D1171500

The
University of
Chicago
School
Mathematics
Project

Teacher's Edition

VOLUME 2 • CHAPTERS 7–13

Authors

James Flanders
Marshall Lassak
Jean Sech
Michelle Eggerding
Paul J. Karafiol
Lin McMullin
Neal Weisman
Zalman Usiskin

Director of Evaluation

Denisse R. Thompson

The McGraw·Hill Companies

Authors

3rd EDITION AUTHORS

James Flanders
Researcher and Technology Integration
Center for Elementary Mathematics and Science Education
The University of Chicago

Marshall Lassak
Associate Professor of Mathematics and Computer Science
Eastern Illinois University, Charleston, IL

Jean Sech *Mathematics Teacher*
Mattawan High School, Mattawan, MI

Michelle Eggerding *Mathematics Teacher*
Schaumburg High School, Schaumburg, IL

Paul J. Karafiol *Mathematics Teacher*
Walter Payton College Prep High School, Chicago, IL

Lin McMullin *Mathematics Teacher (retired)*
Burnt Hills-Ballston Lake High School, Burnt Hills, NY

Neal Weisman *Mathematics Teacher*
Oak Park/River Forest High School, Oak Park, IL

Zalman Usiskin *Professor of Education*
The University of Chicago

AUTHORS OF EARLIER EDITIONS

Sharon L. Senk
Associate Professor of Mathematics
Michigan State University, East Lansing, MI

Natalie Jakucyn *Mathematics Teacher*
Glenbrook South High School, Glenview, IL

Denisse R. Thompson
Assistant Professor of Mathematics Education
University of South Florida, Tampa, FL

Steven S. Viktora
Chairman, Mathematics Department
New Trier High School, Winnetka, IL

Nils P. Ahbel *Mathematics Teacher*
Kent School, Kent, CT

Suzanne Levin
UCSMP

Marcia L. Weinhold *Mathematics Teacher*
Kalamazoo Area Mathematics and Science Center, Kalamazoo, MI

Rheta N. Rubenstein *Mathematics Department Head*
Renaissance High School, Detroit, MI

Judith Halvorson Jaskowiak *Mathematics Teacher*
John F. Kennedy High School, Bloomington, MN

Gerald Pillsbury
UCSMP

www.WrightGroup.com

Printed in the United State of America.
Send all inquiries to:
Wright Group/McGraw-Hill
P.O. Box 812960
Chicago, IL 60681

ISBN 978-0-07-621394-8
MHID 0-07-621394-3

1 2 3 4 5 6 7 8 9 VHJ 14 13 12 11 10 09

The McGraw·Hill Companies

UCSMP EVALUATION, EDITORIAL, AND PRODUCTION

Director of Evaluation
Denisse R. Thompson
Professor of Mathematics Education
University of South Florida, Tampa, FL

Coordinator of School Relations
Carol Siegel

Executive Managing Editor
Clare Froemel

Production Coordinator
Benjamin R. Balskus

Editorial Staff
Kathryn Rich, Gary Spencer, Carlos Encalada, Evan Jenkins, Currence Monson, Yan Yan Wang, Nathaniel Loman

Evaluation Consultant
Sharon L. Senk, *Professor of Mathematics*
Michigan State University, East Lansing, MI

Evaluation Assistants
Allison Burlock,
Julian Owens, Sophia Zhang, Zhuo Zheng,
Gladys Mitchell, Shravani Pasupneti, Alex Yablon

Production Assistants
Paul Campbell, Gretchen Neidhardt,
Sara Mahoney, Nurit Kirschenbaum

Technology Assistant
Luke I. Sandberg

Since the first two editions of *Advanced Algebra* were published, millions of students and thousands of teachers have used the materials. Prior to the publication of this third edition, the following teachers and schools participated in evaluations of the trial version during 2006–2007.

Clay Brown
Greenwood High School
Greenwood, Arkansas

Kathy Coskey
Glenbrook South High School
Glenview, Illinois

Audra Spicer
New Trier High School
Winnetka, Illinois

Craig Flietstra
Unity Christian High School
Hudsonville, Michigan

Catherine Feuerstein
Westfield High School
Westfield, New Jersey

Michael Buescher
Hathaway Brown School
Shaker Heights, Ohio

Cathy Buckingham
Nolan Catholic High School
Ft. Worth, Texas

Tami Wittkopf
Kewaskum High School
Kewaskum, Wisconsin

The following schools participated in field studies in 1993–1994, 1987–1988, 1986–1987, or 1985–1986 as part of the first edition or the second edition research.

Brentwood School
Los Angeles, California

Boulder High School
Boulder, Colorado

Hernando High School
Brooksville, Florida

Lassiter High School
Marietta, Georgia

Taft High School
Chicago, Illinois

Whitney Young High School
Chicago, Illinois

Kenwood Academy
Chicago, Illinois

Steinmetz Academic Center
Chicago, Illinois

Glenbrook South High School
Glenview, Illinois

Thornton Fractional South High School
Lansing, Illinois

Mt. Zion High School
Mt. Zion, Illinois

Rich South High School
Richton Park, Illinois

Lake Park West High School
Roselle, Illinois

Argo Community High School
Summit, Illinois

Shawnee Mission NW High School
Shawnee, Kansas

Framingham High School
Framingham, Massachusetts

Renaissance High School
Detroit, Michigan

Pontotoc High School
Pontotoc, Mississippi

Sentinel High School
Missoula, Montana

West Genessee High School
Camillus, New York

Lake Oswego High School
Lake Oswego, Oregon

Springfield High School
Springfield, Pennsylvania

Hanks High School
El Paso, Texas

We wish to acknowledge the generous support of the **Amoco (now BP) Foundation** and the **Carnegie Corporation of New York** in helping to make it possible for the first edition of these materials to be developed, tested, and distributed, and the additional support of the **Amoco (now BP) Foundation** for the second edition.

We wish also to acknowledge the contribution of the text *Advanced Algebra with Transformations and Applications*, by Zalman Usiskin (Laidlaw, 1975), to some of the conceptualizations and problems used in this book.

Contents

VOLUME 1

Chapter 3 148
Linear Functions and Sequences

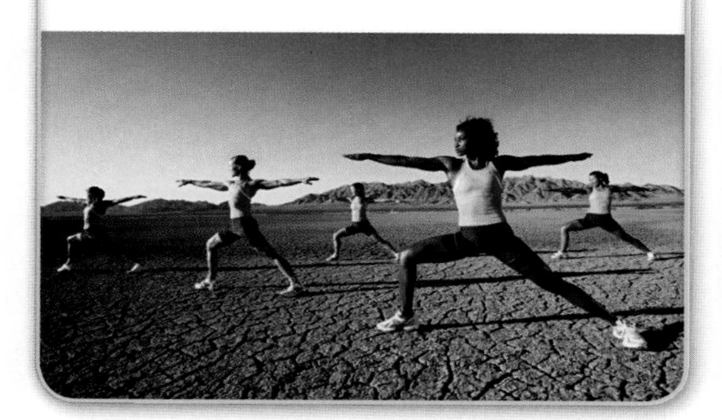

Chapter 4 220
Matrices

Chapter 5 298
Systems

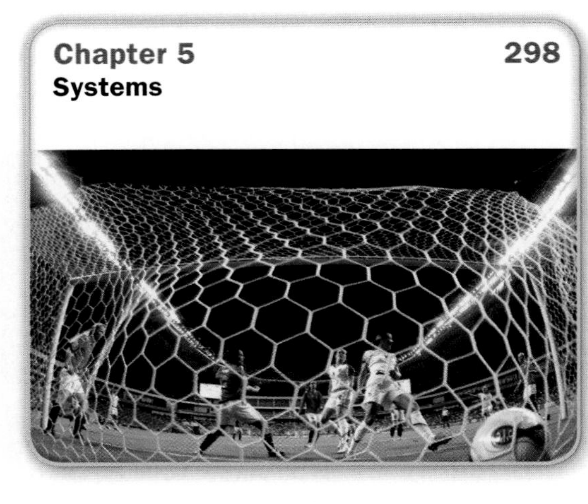

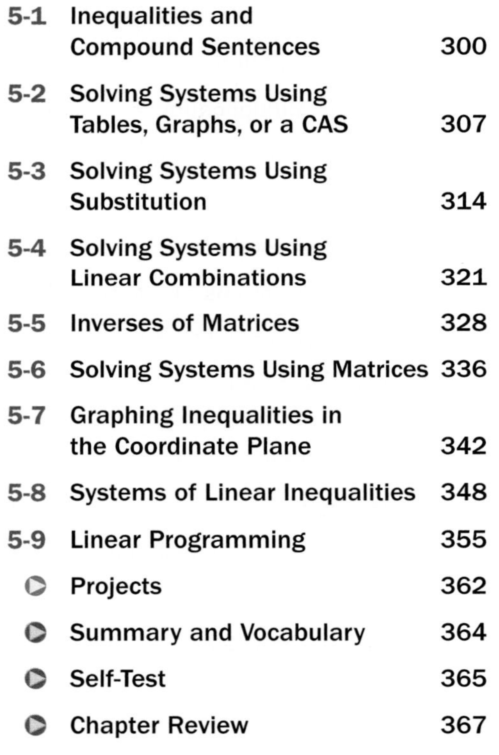

Chapter 6 372
Quadratic Functions

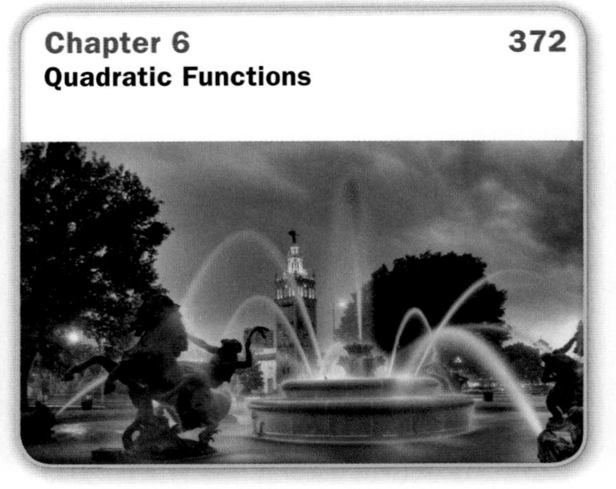

VOLUME 2

Chapter 7 450
Powers

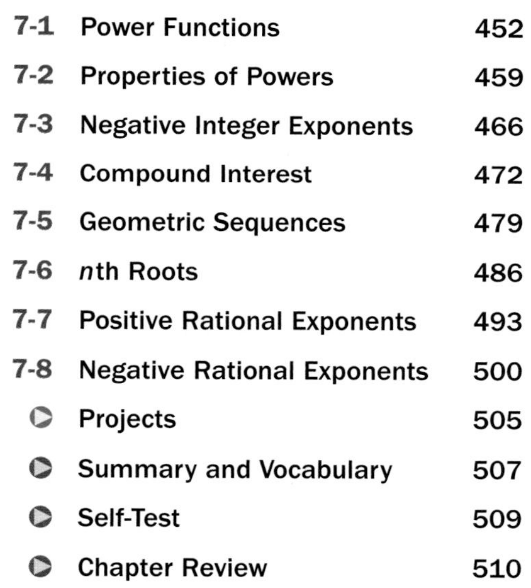

Chapter 8 514
Inverses and Radicals

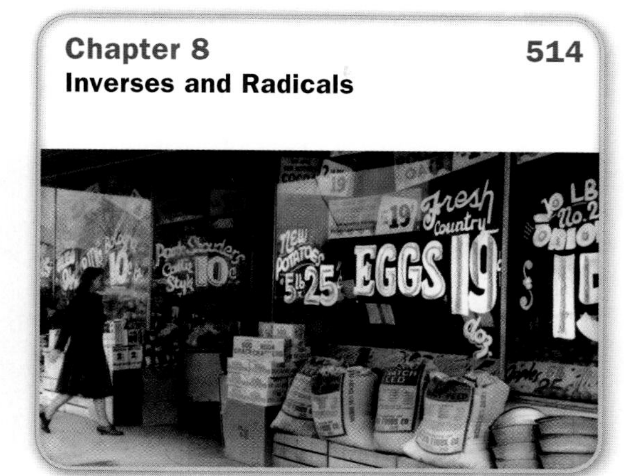

Chapter 11 728
Polynomials

Chapter 12 796
Quadratic Relations

Chapter

7 Powers

Chapter Overview

		Local Standards	Pacing (*in days*)		
			Average	Advanced	Block
7-1	**Power Functions** **F** Solve real-world problems that can be modeled by expressions with *n*th powers or *n*th roots. **I** Graph *n*th power functions.		1	0.75	0.5
7-2	**Properties of Powers** **A** Evaluate b^n when $b > 0$ and n is a rational number. **B** Simplify expressions or solve equations using properties of exponents. **E** Recognize properties of *n*th powers and *n*th roots.		1	0.75	0.5
7-3	**Negative Integer Exponents** **A, B** See 7-2.		1	0.75	0.5
	QUIZ 1		0.5	0.5	0.25
7-4	**Compound Interest** **G** Apply the compound interest formulas.		1	0.75	0.5
7-5	**Geometric Sequences** **C** Describe geometric sequences explicitly and recursively. **H** Solve real-world problems involving geometric sequences.		1	0.75	0.5
7-6	***n*th Roots** **A** Evaluate b^n when $b > 0$ and n is a rational number. **D** Find all real solutions to equations of the form $x^n = b$, where $x \geq 0$ and n is a rational number. **E** Recognize properties of *n*th powers and *n*th roots. **F** Solve real-world problems that can be modeled by expressions with *n*th powers or *n*th roots.		1	0.75	0.5
	QUIZ 2		0.5	0.5	0.25
7-7	**Positive Rational Exponents** **A** Evaluate b^n when $b > 0$ and n is a rational number. **B** Simplify expressions or solve equations using properties of exponents. **D** Find all real solutions to equations of the form $x^n = b$, where $x \geq 0$ and n is a rational number. **E** Recognize properties of *n*th powers and *n*th roots. **F** Solve real-world problems that can be modeled by expressions with *n*th powers or *n*th roots.		1	0.75	0.5
7-8	**Negative Rational Exponents** **A, B, D, E, F** See 7-7.		1	0.75	0.5
		Self-Test	1	0.75	0.5
		Chapter Review	2	1	0.5
		Test	1	1	0.5
		TOTAL	13	9.75	6

Technology Resources

Teacher's Assessment Assistant, Ch. 7
Electronic Teacher's Edition, Ch. 7

Differentiation Options  Universal Access

	Accommodating the Learner	Vocabulary Development	Ongoing Assessment	Materials
7-1	pp. 454, 457	p. 455	written, p. 458	CAS or graphing calculator
7-2	pp. 461, 462		group, p. 465	
7-3	p. 468		group, p. 471	CAS
7-4	pp. 473, 475	p. 474	written, p. 478	
7-5	pp. 482, 484	p. 480	written, p. 485	
7-6	pp. 489, 492	p. 488	group, p. 492	
7-7	pp. 494, 495		group, p. 499	CAS (optional)
7-8	pp. 501, 504		written, p. 504	

Objectives

	Lessons	Self-Test Questions	Chapter Review Questions
Skills			
A Evaluate b^n when $b > 0$ and n is a rational number.	7-2, 7-3, 7-6, 7-7, 7-8	2-4, 10	1-9
B Simplify expressions or solve equations using properties of exponents.	7-2, 7-3, 7-7, 7-8	5-7	10-18
C Describe geometric sequences explicitly and recursively.	7-5	14, 15	19-26
D Find all real solutions to equations of the form $x^n = b$, where $x \geq 0$ and n is a rational number.	7-6, 7-7, 7-8	9, 18	27-35
Properties			
E Recognize properties of *n*th powers and *n*th roots.	7-2, 7-6, 7-7, 7-8	1, 8, 19	36-49
Uses			
F Solve real-world problems that can be modeled by expressions with *n*th powers or *n*th roots.	7-1, 7-6, 7-7, 7-8	16, 17	50-56
G Apply the compound interest formulas.	7-4	20, 21	57-61
H Solve real-world problems involving geometric sequences.	7-5	12	62-64
Representations			
I Graph *n*th power functions.	7-1	11, 13	65-69

Resource Masters Chapter 7

Resource Master 3, Graphing Utility Grids (page 4), can be used with Lesson 7-1.

Resource Master 119 Lesson 7-1

Resource Master 118 Lesson 7-1

Warm-Up

In 1–7, evaluate the power.

1. 3^5
2. $(-3)^5$
3. -3^5
4. 3^{-5}
5. -3^{-5}
6. $3^{0.5}$
7. $3^{-0.5}$

Additional Examples

1. Suppose that the probability that an event will occur is p. Let A be the probability that the event will occur 5 times in a row.
   a. Write a formula for A in terms of p.
   b. Prepare a table of values for p between 0 and 1 and draw a graph.

2. Draw a graph and state the domain and range for the function with equation $f(x) = x^4$.

Resource Masters for Lesson 7-1

Resource Master 120 Lesson 7-2

Warm-Up

1. ABC, NBC, and CBS are 3-letter acronyms. How many different 3-letter acronyms are possible using the 26 letters of the English alphabet?
2. ESPN and NCAA are 4-letter acronyms. How many different 4-letter acronyms are possible using the 26 letters of the English alphabet?
3. WYSIWYG is a 7-letter acronym. How many different 7-letter acronyms are possible using the 26 letters of the English alphabet?
4. Why must the answer to Warm-Up 3 must be the product of the answers to Warm-Up 1 and 2?

Additional Examples

1. Solve $18^4 \cdot 18^x = 18^{12}$.
   Solution Write a correspondence: $18^4 \cdot 18^x = 18^{12}$ and ____ + x = ____. Now solve for x: x = ____.

2. How many zeros are at the end of the number $N = 5^5 \cdot 2^5 \cdot 32$ when N is written in base 10?

3. A multiple-choice English quiz is 2 pages long. Each page has 6 questions. Each question has c possible choices. How many different ways can you complete the quiz if you leave no answer blank?

Resource Master for Lesson 7-2

Resource Master 121 Lesson 7-2

Additional Examples

4. The mass of Earth is about 5.9×10^{24} kilograms, while the mass of Jupiter is about 1.9×10^{27} kilograms. The mass of Jupiter is about how many times the mass of Earth?

5. A cylindrical can containing three tennis balls fits tightly in a rectangular box, as shown at the right. What percent of the volume of the box is taken up by the cylinder?

   Solution The diameter of the base of the cylinder and the side length of the base of the box are $2r$, where r is the radius of a tennis ball. The height of the cylinder and the box is $6r$. The volume of the cylinder is $\pi r^2 h = \pi r^2 \cdot 6r = 6\pi r^3$. The volume of the box is ____ · ____ · ____ = ____. To find the percent, divide the volume of the cylinder by the volume of the box:

   $\frac{\text{volume of cylinder}}{\text{volume of box}} = \frac{6\pi r^3}{\_\_\_\_} = \_\_\_\_$.

   So the percent of the volume of the box taken up by the cylinder is approximately ____%.

Resource Master for Lesson 7-2

Resource Master 122 Lesson 7-2

Properties of Powers Summary

Product of Powers Postulate: For any nonnegative base b and nonzero real exponents m and n, or any nonzero base b and integer exponents m and n, $b^m \cdot b^n = b^{m+n}$.

Power of a Product Postulate: For any nonnegative bases a and b and real exponent m, or any nonzero bases a and b and integer exponent m, $(ab)^m = a^m b^m$.

Quotient of Powers Theorem: For any positive base b and real exponents m and n, or any nonzero base b and integer exponents m and n,
$\frac{b^m}{b^n} = b^{m-n}$.

Power of a Quotient Theorem: For any positive base a and b and real exponent n, or any nonzero bases a and b and integer exponent n,
$\left(\frac{a}{b}\right)^n = \frac{a^n}{b^n}$.

Zero Exponent Theorem: If b is a nonzero real number, $b^0 = 1$.

Power of a Power Postulate: For any positive base b and nonzero real exponents m and n, or any nonzero base b and integer exponents m and n, $(b^m)^n = b^{mn}$.

Question 34a.

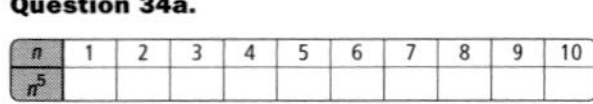

n	1	2	3	4	5	6	7	8	9	10
n^5										

Question 34b.

n	10	20	30	40	50	60	70	80	90	100
n^5										

Resource Master for Lesson 7-2

Resource Master 124 Lesson 7-3

Resource Master 123 Lesson 7-3

Warm-Up

Calculate powers of the fraction $\frac{3}{5}$. What pattern emerges?

1. $\left(\frac{3}{5}\right)^4$
2. $\left(\frac{3}{5}\right)^3$
3. $\left(\frac{3}{5}\right)^2$
4. $\left(\frac{3}{5}\right)^1$
5. $\left(\frac{3}{5}\right)^0$
6. $\left(\frac{3}{5}\right)^{-1}$
7. $\left(\frac{3}{5}\right)^{-2}$

Additional Examples

1. Write 4^{-3} as a decimal.
   Solution By the Negative Exponent Theorem, 4^{-3} = ____ as a fraction and ____ as a decimal.

2. Rewrite Newton's Law of Universal Gravitation, $F_g = \frac{Gm_1m_2}{r^2}$, using negative exponents. In this formula, F_g is the gravitational force between two objects, m_1 and m_2 are the masses of the two objects, r is the distance between the objects, and G is the universal gravitational constant.

Resource Masters for Lesson 7-3

Resource Master 126 Lesson 7-4

Resource Master 125 Lesson 7-4

Warm-Up

In 1–4, use a calculator to evaluate each expression to the nearest hundredth.

1. $300(1.0535)^3$
2. $1500\left(1 + \frac{0.07}{360}\right)^{365}$
3. $1239.47 + 1239.47 \cdot 0.038$
4. $10{,}000\left(1 + \frac{0.0634}{12}\right)^{12 \cdot 5}$

Additional Example

1. Suppose \$1000 is deposited in an account that pays interest at a rate of 3.5%. How much will be earned in the first year if the interest is compounded as indicated below?
   a. annually
   b. semiannually
   c. quarterly

Resource Masters for Lesson 7-4

Resource Master 127 Lesson 7-5

Warm-Up

Jacobi wants to enlarge a portion of a photograph to 10 times its size. However, the photocopier's largest enlargement factor is 120%. Indicate the sequence of size-change factors (rounded to the nearest hundredth) that result from using the copier 1, 2, 3, ... times until the final enlargement is at least 10 times the size of the original photograph.

Additional Examples

1. Give the first six terms and the constant multiplier in the geometric sequence g, where
$\begin{cases} g_1 = 5 \\ g_n = 4g_{n-1} \end{cases}$, for integers $n \geq 2$.

2. Write the 1st, 5th, 10th, 20th, and 25th terms of the sequence a defined by $a_n = 3(-2)^{n-1}$.

Solution Substitute $n = 1, 5, 10, 20$, and 25 into the formula for the sequence.

$a_1 = 3(-2)^{1-1} = 3 \cdot$ ____ = ____

$a_5 = 3(-2)^{\_\_\_\_} = 3 \cdot$ ____ = ____

$a_{10} =$ ____ = ____

A calculator display of a_{20} and a_{25} is shown below.

$3\cdot(-2)^{19}$	-152864
$3\cdot(-2)^{24}$	50331648

Resource Master for Lesson 7-5

Resource Master 128 Lesson 7-5

Additional Example

3. Suppose a ball is dropped from a height of 12 feet and bounces up to 90% of its previous height after each bounce. (A bounce is counted when the ball hits the ground.) Let h_n be the maximum height of the ball after the nth bounce. Refer to the diagram below.

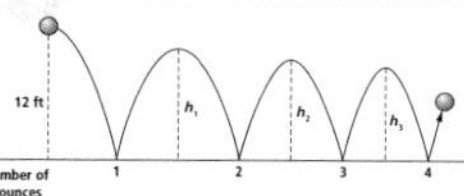

a. Find an explicit formula for h_n.

b. Find the maximum height of the ball after the sixth bounce.

Extension

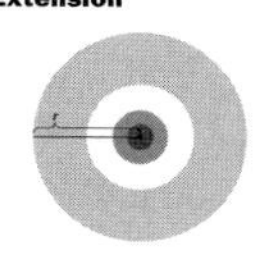

Resource Master for Lesson 7-5

Resource Master 129 Lesson 7-6

Warm-Up

In 1–6, solve. If the solution is not exact, estimate it to the nearest hundredth.

1. $x^5 = -1$
2. $y^3 = 24$
3. $z^8 - 256 = 0$
4. $9a^2 = 4$
5. $10^{10}n^{10} = 0$
6. $-16 + v^4 = 0$

Additional Examples

1. Approximate the real 8th roots of 3.

2. Approximate all real solutions to $x^4 = 100$ to the nearest thousandth.

Solution By the definition of nth root, the real solutions of $x^4 = 100$ are the real ____ roots of ____. So one solution is $x = 100^{\_\_\_\_}$. Enter 100^(1 ÷ 4) into a calculator. The result, to the nearest thousandth is ____. So $100^{\frac{1}{4}} \approx$ ____. By the Number of Real Roots Theorem, there are two real solutions to $x^4 = 100$ because 4 is a(n) ________ number. The solutions are $x \approx$ ____ and $x \approx$ ____.

3. Use the cSolve or Solve command on a CAS to find all the 4th roots of 2401.

Resource Master for Lesson 7-6

Resource Master 130 Lesson 7-6

How Many Real *n*th Roots Does a Real Number Have?

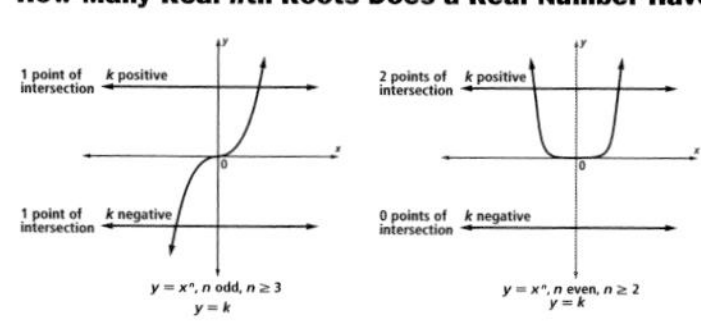

Number of Real Roots Theorem

Every positive real number has

- 2 real nth roots, when n is even.
- 1 real nth root, when n is odd.

Every negative real number has

- 0 real nth roots, when n is even.
- 1 real nth root, when n is odd.

Zero has

- 1 real nth root.

Resource Master for Lesson 7-6

Resource Master 131 Lesson 7-7

Warm-Up

1. Write 9^x for integer values of x from -4 to 4.
2. Write $9^{-4}, 9^{-3}, 9^{-2}, \ldots, 9^4$ as powers of 3. Insert the missing integer powers of 3. What powers of 9 do these powers of 3 represent?

Additional Examples

1. Suppose $x \geq 0$. Simplify $(27x^6)^{\frac{2}{3}}$.
2. Solve $x^{\frac{5}{4}} = 6.8$.
3. The price of a Volkswagen Beetle in 1959 was about \$1700. In 2008, the price of the same model was about \$17,000. What was the average annual percent increase in price over these years?

Activity 1

Rational Power	8^0	$8^{\frac{1}{3}}$	$8^{\frac{1}{2}}$	$8^{\frac{3}{4}}$	8^1	$8^{\frac{5}{4}}$	$8^{\frac{3}{2}}$	$8^{\frac{5}{3}}$	8^2
Decimal Power	8^0	$8^{0.\overline{3}}$		$8^{0.75}$	8^1				8^2
Value	1				8				64

Resource Master for Lesson 7-7

Resource Master 132 Lesson 7-7

Question 19

Rational Power	Decimal Power	Value
$\left(\frac{1}{4}\right)^0$	$\left(\frac{1}{4}\right)^0$	1
$\left(\frac{1}{4}\right)^{\frac{1}{4}}$		
$\left(\frac{1}{4}\right)^{\frac{1}{2}}$		
$\left(\frac{1}{4}\right)^{\frac{2}{3}}$		
$\left(\frac{1}{4}\right)^1$	$\left(\frac{1}{4}\right)^1$	0.25
$\left(\frac{1}{4}\right)^{\frac{4}{3}}$		
$\left(\frac{1}{4}\right)^{\frac{3}{2}}$		
$\left(\frac{1}{4}\right)^{\frac{7}{4}}$		
$\left(\frac{1}{4}\right)^2$	$\left(\frac{1}{4}\right)^2$	0.063

Resource Master for Lesson 7-7

Resource Master 133 Lesson 7-8

Warm-Up

1. Find each power. Note that the exponents decrease by $\frac{1}{3}$.

$343^2 = 117{,}649$ $\qquad$ $343^{\frac{5}{3}} = \left(343^{\frac{1}{3}}\right)^5 = 16{,}807$

$343^{\frac{4}{3}} =$ ____ $\qquad$ $343^1 =$ ____

$343^{\frac{2}{3}} =$ ____ $\qquad$ $343^{\frac{1}{3}} =$ ____

$343^0 =$ ____

2. Continue to decrease the exponent by $\frac{1}{3}$.

$343^{-\frac{1}{3}} = \left(343^{\frac{1}{3}}\right)^{-1} = \frac{1}{7}$ $\qquad$ $343^{-\frac{2}{3}} =$ ____

$343^{-1} =$ ____ $\qquad$ $343^{-\frac{4}{3}} =$ ____

$343^{-\frac{5}{3}} =$ ____ $\qquad$ $343^{-2} =$ ____

Resource Master for Lesson 7-8

Resource Master 134 Lesson 7-8

Additional Example

1. Evaluate $\left(\frac{27}{1000}\right)^{-\frac{2}{3}}$ in three different ways using a different power first.

Solution

Method 1: Find the reciprocal of $\frac{27}{1000}$, take the third root, and then calculate the second power.

$\left(\frac{27}{1000}\right)^{-\frac{2}{3}} = \left(\left(\left(\frac{27}{1000}\right)^{-1}\right)^{\frac{1}{3}}\right)^2 = \left((\_\_\_\_)^{\frac{1}{3}}\right)^2 = (\_\_\_\_)^2 =$ ____

Method 2: Take the third root of $\frac{27}{1000}$, then calculate the second power, and then find the reciprocal.

$\left(\frac{27}{1000}\right)^{-\frac{2}{3}} = \left(\left(\left(\frac{27}{1000}\right)^{\frac{1}{3}}\right)^2\right)^{-1} = ((\_\_\_\_)^2)^{-1} = (\_\_\_\_)^{-1} =$ ____

Method 3: Calculate the second power of $\frac{27}{1000}$, then take the third root, and then find the reciprocal.

$\left(\frac{27}{1000}\right)^{-\frac{2}{3}} = \left(\left(\left(\frac{27}{1000}\right)^2\right)^{\frac{1}{3}}\right)^{-1} = \left((\_\_\_\_)^{\frac{1}{3}}\right)^{-1} = (\_\_\_\_)^{-1} =$ ____

Resource Master for Lesson 7-8

Resource Master 135 Lesson 7-8

Additional Examples

2. Use the formula $r = 241w^{-\frac{1}{4}}$, where w is the weight in kilograms, to estimate a person's resting heart rate in beats per minute if the person weighs 240 pounds.

3. Suppose Gary has \$75,000 of the \$200,000 he hopes to have in a retirement account in $8\frac{1}{2}$ years. What interest rate does Gary need to meet his savings goal?

Resource Master for Lesson 7-8

Chapter

7

Pacing

Each lesson in this chapter is designed to be covered in 1 day. At the end of the chapter, you should plan to spend 1 day to review the Self-Test, 1 to 2 days for the Chapter Review, and 1 day for a test. You may wish to spend a day on projects and possibly a day is needed for quizzes. This chapter should therefore take 11 to 14 days. We strongly advise you not to spend more than 15 days on this chapter.

Overview

Whenever there is an nth power, there is also an nth root: If $x^n = k$, then x is an nth root of k. Thus, it is natural to discuss powers and roots together.

Students may not realize that the picture at the top on page 451 shows half of the shell at the bottom, after it has been cut parallel to the plane of the page (perpendicular to the line of sight). The animal known as the nautilus uses this shell for protection. Its body is partially inside the shell. Its tentacles, looking like those of squids, are outside the shell and are used for grabbing food and for locomotion. Question 18 of Lesson 7-6 refers to the figures on page 451.

Chapter

Powers

Contents

The expression x^n stands for the *nth power of x*. In this chapter you will study powers and related functions. You will see how to interpret powers when the exponent n is not an integer, and how to solve equations involving powers.

Powers have many applications. You are familiar with applications involving x^2, the 2nd power of x, in area problems, counting problems, and a variety of physics problems including those that involve projectiles. Expressions involving x^3, the 3rd power of x, arise from problems involving volume. Both positive and negative exponents are used in writing numbers in scientific notation.

Applications involving powers also arise in money matters dealing with interest rates, amounts owed, or amounts paid, as well as in counting problems and probability. Solving equations in any of these situations can lead to powers of the form $x^{\frac{1}{n}}$ or $x^{\frac{m}{n}}$, where m and n are integers.

Sequences determined by the successive powers of a number also have many applications in the physical world, including music and exponential growth and decay. One of these sequences is shown above in the cross-section of a shell of a *chambered nautilus*, a member of the squid family. The full shell is shown at the right.

Chapter 7 Overview

Chapter 7 covers the skills, properties, uses, and representations related to powers. We assume students have studied the following topics in previous courses: positive integral powers, zero powers, negative integral powers of 10 (at least in conjunction with scientific notation), rewriting square roots such as $\sqrt{75} = 5\sqrt{3}$, and using $\frac{1}{2}$ as an exponent. In this chapter, we extend the study of powers to those involving rational powers and roots.

Graphs of the power functions are introduced in Lesson 7-1 and provide a foundation for the real nth roots to be studied later in the chapter. Lesson 7-2 reviews the properties of powers with which students should be familiar. Lesson 7-3 uses these properties to develop the meaning of negative integer exponents. Lessons 7-4 and 7-5 motivate the use of power functions through compound interest and geometric sequence problems.

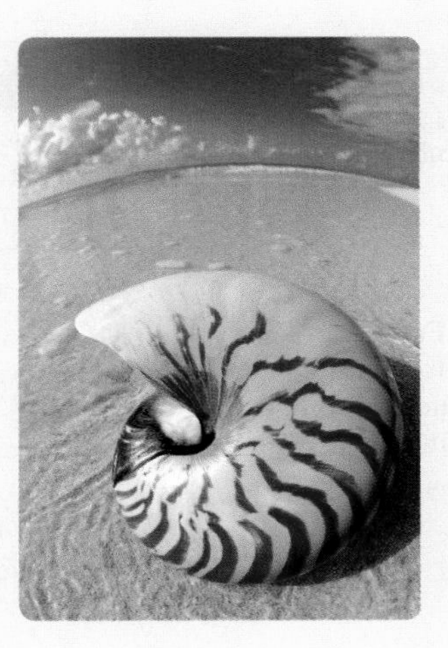

The chambers in the shell may look like they were made by a machine, but it is a natural shell. As the nautilus matures, it builds successively larger chambers to accommodate its growth. Let L represent the length of some part of the smallest chamber. The lengths of corresponding parts in adjacent chambers are all related by a common ratio, x. The sequence of chamber lengths can, thus, be represented as L, Lx^1, Lx^2, and so on. In this chapter you will determine that in this case $x \approx 2^{0.1} \approx 1.07$.

451

Lessons 7-6 through 7-8 deal with exponents of the form $\frac{1}{n}$, positive rational exponents, and negative rational exponents, respectively.

Students will have studied all the rational powers after completing this chapter.

A basic question throughout the chapter is the domain of the base and the domain of the exponent in the power x^n. Two pairs of domains are found throughout the chapter: (1) When n is an integer, x can be any real number, with the single exception 0^0, which is not defined. (2) When n is not an integer, x can be any nonnegative real number.

The discussion of radical notation $\sqrt[n]{}$ for nth roots is delayed until Chapter 8 because still another pair of domains must be considered.

Using Pages 450–451

In the poem "The Chambered Nautilus," Oliver Wendell Holmes (1809–1894) described how the nautilus builds successive chambers as it grows. You might have a student read this poem to the class. The poem can be found on the Internet, for example, http://poetry.com/GreatestPoems/poem.asp?id=502.

More information about the chambered nautilus can be found on many Web sites, including http://www.seasky.org/deep-sea/chambered-nautilus.html.

Chapter 7 Projects

At the end of each chapter, you will find projects related to the chapter. At this time you might want to have students look over the projects on pages 505 and 506. You might want to have students tentatively select a project on which to work. Then, as students read and progress through the chapter, they can finalize their project choices.

Sometimes students might work alone. At other times, you might let them collaborate with classmates for a presentation and discussion. We recommend that you allow for diversity and encourage students to use their imaginations when presenting their projects. As students work on projects throughout the year, they should see many uses of mathematics in the real world.

Lesson 7-1

GOAL

Discuss functions with the equation $y = x^n$, when n is a positive integer.

SPUR Objectives

The SPUR Objectives for all of Chapter 7 are found in the Chapter Review on pages 510–513.

F Solve real-world problems that can be modeled by expressions with nth powers.

I Graph nth power functions.

Materials/Resources

- Lesson Masters 7-1A and 7-1B
- Resource Masters 3, 118, and 119
- CAS or graphing calculator

HOMEWORK

Suggestions for Assignment

- Questions 1–25
- Question 26 (extra credit)
- Reading Lesson 7-2
- Covering the Ideas 7-2

Local Standards

1 Warm-Up

In 1–7, evaluate the power.

1. 3^5 243
2. $(-3)^5$ -243
3. -3^5 -243
4. 3^{-5} $\frac{1}{243}$
5. -3^{-5} $-\frac{1}{243}$
6. $3^{0.5}$ $\sqrt{3}$
7. $3^{-0.5}$ $\frac{1}{\sqrt{3}}$

Lesson 7-1 Power Functions

BIG IDEA When n is a positive integer greater than 1, x^n can be interpreted as repeated multiplication.

Vocabulary

powering, exponentiation
base
exponent
power
nth-power function
identity function
squaring function
cubing function

Recall that the expression x^n, read "x to the nth power" or "the nth power of x", is the result of an operation called **powering** or **exponentiation**. The variable x is called the **base**, n is called the **exponent**, and the expression x^n is called a **power**.

Mental Math

Give a number that fits the description or tell if no such number exists.

a. an integer that is not a natural number

b. an irrational number that is not a real number

c. a complex number that is not a pure imaginary number

d. a real number that is not a complex number

Defining b^n When n Is a Positive Integer

When n is a positive integer and b is any real number, one way to think of b^n is as the nth term of the sequence

$$b^1, b^2, b^3, \dots b^n, \dots .$$

This sequence can be defined recursively as

$$\begin{cases} b^1 = b \\ b^n = b \cdot b^{n-1}, \text{ for } n > 1 . \end{cases}$$

For example, $14^1 = 14$, $14^2 = 14 \cdot 14^1 = 196$, $14^3 = 14 \cdot 14^2 = 14 \cdot 196 = 2744$, and so on.

 QY1

As a result of the recursive definition of b^n for any real number b, when n is a positive integer ≥ 2,

$$b^n = \underbrace{b \cdot b \cdot b \cdot \dots \cdot b}_{n \text{ factors}} .$$

This is the *repeated multiplication* definition of a power. For instance, $x^6 = x \cdot x \cdot x \cdot x \cdot x \cdot x$. The definition enables you to use multiplication to calculate positive integer powers of any number without having to calculate each preceding power. For example,

$$-\left(\frac{2}{3}\right)^5 = -\frac{2}{3} \cdot -\frac{2}{3} \cdot -\frac{2}{3} \cdot -\frac{2}{3} \cdot -\frac{2}{3}$$
$$= -\frac{32}{243}.$$

QY1

Calculate 14^4 without a calculator given that $14^3 = 2744$.

Mental Math

a. Answers vary. Sample: -13

b. does not exist

c. Answers vary. Sample: $12 + 6i$

d. does not exist

Background

Despite its length, this is a good lesson for students to read independently. It provides another opportunity for practice with function notation and the concepts of domain and range; it can also bolster student confidence—even a lesson with a great deal of reading can be conquered!

Defining b^n when b is a positive integer Students have often seen the explicit definition of b^n as shown after QY1. However, the explicit definition does not apply when $n = 1$. An advantage of the recursive definition is that it applies to *all* positive integer exponents.

An example of a power function The example here shows that with numbers between 0 and 1 as the base, a given power of a positive number increases as the base increases. Students have seen this pattern with the 2nd power but not with higher powers. The application of probability in Example 1 allows values of the base from 0

An Example of a Power Function

Powers often arise in counting and probability situations. For example, in the play *Rosencrantz & Guildenstern are Dead,* by Tom Stoppard, the character Rosencrantz spends a lot of time flipping a fair coin. It always lands heads up! This, of course, is very unlikely. The probability that a fair coin lands heads up is $\frac{1}{2}$. Because each flip is independent, the probability of as few as four heads in a row is very small:

$$\frac{1}{2} \cdot \frac{1}{2} \cdot \frac{1}{2} \cdot \frac{1}{2} = \left(\frac{1}{2}\right)^4 = 0.0625.$$

Had Rosencrantz been tossing a 6-sided die, his probability of tossing the same number four times in a row would have been even smaller:

$$\frac{1}{6} \cdot \frac{1}{6} \cdot \frac{1}{6} \cdot \frac{1}{6} = \left(\frac{1}{6}\right)^4 \approx 0.0007716.$$

Example 1 generalizes Rosencrantz's situation.

Example 1

Suppose that the probability of an event happening is p. Let A be the probability of the event happening four times in a row.

a. Find a formula for A in terms of p.

b. Make a table of values and a graph for typical values of p.

Solution

a. The probability of the event happening four times in a row is $p \cdot p \cdot p \cdot p$, so $A = p^4$.

b. The probability p must be a number from 0 to 1. A table and graph are shown below.

p	$A = p^4$
0	0
0.1	0.0001
0.2	0.0016
0.25	0.0039
0.3	0.0081
0.4	0.0256
0.5	0.0625
0.6	0.1296
0.7	0.2401
0.8	0.4096
0.9	0.6561
0.95	0.8145
1	1

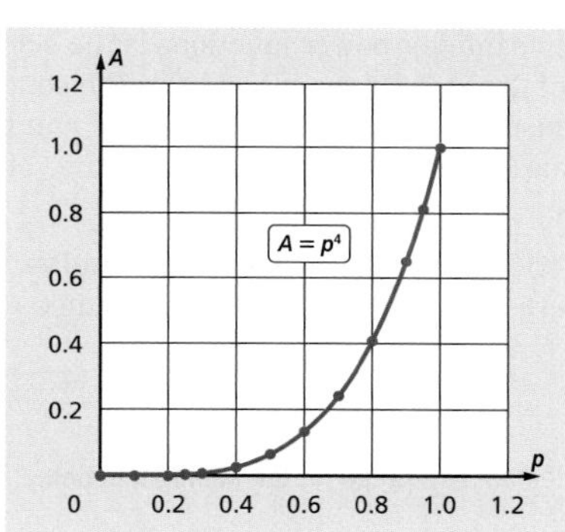

to 1 only, but the values of the function with equation $y = x^6$ continue to increase as x increases beyond 1.

Properties of power functions When examining a function, there are several characteristics to consider. In addition to domain and range, this lesson considers symmetry. Symmetry is useful when evaluating a function because one needs to calculate only the values for a portion of the domain; the other values can be found using that symmetry.

We do not introduce the terms *even function* and *odd function* here. They derive from the power functions and also characterize functions that are not power functions yet have the same symmetries as power functions do.

2 Teaching

Notes on the Lesson

Example 1 You might ask students the following questions: A professional bowler might make strikes 60% of the time. What is the probability that a professional bowler will begin a game with 6 strikes in a row? $0.60^6 = 0.046656$, or about $\frac{1}{21}$

An average bowler might make strikes 20% of the time. What is the average bowler's probability of beginning a game with 6 strikes in a row?
$0.20^6 \approx 0.000064$, or $\frac{1}{15{,}625}$

Additional Example

Example 1 Suppose that the probability that an event will occur is p. Let A be the probability that the event will occur five times in a row.

a. Write a formula for A in terms of p. $A = p^5$

b. Prepare a table of values for p between 0 and 1 and draw a graph.

p	$A = p^5$
0	0
0.1	0.00001
0.2	0.00032
0.25	0.0009766
0.3	0.00243
0.4	0.01024
0.5	0.03125
0.6	0.07776
0.7	0.16807
0.8	0.32768
0.9	0.59049
0.95	0.7737809
1	1

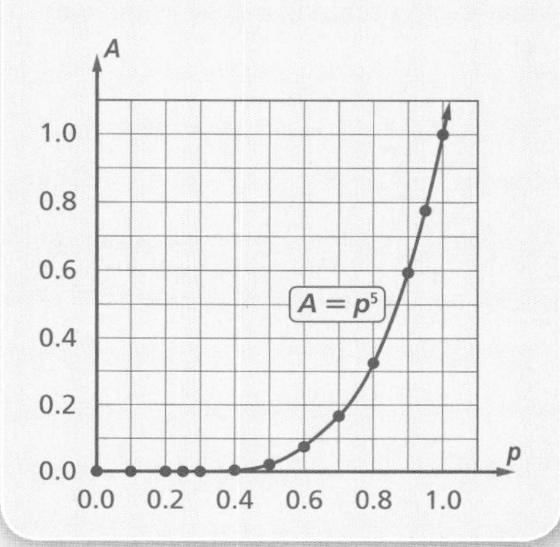

7-1

Notes on the Lesson

After reading Lesson 7-1, many students conclude that as the positive integer n increases, the values of $f(x) = x^n$ increase more rapidly. This is true for values of $x > 1$ and can be seen by plotting various power functions on the same set of axes or by reasoning about powers. For $x > 1$, the graph of $f(x) = x^5$ is steeper than the graph of $f(x) = x^4$, which in turn is steeper than the graph of $f(x) = x^3$, and so on. However, some students may not realize that for values of x between -1 and 1, the order of the steepness is reversed.

Additional Example

Example 2 Draw a graph and state the domain and range for the function with equation $f(x) = x^4$.

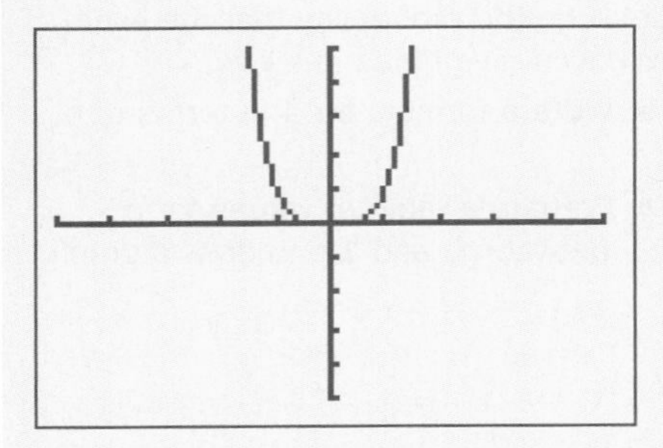

Because x can be any real number, the domain is the set of real numbers. Because x^4 cannot be negative, the range is the set of nonnegative real numbers.

Note-Taking Tips

Have students add to their journal the Probability of Repeated Independent Events. Have them include an example of an event and give the probability of that event occurring a specific number of times.

Notice from Example 1 that an event with as large as a 90% chance of happening has only a $(0.90)^4 \approx 0.6561$ probability of happening four times in a row. That's less than a 66% chance.

The general formula is a simple application of nth powers.

Probability of Repeated Independent Events

If an event has probability p, and if each occurrence of the event is independent of all other occurrences, then the probability that the event occurs n times in a row is p^n.

Caution: The events must be independent. For instance, if there is a 40% probability of rain on a typical day in a particular location, there is not a $(40\%)^7$ chance that there will be rain all 7 days because rain on one day can affect the chances of rain on the next day.

STOP QY2

▶ QY2

If the probability of an independent event happening is 0.6, what is the probability that the event will occur n times in a row?

Some Simple Power Functions

In general, the function f defined by $f(x) = x^n$, where n is a positive integer, is called the **nth-power function**. The function with equation $y = x^5$ is the 5th-power function. The graph in Example 1 is a part of the graph of the 4th-power function.

The simplest power function has the equation $f(x) = x^1$ and is called the **identity function** because the output is identical to the input. The quadratic function f with $f(x) = x^2$ is the 2nd-power, or **squaring function**.

Any real number can be raised to the first or second power. So the domain of each of these positive integer power functions is the set of all real numbers. The range of the identity function is also the set of real numbers. However, because the result of squaring a real number is always nonnegative, the range of the squaring function is the set of all nonnegative real numbers.

The function with equation $f(x) = x^3$ is called the **cubing function**. The nth-power functions where $n > 3$ do not have special names.

Example 2

Draw a graph and state the domain and range for the cubing function.

Solution Make a table of values and plot points. Connect the points with a smooth curve.

Accommodating the Learner

Some students mistakenly think of an exponent as "the number of *times* a base is multiplied by itself" rather than as "the number of identical *factors*." So, they think an exponent is the number of multiplication signs and write x^3 as $x \cdot x \cdot x \cdot x$. Stress that for x^n, there are n factors but $n - 1$ multiplication signs. Similarly, $2x$ does not mean two *additions*, as in $x + x + x$, but two *addends*, as in $x + x$.

x	$f(x) = x^3$
-5	$(-5)^3 = -125$
-4	$(-4)^3 = -64$
-3	$(-3)^3 = -27$
-2	$(-2)^3 = -8$
-1	$(-1)^3 = -1$
0	$0^3 = 0$
1	$1^3 = 1$
2	$2^3 = 8$
3	$3^3 = 27$
4	$4^3 = 64$
5	$5^3 = 125$

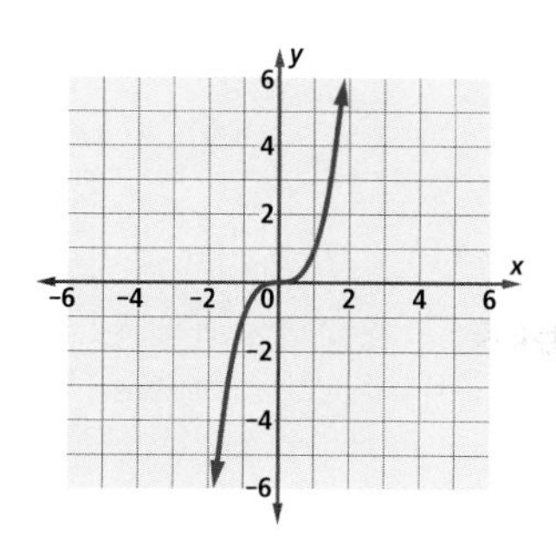

Because x can be any real number, the domain is the set of real numbers.

Because x^3 can be as large or as small as we want, positive or negative, the range is the set of real numbers.

Properties of Power Functions

Activity

MATERIALS CAS or graphing calculator

Work with a partner.

Step 1 Graph several functions of the form $y = x^n$ in a window where $\{x \mid -5 \le x \le 5\}$ and $\{y \mid -5 \le y \le 5\}$. One of you should graph functions for even values of n and the other should graph functions for odd values of n. Graph at least four functions each in the same window. Sketch your results on a separate sheet of paper and label each function.

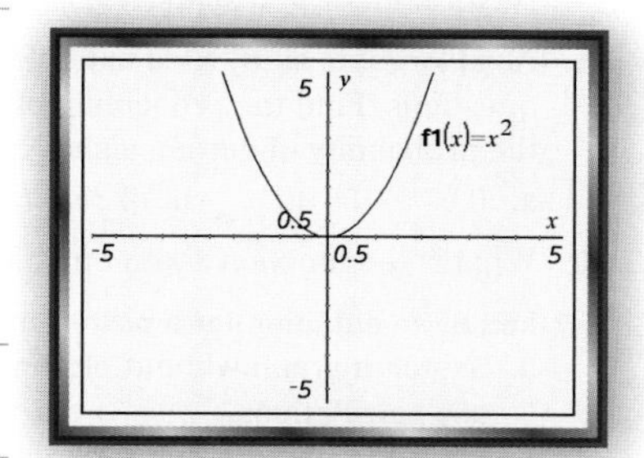

Step 2 State the domain and range for each of the functions you graphed. See margin.

Step 3 Compare and contrast your graphs, then discuss the results with your partner. What other properties do these functions seem to have? See margin.

The table on the next page summarizes some properties of the nth power functions f with $f(x) = x^n$, where n is a positive integer. As in the Activity, these properties depend on whether n is even or odd.

Activity
Step 1.
Even powers:

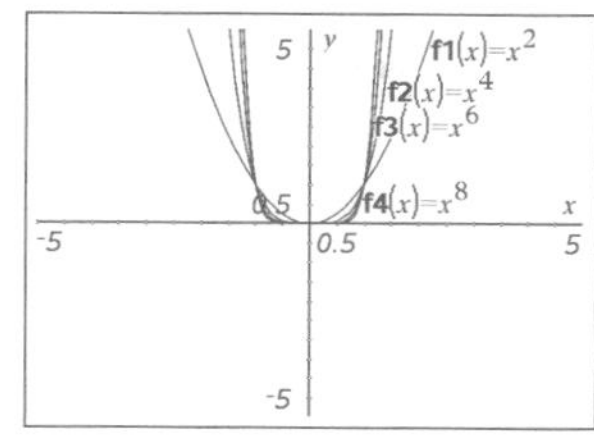

Odd powers:

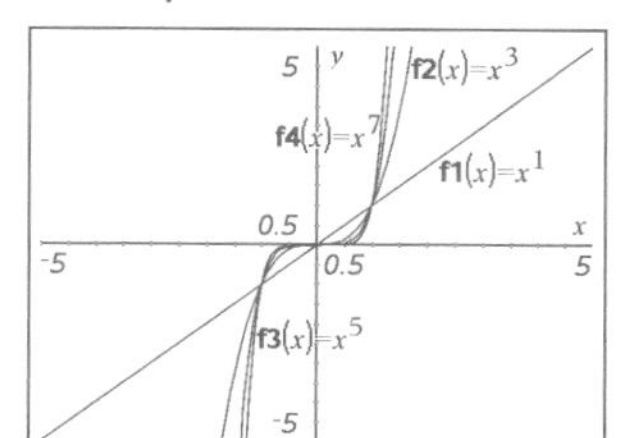

Notes on the Lesson

Activity Discuss with students why $f(x) = x^5$ is "flatter" than $f(x) = x^4$, which in turn is "flatter" than $f(x) = x^3$, and so on, when $0 < x < 1$.

Additional Answers

Activity

Step 2. Even powers: The domain is the set of all real numbers, and the range is $\{y \mid y \ge 0\}$; Odd powers: The domain is the set of all real numbers, and the range is the set of all real numbers.

Step 3. Answers vary. Sample: The graphs of even-power functions are in Quadrants I and II, and they are symmetric to the y-axis. The graphs of odd-power functions are in Quadrants I and III, and they are symmetric about the origin.

ENGLISH LEARNERS

Vocabulary Development

Review the terms *base, exponent,* and *factor* with this diagram:

Exponent
Base → $2^5 = 2 \cdot 2 \cdot 2 \cdot 2 \cdot 2$
5 factors

Explain that 2^5 is read as "the fifth *power* of 2" or as "2 to the 5th power." Write other examples on the board and have students identify the parts of the expression and practice reading the powers.

Review function notation and relate the *squaring function* and the *cubing function* to the area of a square and the volume of a cube, respectively.

Notes on the Lesson

Discuss the properties of power functions listed on page 456. These properties are very helpful in sketching and recognizing graphs of power functions. Though it may seem like a formidable list of properties, actually all the properties can be seen from Example 2 and the Activity.

3 Assignment

Recommended Assignment

- Questions 1–25
- Question 26 (extra credit)
- Reading Lesson 7-2
- Covering the Ideas 7-2

Additional Answers

7a.

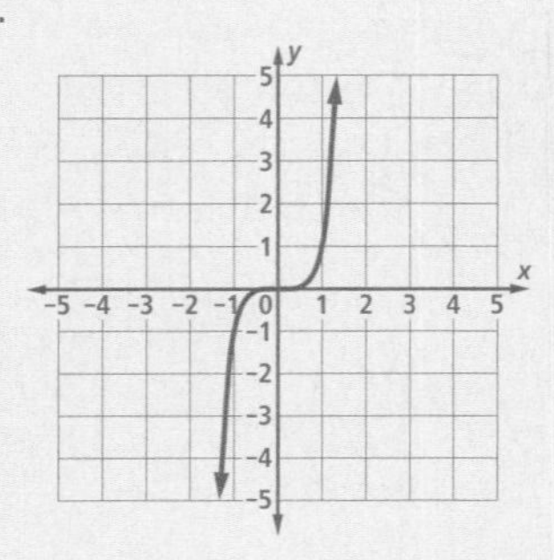

7b. domain: all real numbers; range: all real numbers

7c. rotation symmetry about the origin

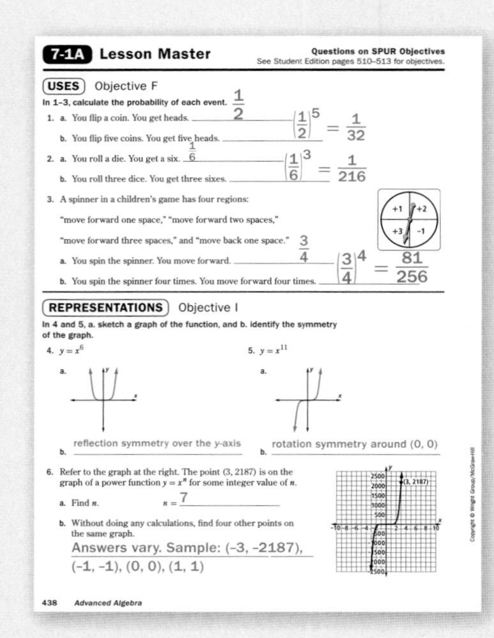

7-1A Lesson Master Questions on SPUR Objectives
See Student Edition pages 510–513 for objectives.

USES Objective F

In 1–3, calculate the probability of each event.

1. a. You flip a coin. You get heads. $\frac{1}{2}$
   b. You flip five coins. You get five heads. $\left(\frac{1}{2}\right)^5 = \frac{1}{32}$
2. a. You roll a die. You get a six. $\frac{1}{6}$
   b. You roll three dice. You get three sixes. $\left(\frac{1}{6}\right)^3 = \frac{1}{216}$
3. A spinner in a children's game has four regions: "move forward one space," "move forward two spaces," "move forward three spaces," and "move back one space."
   a. You spin the spinner. You move forward. $\frac{3}{4}$
   b. You spin the spinner four times. You move forward four times. $\left(\frac{3}{4}\right)^4 = \frac{81}{256}$

REPRESENTATIONS Objective I

In 4 and 5, a. sketch a graph of the function, and b. identify the symmetry of the graph.

4. $y = x^6$
   b. reflection symmetry over the y-axis
5. $y = x^{11}$
   b. rotation symmetry around (0, 0)
6. Refer to the graph at the right. The point (3, 2187) is on the graph of a power function $y = x^n$ for some integer value of n.
   a. Find n. $n = 7$
   b. Without doing any calculations, find four other points on the same graph.
   Answers vary. Sample: (–3, –2187), (–1, –1), (0, 0), (1, 1)

438 *Advanced Algebra*

Properties of Power Functions with Equations $y = x^n$, for integers $n > 0$	n is even.	n is odd.
Some ordered pairs on the graph	(0, 0) (1, 1) (–1, 1)	(0, 0) (1, 1) (–1, –1)
Domain	set of all real numbers	set of all real numbers
Range	$\{y \mid y \geq 0\}$	set of all real numbers
Quadrants	I and II	I and III
Symmetry	Reflection symmetry over the y-axis For all x, $f(x) = f(-x)$.	Rotation symmetry of 180° about the origin For all x, $f(-x) = -f(x)$.

STOP QY3

> **QY3**
> What type of symmetry does the graph of $y = x^{19}$ have?

Questions

COVERING THE IDEAS

1. Given that $2^{10} = 1024$, calculate 2^{11} and 2^{12} without a calculator. 1. 2048; 4096
2. What is the first term of the sequence s with $s_n = (0.9)^n$ in which $s_n < 0.01$? $s_{44} \approx 0.0097$
3. Refer to Example 1. What is the meaning of the number 0.0081 in the table? 3. The probability of an independent event with probability $p = 0.3$ happening four times in a row is 0.0081.
4. A spinner has 5 congruent sectors, as pictured at the right. If the spinner is fair, what is the probability of landing in the blue sector 6 times in 6 spins? $\left(\frac{1}{5}\right)^6 = 0.000064$

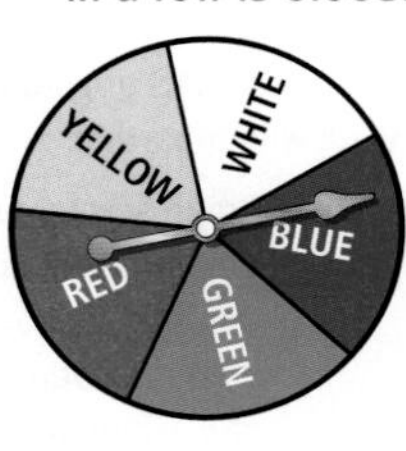

5. Alvin forgot to study for a multiple-choice test with 10 independent questions. Find the probability of getting all questions correct if the probability of getting a single question correct is
   a. 0.5. 0.00098
   b. 0.25. 0.00000095
   c. p. p^{10}
6. What is the function f with equation $f(x) = x^3$ called? the cubing function

In 7 and 8, an equation for a power function f is given.
a. Sketch a graph without plotting points or doing any calculations.
b. State the domain and range of the function.
c. Describe any symmetry the graph may have. 7–8. See margin.

7. $f(x) = x^5$
8. $f(x) = x^{10}$
9. **Fill in the Blanks** If n is even, the range of $y = x^n$ is __?__ and the graph is in Quadrants __?__ and __?__. $\{y \mid y \geq 0\}$; I; II
10. **Fill in the Blanks** If n is odd, the range of $y = x^n$ is __?__ and the graph is in Quadrants __?__ and __?__. all real numbers, I; III

Extension

Have students answer the following questions, where $f(x) = x^n$ and n is a positive integer.

1. If n is even, the graph of every function of this form passes through the same three points. What are the points? (0, 0), (1, 1), and (–1, 1)
2. If n is odd, the graph of every function of this form passes through the same three points. What are the points? (0, 0), (1, 1), and (–1, –1)
3. Do any two different functions of this form have any other points in common? No
4. If n is even, then $f(x) = f(-x)$. Such functions are called *even functions*. Give two examples of functions other than power functions that are even. Answers vary. Sample: $f(x) = |x|$ and $f(x) = \sqrt{x^2 + 5}$
5. If n is odd, then $f(x) = -f(-x)$. Such functions are called *odd functions*. Give two examples of functions other than power functions that are odd. (*Note:* Encourage students to look in a trigonometry book for examples.) Answers vary. Sample: $f(x) = \sin x$ and $f(x) = \tan x$

11. **Multiple Choice** Which of the following graphs could represent the function with equation $y = x^8$? Justify your answer.

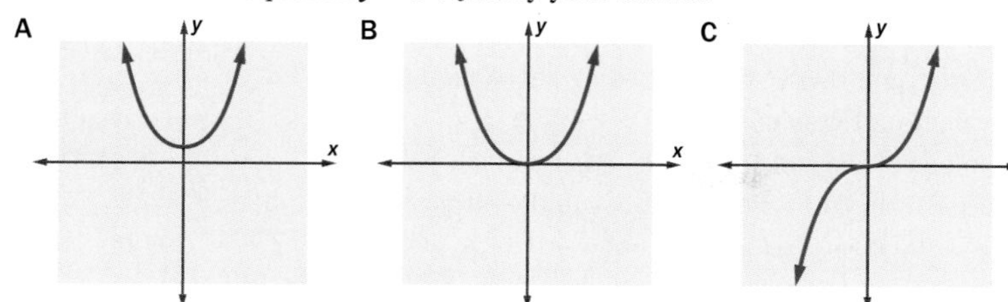

11. B; The graph should pass through the origin and be symmetric over the y-axis. B is the only graph that meets both of these requirements.

APPLYING THE MATHEMATICS

12. Refer to Example 1. Suppose Rosencrantz gets a new fair coin to flip. This coin always seems to alternate heads and tails with each flip: H T H T H T H T H .... Is the pattern H T H T more likely, less likely, or equally as likely as four heads in a row? Justify your answer.

12. equally likely; The probability of each outcome is 0.5, so for any set of four outcomes, $p = (0.5)^4 = 0.0625$.

13. Izzie Wright forgets to study for a history quiz and makes random guesses at each answer. The quiz has 5 true/false questions and 10 multiple-choice questions with 4 choices each.
   a. What is the probability Izzie will guess the correct answer on a true/false question? 0.5
   b. What is the probability Izzie will guess the correct answer on a multiple-choice question? 0.25
   c. Calculate the probability that Izzie will answer all 15 questions correctly. about 2.98×10^{-8} or 0.0000000298

14. **True or False** The graphs of the odd power functions have no minimum or maximum values. true

15. Consider the graph of each function. For what values of x is the graph above the x-axis, and for what values of x is the graph below the x-axis?
   a. $f : x \rightarrow x^{33}$ $x > 0$; $x < 0$
   b. $g : x \rightarrow x^n$, where n is even

15b. all real numbers x such that $x \neq 0$; none

In 16 and 17, write an equation for the *n*th-power function that is graphed.

16.

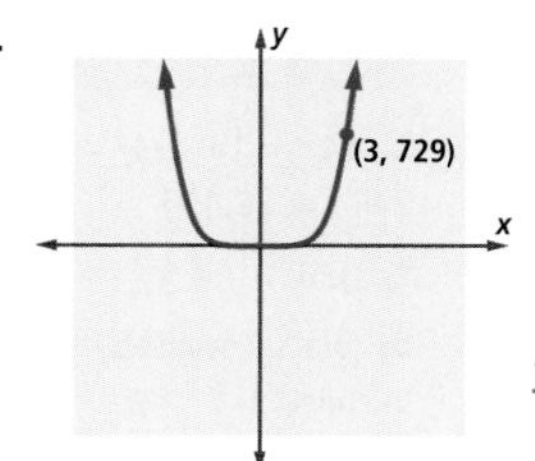

$y = x^6$

17.

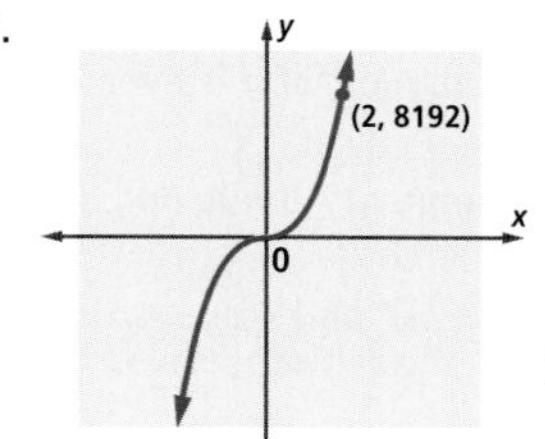

$y = x^{13}$

Notes on the Questions

Question 12 Any particular sequence of 4 H's and T's has the same probability of occurring. However, when dealing with a longer string of flips, certain sequences of 4 H's and T's are more likely to occur sooner than others.

Questions 16 and 17 When discussing these questions, stress that a specific equation is expected. It is easy to see in Question 17 that the equation must be of the form $y = x^n$, where n is odd. The specific point given, (2, 8192), leads to the equation $8192 = 2^n$, from which students can deduce that $n = 13$.

Additional Answers

8a.

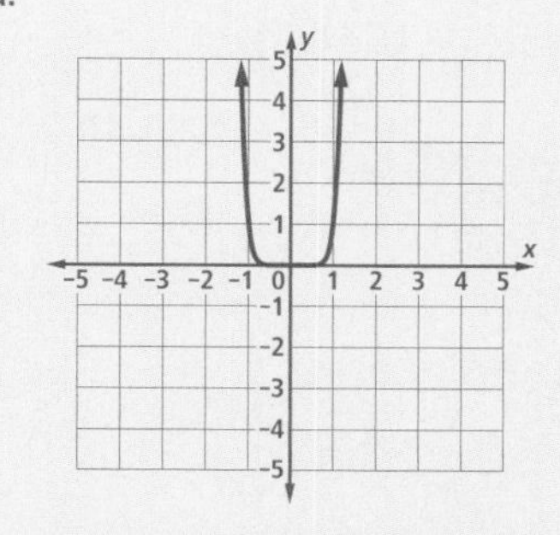

8b. domain: all real numbers; range: $\{y \mid y \geq 0\}$

8c. reflection symmetry over the y-axis

Accommodating the Learner

After completing the lesson, have students work in pairs or small groups. Have them use a graphing utility to graph $f(x) = x^5$, $g(x) = -x^4$, $h(x) = -x^7$, and $k(x) = x^6$. Ask students to describe the similarities and differences among the graphs in relation to the origin and the quadrants in which the graphs are located. Then have students develop a general rule identifying the pairs of quadrants that the graphs of the functions $p(x) = x^n$ and $q(x) = -x^n$ pass through for even and odd values of n.

All four graphs pass through the origin. The graph of $p(x) = x^n$ is in Quadrants I and II for even values of n and in Quadrants I and III for odd values of n. The graph of $q(x) = -x^n$ is in Quadrants III and IV when n is even and in Quadrants II and IV when n is odd.

7-1

Notes on the Questions

Question 25 This question should be discussed, as it sets up Lesson 7-2.

4 Wrap-Up

Ongoing Assessment

Refer students to Example 1 on page 453. Have them write a paragraph explaining how the table would change if the event happened only three times in a row instead of four times. Students should note that the equation for the power function would be $A = p^3$ rather than $A = p^4$, and they should give appropriate values for the second column for this function.

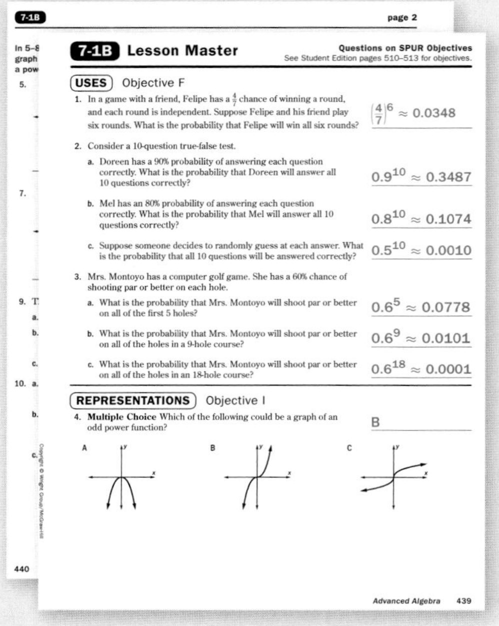

7-1B page 2

In 5–8 graph a pow

7-1B Lesson Master Questions on SPUR Objectives
See Student Edition pages 510–513 for objectives.

USES Objective F

1. In a game with a friend, Felipe has a $\frac{4}{7}$ chance of winning a round, and each round is independent. Suppose Felipe and his friend play six rounds. What is the probability that Felipe will win all six rounds? $\left(\frac{4}{7}\right)^6 \approx 0.0348$
2. Consider a 10-question true-false test.
   a. Doreen has a 90% probability of answering each question correctly. What is the probability that Doreen will answer all 10 questions correctly? $0.9^{10} \approx 0.3487$
   b. Mel has an 80% probability of answering each question correctly. What is the probability that Mel will answer all 10 questions correctly? $0.8^{10} \approx 0.1074$
   c. Suppose someone decides to randomly guess at each answer. What is the probability that all 10 questions will be answered correctly? $0.5^{10} \approx 0.0010$
3. Mrs. Montoyo has a computer golf game. She has a 60% chance of shooting par or better on each hole.
   a. What is the probability that Mrs. Montoyo will shoot par or better on all of the first 5 holes? $0.6^5 \approx 0.0778$
   b. What is the probability that Mrs. Montoyo will shoot par or better on all of the holes in a 9-hole course? $0.6^9 \approx 0.0101$
   c. What is the probability that Mrs. Montoyo will shoot par or better on all of the holes in an 18-hole course? $0.6^{18} \approx 0.0001$

REPRESENTATIONS Objective I

4. **Multiple Choice** Which of the following could be a graph of an odd power function? B

A B C

Copyright © Wright Group/McGraw-Hill

440

Advanced Algebra 439

18. The point (-7, 2401) is on the graph of an even nth power function. What point (other than the origin, (1, 1), and (-1, 1)) must also be on the graph of this function? Why?

18. (7, 2401); Explanations vary. Sample: This must be on the graph because (7, 2401) is the reflection image of image of (-7, 2401) over the y-axis.

19. a. Graph $f(x) = x^2$ and $g(x) = x^6$ on the same set of axes.
    b. For what value(s) of x is $f(x) = g(x)$? $x = -1, 0, 1$
    c. For what values of x is $f(x) > g(x)$? $\{x \mid -1 < x < 1, x \neq 0\}$
    d. As x increases from 0 to 1, what happens to the difference between $f(x)$ and $g(x)$? The difference between $f(x)$ and $g(x)$ increases, then decreases as x increases from 0 to 1.

19a. See margin.

REVIEW

20. **Fill in the Blanks** The graph of the quadratic function Q where $Q(x) = x^2 + 5x + 2$ intersects the x-axis in __?__ point(s) and the y-axis in __?__ point(s). **(Lesson 6-10)** 2; 1

21. a. Write $(1 + i)(1 - i)$ in $a + bi$ form. 2
    b. Calculate $(1 + i)(2 + 3i)(1 - i)$. **(Lesson 6-9)** $4 + 6i$

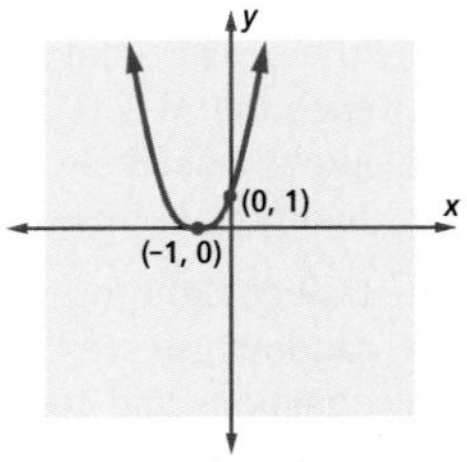

22. Give an equation for the quadratic function graphed at the right. **(Lesson 6-3)** $y = (x + 1)^2$

23. Solve $\begin{cases} x + 2y - 4z = -8 \\ 2x + z = 2 \\ 4x - 4y - z = 16 \end{cases}$. **(Lesson 5-6)** $x = \frac{3}{4}, y = -\frac{27}{8}, z = \frac{1}{2}$

24. In 2006, the St. Louis Cardinals defeated the Detroit Tigers in baseball's World Series. The win-loss records for the two teams in the three regular seasons leading up to this World Series are given in the matrices below. Find a matrix for the total win-loss record of each team over all three seasons. **(Lesson 4-2)** See margin.

	2004 Wins	2004 Losses		2005 W	2005 L		2006 W	2006 L
Detroit	72	90	D	71	91	D	95	67
St. Louis	105	57	SL	100	62	SL	83	78

25. **Fill in the Blank** $2x^{15} \cdot$ __?__ $= 3x^{18}$ **(Previous Course)** $\frac{3}{2}x^3$

EXPLORATION

26. Consider nth power functions with equations of the form $f(x) = ax^n$, where a is any real number. 26a–b. See margin.
    a. What are the domain and range of f if n is even and a is negative?
    b. What are the domain and range of f if n is odd and a is negative?
    c. How do the graphs of $f(x) = ax^n$ and $f(x) = -ax^n$ compare? They are reflection images of each other over the x-axis.

QY ANSWERS

1. $14^4 = 14 \cdot 14^3 = 14 \cdot 2744 = 38{,}416$
2. $(0.6)^n$
3. rotation symmetry about the origin

Additional Answers

24. $\begin{bmatrix} 238 & 248 \\ 288 & 197 \end{bmatrix}$

26a. domain: all real numbers; range: $\{y \mid y \leq 0\}$

26b. domain: all real numbers; range: all real numbers

Lesson 7-2 Properties of Powers

▸ **BIG IDEA** There are single powers equivalent to $x^m \cdot x^n$, $\frac{x^m}{x^n}$, $x^m \cdot y^m$, $\frac{x^m}{y^m}$, and $(x^m)^n$ for all x and y for which these powers are defined.

This lesson reviews the properties of powers for positive integer exponents that you have learned in previous courses. In Lessons 7-3 and 7-7, you will see that these properties also apply to exponents that are negative integers or nonzero rational numbers.

Activity 1

Set a CAS to real-number mode and clear all variables.

Step 1 What does the CAS display when you enter each product of powers?

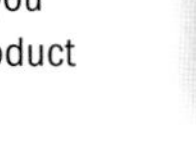

$x^1 \cdot x^1$

a. x^1x^1 x^2 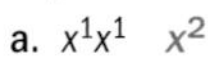 b. x^6x^4 x^{10} 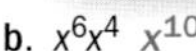 c. x^3x^{12} x^{15}

Step 2 Based on your results in Step 1, write the general property: For all positive integers m and n, $x^mx^n =$ __?__. x^{m+n}

Step 3 What does the CAS display when you enter each power of products?

a. $(x \cdot y)^5$ $x^5 \cdot y^5$ b. $(x \cdot y)^2$ $x^2 \cdot y^2$ c. $(x \cdot y)^{15}$ $x^{15} \cdot y^{15}$

Step 4 Based on your results in Step 3, make a conjecture: $(xy)^m =$ __?__. $x^m \cdot y^m$

Mental Math

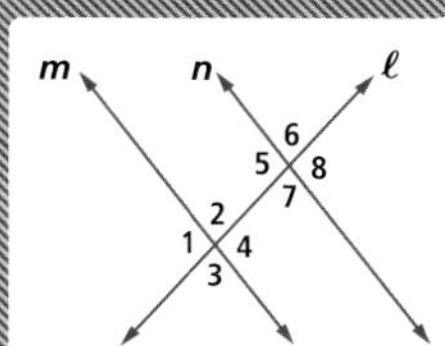

Refer to the diagram above. Assume *m* and *n* are parallel. True or false?

a. ∠1 and ∠7 form a linear pair. false

b. ∠1 and ∠7 are supplementary. true

c. $m\angle 3 = m\angle 6$ true

d. $m\angle 1 + m\angle 8 = m\angle 5 + m\angle 4$ true

Products and Quotients of Powers with the Same Base

The general pattern in Step 2 of Activity 1 is summarized in the following postulate.

Product of Powers Postulate

For any nonnegative base b and nonzero real exponents m and n, or any nonzero base b and integer exponents m and n, $b^m \cdot b^n = b^{m+n}$.

Lesson 7-2

GOAL

Review the six properties of powers in preparation for developing the properties of powers with rational exponents in the lessons that follow.

SPUR Objectives

A Evaluate b^n when $b > 0$ and n is a positive integer.

B Simplify expressions or solve equations using properties of exponents.

E Recognize properties of nth powers.

Materials/Resources

- Lesson Masters 7-2A and 7-2B
- Resource Masters 120–122

HOMEWORK

Suggestions for Assignment

- Questions 1–33
- Question 34 (extra credit)
- Reading Lesson 7-3
- Covering the Ideas 7-3

Local Standards

1 Warm-Up

1. ABC, NBC, and CBS are 3-letter acronyms. How many different 3-letter acronyms are possible using the 26 letters of the English alphabet? 26^3
2. ESPN and NCAA are 4-letter acronyms. How many different 4-letter acronyms are possible using the 26 letters of the English alphabet? 26^4
3. WYSIWYG is a 7-letter acronym. How many different 7-letter acronyms are possible using the 26 letters of the English alphabet? 26^7
4. Why must the answer to Warm-Up 3 be the product of the answers to Warm-Ups 1 and 2? Every 7-letter acronym can be viewed as a choice of a 3-letter acronym followed by a choice of a 4-letter acronym.

Background

Four themes that appear throughout the chapter are found in this lesson: (1) converting between equivalent forms and notations, (2) using the properties of powers to extend the concept of exponents, (3) using a calculator to do certain calculations, and (4) doing mental arithmetic.

Students should not be expected to memorize the names of the properties. However, because the names given here are descriptive, students should be able to give a generalization of a property when given its name. For example, they should know that the Quotient of Powers Theorem deals with the expression $\frac{b^m}{b^n}$ and that the result is b^{m-n}.

Notice that the properties of powers in this lesson are *assumed* for any nonnegative bases and real exponents. This enables us to *prove* such properties as $x^{-n} = \frac{1}{x^n}$. We believe this is more intuitive and efficient

(continued on next page)

2 Teaching

Notes on the Lesson

Even though most students are familiar with them, it is important to discuss the properties of powers because they confuse so many students. When dealing with positive bases and positive integral exponents, the properties seem almost intuitive. However, when negative bases and/or rational exponents are introduced, the properties become less intuitive, and therefore become more important. Point out to students that the properties of powers and roots are also listed in the Summary and Vocabulary on pages 507 and 508.

Activities 1 and 2 The patterns of multiplication and powers of powers are derived in Activities 1 and 2. Students may be able to enter these expressions but not be able to find the decimal equivalents of powers with their calculators. Make certain that students can do this. The most common power key representations are [^], [y^x], and [x^y]. Emphasize that the order of input is as follows: base number, [^], exponent number, and [=].

This and the previous lesson deal primarily with nonnegative bases. Only the repeated multiplication model for powering and the Zero Exponent Theorem allow all bases; this is because they involve integer exponents only. When checking answers with their calculators, some students will likely try powers with negative bases. Students are often surprised to find out that some calculators will not calculate powers with negative bases. To have them test whether or not theirs will, have them try to calculate $(-2.1)^5$. If an error message appears, that particular calculator will not allow the input of a negative base. These students will have to key in the base as a positive number and calculate the sign mentally, using the calculator to find the absolute value of the power.

Consider $10^4 \cdot 10^8 = 10^{12}$. The Product of Powers Postulate shows a correspondence between a product of powers and a sum of exponents.

$$10^4 \cdot 10^8 = 10^{12} \quad \text{and} \quad 4 + 8 = 12.$$

Related facts yield two other correspondences, between quotients of powers and differences of exponents.

$$\frac{10^{12}}{10^4} = 10^8 \quad \text{and} \quad 12 - 4 = 8;$$

$$\frac{10^{12}}{10^8} = 10^4 \quad \text{and} \quad 12 - 8 = 4.$$

In general, from the Product of Powers Postulate, we can prove a theorem about quotients of powers.

Quotient of Powers Theorem

For any positive base b and real exponents m and n, or any nonzero base b and integer exponents m and n, $\frac{b^m}{b^n} = b^{m-n}$.

GUIDED

Example 1

Solve $14^3 \cdot 14^x = 14^{10}$.

Solution Write a correspondence like the one above:

$14^3 \cdot 14^x = 14^{10}$ and ___?___ $+ x =$ ___?___. 3; 10

Now solve for x: $x =$ ___?___. 7

Power of a Product or a Quotient

The general pattern in Step 4 of Activity 1 is summarized in the following postulate.

Power of a Product Postulate

For any nonnegative bases a and b and nonzero real exponent m, or any nonzero bases a and b and integer exponent m, $(ab)^m = a^m b^m$.

You can think about the Power of a Product Postulate as meaning that *powering distributes over multiplication.*

STOP QY1

QY1

Give an example to show that powering does not distribute over addition.

than defining negative exponents and then using the definition to deduce the familiar properties.

The Zero Exponent Theorem, $b^0 = 1$, is proved here for any nonzero real b. When $b = 0$, 0^0 is not defined because it cannot be done in a way such that $z = x^y$ is a continuous function in x and y. Specifically, because $b^0 = 1$, the sequence $1^0, 0.1^0, 0.01^0, 0.001^0, \ldots$ suggests that $0^0 = 1$. However, now consider the sequence $0^1, 0^{0.1}, 0^{0.01}, 0^{0.001}, \ldots$. Because each of these equals 0, as the base is getting closer to zero, it would appear that $0^0 = 0$. This ambiguity is the reason for leaving 0^0 undefined.

Example 2

How many zeros are at the end of the number $N = 2^6 \cdot 5^6 \cdot 17$ when written in base 10?

Solution Use the Power of a Product Postulate.

$2^6 \cdot 5^6 = (2 \cdot 5)^6 = 10^6$. So, $N = 17 \cdot 10^6$, which is 17 followed by six zeros. There are six zeros at the end of the number.

Check Multiply: $2^6 \cdot 5^6 \cdot 17 = 17{,}000{,}000$. It checks.

 QY2

▶ **QY2**

How many zeros are at the end of $5^3 \cdot 13 \cdot 2^3$ when written in base 10?

From the Power of a Product Postulate, a theorem about the power of a quotient can be deduced.

Power of a Quotient Theorem

For any positive bases a and b and real exponent n, or any nonzero bases a and b and integer exponent n, $\left(\frac{a}{b}\right)^n = \frac{a^n}{b^n}$.

Zero as an Exponent

Suppose you divide any power by itself. For instance, consider $\frac{3^7}{3^7}$. By the Quotient of Powers Theorem, $\frac{3^7}{3^7} = 3^{7-7} = 3^0$. But it is also true that $\frac{3^7}{3^7} = 1$. These statements and the Transitive Property of Equality prove that $3^0 = 1$.

In general, for any nonzero real number b,

	$\frac{b^n}{b^n} = b^{n-n}$	Quotient of Powers Theorem
	$= b^0$	Arithmetic
Also,	$\frac{b^n}{b^n} = 1$	A number divided by itself is 1.
So,	$b^0 = 1$	Transitive Property of Equality

This proves the following theorem.

Zero Exponent Theorem

If b is a nonzero real number, $b^0 = 1$.

Notice that the argument above does not work when $b = 0$. 0^0 is not defined because it would involve dividing by 0.

Additional Examples

Example 1 Solve $18^4 \cdot 18^x = 18^{12}$.

Solution Write a correspondence: $18^4 \cdot 18^x = 18^{12}$ and _?_ + x = _?_. 4; 12
Now solve for x: x = _?_. 8

Example 2 How many zeros are at the end of the number $N = 5^5 \cdot 2^5 \cdot 32$ when N is written in base 10? 5

Notes on the Lesson

Zero as an exponent Another justification of the Zero Exponent Theorem is as follows: For any nonzero b and any m, consider $b^0 \cdot b^m$. Using the Product of Powers Postulate, $b^0 \cdot b^m = b^{0+m} = b^m$. Because $b^0 \cdot b^m = b^m$, b^0 must be the multiplicative identity, so it must equal 1.

Note-Taking Tips

Have students include all the postulates and theorems in this lesson in their journals. With each, they should include a numerical example of the statement.

Accommodating the Learner

Two postulates in this lesson—Product of Powers and Power of a Power—are very similar in appearance and may cause some students difficulty. These students may assume that $b^m \cdot b^n = b^{m \cdot n}$. Remind them that if they are unsure how to simplify an expression, they can substitute simple numerical values and evaluate each expression to determine which is correct. For example, is $x^2 \cdot x^3$ equal to x^5 or x^6? For $x = 4$, $16 \cdot 64 = 1024$ and $4^5 = 1024$, while $4^6 = 4096$. They can also use the meaning of positive integer exponents as repeated multiplication to check which is correct: $x^2 \cdot x^3 = (x \cdot x) \cdot (x \cdot x \cdot x) = x^5$, not x^6.

Notes on the Lesson

Example 4 Students should realize that when dealing with numbers written in scientific notation, the user must be facile in dealing with the properties of powers.

Additional Examples

Example 3 A multiple-choice English quiz is 2 pages long. Each page has 6 questions. Each question has c possible choices. How many different ways can you complete the quiz if you leave no answer blank? If each of the 6 questions on one page has c possible choices, there are c^6 ways to answer the questions on that page. Because there are 2 pages, there are $(c^6)^2 = c^{6 \cdot 2} = c^{12}$ ways to complete the quiz.

Example 4 The mass of Earth is about 5.9×10^{24} kilograms, while the mass of Jupiter is about 1.9×10^{27} kilograms. The mass of Jupiter is about how many times the mass of Earth? $\frac{\text{mass of Jupiter}}{\text{mass of Earth}} \approx \frac{1.9 \times 10^{27} \text{ kg}}{5.9 \times 10^{24} \text{ kg}} \approx 0.3 \times 10^{27-24} \approx 0.3 \times 10^3$; the mass of Jupiter is about 300 times the mass of Earth.

Powers of Powers

Activity 2

Set a CAS to real-number mode and clear all variables.

Step 1 What does the CAS display when you enter each power of powers? a. x^6 b. y^{20} c. z^{18} d. 1

a. $(x^3)^2$ **b.** $(y^5)^4$ **c.** $(z^6)^3$ **d.** $(m^0)^5$

Step 2 Based on your results in Step 1, make a conjecture: $(x^m)^n = \underline{\ ?\ }$. x^{mn}

The general pattern in Activity 2 is the last assumed property of powers.

Power of a Power Postulate

For any nonnegative base b and nonzero real exponents m and n, or any nonzero base b and integer exponents m and n, $(b^m)^n = b^{mn}$.

For example, using the Power of a Power Postulate,

$$(a^7)^4 = a^{7 \cdot 4} = a^{28}.$$

You can check this with the Product of Powers Postulate.

$$(a^7)^4 = a^7 \cdot a^7 \cdot a^7 \cdot a^7 = a^{7+7+7+7} = a^{28}$$

Example 3

A multiple-choice test is 3 pages long. Each page has 5 questions. Each question has c possible choices. How many different ways can you complete the test if you leave no answer blank?

Solution 1 If each of the 5 questions on one page has c possible choices, there are c^5 ways to answer the questions on that page. Because there are 3 pages, there are $(c^5)^3 = c^{5 \cdot 3} = c^{15}$ ways to complete the test.

Solution 2 The whole test has $5 \cdot 3 = 15$ questions, each with c choices. So, there are c^{15} ways to answer the questions on the test.

Using the Properties of Powers

Properties of powers are often used when working with numbers expressed in scientific notation.

Accommodating the Learner

Ask students whether $(x^2)^3 = x^{2^3}$. Have them explain their reasoning. $(x^2)^3 \neq x^{2^3}$; Answers vary. Sample: $(x^2)^3 = x^2 \cdot x^2 \cdot x^2 = x^6$ but $x^{2^3} = x^{2 \cdot 2 \cdot 2} = x^8$.

Example 4

In 2005, astronomers using the Hubble Space Telescope discovered two tiny moons, named Hydra and Nix, orbiting Pluto. Hydra's mass is believed to be between 1×10^{17} kg and 9×10^{18} kg. Assume that Hydra's mass is actually 2.4×10^{18} kg. The mass of Earth's moon is 7.35×10^{22} kg. About how many times as massive is Earth's moon as Hydra?

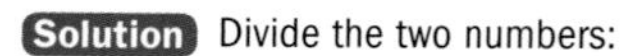

Solution Divide the two numbers:

$$\frac{\text{mass of Earth's moon}}{\text{mass of Hydra}} \approx \frac{7.35 \cdot 10^{22}\text{ kg}}{2.4 \cdot 10^{18}\text{ kg}} = \frac{7.35}{2.4} \cdot \frac{10^{22}}{10^{18}}$$

$$\approx 3 \cdot 10^{22-18} = 3 \cdot 10^4$$

Earth's moon is about 30,000 times as massive as Hydra.

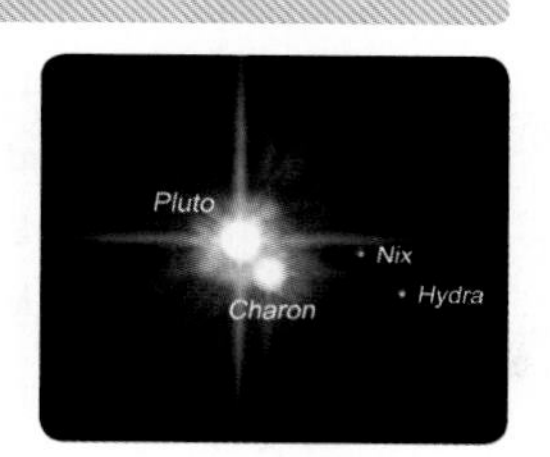

All four of these names have their base in Greek mythology. Nix was named for Nyx, the mother of Charon, and Hydra was named for the nine-headed serpent that guarded Pluto's realm.

Properties of powers can also be used to simplify quotients or products of algebraic expressions containing exponents.

GUIDED

Example 5

Farmers often use circular irrigators on square plots of land, leaving the regions at the corners unirrigated. How does the percentage of irrigated land depend on the radius of the circle?

Solution The diameter of the circle and the side of the square are each $2r$. The area of the circle is πr^2 and the area of the square is $(\underline{\ ?\ })^2 = \underline{\ ?\ }$ by the Power of a Product Postulate. To find the percentage of irrigated land, divide: $2r$; $4r^2$

$$\frac{\text{Area of circle}}{\text{Area of square}} = \frac{\pi r^2}{?} = \frac{\pi}{?} \approx \underline{\ ?\ }.$$ $4r^2$; 4; 0.785

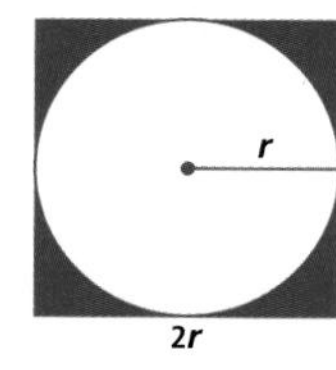

So, regardless of the radius of the circle, $\underline{\ ?\ }$% of the land is irrigated. 78.5

Questions

COVERING THE IDEAS

In 1–5, give an example to illustrate each postulate or theorem.

1. Product of Powers Postulate
2. Power of a Product Postulate
3. Power of a Power Postulate
4. Quotient of Powers Theorem
5. Power of a Quotient Theorem Answers vary. Sample: $\left(\frac{3}{5}\right)^4 = \frac{3^4}{5^4}$

In 6–8, write the expression as a single power using a postulate or theorem from this lesson. Then, check your answer using the repeated multiplication model of powering. 6–8. See margin.

6. $17^3 \cdot 17^4$
7. $(5^2)^3$
8. $\frac{10^5}{10^2}$

1. Answers vary. Sample: $3^2 \cdot 3^3 = 3^5$
2. Answers vary. Sample: $(2 \cdot 5)^2 = 2^2 \cdot 5^2$
3. Answers vary. Sample: $(7^2)^3 = 7^6$
4. Answers vary. Sample: $\frac{5^6}{5^4} = 5^2$

Additional Answers

6. 17^7; $17^3 \cdot 17^4 = (17 \cdot 17 \cdot 17) \cdot (17 \cdot 17 \cdot 17 \cdot 17) = 17 \cdot 17 \cdot 17 \cdot 17 \cdot 17 \cdot 17 \cdot 17 = 17^7$
7. 5^6; $(5^2)^3 = (5 \cdot 5)^3 = (5 \cdot 5)(5 \cdot 5)(5 \cdot 5) = 5 \cdot 5 \cdot 5 \cdot 5 \cdot 5 \cdot 5 = 5^6$
8. 10^3; $\frac{10^5}{10^2} = \frac{10 \cdot 10 \cdot 10 \cdot 10 \cdot 10}{10 \cdot 10} = 10 \cdot 10 \cdot 10 = 10^3$

Notes on the Lesson

Example 5 This example shows the value of not substituting an approximation of π until the problem is finished or nearly completed.

Additional Example

Example 5 A cylindrical can containing three tennis balls fits tightly in a rectangular box, as shown. What percent of the volume of the box is taken up by the cylinder?

TENNIS BALLS

Solution The diameter of the base of the cylinder and the side length of the base of the box are $2r$, where r is the radius of a tennis ball. The height of the cylinder and the box is $6r$. The volume of the cylinder is $\pi r^2 h = \pi r^2 \cdot 6r = 6\pi r^3$. The volume of the box is $\underline{\ ?\ } \cdot \underline{\ ?\ } \cdot \underline{\ ?\ } = \underline{\ ?\ }$. $2r$; $2r$; $6r$; $24r^3$ To find the percent, divide the volume of the cylinder by the volume of the box: $\frac{\text{volume of cylinder}}{\text{volume of box}} = \frac{6\pi r^3}{?} = \underline{\ ?\ }$. $24r^3$; $\frac{\pi}{4}$ So the percent of the volume of the box taken up by the cylinder is approximately $\underline{\ ?\ }$%. 79

3 Assignment

Recommended Assignment

- Questions 1–33
- Question 34 (extra credit)
- Reading Lesson 7-3
- Covering the Ideas 7-3

Notes on the Questions

Questions 11–16 These questions are direct applications of the properties of powers. You might ask students to indicate which property or properties can be used to simplify each expression. There are two ways to indicate the property: by name or by its description using variables.

Question 20 It is a surprise to most students that the answer is identical to that in Example 5. Ask whether anyone can see why without calculating. Each of the 4 circles is inscribed in a square that is $\frac{1}{4}$ the area of the farm. Each circle fills the same percent of the area of that fourth as the larger circle fills of the whole farm, so together they fill the same percent of the total area.

Question 23 You might also ask for the prime factorization of 875^{14}. $5^{42} \cdot 7^{14}$

7-2A Lesson Master — Questions on SPUR Objectives. See Student Edition pages 510–513 for objectives.

SKILLS Objective A

In 1–3, write as a whole number or simple fraction. Do all of the work in your head.

1. $147^1 =$ 147
2. $\left(\frac{2}{3}\right)^4 =$ $\frac{16}{81}$
3. $423^0 =$ 1

SKILLS Objective B

In 4–6, rewrite as a single power. Do all of the work in your head.

4. $43^2 \cdot 43^7 =$ 43^9
5. $2^8 \cdot 5^8 =$ 10^8
6. $\frac{12^{13}}{12^{11}} =$ 12^2

In 7–12, simplify the expression by hand; check with a CAS if necessary.

7. $x^3 \cdot x^5$ x^8
8. $(3a)^2(2a)^3$ $72a^5$
9. $\frac{12t^7}{3t^4}$ $4t^3$
10. $(-12n)^2(-5n^2)^3$ $-18{,}000n^8$
11. $\frac{(6c)^2}{(2d^3)^2}$ $\frac{9c^2}{d^6}$
12. $\frac{a^2b^3c^4}{bc^2d^4}$ $\frac{a^2b^2c^2}{d^4}$
13. Solve for a: $4^a \cdot 4^7 = 4^9$ $a = 2$
14. Solve for n: $(5^2)^n = 5^{12}$ $n = 6$

PROPERTIES Objective E

15. If $a = 7$ and $b = 4$, then $x^a \cdot x^b = x^{11}$. Find three other pairs of positive integers that are solutions to this equation. Answers vary. Samples: $a = 1$ and $b = 10$, $a = 3$ and $b = 8$, $a = 6$ and $b = 5$
16. How many zeros are at the end of the number $N = 2^{16} \cdot 3^{17} \cdot 5^{18} \cdot 19$ when written in base 10? 16
17. Write an expression equivalent to $24x^{10}$ using Answers vary. Samples are given.
    a. the Product of Powers Postulate. $6x^3 \cdot 4x^7$
    b. the Quotient of Powers Theorem. $\frac{48x^{12}}{2x^2}$
    c. more than one of the postulates and theorems in this lesson. $\frac{(9x^2)(2x^5)^3}{3x^7}$

Advanced Algebra 441

9. What postulate or theorem justifies $\left(\frac{2}{y}\right)^4 = \frac{16}{y^4}$? 9. Power of a Quotient Theorem
10. Solve $6^{2x} \cdot 6^3 = 6^7$ for x. $x = 2$

In 11–16, simplify by hand and check using a CAS.

11. $\frac{n^{77}}{n^7}$ n^{70}
12. $60m^6 \cdot \frac{m^3}{6}$ $10m^9$
13. $(3x^4)^3$ $27x^{12}$
14. $\frac{w^8}{(w^4)^2}$ 1
15. $v^2 \cdot v^{a-2}$ v^a
16. $j^{289} \cdot j^0$ j^{289}
17. How many zeros are at the end of $2^8 \cdot 3^{10} \cdot 5^6$ when written in base 10? 6
18. A multiple-choice test has 6 pages and 5 questions on each page. If each question can be answered in a different ways, how many ways are there to complete the test? a^{30}
19. Refer to Example 4. Pluto itself has a mass of approximately 1.3×10^{22} kg. How many times as massive is Pluto than its moon Hydra? about 5417 times

APPLYING THE MATHEMATICS

20. Refer to Example 5. Suppose the farmer decides to split the field into four smaller squares of side length r and irrigate each one separately.
    a. Compute the total area of the four circles. πr^2
    b. Compute the percent of the field that is irrigated in the new arrangement. about 78.5%

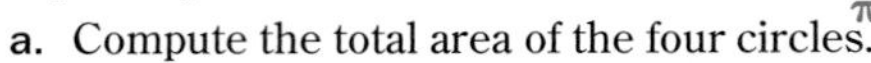

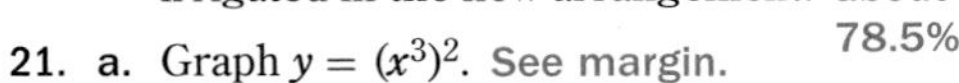

Many farmers irrigate their crops using a center pivot irrigation system.

21. a. Graph $y = (x^3)^2$. See margin.
    b. Find a number n such that the graph of $y = x^n$ coincides with the graph in Part a. 6
22. a. Check that $\left(\frac{x^{12}}{x^{10}}\right)\left(\frac{x}{2}\right)^2 = \frac{x^4}{4}$ by graphing the functions $f(x) = \left(\frac{x^{12}}{x^{10}}\right)\left(\frac{x}{2}\right)^2$ and $g(x) = \frac{x^4}{4}$ separately. See margin.
    b. Is this check more or less reliable than testing whether the equation is true for a single value of x?

    22b. It is a more reliable check because graphing allows you to compare the equations over a range of values rather than at only one value.
23. The prime factorization of 875 is $5^3 \cdot 7$. The prime factorization of 8575 is $5^2 \cdot 7^3$. Use this information to find the prime factorization of $875 \cdot 8575$. $5^5 \cdot 7^4$
24. Waneta computed $(40)^3$ and obtained the answer 640. Does her answer end with enough zeros to be correct? How do you know? What is the correct answer?
    No her answer does not have enough zeros; since $(40)^3 = (4 \cdot 10)^3 = 4^3 \cdot 1000 = 64{,}000$, the answer ends with three zeros.

Additional Answers

21a.

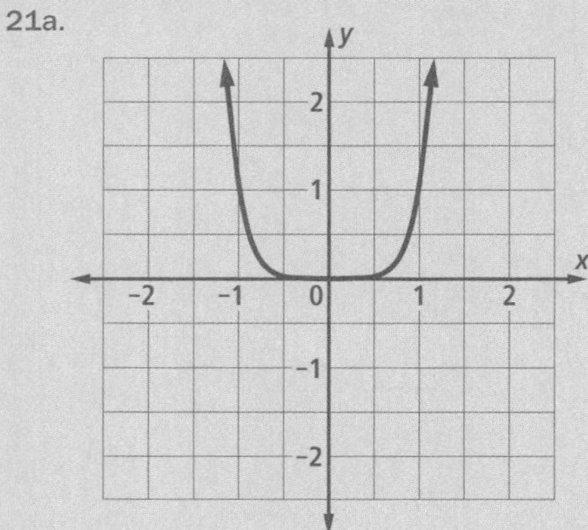

22a. Both graphs are identical to the one below.

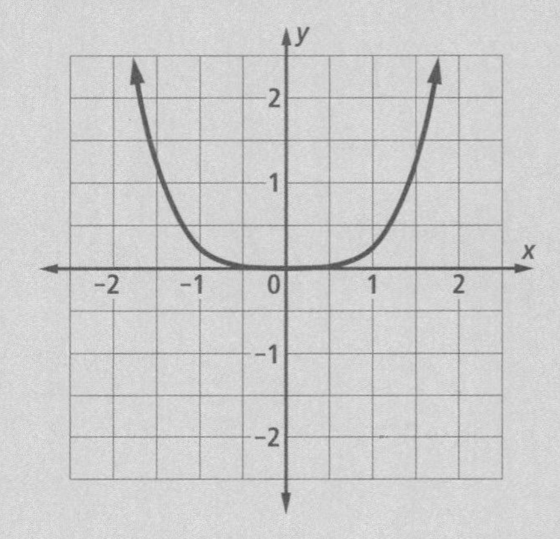

25. x^3 and x^4 are powers of x whose product is x^7. Find three more pairs of powers of x whose product is x^7.

26. Below is a proof of the Quotient of Powers Theorem. Suppose b is a nonzero real number, and n and m are integers. Fill in each justification.

$b^{m-n} \cdot b^n = b^{(m-n)+n}$ a. ___?___

$= b^{m+(-n+n)}$ b. ___?___

$= b^{m+0}$ c. ___?___

$b^{m-n} \cdot b^n = b^m$ d. ___?___

$b^{m-n} = \frac{b^m}{b^n}$ e. ___?___

In 27–29, write an equivalent expression in which each variable appears once.

27. $\frac{18x^4}{(-3x^2)^3}$ $\frac{-2}{3x^2}$

28. $\frac{8a^2b^6c^8}{(4a)^2b^6c^6}$ $\frac{c^2}{2}$

29. $\left(\frac{8}{w^3}\right)^2\left(\frac{w^2}{4}\right)^3$ 1

25. Answers vary. Sample: $x^2 \cdot x^5$; $x^1 \cdot x^6$; $x^0 \cdot x^7$

26a. Product of Powers Postulate

26b. Associative Property of Addition

26c. additive inverses

26d. additive identity

26e. Divide both sides by b^n.

REVIEW

30. **Fill in the Blank** The graph of $f(x) = x^n$ has rotation symmetry whenever n is ___?___. **(Lesson 7-1)** odd

31. **Fill in the Blank** The graph of $f(x) = x^n$ has reflection symmetry whenever n is ___?___. **(Lesson 7-1)** even

32. How many real roots does the quadratic equation $2p^2 - 4p + 2 = 0$ have? **(Lesson 6-10)** 1

33. Calculate $\sqrt{-3} \cdot \sqrt{-5} \cdot \sqrt{-15}$. **(Lesson 6-8)** $-15i$

EXPLORATION

34. a. Copy and fill in the table at the right. What do you notice about the last digits of your answers? 34a–b. See margin.

n	1	2	3	4	5	6	7	8	9	10
n^5	?	?	?	?	?	?	?	?	?	?

b. Copy and fill in the table at the right using scientific notation. Round the constant to the nearest tenth.

n	10	20	30	40	50	60	70	80	90	100
n^5	?	?	?	?	?	?	?	?	?	?

c. An old magic trick has a member of the audience pick a number n between 1 and 99, compute n^5, and tell the magician the result. The magician then instantly tells the audience member the original number by using the observation in Part a to determine the number's last digit, and by comparing the size of the number to the values in the second table (which the magician memorizes) to determine the number's first digit. For example, the audience member might say the number 1,419,857. Use the tables above (but no calculator) to determine the original number. 17

QY ANSWERS

1. Answers vary. Sample: $(a + b)^3 \neq a^3 + b^3$. Let $a = 1$, $b = 1$. The left side is equal to 8, the right side is equal to 2.

2. 3 zeros

Additional Answers

34a.

n	1	2	3	4	5
n^5	1	32	243	1,024	3,125

n	6	7	8	9	10
n^5	7,776	16,807	32,768	59,049	100,000

The last digit is n.

34b.

n	10	20	30	40	50
n^5	1.0×10^5	3.2×10^6	2.4×10^7	1.0×10^8	3.1×10^8

n	60	70	80	90	100
n^5	7.8×10^8	1.7×10^9	3.3×10^9	5.9×10^9	1.0×10^{10}

Notes on the Questions

Question 25 By extending the pattern $x^2 \cdot x^5 = x^7$, $x^1 \cdot x^6 = x^7$, $x^0 \cdot x^7 = x^7$, one sees that $x^{-1} \cdot x^8$ also equals x^7. This leads directly into Lesson 7-3.

Question 26 Neither the theorem nor this proof requires that m and n be integers, but we have not yet discussed powers with rational exponents.

4 Wrap-Up

Ongoing Assessment

Have students work in pairs. Have each student write five expressions that can be simplified by applying the properties of powers in this lesson. Have students exchange papers with their partner and simplify the expressions. Then have students correct each other's work and discuss any errors. Students should correctly apply the power properties to simplify expressions with exponents.

Project Update

Project 3, *Sums of Powers,* on page 505 relates to the content of this lesson.

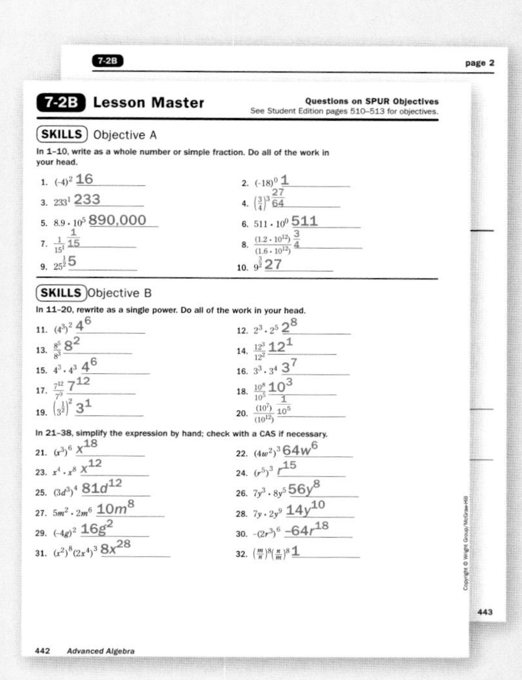
7-2B page 2

7-2B Lesson Master

Questions on SPUR Objectives
See Student Edition pages 510–513 for objectives.

SKILLS Objective A

In 1–10, write as a whole number or simple fraction. Do all of the work in your head.

1. $(-4)^2$ 16
2. $(-18)^0$ 1
3. 233^1 233
4. $\left(\frac{3}{4}\right)^3$ $\frac{27}{64}$
5. $8.9 \cdot 10^5$ 890,000
6. $511 \cdot 10^0$ 511
7. $\frac{1}{15^1}$ $\frac{1}{15}$
8. $\frac{(1.2 \cdot 10^{12})}{(1.6 \cdot 10^{12})}$ $\frac{3}{4}$
9. $25^{\frac{1}{2}}$ 5
10. $9^{\frac{3}{2}}$ 27

SKILLS Objective B

In 11–20, rewrite as a single power. Do all of the work in your head.

11. $(4^3)^2$ 4^6
12. $2^3 \cdot 2^5$ 2^8
13. $\frac{8^5}{8^3}$ 8^2
14. $\frac{12^3}{12^2}$ 12^1
15. $4^3 \cdot 4^3$ 4^6
16. $3^3 \cdot 3^4$ 3^7
17. $\frac{7^{12}}{7^0}$ 7^{12}
18. $\frac{10^8}{10^5}$ 10^3
19. $\left(3^{\frac{1}{2}}\right)^2$ 3^1
20. $\frac{(10^7)}{(10^{12})}$ $\frac{1}{10^5}$

In 21–38, simplify the expression by hand; check with a CAS if necessary.

21. $(x^3)^6$ x^{18}
22. $(4w^2)^3$ $64w^6$
23. $x^4 \cdot x^8$ x^{12}
24. $(r^5)^3$ r^{15}
25. $(3d^3)^4$ $81d^{12}$
26. $7y^3 \cdot 8y^5$ $56y^8$
27. $5m^2 \cdot 2m^6$ $10m^8$
28. $7y \cdot 2y^9$ $14y^{10}$
29. $(-4g)^2$ $16g^2$
30. $-(2r^3)^6$ $-64r^{18}$
31. $(x^2)^8(2x^4)^3$ $8x^{28}$
32. $\left(\frac{m}{n}\right)^8\left(\frac{n}{m}\right)^8$ 1

Copyright © Wright Group/McGraw-Hill

443

442 Advanced Algebra

Lesson 7-3

GOAL

Learn and apply the property $x^{-n} = \frac{1}{x^n}$ to evaluate and work with negative exponents.

SPUR Objectives

A Evaluate b^n when $b > 0$ and n is a negative integer.

B Simplify expressions or solve equations using properties of exponents.

Materials/Resources

- Lesson Masters 7-3A and 7-3B
- Resource Masters 123 and 124
- Quiz 1
- CAS

HOMEWORK

Suggestions for Assignment

- Questions 1–31
- Question 32 (extra credit)
- Reading Lesson 7-4
- Covering the Ideas 7-4

Local Standards

1 Warm-Up

Calculate powers of the fraction $\frac{3}{5}$. What pattern emerges?

1. $\left(\frac{3}{5}\right)^4$ $\frac{81}{625}$
2. $\left(\frac{3}{5}\right)^3$ $\frac{27}{125}$
3. $\left(\frac{3}{5}\right)^2$ $\frac{9}{25}$
4. $\left(\frac{3}{5}\right)^1$ $\frac{3}{5}$
5. $\left(\frac{3}{5}\right)^0$ 1
6. $\left(\frac{3}{5}\right)^{-1}$ $\frac{5}{3}$
7. $\left(\frac{3}{5}\right)^{-2}$ $\frac{25}{9}$

Each answer is the previous answer divided by $\frac{3}{5}$.

Lesson 7-3 Negative Integer Exponents

BIG IDEA The powers x^m and x^{-m} represent reciprocals when they are both defined.

Because of the Quotient of Powers Theorem, for any positive base b and real exponents m and n, or any nonzero base b and integer exponents m and n,

$$\frac{b^m}{b^n} = b^{m-n}.$$

Let us look at this theorem in terms of the values of m and n. If $m > n$, then $m - n$ is positive and b^{m-n} is the product of $(m - n)$ b's. If $m = n$, then $m - n = 0$, and $b^{m-n} = b^0 = 1$. What happens when $m < n$? Then $m - n < 0$, and b^{m-n} has a negative exponent. You have seen negative exponents with base 10 before when writing numbers in scientific notation. For example,

$$10^6 = 1{,}000{,}000 = \text{one million}$$
$$10^{-6} = 0.000001 = \text{one millionth.}$$

Note that $1{,}000{,}000 \cdot 0.000001 = 1$. This means 10^6 and 10^{-6} are reciprocals. The same kind of relationship holds for bases other than 10.

Mental Math

What must be added to each expression to create a perfect-square trinomial?

a. $x^2 + 4x$ 4

b. $x^2 + 4x - 7$ 11

c. $x^2 + bx$ $\left(\frac{b}{2}\right)^2$

d. $x^2 + bx + c$ $\left(\frac{b}{2}\right)^2 - c$

Activity

MATERIALS CAS

Step 1 What does a CAS display when you enter the following powers of x?

a. x^{-3} $\frac{1}{x^3}$ b. x^{-8} $\frac{1}{x^8}$ c. x^{-11} $\frac{1}{x^{11}}$

Step 2 Based on the results of Step 1, make a conjecture: $x^{-n} =$ __?__. Test your conjecture by entering x^{-n} into a CAS. If your calculator does not rewrite x^{-n}, use `expand(x^-n)` to create an equivalent expression with only positive exponents. $\frac{1}{x^n}$

The results of the Activity should be instances of the theorem at the top of the next page.

Background

In many developments of exponents, one first *supposes* that the properties of powers are true for negative exponents. One then deduces that x^{-n} would have to equal the reciprocal of x^n if the properties are still to be satisfied, and x^{-n} is defined to agree with that treatment. Finally, if one wishes to be rigorous, the properties of powers are deduced for negative exponents.

The approach taken in this book is simpler. We have already *assumed* that the properties of powers hold for all real exponents. Then, from these properties, we *prove* that x^{-n} is the reciprocal of x^n.

Notice that the Negative Exponent Theorem holds for both integer and noninteger negative exponents, but at this point students are expected to understand the Negative Exponent Theorem only when the exponent is an integer. The reason that the theorem does not hold when the base is negative and the exponent is not an integer is explained in Lesson 7-7.

Negative Exponent Theorem

For any positive base b and real exponent n, or any nonzero base b and integer exponent n, $b^{-n} = \frac{1}{b^n}$.

Proof

1.	Suppose $b^{-n} = x$.	We want to determine x.
2.	$b^n \cdot b^{-n} = b^n \cdot x$	Multiplication Property of Equality (Multiply both sides by b^n.)
3.	$b^0 = b^n \cdot x$	Product of Powers Postulate
4.	$1 = b^n \cdot x$	Zero Exponent Theorem
5.	$\frac{1}{b^n} = x$	Divide both sides by b^n (which can always be done because $b \neq 0$).
6.	Thus $b^{-n} = \frac{1}{b^n}$.	Transitive Property of Equality (Steps 1 and 5)

It helps to think of the Negative Exponent Theorem as stating that b^n and b^{-n} are reciprocals. In particular, $b^{-1} = \frac{1}{b}$, so b^{-1} is the reciprocal of b.

GUIDED

Example 1

Write 2^{-5} as a decimal.

Solution By the Negative Exponent Theorem, $2^{-5} = \frac{1}{?}$ as a fraction and __?__ as a decimal. 2^5; 0.03125

The Negative Exponent Theorem allows expressions with fractions to be rewritten without them.

Example 2

Critical buckling load **is the minimum weight that would cause a column to buckle. Rewrite Euler's formula for critical buckling load, $P = \frac{\pi^2 EI}{L^2}$, using negative exponents and no fractions. (In this formula, E is a constant related to the material used to construct the column, I is the moment of inertia of a cross-section of the column, and L is the length of the column.)**

Solution $P = \frac{\pi^2 EI}{L^2}$

$P = \pi^2 EI \frac{1}{L^2}$ Algebraic definition of division

$P = \pi^2 EIL^{-2}$ Negative Exponent Theorem

READING MATH

In many math-related fields the term *critical* refers to a point or measurement at which some quality undergoes a drastic change. In the case of critical buckling load, this change is from stable to collapsed.

Extension

Have students use a graphing utility to graph power functions with negative integer exponents. Then have them summarize characteristics in the same way as the properties of power functions with positive integer exponents were summarized in Lesson 7-1. Answers vary. Sample: Each graph approaches the x-axis and the y-axis without touching either of them. Each function has as its domain the set of all real numbers except zero. If the exponent is an even negative integer, the range is the set of all real numbers greater than zero. If the exponent is an odd negative integer, the range is the set of all real numbers except zero. If the exponent is even, the graph is symmetric about the y-axis. If the exponent is odd, the graph is symmetric about the origin.

2 Teaching

Notes on the Lesson

Many students will be familiar with negative integers as exponents from their work with scientific notation. In many cases, however, their concept of this notation involves "moving the decimal point," not the operation of multiplication or division that is involved.

Point out that multiplying by 10^6 moves the decimal point of the other factor 6 places to the right because we are multiplying by 1,000,000. When we multiply by 10^{-6}, we are multiplying by 0.000001, or dividing by 1,000,000. Remind students that multiplying by 10^{-6} is the same as dividing by 10^6. So $10^{-6} = \frac{1}{10^6}$.

Stress that the negative sign before an exponent should be a flag to students that says "reciprocal of the base" each time they see it. A negative sign in an exponent *never* affects the sign of the power.

In addition to evaluating expressions such as 5^{-3}, 3^{-6}, and $10^{-3} \cdot 10^{-6}$, students should learn to handle negative exponents in expressions and sentences with variables, as illustrated in Example 2. This is an excellent time to review inverse and combined variation problems. If y varies directly as the nth power of x, then y varies inversely as the $-n$th power of x.

The use of negative exponents, in fact, leads to an alternate definition of variation: A variation is a relationship of the form $y = kx^n$. When $n > 0$, it is a direct variation; when $n < 0$, it is an inverse variation.

Error Analysis When students are asked to write an equation with only positive exponents, many will make a common error. When a term consists of more than one variable, such as $z = xy^{-3}$, some students will write $z = \frac{1}{xy^3}$. Stress that in xy^{-3}, only y can be thought of as being to the -3 power. So $z = xy^{-3} = \frac{x}{y^3}$.

Additional Examples

Example 1 Write 4^{-3} as a decimal.

Solution By the Negative Exponent Theorem, $4^{-3} = \underline{\ ?\ }$ as a fraction and $\underline{\ ?\ }$ as a decimal. $\frac{1}{4^3}$; 0.015625

Example 2 Rewrite Newton's Law of Universal Gravitation, $F_g = \frac{Gm_1m_2}{r^2}$, using negative exponents and no fractions. In this formula, F_g is the gravitational force between two objects, m_1 and m_2 are the masses of the two objects, r is the distance between the objects, and G is the universal gravitational constant. $F_g = Gm_1m_2r^{-2}$

Example 3 Rewrite each expression using a single exponent.

a. $\frac{p^9}{p^{14}}$ (assume $p > 0$)

b. $5^{-4} \cdot 5^8$

c. $(4 \cdot 2^5)^2 \cdot (2.5 \cdot 2^{-3})$

Solution

a. Use the Quotient of Powers Theorem:
$\frac{p^9}{p^{14}} = p^{\underline{\ ?\ } - \underline{\ ?\ }} = p^{\underline{\ ?\ }}$
9; 14; –5

b. Use the Product of Powers Postulate:
$5^{-4} \cdot 5^8 = 5^{\underline{\ ?\ } + \underline{\ ?\ }} = 5^{\underline{\ ?\ }}$
–4; 8; 4

c. Use the Power of a Product and Power of a Power Postulates:
$(4 \cdot 2^5)^2 \cdot (2.5 \cdot 2^{-3}) =$
$(\underline{\ ?\ } \cdot 2^{\underline{\ ?\ }}) \cdot (2.5 \cdot 2^{-3})$
4^2; 10
Use the Commutative Property of Multiplication and the Product of Powers Postulate:
$\underline{\ ?\ } \cdot (2^{\underline{\ ?\ }})(2^{-3}) = \underline{\ ?\ } \cdot 2^{\underline{\ ?\ }}$
16 · 2.5; 10; 40; 7

Example 4 Rewrite $(4a)^4(2a)^{-3}$ as a fraction with the variable a appearing only once. $\frac{4^4 \cdot a}{2^3}$

Note-Taking Tips

Have students add the Negative Exponent Theorem and an appropriate example to their journals.

Properties of Negative Integer Exponents

All the postulates and theorems involving powers stated in Lesson 7-2 hold when the exponents are negative integers.

GUIDED

Example 3

Rewrite each expression as a single power or a single number in scientific notation.

a. $\frac{r^5}{r^{12}}$ (Assume $r > 0$.) b. $4^{-3} \cdot 4^5$ c. $(2 \cdot 10^3)^2 \cdot (1.5 \cdot 10^{-2})$

Solution

a. Use the Quotient of Powers Theorem.
$\frac{r^5}{r^{12}} = r^{\underline{\ ?\ } - \underline{\ ?\ }} = r^{\underline{\ ?\ }}$ 5; 12; –7

b. Use the Product of Powers Postulate.
$4^{-3} \cdot 4^5 = 4^{\underline{\ ?\ } + \underline{\ ?\ }} = 4^{\underline{\ ?\ }}$ –3; 5; 2

c. Use the Power of a Product and Power of a Power Postulates.
$(2 \cdot 10^3)^2 \cdot (1.5 \cdot 10^{-2}) = (\underline{\ ?\ } \cdot 10^{\underline{\ ?\ }}) \cdot (1.5 \cdot 10^{-2})$ 4; 6
Use the Commutative Property of Multiplication and the Product of Powers Postulate.
$\underline{\ ?\ } \cdot 10^{\underline{\ ?\ }}(10^{-2}) = \underline{\ ?\ } \cdot 10^{\underline{\ ?\ }}$ 6; 6; 6; 4

Check Use a CAS to check whether the original expression and your answer are equivalent.

Caution: A negative number in an exponent does not make the value of an expression negative. All powers of positive numbers are positive.

Example 4

Rewrite $(3c)^{-3}(2c)^4$ as a fraction with the variable c appearing only once.

Solution 1

$(3c)^{-3}(2c)^4 = 3^{-3} \cdot c^{-3} \cdot 2^4 \cdot c^4$	Power of a Product Postulate
$= 3^{-3} \cdot 2^4 \cdot c^{-3} \cdot c^4$	Commutative Property of Multiplication
$= 3^{-3} \cdot 2^4 \cdot c$	Product of Powers Postulate
$= \frac{1}{3^3} \cdot 2^4 \cdot c$	Negative Exponent Theorem
$= \frac{16c}{27}$	

Accommodating the Learner ↑

Have students simplify and rewrite $\left(\frac{2x^{-3}}{y^{-4}z^5}\right)^{-2}$ without negative exponents. $\frac{x^6z^{10}}{4y^8}$

Accommodating the Learner ↓

If students are having difficulty understanding the meaning of negative exponents, you might have them choose a positive value of x and any real value of n. Have them evaluate x^n and x^{-n} with their calculators. Then have them find the reciprocal of each expression to verify that it is equal to the other expression.

Solution 2

$(3c)^{-3}(2c)^4 = \frac{1}{(3c)^3} \cdot (2c)^4$ Negative Exponent Theorem

$= \frac{(2c)^4}{(3c)^3}$ Multiply.

$= \frac{2^4 \cdot c^4}{3^3 \cdot c^3}$ Power of a Product Postulate

$= \frac{2^4 c}{3^3}$ Quotient of Powers Postulate

$= \frac{16c}{27}$

Questions

COVERING THE IDEAS

In 1 and 2, write as a single power.

1. $\frac{t^3}{t^{10}}$ t^{-7}
2. $\frac{6^6}{6^7}$ 6^{-1}

In 3 and 4, write an equivalent expression without negative exponents.

3. x^{-4} $\frac{1}{x^4}$
4. 3^{-7} $\frac{1}{3^7}$
5. Solve for n: $8^{-7} = \frac{1}{8^n}$. 7
6. If $p^{-1} = \frac{4}{13}$, find p. $\frac{13}{4}$
7. Write as a whole number or a fraction without an exponent.
   a. 1.8^0 1
   b. 1.8^{-1} $\frac{5}{9}$
   c. 1.8^{-2} $\frac{25}{81}$
8. Write as a fraction without an exponent.
   a. 9^{-1} $\frac{1}{9}$
   b. 9^{-3} $\frac{1}{729}$
   c. 9^{-5} $\frac{1}{59{,}049}$
9. Write 8^{-3}
   a. as a decimal. 0.001953125
   b. in scientific notation. $1.953125 \cdot 10^{-3}$
10. The time t it takes you to read a book is inversely proportional to the number p of pages in the book. Let k be the constant of variation.
    a. Write an inverse variation equation to represent this situation using positive exponents. $t = \frac{k}{p}$
    b. Rewrite your inverse variation equation using negative exponents. $t = kp^{-1}$

In 11–13, write an equivalent expression without negative exponents.

11. $\frac{10y}{15y^{-2}}$ $\frac{2y^3}{3}$
12. $(3e^2)^{-3}(5e)^4$ $\frac{625}{27e^2}$
13. $\frac{2a^{-3}}{b^4}$ $\frac{2}{a^3b^4}$

In 14–16, write an equivalent expression without an exponent.

14. $10^4 \cdot 10^{-5}$ $\frac{1}{10}$
15. $1.982^0 \cdot 1^{47}$ 1
16. $3^{-3} \cdot \left(\frac{1}{3}\right)^{-1}$ $\frac{1}{9}$

3 Assignment

Recommended Assignment

- Questions 1–31
- Question 32 (extra credit)
- Reading Lesson 7-4
- Covering the Ideas 7-4

Notes on the Questions

Questions 14–16 Encourage students to simplify these expressions by using mental arithmetic.

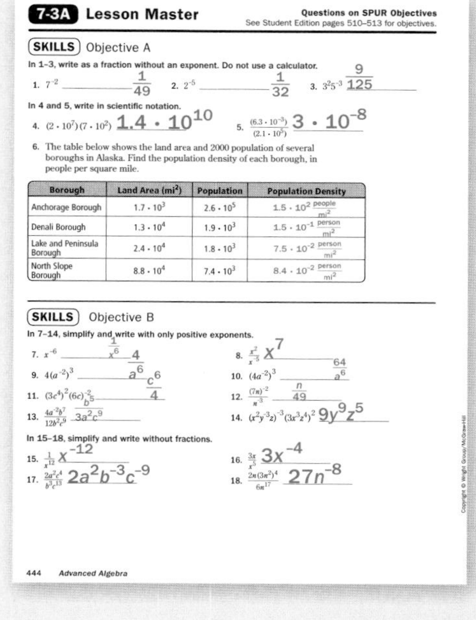

7-3A Lesson Master Questions on SPUR Objectives
See Student Edition pages 510–513 for objectives.

SKILLS Objective A

In 1–3, write as a fraction without an exponent. Do not use a calculator.

1. 7^{-2} $\frac{1}{49}$
2. 2^{-5} $\frac{1}{32}$
3. $3^2 5^{-3}$ $\frac{9}{125}$

In 4 and 5, write in scientific notation.

4. $(2 \cdot 10^7)(7 \cdot 10^2)$ $1.4 \cdot 10^{10}$
5. $\frac{(6.3 \cdot 10^{-3})}{(2.1 \cdot 10^5)}$ $3 \cdot 10^{-8}$
6. The table below shows the land area and 2000 population of several boroughs in Alaska. Find the population density of each borough, in people per square mile.

Borough	Land Area (mi^2)	Population	Population Density
Anchorage Borough	$1.7 \cdot 10^3$	$2.6 \cdot 10^5$	$1.5 \cdot 10^2 \frac{people}{mi^2}$
Denali Borough	$1.3 \cdot 10^4$	$1.9 \cdot 10^3$	$1.5 \cdot 10^{-1} \frac{person}{mi^2}$
Lake and Peninsula Borough	$2.4 \cdot 10^4$	$1.8 \cdot 10^3$	$7.5 \cdot 10^{-2} \frac{person}{mi^2}$
North Slope Borough	$8.8 \cdot 10^4$	$7.4 \cdot 10^3$	$8.4 \cdot 10^{-2} \frac{person}{mi^2}$

SKILLS Objective B

In 7–14, simplify and write with only positive exponents.

7. x^{-6} $\frac{1}{x^6}$
8. $\frac{x^2}{x^{-5}}$ x^7
9. $4(a^{-2})^3$ $\frac{4}{a^6}$
10. $(4a^{-2})^3$ $\frac{64}{a^6}$
11. $(3c^4)^2(6c)^{-2}$ $\frac{c^6}{4}$
12. $\frac{(7n)^{-2}}{n^{-3}}$ $\frac{n}{49}$
13. $\frac{4a^{-2}b^7}{12b^2c^9}$ $\frac{b^5}{3a^2c^9}$
14. $(x^2y^{-3}z)^{-3}(3x^3z^4)^2$ $9y^9z^5$

In 15–18, simplify and write without fractions.

15. $\frac{1}{x^{12}}$ x^{-12}
16. $\frac{3x}{x^5}$ $3x^{-4}$
17. $\frac{2a^2c^4}{b^3c^{13}}$ $2a^2b^{-3}c^{-9}$
18. $\frac{2n(3n^2)^4}{6n^{17}}$ $27n^{-8}$

17. **Multiple Choice** If $b > 0$, for what integer values of n is $b^n < 0$? D

    A $n < 0$ B $0 < n < 1$

    C all values of n D no values of n

18. If $y^{-6} = 9$, what is the value of y^6? $\frac{1}{9}$

APPLYING THE MATHEMATICS

In 19 and 20, rewrite the right side of the formula using negative exponents and no fractions.

19. $A = \frac{kh}{g^5}$ $A = khg^{-5}$

20. $T = \frac{k}{m^2n^5}$ $T = km^{-2}n^{-5}$

21. Write an expression equivalent to $\left(\frac{3x^{-3}y}{2z^{-5}}\right)^{-2}\left(\frac{x^4y^{-3}}{z^3}\right)^8$ without any negative exponents. $\frac{4x^{38}}{9y^{26}z^{34}}$

22. Write each expression in standard scientific notation $x \cdot 10^n$, where $1 \le x < 10$ and n is an integer.

    a. $(3 \cdot 10^{-4})^2$ $9 \cdot 10^{-8}$

    b. $(6.2 \cdot 10^{-6})(4.6 \cdot 10^9)$ $2.852 \cdot 10^4$

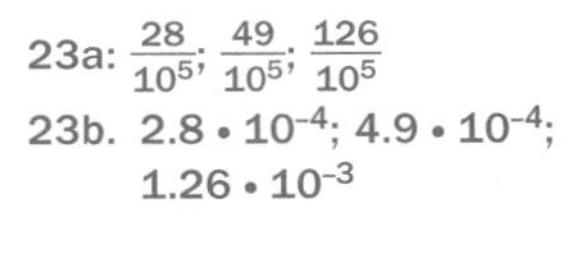

23a: $\frac{28}{10^5}$; $\frac{49}{10^5}$; $\frac{126}{10^5}$

23b. $2.8 \cdot 10^{-4}$; $4.9 \cdot 10^{-4}$; $1.26 \cdot 10^{-3}$

23. Carbon dioxide is a colorless and odorless gas that absorbs radiation from the sun and contributes to global warming. Before the industrial age, carbon dioxide made up about 280 parts per million (ppm) of the atmosphere. Carbon dioxide is released when coal, gasoline, and other fossil fuels are burned, so the level of the gas in the atmosphere has been increasing. Some scientific models have predicted that by 2100, the concentration will range from 490 ppm to 1260 ppm.

    a. Write all three rates as fractions using positive powers of 10.

    b. Write each rate in scientific notation.

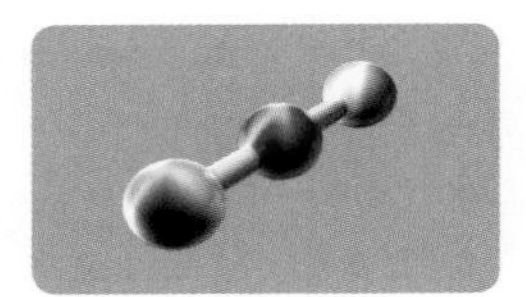

The molecular structure of carbon dioxide shows that one carbon atom in the center is flanked by two oxygen atoms.

24. Benjamin Franklin was one of the most famous scientists of his day. In one experiment he noticed that oil dropped on the surface of a lake would not spread out beyond a certain area. In modern units, he found that 0.1 cm^3 of oil spread to cover about 40 m^2 of the lake. About how thick is such a layer of oil? Express your answer in scientific notation. (We now know that the layer of oil stops spreading when it is one molecule thick. Although in Franklin's time no one knew about molecules, Franklin's experiment resulted in the first estimate of a molecule's size.) $2.5 \cdot 10^{-7}$ cm

Benjamin Franklin

In 25 and 26, write an equivalent expression without a fraction.

25. $\frac{4x^2}{y^3}$ $4x^2y^{-3}$

26. $\frac{12a^4}{19b^5c^2}$ $12 \cdot 19^{-1} \cdot a^4b^{-5}c^{-2}$

REVIEW

In 27 and 28, write without a fraction. (Lesson 7-2)

27. $\left(\frac{a^3}{a^2}\right)^3 \cdot 20a$ $20a^4$

28. $\frac{(xy)^m y^n}{x^2}$ $x^{m-2}y^{m+n}$

29. **Multiple Choice** Which of the following could be the graph of $y = x^4 + 1$? Justify your answer. **(Lessons 7-1, 6-3)**

A

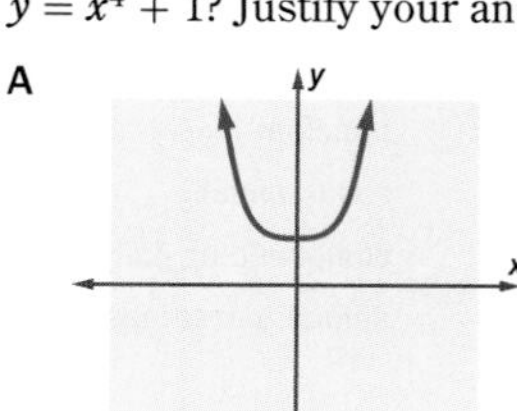

B

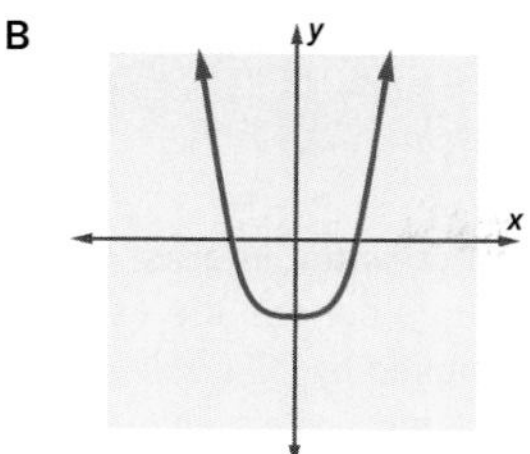

C

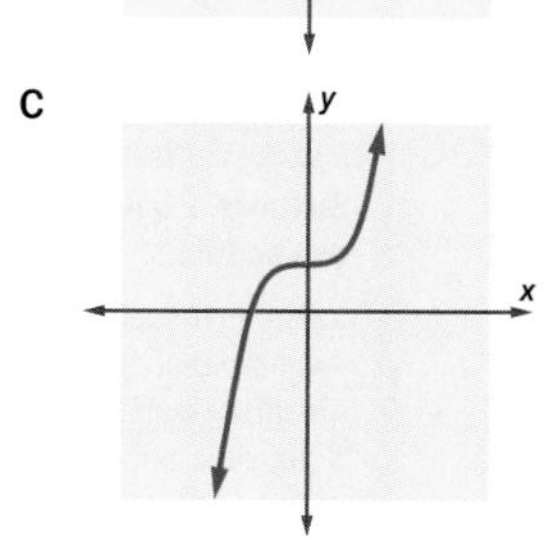

D

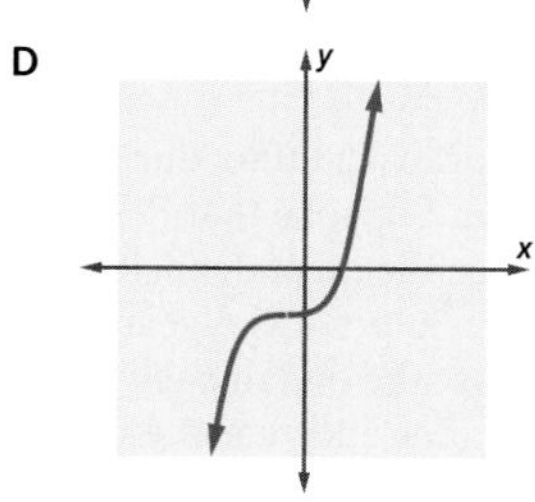

30. A bowler needs 12 strikes in a row to bowl a perfect game of 300.
   a. If the probability that Khadijah gets a strike is $\frac{1}{8}$ and strikes are independent of each other, what is the probability that Khadijah's next game will be a perfect game? $\left(\frac{1}{8}\right)^{12}$
   b. Is your answer to Part a greater than or less than one billionth? **(Lesson 7-1)** less than

31. a. What are the domain and range of the function with equation $y = -\frac{4}{x^2}$?
   b. What are the domain and range of the function with equation $y = -\frac{4}{x}$? **(Lesson 2-6)**

EXPLORATION

32. a. Examine the table at the right closely. Describe two patterns relating the powers of 5 on the left to the powers of 2 on the right.
   b. Make a chart similar to the one in Part a using the powers of 4 and of 2.5. See margin.
   c. Describe how the patterns in the chart from Part b are similar to the patterns in Part a.
   d. Find another pair of numbers with the same properties.

Powers of 5	Powers of 2
$5^6 = 15{,}625$	$2^6 = 64$
$5^5 = 3125$	$2^5 = 32$
$5^4 = 625$	$2^4 = 16$
$5^3 = 125$	$2^3 = 8$
$5^2 = 25$	$2^2 = 4$
$5^1 = 5$	$2^1 = 2$
$5^0 = 1$	$2^0 = 1$
$5^{-1} = 0.2$	$2^{-1} = 0.5$
$5^{-2} = 0.04$	$2^{-2} = 0.25$
$5^{-3} = 0.008$	$2^{-3} = 0.125$
$5^{-4} = 0.0016$	$2^{-4} = 0.0625$
$5^{-5} = 0.00032$	$2^{-5} = 0.03125$
$5^{-6} = 0.000064$	$2^{-6} = 0.015625$

29. A; the range contains no negative numbers.

31a. domain: all real numbers except 0; range: all negative real numbers

31b. domain: all real numbers except 0; range: all real numbers except 0

32a. Answers vary. Sample: The two columns of powers contain the same nonzero digits in reverse order. $2^n = 5^{-n} \cdot 10^n$

32c. Answers vary. Sample: As in Part a, the two columns of powers contain the same nonzero digits in reverse order. The equation in Part a holds true if you substitute 2.5 for 2 and 4 for 5: $2.5^n = 4^{-n} \cdot 10^n$.

32d. Answers vary. Sample: 8 and 1.25

Additional Answers

32b.

$4^6 = 4096$	$2.5^6 = 244.140625$
$4^5 = 1024$	$2.5^5 = 97.65625$
$4^4 = 256$	$2.5^4 = 39.0625$
$4^3 = 64$	$2.5^3 = 15.625$
$4^2 = 16$	$2.5^2 = 6.25$
$4^1 = 4$	$2.5^1 = 2.5$
$4^0 = 1$	$2.5^0 = 1$
$4^{-1} = 0.25$	$2.5^{-1} = 0.4$
$4^{-2} = 0.0625$	$2.5^{-2} = 0.16$
$4^{-3} = 0.015625$	$2.5^{-3} = 0.064$
$4^{-4} = 0.00390625$	$2.5^{-4} = 0.0256$
$4^{-5} = 0.0009765625$	$2.5^{-5} = 0.01024$
$4^{-6} = 0.000244140625$	$2.5^{-6} = 0.004096$

4 Wrap-Up

Ongoing Assessment

Have students work in pairs. Have each student write five expressions—similar to those in this lesson—that can be simplified by applying the postulates and theorems in Lessons 7-2 and 7-3. Have students exchange papers with their partner and simplify the expressions. Then have students correct each other's work and discuss any errors. Students should correctly apply the postulates and theorems in Lessons 7-2 and 7-3 to simplify expressions with exponents.

Administer Quiz 1 (or a quiz of your own) after students complete this lesson.

Project Update

Project 2, *Powers of 10*, on page 505 relates to the content of this lesson.

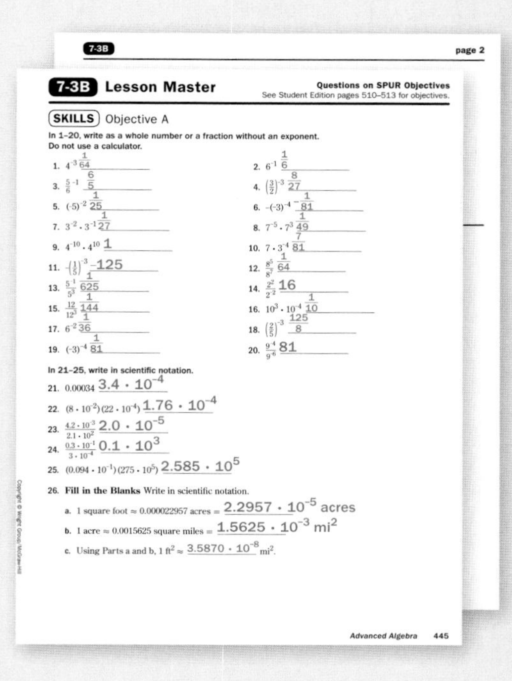
7-3B page 2

7-3B **Lesson Master**

Questions on SPUR Objectives
See Student Edition pages 510–513 for objectives.

SKILLS Objective A

In 1–20, write as a whole number or a fraction without an exponent. Do not use a calculator.

1. 4^{-3} $\frac{1}{64}$
2. 6^{-1} $\frac{1}{6}$
3. $\frac{5}{6}^{-1}$ $\frac{6}{5}$
4. $\left(\frac{3}{2}\right)^{-3}$ $\frac{8}{27}$
5. $(-5)^{-2}$ $\frac{1}{25}$
6. $-(-3)^{-4}$ $-\frac{1}{81}$
7. $3^{-2} \cdot 3^{-1}$ $\frac{1}{27}$
8. $7^{-5} \cdot 7^3$ $\frac{1}{49}$
9. $4^{-10} \cdot 4^{10}$ 1
10. $7 \cdot 3^{-4}$ $\frac{7}{81}$
11. $-\left(\frac{1}{5}\right)^{-3}$ −125
12. $\frac{8^5}{8^7}$ $\frac{1}{64}$
13. $\frac{5^{-1}}{5^3}$ $\frac{1}{625}$
14. $\frac{2^2}{2^{-2}}$ 16
15. $\frac{12}{12^3}$ $\frac{1}{144}$
16. $10^3 \cdot 10^{-4}$ $\frac{1}{10}$
17. 6^{-2} $\frac{1}{36}$
18. $\left(\frac{2}{5}\right)^{-3}$ $\frac{125}{8}$
19. $(-3)^{-4}$ $\frac{1}{81}$
20. $\frac{9^{-4}}{9^{-6}}$ 81

In 21–25, write in scientific notation.

21. 0.00034 $3.4 \cdot 10^{-4}$
22. $(8 \cdot 10^{-2})(22 \cdot 10^{-4})$ $1.76 \cdot 10^{-4}$
23. $\frac{4.2 \cdot 10^{-3}}{2.1 \cdot 10^2}$ $2.0 \cdot 10^{-5}$
24. $\frac{0.3 \cdot 10^{-1}}{3 \cdot 10^{-4}}$ $0.1 \cdot 10^3$
25. $(0.094 \cdot 10^{-1})(275 \cdot 10^5)$ $2.585 \cdot 10^5$
26. **Fill in the Blanks** Write in scientific notation.
   a. 1 square foot ≈ 0.000022957 acres = $2.2957 \cdot 10^{-5}$ acres
   b. 1 acre ≈ 0.0015625 square miles = $1.5625 \cdot 10^{-3}$ mi^2
   c. Using Parts a and b, 1 ft^2 ≈ $3.5870 \cdot 10^{-8}$ mi^2.

Advanced Algebra 445

Lesson 7-4

GOAL

Learn the definition of and discuss compound interest.

SPUR Objectives

G Apply the compound interest formulas.

Materials/Resources

- Lesson Masters 7-4A and 7-4B
- Resource Masters 125 and 126

HOMEWORK

Suggestions for Assignment

- Questions 1–19
- Question 20 (extra credit)
- Reading Lesson 7-5
- Covering the Ideas 7-5

Local Standards

1 Warm-Up

In 1–4, use a calculator to evaluate each expression to the nearest hundredth.

1. $300(1.0535)^3$ 350.77
2. $1500\left(1 + \frac{0.07}{360}\right)^{365}$ 1610.32
3. $1239.47 + 1239.47 \cdot 0.038$ 1286.57
4. $10{,}000\left(1 + \frac{0.0634}{12}\right)^{12 \cdot 5}$ 13,718.57

Lesson 7-4 Compound Interest

Vocabulary

annual compound interest
principal
semi-annually
compounding daily
annual percentage yield, APY

BIG IDEA If money grows at a constant interest rate r in a single time period, then after n time periods the value of the original investment has been multiplied by $(1 + r)^n$.

Interest Compounded Annually

Penny Wise, a high school junior, works part-time during the school year and full-time during the summer. Suppose that Penny decides to deposit $3000 this year in a 3-year certificate of deposit (CD). The investment is guaranteed to earn interest at a yearly rate of 4.5%. The interest is added to the account at the end of each year. If no money is added or withdrawn, then after one year the CD will have the original amount invested, plus 4.5% interest.

amount after 1 year: $3000 + 0.045(3000) = 3000(1 + 0.045)^1$
$= 3000(1.045)$
$= 3135$

Penny's CD is worth $3135 after one year.

Notice that to find the amount after 1 year, you do not have to add the interest separately; you can just multiply the original amount by 1.045. Similarly, at the end of the second year, there will be 1.045 times the *balance* (the ending amount in the account) from the first year.

amount after 2 years: $3000(1.045)(1.045) = 3000(1.045)^2$
≈ 3276.075

Since banks round down, Penny's CD is worth $3276.07 after two years.

amount after 3 years: $3000(1.045)^2(1.045) = 3000(1.045)^3$
≈ 3423.49

The value of Penny's CD has grown to $3423.49 after three years. Notice the general pattern.

amount after t years: $3000(1.045)^t$

Mental Math

Suppose a quiz has two sections.

a. The first section has 4 multiple-choice questions each with 3 possible answers. What is the probability of guessing all answers in this section correctly? $\frac{1}{81}$

b. The second section has 3 true/false questions. What is the probability of guessing all answers in this section correctly? $\frac{1}{8}$

c. What is the probability of guessing correctly on all the quiz questions? $\frac{1}{648}$

Background

Virtually everyone wants to know how to predict the value of his or her money in the future or how to shop for the best buy. Thus the content in this lesson is very interesting to most students.

A generation ago, compound interest could not be discussed until students studied logarithms because there was no other way to calculate large powers. The scientific calculator changed that, and we introduce compound interest in UCSMP *Transition Mathematics* and discuss it in some detail in UCSMP *Algebra*. In testing, we found compound-interest questions to have some of the greatest differences in performance between UCSMP students and other students. Indeed, other students often score less than chance on multiple-choice questions about this topic. So you can expect that students who have not studied this topic not only have little knowledge about compound interest, but what they think they know may be wrong!

When interest is earned at the end of each year, it is called *annual compound interest*. To find a more general formula for interest, replace 4.5% with r, the annual interest rate, and 3000 with P, the **principal** or original amount invested.

Annual Compound Interest Formula

Let P be the amount of money invested at an annual interest rate r compounded annually. Let A be the total amount after t years. Then

$$A = P(1 + r)^t.$$

In the Annual Compound Interest Formula, notice that A varies directly as P. For example, doubling the principal doubles the amount at the end. However, A does not vary directly as r; doubling the rate does not necessarily double the amount earned.

 QY

Interest Compounded More Than Once a Year

In most savings accounts, interest is compounded more than once a year. If money is compounded **semi-annually**, the interest rate at each compounding is *half of the annual interest rate* but there are *two compoundings each year* instead of just one. So if your account pays 4.5% compounded semi-annually, you earn 2.25% on the balance every six months. At the end of t years, interest paid semi-annually will have been paid $2t$ times. Therefore, the compound interest formula becomes

$$A = P\left(1 + \frac{r}{2}\right)^{2t}.$$

If money is compounded *quarterly*, the compound interest formula becomes

$$A = P\left(1 + \frac{r}{4}\right)^{4t}.$$

This pattern leads to a general compound interest formula.

General Compound Interest Formula

Let P be the amount invested at an annual interest rate r compounded n times per year. Let A be the amount after t years. Then

$$A = P\left(1 + \frac{r}{n}\right)^{nt}.$$

The number of times that the interest is compounded makes a difference in the amount of interest earned.

QY

How much more money would Penny earn if she were able to earn 9% rather than the 4.5% for 3 years?

2 Teaching

Notes on the Lesson

The development of the General Compound Interest Formula is straightforward. You may want to mimic this development with an annual rate of interest available in your area. Consider introducing this lesson by bringing in ads from a local newspaper about current interest rates on savings accounts or by asking students if they know a current rate of interest paid by a financial institution in their community.

In particular, many students have been taught the simple interest formula $I = prt$ (interest = principal × rate × time) and think this is the way that all interest is calculated. Actually, that formula is rather dated; it seldom applies except when $t = 1$. (See Question 9.)

Accommodating the Learner 

Present the *Rule of 72* to students: If money is invested at r% annual yield, it will double in about $\frac{72}{r}$ years. Have students test this rule with several different interest rates and amounts of money invested.

7-4

Notes on the Lesson

Example 1 Many students are surprised to learn that a rate of $r\%$ interest compounded semiannually means that you earn $\frac{r}{2}\%$ interest every 6 months. They think you get $r\%$ every 6 months. To help emphasize how the number of compounding periods affects the return of the investment, we recommend setting up expressions for the amount an investment is worth after several years under a fixed rate of interest for different numbers of compoundings. For example, the value of \$1000 invested for 3 years at an 8% annual interest rate when compounded annually, semiannually, quarterly, monthly, or daily is as follows:

- Annually: $\$1000(1 + 0.08)^3 = 1000(1.08)^3 = \$1259.71$
- Semiannually: $\$1000\left(1 + \frac{0.08}{2}\right)^{2 \cdot 3} = 1000(1.04)^6 = \$1265.31$
- Quarterly: $\$1000\left(1 + \frac{0.08}{4}\right)^{4 \cdot 3} = 1000(1.02)^{12} = \$1268.24$
- Monthly: $\$1000\left(1 + \frac{0.08}{12}\right)^{12 \cdot 3} \approx 1000(1.00667)^{36} \approx \$1270.23$
- Daily: $\$1000\left(1 + \frac{0.08}{365}\right)^{365 \cdot 3} \approx 1000(1.00022)^{1095} \approx \$1271.21$

The above calculations, particularly the last two, force students to focus carefully on the order of operations with their calculators. You may wish to check that students do such calculations correctly before assigning the questions as homework.

Students may wonder why financial institutions charge different rates of interest. Some students may not realize that these institutions make money on their money by lending it to others; the more money they have to lend, the more money they make. Financial institutions need to weigh the financial consequences of paying low interest rates, which increase their profit, and high interest rates, which encourage people to deposit funds that can be used by the bank.

Example 1

Suppose \$10,000 is placed into an account that pays interest at a rate of 5%. How much will be earned in the account in the first year if the interest is compounded as indicated?

a. annually **b. semi-annually** **c. quarterly**

Solution

a. Since interest is compounded only once, the interest is simply $0.05 \cdot \$10{,}000 = \$500$. The account will earn \$500.

b. and c. Substitute into the General Compound Interest Formula to determine the account's value.

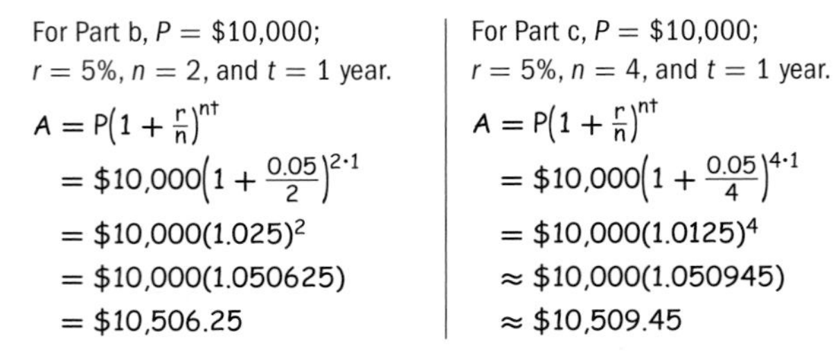

For Part b, $P = \$10{,}000$; $r = 5\%$, $n = 2$, and $t = 1$ year.

$$A = P\left(1 + \frac{r}{n}\right)^{nt} = \$10{,}000\left(1 + \frac{0.05}{2}\right)^{2 \cdot 1} = \$10{,}000(1.025)^2 = \$10{,}000(1.050625) = \$10{,}506.25$$

For Part c, $P = \$10{,}000$; $r = 5\%$, $n = 4$, and $t = 1$ year.

$$A = P\left(1 + \frac{r}{n}\right)^{nt} = \$10{,}000\left(1 + \frac{0.05}{4}\right)^{4 \cdot 1} = \$10{,}000(1.0125)^4 \approx \$10{,}000(1.050945) \approx \$10{,}509.45$$

Now subtract the \$10,000 principal to find the amount of interest that was earned.

The account will earn \$506.25.

The account will earn \$509.45.

In Example 1, the difference after one year between compounding semi-annually and compounding quarterly is only \$3.20. However, if you withdraw your money before a year is up, you may have received interest in the account that pays quarterly while you may not have received interest in the account that pays semi-annually. For instance, if interest is compounded quarterly and you withdraw your money after 10 months, you will have received 3 of the 4 quarterly compound interest payments and have a total of $10{,}000\left(1 + \frac{0.05}{4}\right)^{3 \cdot 1} \approx \$10{,}379.70$.

However, if interest is compounded semi-annually, then after 10 months you will have received 1 of 2 semi-annual compound interest payments and have only $10{,}000\left(1 + \frac{0.05}{2}\right)^{1 \cdot 1} = \$10{,}250$, a difference of over \$125!

To avoid angering their customers, most savings institutions guarantee that accounts will earn interest "from the date of deposit until the date of withdrawal." They can do this by **compounding daily**. Daily compounding uses either 360 or 365 as the number of days in a year.

ENGLISH LEARNERS

Vocabulary Development

Discuss with students the idea of *interest* as the money paid for the use of money invested (or borrowed). Review the meanings of the variables in the compound interest formulas: P is the *principal,* or original amount invested (or loaned); r is the annual interest *rate;* n is the number of compoundings per year; t is the *time* in years that money is invested (or borrowed); and A is the total *amount* of the investment (or loan) after t years. Be sure that students know that, in these formulas, t always represents years, not months or parts of years.

Discuss the differences between *simple* and *compound* interest and have students determine amounts of investments made under each plan. (See Question 9.) When discussing compound interest, be sure students know the meanings of *annually, semiannually,* and *quarterly*. Relate the terms to other terms that your students know.

Annual Percentage Yield

Because of the many different ways of calculating interest, savings institutions are required by federal law to disclose the **annual percentage yield**, or **APY**, of an account after all the compoundings for a year have taken place. This allows consumers to compare savings plans. For instance, to determine the APY of an account paying 5% compounded quarterly (as in Example 1), find the interest $1 would earn in the account in one year.

$$1 \cdot \left(1 + \frac{0.05}{4}\right)^{4 \cdot 1} \approx 1.0509$$

So the interest earned is $1.0509 – $1 = $0.0509. This means that the APY on an account paying 5% compounded quarterly is 5.09%.

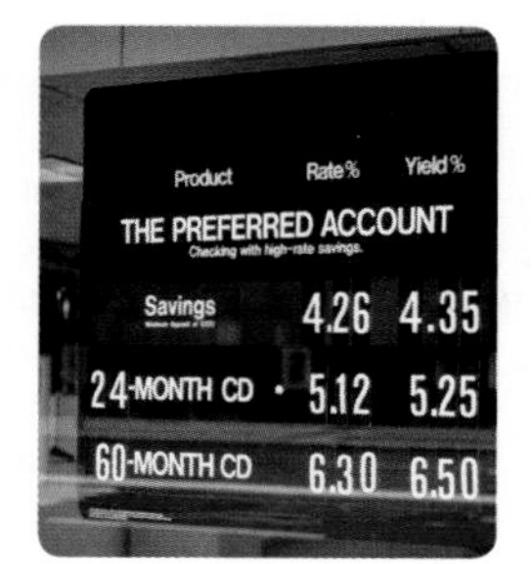

GUIDED

Example 2

What is the APY for a 5.5% interest rate compounded

a. quarterly?

b. daily, for 365 days per year?

Solution To find the APY on an account, use $1 as the principal amount to keep the computations simple.

a. $1 \cdot \left(1 + \frac{?}{4}\right)^{4 \cdot 1} \approx$ _?_ 0.055; 1.0561

So, the interest earned is \$_?_ – \$1 = \$_?_.

This is an APY of _?_%. 1.0561; 0.0561; 5.61

b. $1 \cdot \left(1 + \frac{?}{?}\right)^{?} \approx$ _?_ 0.055, 365; 365 • 1; 1.0565

So, the interest earned is \$_?_ – \$1 = \$_?_.

This is an APY of _?_%. 1.0565; 0.0565; 5.65

Going Back in Time

In both compound interest formulas, you can think of P either as the principal or as the *present amount*. In each of the previous examples, A is an amount that is determined after compounding. Then, because A comes after P, the time t is represented by a positive number. But it is also possible to think of A as an amount some years ago that was compounded to get the present amount P. Then the time t is represented by a negative number.

Additional Examples

Example 1 Suppose $1000 is deposited in an account that pays interest at a rate of 3.5%. How much will be earned in the first year if the interest is compounded as indicated below?

a. annually 0.035 • \$1000 = \$35

b. semiannually $\$1000\left(1 + \frac{0.035}{2}\right)^{2 \cdot 1} = \$1035.30$; \$1035.30 – \$1000 = \$35.30

c. quarterly $\$1000\left(1 + \frac{0.035}{4}\right)^{4 \cdot 1} \approx \$1035.46$; \$1035.46 – \$1000 = \$35.46

Example 2 What is the APY for a 4.5% interest rate compounded

a. semiannually?

b. daily, 360 days per year?

Solution To find the APY on an account, use $1 as the principal amount to keep the computations simple.

a. $1 \cdot \left(1 + \frac{?}{2}\right)^{2 \cdot 1} =$ _?_

0.045; 1.0455

The interest earned is \$_?_ – \$1 = \$_?_. 1.0455; 0.0455 So the APY is _?_%. 4.55

b. $1 \cdot \left(1 + \frac{?}{?}\right)^{? \cdot 1} =$ _?_

0.045; 360; 360; 1.0460

The interest earned is \$_?_ – \$1 = \$_?_. 1.0460; 0.0460 So the APY is _?_%. 4.60

Accommodating the Learner

Help students to understand why, in the General Compound Interest Formula, the principal is multiplied by a power of $(1 + r)$ rather than by just a power of r. Remind them that each compounding period, the interest is added to the beginning principal to get the new principal a year later. If P is the beginning principal, then Pr is the interest. So $P + Pr$ is the principal after the compounding period. Have students note that $P + Pr = P(1 + r)$.

Additional Example

Example 3 A bond paying 7% interest compounded annually has matured after 8 years, giving the owner \$10,000. How much was invested 8 years ago? \$5820.09

Note-Taking Tips

Have students add the two Compound Interest Formulas to their journals and supply an example for each.

3 Assignment

Recommended Assignment

- Questions 1–19
- Question 20 (extra credit)
- Reading Lesson 7-5
- Covering the Ideas 7-5

7-4A Lesson Master

Questions on SPUR Objectives
See Student Edition pages 510–513 for objectives.

VOCABULARY

1. In the General Compound Interest Formula $A = P\left(1 + \frac{r}{n}\right)^{nt}$, give the meaning of

 a. r. interest rate b. n. compoundings per year c. P. principal

2. What does APY stand for? annual percentage yield

USES Objective G

3. Asdrubal puts \$12,000 in a certificate of deposit paying 4.8% annually.
 a. Find the value of the account after 5 years. \$15,170.07
 b. How much interest does he earn in the 6th year? \$728.17
4. Write the General Compound Interest Formula, if interest is compounded quarterly. $A = P\left(1 + \frac{r}{4}\right)^{4t}$
5. Toni opens a bank account with \$500. Find the amount in the account after 3 years if the bank pays 2.9% interest, compounded quarterly. \$545.28
6. Find the APY on a bank account that pays 3.20% compounded daily for 360 days per year. ≈ 3.25%
7. Bank A pays 1.9% interest on a savings account, compounded monthly. Bank B pays 1.85% interest, compounded daily for 360 days per year.
 a. Which bank should you use? Bank A
 b. You have \$2000 to save for five years. How much more money will you have at the end of five years with Bank A than you would have at the other bank? \$5.33 more
8. A credit card charges 18.6% interest, compounded monthly. If you charge \$1500 on the card, how much interest will you pay in the first month? \$23.25
9. If you take a loan at a 6% annual rate with monthly payments, each month you will pay one-twelfth of 6%, or 0.5% interest. Some "payday lending" stores charge a \$15 fee to get a two-week advance of \$100. Find the annual rate that corresponds to 15% every two weeks (use 1 year = 52 weeks). 390%
10. In 1986, Bill Gates, the founder of Microsoft, had approximately \$234 million. Over the next twenty years, his wealth grew at an annual rate of approximately 23.4%. How much money did he have in 2006? \$15.7 billion

Advanced Algebra 447

Example 3

Zero-coupon bonds do not pay interest during their lifetime, typically 20 or 30 years. They are bought for much less than their final value and earn a fixed rate of interest over their life. When a bond *matures*, its value is equal to the initial investment plus all the interest earned over its lifetime. Suppose a 30-year zero-coupon bond has a value at maturity of \$20,000 and is offered at 5.5% interest compounded semi-annually. How much do you need to invest to buy this bond?

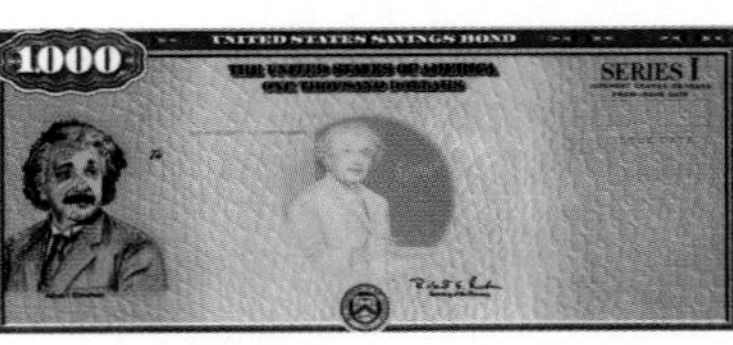

Series I savings bonds are sold at face value and earn interest based on a fixed interest rate and inflation. The interest earned is tax free when the bond is used to pay for higher education expenses. Albert Einstein appears on the \$1000 Series I savings bond.

Solution 1 Think of how much you would need to have invested 30 years ago to have \$20,000 now. Use the General Compound Interest Formula with a present value of $P = 20{,}000$, $r = 0.055$, $n = 2$, and $t = -30$.

$A = P\left(1 + \frac{r}{n}\right)^{nt}$ General Compound Interest Formula

$A = 20{,}000\left(1 + \frac{0.055}{2}\right)^{2 \cdot -30}$ Substitution

$A = \frac{20{,}000}{1.0275^{60}}$ Arithmetic and Negative Exponent Theorem

$A \approx 3927.54$ Arithmetic

You need to invest \$3927.54 to buy this bond.

Solution 2 Use the General Compound Interest Formula. You know $A = 20{,}000$, $r = 0.055$, $n = 2$, and $t = 30$. Solve for P.

$A = P\left(1 + \frac{r}{n}\right)^{nt}$ General Compound Interest Formula

$20{,}000 = P\left(1 + \frac{0.055}{2}\right)^{2 \cdot 30}$ Substitution

$20{,}000 \approx P(1.0275)^{60}$ Arithmetic

$P \approx 3927.54$ Divide both sides by 1.0275^{60}

You need to invest \$3927.54 to buy this bond.

Questions

COVERING THE IDEAS

1. Suppose Penny Wise buys \$2500 worth of government bonds that pay 3.7% interest compounded quarterly. If no money is added or withdrawn, find out how much the bonds will be worth after 1, 2, 3, 4, and 5 years. \$2593.79; \$2691.10; \$2792.06; \$2896.81; \$3005.49
2. Find the interest earned in the fourth year for Penny's 4.5% CD described in this lesson. \$154.06

3. Write the compound interest formula for an account that earns interest compounded
   a. monthly. $A = P\left(1 + \frac{r}{12}\right)^{12t}$ b. daily in a leap year. $A = P\left(1 + \frac{r}{366}\right)^{366t}$
4. To what amount will \$8000 grow if it is invested for 12 years at 6% compounded quarterly? \$16,347.82
5. Find the APY of a savings account earning 4% interest compounded daily. Use 360 for the number of days in a year. 4.08%
6. Suppose a zero-coupon bond matures and pays the owner \$30,000 after 10 years, paying 4.5% interest annually. How much was invested 10 years ago? \$19,317.83
7. **True or False** An account earning 8% compounded annually earns exactly twice as much interest in 6 years as an account earning 8% compounded annually earns in 3 years. Explain your answer.
8. **True or False** Justify your answer. In the General Compound Interest Formula,
   a. A varies directly as t.   b. A varies directly as P.
   c. A varies inversely as n.   d. A varies directly as r.

7. False; because the starting balance gets larger each year, the interest earned each year increases.

8a. False; Answers vary. Sample: When t is multiplied by a constant k, A is raised to the kth power.

8b. True; Answers vary. Sample: When P is multiplied by a constant k, A is also multiplied by k.

8c. False; Answers vary. Sample: When n is multiplied by a constant k, A is not divided by k.

8d. False; Answers vary. Sample: If r is doubled, A is not necessarily doubled.

APPLYING THE MATHEMATICS

9. Refer to Penny's certificate of deposit.
   a. Calculate the value of Penny's CD at the end of 3 years using the **simple interest formula** $I = Prt$, where I is the amount of interest earned, P is the principal, r is the annual percentage rate, and t is time in years. \$3405
   b. How much money would Penny have if she earned annual compound interest over the same 3 years? \$3423.49
   c. Should Penny prefer simple interest to annual compound interest? Explain why or why not. See margin.
10. On a CAS, define a function `gencompint(p,r,n,t)` to calculate the value of an investment using the General Compound Interest Formula. Use the function to verify the answers to Example 1. See margin.

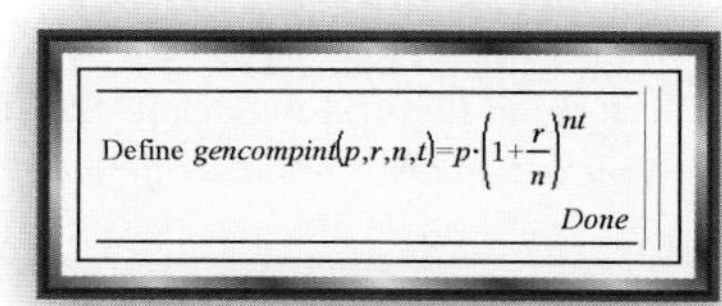

11. Rich takes a \$2000 cash advance against his credit card to fund an investment opportunity he saw on the Internet. The credit card charges an annual rate of 18% and compounds the interest monthly on all cash advances. How much interest does Rich owe if he does not make any payments for 3 months? \$91.36

7-4

Notes on the Questions

Question 3b Some banks use a 360-day year rather than a 365-day year for calculating daily interest. You may want to ask students to do this question using $n = 360$ and compare it with $n = 365$ to find out what difference, if any, this makes in the interest earned.

Questions 9 This question compares compound interest with simple interest. The difference is critical and should be stressed.

Additional Answers

10.

Define $gencompint(p,r,n,t)=p\cdot\left(1+\frac{r}{n}\right)^{n\cdot t}$	Done
gencompint(10000,.05,1,1)	10500.
gencompint(10000,.05,2,1)	10506.25
gencompint(10000,.05,4,1)	10509.45

Notes on the Questions

Question 12 Discuss this question; being aware of the situation could save one or more of your students a great deal of money in the future.

Question 14 Several expressions involve powers of π. For example, the sum of the reciprocals of the squares of all the positive integers is $\frac{\pi^2}{6}$. The sum of the reciprocals of the fourth powers of all the positive integers is $\frac{\pi^4}{90}$.

Question 19 This question sets the stage for Lesson 7-5.

4 Wrap-Up

Ongoing Assessment

Have students write a paragraph explaining why r% interest compounded annually on a given amount of money for several years is less than r% interest compounded monthly on the same amount of money for the same length of time. Students should describe how the amount of interest increases with the number of compoundings.

Project Update

Project 1, *Financing Post-High School Education,* on page 505 and Project 4, *The $200,000 Cell Phone,* on page 506 relate to the content of this lesson.

7-4B page 2

7-4B Lesson Master **Questions on SPUR Objectives** See Student Edition pages 510–513 for objectives.

VOCABULARY

Fill in the Blanks In 1–3, complete the statement.

1. The original amount of money placed in an investment is called the principal.
2. If a savings account earns *compound interest*, it means that Answers vary. Sample: The interest, as well as the principal, earns interest.
3. The annual rate of interest earned after all the compounding has taken effect is called the annual percentage yield.

USES Objective G

In 4–8, find the annual percentage yield on the account with the given description.

4. 6% interest, compounded quarterly $\approx$ 6.14%
5. 8% interest, compounded semi-annually 8.16%
6. 18.5% interest, compounded monthly $\approx$ 20.15%
7. 5.25% interest, compounded daily for 360 days per year $\approx$ 5.39%
8. 3.75% interest, compounded daily for 365 days per year $\approx$ 3.82%
9. Yu invests $500 in a savings account that pays 3.2% interest compounded annually. How much money will be in his account after 5 years if no deposits or withdrawals take place during the 5 years? $585.29
10. Debbie invested $5000 in a 5-year CD (certificate of deposit) that pays 7.8% interest compounded quarterly. The CD matures next February. If no deposits or withdrawals have taken place during the 5-year period, how much money will the CD be worth when it matures? $7357.23
11. Maria invests $6000 in an IRA (individual retirement account) 25 years before she plans to retire. With a 4% annual yield, if Maria makes no deposits or withdrawals during the 25 years, what will be the value of the IRA when it matures? $15,995.02
12. Bank X pays 2.75% interest on a savings account, compounded monthly. Bank Y pays 2.75% interest, compounded daily for 365 days per year.
    a. Which bank should you use? Bank Y
    b. You have $3500 to save for three years. How much more money will you have at the end of three years with the bank you chose in Part a? $\approx$ $0.35 more

448 *Advanced Algebra*

12. Stores often advertise a "90-day same as cash" method for making purchases. This means that interest is compounded starting the day of purchase (the interest *accrues*), but no interest is charged if the bill is paid in full before 90 days go by. However, on the 91st day, the accrued interest is added to the purchase price. Suppose Manny purchased a sofa for $3000 under this plan with an annual interest rate of 20.5% compounded monthly. If Manny forgets to pay the purchase in full, how much will he owe on the 91st day? $3156.39

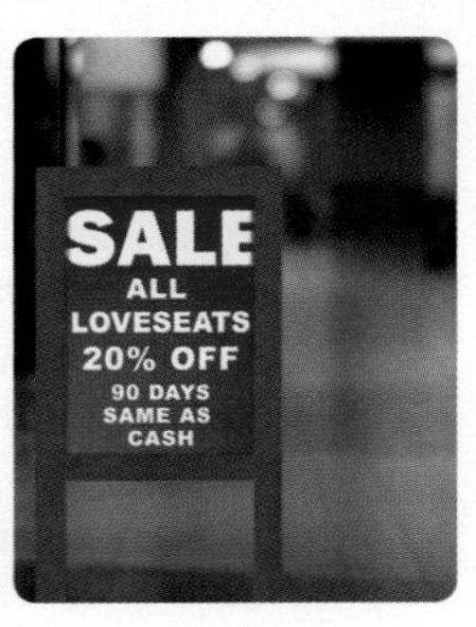

Many stores offer 90 days same as cash during sales.

REVIEW

13. Rewrite $\left(\frac{1}{3^{-3}}\right)^{-2}$ without exponents. **(Lesson 7-3)** $\frac{1}{729}$
14. The Stefan-Boltzmann constant in physics is $\frac{2\pi^5k^4}{15h^3c^2}$. Rewrite this expression in the form $\frac{2}{15}M$, where M is an expression that does not involve fractions. **(Lesson 7-3)** $\frac{2}{15}(\pi^5k^4h^{-3}c^{-2})$
15. **True or False** For all positive integers a, b, and c, $(a^b)^c = a^{(b^c)}$. Justify your answer. **(Lesson 7-2)**
16. Solve $x^2 - 3x + 7 = 2x^2 + 5x - 9$ by
    a. graphing. See margin.
    b. using the Quadratic Formula. **(Lessons 6-7, 6-4)**
17. What translation maps the graph of $y = \sqrt{x - 3} + 5$ onto the graph of $y = \sqrt{x} - 3$? **(Lesson 6-3)** $T_{-3,\,-8}$
18. The graph at the right appears to have a certain symmetry. Give a matrix describing a transformation that would map this graph onto itself. **(Lesson 4-8)**

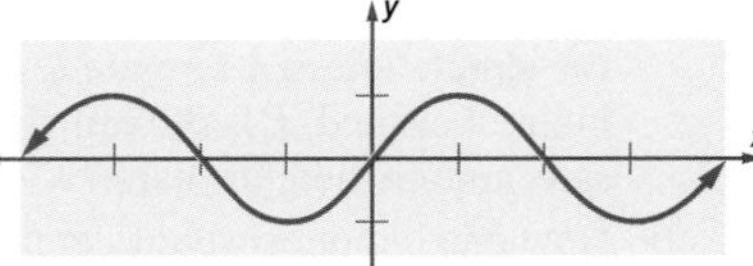

19. Consider the sequence t_n defined recursively as follows. **(Lessons 3-6, 1-8)**
$$\begin{cases} t_1 = 4 \\ t_n = 3t_{n-1} \text{ for } n \ge 2 \end{cases}$$
    a. Find the first five terms of the sequence. 4, 12, 36, 108, 324
    b. Is t an arithmetic sequence? Why or why not?

15. False; Answers vary. Sample: $(2^3)^5$ is not the same as 2^{3^5}. $(2^3)^5 = 2^{15}$ but $2^{3^5} = 2^{243}$.

16b. $x = -4 + 4\sqrt{2} \approx 1.66$, or $x = -4 - 4\sqrt{2} \approx -9.66$

18. $\begin{bmatrix} -1 & 0 \\ 0 & -1 \end{bmatrix}$

19b. No; the terms do not increase by a constant amount.

EXPLORATION

20. Find an interest rate and an APY for a 3-year CD at a savings institution in your area. Show how to calculate the APY from the interest rate. See margin.

QY ANSWER

$461.59

Additional Answers

16a.

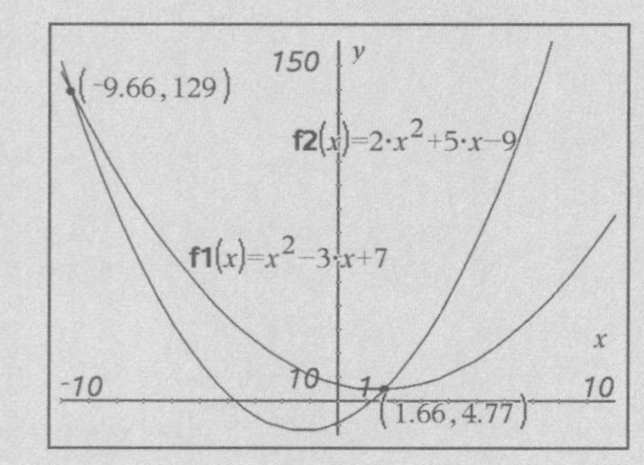

The solutions are $x \approx -9.66$ and $x \approx 1.66$.

20. Answers vary. Sample: During May 2008, a Chicago-area bank offered a 9-month CD with a 2.75% APY and a 2.71% interest rate compounded daily. Here, $P\left(1 + \frac{0.0271}{365}\right)^{365 \cdot 1} = 1.02747P$, which means the APY $\approx$ 2.75%.

Lesson

7-5 Geometric Sequences

Vocabulary

geometric sequence, exponential sequence
constant multiplier
constant ratio

▸ **BIG IDEA** Geometric sequences are generated by multiplying each term by a constant to get the next term, just as arithmetic sequences are generated by adding a constant to each term to get the next.

In 2005, a major television manufacturer filmed an advertisement featuring 250,000 balls bouncing down the hills of San Francisco. The maximum height of a ball after each bounce can be modeled by a *geometric sequence.*

Mental Math

Tell whether the sequence could be arithmetic. If it could be, give the constant difference.

a. $1\frac{5}{6}, \frac{5}{6}, -\frac{5}{6}, -1\frac{5}{6}, -2\frac{5}{6}, \ldots$ no

b. 17, 28, 39, 50, ... yes; 11

c. 1.017, 0.917, 0.817, 0.717, ... yes; −0.1

d. 2, −4, 6, −8, ... no

Recursive Formulas for Geometric Sequences

Recall that, in an arithmetic (linear) sequence, each term after the first is found by adding a constant difference to the previous term. If, instead, each term after the first is found by *multiplying* the previous term by a constant, then a **geometric** (or **exponential**) **sequence** is formed.

The constant in a geometric sequence is called a **constant multiplier**. For instance, the geometric sequence with first term 30 and constant multiplier 2 is

$$30, 60, 120, 240, 480, 960, \ldots.$$

Replace 30 by g_1 and 2 by r and you have the general form for a geometric sequence.

Recursive Formula for a Geometric Sequence

Let r be a nonzero constant. The sequence g defined by the recursive formula

$$\begin{cases} g_1 = x \\ g_n = rg_{n-1}, \text{ for integers } n \geq 2 \end{cases}$$

is the geometric, or exponential, sequence with first term x and constant multiplier r.

Background

Arithmetic and geometric sequences are of special interest in an advanced algebra course because they are discrete special cases of functions studied in the course, both explicit and recursive formulas for them are easily derived, and they model many real-world situations. Arithmetic (or linear) sequences were studied in Chapter 3. Geometric, or exponential, sequences are introduced in this lesson.

The term *exponential sequence* is appropriate because every geometric sequence can be considered as an exponential function whose domain is the set of natural numbers. Thus, a geometric sequence is an example of a discrete exponential function.

Lesson 7-5

GOAL

Learn the terminology and some applications of geometric sequences.

SPUR Objectives

C Describe geometric sequences explicitly and recursively.

H Solve real-world problems involving geometric sequences.

Materials/Resources

- Lesson Masters 7-5A and 7-5B
- Resource Masters 127 and 128

HOMEWORK

Suggestions for Assignment

- Questions 1–23
- Question 24 (extra credit)
- Reading Lesson 7-6
- Covering the Ideas 7-6

Local Standards

1 Warm-Up

Jacobi wants to enlarge a portion of a photograph to 10 times its size. However, the photocopier's largest enlargement factor is 120%. Indicate the sequence of size-change factors (rounded to the nearest hundredth) that result from using the copier 1, 2, 3, ... times until the final enlargement is at least 10 times the size of the original photograph. 1.20, 1.44, 1.73, 2.07, 2.49, 2.99, 3.58, 4.30, 5.16, 6.19, 7.43, 8.92, 10.70; 13 enlargements are needed.

Solving the sentence $g_n = rg_{n-1}$ for r yields $\frac{g_n}{g_{n-1}} = r$. This indicates that in a geometric sequence, the ratio of successive terms is constant. For this reason, the constant multiplier r is also called the **constant ratio**.

Alternatively, you can write a recursive formula for a geometric sequence g using the $(n + 1)$st term as

$$\begin{cases} g_1 = x \\ g_{n+1} = rg_n, \text{ for integers } n \geq 1. \end{cases}$$

Example 1

Give the first six terms and the constant multiplier of the geometric sequence g where

$$\begin{cases} g_1 = 6 \\ g_n = 3g_{n-1}, \text{ for integers } n \geq 2. \end{cases}$$

Solution 1 The value $g_1 = 6$ is given. The rule for g_n tells you that each term after the first is found by multiplying the previous term by 3.

The constant multiplier is 3.

$g_2 = 3g_1 = 3 \cdot 6 = 18$
$g_3 = 3g_2 = 3 \cdot 18 = 54$
$g_4 = 3g_3 = 3 \cdot 54 = 162$
$g_5 = 3g_4 = 3 \cdot 162 = 486$
$g_6 = 3g_5 = 3 \cdot 486 = 1458$

The first six terms of the sequence are 6, 18, 54, 162, 486, 1458.

Solution 2 Use a spreadsheet.

Enter 6 in cell A1. Then enter = 3*A1 in cell A2.

Copy and paste cell A2 into cells A3–A6.

	A	B	C	D	E	F
1	6					
2	18					
3	54					
4	162					
5	486					
6	1458					

A6 =3·a5

 QY

▶ QY

Write a recursive formula for the geometric sequence in Example 1 using g_{n+1}.

Explicit Formulas for Geometric Sequences

You may have received a letter or e-mail that promises good luck as long as you send the letter to five friends asking each to forward it to five of their friends, and so on. Such chain letters are illegal in the U.S. if the mailer asks for money.

2 Teaching

Notes on the Lesson

To help students focus on the salient features of geometric sequences, compare and contrast geometric and arithmetic sequences as follows:

- Arithmetic sequence
  Explicit formula: $a_n = a_1 + (n - 1)d$
  Recursive formula:
  $\begin{cases} a_1 \\ a_n = a_{n-1} + d, \text{ for integers } n \geq 2 \end{cases}$
  Constant: $a_n - a_{n-1} = d$ (constant difference)
- Geometric sequence
  Explicit formula: $g_n = g_1 r^{(n-1)}$
  Recursive formula:
  $\begin{cases} g_1 \\ g_n = g_{n-1} \cdot r, \text{ for integers } n \geq 2 \end{cases}$
  Constant: $\frac{g_n}{g_{n-1}} = r$, (constant ratio)

Example 1 Point out that the difference between successive terms of a geometric sequence with a constant ratio greater than 1 increases as one considers later terms of a sequence. You can use the compound interest example at the beginning of Lesson 7-4 to show this; the differences are 135, 141.07, 147.42, ... The implications of this property are important; keeping money invested for twice as long generates more than twice the interest.

ENGLISH LEARNERS

Vocabulary Development

On the board, copy the list of sequence characteristics from the Notes on the Lesson on this page. Discuss the differences and similarities between *arithmetic sequences* and *geometric sequences*. Have students note that $(n - 1)$ in the arithmetic sequence explicit formula is a multiplier, while $(n - 1)$ in the geometric sequence explicit formula is an exponent. Also have them note that an arithmetic sequence is based on a *constant difference*, while a geometric sequence is based on a *constant multiplier*. Be sure that students know that *constant multiplier* and *constant ratio* have the same meaning.

Review the definitions of explicit and recursive formulas and write examples of both on the board to help students distinguish between them. You may also want to have students refer to the Glossary for these definitions.

Part of the appeal of chain letters is that a very large number of people can receive them quickly. This is because the number of letters sent by each *generation* of mailers forms a geometric sequence. The data at the right represent the first five generations of a chain letter in which a person sends an e-mail to 12 people and asks each person receiving the e-mail to forward it to 4 other friends, and no person receives two letters.

Generation	Number of Letters Sent
1	12
2	$12 \cdot 4 = 48$
3	$12 \cdot 4^2 = 192$
4	$12 \cdot 4^3 = 768$
5	$12 \cdot 4^4 = 3072$

In this sequence, the constant multiplier is $r = 4$. If $g_1 = 12$, the number of letters the first person sends out, then g_2 is the number of letters sent out by everyone in generation 2, and $g_n = 12(4)^{n-1}$ is the number of letters sent out in generation n. This pattern can be generalized to find an explicit formula for the nth term of any geometric sequence.

Explicit Formula for a Geometric Sequence

In the geometric sequence g with first term g_1 and constant ratio r,
$g_n = g_1(r)^{n-1}$, for integers $n \geq 1$.

Notice that in the explicit formula, the exponent of the nth term is $n - 1$. When you substitute 1 for n to find the first term, the constant multiplier has an exponent of zero.

$$g_1 = g_1(r)^{1-1}$$
$$= g_1 r^0$$

This is consistent with the Zero Exponent Theorem which states that for all $r \neq 0$, $r^0 = 1$.

Constant multipliers in a geometric sequence can be negative. Then the terms of the sequence alternate between positive and negative values.

GUIDED

Example 2

Write the 1st, 5th, 10th, 35th, and 50th terms of the sequence a defined by $a_n = 4(-3)^{n-1}$.

Solution Substitute $n = 1, 5, 10, 35$, and 50 into the formula for the sequence.

$a_1 = 4(-3)^{1-1} = 4 \cdot$ ___?___ $=$ ___?___ 1; 4

$a_5 = 4(-3)^{\underline{?}} = 4 \cdot$ ___?___ $=$ ___?___ 5 – 1; 81; 324

$a_{10} =$ ___?___ $=$ ___?___ $= -78{,}732$ $4(-3)^{10-1}$; 4(–19,683)

A calculator display of a_{35} and a_{50} is shown at the right.

$4 \cdot (-3)^{34}$	66708726798666276
$4 \cdot (-3)^{49}$	-95719731692247018360332

Extension

Give students the diagram of concentric circles shown at the right, in which the radius of each circle is half the radius of the next larger circle. Tell them the radius of the largest circle is r and to imagine that the pattern continues indefinitely. Have students find the area of the outermost ring. $\frac{3}{4}\pi r^2$ Then have them find the area of the second, third, and fourth rings. $\frac{3}{16}\pi r^2$; $\frac{3}{64}\pi r^2$; $\frac{3}{256}\pi r^2$ Finally, have students write an explicit formula for the area of the nth ring and find the area of the sixth ring. $A_n = \frac{3}{4}\pi r^2\left(\frac{1}{4}\right)^{n-1}$; $\frac{3}{4096}\pi r^2$

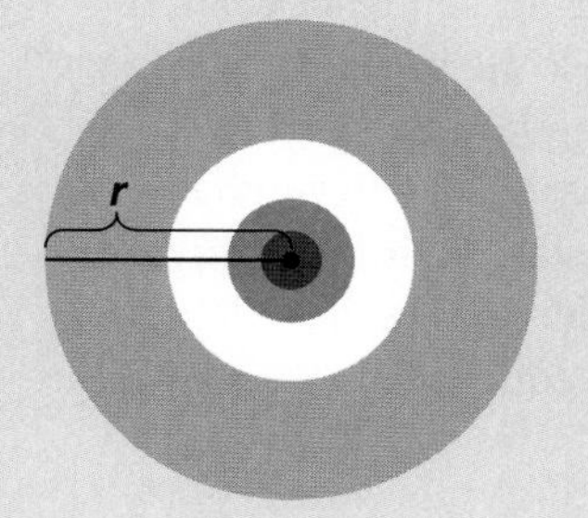

Notes on the Lesson

Example 2 This example shows that a geometric sequence can have a negative constant multiplier. This is the only time in the chapter where a negative multiplier is used. This is because negative bases present problems if the exponents are not integers, as students will learn in Lesson 7-7.

Additional Examples

Example 1 Give the first six terms and the constant multiplier of the geometric sequence g where

$$\begin{cases} g_1 = 5 \\ g_n = 4g_{n-1}, \text{ for integers } n \geq 2. \end{cases}$$

$g_1 = 5$; $g_2 = 4g_1 = 4 \cdot 5 = 20$; $g_3 = 4g_2 = 4 \cdot 20 = 80$; $g_4 = 4g_3 = 4 \cdot 80 = 320$; $g_5 = 4g_4 = 4 \cdot 320 = 1280$; $g_6 = 4g_5 = 4 \cdot 1280 = 5120$; the first six terms of the sequence are 5, 20, 80, 320, 1280, and 5120. The constant multiplier is 4.

Example 2 Write the 1st, 5th, 10th, 20th, and 25th terms of the sequence a defined by $a_n = 3(-2)^{n-1}$.

Solution Substitute $n = 1, 5, 10, 20$, and 25 into the formula for the sequence.

$a_1 = 3(-2)^{1-1} =$
$3 \cdot$ ___?___ $=$ ___?___ 1; 3
___?___

$a_5 = 3(-2)$
$= 3 \cdot$ ___?___ $=$ ___?___ 5 – 1; 16; 48

$a_{10} =$ ___?___ $=$ ___?___ $3(-2)^{10-1}$; –1536

A calculator display of a_{20} and a_{25} is shown below.

$3 \cdot (-2)^{19}$	-152864
$3 \cdot (-2)^{24}$	50331648

Note-Taking Tips

Have students add the Recursive Formula for a Geometric Sequence and the Explicit Formula for a Geometric Sequence to their journals and supply an example for each.

Notes on the Lesson

Example 3 When dropped, toy rubber balls and other similar products bounce to as high as 90% of their previous height. In Question 11 of Lesson 13-2, students are asked to consider the total vertical distance traveled by such a ball after a certain number of bounces.

Additional Example

Example 3 Suppose a ball is dropped from a height of 12 feet and bounces up to 90% of its previous height after each bounce. (A bounce is counted when the ball hits the ground.) Let h_n be the maximum height of the ball after the nth bounce.

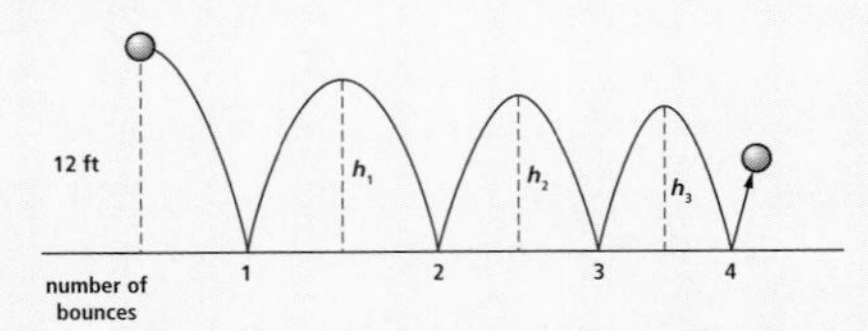

a. Find an explicit formula for h_n. $h_n = 10.8(0.9)^{n-1}$

b. Find the maximum height of the ball after the sixth bounce. ≈ 6.38 ft

3 Assignment

Recommended Assignment

- Questions 1–23
- Question 24 (extra credit)
- Reading Lesson 7-6
- Covering the Ideas 7-6

Notes on the Questions

Question 1 The analogy goes farther than just the way the sequence is formed. As the list of characteristics in the Notes on the Lesson on page 480 show, the formulas for the nth term are analogous.

Constant multipliers in a geometric sequence can also be between 0 and 1. This is the case for the sequence that models the height of a bouncing ball.

Example 3

Suppose a ball is dropped from a height of 10 meters, and it bounces up to 80% of its previous height after each bounce. (A bounce is counted when the ball hits the ground.) Let h_n be the maximum height of the ball after the nth bounce.

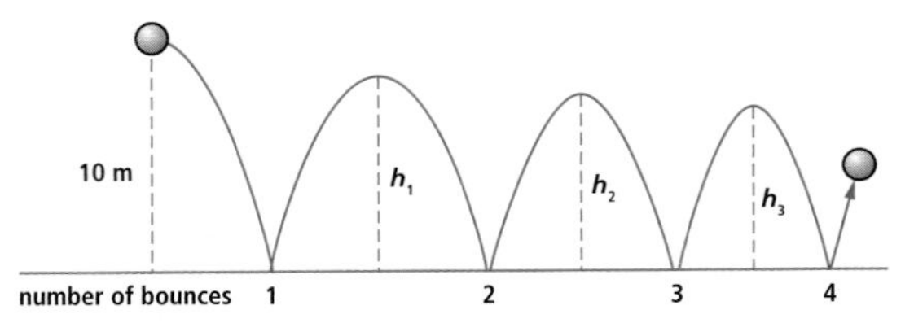

a. Find an explicit formula for h_n.

b. Find the maximum height of the ball after the seventh bounce.

Solution

a. Because each term is 0.8 times the previous term, the sequence is geometric. On the first bounce, the ball bounces up to 10(0.8) meters, or 8 meters. So, $h_1 = 8$. Also, $r = 0.8$. So,

$$h_n = 8(0.8)^{n-1}.$$

b. On the seventh bounce, $n = 7$, so

$$h_7 = 8(0.8)^{7-1} \approx 2.10.$$

So, after the seventh bounce, the ball will rise to a height of about 2.10 meters.

Look back at the sequences generated in Examples 1 to 3. Notice that in Example 1, $r > 1$ and g_n increases as n increases. In Example 3, $0 < r < 1$ and g_n decreases as n increases. In Example 2, $r < 0$ and as n increases, g_n alternates between positive and negative values. These properties are true for all geometric sequences.

Questions

COVERING THE IDEAS

1. **Fill in the Blanks** In an arithmetic sequence, each term after the first is found by __?__ a constant to the previous term. In a geometric sequence, each term after the first is found by __?__ the previous term by a constant. adding; multiplying

In 2–4, state whether the numbers can be consecutive terms of a geometric sequence. If they can, find the constant ratio and write an explicit formula.

2. 12, 48, 192, ...
3. 5, 10, 20, 25, ... no
4. $12, \frac{4}{3}, \frac{1}{6}, \frac{1}{48}$ ... no

2. yes; 4; $g_n = 12(4)^{n-1}$

Accommodating the Learner

Some students might still have difficulty differentiating between explicit and recursive formulas for sequences. These students can review the meaning of explicit and recursive formulas by referring to Lesson 1-8 and Lessons 3-6 through 3-8. Help them to translate their thinking from the arithmetic sequences in those lessons to the geometric sequences in this lesson.

5. Let g be a sequence with $g_n = 200 \cdot (0.10)^{n-1}$.
   a. Find terms 1, 5, 20, and 50. $200, 0.02, 2 \cdot 10^{-17}, 2 \cdot 10^{-47}$
   b. Use a spreadsheet to generate the first 15 terms of g.

6. Find the first five terms of the sequence $\begin{cases} t_1 = 1.2 \\ t_n = 5 \cdot t_{n-1}, \text{ for integers } n \geq 2. \end{cases}$ 1.2, 6, 30, 150, 750

7. Consider $\begin{cases} g_1 = x \\ g_{n+1} = rg_n, \text{ for integers } n \geq 1 \end{cases}$.
   a. Write r in terms of g_{n+1} and g_n. $r = \frac{g_{n+1}}{g_n}$
   b. Write an explicit formula for g_{n+1}. $g_{n+1} = x(r)^n$

8. a. Write the first six terms of the geometric sequence whose first term is -3 and whose constant ratio is -2.
   b. Give a recursive formula for the sequence in Part a.
   c. Give an explicit formula for the sequence in Part a.

9. Suppose $g_n = 1.85 \cdot 0.38^{n-1}$ for integers $n \geq 1$.
   a. Find each ratio. 9a. i–iv. 0.38
      i. $\frac{g_2}{g_1}$ ii. $\frac{g_3}{g_2}$ iii. $\frac{g_4}{g_3}$ iv. $\frac{g_{20}}{g_{19}}$
   b. What is true about the values in Part a? They are all equal.

10. **Matching** Each graph below is a graph of a geometric sequence. Match each graph with its range of possible common ratios r.
    i. $r > 1$ ii. $r < 0$ iii. $0 < r < 1$

a. iii

b. i

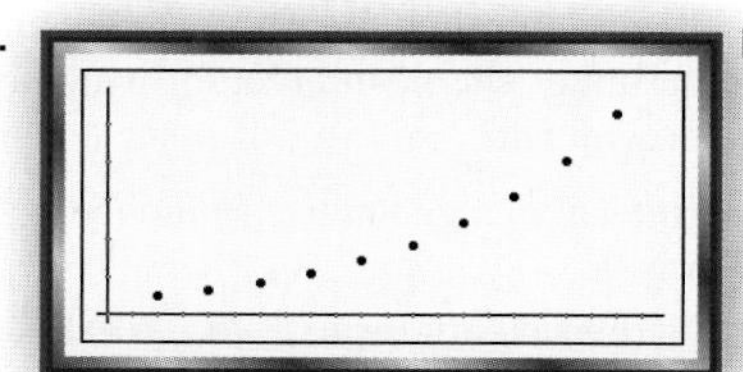

c. ii

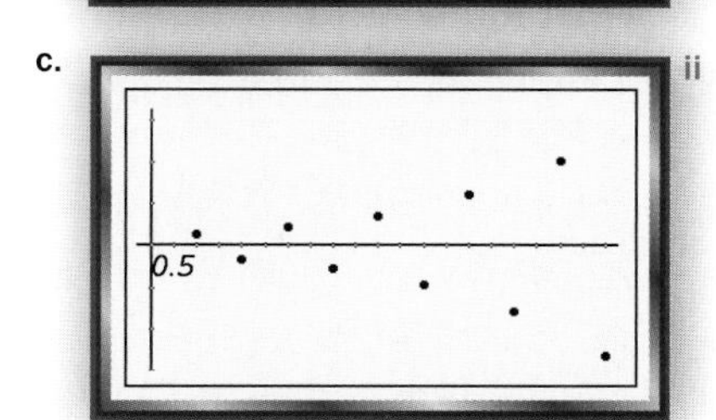

5b. The first 15 terms are 200, 20, 2, 0.2, 0.02, 0.002, 0.0002, $2 \cdot 10^{-4}$, ..., $2 \cdot 10^{-12}$.

	A n	B	C	D	E
◆		=200*(.1)^('n-1)			
1	1	200.			
2	2	20.			
3	3	2.			
4	4	.2			
5	5	.02			

B =200·(.1)^('n-1)

8a. -3, 6, -12, 24, -48, 96

8b. $\begin{cases} g_1 = -3 \\ g_n = -2g_{n-1}, \text{ for integers } n \geq 2 \end{cases}$

8c. $g_n = -3(-2)^{n-1}$

7-5A Lesson Master

Questions on SPUR Objectives
See Student Edition pages 510–513 for objectives.

SKILLS Objective C

In 1–4, give the first four terms of the geometric sequence described.

1. The first term is 5; the constant ratio is 2. 5, 10, 20, 40
2. The first term is 180; the constant ratio is $\frac{2}{3}$. 180, 120, 80, $\frac{160}{3}$
3. $\begin{cases} g_1 = 8 \\ g_n = -1.5g_{n-1}, \text{ for integers } n \geq 2 \end{cases}$ 8, -12, 18, -27
4. $t_n = 220(1.06)^{n-1}$ 220, 233.2, 247.192, 262.02352
5. Write recursive and explicit formulas for the geometric sequence 4, 12, 36, 108, ...
   a. Recursive: $\begin{cases} g_1 = 4 \\ g_n = 3g_{n+1}, \text{ for integers } n \geq 1 \end{cases}$
   b. Explicit: $g_n = 4 \cdot 3^{n-1}$
6. A geometric sequence is defined recursively by $\begin{cases} g_1 = 0.75 \\ g_n = 2g_{n-1} \end{cases}$. Write an explicit formula for the sequence. $g_n = 0.75 \cdot 2^{n-1}$
7. **Multiple Choice** Which of the following sequences could be geometric? B
   A 3, 6, 9, ... B $2, \frac{1}{4}, \frac{1}{32}, ...$ C -5, -10, 20, ... D 1.2, 1.0, 0.8, ...

USES Objective H

8. A child on a swing moves 1.5 m on her first swing. On each following swing, she moves 120% of the distance she moved on the previous swing.
   a. How far does she move on the 4th swing, to the nearest centimeter? 259 cm
   b. How far does she move on the nth swing? $1.5 \cdot 1.20^{n-1}$
9. The figures below are the first four terms in a sequence creating a figure called the Sierpinski Triangle. In each step, one-quarter of each dark triangle is removed. Suppose the area of the first triangle is 1 square unit.
   a. Find the area of the shaded triangle(s) in each step. $1, \frac{3}{4}, \frac{9}{16}, \frac{27}{64}$
   b. Find the area of the shaded triangles in the nth step. $\left(\frac{3}{4}\right)^{n-1}$

Notes on the Questions

Question 18 This is an example of multiplying terms of two geometric sequences. In general, the term-by-term product of two geometric sequences is a geometric sequence. (Also, the term-by-term sum of two arithmetic sequences is an arithmetic sequence.)

11. Suppose a ball dropped from a height of 11 feet bounces up to 60% of its previous height after each bounce.
   a. Find an explicit formula for the maximum height of the ball after the nth bounce. $g_n = 6.6(0.6)^{n-1}$
   b. Find the height of the ball, to the nearest inch, after the tenth bounce. 1 in.

12. In the figure at the right, the midpoints of the sides of the largest equilateral triangle have been connected to create the next smaller equilateral triangle, and this process has been continued. If the side length of the largest triangle is s, then the side length of the next smaller triangle is $\frac{1}{2}s$. The sides of the consecutively smaller triangles form a geometric sequence.

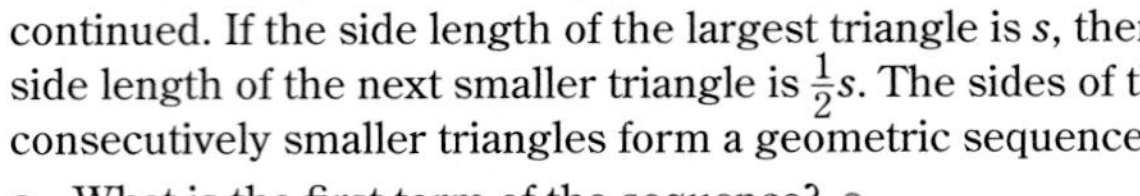

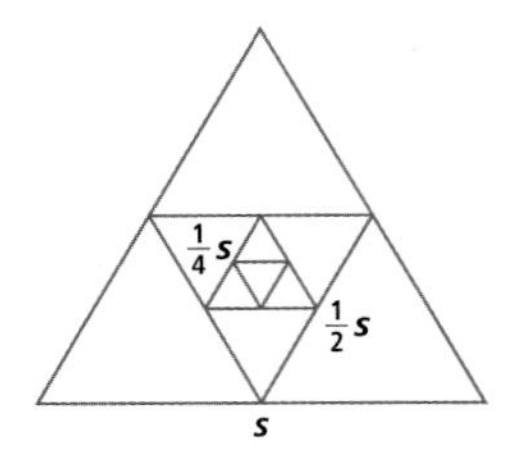

   a. What is the first term of the sequence? s
   b. What is the constant multiplier? $\frac{1}{2}$

APPLYING THE MATHEMATICS

13. Willie Savit invested \$5000 in an account at 2.25% interest compounded annually after t years.
   a. Write an explicit formula for how much money Willie will have in his account after t years. $g_t = 5000(1.0225)^t$
   b. How much money will Willie have after 20 years? \$7802.54
   c. If Willie had received simple interest instead of compound interest, the value of his investment over the first five years would be as shown at the right. Do the amounts in his account under simple interest form a geometric sequence? Why or why not? No; there is not a constant ratio between amounts.

Year	Amount (\$)
0	\$5000.00
1	\$5112.50
2	\$5225.00
3	\$5337.50
4	\$5450.00

14. The fourth term of a geometric sequence is 1. The constant multiplier is $\frac{1}{5}$.
   a. What is the seventh term? b. What is the first term? 125

14a. $\frac{1}{125}$

In 15 and 16, the first few terms of a geometric sequence are given. Find the next two terms. Then, find an explicit formula for the nth term of the geometric sequence.

15. 14, 28, 56, 112, ...

16. 9, 3, 1, ... $\frac{1}{3}, \frac{1}{9}$; $g_n = 9\left(\frac{1}{3}\right)^{n-1}$

15. 224, 448; $g_n = 14(2)^{n-1}$

17. a. Write a recursive formula for the geometric sequence whose first four terms are 23, -23, 23, -23, ...
   b. Write an explicit formula for the sequence in Part a.

17a. $\begin{cases} g_1 = 23 \\ g_n = -g_{n-1}, \text{ for integers } n \geq 2 \end{cases}$

17b. $g_n = 23(-1)^{n-1}$

18. y, xy^2, x^2y^3, x^3y^4, and x^4y^5 are the first five terms of a sequence s.
   a. Find each ratio. For all parts, the ratio is xy.
      i. $\frac{s_2}{s_1}$ ii. $\frac{s_3}{s_2}$ iii. $\frac{s_4}{s_3}$ iv. $\frac{s_5}{s_4}$
   b. Could s be a geometric sequence? Explain why or why not.

18b. Yes; xy is the constant ratio between consecutive terms.

Accommodating the Learner

Refer pairs of students to Question 12. Have them write an explicit formula for the side length of the nth triangle formed. Then have them write an explicit formula for the area of the nth triangle. $s_n = s_1\left(\frac{1}{2}\right)^{n-1}$; $A_n = A_1\left(\frac{1}{4}\right)^{n-1}$

19. In the figure at the right, the midpoints of the sides of each square are connected to form the next smaller square. The ratios of the areas of consecutive shaded regions are equal. This is called a Baravelle Spiral. Assume that the side of the largest square has length 1 unit.
    a. Find the area of region A_1. $\frac{1}{8}$
    b. The areas of the consecutively smaller and smaller regions $A_2, A_3, A_4, \ldots$ form a geometric sequence A. Find an explicit formula for A_n. $A_n = \frac{1}{8}\left(\frac{1}{2}\right)^n$

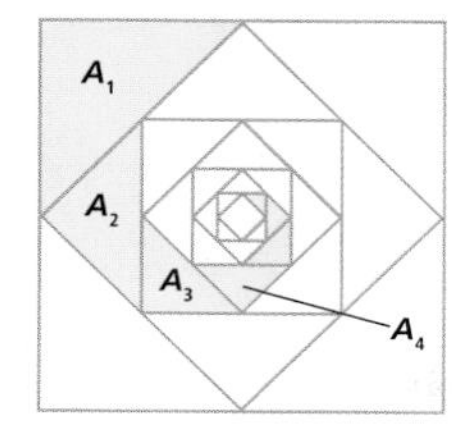

REVIEW

20. A bank account has an annual interest rate of 3.8% compounded daily. **(Lesson 7-4)**
    a. If \$10,000 is placed in this account, calculate the value of the account 5 years from now. \$12,092.37
    b. What is the annual percentage yield of this account? 3.87%
    c. If \$10,000 is placed into an account that compounds interest annually at a rate equal to the annual percentage yield in Part b, what will the value of this new account be in 5 years? How does this amount compare to your answer to Part a?

21. Suppose N varies directly as a and inversely as the square of b and the third power of c. Using negative exponents, write a formula for N that does not contain a fraction. **(Lessons 7-3, 2-8)**

22. Rewrite $y = x^2 - 46x + 497$ in vertex form. **(Lesson 6-5)**

23. A circle and a rectangle have the same area. The circumference of the circle is 20 cm and one side of the rectangle equals the diameter of the circle. Determine whether the perimeter of the rectangle is longer or shorter than the circle's circumference. **(Lesson 6-2)** longer

20c. \$12,090.67, about the same as Part a. (If the rate in Part b were not rounded, the amounts would be the same.)

21. $N = kab^{-2}c^{-3}$

22. $y = (x - 23)^2 - 32$

EXPLORATION

24. a. Refer to the chain letter example from the lesson. The number of e-mails actually sent after the first generation seldom matches the numbers in the table. Why is that?
    b. Suppose only 2 of 4 people who receive an e-mail pass it along to 4 others. What, then, is the minimum number of generations it will take for the e-mail to reach 100 million people? 24 generations

24a. Answers vary. Sample: Some people discard the e-mail instead of passing it on to 5 of their friends.

QY ANSWER

$$\begin{cases} g_1 = 6 \\ g_{n+1} = 3g_n, \text{ for } n \geq 1 \end{cases}$$

Notes on the Questions

Question 24 Chain letters that solicit funds to be sent to others are illegal in most places in the United States.

4 Wrap-Up

Ongoing Assessment

Write an explicit formula for a geometric sequence, such as $g_n = 8(-5)^{n-1}$, on the board. Ask students for the corresponding recursive formula.
$\begin{cases} g_1 = 8 \\ g_n = -5g_{n-1}, \text{ for integers } n \geq 2 \end{cases}$
Have students write the first four terms of the sequence. 8; –40; 200; –1000
Then write a recursive formula for a geometric sequence, such as
$\begin{cases} g_1 = 3 \\ g_n = 5g_{n-1}, \text{ for integers } n \geq 2 \end{cases}$
on the board. Ask students for a corresponding explicit formula. Answers vary. Sample: $g_n = 3(5)^{n-1}$ Then have students write the first four terms of the sequence. 3; 15; 75; 375

Project Update

Project 5, *Family of Equations,* on page 506 relates to the content of this lesson.

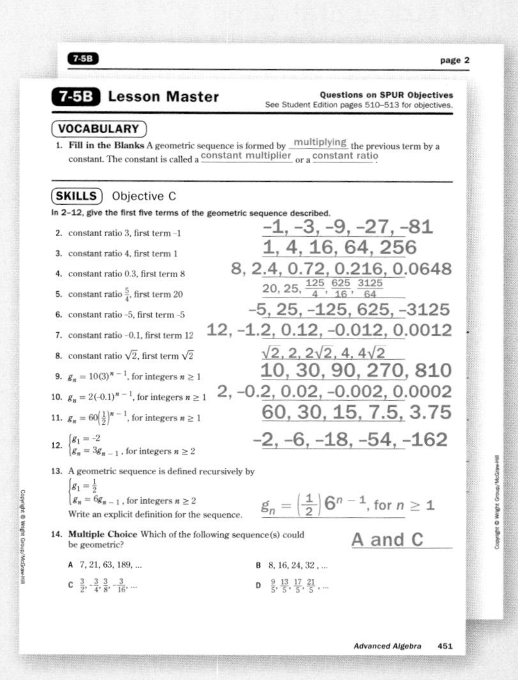

7-5B page 2

7-5B Lesson Master

Questions on SPUR Objectives
See Student Edition pages 510–513 for objectives.

VOCABULARY

1. **Fill in the Blanks** A geometric sequence is formed by multiplying the previous term by a constant. The constant is called a constant multiplier or a constant ratio.

SKILLS Objective C

In 2–12, give the first five terms of the geometric sequence described.

2. constant ratio 3, first term -1 — –1, –3, –9, –27, –81
3. constant ratio 4, first term 1 — 1, 4, 16, 64, 256
4. constant ratio 0.3, first term 8 — 8, 2.4, 0.72, 0.216, 0.0648
5. constant ratio $\frac{5}{4}$, first term 20 — $20, 25, \frac{125}{4}, \frac{625}{16}, \frac{3125}{64}$
6. constant ratio -5, first term -5 — –5, 25, –125, 625, –3125
7. constant ratio -0.1, first term 12 — 12, –1.2, 0.12, –0.012, 0.0012
8. constant ratio $\sqrt{2}$, first term $\sqrt{2}$ — $\sqrt{2}, 2, 2\sqrt{2}, 4, 4\sqrt{2}$
9. $g_n = 10(3)^{n-1}$, for integers $n \geq 1$ — 10, 30, 90, 270, 810
10. $g_n = 2(-0.1)^{n-1}$, for integers $n \geq 1$ — 2, –0.2, 0.02, –0.002, 0.0002
11. $g_n = 60\left(\frac{1}{2}\right)^{n-1}$, for integers $n \geq 1$ — 60, 30, 15, 7.5, 3.75
12. $\begin{cases} g_1 = -2 \\ g_n = 3g_{n-1}, \text{ for integers } n \geq 2 \end{cases}$ — –2, –6, –18, –54, –162
13. A geometric sequence is defined recursively by
    $\begin{cases} g_1 = \frac{1}{2} \\ g_n = 6g_{n-1}, \text{ for integers } n \geq 2 \end{cases}$
    Write an explicit definition for the sequence. $g_n = \left(\frac{1}{2}\right)6^{n-1}$, for $n \geq 1$
14. **Multiple Choice** Which of the following sequence(s) could be geometric? A and C
    A 7, 21, 63, 189, ...
    B 8, 16, 24, 32, ...
    C $\frac{3}{2}, -\frac{3}{4}, \frac{3}{8}, -\frac{3}{16}, \ldots$
    D $\frac{9}{5}, \frac{13}{5}, \frac{17}{5}, \frac{21}{5}, \ldots$

Advanced Algebra 451

Lesson

7-6

GOAL

Discuss the meaning and some applications of exponents that are unit fractions; introduce nth roots.

SPUR Objectives

A Evaluate b^n when $b > 0$ and n is the reciprocal of a positive integer.

D Find all real solutions to equations of the form $x^n = b$, where $x \geq 0$ and n is a rational number.

E Recognize properties of nth roots.

F Solve real-world problems that can be modeled by expressions with nth roots.

Materials/Resources

- Lesson Masters 7-6A and 7-6B
- Resource Masters 129–130
- Quiz 2

HOMEWORK

Suggestions for Assignment

- Questions 1–30
- Question 31 (extra credit)
- Reading Lesson 7-7
- Covering the Ideas 7-7

Local Standards

1 Warm-Up

In 1–6, solve. If the solution is not exact, estimate it to the nearest hundredth.

1. $x^5 = -1$ -1
2. $y^3 = 24$ 2.88
3. $z^8 - 256 = 0$ 2 or -2
4. $9a^2 = 4$ $\frac{2}{3}$ or $-\frac{2}{3}$
5. $10^{10}n^{10} = 0$ 0
6. $-16 + v^4 = 0$ 2 or -2

Lesson

7-6 nth Roots

Vocabulary

cube root

nth root

▸ **BIG IDEA** If y is the nth power of x, then x is an nth root of y. Real numbers may have 0, 1, or 2 real nth roots.

Geometric Sequences in Music

A piano tuner adjusts the tension on the strings of a piano so the notes are at the proper pitch. Pitch depends on frequency, measured in hertz or cycles per second. It is common today to tune the A above middle C to 440 hertz. Pythagoras and his followers discovered that a note has exactly half the frequency of the note one octave higher. Thus, the A below middle C is tuned to a frequency of 220 hertz. In most music today, an octave is divided into twelve notes as shown below.

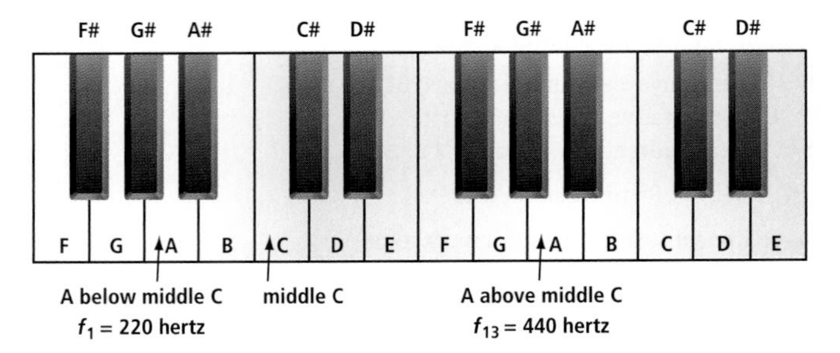

In order for a musical piece to sound much the same in any key, notes in the scale are tuned so that ratios of the frequencies of consecutive notes are equal. To find these frequencies, let f_1 = the frequency of the A below middle C and f_n = the frequency of the nth note in the scale. Then f_{n+1} is the frequency of the next higher note. The frequency of A *above* middle C is f_{13} because there are 12 notes in each octave.

Let r = the ratio of the frequencies of consecutive notes. Then for all integers $n \geq 1$,

$$\frac{f_{n+1}}{f_n} = r.$$

Multiply both sides of this equation by f_n.

$$f_{n+1} = rf_n, \text{ for all integers } n \geq 1$$

Mental Math

Determine whether the discriminant of the quadratic equation is positive, negative, or zero. Then, tell how many real roots the equation has.

a. $5x^2 + 2x - 1 = 0$

b. $-t^2 - 4t + 1 = 0$

c. $2h^2 + 3h + 2 = 0$

d. $s^2 - 6s + 9 = 0$

a. positive, two

b. positive, two

c. negative, none

d. zero, one

Background

Most advanced algebra students will probably have studied square roots and cube roots in previous courses. In this lesson, we extend the meaning of nth roots to all integers n greater than 1.

Geometric sequences in music Example 1 may be surprising, even to musicians. Students may know that mathematics and music are connected but not realize the fundamental nature of such connections. In UCSMP *Geometry,* Lesson 4-8 is devoted to transformations and music, but frequencies are not discussed. Some of the relationships between frequencies and lengths of strings were discovered by the Pythagoreans, but the use of the 12th root of 2 to tune instruments dates only from around the 1700s, during the time of J. S. Bach. In fact, in the title of the famous set of Bach piano pieces entitled "The Well-Tempered Clavier," *well-tempered* meant a set of notes that were tuned in geometric progression. Until that time, instruments were tuned so that a piece would sound good in a particular key, but pieces could not be played in all keys.

Together with the known value $f_1 = 220$, this is a recursive formula for a geometric sequence. It indicates that the frequencies of consecutive notes on a piano (when in tune) are the elements of a geometric sequence. The first term is $f_1 = 220$ and the 13th term of this sequence is $f_{13} = 440$.

From the explicit formula for the nth term of a geometric sequence, substituting 13 for n,

$$f_{13} = 220r^{13-1} = 220r^{12}.$$

To find r, substitute 440 for f_{13}. $440 = 220r^{12}$

Divide both sides by 220. $2 = r^{12}$

The ratio of the frequencies of consecutive in-tune keys on a piano is called a *12th root* of 2.

A piano being tuned

What Is an nth Root?

Recall that x is a square root of t if and only if $x^2 = t$. Similarly, x is a **cube root** of t if and only if $x^3 = t$. For instance, 4 is a cube root of 64 because $4^3 = 64$. Square roots and cube roots are special cases of the following more general idea.

Definition of nth Root

Let n be an integer greater than 1. Then b is an ***n*th root** of x if and only if $b^n = x$.

For example, $-\frac{1}{3}$ is a 5th root of $-\frac{1}{243}$ because $\left(-\frac{1}{3}\right)^5 = -\frac{1}{243}$. There are no special names for nth roots other than *square roots* (when $n = 2$) and *cube roots* (when $n = 3$). Other nth roots are called *fourth roots*, *fifth roots*, and so on. In the piano-tuning example above, $r^{12} = 2$. This is why r is a 12th root of 2. And because $(-r)^{12} = r^{12}$ for all real numbers r, there is a negative number that is also a 12th root of 2.

Example 1

Approximate the real 12th roots of 2 to find the ratio r of the frequencies of consecutive in-tune notes, to the nearest hundred-thousandth.

Solution The real 12th roots of 2 are the real solutions to $x^{12} = 2$. So they are the x-coordinates of the points of intersection of $y = x^{12}$ and $y = 2$. Graph these functions using a graphing utility.

(continued on next page)

Every student needs to be able to evaluate nth roots on a calculator. Students are often surprised to find out that most calculators (1) will not give both real nth roots of a positive number when n is even and (2) calculate odd nth roots of negative numbers. This provides added support for the restrictions we must impose on the base when the exponent is not an integer.

Just as there was a Negative Exponent Theorem, so there is a $\frac{1}{n}$ Exponent Theorem. The fundamental property of $x^{\frac{1}{n}}$ as an nth root is not given as a definition but deduced from the power properties.

We purposely delay the introduction of the radical notation $\sqrt[n]{x}$ for an nth root of x because that notation has more complicated domains for x and n than $x^{\frac{1}{n}}$ has. The radical sign for nth roots first appears in Lesson 8-4.

2 Teaching

Notes on the Lesson

Students usually do not have much difficulty with the definition of nth root. Point out that the definition of nth root requires n to be both positive and an integer greater than 1. Stress that the symbol $x^{\frac{1}{n}}$ stands for the largest real nth root of x.

Geometric sequences in music Many of your students may be unfamiliar with keyboards and the musical terminology in this lesson. Try to borrow a piano or other keyboard instrument from the music department at your school. Then you can demonstrate the successive notes on a keyboard as they are discussed in the lesson. Emphasize the connection between 12th roots and the successive frequencies. If you cannot borrow a keyboard, you could use one of many working keyboard Web sites, for example, http://www.pianoworld.com/fun/javapiano/javapiano.htm.

Additional Example

Example 1 Approximate the real 8th roots of 3.

Graph $y = x^8$ and $y = 3$.

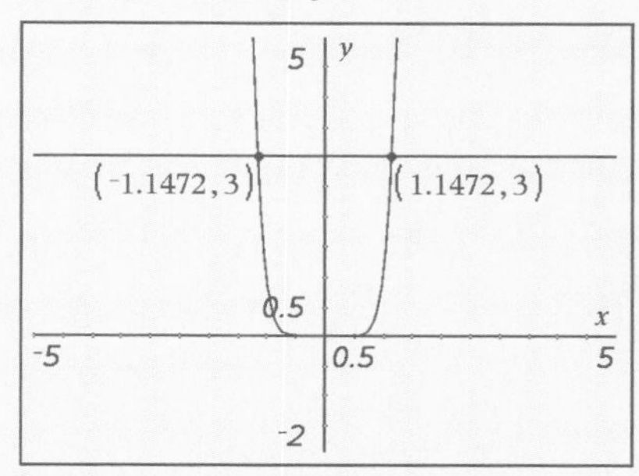

The points of intersection are (1.1472, 3) and (–1.1472, 3), so the approximate real 8th roots of 3 are 1.1472 and -1.1472.

Notes on the Lesson

Quiz Yourself 1 Students may not understand why the frequency of D is the sixth term of the geometric sequence of piano frequencies. They may think that D should be the fourth term of the sequence because A is the first white key and D is the fourth white key. Point out to your students that the black keys are counted as well, which is why the frequency of D is the sixth term of the sequence.

How many real *n*th roots does a real number have? Notice the connection between the real *n*th roots of a number and the graph of $y = x^n$. When *n* is even, the graph does not have any negative *y*-values, and all positive *y*-values correspond to two *x*-values. This indicates that negative numbers do not have real even *n*th roots, and positive numbers have two real even *n*th roots.

The situation with *n*th roots when *n* is odd is much easier. The graph of $y = x^n$ intersects each horizontal line exactly once, so every *y*-value has exactly one corresponding *x*-value, and every real number has exactly one real odd *n*th root.

From the graph at the right, you can see that that there are two real 12th roots of 2. This calculator shows that the real 12th roots of 2 are approximately –1.05946 and 1.05946. Only the positive root has meaning in this context. So, the ratio *r* of the frequencies of consecutive in-tune keys is about 1.05946.

Check Use a CAS in real-number mode to solve $x^{12} = 2$.

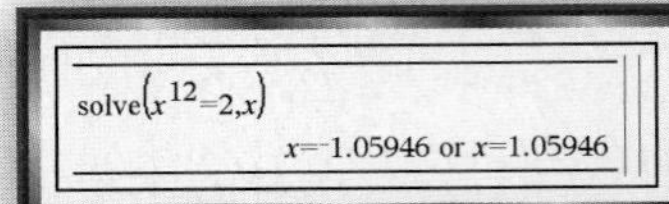

The positive value $x = 1.05946$ checks.

STOP QY1

> **QY1**
> If the A below middle C is tuned to 220 cycles per second, find the frequency of the D above middle C, the 5th note above this A.

How Many Real *n*th Roots Does a Real Number Have?

The number of real *n*th roots of a real number *k* is the number of points of intersection of the line $y = k$ with the power function $y = x^n$. The number of intersections is determined by whether the value of *n* is odd or even, and whether the real number *k* is positive or negative, as illustrated in the graphs below.

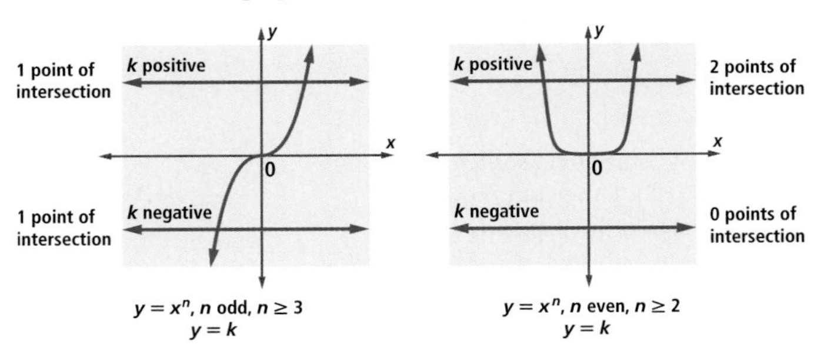

Each intersection determines an *n*th root of *k*, suggesting the following theorem.

Number of Real Roots Theorem

Every positive real number has:	2 real *n*th roots, when *n* is even. 1 real *n*th root, when *n* is odd.
Every negative real number has:	0 real *n*th roots, when *n* is even. 1 real *n*th root, when *n* is odd.
Zero has:	1 real *n*th root.

ENGLISH LEARNERS

Vocabulary Development

Review with students the ordinal numbers *first, second, third, fourth,* and so on. Have them note the endings of abbreviations for the terms. The first three terms, 1st, 2nd, and 3rd, end in *-st, -nd,* and *-rd,* respectively. The 4th through 10th terms end with *-th*. Explain that the term ***nth*** is like a variable in that it can represent any one of the ordinal numbers.

Then call attention to the fact that only the 2nd and 3rd roots have special names—*square root* and *cube root,* respectively.

For instance, –4 has no real square roots, 4th roots, or 6th roots. It has one real cube root, one real 5th root, and one real 7th root.

Roots and Powers

One reason that powers are important is that the positive *n*th root of a positive number *x* is a power of *x*. The power is directly related to the root: the square root is the $\frac{1}{2}$ power; the cube root is the $\frac{1}{3}$ power; and so on. The general property is stated in the following theorem and can be proved using properties of powers you already know.

$\frac{1}{n}$ Exponent Theorem

When $x \geq 0$ and n is an integer greater than 1, $x^{\frac{1}{n}}$ is an nth root of x.

Proof By the definition of *n*th root, b is an nth root of x if and only if $b^n = x$.

Suppose $b = x^{\frac{1}{n}}$.

Then $b^n = \left(x^{\frac{1}{n}}\right)^n$ Raise both sides to the *n*th power.

$= x^{\left(\frac{1}{n} \cdot n\right)}$ Power of a Power Postulate

$= x^1$

$= x.$

Thus, $x^{\frac{1}{n}}$ is an *n*th root of x.

Mathematicians could decide to let the symbol $x^{\frac{1}{n}}$ be any of the *n*th roots of *x*. However, to ensure that $x^{\frac{1}{n}}$ has exactly one value, we restrict the base *x* to be a nonnegative real number and let $x^{\frac{1}{n}}$ stand for the ***unique nonnegative*** *n*th root. For example, $x^{\frac{1}{2}}$ is the positive square root of *x*, and $2^{\frac{1}{4}}$ is the positive fourth root of 2.

Pay close attention to parentheses when applying the $\frac{1}{n}$ Exponent Theorem. Do not consider negative bases with these exponents because there are properties of powers that do not apply to them. You may use your calculator to find the *n*th roots of a nonnegative number *b* by entering `b^(1÷n)`, as in the next Example. You will read more about how your calculator interprets numbers like $(-8)^{\frac{1}{3}}$ in Lesson 7-7.

GUIDED

Example 2

Approximate all real solutions to $x^5 = 77$ to the nearest thousandth.

(continued on next page)

Accommodating the Learner

Have students work in pairs to write examples of the function $y = x^n$ for even and odd values of $n \geq 2$. Have each pair use a different value for *n*. Then ask them to graph each function along with various horizontal lines to verify the Number of Real Roots Theorem.

Notes on the Lesson

Roots and Powers The proof of the $\frac{1}{n}$ Exponent Theorem on page 489 is similar to other proofs students have seen in this chapter. If students have trouble with the proof, you might begin by asking students what the symbol $9^{\frac{1}{2}}$ means. Use the Power of a Power Postulate to show that $\left(9^{\frac{1}{2}}\right)^2 = 9^{\frac{1}{2} \cdot 2} = 9^1 = 9$. This proves that $9^{\frac{1}{2}}$ is a square root of 9. Similarly, $\left(9^{\frac{1}{n}}\right)^n = 9$, so $9^{\frac{1}{n}}$ is an *n*th root of 9. Now work through the general case for the proof of the $\frac{1}{n}$ Exponent Theorem.

Additional Examples

Example 2 Approximate all real solutions to $x^4 = 100$ to the nearest thousandth.

Solution By the definition of nth root, the real solutions of $x^4 = 100$ are the real __?__ roots of __?__. 4th; 100 So one solution is $x = 100^{\underline{?}}$. $\frac{1}{4}$ Enter 100 [^] (1 [÷] 4) into a calculator. The result, to the nearest thousandth is __?__. 3.162 So $100^{\frac{1}{4}} \approx$ __?__. 3.162 By the Number of Real Roots Theorem, there are two real solutions to $x^4 = 100$ because 4 is a(n) __?__ number. even The solutions are $x \approx$ __?__ and $x \approx$ __?__. 3.162, -3.162

Example 3 Use the cSolve or Solve command on a CAS to find all the 4th roots of 2401. 7, -7, 7*i*, -7*i*

3 Assignment

Recommended Assignment

- Questions 1–30
- Question 31 (extra credit)
- Reading Lesson 7-7
- Covering the Ideas 7-7

7-6A Lesson Master — Questions on SPUR Objectives — See Student Edition pages 510–513 for objectives.

SKILLS Objective A

In 1–5, give a positive real number answer. Do all of the work in your head.

1. a square root of 121 11
2. a cube root of 27 3
3. $125^{\frac{1}{3}} =$ 5
4. $16^{\frac{1}{4}} =$ 2
5. $\left(\frac{49}{81}\right)^{\frac{1}{2}} =$ $\frac{7}{9}$

In 6–8, estimate to the nearest thousandth.

6. $18^{\frac{1}{6}} =$ 1.619
7. $0.86^{\frac{1}{4}} =$ 0.963
8. $32{,}176^{\frac{1}{10}} =$ 2.823

SKILLS Objective D

In 9–12, find all real solutions to the equation. Round to the nearest thousandth when necessary.

9. $p^3 = \frac{27}{8}$ $p = \frac{3}{2}$
10. $3x^4 + 2 = 50$ $x = 2$ or -2
11. $a^5 = 20$ $a = 1.821$
12. $200 = 100r^8$ $r = 1.091$ or -1.091

PROPERTIES Objective E

13. How many real solutions does the equation $x^n = a$ have if a is positive and
    a. n is even? two
    b. n is odd? one
14. In this lesson, the expression $b^{\frac{1}{4}}$ is defined for what values of b? $b \geq 0$

USES Objective F

15. Recall that the frequencies of notes in the musical scale can be modeled using a geometric sequence with constant ratio $2^{\frac{1}{12}}$. On most pianos, the lowest note is an A with a frequency of 27.50 Hz. Find the frequency of the C above this A, which is the fourth-lowest note on a piano. Round to the nearest tenth. 32.7 Hz
16. The average price of a gallon of whole milk in the United States in 1998 was \$2.63. In 2008, it was \$3.87. Use the compound interest formula and solve for r to find the average annual increase in the price of a gallon of milk. ≈ 3.9%

Solution By the definition of nth root, the real solutions of $x^5 = 77$ are the real __?__ roots of __?__. So, one solution is $x = 77^{\underline{?}}$. 5th; 77; $\frac{1}{5}$

Enter `77^(1÷5)` into a calculator. The result, to the nearest thousandth is __?__. So, $77^{\frac{1}{5}} \approx$ __?__. By the Number of Real Roots Theorem, 2.384; 2.384 $x \approx$ __?__ is the only real solution because 5 is a(n) __?__ number. 2.384; odd

QY2

> **QY2**
> Approximate the real solution to $4n^3 = -100$ to the nearest hundredth.

Nonreal nth Roots

Some of the nth roots of a real number are not real.

Example 3

Use the cSolve or Solve command on a CAS to find all 4th roots of 81.

Solution Set a CAS to complex-number mode. z is a 4th root of 81 if and only if $z^4 = 81$. So solve $z^4 = 81$. One CAS shows four solutions: $z = 3i, -3i, -3$, or 3.

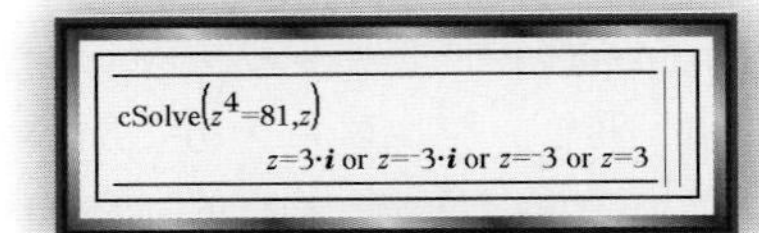

Check Verify that each solution satisfies $z^4 = 81$.

$$3^4 = 3 \cdot 3 \cdot 3 \cdot 3 = 81$$
$$(-3)^4 = (-3)(-3)(-3)(-3) = 81$$
$$(3i)^4 = 3^4 \cdot i^4 = 81 \cdot 1 = 81$$
$$(-3i)^4 = (-3)^4 \cdot i^4 = 81 \cdot 1 = 81$$

So, 3, −3, 3i, and −3i are fourth roots of 81.

It can be proved that every nonzero real number has n distinct nth roots. In a later mathematics course you will learn how to find them.

Questions

COVERING THE IDEAS

In 1–3, refer to the discussion of the musical scale at the start of this lesson.

1. What is the exact ratio of the frequencies of consecutive notes in this scale? $2^{\frac{1}{12}}$
2. What is the frequency of E above the middle C, to the nearest hundredth? 329.63 Hz
3. In 1879, the Steinway & Sons piano manufacturing company tuned the note A above middle C to 457.2 hertz. Given this frequency, what is the frequency of A below middle C? 228.6 Hz

4. **Fill in the Blank** Let n be an integer greater than 1. Then x is an nth root of d if and only if ___?___. $x^n = d$

In 5–7, find the positive real root without a calculator.

5. fourth root of 81 3
6. cube root of 64 4
7. fifth root of 32 2

In 8–10, suppose the graphs of $y = x^n$ and $y = k$ are drawn on the same set of axes.

8. How are the points of intersection related to the nth roots of k?
9. If n is odd and $k > 0$, at how many points do the graphs intersect? 1
10. If $k < 0$ and the graphs do not intersect, is n even or odd? even
11. Approximate all real solutions of $m^7 = 5$ to the nearest hundredth. 1.26

8. The x-coordinates of the points of intersection are the real nth roots of k.

In 12 and 13, use a CAS to find all solutions of the equation.

12. $x^3 = 1331$
13. $x^4 = 20{,}736$
14. a. Find two solutions to $x^4 = \frac{81}{625}$ in your head. $\frac{3}{5}, -\frac{3}{5}$
    b. Your answers to Part a are nth roots of $\frac{81}{625}$. What is n? 4
15. **True or False** $x^{\frac{1}{n}}$ is defined for $x \geq 0$ and any real number n. false
16. Explain why $(-7)^4 = 2401$, but $2401^{\frac{1}{4}} \neq -7$.
17. **Multiple Choice** Which of the following is *not* a 4th root of 6561? Justify your answer. D; The exponent is negative, so it cannot be an nth root.

    A $6561^{\frac{1}{4}}$ B -9 C $9i$ D $6561^{-\frac{1}{4}}$

12. $x = 11, -\frac{11}{2} + \frac{11\sqrt{3}}{2}i, -\frac{11}{2} - \frac{11\sqrt{3}}{2}i$

13. $x = 12, -12, 12i, -12i$

16. $x^{\frac{1}{n}}$ stands for the positive nth root of x.

APPLYING THE MATHEMATICS

18. In the nautilus shell discussed on the first page of the chapter, the eleventh chamber is about twice as long as the smallest chamber. Assuming that the ratio r of the lengths of two adjacent chambers is constant, estimate r to the nearest hundredth. 1.07

In 19 and 20, use the Compound Interest Formula and nth roots to determine a rate of growth.

19. In an old animated show, the main character travels to the future and finds out he is a billionaire. Assume that he started with \$563 in his account and after 248 years the account held \$1,000,000,000. If the interest rate is constant for the entire time period, what is the annual percentage yield? 6%
20. Suppose a house was purchased in 1990 for \$100,000.
    a. If its value is increasing by r% each year, what is its value n years after 1990? $100{,}000 \cdot \left(1 + \frac{r}{100}\right)^n$
    b. If its value in 2005 was \$180,000, estimate r to the nearest tenth. 4.0
21. Give a value of x that makes the inequality $x^{\frac{1}{2}} > x$ true. Answers vary. Sample: $x = \frac{1}{4}$

7-6B page 2

7-6B Lesson Master

Questions on SPUR Objectives
See Student Edition pages 510–513 for objectives.

SKILLS Objective A

In 1–14, give a positive real number answer. Do all of the work in your head.

1. $64^{\frac{1}{3}}$ 4
2. $64^{\frac{1}{6}}$ 2
3. $10{,}000^{\frac{1}{4}}$ 10
4. $(0.04)^{\frac{1}{2}}$ 0.2
5. $36^{\frac{1}{2}}$ 6
6. $625^{\frac{1}{4}}$ 5
7. $81^{\frac{1}{2}}$ 9
8. $125^{\frac{1}{3}}$ 5
9. $\left(\frac{1000}{27}\right)^{\frac{1}{3}}$ $\frac{10}{3}$
10. $1.44^{\frac{1}{2}}$ 1.2
11. $1^{\frac{1}{2}}$ 1
12. $\left(\frac{16}{121}\right)^{\frac{1}{2}}$ $\frac{4}{11}$
13. $32^{\frac{1}{5}}$ 2
14. $343^{\frac{1}{3}}$ 7

In 15–20, estimate to the nearest integer.

15. $52^{\frac{1}{2}}$ 7
16. $9^{\frac{1}{3}}$ 2
17. $153^{\frac{1}{2}}$ 12
18. $300^{\frac{1}{5}}$ 3
19. $99^{\frac{1}{2}}$ 10
20. $102^{\frac{1}{2}}$ 10

In 21–26, estimate to the nearest thousandth.

21. $5^{\frac{1}{2}}$ 2.236
22. $22^{\frac{1}{3}}$ 2.802
23. $10^{\frac{1}{4}}$ 1.778
24. $2^{\frac{1}{10}}$ 1.072
25. $600^{\frac{1}{6}}$ 2.904
26. $(-0.5)^{\frac{1}{9}}$ −0.925

SKILLS Objective D

In 27–34, find all real solutions to the equation. Round to the nearest thousandth when necessary.

27. $d^3 = 14$ $d \approx 2.410$
28. $w^2 = 218$ $w \approx 14.765$ or -14.765
29. $m^5 + 6 = 9$ $m \approx 1.246$
30. $2v^{10} = 24$ $v \approx 1.282$ or -1.282
31. $n^6 = \frac{64}{729}$ $n = \frac{2}{3}$
32. $3x^4 = 30$ $x \approx 1.778$ or -1.778
33. $u^7 - 25 = 45$ $u \approx 1.835$
34. $5c^5 + 17 = -3$ $c \approx -1.320$

455

454 Advanced Algebra

Notes on the Questions

Question 22 $9^{\frac{1}{4}} \neq i\sqrt{3}$ because $9^{\frac{1}{4}}$ indicates the greatest *real* 4th root of 9, which is approximately 1.732. Note that the 4th root of 9 equals the square root of 3 because $9^{\frac{1}{4}} = (3^2)^{\frac{1}{4}} = 3^{2 \cdot \frac{1}{4}} = 3^{\frac{1}{2}}$.

Questions 23 and 24 Both questions can be answered either by reasoning from the properties of powers or by direct calculation. Students should be able to answer each question without a calculator.

Question 31 You might use this question to pique student interest in the *n*th roots of 1, which have many interesting properties. Some of these will be encountered in later UCSMP courses.

4 Wrap-Up

Ongoing Assessment

Have students work in small groups. Have one student write an equation in the form $b^n = x$, for example, $5^3 = 125$. Have a second student write a sentence that applies the definition of an *n*th root. For $5^3 = 125$, the student would write "5 is the cube root of 125." Then have a third student apply the $\frac{1}{n}$ Exponent Theorem to the preceding sentence, in this case, "$125^{\frac{1}{3}}$ is the cube root of 125." Be sure students include some cases in which *b* is not an integer. Students should correctly apply the definition of *n*th root to examples of the form $b^n = x$ and then correctly apply the $\frac{1}{n}$ Exponent Theorem.

Administer Quiz 2 (or a quiz your own) after students complete this lesson.

22. a. Verify that $i\sqrt{3}$ is a 4th root of 9.
    b. Why is $9^{\frac{1}{4}} \neq i\sqrt{3}$?

Fill in the Blank In 23 and 24, which symbol, <, =, or >, makes it a true statement?

23. $(16.1)^{\frac{1}{4}}$ __?__ 2 >

24. $0.25^{\frac{1}{2}}$ __?__ $0.25^{\frac{1}{3}}$ <

REVIEW

25. A Baravelle spiral is shown at the right. The ratios of the areas of consecutive shaded regions are equal. Suppose the area of region $A_1 = 32$ square units and the area of region $A_4 = \frac{1}{2}$ square unit. What is the ratio of consecutive areas? (Lesson 7-5) $\frac{1}{4}$

In 26–28, determine whether the sequence is geometric. If it is, write an explicit formula for its *n*th term. (Lesson 7-5)

26. 4, 9, 16, 25, ...

27. 5, 10, 20, 40, ...

28. 6, -2, $\frac{2}{3}$, $-\frac{2}{9}$, ...

29. **True or False** If two savings accounts have the same published interest rate, then the one with more compoundings per year will always have a higher annual percentage yield. (Lesson 7-4) true

30. **Multiple Choice** Which of the following graphs show *y* as a function of *x*? There may be more than one correct answer. (Lesson 1-4) A, C, D

A
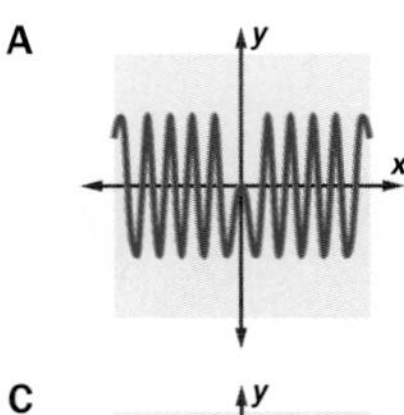

B
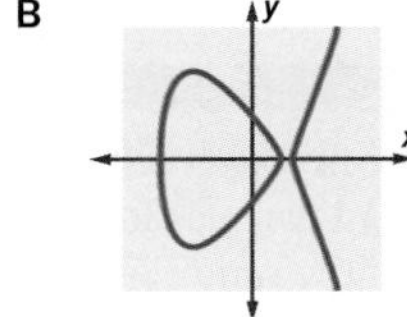

C
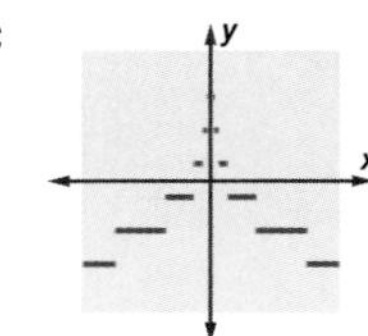

D
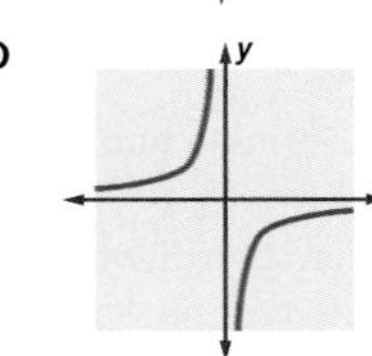

EXPLORATION

31. Use a CAS to find all the complex solutions to $x^8 = 1$.
    a. Choose any two solutions and multiply them. What do you notice? Their product is another root.
    b. Add all of the solutions. What do you notice? The sum is 0.
    c. Repeat Parts *a* and *b* for the solutions for $x^9 = 1$. Make two conjectures about your findings.

22a. $(i\sqrt{3})^4 = i^4 \cdot (\sqrt{3})^4 = 1 \cdot 3^2 = 9$

22b. The $9^{\frac{1}{4}}$ is the positive real solution to $x^4 = 9$, or $\sqrt{3}$.

A_1, A_2, A_3, A_4

26. not geometric

27. geometric; $g_n = 5 \cdot 2^{n-1}$

28. geometric; $g_n = 6 \cdot \left(-\frac{1}{3}\right)^{n-1}$

31c. Answers vary. Sample: For integers $n > 1$, the product of any two complex roots of $x^n = 1$ is another root, and the sum of all of the *n*th roots of 1 is 0.

QY ANSWERS

1. about 293.660 Hz
2. $n \approx -2.92$

Accommodating the Learner

After students complete the lesson, have them work in groups to explain the differences among 2^n, $\left(\frac{1}{2}\right)^n$, and $2^{\frac{1}{n}}$. Answers vary. Sample: 2^n is the *n*th power of 2, while $2^{\frac{1}{n}}$ is the largest *n*th root of 2. $\left(\frac{1}{2}\right)^n$ is not equal to either of the other expressions; it is the *n*th power of $\frac{1}{2}$, which is $\frac{1}{2^n}$, the reciprocal of 2^n.

Lesson 7-7

Positive Rational Exponents

▸ **BIG IDEA** The expression $x^{\frac{m}{n}}$ is only defined when x is nonnegative and stands for the positive nth root of the mth power of x, or, equivalently, the mth power of the positive nth root of x.

The Meaning of Positive Rational Powers

In Lesson 7-6, you learned that $x^{\frac{1}{n}}$ stands for the positive nth root of x. For instance, $64^{\frac{1}{6}}$ is the positive 6th root of 64. In this lesson, we ask what $x^{\frac{m}{n}}$ means when m and n are positive integers. For instance, what does $64^{\frac{5}{6}}$ mean? The answer can be found by rewriting the fraction $\frac{5}{6}$ and using the Power of a Power Postulate.

$$64^{\frac{5}{6}} = 64^{\left(\frac{1}{6}\cdot 5\right)} \qquad \frac{5}{6} = \frac{1}{6}\cdot 5$$

$$= \left(64^{\frac{1}{6}}\right)^5 \qquad \text{Power of a Power Postulate}$$

Thus, $64^{\frac{5}{6}}$ is the 5th power of the positive 6th root of 64. With this interpretation, $64^{\frac{5}{6}} = \left(64^{\frac{1}{6}}\right)^5 = 2^5 = 32$.

Notice also that $64^{\frac{5}{6}} = 64^{\left(5\cdot\frac{1}{6}\right)} = (64^5)^{\frac{1}{6}}$.

So $64^{\frac{5}{6}}$ is also the positive 6th root of the 5th power of 64. With this interpretation, $64^{\frac{5}{6}}$ can be simplified as follows:

$$64^{\frac{5}{6}} = (64^5)^{\frac{1}{6}} = (1{,}073{,}741{,}824)^{\frac{1}{6}} = 32.$$

In general, when an exponent is a simple fraction, the numerator is the power and the denominator is the root. The proof is a generalization of the argument above.

Rational Exponent Theorem

For any nonnegative real number x and positive integers m and n, $x^{\frac{m}{n}} = \left(x^{\frac{1}{n}}\right)^m$, the mth power of the positive nth root of x, and $x^{\frac{m}{n}} = (x^m)^{\frac{1}{n}}$, the positive nth root of the mth power of x.

Mental Math

Tyra is painting her bedroom. The room is 8 feet by 12 feet and has 10-foot ceilings. One quart of paint covers about 90 square feet. How many quarts of paint does Tyra need if she wants to paint

a. only the largest wall? 2 qt

b. all four walls, not including a 24-square-foot window and a 28-square-foot doorway? 4 qt

Background

The relevant property of powers for the evaluation of powers with rational exponents is $x^{\frac{m}{n}} = \left(x^{\frac{1}{n}}\right)^m = (x^m)^{\frac{1}{n}}$. Like other properties, this property is deduced from the fundamental properties mentioned in Lesson 7-2, in this case, the Power of a Power Postulate.

Note the semantic problem: Virtually everyone speaks of the "rational power" of a number when they mean more precisely "a power with a rational exponent." The value of the power is usually not a rational number. This issue is addressed in the Accommodating the Learner Down activity on page 494.

The Rational Exponent Theorem has two major uses. First, it interprets rational powers in terms of integer powers and roots. Second, it implies that if both a power and a root are to be applied to the same base, the order in which they are calculated is irrelevant.

(continued on next page)

Lesson 7-7

GOAL

Learn skills, properties, and uses involving positive rational exponents, using both mental computation and calculator arithmetic.

SPUR Objectives

A Evaluate b^n when $b > 0$ and n is a rational number.

B Simplify expressions or solve equations using properties of exponents.

D Find all real solutions to equations of the form $x^n = b$, where $x \geq 0$ and n is a rational number.

E Recognize properties of nth powers and nth roots.

F Solve real-world problems that can be modeled by expressions with nth powers or nth roots.

Materials/Resources

- Lesson Masters 7-7A and 7-7B
- Resource Masters 131 and 132
- CAS (optional)

HOMEWORK

Suggestions for Assignment

- Questions 1–33
- Question 34 (extra credit)
- Reading Lesson 7-8
- Covering the Ideas 7-8

Local Standards

1 Warm-Up

1. Write 9^x for integer values of x from –4 to 4. $\frac{1}{6561}, \frac{1}{729}, \frac{1}{81}, \frac{1}{9}$, 1, 9, 81, 729, 6561

2. Write $9^{-4}, 9^{-3}, 9^{-2}, \ldots, 9^4$ as powers of 3. Insert the missing integer powers of 3. What powers of 9 do these powers of 3 represent? $3^{-8}, 3^{-7}, 3^{-6}, 3^{-5}, 3^{-4}, 3^{-3}, 3^{-2}, 3^{-1}, 3^0, 3^1, 3^2, 3^3, 3^4, 3^5, 3^6, 3^7, 3^8$; -4, -3.5, -3, -2.5, -2, -1.5, -1, -0.5, 0, 0.5, 1, 1.5, 2, 2.5, 3, 3.5, 4

7-7

2 Teaching

Notes on the Lesson

Although the Rational Exponent Theorem looks as if it applies only to powers with simple fractions as exponents, there are places throughout the lesson where the theorem can help to evaluate powers with decimal exponents. In other places, you might point out that the rational exponent could be written as a decimal. Then $64^{\frac{5}{6}}$ becomes $64^{0.8\overline{3}}$, and $x^{\frac{3}{4}} = 7.2$ (Example 2) becomes $x^{0.75} = 7.2$.

The advantage of decimal over fractional exponents is that the size of the answer is more easily estimated. For example, $64^{0.8\overline{3}}$ should be between $64^{0.5}$ and 64^1, that is, between 8 and 64.

Proof $x^{\frac{m}{n}} = x^{\frac{1}{n}\cdot m}$ $\quad \frac{m}{n} = \frac{1}{n}\cdot m$

$= \left(x^{\frac{1}{n}}\right)^m$ $\quad$ Power of a Power Postulate

Also, $x^{\frac{m}{n}} = x^{m\cdot\frac{1}{n}}$ $\quad \frac{m}{n} = m\cdot\frac{1}{n}$

$= (x^m)^{\frac{1}{n}}.$ $\quad$ Power of a Power Postulate

To simplify an expression with a rational exponent you can find powers first or roots first. By hand, it is usually easier to find the root first because you end up working with smaller numbers and fewer digits. With a calculator, you can work more directly.

STOP QY1

> **QY1**
>
> **a.** Estimate $7^{\frac{2}{5}}$ by using the key sequence 7^(2÷5).
>
> **b.** Is $7^{\frac{2}{5}}$ greater than, equal to, or less than $7^{0.4}$?

Properties of Positive Rational Exponents

The exponent gives information about the value of each power relative to the base.

Activity 1

Step 1 Complete the following chart for powers of 8.

Rational Power	8^0	$8^{\frac{1}{3}}$	$8^{\frac{1}{2}}$	$8^{\frac{3}{4}}$	8^1	$8^{\frac{5}{4}}$	$8^{\frac{3}{2}}$	$8^{\frac{5}{3}}$	8^2
Decimal Power	8^0	$8^{0.\overline{3}}$	?	$8^{0.75}$	8^1	?	?	?	8^2
Value	1	?	?	?	8	?	?	?	64

$8^{0.5}$; $8^{1.25}$; $8^{1.5}$; $8^{1.\overline{6}}$

2; 2.83; 4.76; 13.45; 22.63; 32

Step 2 When the exponent n is between 0 and 1, between what values is 8^n? It is between 1 and 8.

Step 3 When the exponent n is between 1 and 2, between what values is 8^n? It is between 8 and 64.

Step 4 As the exponent n gets larger, what happens to the value of 8^n?

Step 5 Without calculating, predict between what values $8^{\frac{7}{4}}$ will be. Explain your answer.

Step 4. It gets larger.

Step 5. Answers vary. Sample: It will be between 32 and 64, since the exponent is between $\frac{5}{3}$ and 2.

In general, if the base is greater than 1, then the greater the exponent, the greater the value. Thus, even without calculating, you can conclude that $8^{\frac{7}{5}}$ is between 8 and 64 because $\frac{7}{5} = 1.4$ is between 1 and 2. In Question 19, you are asked to examine what happens if the base is less than 1 but greater than zero.

STOP QY2

> **QY2**
>
> Which is smaller, $47^{\frac{3}{4}}$ or $47^{0.78}$?

Activity 2 This Activity is designed to show why rational exponents are not considered with negative bases. The basic idea is that the operation of powering is not well defined when there are negative bases. That is, when $x < 0$, it is possible to have $m = n$, but $x^m \neq x^n$.

Accommodating the Learner 

This lesson, and virtually every text that deals with rational exponents, uses the term *rational power* of a number when more precisely we mean "a power with a rational exponent." All students may benefit from an explicit discussion of this shorthand usage. You may want to give students examples of "rational powers" so they see that the value of the power is not usually a rational number.

The properties of powers in Lesson 7-2 hold for all positive exponents.

Example 1

Suppose $y \geq 0$. Simplify $(64y^9)^{\frac{4}{3}}$.

Solution

$(64y^9)^{\frac{4}{3}} = (64)^{\frac{4}{3}}(y^9)^{\frac{4}{3}}$ Power of a Product Postulate

$= 64^{\frac{4}{3}} \cdot y^{\frac{36}{3}}$ Power of a Power Postulate

$= \left(64^{\frac{1}{3}}\right)^4 \cdot y^{12}$ Rational Exponent Theorem

$= 4^4 \cdot y^{12}$ $\frac{1}{n}$ Exponent Theorem

$= 256y^{12}$ Arithmetic

Check This CAS display shows that $(64y^9)^{\frac{4}{3}} = 256y^{12}$.

Solving Equations with Positive Rational Exponents

Properties of powers can be used to solve equations with positive rational exponents. To solve an equation of the form $x^{\frac{m}{n}} = k$, raise each side of the equation to the $\frac{n}{m}$ power. This can be done because in general, if $a = b$, then $a^n = b^n$.

Example 2

Solve $x^{\frac{3}{4}} = 7.2$ for x.

Solution

$\left(x^{\frac{3}{4}}\right)^{\frac{4}{3}} = (7.2)^{\frac{4}{3}}$ Raise both sides to the $\frac{4}{3}$ power.

$x^1 = (7.2)^{\frac{4}{3}}$ Power of a Power Postulate

$x \approx 13.9$ Arithmetic

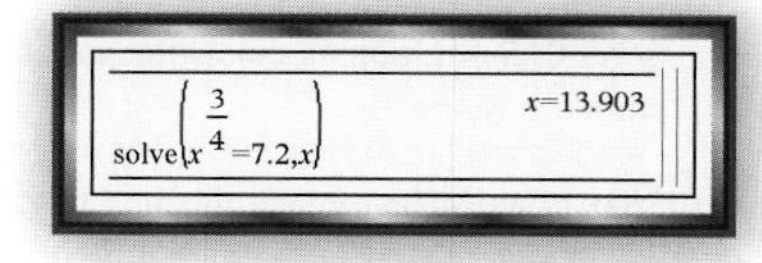

Check Solve on a CAS as shown at the right.

 QY3

QY3

Find a solution to the nearest thousandth for $x^{\frac{8}{5}} = 50$.

Accommodating the Learner

Write $2^{\frac{3}{2}}, \left(\frac{1}{2}\right)^3, 2^{-4}, 2^{\frac{3}{5}}, \left(\frac{1}{2}\right)^{-5}$ on the board and have students work in groups to order them from least to greatest without using a calculator. Have students explain their reasoning. $2^{-4}; \left(\frac{1}{2}\right)^3; 2^{\frac{3}{5}}; 2^{\frac{3}{2}}; \left(\frac{1}{2}\right)^{-5}$; Answers vary. Sample: By rewriting the numbers of powers of 2, we can order them by their exponents. $2^{-4} = 2^{-4}; \left(\frac{1}{2}\right)^3 = 2^{-3}; 2^{\frac{3}{5}} = 2^{\frac{3}{5}}; 2^{\frac{3}{2}} = 2^{\frac{3}{2}}; \left(\frac{1}{2}\right)^{-5} = 2^5$. The number with the greatest exponent is the greatest number.

7-7

Notes on the Lesson

Example 2 Before discussing the solutions of equations containing rational exponents, be certain students can solve simple equations such as $x^3 = 64$ and $y^5 = 32$. Note that one method is to take each side to the same (fractional) power.

Additional Examples

Example 1 Suppose $x \geq 0$. Simplify $(27x^6)^{\frac{2}{3}}$. $9x^4$

Example 2 Solve $x^{\frac{5}{4}} = 6.8$. $x \approx 4.6$

Error Analysis Most students have little difficulty simplifying expressions in the form $x^{\frac{m}{n}}$. However, problems may occur when they are asked to solve equations. Some students will attempt to solve the equation $x^{\frac{m}{n}} = b$ by calculating $b^{\frac{m}{n}}$. Stress that, in a solution, the exponent of x must be 1. Because $x^{\frac{m}{n}}$ must be raised to the reciprocal power, $\frac{n}{m}$, the right-hand side must also be raised to the $\frac{n}{m}$ power.

Additional Example

Example 3 The price of a Volkswagen Beetle in 1959 was about $1700. In 2008, the price of the same model was about $17,000. What was the average annual percent increase in price over these years? 4.81%

Notes on the Lesson

Activity 2 The results in this Activity may startle some students, confuse others, and be obvious to still others. These varying reactions are to be expected and should make for rich discussion. The basic conclusion should be emphasized: Counterexamples to all the properties of powers in Lesson 7-2 can be found if negative bases are allowed; consequently, none of these properties hold for negative bases. However, do not lose the opportunity to point out that the graphs confirm that all the properties do hold for positive bases.

Step 1 can be particularly confusing. Some calculators will allow a domain of any real number for Part c, even though we do not.

Steps 1 and 2 both show that the Power of a Power Postulate does not hold for negative bases. Step 3 shows that even the Product of Powers Postulate does not hold for negative bases; most people would argue that this is the most basic property of all.

Note-Taking Tips

Have students add the Rational Exponent Theorem to their journals, along with a numerical example of each part.

Applications of Rational Exponents

Rational exponents have many applications, including growth situations, investments, and radioactive decay.

Example 3

The base price of a convertible sports car was $4037 in 1963 and $51,390 in 2006. What was the average annual percent increase in price over these years?

A 1963 Austin-Healey Model 3000

Solution Let p_t be the price of the sports car where $t = 1$ represents 1963 and $t = 44$ represents 2006. Then $p_1 = 4037$ and $p_{44} = 51{,}390$. Use a geometric sequence P with $p_t = p_1 r^{t-1}$ to model this situation.

$p_{44} = p_1 r^{44-1}$	Geometric sequence model
$51{,}390 = 4037r^{43}$	Substitution
$12.730 \approx r^{43}$	Divide both sides by 4037.
$(12.730)^{\frac{1}{43}} \approx r$	Raise each side to the $\frac{1}{43}$ power.
$1.0609 \approx r$	Arithmetic

The constant ratio r represents the previous year's price plus the increase of $0.0609 = 6.09\%$. So, the price of the car increased by about 6.09% per year from 1963 to 2006.

Why Don't We Use Rational Exponents with Negative Bases?

Difficulties arise when working with noninteger rational exponents when the base is negative.

Activity 2

MATERIALS CAS (optional)

Set a CAS or graphing calculator to real-number mode and use the standard window.

Step 1 a. Do you think the graph of $y = \left(x^{\frac{1}{6}}\right)^2$ will be the same as the graph of $y = x^{\frac{1}{3}}$? Why or why not?

b. Graph $y = x^{\frac{1}{3}}$.

c. Clear the window and graph $y = \left(x^{\frac{1}{6}}\right)^2$. Was your prediction correct? See margin.

Step 1a. No; because there is no real 6th root of a negative number, so the first graph will only be defined for nonnegative numbers.

Step 1b.

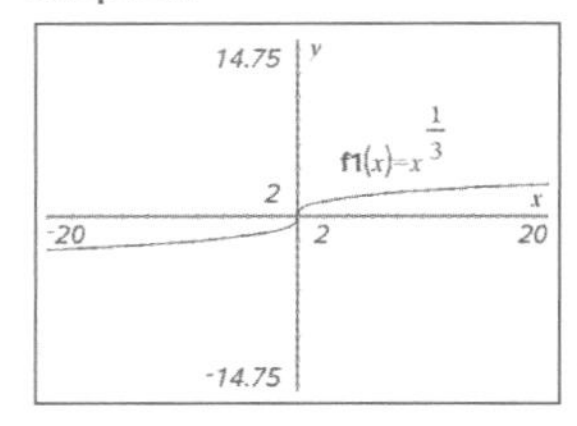

Extension

Give students these problems. Suppose $p^9 = 27$. In 1–5, find each value, using only the properties of powers. (*Hint:* Have students first express the answer as a power of 27.)

1. p^{27} 27^3, or 19,683
2. $p^{\frac{9}{2}}$ $27^{\frac{1}{2}}$, or $\sqrt{27}$
3. p^6 $27^{\frac{2}{3}}$, or 9
4. $p^{\frac{3}{2}}$ $27^{\frac{1}{6}}$, or $\sqrt{3}$
5. p^0 27^0, or 1

6. a. Solve $p^9 = 27$ for p. $p = 27^{\frac{1}{9}}$
   b. Use a calculator to find p to 5 decimal places. 1.44225

Step 2 a. Repeat Step 1 with $y = (x^{10})^{\frac{1}{2}}$ and $y = x^5$. Step 2b–3. See margin.

b. Predict what the graph of $y = \left(x^{\frac{1}{2}}\right)^{10}$ will look like. Clear the graph screen and check your prediction by graphing $y = \left(x^{\frac{1}{2}}\right)^{10}$.

Step 3 Predict what the graph of $y = x^{0.5} \cdot x^{0.5}$ will look like. Then clear the screen and graph the equation to check your prediction.

Step 4 Based on these examples, what properties of powers do not hold for noninteger rational exponents with negative bases? Compare your results with the others in your class and discuss any differences.

The results of Activity 2 illustrate that to keep the properties of powers valid, the Rational Exponent Theorem requires that the base be a nonnegative real number.

Step 2a.
No; the 5th power of a negative number is negative, but the square root of the 10th power of a negative number is a positive number.

Step 2ab.

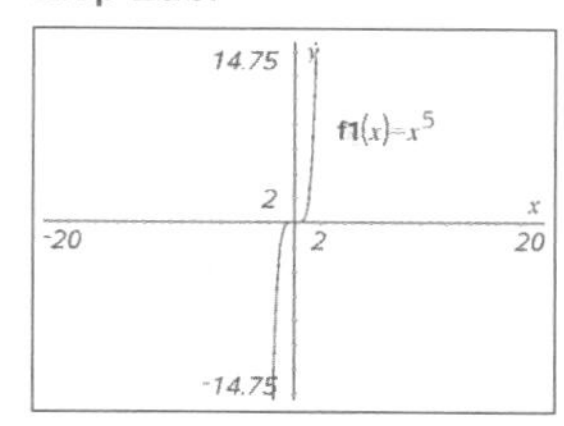

Step 2ac.

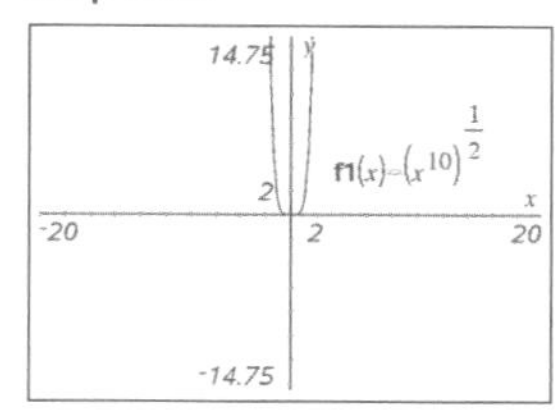

Step 4.
The Power of a Power and Power of a Product Postulates do not hold for noninteger rational exponents with negative bases.

Questions

COVERING THE IDEAS

In 1 and 2, write as a power of *x*.

1. the 3rd power of the 7th root of x $x^{\frac{3}{7}}$
2. the fifth root of the square of x $x^{\frac{2}{5}}$
3. a. Rewrite $10{,}000{,}000^{\frac{4}{7}}$ in two ways as a power of a power of 10,000,000. $(10{,}000{,}000^4)^{\frac{1}{7}}$, $\left(10{,}000{,}000^{\frac{1}{7}}\right)^4$
   b. Which way is easier to calculate mentally? $\left(10{,}000{,}000^{\frac{1}{7}}\right)^4$
   c. Calculate $10{,}000{,}000^{\frac{4}{7}}$. 10,000

In 4–6, simplify without a calculator.

4. $16^{\frac{3}{4}}$ 8
5. $8^{\frac{5}{3}}$ 32
6. $49^{\frac{3}{2}}$ 343

In 7–9, evaluate with a calculator.

7. $243^{\frac{3}{5}}$ 27
8. $(1.331)^{\frac{4}{3}}$ 1.4641
9. $169^{1.50}$ 2197

In 10–12, suppose that the value of each variable is nonnegative. Simplify.

10. $(27x^9)^{\frac{2}{3}}$ $9x^6$
11. $C^{\frac{3}{4}} \cdot C^{\frac{8}{6}}$ $C^{\frac{25}{12}}$
12. $\frac{7}{8}y^{\frac{7}{8}} \cdot \frac{8}{7}y^{\frac{8}{7}}$ $y^{\frac{113}{56}}$

In 13–15, solve.

13. $R^{\frac{2}{5}} = 100$ $R = 100{,}000$
14. $j^{\frac{4}{3}} = 3^4$ $j = 27$
15. $s^{\frac{4}{7}} - 10 = 0$ $s = 10^{\frac{7}{4}}$
16. **True or False** For all real numbers x, $x^{\frac{4}{14}} = x^{\frac{2}{7}}$. Explain your answer.

16. False; rational exponents are only defined for nonnegative real numbers.

Fill in the Blank In 17 and 18, complete with >, <, or =.

17. When $y > 1$, $y^{\frac{3}{4}}$ __?__ $y^{\frac{4}{3}}$. <
18. When $0 < z < 1$, $z^{\frac{5}{6}}$ __?__ $z^{\frac{3}{4}}$. <

3 Assignment

Recommended Assignment

- Questions 1–33
- Question 34 (extra credit)
- Reading Lesson 7-8
- Covering the Ideas 7-8

Notes on the Questions

Questions 10–12 Because of their rational exponents, these questions are not as easily done using algebraic intuition as the same problems with integral exponents. Remind students of the properties of powers in Lesson 7-2.

Additional Answers

Activity 2
Step 1c. Answers vary. Sample: Yes, my prediction was correct.

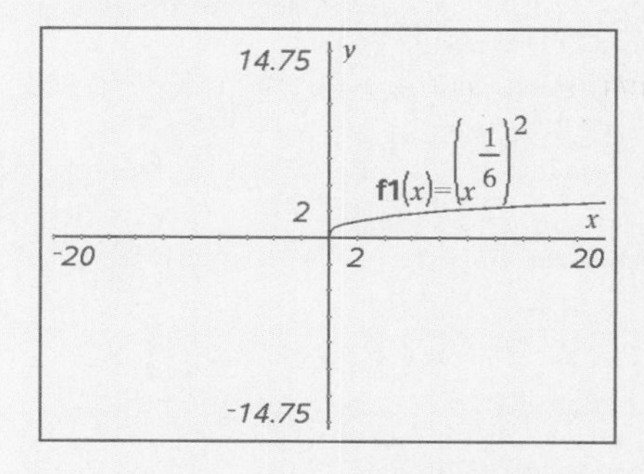

Additional Answers

Activity 2
Step 2b. Answers vary. Sample: I predict the graph will look like the sections of the graphs in Part a that are in Quadrant I.

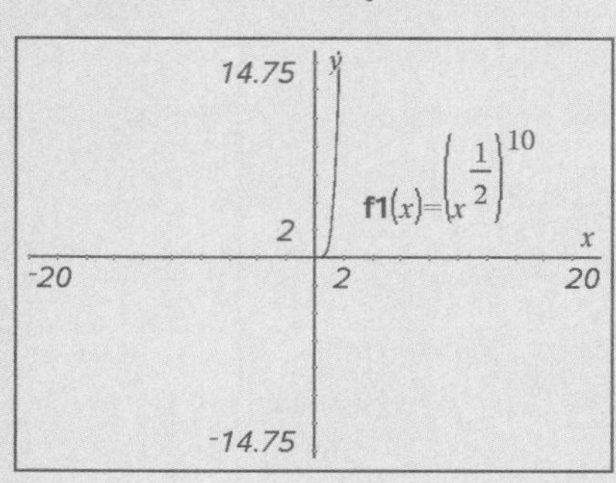

Step 3. Answers vary. Sample: I predict the graph will be a ray in Quadrant I.

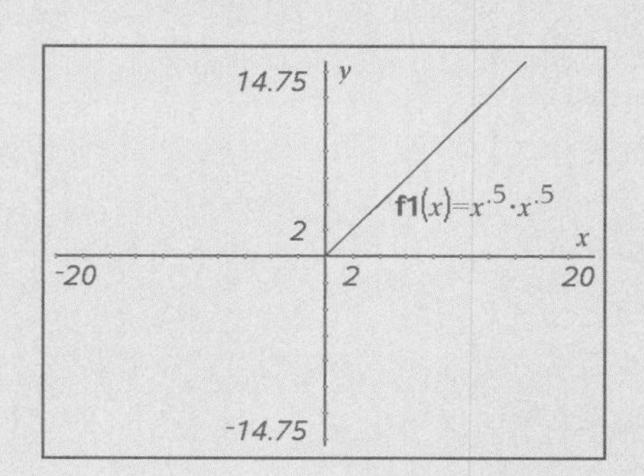

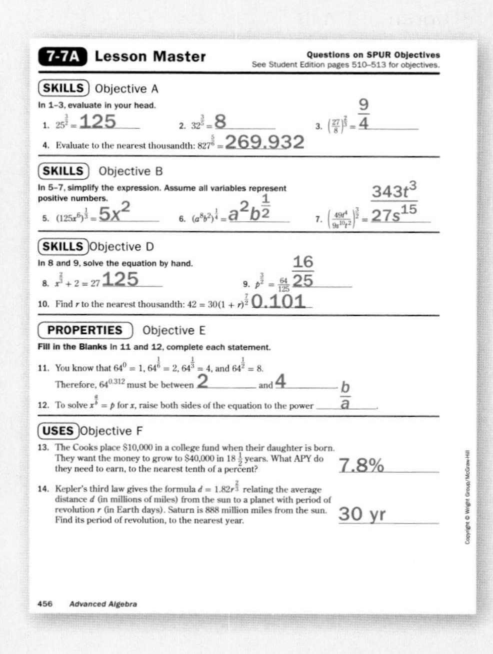

7-7A Lesson Master Questions on SPUR Objectives
See Student Edition pages 510–513 for objectives.

SKILLS Objective A

In 1–3, evaluate in your head.

1. $25^{\frac{3}{2}} =$ 125
2. $32^{\frac{3}{5}} =$ 8
3. $\left(\frac{27}{8}\right)^{\frac{2}{3}} =$ $\frac{9}{4}$
4. Evaluate to the nearest thousandth: $827^{\frac{5}{6}} =$ 269.932

SKILLS Objective B

In 5–7, simplify the expression. Assume all variables represent positive numbers.

5. $(125x^6)^{\frac{1}{3}} =$ $5x^2$
6. $(a^8b^2)^{\frac{1}{4}} =$ $a^2b^{\frac{1}{2}}$
7. $\left(\frac{49t^4}{9s^{10}t^2}\right)^{\frac{3}{2}} =$ $\frac{343t^3}{27s^{15}}$

SKILLS Objective D

In 8 and 9, solve the equation by hand.

8. $x^{\frac{2}{3}} + 2 = 27$ 125
9. $p^{\frac{3}{2}} = \frac{64}{125}$ $\frac{16}{25}$
10. Find r to the nearest thousandth: $42 = 30(1 + r)^{\frac{7}{2}}$ 0.101

PROPERTIES Objective E

Fill in the Blanks In 11 and 12, complete each statement.

11. You know that $64^0 = 1$, $64^{\frac{1}{6}} = 2$, $64^{\frac{1}{3}} = 4$, and $64^{\frac{1}{2}} = 8$. Therefore, $64^{0.312}$ must be between 2 and 4
12. To solve $x^{\frac{a}{b}} = p$ for x, raise both sides of the equation to the power $\frac{b}{a}$.

USES Objective F

13. The Cooks place \$10,000 in a college fund when their daughter is born. They want the money to grow to \$40,000 in $18\frac{1}{2}$ years. What APY do they need to earn, to the nearest tenth of a percent? 7.8%
14. Kepler's third law gives the formula $d = 1.82r^{\frac{2}{3}}$ relating the average distance d (in millions of miles) from the sun to a planet with period of revolution r (in Earth days). Saturn is 888 million miles from the sun. Find its period of revolution, to the nearest year. 30 yr

456 *Advanced Algebra*

Notes on the Questions

Question 22 This question continues the discussion on the restriction of base values to positive numbers when using rational exponents that was started in Activity 2.

Question 26b General Sherman is actually about 84.8 meters (or 275 feet) tall. It is not the tallest living tree. The tallest living tree is a coast redwood, 112 meters (367.5 feet) tall, in Montgomery State Reserve near Ukiah, California. It has a diameter of 3.14 meters (10 feet 4 inches), so it is not as massive as General Sherman.

19. Refer to Activity 1.
    a. Complete the table at the right. See margin.
    b. As the exponent n gets larger, what happens to the value of $\left(\frac{1}{4}\right)^n$? $\left(\frac{1}{4}\right)^n$ gets smaller as n gets larger.
    c. Without calculating, predict values that $\left(\frac{1}{4}\right)^{\frac{5}{3}}$ will be between. Explain your answer.
    d. **Fill in the Blank** Complete the following statement: If the base is smaller than 1 (but greater than zero), as the exponent gets larger, the value gets __?__. smaller

Rational Power	Decimal Power	Value
$\left(\frac{1}{4}\right)^0$	$\left(\frac{1}{4}\right)^0$	1
$\left(\frac{1}{4}\right)^{\frac{1}{4}}$	?	?
$\left(\frac{1}{4}\right)^{\frac{1}{2}}$	?	?
$\left(\frac{1}{4}\right)^{\frac{2}{3}}$	?	?
$\left(\frac{1}{4}\right)^1$	$\left(\frac{1}{4}\right)^1$	0.25
$\left(\frac{1}{4}\right)^{\frac{4}{3}}$	?	?
$\left(\frac{1}{4}\right)^{\frac{3}{2}}$	?	?
$\left(\frac{1}{4}\right)^{\frac{7}{4}}$	?	?
$\left(\frac{1}{4}\right)^2$	$\left(\frac{1}{4}\right)^2$	0.063

20. Refer to Example 3. Estimate what the base price of the sports car was in 2007. about \$54,520

APPLYING THE MATHEMATICS

21. Suppose n is a positive integer. Write $32^{\frac{n}{5}}$ as an integer power of an integer. 2^n

22. **Fill in the Blanks** This question gives one reason why rational exponents are used only with positive bases.
    a. If $(-27)^{\frac{1}{3}}$ were to equal the cube root of -27, then $(-27)^{\frac{1}{3}} =$ __?__. -3
    b. If $(-27)^{\frac{2}{6}}$ follows the Rational Exponent Theorem, then $(-27)^{\frac{2}{6}} = \left((-27)^2\right)^{\frac{1}{6}} =$ __?__; and $(-27)^{\frac{2}{6}} = \left(-27^{\frac{1}{6}}\right)^2 =$ __?__. 3; undefined
    c. In this question, does $(-27)^{\frac{1}{3}} = (-27)^{\frac{2}{6}}$? no
    d. Check the answers to this question on a CAS. Is there a difference? yes
    e. Reread the Rational Exponent Theorem's hypothesis and explain why the base is restricted to nonnegative numbers. See margin.

19c. Answers vary. Sample: Since $\frac{3}{2} < \frac{5}{3} < \frac{7}{4}$, $0.125 > \left(\frac{1}{4}\right)^{\frac{5}{3}} > 0.088$.

In 23–25, apply the Power of a Quotient Theorem, $\left(\frac{a}{b}\right)^m = \frac{a^m}{b^m}$, to simplify.

23. $\left(\frac{16}{81}\right)^{\frac{3}{4}}$ $\frac{8}{27}$

24. $\left(\frac{125}{27}\right)^{\frac{2}{3}}$ $\frac{25}{9}$

25. $(0.00032)^{\frac{3}{5}}$ 0.008

26. The diameter D of the base of a tree of a given species roughly varies directly with the $\frac{3}{2}$ power of its height h.
    a. Suppose a young sequoia 6 meters tall has a base diameter of 20 centimeters. Find the constant of variation. 0.0136
    b. The most massive living tree is a California sequoia called General Sherman. Its base diameter is about 11.1 meters. According to the variation in Part a, about how tall is General Sherman? about 87.3 m

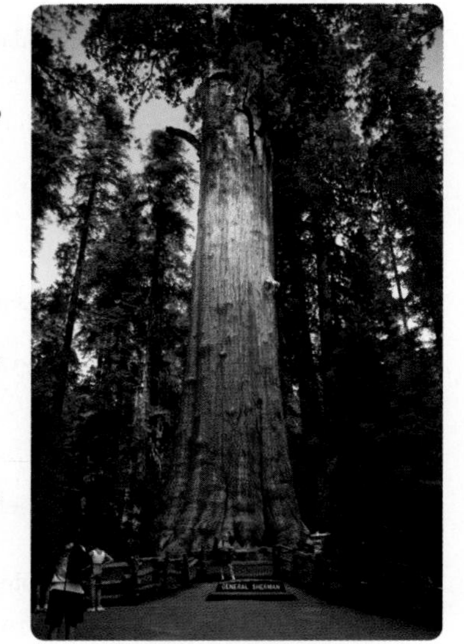

General Sherman

Additional Answers

19a.

Rational Power	$\left(\frac{1}{4}\right)^0$	$\left(\frac{1}{4}\right)^{\frac{1}{4}}$	$\left(\frac{1}{4}\right)^{\frac{1}{2}}$	$\left(\frac{1}{4}\right)^{\frac{2}{3}}$	$\left(\frac{1}{4}\right)^1$	$\left(\frac{1}{4}\right)^{\frac{4}{3}}$	$\left(\frac{1}{4}\right)^{\frac{3}{2}}$	$\left(\frac{1}{4}\right)^{\frac{7}{4}}$	$\left(\frac{1}{4}\right)^2$
Decimal Power	$\left(\frac{1}{4}\right)^0$	$\left(\frac{1}{4}\right)^{0.25}$	$\left(\frac{1}{4}\right)^{0.5}$	$\left(\frac{1}{4}\right)^{0.\overline{6}}$	$\left(\frac{1}{4}\right)^1$	$\left(\frac{1}{4}\right)^{1.\overline{3}}$	$\left(\frac{1}{4}\right)^{1.5}$	$\left(\frac{1}{4}\right)^{1.75}$	$\left(\frac{1}{4}\right)^2$
Value	1	0.707	0.5	0.397	0.25	0.157	0.125	0.088	0.063

22e. Answers vary: Sample: If the base is not restricted to nonnegative numbers, then it is possible for $m = n$, but $x^m \neq x^n$.

27. Recall from Lesson 2-3 the ancient rodent *Phoberomys*. There you used the direct variation equation $w = kd^3$ to estimate the weight of the rodent given its femur diameter d. This equation actually gives an overestimate of *Phoberomys*'s weight. Scientists have concluded that a better model is $w = kd^{2.5}$. Use this newer model to estimate how the weight of the rodent compares to the weight of a modern guinea pig if the *Phoberomys's* femur diameter is 18 times that of the guinea pig. How does this compare to your estimate in Lesson 2-3? 1374.6 times as heavy; it is less than the original estimate.

REVIEW

28. In Byzantine music theory, an octave is divided into 72 notes. What is the ratio of the frequency of a note to the frequency of the note below it in this system? Assume that the ratios between consecutive notes are equal. **(Lesson 7-6)** $2^{\frac{1}{72}}$

29. Verify that $-1 - \sqrt{3}i$ is a third root of 8. **(Lessons 7-6, 6-9)** $(-1 - \sqrt{3}i)^3 = 8$

30. **Fill in the Blanks** Write <, =, or > in each blank. Suppose the geometric sequence with formula $g_n = ar^{n-1}$ has $g_1 < 0$ and $g_2 > 0$. Then a __?__ 0 and r __?__ 0. **(Lesson 7-5)** <; <

31. If you graph the function $y = x^n$ for $x \le 0$, what is the range when n is
    a. even? nonnegative numbers **b.** odd? **(Lesson 7-1)** nonpositive numbers

32. Suppose $f(x) = 3x^2 + 5$. Write an expression for $f(8 - 2x)$ in the standard form of a quadratic. **(Lessons 6-1, 1-3)** $12x^2 - 96x + 197$

33. Find a transformation T such that $T \circ (S_3 \circ S_{0.5,4}) = I$. **(Lessons 4-7, 4-5, 4-4)** $T = S_{\frac{2}{3}, \frac{1}{12}}$

EXPLORATION

34. Sandwiching irrational powers, such as $x^{\sqrt{2}}$ or x^{π}, between two close rational powers is one way to give a meaning to irrational powers of nonnegative numbers. Set a CAS to approximate mode so your answers will be decimals.
    a. Evaluate several irrational powers such as $5^{\sqrt{2}}$, $7^{\sqrt{6}}$, and $\sqrt{2}^{\sqrt{3}}$ and some others of your choosing.
    b. Recall that $1.41 < \sqrt{2} < 1.42$. Show that $5^{1.41} < 5^{\sqrt{2}} < 5^{1.42}$.
    c. Given that $\sqrt{6} \approx 2.4494$, is it true that $7^{\sqrt{6}}$ is between $7^{2.449}$ and $7^{2.450}$? yes

34a. 9.74; 117.51, 1.82

34b. $5^{1.41} \approx 9.67$, $5^{\sqrt{2}} \approx 9.74$, and $5^{1.42} \approx 9.83$

QY ANSWERS

1. **a.** ≈ 2.1779
   b. equal
2. $47^{\frac{3}{4}}$
3. 11.531

Notes on the Questions

Question 34 This question indicates how powers with irrational exponents are calculated. Sandwich the irrational number between two rationals, and the power with the irrational exponent will be sandwiched between the powers with those two rational exponents.

4 Wrap-Up

Ongoing Assessment

Have students work in pairs. Have each student write an expression of the type in Example 1. Have partners exchange papers and simplify the expression. Then have pairs work to check each simplification. Students should correctly apply the Rational Exponent Theorem to simplify expressions involving fractional exponents.

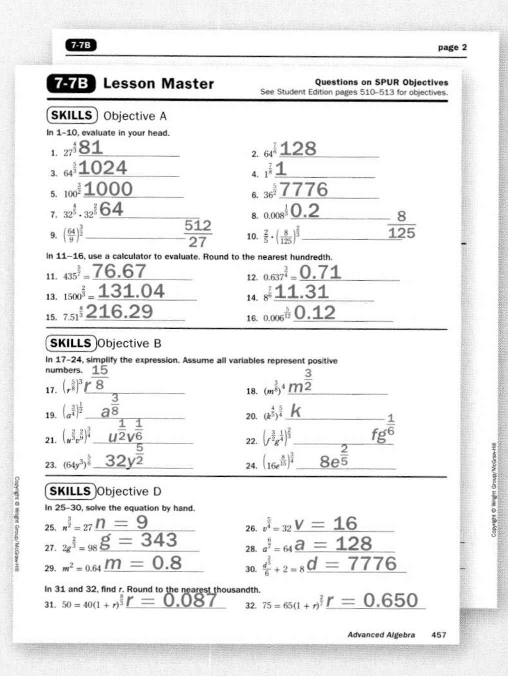
7-7B page 2

7-7B Lesson Master — Questions on SPUR Objectives. See Student Edition pages 510–513 for objectives.

SKILLS Objective A

In 1–10, evaluate in your head.

1. $27^{\frac{4}{3}}$ 81
2. $64^{\frac{7}{6}}$ 128
3. $64^{\frac{5}{3}}$ 1024
4. $1^{\frac{7}{8}}$ 1
5. $100^{\frac{3}{2}}$ 1000
6. $36^{\frac{5}{2}}$ 7776
7. $32^{\frac{4}{5}} \cdot 32^{\frac{2}{5}}$ 64
8. $0.008^{\frac{1}{3}}$ 0.2
9. $\left(\frac{64}{9}\right)^{\frac{3}{2}}$ $\frac{512}{27}$
10. $\frac{2}{5} \cdot \left(\frac{8}{125}\right)^{\frac{2}{3}}$ $\frac{8}{125}$

In 11–16, use a calculator to evaluate. Round to the nearest hundredth.

11. $435^{\frac{5}{7}} =$ 76.67
12. $0.637^{\frac{3}{4}} =$ 0.71
13. $1500^{\frac{2}{3}} =$ 131.04
14. $8^{\frac{7}{6}}$ 11.31
15. $7.51^{\frac{8}{3}}$ 216.29
16. $0.006^{\frac{5}{12}}$ 0.12

SKILLS Objective B

In 17–24, simplify the expression. Assume all variables represent positive numbers.

17. $\left(r^{\frac{5}{8}}\right)^3$ $r^{\frac{15}{8}}$
18. $\left(m^{\frac{3}{8}}\right)^4$ $m^{\frac{3}{2}}$
19. $\left(a^{\frac{3}{4}}\right)^{\frac{1}{2}}$ $a^{\frac{3}{8}}$
20. $\left(k^{\frac{4}{5}}\right)^{\frac{5}{4}}$ k
21. $\left(u^{\frac{2}{3}}v^{\frac{2}{9}}\right)^{\frac{3}{4}}$ $u^{\frac{1}{2}}v^{\frac{1}{6}}$
22. $\left(f^{\frac{3}{2}}g^{\frac{1}{4}}\right)^{\frac{2}{3}}$ $fg^{\frac{1}{6}}$
23. $(64y^3)^{\frac{5}{6}}$ $32y^{\frac{5}{2}}$
24. $\left(16e^{\frac{8}{15}}\right)^{\frac{3}{4}}$ $8e^{\frac{2}{5}}$

SKILLS Objective D

In 25–30, solve the equation by hand.

25. $n^{\frac{3}{2}} = 27$ $n = 9$
26. $v^{\frac{5}{4}} = 32$ $v = 16$
27. $2g^{\frac{2}{3}} = 98$ $g = 343$
28. $a^{\frac{6}{7}} = 64$ $a = 128$
29. $m^2 = 0.64$ $m = 0.8$
30. $\frac{d^{\frac{2}{5}}}{6} + 2 = 8$ $d = 7776$

In 31 and 32, find r. Round to the nearest thousandth.

31. $50 = 40(1 + r)^{\frac{8}{3}}$ $r = 0.087$
32. $75 = 65(1 + r)^{\frac{2}{7}}$ $r = 0.650$

Advanced Algebra 457

Lesson 7-8

GOAL

Use what has been learned about exponents to evaluate all rational powers of any given positive base.

SPUR Objectives

A Evaluate b^n when $b > 0$ and n is a rational number.

B Simplify expressions or solve equations using properties of exponents.

D Find all real solutions to equations of the form $x^n = b$, where $x \geq 0$ and n is a rational number.

E Recognize properties of nth powers and nth roots.

F Solve real-world problems that can be modeled by expressions with nth powers or nth roots.

Materials/Resources

- Lesson Masters 7-8A and 7-8B
- Resource Masters 133–135

HOMEWORK

Suggestions for Assignment

- Questions 1–32
- Question 33 (extra credit)
- Self-Test

Local Standards

1 Warm-Up

1. Find each power. Note that the powers decrease by $\frac{1}{3}$.

$343^2 = 117{,}649$
$343^{\frac{5}{3}} = \left(343^{\frac{1}{3}}\right)^5 = 16{,}807$
$343^{\frac{4}{3}} = \underline{\ ?\ }$ 2401
$343^1 = \underline{\ ?\ }$ 343
$343^{\frac{2}{3}} = \underline{\ ?\ }$ 49
$343^{\frac{1}{3}} = \underline{\ ?\ }$ 7
$343^0 = \underline{\ ?\ }$ 1

Lesson 7-8 Negative Rational Exponents

BIG IDEA The expressions $x^{\frac{m}{n}}$ and $x^{-\frac{m}{n}}$ are reciprocals.

For mammals, a typical relationship between body weight w in kilograms and resting heart rate r in $\frac{\text{beats}}{\text{minute}}$ is modeled by $r = 241w^{-\frac{1}{4}}$. So far in this chapter you have deduced theorems from the postulates of powers that provide meaning for all positive rational exponents. Now you will use the properties of powers to determine the meaning of negative rational exponents, enabling you to work with equations such as this resting heart rate formula.

Mental Math

Calculate.

a. $16 \cdot 256^{\frac{1}{4}}$ 64
b. $16^{\frac{1}{4}} \cdot 256^{\frac{1}{4}}$ 8
c. $(16 \cdot 256)^{\frac{1}{4}}$ 8

Evaluating Powers with Negative Rational Exponents

Consider the power $x^{-\frac{m}{n}}$. Because $-\frac{m}{n} = -1 \cdot m \cdot \frac{1}{n}$, and the factors can be multiplied in any order, you have the choice of taking the reciprocal, the mth power, or the nth root first.

GUIDED

Example 1

Evaluate $\left(\frac{16}{625}\right)^{-\frac{3}{4}}$ in three different ways.

Solution

Method 1: First find the reciprocal of $\frac{16}{625}$, then take the fourth root, and then calculate the third power.

$\left(\frac{16}{625}\right)^{-\frac{3}{4}} = \left(\left(\left(\frac{16}{625}\right)^{-1}\right)^{\frac{1}{4}}\right)^3 = \left((\underline{\ ?\ })^{\frac{1}{4}}\right)^3 = (\underline{\ ?\ })^3 = \underline{\ ?\ }$ $\frac{625}{16}$; $\frac{5}{2}$; $\frac{125}{8}$

Method 2: First take the fourth root of $\frac{16}{625}$, then calculate the third power, and then find the reciprocal.

$\left(\frac{16}{625}\right)^{-\frac{3}{4}} = \left(\left(\left(\frac{16}{625}\right)^{\frac{1}{4}}\right)^3\right)^{-1} = \left((\underline{\ ?\ })^3\right)^{-1} = (\underline{\ ?\ })^{-1} = \underline{\ ?\ }$ $\frac{2}{5}$; $\frac{8}{125}$; $\frac{125}{8}$

Method 3: First calculate the third power of $\frac{16}{625}$, then take the fourth root, and then find the reciprocal.

$\left(\frac{16}{625}\right)^{-\frac{3}{4}} = \left(\left(\left(\frac{16}{625}\right)^3\right)^{\frac{1}{4}}\right)^{-1} = \left((\underline{\ ?\ })^{\frac{1}{4}}\right)^{-1} = (\underline{\ ?\ })^{-1} = \underline{\ ?\ }$ $\frac{4096}{244{,}140{,}625}$; $\frac{8}{125}$; $\frac{125}{8}$

Background

This lesson consolidates the material of the previous lessons and finishes the discussion of rational exponents.

Example 2

Use the formula $r = 241w^{-\frac{1}{4}}$ to estimate a 180-lb person's resting heart rate in beats per minute.

Solution In the formula, w is in kilograms, so convert the weight in pounds to kilograms.

$$180 \text{ pounds} \cdot \frac{1 \text{ kilogram}}{2.2 \text{ pounds}} \approx 81.8 \text{ kilograms}$$

Substitute $w = 81.8$ into the formula and evaluate using a calculator.

$$r = 241(81.8)^{-\frac{1}{4}}$$

$$r \approx 80$$

So, a normal resting heart rate for a 180-lb person is about 80 beats per minute. Note, however, that resting heart rate is affected by many factors and that there is a wide range of variability in human heart rates. Any rate in the range $50 \le r \le 100$ might be considered normal for an individual.

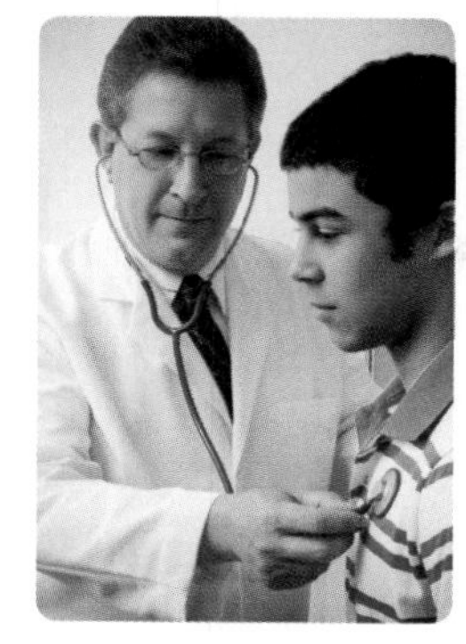

Diet, fitness, and other health-related issues can all affect a person's resting heart rate.

Solving Equations Involving Negative Rational Exponents

The ideas used in Lesson 7-7 to solve equations with positive rational exponents can be used with negative rational exponents as well. For example, if you have a savings goal of G dollars and you already have saved S dollars, then a formula relating S and G to the annual percentage yield r needed over time t in years to reach the savings goal is

$$S = G(1 + r)^{-t}.$$

Example 3

Suppose Jett has \$50,000 of the \$150,000 he hopes to have for his child's college education in $12\frac{1}{2}$ years. Find the interest rate Jett needs in order to meet his savings goal.

Solution Substitute $G = 150{,}000$, $S = 50{,}000$, and $t = 12\frac{1}{2} = \frac{25}{2}$ into the formula above.

$$150{,}000(1 + r)^{-\frac{25}{2}} = 50{,}000$$

$$(1 + r)^{-\frac{25}{2}} = \frac{1}{3}$$

(continued on next page)

2. Continue to decrease the exponent by $\frac{1}{3}$.

$343^{-\frac{1}{3}} = \left(343^{\frac{1}{3}}\right)^{-1} = \frac{1}{7}$

$343^{-\frac{2}{3}} = \underline{\ ?\ }\ \frac{1}{49}$

$343^{-1} = \underline{\ ?\ }\ \frac{1}{343}$

$343^{-\frac{4}{3}} = \underline{\ ?\ }\ \frac{1}{2401}$

$343^{-\frac{5}{3}} = \underline{\ ?\ }\ \frac{1}{16{,}807}$

$343^{-2} = \underline{\ ?\ }\ \frac{1}{117{,}649}$

Note: Finding the ratio of any two powers of 343 above provides practice in applying the Quotient of Powers Theorem. Finding the ratio of the values of any two of these powers provides practice in dividing fractions, which is an opportunity to check answers.

2 Teaching

Notes on the Lesson

Example 1 Emphasize the sentence immediately preceding this example. Three ways to do the same calculation are shown. Ask students which way they prefer and why.

You might wish to summarize the evaluation of negative rational exponents by noting that the opposites in exponents signify reciprocals, the numerators signify powers, and the denominators signify roots. This will pave the way for the properties of logarithms, which will be encountered in Chapter 9.

Accommodating the Learner

Emphasize the paragraph immediately preceding Example 1. You might have students read the paragraph aloud during class. Then discuss the various orders in which the operations could be done. Have students try the orders other than the three shown in the example to verify that any of the six methods are valid.

Additional Examples

Example 1 Evaluate $\left(\frac{27}{1000}\right)^{-\frac{2}{3}}$ in three different ways using a different power first.

Solution

Method 1: Find the reciprocal of $\frac{27}{1000}$, then take the third root, and then calculate the second power.

$\left(\frac{27}{1000}\right)^{-\frac{2}{3}} = \left(\left(\left(\frac{27}{1000}\right)^{-1}\right)^{\frac{1}{3}}\right)^{2} =$

$\left((\underline{\ ?\ })^{\frac{1}{3}}\right)^{2} = (\underline{\ ?\ })^{2} = \underline{\ ?\ }$

$\frac{1000}{27}; \frac{10}{3}; \frac{100}{9}$

Method 2: Take the third root of $\frac{27}{1000}$, then calculate the second power, and then find the reciprocal.

$\left(\frac{27}{1000}\right)^{-\frac{2}{3}} = \left(\left(\left(\frac{27}{1000}\right)^{\frac{1}{3}}\right)^{2}\right)^{-1} =$

$((\underline{\ ?\ })^{2})^{-1} = (\underline{\ ?\ })^{-1} = \underline{\ ?\ }$

$\frac{3}{10}; \frac{9}{100}; \frac{100}{9}$

Method 3: Calculate the second power of $\frac{27}{1000}$, then take the third root, and then find the reciprocal.

$\left(\frac{27}{1000}\right)^{-\frac{2}{3}} = \left(\left(\left(\frac{27}{1000}\right)^{2}\right)^{\frac{1}{3}}\right)^{-1} =$

$\left((\underline{\ ?\ })^{\frac{1}{3}}\right)^{-1} = (\underline{\ ?\ })^{-1} = \underline{\ ?\ }$

$\frac{729}{1{,}000{,}000}; \frac{9}{100}; \frac{100}{9}$

Example 2 Use the formula $r = 241w^{-\frac{1}{4}}$, where w is the weight in kilograms, to estimate a person's resting heart rate in beats per minute if the person weighs 240 pounds.
$\approx$ 75 beats per min

Example 3 Suppose Gary has \$75,000 of the \$200,000 he hopes to have in a retirement account in $8\frac{1}{2}$ years. What interest rate does Gary need to meet his savings goal? Substitute $G = 200{,}000$; $S = 75{,}000$; and $t = \frac{17}{2}$ into the formula $S = G(1 + r)^{-t}$; $r \approx 0.122 = 12.2\%$

The reciprocal of $-\frac{25}{2}$ is $-\frac{2}{25}$, so raise each side to the $-\frac{2}{25}$ power.

$$\left((1 + r)^{-\frac{25}{2}}\right)^{-\frac{2}{25}} = \left(\frac{1}{3}\right)^{-\frac{2}{25}}$$

$$(1 + r) = \left(\frac{1}{3}\right)^{-\frac{2}{25}} \approx 1.092$$

$$r \approx 0.092$$

Jett needs to find an investment with an APY of about 9.2% to meet his savings goal.

Check Check by substitution.
Is $150{,}000(1 + r)^{-\frac{25}{2}} \approx 50{,}000$? $150{,}000(1.092)^{-\frac{25}{2}} \approx 49{,}924$. This is close enough to 50,000 given the estimate, so it checks.

In 2008, the average in-state public 4-year college tuition was over \$6000 per year. For private institutions it was over \$23,000.

Questions

COVERING THE IDEAS

In 1–3, evaluate without using a calculator.

1. $1000^{-\frac{1}{3}}$ $\frac{1}{10}$
2. $16^{-\frac{3}{2}}$ $\frac{1}{64}$
3. $\left(\frac{625}{81}\right)^{-\frac{3}{4}}$ $\frac{27}{125}$
4. Tell whether or not the expression equals $a^{-\frac{2}{3}}$ for $a > 0$.
   a. $\left(-a^{\frac{1}{3}}\right)^{2}$ no
   b. $\frac{1}{(a^2)^{\frac{1}{3}}}$ yes
   c. $\left((a^{-1})^{-2}\right)^{-\frac{1}{3}}$ yes
   d. $-a^{\frac{2}{3}}$ no
   e. $\left(a^{\frac{1}{3}}\right)^{-2}$ yes
   f. $\frac{1}{a^{\frac{2}{3}}}$ yes

In 5–7, approximate to the nearest thousandth.

5. $75^{-\frac{1}{2}}$ 0.115
6. $20 \cdot 4.61^{-\frac{3}{5}}$ 7.995
7. $8^{-0.056}$ 0.890

In 8 and 9, refer to Example 2.

8. An adult mouse weighs about 20 grams. Estimate its heart rate in beats per minute. about 641 beats per min
9. If the resting heart rate of an Asian elephant is about 30 beats per minute, estimate its weight. about 4165 kg

Asian elephants may live as long as 60 years.

In 10–12, solve without using a calculator.

10. $r^{-\frac{1}{3}} = 3$ $r = \frac{1}{27}$
11. $w^{-\frac{2}{5}} = 4$ $w = \frac{1}{32}$
12. $4z^{-\frac{3}{2}} = \frac{1}{16}$ $z = 16$

Extension

Give students this situation. Suppose a certain radioactive material is decaying according to the formula $y = 300 \cdot 2^{-0.5t}$, where t is the time in days and y is the amount of the material in grams.

1. Find the amount of radioactive material present after 1, 2, 3, 4, and 5 days. 212.13 g; 150 g; 106.07 g; 75 g; and 53.03 g

2. What kind of sequence do your answers to Question 1 form? a geometric sequence, with $r = 2^{-0.5}$

13. Solve $\frac{x^{-\frac{2}{3}}}{2} - 11 = 0$ to the nearest thousandth. $x \approx 0.010$

In 14 and 15, refer to Example 3.

14. a. Rewrite the formula for G in terms of S. $G = S(1 + r)^t$
    b. Jett adopts another child and now needs to save \$300,000 in 14.5 years. What APY is needed to meet this goal? 13.2%

15. A \$2.00 hamburger in 2007 cost as little as 5¢ in 1923. What yearly percentage growth in the price of the hamburger does this represent? 4.5%

APPLYING THE MATHEMATICS

In 16–18, True or False. Justify your answer.

16. The value of an expression with a negative exponent is always less than zero.

17. If $y = x^{-\frac{1}{5}}$ and $z = -5$, then $y^z = x$. True; $\left(x^{-\frac{1}{5}}\right)^{-5} = x$.

18. $\left(125^{-\frac{1}{3}}\right)^0 = 0$ False; for any $x \neq 0$, $x^0 = 1$.

19. Find t if $\left(\frac{99}{100}\right)^{-\frac{1}{2}} = \left(\frac{100}{99}\right)^t$. $t = \frac{1}{2}$

20. The amount F of food in grams that a mouse with body mass m must eat daily to maintain its mass is estimated by $F = km^{\frac{2}{3}}$. For a 25-gram mouse, suppose $k = 11.7$. Find the amount of food in grams that this mouse must eat daily to maintain its weight. about 100 grams

In 21–24, rewrite each expression in the form ax^n. Check your answer by substituting a value for x in both the original and the rewritten expression.

21. $(x^{-4})^{-\frac{1}{4}}$

22. $(36x^{-2})^{-\frac{3}{2}}$

23. $\frac{x}{6x^{-\frac{4}{3}}}\left(3x^{\frac{1}{3}}\right)$

24. $\frac{-\frac{5}{6}x^{-\frac{5}{6}}}{\frac{1}{6}x^{\frac{1}{6}}}$

REVIEW

In 25–27, simplify without a calculator. (Lesson 7-7)

25. $100{,}000{,}000{,}000^{\frac{5}{11}}$ 100,000

26. $12 \cdot 81^{\frac{3}{4}}$ 324

27. $0.064^{\frac{2}{3}}$ 0.16

22. $\frac{|x|^3}{216}$; Let $x = 4$: $(36(4)^{-2})^{-\frac{3}{2}} = \left(36 \cdot \frac{1}{16}\right)^{-\frac{3}{2}} = \left(\frac{9}{4}\right)^{-\frac{3}{2}} = \frac{8}{27}, \frac{|4|^3}{216} = \frac{64}{216} = \frac{8}{27}$.

23. $\frac{1}{2}x^{\frac{8}{3}}$; Let $x = 27$: $\frac{27}{6(27)^{-\frac{4}{3}}}\left(3(27)^{\frac{1}{3}}\right) = \frac{27}{6 \cdot \frac{1}{81}}(9) = \frac{6561}{2}, \frac{1}{2}(27)^{\frac{8}{3}} = \frac{1}{2} \cdot 3^8 = \frac{6561}{2}$.

24. $-5x^{-1}$; Let $x = 64$: $\frac{-\frac{5}{6}(64)^{-\frac{5}{6}}}{\frac{1}{6}(64)^{\frac{1}{6}}} = \frac{-5\left(\frac{1}{32}\right)}{2} = \frac{-5}{64}, -5(64)^{-1} = -5\left(\frac{1}{64}\right) = \frac{-5}{64}$.

16. False; All powers of positive numbers are positive. For example, $3^{-2} = \frac{1}{9}$.

Baby mice raised in captivity without their mother may be fed milk or formula.

21. x; Let $x = 2$: $(2^{-4})^{-\frac{1}{4}} = \left(\frac{1}{16}\right)^{-\frac{1}{4}} = 16^{\frac{1}{4}} = 2$.

3 Assignment

Recommended Assignment

- Questions 1–32
- Question 33 (extra credit)
- Self-Test

Notes on the Questions

Question 3 There are six possible orders in taking the exponents -1, 3, and $\frac{1}{4}$. You might have students try as many of these as they can.

Question 4 The only expressions in this question that are *not* equivalent to $a^{-\frac{2}{3}}$ are (a) and (d). Remind students that the sign of an exponent never affects the sign of the power itself. A negative sign never "moves" from an exponent to its base.

Questions 21–24 You might want to work through these questions with students. This would be a good time to discuss what form the answer to a powers problem should take. Sometimes there are several representations of the same answer, each of which could be considered simplest form. For example, it is debatable whether $\frac{1}{y^4}$ is simpler than y^{-4} or vice versa. Occasionally, the problem itself will ask for a particular form of the answer, as these do.

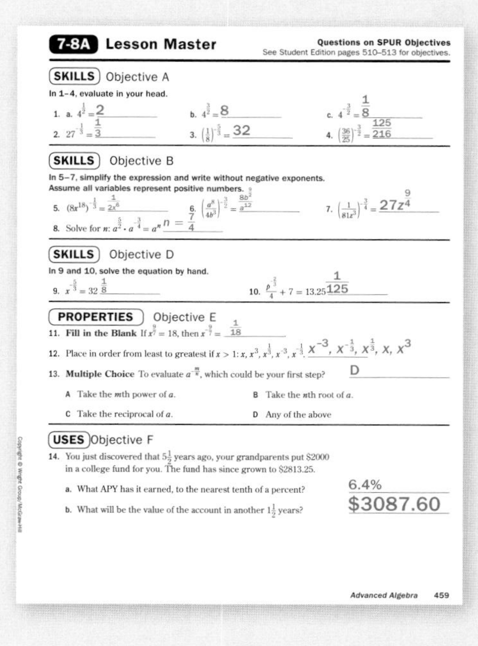

7-8A Lesson Master

Questions on SPUR Objectives
See Student Edition pages 510–513 for objectives.

SKILLS Objective A

In 1–4, evaluate in your head.

1. a. $4^{\frac{1}{2}} =$ 2   b. $4^{\frac{3}{2}} =$ 8   c. $4^{-\frac{3}{2}} =$ $\frac{1}{8}$
2. $27^{-\frac{1}{3}} =$ $\frac{1}{3}$
3. $\left(\frac{1}{8}\right)^{-\frac{5}{3}} =$ 32
4. $\left(\frac{36}{25}\right)^{-\frac{3}{2}} =$ $\frac{125}{216}$

SKILLS Objective B

In 5–7, simplify the expression and write without negative exponents. Assume all variables represent positive numbers.

5. $(8x^{18})^{-\frac{1}{3}} =$ $\frac{1}{2x^6}$
6. $\left(\frac{a^8}{4b^3}\right)^{-\frac{3}{2}} =$ $\frac{8b^{\frac{9}{2}}}{a^{12}}$
7. $\left(\frac{1}{81z^3}\right)^{-\frac{3}{4}} =$ $27z^{\frac{9}{4}}$
8. Solve for n: $a^{\frac{5}{2}} \cdot a^{-\frac{3}{4}} = a^n$ $n = \frac{7}{4}$

SKILLS Objective D

In 9 and 10, solve the equation by hand.

9. $x^{-\frac{5}{3}} = 32$ $\frac{1}{8}$
10. $\frac{p^{-\frac{2}{3}}}{4} + 7 = 13.25$ $\frac{1}{125}$

PROPERTIES Objective E

11. **Fill in the Blank** If $x^{\frac{9}{7}} = 18$, then $x^{-\frac{9}{7}} =$ $\frac{1}{18}$.
12. Place in order from least to greatest if $x > 1$: $x, x^3, x^{\frac{1}{3}}, x^{-3}, x^{-\frac{1}{3}}$. $x^{-3}, x^{-\frac{1}{3}}, x^{\frac{1}{3}}, x, x^3$
13. **Multiple Choice** To evaluate $a^{-\frac{m}{n}}$, which could be your first step? D
    A Take the mth power of a.
    B Take the nth root of a.
    C Take the reciprocal of a.
    D Any of the above

USES Objective F

14. You just discovered that $5\frac{1}{2}$ years ago, your grandparents put \$2000 in a college fund for you. The fund has since grown to \$2813.25.
    a. What APY has it earned, to the nearest tenth of a percent? 6.4%
    b. What will be the value of the account in another $1\frac{1}{2}$ years? \$3087.60

4 Wrap-Up

Ongoing Assessment

Have students write an equation similar to those in Questions 10–12. Have them solve the equation, giving the solution to the nearest thousandth. Then have students write a paragraph explaining the procedure they used to solve the equation. Students should write an equation involving a negative rational exponent, solve the equation, and explain their solution procedure.

7-8B page 2

7-8B Lesson Master — Questions on SPUR Objectives. See Student Edition pages 510–513 for objectives.

SKILLS Objective A

In 1–14, evaluate in your head.

1. $125^{-\frac{4}{3}}$ $\frac{1}{625}$
2. $36^{-\frac{3}{2}}$ $\frac{1}{216}$
3. $64^{-\frac{4}{3}}$ $\frac{1}{256}$
4. $100^{-\frac{3}{2}}$ $\frac{1}{1000}$
5. $625^{-\frac{1}{4}}$ $\frac{1}{5}$
6. $81^{-\frac{3}{4}}$ $\frac{1}{27}$
7. $\left(\frac{25}{49}\right)^{-\frac{3}{2}}$ $\frac{343}{125}$
8. $\left(\frac{1}{27}\right)^{-\frac{1}{3}}$ 3
9. $6 \cdot 32^{-\frac{4}{5}}$ $\frac{3}{8}$
10. $9.3 \cdot 10{,}000^{-\frac{1}{2}}$ 0.093
11. $4 \cdot 16^{-\frac{3}{4}}$ $\frac{1}{2}$
12. $\left(\frac{8}{125}\right)^{-\frac{4}{3}}$ $\frac{625}{16}$
13. $8 \cdot 128^{-\frac{5}{7}}$ $\frac{1}{4}$
14. $\left(\frac{1}{32}\right)^{-\frac{2}{5}}$ 4

SKILLS Objective B

In 15–24, simplify the expression and write without negative exponents. Assume all variables represent positive numbers.

15. $\frac{-15x^7y^{-\frac{2}{3}}}{5x^{-10}y^{\frac{1}{3}}}$ $\frac{-3x^{17}}{y}$
16. $(m^2n^4)^{-\frac{3}{4}}$ $\frac{1}{m^{\frac{3}{2}}n^3}$
17. $\left(\frac{a}{b}\right)^{-\frac{1}{2}}$ $\left(\frac{b}{a}\right)^{\frac{1}{2}}$
18. $\left(\frac{1}{h}\right)^{-\frac{3}{4}}$ $h^{\frac{3}{4}}$
19. $e^{-\frac{2}{3}}$ $\left(\frac{1}{e}\right)^{\frac{2}{3}}$
20. $(r^3)^{-\frac{3}{8}}$ $\frac{1}{r^{\frac{9}{8}}}$
21. $v^{-\frac{1}{2}} \cdot w^3$ $\frac{w^3}{v^{\frac{1}{2}}}$
22. $\left(x^{-\frac{3}{2}}y^{\frac{1}{4}}\right)^{-2}$ $\frac{x^3}{y^{\frac{1}{2}}}$
23. $\frac{a^{-\frac{4}{5}}}{a^{\frac{6}{5}}}$ $\frac{1}{a^2}$
24. $\frac{-20xy^{-\frac{1}{2}}}{4x^3y^{-\frac{3}{4}}}$ $\frac{-5y^{\frac{1}{4}}}{x^2}$
25. Solve for x: $b^{\frac{4}{3}} \cdot b^{-\frac{1}{6}} = b^x$ $x = \frac{7}{6}$
26. Solve for y: $c^{-\frac{3}{8}} \cdot c^{-\frac{5}{2}} = c^y$ $y = -\frac{23}{8}$
27. Solve for z: $d^{\frac{3}{2}} \cdot d^z = d^{\frac{1}{4}}$ $z = -\frac{5}{4}$

SKILLS Objective D

In 28–33, solve the equation by hand.

28. $y^{-\frac{2}{3}} = 16$ $y = \frac{1}{64}$
29. $w^{-\frac{8}{5}} = 256$ $\frac{1}{32}$
30. $6v^{-5} = 1458$ $\frac{1}{3}$
31. $9p^{-\frac{1}{3}} = 45$ $\frac{1}{125}$
32. $\frac{m^{-\frac{3}{2}}}{3} + 5 = 14$ $m = \frac{1}{9}$
33. $2y^{-\frac{4}{5}} - 4 = 28$ $\frac{1}{32}$

460 Advanced Algebra

28. German astronomer Johannes Kepler (1571–1630) made observations on planetary orbits. His results became known as Kepler's laws of planetary motion. Kepler's third law states that the ratio of the squares of the periods of any two planets equals the ratio of the cubes of their mean distances from the Sun. (The period of a planet is the length of time it takes the planet to go around the Sun.) If the periods of any two planets are t and T, and their mean distances from the sun are d and D, respectively, then $\frac{T^2}{t^2} = \frac{D^3}{d^3}$. Find the ratio of the periods, $\frac{T}{t}$. (Lesson 7-7) $\frac{D^{\frac{3}{2}}}{d^{\frac{3}{2}}}$

29. Use a graph to explain why negative real numbers have no real nth roots when n is even. (Lessons 7-6, 7-1)

30. Cassandra is playing a board game where she rolls two 6-sided dice each turn, and then she adds the two rolls to find how many squares she should move forward. In 50 turns, Cassandra moved forward 2 squares five times. Cassandra thinks the dice might be unfair.
   a. What was her relative frequency of rolling two 1s with these dice? $\frac{1}{10}$
   b. What seems to be the probability of rolling two 1s with these dice? Is Cassandra's concern valid? (Lesson 7-6)

31. Simplify $\left(\frac{a}{b}\right)^3 \cdot \frac{a^2b}{(2ab^2)^2}$. (Lesson 7-2) $\frac{a^3}{4b^6}$

32. Expand $(2x + 3y)^2$. (Lesson 6-1) $4x^2 + 12xy + 9y^2$

Johannes Kepler

29. Since $y = k$ does not intersect $y = x^n$ for $k < 0$ and n even, there are no real solutions.

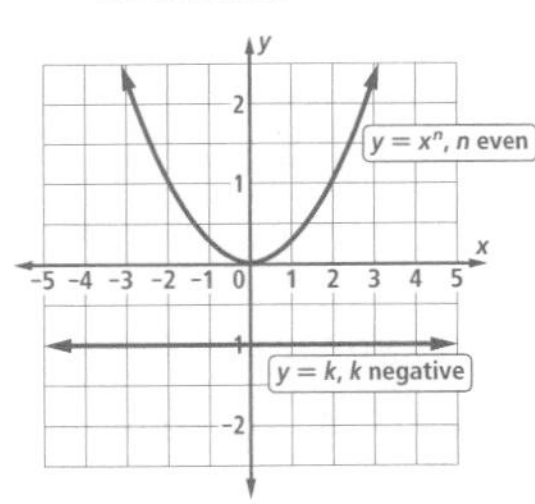

30b. $\frac{1}{10}$; Answers vary. Sample: With fair dice, the probability of rolling two 1s is $\frac{1}{6} \cdot \frac{1}{6} \approx 0.028$. Based on Cassandra's 50 turns, it is about 3.6 times as likely that two 1s are rolled on her dice than on fair dice. So, Cassandra might have a valid concern.

EXPLORATION

33. Research the average adult weight and heart rate of a mouse and of an Asian elephant. Compare these data to your answers for Questions 8 and 9. How accurate does the model $r = 241w^{-\frac{1}{4}}$ seem to be for predicting the heart rates of these two mammals? Does the weight of the mammal seem to affect the accuracy of the model?

Answers vary. Sample: Adult Asian elephants weigh about 4000 kg and their average heart rate is about 30 beats per minute. The model predicts heart rate and weight very accurately for elephants. Mice weigh about 20 g and their average heart rate is about 600 beats per minute. The model also predicts heart rate and weight accurately for mice. The weight of the mammal does not seem to affect the accuracy of the model.

Accommodating the Learner

At the end of the lesson, ask students to answer the following questions.

1. How could you interpret a power such as $4^{2.5}$ as a rational power? Answers vary. Sample: Think of 2.5 as $\frac{25}{10}$. Then $4^{2.5}$ is the 10th root of the 25th power of 4.

2. What would you enter into your calculator to evaluate $4^{2.5}$? What is $4^{2.5}$? Answers vary. Sample: 4 [y^x] 2.5 [=]; 32

Chapter 7 Projects

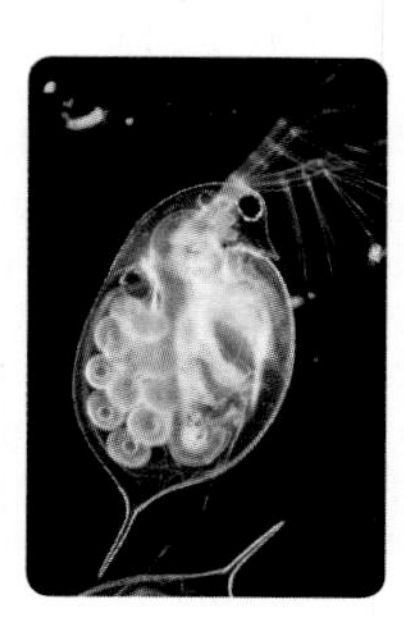

1 Financing Post-High School Education

a. Select a college or post-secondary school you have heard about or are interested in attending. Find out its yearly tuition for each year of the past decade.

b. Based on the data in Part a, estimate what tuition will cost during the years you would attend. Explain your answer.

c. Suppose that 15 years ago, a benefactor set up an account for your education. This benefactor made a single deposit of $20,000 that has been earning 6% interest compounded monthly. Since the deposit 15 years ago, no money has been added to or taken from the account. Will this account be sufficient to cover tuition for all four years?

d. Find the smallest annual interest rate for the account to be sufficient to pay for the tuition for the years you will attend.

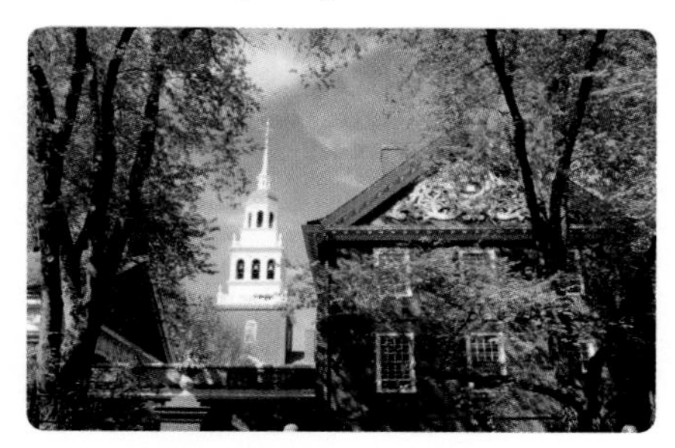

In 2008 Harvard College, the undergraduate portion of Harvard University, adjusted their financial aid program to become more affordable for middle-income families.

2 Powers of 10

Several sites on the Internet show pictures of objects of sizes from 10^{-15} m long to 10^{20} m long, that is, from the smallest particles to the largest multigalactic structures in the universe. Make a table similar to these sites using mass rather than length, from 10^{-30} kg, the mass of an electron, to 10^{30} kg, the mass of our solar system. For various powers of 10, fill in an object that has a mass close to that number in kilograms. For example, the dry mass of an adult water flea is about 10^{-7} kg. The one shown above is carrying eggs.

3 Sums of Powers

In 1637, the French mathematician and lawyer Pierre Fermat asserted that there were no positive integers x, y, and z for which $x^n + y^n = z^n$ for any integer $n > 2$. He wrote that he had a proof but it would not fit in the margin of the book he was writing in. Fermat's "Last Problem," as this assertion was sometimes called, was finally solved by Princeton mathematician Andrew Wiles in 1995. In the over 350 years people worked on this problem, many related problems were posed and solved. Write about efforts to find positive integer solutions to the following equations.

$$w^4 + x^4 + y^4 = z^4$$

$$v^5 + w^5 + x^5 + y^5 = z^5$$

Project Rubric

Advanced	Student correctly provides all of the details asked for in the project as well as additional correct independent conclusions.
Proficient	Student correctly provides all of the details asked for in the project.
Partially proficient	Student correctly provides some of the details asked for in the project or provides all details with some inaccuracies.
Not proficient	Student correctly provides few of the details asked for in the project or provides all details with many inaccuracies.
No attempt	Student makes little or no attempt to complete the project.

Chapter 7

The projects relate to the content of the lessons of this chapter as follows:

Project	Lesson
1	7-4
2	7-3
3	7-2
4	7-4
5	7-5

1 Financing Post-High School Education

Students who select this project may use a variety of assumptions. For private institutions, the yearly tuition data will be fairly straightforward. For state institutions, students should research whether their tuition figures are for residents or nonresidents of the states in question. Point out to students that in Part c, they will find the amount in the account after a total of 15 years plus the number of years until they start paying college tuition.

2 Powers of 10

Suggest that students who choose this project work together to complete the table. If there are several students in the group, the number of powers of 10 can be divided equally among the group members to research. If there are only a few students in the group, you might restrict the powers of 10 to multiples of 5. Students can include with their table pictures of the items they have listed.

3 Sums of Powers

Students can find information on the history of Fermat's Last Theorem in any mathematics history book. Have students especially research the solution of Andrew Wiles. They can find numerous references on the Internet.

4 The $200,000 Cell Phone

You might have students work in groups of three on this project, with each student completing one of the three parts. Then have each group prepare a report or a poster on their work to share with the class. If students do not have access to bills and interest rates, supply figures for them.

5 Family of Equations

Project 4 in Chapter 3 deals with a similar problem, in which the coefficients are in an arithmetic sequence. Students may need to look at more than 10 graphs on the same axes to identify the pattern. Stress that a proper viewing window is important.

If students have difficulty identifying equations that fit the criteria, suggest that they can rewrite $ax + by = c$ as $ax + ary = ar^2$, where r is the common ratio. Then this equation can be rewritten as $y = -\frac{1}{r}x + r$.

Sample answers for projects are in the Solution Manual in the Electronic Teacher's Edition.

4 The $200,000 Cell Phone

Suppose that, instead of paying $55 per month for cell phone charges, you invest that amount at a 6% interest rate compounded monthly until you retire 50 years from now. A periodic payment (*Pmt*) like this one is called an ***annuity*** and the amount you will have at retirement is the ***future value*** (*FV*) of the annuity. A formula for the future value of the annuity is related to the compound interest formula. If i = the interest rate at each compounding and n = the number of compoundings, $FV = Pmt \cdot \left[\frac{(1+i)^n - 1}{i}\right]$.

In this case, you would have

$FV = 55 \cdot \left[\frac{(1 + 0.005)^{600} - 1}{0.005}\right]$ or $208,295.51

at retirement.

a. Use your average cell phone bill or that of a friend. Calculate the future value of those payments 50 years from now if invested at an interest rate from your local bank.

b. Many household expenses recur monthly, such as utility and satellite or cable TV bills. Pick one of these recurring expenses and calculate the future value of that annuity 50 years from now.

c. Find the price of a cup of coffee at a local coffee shop and the price of your favorite car. Assume that car prices increase 3% per year and that you can invest money at a 5% interest rate compounded monthly. Can you buy the car when you retire 50 years from now if you give up a daily cup of coffee?

5 Family of Equations

Graph at least 10 members of the family of equations of the form $ax + by = c$, where a, b, and c are consecutive terms in a geometric sequence. Sketch the graphs. What pattern do you see? You may have to experiment to determine the values to use in the window you have chosen. How can you explain the results?

Notes

Chapter 7 Summary and Vocabulary

- When $x > 0$, the expression x^m is defined for any real number m. This chapter covers the meanings and properties of x^m when m is a positive or negative rational number.
- In previous courses, you have learned basic properties of **powers**. For any nonnegative **bases** and nonzero real **exponents**, or any nonzero bases and integer exponents:

Product of Powers Postulate	$x^m \cdot x^n = x^{m+n}$
Power of a Power Postulate	$(x^m)^n = x^{mn}$
Power of a Product Postulate	$(xy)^n = x^n y^n$

- The following theorems can be deduced from these postulates. For any positive bases and real number exponents and any nonzero bases and integer exponents:

Quotient of Powers Theorem	$\frac{x^m}{x^n} = x^{m-n}$
Power of a Quotient Theorem	$\left(\frac{x}{y}\right)^m = \frac{x^m}{y^m}$
Zero Exponent Theorem	$x^0 = 1$
Negative Exponent Theorem	$x^{-m} = \frac{1}{x^m}$
Exponent Theorem	$x^{\frac{1}{n}}$ is the positive solution to $b^n = x$.
Rational Exponent Theorem	$x^{\frac{m}{n}} = (x^m)^{\frac{1}{n}} = \left(x^{\frac{1}{n}}\right)^m$

- From these properties, we see that $x^{\frac{1}{n}}$ is the positive root of x, and $x^{\frac{m}{n}}$ is both the mth power of the positive ***n*th root** of x, and the positive nth root of the mth power of x. These properties are not always true when $x < 0$, so we do not define x^m when $x < 0$ and m is not an integer. You can use these properties to simplify expressions and to solve equations of the form $x^n = b$. To solve such an equation, raise each side of the equation to the $\frac{1}{n}$ power.

Vocabulary

Lesson 7-1
powering, exponentiation
*base
*exponent
*power
**n*th-power function
identity function
squaring function
cubing function

Lesson 7-4
annual compound interest
principal
semi-annually
compounding daily
annual percentage yield, APY

Lesson 7-5
*geometric sequence, exponential sequence
constant multiplier
constant ratio

Lesson 7-6
cube root, *n*th root

Chapter 7

Summary and Vocabulary

The Summary gives an overview of the entire chapter and provides an opportunity for students to consider the material as a whole. Thus, the Summary can be used to help students relate and unify the concepts presented in the chapter.

Vocabulary words and symbols are listed by lesson to provide a checklist of concepts that students must know. Emphasize to students that they should read the vocabulary list carefully before starting the Self-Test on page 509. If students do not understand the meaning of a vocabulary word, they should refer back to the indicated lesson.

Theorems and Properties covered in the chapter are listed below the Summary with page references included to lead students back to the location in the chapter where the theorem or property is stated.

Additional Answers

1. Exponents do not distribute over addition. $(3 + 4)^{\frac{1}{2}} = 7^{\frac{1}{2}} \approx 2.65$, while $3^{\frac{1}{2}} + 4^{\frac{1}{2}} \approx 3.73$.
2. $7^{-2} = \frac{1}{7^2} = \frac{1}{49}$
3. $(214, 358, 881)^{\frac{1}{8}} = 11$ because $11^8 = 214{,}358{,}881$.
4. $\left(\frac{343}{27}\right)^{-\frac{4}{3}} = \left(\frac{27}{343}\right)^{\frac{4}{3}} = \left(\frac{3}{7}\right)^4 = \frac{81}{2401}$
5. $\frac{7.3 \cdot 10^3}{10^{-4}} = 7.3 \cdot 10^3 \cdot 10^4 = 7.3 \cdot 10^7 = 173{,}000{,}000$
6. $\left(1728x^9y^{27}\right)^{\frac{1}{3}} = 1728^{\frac{1}{3}}x^{\frac{9}{3}}y^{\frac{27}{3}} = 12x^3y^9$
7. $\frac{84x^{21}y^5}{6x^3y^7} = \frac{84}{6}x^{21-3}y^{5-7} = 14x^{18}y^{-2}$ or $\frac{14x^{18}}{y^2}$

8a. True; $-5^{\frac{1}{3}}$ is negative, and $5^{-\frac{1}{3}}$ is positive.

8b. False; $3^{-6.4} = \frac{1}{3^{6.4}}$, $3^{-6.5} = \frac{1}{3^{6.5}}$, and $\frac{1}{3^{6.4}} > \frac{1}{3^{6.5}}$.

9. $(x^{\frac{3}{2}})^{\frac{2}{3}} = 0.8^{\frac{2}{3}}$; $x = 0.8^{\frac{2}{3}}$; $x \approx 0.862$

11. n is even because the graph has reflection symmetry over the y-axis.

12a. $h_1 = 5$; $h_2 = 0.85 \cdot 5 = 4.25$; $h_3 = 0.85 \cdot 4.25 \approx 3.61$; $h_4 \approx 0.85 \cdot 3.61 \approx 3.07$.

13. False; the range of $y = x^2$ is all real numbers greater than or equal to zero, so $y = x^2$ is a counterexample.

- Equations involving powers are found in many fields, including investments, science, and music. In the **General Compound Interest Formula** $A = P\left(1 + \frac{r}{n}\right)^{nt}$, A is the value of an investment of P dollars earning interest at a rate r compounded n times per year for t years. When P, r, n, and t are given, you can solve for A; when A, r, n, and t are known, you can solve for P. Because of the multitude of ways to calculate interest, federal law requires institutions to advertise the **annual percentage yield (APY)** of their accounts.

- A **geometric sequence** is a sequence in which the ratios of consecutive terms are constant; each term is a constant multiple r of the preceding term. In symbols, given g_1, then for all $n \geq 2$, $g_n = rg_{n-1}$. The nth term of a geometric sequence can be found explicitly using the formula $g_n = g_1r^{n-1}$.

Postulates and Theorems

Probability of Repeated Independent Events (p. 454)
Product of Powers Postulate (p. 459)
Quotient of Powers Theorem (p. 460)
Power of a Product Postulate (p. 460)
Power of a Quotient Theorem (p. 461)
Zero Exponent Theorem (p. 461)
Power of a Power Postulate (p. 462)
Negative Exponent Theorem (p. 467)
Annual Compound Interest Formula (p. 473)
General Compound Interest Formula (p. 473)
Recursive Formula for a Geometric Sequence (p. 479)
Explicit Formula for a Geometric Sequence (p. 481)
Number of Real Roots Theorem (p. 488)
$\frac{1}{n}$ Exponent Theorem (p. 489)
Rational Exponent Theorem (p. 493)

Chapter 7 Self-Test

Take this test as you would take a test in class. You will need a calculator. Then use the Selected Answers section in the back of the book to check your work.

1. A student writes $(3 + 4)^{\frac{1}{2}} = 3^{\frac{1}{2}} + 4^{\frac{1}{2}}$. Explain why this sentence is not true. See margin.

In 2–4, write as a whole number or simple fraction. 2–4. See margin.

2. 7^{-2} 3. $(214{,}358{,}881)^{\frac{1}{8}}$ 4. $\left(\frac{343}{27}\right)^{-\frac{4}{3}}$

5. Write without an exponent: $\frac{7.3 \cdot 10^3}{10^{-4}}$. See margin.

In 6 and 7, simplify. Assume $x > 0$ and $y > 0$.

6. $\left(1728x^9y^{27}\right)^{\frac{1}{3}}$ 7. $\frac{84x^{21}y^5}{6x^3y^7}$ 6–7. See margin.

8. **True or False** Justify your answer. See margin.
   a. $-5^{\frac{1}{3}} < 5^{-\frac{1}{3}}$ b. $3^{-6.4} < 3^{-6.5}$

9. Solve $x^{\frac{3}{2}} = 0.8$ for x. Round your answer to the nearest thousandth. See margin.

10. Approximate $4.26^{\frac{1}{6}}$ to the nearest hundredth. 1.27

11. A graph of a power function, $y = x^n$, is shown at the right. Is n even or odd? Justify your answer. See margin.

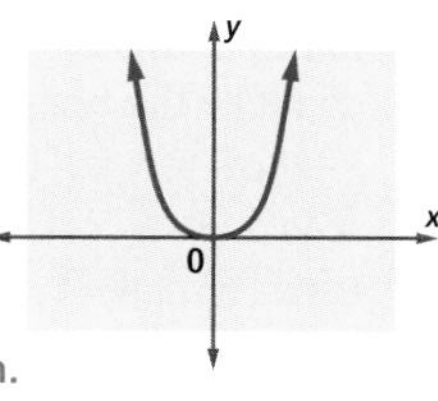

12. Consider this sequence, which gives the maximum height of a bouncing ball after the nth bounce:
$$\begin{cases} h_1 = 5 \\ h_n = 0.85h_{n-1}, \text{ for integers } n \geq 2. \end{cases}$$
   a. Find the height of the ball after the 1st, 2nd, 3rd, and 4th bounces. See margin.
   b. Write an explicit formula for this sequence. $h_n = 5(0.85)^{n-1}$

13. **True or False** The range of all power functions is the set of real numbers. Justify your answer. See margin.

In 14 and 15, the first few terms of a geometric sequence are given. 14–15. See margin.

a. Find the next two terms.
b. Write a recursive formula for the sequence.
c. Write an explicit formula for the nth term of the sequence.

14. 3, 0.6, 0.12, 0.024, ...

15. -4, -12, -36, -108, ...

16. A quiz has 10 multiple choice questions. Each question has three choices. What is the probability of guessing all 10 questions correctly? $\left(\frac{1}{3}\right)^{10} \approx 0.000017$

17. The formula $m = 1.23 \cdot (1.2)^b$ gives the approximate number of minutes m that b bacon slices will take to cook in a typical microwave. How long will it take 2 slices of bacon to cook? Give your answer in minutes and seconds. See margin.

18. Identify all real 10th roots of 1024. See margin.

19. **True or False** $625^{\frac{1}{4}} = -5$. Justify your answer. See margin.

20. A bank account pays 4.25% annual interest. Suppose you deposit \$500 in the account and then do not deposit or withdraw any money for 6 years. 20a–b. See margin.
   a. How much will you have in the account after 6 years if the interest is compounded annually?
   b. What is the APY if the interest is compounded quarterly?

21. A zero-coupon bond paying 6.8% interest compounded monthly for 7 years has matured, giving the investor \$7854. How much did the investor pay for the bond 7 years ago? See margin.

Self-Test

For the development of mathematical competence, feedback and correction, along with the opportunity for practice, are necessary. The Self-Test provides the opportunity for feedback and correction; the Chapter Review provides additional opportunities for practice. We cannot overemphasize the importance of these end-of-chapter materials. It is at this point that the material gels for many students, allowing them to solidify skills and understanding. In general, student performance should improve after these pages.

Assign the Self-Test as a one-night assignment. Worked-out solutions for all questions are in the Selected Answers section of the student book. Encourage students to take the Self-Test honestly, grade themselves, and then be prepared to discuss the test in class.

Advise students to pay special attention to those Chapter Review questions (pages 510–513) that correspond to the questions they missed on the Self-Test.

Additional Answers

14a. $r = \frac{0.6}{3} = 0.2$; $0.024 \cdot 0.2 = 0.0048$, $0.0048 \cdot 0.2 = 0.00096$

14b. $\begin{cases} h_1 = 3 \\ h_n = 0.2h_{n-1}, \text{ for integers } n \geq 2 \end{cases}$

14c. $h_n = 3(0.2)^{n-1}$

15a. $r = \frac{-12}{-4} = 3$; $-108 \cdot 3 = -324$, $-324 \cdot 3 = -972$

15b. $\begin{cases} h_1 = -4 \\ h_n = 3h_{n-1}, \text{ for integers } n \geq 2 \end{cases}$

15c. $h_n = -4(3)^{n-1}$

17. $1.23 \cdot (1.2)^2 \approx 1.77$ minutes = 1 minute 46.2 seconds

18. Solve $x^{10} = 1024$ for x. A CAS in real-number mode shows that $x = 2$ or $x = -2$, so the real 10th roots of 1024 are 2 and -2.

19. False; $-4(3)^{n-1}$ represents only the positive 4th root of 625, which is 5.

20a. $500(1 + 0.0425)^6 \approx \$641.83$

20b. $\left(1 + \frac{0.0425}{4}\right)^4 \approx 1.0432$, so the APY is about 4.32%.

21. $7854 = P\left(1 + \frac{0.068}{12}\right)^{12 \cdot 7}$, so $P \approx \$4{,}885.96$.

Chapter Review

The main objectives for the chapter are organized in the Chapter Review under the four types of understanding this book promotes: Skills, Properties, Uses, and Representations.

Whereas end-of-chapter material may be considered optional in some texts, in UCSMP *Advanced Algebra* we have selected these objectives and questions with the expectation that they will be covered. Students should be able to answer these questions with about 85% accuracy after studying the chapter.

You may assign these questions over a single night to help students prepare for a test the next day or you may assign the questions over a two-day period. If you work the questions over two days, we recommend assigning the evens for homework the first night so that students get feedback in class the next day, and then assigning the odds the night before the test because the answers are provided to the odd-numbered questions in the Selected Answers section at the back of the book.

It is effective to ask students which questions they still do not understand and use the day as a total class discussion of the material that the class finds most difficult.

Resources

- Assessment Resources: Chapter 7 Test Forms A–D; Chapter 7 Test, Cumulative Form

Technology Resources

Teacher's Assessment Assistant, Ch. 7
Electronic Teacher's Edition, Ch. 7

Chapter 7 Chapter Review

SKILLS
PROPERTIES
USES
REPRESENTATIONS

SKILLS Procedures used to get answers

OBJECTIVE A Evaluate b^n when $b > 0$ and n is a rational number. (Lessons 7-2, 7-3, 7-6, 7-7, 7-8)

In 1–6, write as a simple fraction or whole number. Do not use a calculator.

1. 17^0 1
2. 2^{-3} $\frac{1}{8}$
3. $\left(\frac{5}{3}\right)^{-1}$ $\frac{3}{5}$
4. $64^{-\frac{1}{2}}$ $\frac{1}{8}$
5. $8^{\frac{4}{3}}$ 16
6. $1{,}000{,}000^{\frac{1}{3}}$ 100

In 7–9, approximate to the nearest hundredth.

7. $123^{\frac{2}{3}}$ 7–9. See margin.
8. $5 \cdot 8^{\frac{1}{4}}$
9. $7^{1.5}$

OBJECTIVE B Simplify expressions or solve equations using properties of exponents. (Lessons 7-2, 7-3, 7-7, 7-8)

In 10–12, solve.

10. $13^4 \cdot 13^{12} = 13^x$ $x = 16$
11. $\frac{2^6}{2^{-3}} = 2^y$ $y = 9$
12. $(7^z)^3 = 7^9$ $z = 3$

In 13–18, simplify. Assume all variables represent positive numbers. 13–18. See margin.

13. $(-2x^3)^2$
14. $\left(-2x^2\right)^3$
15. $\left(\frac{p}{q}\right)^7\left(\frac{5q}{3p}\right)^3$
16. $\frac{21b}{(7b^{-5})(6b^5)}$
17. $\frac{-16x^8y^{\frac{5}{2}}}{4x^2y^{\frac{1}{2}}}$
18. $\frac{(r^3s^2)^{\frac{1}{2}}}{r^2s^3}$

OBJECTIVE C Describe geometric sequences explicitly and recursively. (Lesson 7-5)

In 19 and 20, the first few terms of a geometric sequence are given.
a. Find an explicit formula for the nth term.
b. Find a recursive formula for the sequence.
c. Find the 16th term. 19–20. See margin.

19. 4, -12, 36, -108, 324, …
20. 2, 0.5, 0.125, 0.03125, …
21. Find the 25th term of a geometric sequence whose first term is 4 and whose constant multiplier is 1.075. Express your answer
    a. exactly. $4(1.075)^{24}$
    b. to the nearest thousandth. 22.691
22. **Multiple Choice** Which of the following could be the first three terms of a geometric sequence? B
    A 9, 3, -6, …
    B $6\frac{2}{3}, 66\frac{2}{3}, 666\frac{2}{3}, \ldots$
    C $\frac{4}{7}, \frac{11}{7}, \frac{18}{7}, \ldots$
    D 0.4, 0.16, 0.64, …

In 23–26, give the first four terms of the geometric sequence described. 23–26. See margin.

23. constant ratio of 3, first term 7
24. first term is $\frac{2}{3}$, fourth term is $\frac{16}{81}$
25. $\begin{cases} t_1 = 6 \\ t_n = \frac{2}{3}t_{n-1}, \text{ for integers } n \geq 2 \end{cases}$
26. $\begin{cases} h_1 = -4 \\ h_{n+1} = -1.5h_n, \text{ for integers } n \geq 1 \end{cases}$

Additional Answers

7. 24.73
8. 8.41
9. 18.52
13. $4x^6$
14. $-8x^6$
15. $\frac{125p^4}{27q^4}$
16. $\frac{1}{2}b$
17. $-4x^6y^2$
18. $r^{-\frac{1}{2}}s^{-2}$

19a. $g_n = 4(-3)^{n-1}$
19b. $\begin{cases} g_1 = 4 \\ g_n = -3g_{n-1}, \text{ for } n \geq 2 \end{cases}$
19c. $g_{16} = -57{,}395{,}628$
20a. $g_n = \left(2\frac{1}{4}\right)^{n-1}$
20b. $\begin{cases} g_1 = 2 \\ g_n = \frac{1}{4}g_{n-1}, \text{ for } n \geq 2 \end{cases}$
20c. $g_{16} \approx 1.86 \cdot 10^{-9}$
23. 7, 21, 63, 189
24. $\frac{2}{3}, \frac{4}{9}, \frac{8}{27}, \frac{16}{81}$
25. 6, 4, $\frac{8}{3}, \frac{16}{9}$
26. -4, 6, -9, 13.5

OBJECTIVE D Find all real solutions to equations of the form $x^n = b$, where $x \geq 0$ and n is a rational number. (Lessons 7-6, 7-7, 7-8)

In 27–35, find all real solutions.

27. $12x^2 = 432$ $x = \pm 6$
28. $33 = a^3$ $a \approx 3.2$
29. $y^4 = 16$ $y = \pm 2$
30. $p^{-2} = 16$ $p = \pm \frac{1}{4}$
31. $6 = y^{\frac{1}{3}}$ $y = 216$
32. $7q^{-\frac{3}{5}} = 9$ $q \approx 0.658$
33. $x^{\frac{4}{9}} = 12$ $x \approx 268.01$
34. $r^{-\frac{3}{2}} = \frac{1}{8}$ $r = 4$
35. $1.55 = m^{\frac{1}{6}}$ $m \approx 13.87$

PROPERTIES Principles behind the mathematics

OBJECTIVE E Recognize properties of nth powers and nth roots. (Lessons 7-2, 7-6, 7-7, 7-8)

In 36–38, True or False. Justify your answer.

36. $-5 = (390{,}625)^{\frac{1}{8}}$
37. $\pi^{-5.3} < \pi^{-5.4}$ 36–38. See margin.
38. $t^{-\frac{3}{4}} = \frac{1}{(t^3)^{\frac{1}{4}}}$ $(t > 0)$
39. **a.** Identify all the square roots of 121. ± 11
    b. Simplify $121^{\frac{1}{2}}$. 11
40. **True or False** $3i$ is a 4th root of 81. true
41. **True or False** For all $x > 1$, $x^{\frac{1}{4}} < x$. true
42. Suppose $0 < v < 1$. Arrange from least to greatest: v, $v^{\frac{3}{2}}$, v^{-3}, $v^{\frac{1}{3}}$, $v^{-\frac{5}{3}}$. $v^{\frac{3}{2}}, v, v^{\frac{1}{3}}, v^{-\frac{5}{3}}, v^{-3}$

In 43–46, use properties A–D below. Assume $R > 0$, $m \neq 0$, and $n \neq 0$. Identify the property or properties that justify the equality.

A $R^0 = 1$

B $R^{-n} = \frac{1}{R^n}$

C $R^{\frac{1}{n}}$ is the positive solution to $x^n = R$.

D $R^{\frac{m}{n}} = (R^m)^{\frac{1}{n}} = \left(R^{\frac{1}{n}}\right)^m$

43. $(3.456)^{6-6} = 1$ A
44. $\left(q^{\frac{1}{4}}\right)^4 = q$ D
45. $(81)^{-\frac{1}{4}} = \frac{1}{3}$ B, C
46. $\left(\frac{1}{b}\right)^{-\frac{7}{8}} = (b^7)^{\frac{1}{8}}$ B, D
47. **a.** For what integer values of n does the equation $x^n = 19$ have exactly one real solution? odd numbers
    b. How many solutions does it have for other nonzero integer values of n? 2
48. Explain why rational exponents are not defined for negative bases, using $(-125)^{\frac{1}{3}}$ and $(-125)^{\frac{2}{6}}$ as examples. See margin.
49. **Fill in the Blank** The positive nth root of a positive number equals the __?__ power of that number. $\frac{1}{n}$th

USES Real-world applications of mathematics

OBJECTIVE F Solve real-world problems that can be modeled by expressions with nth powers or nth roots. (Lessons 7-1, 7-6, 7-7, 7-8)

50. To qualify for a quiz show, a person must answer all questions correctly in three categories: literature, science, and current events. Suppose a person estimates that the probability of getting one question correct in literature is ℓ, in science is s, and in current events is c. If the person is asked 3 literature, 3 science, and 4 current events questions, what is the probability that the person gets all the questions right? $\ell^3 s^3 c^4$

Additional Answers

36. False; the even nth root of a number cannot be negative.
37. False, $\pi^{5.4} > \pi^{5.3}$, thus $\frac{1}{\pi^{5.4}} < \frac{1}{\pi^{5.3}}$.
38. True; $\frac{1}{(t^3)^{\frac{1}{4}}} = \frac{1}{t^{\frac{3}{4}}} = t^{-\frac{3}{4}}$
48. $(-125)^{\frac{1}{3}} = -5$, but $(-125)^{\frac{2}{6}} = (15{,}625)^{\frac{1}{6}} = 5$. Since $\frac{1}{3} = \frac{2}{6}$ but $(-125)^{\frac{1}{3}} = (-125)^{\frac{2}{6}}$, rational exponents are not defined for negative bases.

51. The Merchandise Mart in Chicago has about $4 \cdot 10^6$ ft^2 of floor space. This area is what percent of the $6.6 \cdot 10^6$ ft^2 of floor space in the Pentagon in Washington DC? 61%

52. The intensity I of light varies inversely with the square of the distance d from the light source. Write a formula for I as a function of d using
   a. a positive exponent. $I = \frac{k}{d^2}$
   b. a negative exponent. $I = kd^{-2}$

In 53 and 54, use this information. Kepler's third law states that the ratio of the squares of the periods of any two planets equals the ratio of the cubes of their mean distances from the Sun. If the periods of the planets are t and T and their mean distances from the Sun are d and D, respectively, then $\frac{T^2}{t^2} = \frac{D^3}{d^3}$.

53. Find the ratio $\frac{D}{d}$ of the distance. $\left(\frac{T}{t}\right)^{\frac{2}{3}}$

54. Kepler used his third law to determine how far planets were from the Sun. He knew that for Earth, $t \approx 365$ days and $d \approx 150{,}000{,}000$ km. He also knew that for Mars, $T \approx 687$ days. Use this information to find D, the mean distance from Mars to the Sun. $D \approx 2.29 \times 10^8$ km

In 55 and 56, use this information about similar figures. If A_1 and A_2 are the surface areas of two similar figures and V_1 and V_2 are their volumes, then $\frac{A_1}{A_2} = \left(\frac{V_1}{V_2}\right)^{\frac{2}{3}}$.

55. Two similar figures have volumes 36 cm^3 and 48 cm^3. What is the ratio of the amounts of paint needed to cover their surfaces? $\frac{3\sqrt[3]{6}}{2\sqrt[3]{36}} \approx 0.825$

56. Solve the formula for $\frac{V_1}{V_2}$. $\frac{V_1}{V_2} = \left(\frac{A_1}{A_2}\right)^{\frac{3}{2}}$

OBJECTIVE G Apply the compound interest formulas. (Lesson 7-4)

57. Deion wants to invest now in a bond that will give him \$5000 in 7 years. The bond pays 5.25% interest compounding monthly. How much must Deion invest? \$3465.09

In 58 and 59, Camila put \$10,000 in a 6-year 4.825% savings certificate in which interest is compounded daily 365 days per year.

58. What is the APY of Camila's savings certificate? 4.943%

59. a. How much interest will she earn during the entire 6-year period? \$3357.34
   b. How much interest will she earn during the sixth year? \$629.15

In 60 and 61, Brooklyn now has \$7231 in an account earning interest at a rate of 3.125% compounded quarterly.

60. Assuming she made no deposits or withdrawals in the past four years, how much money was in the account 4 years ago? \$6384.44

61. How much interest did she earn during the past two years? \$436.45

OBJECTIVE H Solve real-world problems involving geometric sequences. (Lesson 7-5)

62. Suppose a ball bounces up to 77% of its previous height after each bounce, and the ball is dropped from a height of 8 m.
   a. Find an explicit formula for the height after the nth bounce. $g_n = 6.16(0.77)^{n-1}$
   b. Find the height of the ball after the tenth bounce, to the nearest decimeter. 6 decimeters

63. Raul set a copy machine to reduce images to 82% of their original size.
   a. If the original image was 20 cm by 25 cm, what are the dimensions of the copy? 18.1 cm × 22.6 cm
   b. If each time Raul made a copy he used the copy as the preimage for the next copy, what are the dimensions of the fifth copy? 15.2 cm × 12.2 cm

64. A weight on a pendulum moves 120 cm on its first swing. On each succeeding swing back or forth it moves 95% of the distance of the previous swing. Write the first four terms of the sequence of swing lengths.
120, 114, 108.3, 102.9

REPRESENTATIONS Pictures, graphs, or objects that illustrate concepts

OBJECTIVE I Graph *n*th power functions. (Lesson 7-1)

In 65 and 66, an *n*th power graph is drawn. Write an equation for each function.

65. $y = x^8$

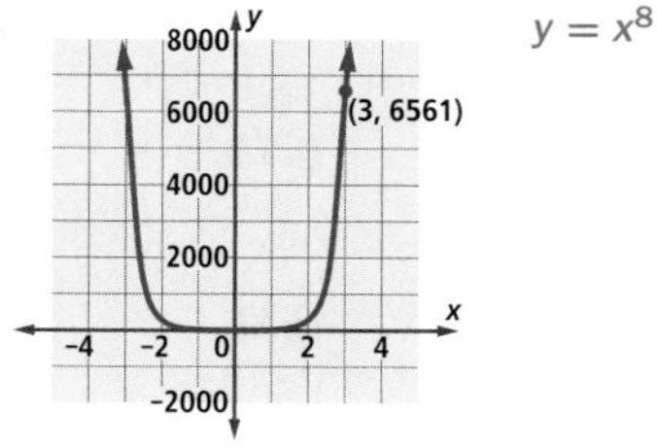

67a.

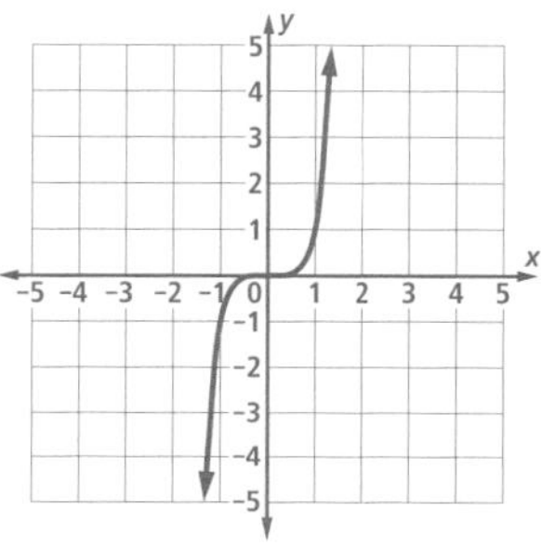

67b. domain: all real numbers; range: all real numbers

67c. rotation symmetry about the origin

66. $y = x^5$

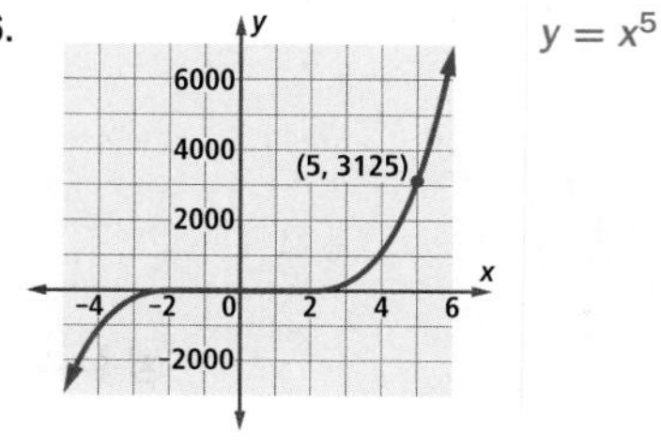

In 67 and 68, a function is given.
a. Graph the function.
b. Identify its domain and range.
c. Describe any symmetries of the graph.

67. $y = x^5$

68. $y = x^4$

69. Use a graph to explain why the equation $x^6 = -5$ has no real solutions.

68a.

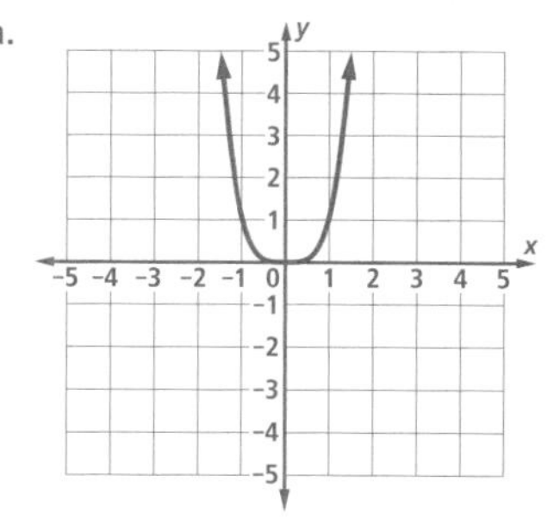

68b. domain: all real numbers; range: $y \geq 0$

68c. reflection symmetry over the y-axis

69.

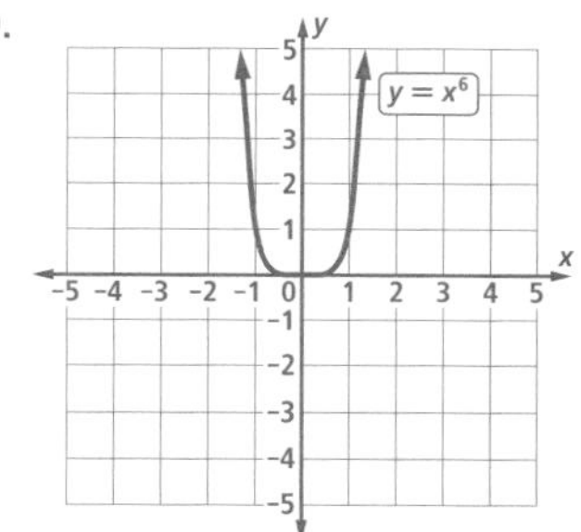

The range $y \geq 0$ does not include $y = -5$.

Assessment

Evaluation The *Assessment Resources* provide four forms of the Chapter 7 Test. Forms A and B present parallel versions of a short-answer format. Form C consists of four to six short-response questions that cover the SPUR objectives from Chapter 7. Form D offers performance assessment that covers a subset (or even just one) of the SPUR objectives for the chapter. The fifth type of test is a Chapter 7 Test, Cumulative Form. About 50% of this test covers Chapter 7, and the remaining 50% covers the previous chapters evenly.

Feedback After students have taken the test for Chapter 7 and you have scored the results, return the tests to students for discussion. Class discussion on the questions that caused trouble for most students can be very effective in identifying and clarifying misunderstandings. You might want to have them note the items they missed and work either in groups or at home to correct them. It is important for students to receive feedback on every chapter test, and we recommend that students see and correct their mistakes before proceeding too far into the next chapter

Suggestions for Assignment Assign Lesson 8-1 for homework the evening of the test. It gives students work to do after they have completed the test and keeps the class moving. If you do not do this, you may cover one less chapter over the course of the year.

Chapter 8

Inverses and Radicals

Chapter Overview

		Local Standards	Pacing (in days) Average	Advanced	Block
8-1	**Composition of Functions** **A** Find values and rules for composites of functions. **H** Solve real-world problems that can be modeled by composite functions.		1	0.75	0.5
8-2	**Inverses of Relations** **B** Find the inverse of a function. **F** Apply properties of the inverse of a function. **J** Make and interpret graphs of inverses of relations and functions.		1	0.75	0.5
8-3	**Properties of Inverse Functions** **B** Find the inverse of a function. **F** Apply properties of the inverse of a function. **J** Make and interpret graphs of inverses of relations and functions.		1	0.75	0.5
	QUIZ 1		0.5	0.5	0.25
8-4	**Radical Notation for *n*th Roots** **C** Evaluate radicals. **G** Apply properties of radicals and *n*th root functions. **I** Solve real-world problems that can be modeled by equations with radicals.		1	0.75	0.5
8-5	**Products with Radicals** **D** Rewrite or simplify expressions with radicals. **G** Apply properties of radicals and *n*th root functions.		1	0.75	0.5
8-6	**Quotients with Radicals** **D** Rewrite or simplify expressions with radicals.		1	0.75	0.5
	QUIZ 2		0.5	0.5	0.25
8-7	**Powers and Roots of Negative Numbers** **C** Evaluate radicals. **D** Rewrite or simplify expressions with radicals. **G** Apply properties of radicals and *n*th root functions.		1	0.75	0.5
8-8	**Solving Equations with Radicals** **E** Solve equations with radicals. **I** Solve real-world problems that can be modeled by equations with radicals.		1	0.75	0.5
		Self-Test	1	0.75	0.5
		Chapter Review	2	1	0.5
		Test	1	1	0.5
		TOTAL	13	9.75	6

Technology Resources

Teacher's Assessment Assistant, Ch. 8

Electronic Teacher's Edition, Ch. 8

Differentiation Options

Universal Access

	Accommodating the Learner	Vocabulary Development	Ongoing Assessment	Materials
8-1	pp. 517, 520	p. 518	group, p. 521	
8-2	pp. 524, 525	p. 523	written, p. 528	
8-3	pp. 531, 532	p. 532	oral, p. 536	CAS
8-4	pp. 539, 540	p. 540	written, p. 544	
8-5	pp. 547, 548	p. 548	oral, p. 550	CAS
8-6	pp. 552, 553	p. 554	group, p. 555	CAS
8-7	p. 558	p. 559	written, p. 561	
8-8	pp. 564, 565	p. 564	oral, p. 567	

Objectives

Skills	Lessons	Self-Test Questions	Chapter Review Questions
A Find values and rules for composites of functions.	8-1	1–3	1–8
B Find the inverse of a function.	8-2, 8-3	5	9–14
C Evaluate radicals.	8-4, 8-7	16	15–22
D Rewrite or simplify expressions with radicals.	8-5, 8-6, 8-7	10–12, 14, 15	23–34
E Solve equations with radicals.	8-8	17, 18	35–40
Properties			
F Apply properties of the inverse of a function.	8-2, 8-3	4, 19	41–45
G Apply properties of radicals and *n*th root functions.	8-4, 8-5, 8-7	8	46–52
Uses			
H Solve real-world problems that can be modeled by composite functions.	8-1	22	53, 54
I Solve real-world problems that can be modeled by equations with radicals.	8-4, 8-8	9, 13, 21	55–59
Representations			
J Make and interpret graphs of inverses of relations and functions.	8-2, 8-3	6, 7, 20	60-67

Resource Masters Chapter 8

None of the generic Resource Masters apply to this Chapter.

Resource Master 136 Lesson 8-1

Warm-Up

In 1–4, describe how to obtain an equivalent result in one step.

1. adding 3 to a number and then adding -7 to the sum
2. multiplying a number by 5 and then multiplying the product by -5
3. cubing a number and then squaring the result
4. getting a 30% discount on an item already marked 40% off

Additional Example

1. Consider the situation in the Activity. Suppose the rebate is $1500 and the discount is 22%, so $r(x) = x - 1500$ and $d(x) = 0.78x$.
   a. Write an equation for $p(x) = r(d(x))$, that is, the price $p(x)$ if the sticker price is x and the discount is taken first followed by the rebate.
   b. Write an equation for $q(x) = d(r(x))$, that is, the price if the rebate is taken first followed by the discount.
   c. Is it true for all x that $p(x) < q(x)$?

Resource Master for Lesson 8-1

Resource Master 137 Lesson 8-1

Additional Examples

2. Let $f(x) = x + 5$ and $g(x) = 2x^2$.
   a. Find an expression for $f \circ g(x)$.
   b. Find an expression for $g \circ f(x)$?

   Solution

   a. $f \circ g(x)$ means first square x and multiply the result by 2, and then add 5 to the result:
   $f \circ g(x) = f(g(x)) = f(\_\_\_\_) = \_\_\_\_ + 5$
   b. To evaluate $g \circ f(x)$, first add 5 to x, then square the result and multiply by 2: $g \circ f(x) = g(f(x)) = g(\_\_\_\_) = 2(\_\_\_\_)^2 =$ $2(\_\_\_\_) = \_\_\_\_$
3. Let x be a real number. Let $t(x) = \frac{1}{x}$ and g be given by $g(x) = x^2 - 100$. What is the domain of $t \circ g$?

Resource Master for Lesson 8-1

Resource Master 138 Lesson 8-2

Warm-Up

In 1–4, identify the operation or sequence of operations that undoes the given operation or sequence.

1. putting on your socks and then putting on your shoes
2. adding 3 to a number and then multiplying the sum by 70
3. squaring a negative number
4. rotating a figure 30° about the origin and then translating the image 6 units up

Additional Examples

1. Let $q = \{(-2, 5), (-1, 7), (0, 3), (1, 7), (2, 1)\}$. Find the inverse of q.
2. Consider the function $y = -2x^2$ with its domain as the set of all real numbers.
   a. What is an equation for the inverse of this function?
   b. Graph the function and its inverse on one set of axes.
   c. Is the inverse a function? Why or why not?

   Solution

   a. To find an equation for the inverse, switch x and y in the rule for the function. The inverse of a function with equation $y = -2x^2$ has equation ________.
   b. The graph of ________ is a parabola. The graph of its inverse is the reflection image of the parabola over the line ________. Graph $y = -2x^2$ and its inverse.
   c. Graphs of functions in rectangular coordinates do not include any two points with the same first coordinate. The inverse (is/is not) a function because ________.

Resource Master for Lesson 8-2

Resource Master 139 Lesson 8-2

Additional Example

3. Two functions are graphed below.

I. II.

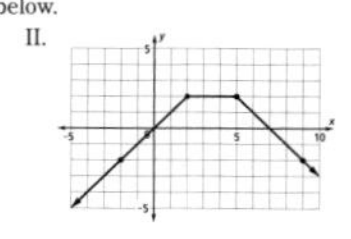

   a. Is the inverse of each function a function? Explain your reasoning.
   b. State the domain and range of each function.
   c. State the domain and range of each inverse.

Guided Example 2

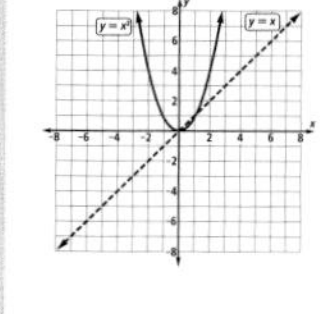

Resource Master for Lesson 8-2

Resource Master 140 Lesson 8-3

Warm-Up

In 1–4, what is the inverse of each object under the given operation?

1. multiplicative inverse of -7
2. additive inverse of 0.625
3. multiplicative inverse of $\begin{bmatrix} 3 & 5 \\ -2 & -4 \end{bmatrix}$
4. inverse under composition of the translation $T_{3,4}$

Additional Example

Let $h : x \rightarrow \frac{4(x+7)-3}{2}$. Find a rule for h^{-1}.

Solution $h(x) = \frac{4(x+7)-3}{2} = \frac{\_\_\_ + \_\_\_}{2}$

Substitute y for $h(x)$: $y = \_\_\_\_\_\_\_\_$. Switching x and y, an equation for the inverse h^{-1} is $x = \_\_\_\_\_\_\_\_$. Solve this equation for y: $2x = \_\_\_\_ + \_\_\_\_$ and $2x - \_\_\_\_ = \_\_\_\_$; $y = \_\_\_\_\_\_\_\_$.

So $h^{-1}(x) = \_\_\_\_\_\_\_\_$.

Resource Master for Lesson 8-3

Resource Master 141 Lesson 8-3

Inverse Functions and the Identity Function

Addition	Functions
0 is the additive identity element $(a + 0 = 0 + a = a)$.	I is the identity function $(f \circ I = I \circ f = f)$.
a and b are additive inverses if and only if $a + b = b + a = 0$, the additive identity element.	f and g are inverses if and only if $f \circ g = g \circ f = I$, the identity function.

Domains of a Function and Its Inverse

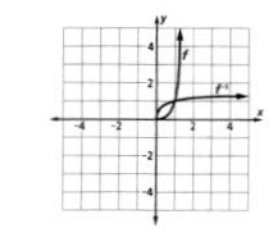

$f(x) = x^6$
Domain of f: set of nonnegative real numbers

$h(x) = x^5$
Domain of h: set of real numbers

$f^{-1}(x) = x^{\frac{1}{6}}$
Domain of f^{-1}: set of nonnegative real numbers

The inverse of h is not a function.

Resource Master for Lesson 8-3

Resource Master 142 Lesson 8-4

Warm-Up

1. Pick any number between 1 and 100. Enter the number into your calculator and repeatedly press the square root key. Describe what happens.
2. Repeat Warm-Up 1 with a number between 0 and 1. Describe what happens.
3. Repeat Warm-Up 1 but use the $-\frac{1}{2}$ power. Describe what happens.

Additional Example

1. The following chart shows the population for eight 1-square-mile regions in the United States.

Sample	1	2	3	4	5	6	7	8
Population	47	68	159	2215	8715	10,512	12,130	45,312

Use the geometric mean to compute an average population density.

Resource Master for Lesson 8-4

Resource Master 143 Lesson 8-4

Additional Examples

2. a. Set a CAS to real-number mode. Evaluate $\sqrt[4]{2401}$ and explain its meaning.
   b. Set a CAS to complex-number mode. Find all the fourth roots of 2401.

Solution

a.

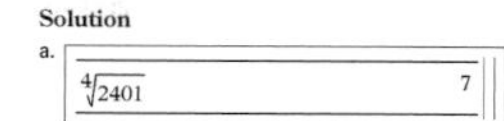

$\sqrt[4]{2401} = (\_\_\_)^{\frac{1}{4}}$ represents the ______ number whose ______ power is 2401.

$(2401)^{\frac{1}{4}} =$ ____ because $(\_\_\_)^4 = 2401$. So $\sqrt[4]{2401} =$ ____.

b. Solve the equation ______ in complex-number mode. The solutions are ____, ____, ____, and ____. These solutions are all the ______ roots of 2401.

3. Rewrite $\sqrt{\sqrt{\sqrt{\sqrt{10}}}}$ using rational exponents. Is this expression an nth root of 10? Justify your answer.

Resource Master for Lesson 8-4

Resource Master 144 Lesson 8-4

Question 19

Years	% Increase (rounded)	Size-Change Factor
1940–1950	150	2.50
1950–1960	62	
1960–1970	43	
1970–1980	178	
1980–1990	68	
1990–2000	51	

Ongoing Assessment

$\sqrt[n]{x^m}$	$(\sqrt[n]{x})^m$	$x^{\frac{m}{n}}$
$\sqrt[5]{p^{20}}$		
		$q^{\frac{17}{3}}$
	$(\sqrt[4]{r})^{12}$	

Resource Master for Lesson 8-4

Resource Master 145 Lesson 8-5

Warm-Up

In 1 and 2, a circle contains the four vertices of a rectangle with dimensions 2 units by 5 units.

1. What is the exact area of the circle?
2. What is the circumference of the circle, to the nearest thousandth of a unit?

Additional Examples

1. Calculate $\sqrt[3]{320} \cdot \sqrt[3]{25}$ without a calculator.
2. Assume that $x \geq 0$. Perform the multiplication $\sqrt[5]{8x^2} \cdot \sqrt[5]{4x^8}$.
   Solution Rewrite using the Root of a Product Theorem.

$$\sqrt[5]{8x^2} \cdot \sqrt[5]{4x^8} = \sqrt[5]{\_\_\_\_}$$
$$= \sqrt[5]{\_\_\_\_} \cdot \sqrt[5]{\_\_\_\_}$$
$$= \_\_\_\_$$

3. Suppose $a \geq 0$ and $b \geq 0$. Simplify $\sqrt[3]{125a^{12}b^{27}}$.
4. Suppose $y \geq 0$. Rewrite $\sqrt[5]{96y^{11}}$ with a smaller power of y inside the radical.

Resource Master for Lesson 8-5

Resource Master 146 Lesson 8-5

Question 20

Year	Percent Increase from Preceding Year	Size-Change Factor
2000	28.5	
2001	-3.6	
2002	-6.5	
2003	16.5	
2004	18.2	
2005	21.9	
2006	12.9	

Resource Master for Lesson 8-5

Resource Master 147 Lesson 8-6

Warm-Up

In 1–3, write in $a + bi$ form.

1. $2i \cdot 3i$
2. $(9 + 16\sqrt{-1})(9 - 16\sqrt{-1})$
3. $\frac{2i - 6}{3 + i}$

Additional Examples

1. Assume $x > 0$. Rationalize the denominator of $\frac{5}{\sqrt{45x}}$.
   Solution 1
   Simplify the denominator and then rationalize:

$$\frac{5}{\sqrt{45x}} = \frac{5}{\sqrt{5 \cdot 9 \cdot x}} = \frac{5}{\sqrt{5} \cdot \sqrt{\_\_\_} \cdot \sqrt{\_\_\_}}$$
$$= \frac{5}{\_\_\_\sqrt{\_\_\_}} \cdot \frac{\_\_\_}{\_\_\_} = \frac{\_\_\_}{\_\_\_}$$

   Solution 2
   Rationalize and then simplify:

$$\frac{5}{\sqrt{45x}} \cdot \frac{\_\_\_}{\_\_\_} = \frac{\_\_\_}{45x} = \_\_\_\_\_\_ = \_\_\_\_\_\_$$

2. Write $\frac{2}{3 - \sqrt{5}}$ in $a + b\sqrt{c}$ form.

Resource Master for Lesson 8-6

Resource Master 149 Lesson 8-7

Resource Master 148 Lesson 8-7

Warm-Up

In 1–4, consider the geometric sequence $g_n = x^n$.
Identify whether the successive terms of this sequence *always increase*, *always decrease*, or *sometimes increase and sometimes decrease* as n increases for the given value of x.

1. $x = 5$
2. $x = -5$
3. $x = \frac{2}{3}$
4. $x = -\frac{2}{3}$
5. In which of the sequences in Warm-Ups 1–4 does the value of g_n approach a limit as $n \to \infty$?

Additional Examples

1. Write $(-5)^{-4}(-5)^7$ without exponents.
   Solution Use the Product of Powers Postulate:
   $(-5)^{-4}(-5)^7 = (-5)^{\_\_\_ + \_\_\_} = (-5)^{\_\_\_} = \_\_\_\_$
2. Evaluate $\sqrt[5]{-32}$.
3. Simplify $\sqrt[3]{-1250}$. Write your answer in radical form.

Resource Masters for Lesson 8-7

Resource Master 150 Lesson 8-8

Warm-Up

Find all the real solutions to $x^{\frac{2}{3}} = 5$ to the nearest hundredth in at least three different ways.

Additional Example

1. Use the formula $V = \sqrt{\frac{Tr}{m}}$ from Example 1, where T is the tension on the string (in newtons), m is the mass of the ball (in kilograms), and r is the length of the string (in meters), and refer to the art below. What tension is needed to allow a 4-kilogram ball on a 2.5-meter string to achieve a velocity of 12 $\frac{\text{meters}}{\text{second}}$?

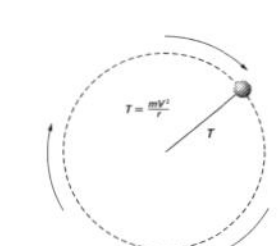

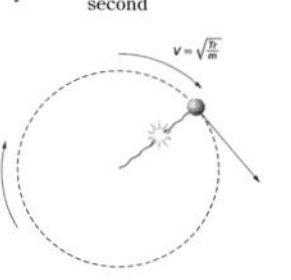

Resource Master for Lesson 8-8

Resource Master 151 Lesson 8-8

Additional Examples

2. Two methods of solving the equation $12 - \sqrt[4]{x} = 20$ given below show that the equation has no real solutions. Complete each method.

   Solution 1

____ = 8	Add ____ to both sides.
$(\_\_\_)^4 = 8^4$	Raise both sides to the 4th power.
$x =$ ____	def. of ____ power, arithmetic

   Check: Substitute $x =$ ____ into the original equation. Does $12 -$ ____ $= 20$? No. So ____ is not a solution. It is extraneous.
   The equation $12 - \sqrt[4]{x} = 20$ has ____ real solutions.

   Solution 2

$-\sqrt[4]{x} = 8$	Add ____ to both sides.

   The left side of the equation is always a negative number because ______. Therefore, the left side cannot equal positive 8. Thus, there are ______ real solutions.

3. Find coordinates for the two points on the line with equation $x = 3$ that are 10 units away from the point (-4, -2).

Question 13a.

Years	% Increase	Size-Change Factor
1950–1960	52	1.52
1960–1970		
1970–1980		
1980–1990		
1990–2000		

Resource Master for Lesson 8-8

Chapter 8

Pacing

Each lesson in this chapter is designed to be covered in 1 day. At the end of the chapter, you should plan to spend 1 day to review the Self-Test, 1 to 2 days for the Chapter Review, and 1 day for a test. You may wish to spend a day on projects, and possibly a day is needed for quizzes. This chapter should therefore take 11 to 14 days. We strongly advise you not to spend more than 15 days on this chapter; there is ample opportunity to review ideas in later chapters. In particular, Chapter 9 continues many of the ideas of this chapter.

Overview

Roughly speaking, the inverse of a function undoes the work of the original function. Students have encountered many examples of inverse functions in prior chapters; for instance, the "adding three" function, with equation $f(x) = x + 3$, has as its inverse the "subtracting three" function, with equation $f(x) = x - 3$. Similarly, with suitable domains, the inverse of the "multiplying by k" function is the "dividing by k" function. Also, for the domain of positive real numbers, the inverse of the squaring function is the square root function, and, more generally, the inverse of the nth power function is the nth root function.

Using Pages 514–515

The concepts in this chapter extend ideas that should be familiar to students. Extending square roots and cube roots leads to radicals of the form $\sqrt[n]{x}$, standing for nth roots. The geometric mean of two numbers that students saw in geometry will generalize to the geometric mean of n numbers.

Chapter 8 Inverses and Radicals

Contents

Year	1940	1950	1960	1970	1980	1990	2000
Median Home Value (unadjusted dollars)	2938	7354	11,900	17,000	47,200	79,100	119,600

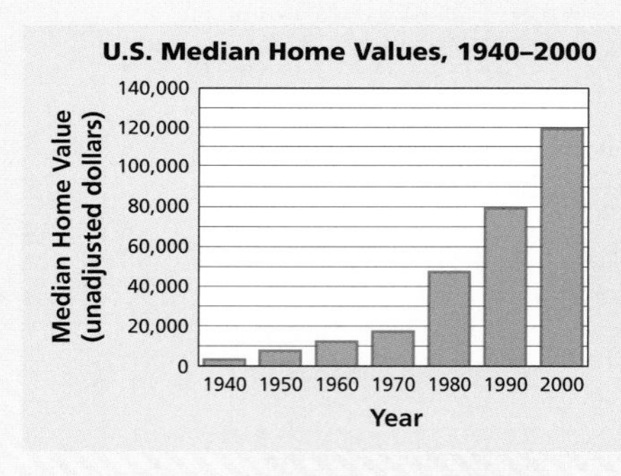

Source: http://www.census.gov/hhes/www/housing/census/historic/values.html

Chapter 8 Overview

Lesson 8-1 covers the composition of functions and the notations $f \circ g(x)$ and $f(g(x))$. The lesson provides practice using this vocabulary and notation and reviews the linear, quadratic, and variation equations studied in earlier chapters. Lesson 8-2 defines the inverse of a relation and introduces the horizontal-line test for inverses. Lesson 8-3 introduces the notation f^{-1} for the inverse function of f and uses the theorem that two functions are inverses of each other if and only if their composite, in either order, is the identity function.

The remainder of the chapter deals with radical expressions for nth roots—expressions that involve the $\sqrt[n]{\ }$ symbol. Care must be taken when dealing with these expressions because the nth root of x, $x^{\frac{1}{n}}$, and $\sqrt[n]{x}$ are defined for different values of x and n. Lessons 8-4 to 8-6 introduce the radical notation for nth roots when x is positive and applies those notations in expressions involving products and quotients, including the geometric mean. Lesson 8-7 discusses radical notation when x is negative, and Lesson 8-8 discusses equations with radicals.

Can you imagine what it would be like to pay these prices: a movie ticket for \$0.30, a new car for \$800, or a house for \$3000? It may be hard to believe, but those were typical prices in the United States in 1940.

Since 1940, the U.S. Census has calculated the median values of single-family homes in the United States. These values are unadjusted for inflation and are shown at the left.

Economists and statisticians analyze price data like these and calculate their rate of change over time using a *geometric mean.* Calculating this mean requires finding nth roots or, using *radical notation,* finding $\sqrt[n]{x}$.

You have seen radical notation before. For example, to find the side length of a cube with a volume of 64 cm^3, you find the cube root of 64, or $\sqrt[3]{64} = 4$ cm. To check the solution, you cube the answer: $4^3 = 64$. The cubing function $y = x^3$ and the "uncubing" function $y = \sqrt[3]{x}$ are examples of *inverse functions;* each function undoes what the other does.

In this chapter, you will study inverses of functions. We begin with the general idea of following one function with another, using the output of the first as the input of the second. After this, you will learn about the properties and graphs of inverse functions, evaluating expressions with radical notation, and other applications of nth roots.

515

You can calculate the average growth rate of the home values given on page 514 in the following way. If the median price of a single-family home was \$2938 in 1940 and \$119,600 in 2000, and there was a constant yearly inflation rate of r, then $2938(1 + r)^{60} = 119{,}600$. From this, $(1 + r)^{60} \approx 40.708$. Taking each side to the $\frac{1}{60}$ power, $1 + r \approx 1.06372$, so $r \approx 0.06372$; the average growth rate over the 60-year time period was about 6.4%. (Question 19 in Lesson 8-4 asks students to calculate the per-decade growth rate using a geometric mean.) A growth rate of 6.4% per year over the 60-year period exceeds the average inflation rate for consumer goods such as food and clothing. This may be due in part to the fact that houses built in 2000 were much bigger than houses built in 1940.

You might want to demonstrate the equation-solving process presented in the previous paragraph for your class. Point out to students that they have just done a problem similar to those they will see at the end of the chapter. This may help them gain confidence that they can handle what is in this chapter.

Chapter 8 Projects

At the end of each chapter, you will find projects related to the chapter. At this time you might want to have students look over the projects on pages 568 and 569. You might want to have students tentatively select a project on which to work. Then, as students read and progress through the chapter, they can finalize their project choices.

Sometimes students might work alone. At other times, you might let them collaborate with classmates for a presentation and discussion. We recommend that you allow for diversity and encourage students to use their imaginations when presenting their projects. As students work on projects throughout the year, they should see many uses of mathematics in the real world.

Lesson 8-1

GOAL

Introduce the operation of composition of functions. Given functions f and g, evaluate $f(g(c))$ or $f \circ g(c)$ for any value of c for which the composite is defined and find an algebraic expression for $f(g(x))$.

SPUR Objectives

The SPUR Objectives for all of Chapter 8 are found in the Chapter Review on pages 574–577.

A Find values and rules for composites of functions.

H Solve real-world problems that can be modeled by composite functions.

Materials/Resources

- Lesson Masters 8-1A and 8-1B
- Resource Masters 136 and 137

HOMEWORK

Suggestions for Assignment

- Questions 1–23
- Question 24 (extra credit)
- Reading Lesson 8-2
- Covering the Ideas 8-2

Local Standards

1 Warm-Up

In 1–4, describe how to obtain an equivalent result in one step.

1. adding 3 to a number and then adding –7 to the sum adding –4 to the original number
2. multiplying a number by 5 and then multiplying the product by –5 multiplying the original number by –25
3. cubing a number and then squaring the result raising the original number to the 6th power
4. getting a 30% discount on an item already marked 40% off multiplying the original cost by 0.42, or paying 42% of the original cost

Lesson 8-1 Composition of Functions

Vocabulary

composite, $g \circ f$

function composition, composition

▶ **BIG IDEA** The function that results from following one function by another is called the *composite of the two functions*; the operation is called *composition*.

Activity

The Lee Muns Car Dealership offers two incentives to car buyers. They give a 12% discount off the \$33,000 sticker price of a new car, as well as a \$2000 rebate for an end-of-the-year clearance. If you were given a choice, which incentive would you take first?

Step 1 Take the discount first and then the rebate. Note that a 12% discount means that you pay 88% of the selling price. How much would you pay for the car if you took the discount first? \$27,040

Step 2 Take the rebate first then apply the discount. How much would you then pay for the car? \$27,280

Step 3 Which method gives you a lower price for the car? How much money would you save over the other option? discount first and then rebate; \$240

Mental Math

Write in $a + bi$ form.

a. $\frac{6+4i}{4}$ $\frac{3}{2} + i$

b. $5i(2i + i^2)$ $-10 - 5i$

c. $(3 + 2i)(3 - 2i)$ 13

d. $(k + ri)(k - ri)$ $k^2 + r^2$

When the supply of available new cars exceeds customer demand, auto dealers may lower the price to increase demand.

The Composite of Two Functions

Will calculating the discount before the rebate always result in a lower price? Will the difference always be the same? To answer these questions, you can use algebra. Let x be the sticker price, d the discount function, and r the rebate function. If you take the discount first, then the price after the discount will be $d(x)$. If you then take the rebate, you can find the final price by taking the output of the discount function and using it as input to the rebate function. This is given by the expression $r(d(x))$, read "r of d of x."

Example 1

Consider the situation in the Activity. Let $r(x) = x - 2000$ and let $d(x) = 0.88x$.

a. Write an equation for $p(x) = r(d(x))$, that is, the price $p(x)$ if the sticker price is x and discount is taken first, then the rebate.

Background

Just as we distinguish between f (a function) and $f(x)$ (its value), so we distinguish between $\circ$ (an operation) and $f \circ g$ (the result of performing the operation). The operation is called *composition;* the result is called the *composite.*

Simple applications of the composition of functions occur frequently in business contexts. The car discount rebate problem in the Activity is a good example to motivate students and to preview key ideas about the composition of functions.

Students in this course first saw composites of transformations in Chapter 4 and they may also have been introduced to composites of transformations and the notation and language introduced here in their geometry courses. Those familiar with composites of transformations will understand that composition is not necessarily commutative.

b. Write an equation for $q(x) = d(r(x))$, that is, the price if the rebate is taken first, then the discount.

c. Is it true for all x that $p(x) < q(x)$?

Solution

a. $p(x) = r(d(x)) = r(0.88x)$ Apply the formula for d.
$= 0.88x - 2000$ Apply the formula for r.

b. $q(x) = d(r(x)) = d(x - 2000)$ Apply the formula for r.
$= 0.88(x - 2000)$ Apply the formula for d.
$= 0.88x - 1760$ Distributive Property

c. Notice that the selling price is $p(x) = r(d(x)) = 0.88x - 2000$ when the discount is given before the rebate, or $q(x) = d(r(x)) = 0.88x - 1760$ when the rebate is given before the discount.

Both p(x) and q(x) are linear equations with the same slope, so the graphs of the functions p and q are parallel lines. The y-intercept of q(x) is \$240 more than the y-intercept of p(x). Hence, p(x) < q(x) for all x. That is, with a 12% discount and a \$2000 rebate, the final selling price is always \$240 less when the discount is taken first, no matter what the sticker price is.

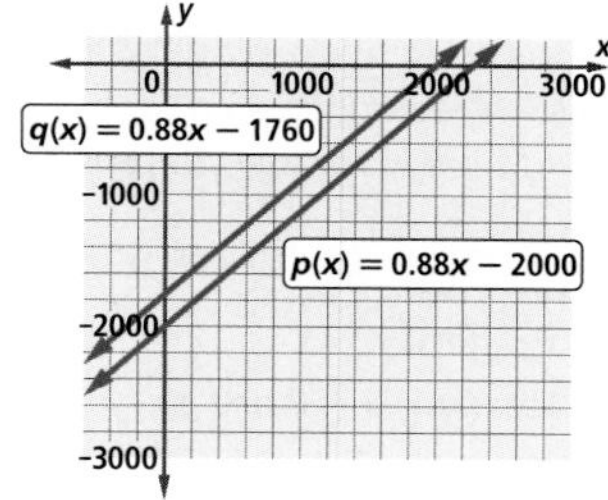

STOP QY1

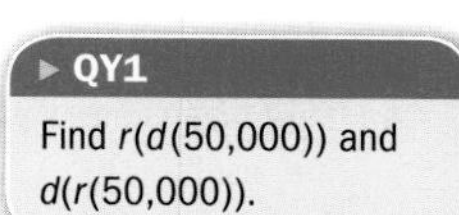
QY1
Find $r(d(50{,}000))$ and $d(r(50{,}000))$.

Example 1 involves the same ideas you saw in Chapter 4 with transformations. Recall that the result of applying one transformation T after another S is called the composite of the two transformations, written $T \circ S$. Likewise, the function that maps x onto $r(d(x))$ is called the *composite* of the two functions d and r, and is written $r \circ d$.

The composite of two functions is a function. You can describe any function if you know its domain and a rule for obtaining its values. Thus, you define the composite of two functions by indicating its rule and domain.

Definition of Composite

The **composite $g \circ f$** of two functions f and g is the function that maps x onto $g(f(x))$, and whose domain is the set of all values in the domain of f for which $f(x)$ is in the domain of g.

The operation signified by the small circle $\circ$ is called **function composition**, or just **composition**. $g \circ f$ is read "the composite f followed by g" "the composite g following f," or "the composite f then g."

2 Teaching

Notes on the Lesson

The composite of two functions
Remind students that, when working with parentheses, one always works from inside to outside. The same procedure applies to the composition of functions. Thus, when the value of a composite of functions is in the form $g(f(x))$, we evaluate the inner function first and then substitute the result for the variable in the rule for the outside function.

Notice how the graph in Example 1 shows students that $d(r(x))$ is always 240 dollars greater than $r(d(x))$. Since the slopes of the two linear functions are equal, the graphs of the functions are parallel lines, and $d(r(x))$ is greater than $r(d(x))$ by the same amount for any value of x.

Additional Example

Example 1 Consider the situation in the Activity. Suppose the rebate is \$1500 and the discount is 22%, so $r(x) = x - 1500$ and $d(x) = 0.78x$.

a. Write an equation for $p(x) = r(d(x))$, that is, the price $p(x)$ if the sticker price is x and the discount is taken first followed by the rebate.
$p(x) = 0.78x - 1500$

b. Write an equation for $q(x) = d(r(x))$, that is, the price if the rebate is taken first followed by the discount. $q(x) = 0.78x - 1170$

c. Is it true for all x that $p(x) < q(x)$?
Answers vary. Sample: For all x, $q(x) - p(x) = .78x - 1170 - (.78x - 1500)) = 330$. So, $p(x)$ is always 330 less than $q(x)$, and $p(x) < q(x)$ for all x.

Accommodating the Learner

An item has a price tag of \$100. You have two coupons: one a rebate for \$10 off and one a discount of 10% off. The store will let you use both coupons.

a. Write the composites of functions r and d (for rebate and discount) in both orders to describe the two ways you can use both coupons. What is the final cost for each way to use the coupons? Answers vary. Sample: Applying the discount first, the final cost is $r \circ d(x)$; $r(d(100)) = r(90) = 80$. Applying the rebate first, the final cost is $d \circ r(x)$; $d(r(100)) = d(90) = 81$.

b. Which order gives you a lower final price? Explain. Answers vary. Sample: Apply the discount first, then the rebate. You want to apply the 10% off coupon to the greatest possible price because that will reduce the price by the greatest dollar amount.

8-1

Notes on the Lesson

A machine analogy is frequently helpful for students trying to understand composition. Try the following schema for the two functions s and f in Example 3.

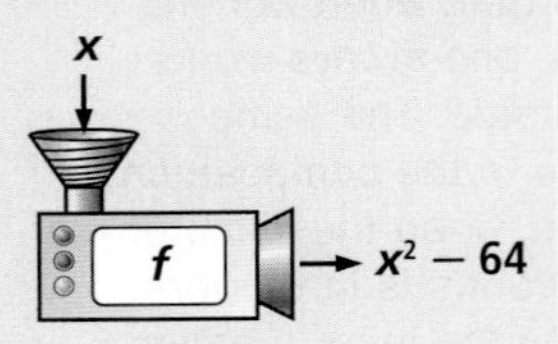

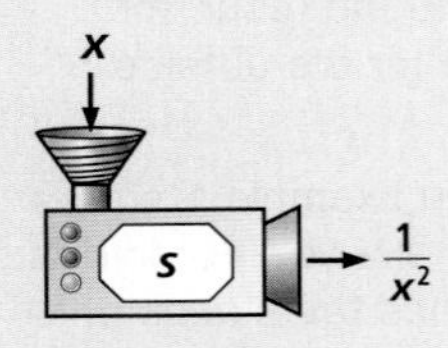

The composite value $s \circ f(7)$ is represented as follows:

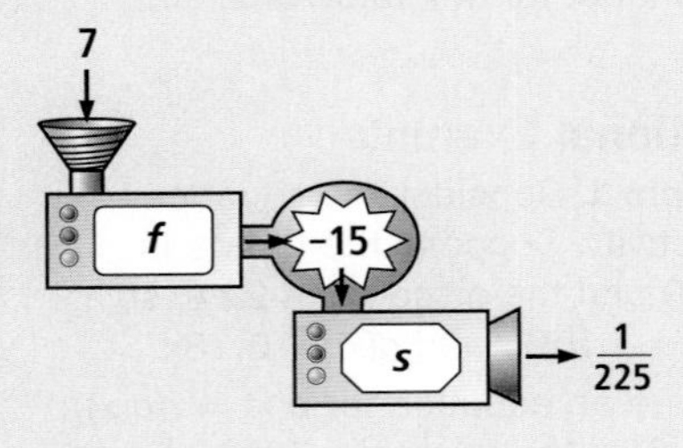

In a similar manner, $f \circ s(7)$ can be represented. This illustrates the noncommutativity of function composition.

Additional Examples

Example 2 Let $f(x) = x + 5$ and $g(x) = 2x^2$.

a. Find an expression for $f \circ g(x)$.

b. Find an expression for $g \circ f(x)$.

Solution

a. $f \circ g(x)$ means first square x and multiply the result by 2, and then add 5 to the result: $f \circ g(x) = f(g(x)) = f(\underline{\ ?\ }) = \underline{\ ?\ } + 5$. $2x^2$; $2x^2$

b. To evaluate $g \circ f(x)$, first add 5 to x, then square the result and multiply by 2: $g \circ f(x) = g(f(x)) = g(\underline{\ \ ?\ \ }) = 2(\underline{\ \ ?\ \ })^2 = 2(\underline{\ \ ?\ \ }) = \underline{\ \ ?\ \ }$. $x + 5$; $x + 5$; $x^2 + 10x + 25$; $2x^2 + 20x + 50$

Example 3 Let x be a real number. Let $t(x) = \frac{1}{x}$ and g be given by $g(x) = x^2 - 100$. What is the domain of $t \circ g$? the set of real numbers except 10 and -10

Ways of Writing a Composite

The ways of writing a composite are the same as those used for composites of transformations. Consider the composite $g \circ f$. You can describe the rule for a composite in two ways.

Mapping notation: $g \circ f: x \rightarrow g(f(x))$

$f(x)$ notation: $g \circ f(x) = g(f(x))$

In Example 1, you wrote $r(d(x))$. You could have written this as $r \circ d(x)$.

QY2

▸ QY2

Write "the composite r then d of x" in

a. mapping notation.

b. $f(x)$ notation.

Is Function Composition Commutative?

From the Activity, $r(d(33{,}000)) = 27{,}040$, and $d(r(33{,}000) = 27{,}280$. This one example is enough to show that *composition of functions is not commutative*. Here is another example.

GUIDED

Example 2

Let $f(x) = x - 2$ and $g(x) = 3x^2$. Calculate

a. $f \circ g(x)$. b. $g \circ f(x)$.

Solution

a. $f \circ g$ means first square x and multiply by 3, then subtract 2 from the result.

$f \circ g(x) = f(g(x)) = f(\underline{\ ?\ }) = \underline{\ ?\ } - 2$ $3x^2$; $3x^2$

b. To evaluate $g \circ f(x)$, first subtract 2 from x, then square the result and multiply by 3.

$g \circ f(x) = g(f(x)) = g(\underline{\ ?\ }) = 3(\underline{\ ?\ })^2 = 3(\underline{\ \ ?\ \ }) = \underline{\ \ ?\ \ }$

b. $x - 2$; $x - 2$; $x^2 - 4x + 4$; $3x^2 - 12x + 12$

Finding the Domain of a Composite of Functions

The domain for a composite is the largest set for which the composition is defined. That is, the domain can include only those values of x for which the first function is defined and that are paired with values that are in the domain of the second function.

ENGLISH LEARNERS

Vocabulary Development

This lesson provides a natural opportunity to review the terms *domain* and *range*. It will also be useful to review set-builder notation such as $\{x \mid x \text{ is a real number}\}$ prior to Lesson 8-2.

Extension

Ask students to explore composites of three functions by having them define three linear functions, such as $f(x) = 2x - 3$, $g(x) = 4x + 1$, and $h(x) = -x + 5$, and asking how many different expressions result from composing the three functions in different orders. There are six orders and six expressions: $f(g(h(x))) = -8x + 39$; $f(h(g(x))) = -8x + 5$; $g(f(h(x))) = -8x + 29$; $g(h(f(x))) = -8x + 33$; $h(f(g(x))) = -8x + 6$; $h(g(f(x))) = -8x + 16$.

Example 3

Let x be a real number. Let $s(x) = \frac{1}{x^2}$, and let f be given by $f(x) = x^2 - 64$. What is the domain of $s \circ f$?

Solution There are no restrictions on the domain of f, but 0 is not in the domain of s. Thus, $f(x)$ cannot be 0. Because $f(x) \neq 0$, $x^2 - 64 \neq 0$; thus, $x^2 \neq 64$. So, x cannot equal 8 or -8. The domain of $s \circ f$ is the set of real numbers other than 8 or -8.

Questions

COVERING THE IDEAS

In 1 and 2, refer to the rebate and discount functions in the Activity.

1. a. If the sticker price is \$25,000 and the rebate is calculated first, what is the selling price of the car? \$20,240
   b. If the sticker price is \$25,000 and the discount is calculated first, what is the selling price of the car? \$20,000
2. Suppose the car dealer changes the rebate to \$3000 and the discount to 15%.
   a. Which gives a lower selling price, taking the rebate first or taking the discount first? Justify your answer.
   b. Will the difference in selling price between taking the discount first versus taking the rebate first always be the same? Explain why or why not.

In 3 and 4, if $f(x) = 2x^3$ and $g(x) = 6x - 4$, evaluate the expression.

3. a. $f(g(-3))$ −21,296 b. $f \circ g(-3)$ −21,296
4. a. $f \circ g(5)$ 35,152 b. $f(g(5))$ 35,152
5. Suppose $f(x) = x + 1$ and $g(x) = x - 3$. Is composition of f and g commutative? Justify your answer.

In 6 and 7, let $f(a) = a^2 + a + 1$ and $g(a) = -4a$.

6. Evaluate each expression.
   a. $g(f(-3))$ -28 b. $f(g(-3))$ 157 c. $g(f(3))$ -52 d. $f(g(3))$ 133
7. Find an expression in standard form for each.
   a. $g(f(a))$ $-4a^2 - 4a - 4$ b. $f(g(a))$ $16a^2 - 4a + 1$
8. Use a CAS to define the functions f and g in Example 2. Evaluate each expression and compare your results with the answers in the example. See margin.
   a. $f(g(x))$ b. $g(f(x))$

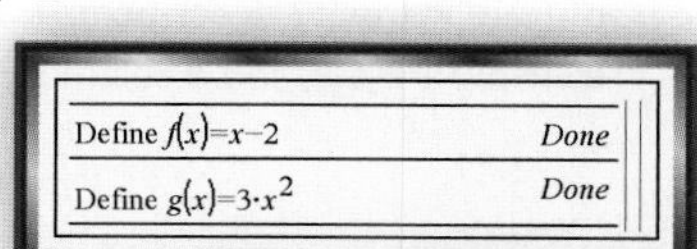

2a. discount first; For any car priced x, if you take the discount first the price will be $0.85x - 3000$, but if you take the rebate first the price will be $0.85(x - 3000) = 0.85x - 2550$.

2b. Yes; the difference will always be $(0.85x - 2550) - (0.85x - 3000) = \$450$.

5. Yes; $f(g(x)) = (x - 3) + 1 = x - 2$, $g(f(x)) = (x + 1) - 3 = x - 2$.

Notes on the Lesson

Example 3 Here is an alternate solution to Example 3:

In $f(x)$, x can be any real number. However, $s \circ f(x) = s(f(x)) = s(x^2 - 64) = \frac{1}{x^2 - 64}$. So to find $s \circ f(x)$, x cannot be 8 or -8. Therefore, the domain of $s \circ f$ is the set of real numbers other than 8 or -8.

Note-Taking Tips

Encourage students to use combined input–output diagrams, such as those in the Notes on the Lesson on page 518, to represent a composite of functions. Such diagrams can help them visualize how the output of the first function is the input for the second function.

3 Assignment

Recommended Assignment

- Questions 1–23
- Question 24 (extra credit)
- Reading Lesson 8-2
- Covering the Ideas 8-2

Notes on the Questions

Questions 6 and 7 These questions show the noncommutativity of composition of functions.

Additional Answers

8a.

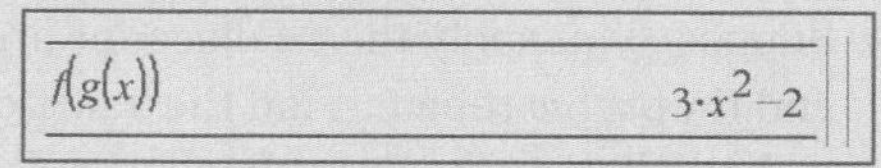

This result is the same as in Example 2.

8b.

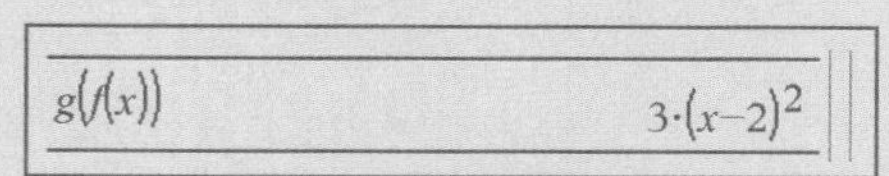

This result is the same as in Example 2.

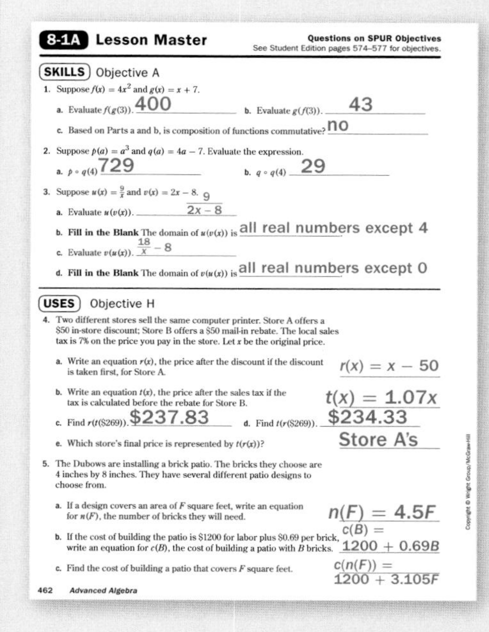

8-1A Lesson Master

Questions on SPUR Objectives
See Student Edition pages 574–577 for objectives.

SKILLS Objective A

1. Suppose $f(x) = 4x^2$ and $g(x) = x + 7$.
   a. Evaluate $f(g(3))$. 400
   b. Evaluate $g(f(3))$. 43
   c. Based on Parts a and b, is composition of functions commutative? no
2. Suppose $p(a) = a^3$ and $q(a) = 4a - 7$. Evaluate the expression.
   a. $p \circ q(4)$ 729
   b. $q \circ q(4)$ 29
3. Suppose $u(x) = \frac{9}{x}$ and $v(x) = 2x - 8$.
   a. Evaluate $u(v(x))$. $\frac{9}{2x - 8}$
   b. **Fill in the Blank** The domain of $u(v(x))$ is all real numbers except 4.
   c. Evaluate $v(u(x))$. $\frac{18}{x} - 8$
   d. **Fill in the Blank** The domain of $v(u(x))$ is all real numbers except 0.

USES Objective H

4. Two different stores sell the same computer printer. Store A offers a \$50 in-store discount; Store B offers a \$50 mail-in rebate. The local sales tax is 7% on the price you pay in the store. Let x be the original price.
   a. Write an equation $r(x)$, the price after the discount if the discount is taken first, for Store A. $r(x) = x - 50$
   b. Write an equation $t(x)$, the price after the sales tax if the tax is calculated before the rebate for Store B. $t(x) = 1.07x$
   c. Find $r(t(\$269))$. \$237.83
   d. Find $t(r(\$269))$. \$234.33
   e. Which store's final price is represented by $t(r(x))$? Store A's
5. The Dubows are installing a brick patio. The bricks they choose are 4 inches by 8 inches. They have several different patio designs to choose from.
   a. If a design covers an area of F square feet, write an equation for $n(F)$, the number of bricks they will need. $n(F) = 4.5F$
   b. If the cost of building the patio is \$1200 for labor plus \$0.69 per brick, write an equation for $c(B)$, the cost of building a patio with B bricks. $c(B) = 1200 + 0.69B$
   c. Find the cost of building a patio that covers F square feet. $c(n(F)) = 1200 + 3.105F$

462 Advanced Algebra

Notes on the Questions

Question 15 Students may not realize that the answer to Part c is the composite of the answers to Parts a and b.

9. Refer to Example 3.
   a. What is the domain of $f \circ s$? the set of real numbers other than 0
   b. Is the domain of $f \circ s$ the same as the domain of $s \circ f$? no

APPLYING THE MATHEMATICS

In 10 and 11, let $g(x) = \frac{1}{x}$ and $h(x) = x^4 - 16$.

10. Find the domain of $g \circ h$.
11. Find the domain of $h \circ g$.
12. Suppose a state has a sales tax of 5% and you buy something at a discount of 20%. Let P be the original price of what you have bought.
   a. Write a formula for $f(P)$, the price after the discount.
   b. Write a formula for $g(P)$, the price after tax. $g(P) = 1.05P$
   c. Which gives you a better final price, discount first or tax first? Explain why.
13. Jarrod earns some extra cash by chauffeuring on the weekends. He rents a limousine from Executive Rentals. According to their rental agreement, Jarrod pays Executive a $300 rental fee plus 40% of his remaining proceeds. Luxury Rental makes Jarrod a different offer. They would charge him $300, but they tell him he will pay them 40% of all collected proceeds *before* deducting the $300 fee. Use function composition to show which offer Jarrod should take.
14. Let $g(x) = x^{\frac{2}{3}}$, where x is a real number. The function g can be rewritten as the composite of two functions m and h. Define m and h so that $h(m(x)) = m(h(x)) = x^{\frac{2}{3}}$.
15. Composite functions can be used to describe relationships between functions of variation. Suppose w varies inversely as z, and z varies directly as the fourth power of x.
   a. Give an equation for w in terms of z. Use your equation to describe a function $f: z \rightarrow w$. $w = \frac{k_1}{z}$; $f: z \rightarrow \frac{k_1}{z}$
   b. Give an equation for z in terms of x. Use your equation to describe a function $g: x \rightarrow z$. $z = k_2x^4$; $g: x \rightarrow k_2x^4$
   c. Give an equation for w in terms of x. Use your equation to describe a function $h: x \rightarrow w$.
   d. Use words to describe how w varies with x.
   e. How are f, g, and h related? $h = f \circ g$

10. the set of real numbers other than 2 and -2

11. the set of real numbers other than 0

12a. $f(P) = 0.8P$

12c. Both give the same price because of the Commutative Property of Multiplication: $f(g(P)) = 0.8(1.05P) = 1.05(0.8P) = g(f(P))$

13. $f(x) = 0.6x$; $g(x) = x - 300$; $f(g(x)) = 0.6(x - 300) = 0.6x - 180$; $g(f(x)) = 0.6x - 300$; He should take Executive Rental's offer.

14. $m(x) = x^{\frac{1}{3}}$; $h(x) = x^2$; $h(m(x)) = \left(x^{\frac{1}{3}}\right)^2 = x^{\frac{2}{3}}$; $m(h(x)) = (x^2)^{\frac{1}{3}} = x^{\frac{2}{3}}$

15c. $w = \frac{k_1}{k_2x^4} = \frac{k_3}{x^4}$; $h: x \rightarrow \frac{k_3}{x^4}$

15d. w varies inversely as the fourth power of x.

Accommodating the Learner

An item has a price tag of $\$x$. You can apply a $\$y$ rebate and a z% discount.

1. Write a composite of the function r (for the rebate) followed by the function d (for the discount) to represent the final cost. What is the final cost when the rebate is taken first? $d \circ r(x)$; $d(r(x)) = d(x - y) = \left(1 - \frac{z}{100}\right)(x - y) = x - y - \frac{xz}{100} + \frac{yz}{100}$
2. Suppose you apply the z% discount first and then a $\$w$ rebate. Find the value of w that will give the same final price as in Question 1. $r \circ d(x) = r(d(x)) = r\left(\left(1 - \frac{z}{100}\right)x\right) = r\left(x - \frac{xz}{100}\right) = x - \frac{xz}{100} - w$. If $x - \frac{xz}{100} - w = x - y - \frac{xz}{100} + \frac{yz}{100}$, then $-w = -y + \frac{yz}{100}$ and $w = y - \frac{yz}{100}$.

16. Let $f(x) = x^2$. What is $f(f(f(x)))$? x^8

17. Consider $t(x) = \frac{1}{x^2}$.
    a. Simplify $t(t(x))$. x^4
    b. When is $t(t(x))$ undefined? when $x = 0$

REVIEW

18. Nancy throws a ball upward at a velocity of 18 $\frac{\text{m}}{\text{sec}}$ from the top of a cliff 35 m above sea level. **(Lesson 6-4)**
    a. Write an equation to describe the height h of the ball after t seconds. $h = -4.9t^2 + 18t + 35$
    b. What is the maximum height of the ball? 51.5 m

19. Find the inverse of the matrix $\begin{bmatrix} a & -7 \\ 0 & 18 \end{bmatrix}$, $a \neq 0$. **(Lesson 5-5)**

20. Consider the transformation $T: (x, y) \to (y, x)$. **(Lesson 4-6)**
    a. Let $A = (-4, 0)$, $B = (-1, 5)$, and $C = (2, 5)$. Graph the image of $\triangle ABC$ under T. See margin.
    b. What transformation does T represent?

21. **True or False** The line with the equation $\pi = x$ is the graph of a function. **(Lesson 1-4)** false

22. The graph at the right shows the height of a flag on a 12-meter pole as a function of time. **(Lesson 1-4)**
    a. Describe what is happening to the flag.
    b. Why are there some horizontal segments on the graph?
    c. What is the domain of the function?
    d. What is its range? all real numbers from 0 to 12

23. a. What number is the additive inverse of $-\frac{13}{4}$? $\frac{13}{4}$
    b. What number is the multiplicative inverse of $-\frac{13}{4}$? **(Previous Course)** $-\frac{4}{13}$

EXPLORATION

24. Let $f(x) = \frac{1}{1-x}$.
    a. Find $f(f(x))$, $f(f(f(x)))$, and $f(f(f(f(x))))$. $-\frac{1}{x} + 1$; x, $\frac{1}{1-x}$
    b. What is the relationship between $f(x)$ and $f(f(f(f(x))))$? They are the same.
    c. Use your answers to Parts a and b to find $f(f(f(f(f(f(f(f(x))))))))$. $-\frac{1}{x} + 1$

19. $\begin{bmatrix} \frac{1}{a} & \frac{7}{18a} \\ 0 & \frac{1}{18} \end{bmatrix}$

20b. a reflection over the line with equation $y = x$

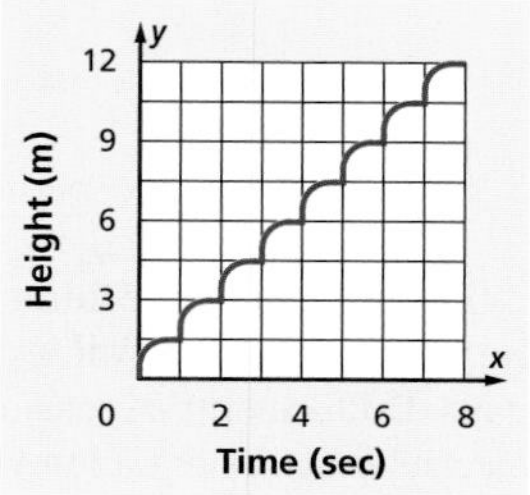

22a. The flag is being raised up the pole.

22b. There are short pauses during the flag raising.

22c. all real numbers from 0 to 8

QY ANSWERS

1. $r(d(50{,}000)) = 42{,}000$; $d(r(50{,}000)) = 42{,}240$
2. a. $d \circ r : x \to d(r(x))$
   b. $d \circ r(x) = d(r(x))$

Notes on the Questions

Question 16 You could ask students to generalize: If $f(x) = x^n$, then $f(f(f(x))) = x^{(n^3)}$.

Question 17 If $t(t(x))$ is written as x^4, then it is never undefined. But if it is written as $t \circ t(x)$, since a composite is defined at most over the domain of the first function performed, the composite is not defined at $x = 0$, and 0 is not in the domain.

Questions 20, 22, and 23 These questions preview ideas in Lesson 8-2 and should be discussed.

Question 24 The sequence of functions $f_1(x) = \frac{1}{1-x}$, $f_{n+1}(x) = f(f_n(x))$ is periodic with degree 3.

4 Wrap-Up

Ongoing Assessment

Have students work in small groups. Ask each group to describe two linear or quadratic functions f and g, select a value of x, and predict which will be greater, $f \circ g(x)$ or $g \circ f(x)$. Then half the group should evaluate $f \circ g(x)$, while the other half evaluates $g \circ f(x)$, to determine whether their predictions were correct. Answers vary. Check students' work.

Additional Answers

20a.

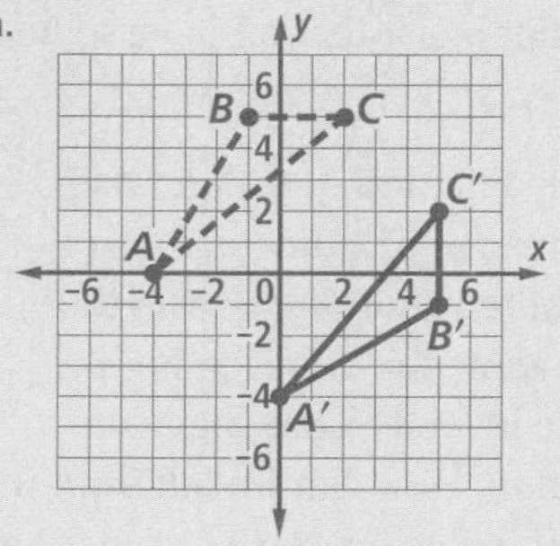

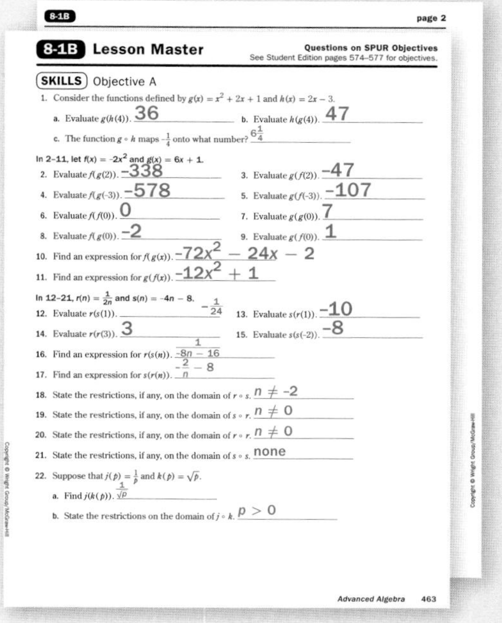

8-1B page 2

8-1B Lesson Master Questions on SPUR Objectives
See Student Edition pages 574–577 for objectives.

SKILLS Objective A

1. Consider the functions defined by $g(x) = x^2 + 2x + 1$ and $h(x) = 2x - 3$.
   a. Evaluate $g(h(4))$. 36
   b. Evaluate $h(g(4))$. 47
   c. The function $g \circ h$ maps $-\frac{1}{4}$ onto what number? $6\frac{1}{4}$

In 2–11, let $f(x) = -2x^2$ and $g(x) = 6x + 1$.

2. Evaluate $f(g(2))$. -338
3. Evaluate $g(f(2))$. -47
4. Evaluate $f(g(-3))$. -578
5. Evaluate $g(f(-3))$. -107
6. Evaluate $f(f(0))$. 0
7. Evaluate $g(g(0))$. 7
8. Evaluate $f(g(0))$. -2
9. Evaluate $g(f(0))$. 1
10. Find an expression for $f(g(x))$. $-72x^2 - 24x - 2$
11. Find an expression for $g(f(x))$. $-12x^2 + 1$

In 12–21, $r(n) = \frac{1}{2n}$ and $s(n) = -4n - 8$.

12. Evaluate $r(s(1))$. $-\frac{1}{24}$
13. Evaluate $s(r(1))$. -10
14. Evaluate $r(r(3))$. 3
15. Evaluate $s(s(-2))$. -8
16. Find an expression for $r(s(n))$. $\frac{1}{-8n - 16}$
17. Find an expression for $s(r(n))$. $-\frac{2}{n} - 8$
18. State the restrictions, if any, on the domain of $r \circ s$. $n \neq -2$
19. State the restrictions, if any, on the domain of $s \circ r$. $n \neq 0$
20. State the restrictions, if any, on the domain of $r \circ r$. $n \neq 0$
21. State the restrictions, if any, on the domain of $s \circ s$. none
22. Suppose that $j(p) = \frac{1}{p}$ and $k(p) = \sqrt{p}$.
    a. Find $j(k(p))$. $\frac{1}{\sqrt{p}}$
    b. State the restrictions on the domain of $j \circ k$. $p > 0$

Advanced Algebra 463

Lesson

8-2

GOAL

Explore the definition of the inverse of a relation (note that, in this book, we allow nonfunctions to have inverses); emphasize that the inverse of a function is not always a function.

SPUR Objectives

B Find the inverse of a function.

F Apply properties of the inverse of a function.

J Make and interpret graphs of inverses of relations and functions.

Materials/Resources

- Lesson Masters 8-2A and 8-2B
- Resource Masters 138 and 139

HOMEWORK

Suggestions for Assignment

- Questions 1–23
- Question 24 (extra credit)
- Reading Lesson 8-3
- Covering the Ideas 8-3

Local Standards

1 Warm-Up

In 1–4, identify the operation or sequence of operations that undoes the given operation or sequence.

1. putting on your socks and then putting on your shoes taking off your shoes and then taking off your socks
2. adding 3 to a number and then multiplying the sum by 70 dividing a number by 70 and then subtracting 3 from the quotient

Lesson

8-2 Inverses of Relations

Vocabulary

inverse of a relation

horizontal-line test

BIG IDEA Every relation has an *inverse*. Some of these inverses are functions.

In 1929, astronomers Edwin Hubble and Milton Humason announced their discovery that other galaxies are moving away or *receding* from our galaxy, the Milky Way. Galaxies that are farther away appear to be receding faster. The relationship between distance and recession speed is given in the table below. Distance is given in megaparsecs (Mpc), with 1 Mpc ≈ 3.26 million light years. Speed is given in kilometers per second.

x = Distance (Mpc)	y = Speed $\left(\frac{\text{km}}{\text{sec}}\right)$
0	0
5	350
10	700
15	1050
20	1400

In this table, the left column has values of the domain variable x and the right column has values of the range variable y. The function that maps distance onto recession speed is called *Hubble's Law* and is described by the equation $y = 70x$.

Astronomers use Hubble's Law to estimate the distance to a galaxy based on its apparent recession speed, which is measured by shifts in the spectrum of light from the galaxy. In other words, the speed becomes the domain variable x and the distance becomes the range variable y. The function mapping the speed onto the distance can be described by the equation $x = 70y$. Solving this equation for y, $y = \frac{x}{70}$.

x = Speed $\left(\frac{\text{km}}{\text{sec}}\right)$	y = Distance (Mpc)
0	0
350	5
700	10
1050	15
1400	20

Mental Math

Nina is pulling chips one at a time out of a bag that contains 4 red chips, 5 black chips, and 1 blue chip. She replaces the chip after each pull. What is the probability that she pulls

a. the blue chip twice in a row? $\frac{1}{100}$

b. a red chip, then a black chip? $\frac{20}{100}$, or $\frac{1}{5}$

c. a red chip n times, then a black chip m times? $\left(\frac{4}{10}\right)^n \cdot \left(\frac{5}{10}\right)^m$, or $\left(\frac{2}{5}\right)^n \cdot \left(\frac{1}{2}\right)^m$

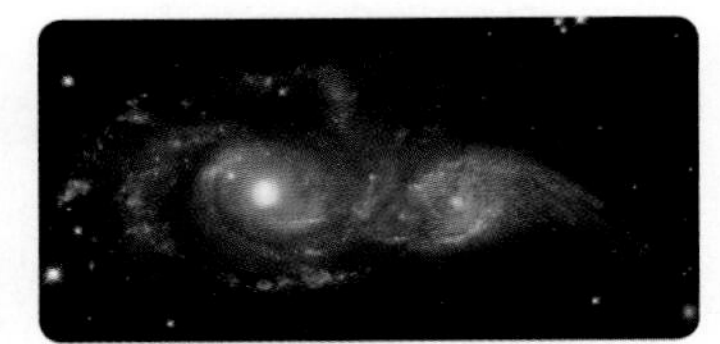

Galaxies NGC 2207 and IC 2163 are 140 million light years away from us in the direction of the Canis Major constellation. They are expected to meld in 500 million years.

Background

We allow every relation to have an inverse. The advantage of that unrestricted definition is that we often want to discuss all the points one gets by switching the x- and y-coordinates of the points of a relation. This approach gives us language for that discussion. For instance, for the inverse of $y = x^2$, it may be more natural to consider the relation $x = y^2$ than the function $y = \sqrt{x}$. Similarly, $\frac{x^2}{4} + \frac{y^2}{9} = 1$ is more naturally compared with $\frac{y^2}{4} + \frac{x^2}{9} = 1$ than any restricted relations that are functions. Thus, we do not insist that an inverse be a function.

However, then a natural question arises: When is the inverse of a function also a function? There is nothing new in the answer—just apply the criterion for a function to the inverse. That suggests another question: How can we tell from the *original* function if its inverse is a function? One answer is given by the horizontal-line test.

The relations with equations $y = 70x$ and $y = \frac{1}{70}x$ are related. The ordered pairs of each one are found by switching the values of x and y in the other. Two relations that have this property are called *inverse relations.*

Definition of Inverse of a Relation

The **inverse of a relation** is the relation obtained by switching the coordinates of each ordered pair in the relation.

Example 1

Let $f = \{(-3, 2), (-1, 4), (0, 3), (2, 8), (5, 7), (7, 8)\}$. Find the inverse of f.

Solution Switch the coordinates of each ordered pair. Call the inverse g. Then $g = \{(2, -3), (4, -1), (3, 0), (8, 2), (7, 5), (8, 7)\}$.

The blue dots at the right are a graph of the function f from Example 1. The red dots are a graph of the inverse g.

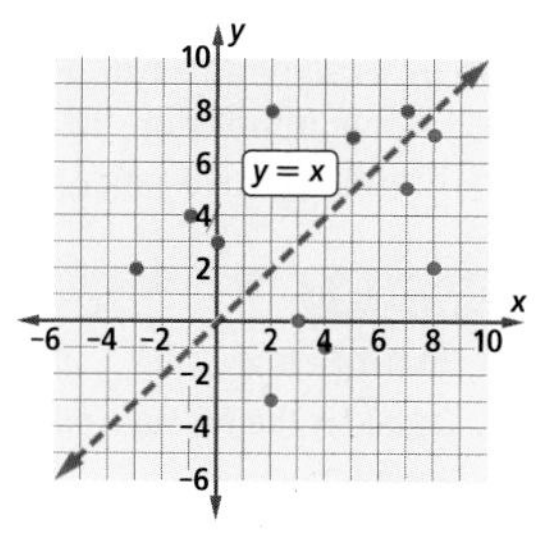

Recall that the points (x, y) and (y, x) are reflection images of each other over the line with equation $y = x$. That is, reflection over this line switches the coordinates of the ordered pairs. The graphs of any relation and its inverse are reflection images of each other over the line $y = x$.

The Domain and Range of a Relation and Its Inverse

Recall that the domain of a relation is the set of possible values for the first coordinate, and the range is the set of possible values for the second coordinate. Because the inverse is found by switching the first and second coordinates, the domain and range of the inverse of a relation are the range and domain, respectively, of the original relation. For instance, in Example 1,

domain of f = range of g = $\{-3, -1, 0, 2, 5, 7\}$,

range of f = domain of g = $\{2, 4, 3, 8, 7\}$.

The theorem on the next page summarizes the ideas you have read so far in this lesson.

We do not use the language of 1-1 correspondence in this lesson, but some students may find it useful: A function has an inverse that is also a function if and only if it is a 1-1 mapping from the domain to the range.

ENGLISH LEARNERS

Vocabulary Development

Ask students to list all the different ways they use the word *inverse* in mathematics. Answers vary. Sample: additive inverse, multiplicative inverse, inverse of a matrix, inverse variation, inverse of a function Emphasize that a single word can have several meanings, and each particular meaning depends on the context in which the word is used.

3. squaring a negative number taking the principal square root of a number and then taking its opposite
4. rotating a figure 30° about the origin and then translating the image 6 units up translating a figure 6 units down and then rotating the image -30° about the origin

2 Teaching

Notes on the Lesson

If a relation is given as a list of ordered pairs, then finding its inverse is usually not difficult for students. Similarly, finding the graph of the inverse from the graph of an original function is also straightforward: Reflections preserve size and shape, so the inverse can be graphed by reversing some ordered pairs from the original graph and then connecting those points to form a figure that is the same size and shape as the original.

Another point to stress is that if y can be written as a function f of x, then x determines y. If, in addition, y also determines x, then the inverse of f is also a function.

Additional Example

Example 1 Let $q = \{(-2, 5), (-1, 7), (0, 3), (1, 7), (2, 1)\}$. Find the inverse of q. If h is the inverse of q, then $h = \{(5, -2), (7, -1), (3, 0), (7, 1), (1, 2)\}$.

Note-Taking Tips

Encourage students to use phrases such as "the domain of f" and "the range of the inverse of f" to label domains and ranges of functions. Besides helping them keep track of various sets of values, the phrases can help emphasize that the range of a function is the domain of its inverse, and the domain of a function is the range of its inverse.

Notes on the Lesson

Inverse-Relation Theorem Be sure to mention the caution that follows this theorem. Students need to realize that *the inverse of a relation* and *inverse variation* are different concepts.

Additional Example

Example 2 Consider the function with equation $y = -2x^2$, with its domain as the set of all real numbers.

a. What is an equation for the inverse of this function?

b. Graph the function and its inverse on one set of axes.

c. Is the inverse a function? Why or why not?

Solution

a. To find an equation for the inverse, switch x and y in the rule for the function. The inverse of a function with equation $y = -2x^2$ has equation ___?___. $x = -2y^2$

b. The graph of ___?___ is a parabola. $y = -2x^2$ The graph of its inverse is the reflection image of the parabola over the line with equation ___?___. $y = x$ Graph $y = -2x^2$ and its inverse.

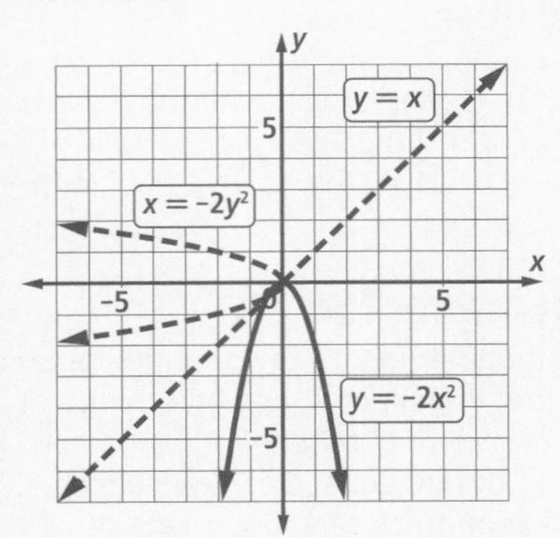

c. Graphs of functions in rectangular coordinates do not include any two points with the same first coordinate. The inverse (is/is not) a function because ___?___. is not; its graph in rectangular coordinates includes two points with the same first coordinate, (-2, 1) and (-2, -1).

Inverse-Relation Theorem

Suppose f is a relation and g is the inverse of f. Then:

1. If a rule for f exists, a rule for g can be found by switching x and y in the rule for f.
2. The graph of g is the reflection image of the graph of f over the line with equation $y = x$.
3. The domain of g is the range of f, and the range of g is the domain of f.

Caution! The word *inverse*, when used in the term *inverse of a relation*, is different than its use in the phrase *inverse variation*.

Determining Whether the Inverse of a Function Is a Function

The inverse of a relation is a relation. But the inverse of a function is not always a function. In Example 1, g is not a function because it contains the two pairs (8, 2) and (8, 7).

GUIDED

Example 2

Consider the function with domain the set of all real numbers and equation $y = x^2$.

a. **What is an equation for the inverse of this function?**

b. **Graph the function and its inverse on the same coordinate axes.**

c. **Is the inverse a function? Why or why not?**

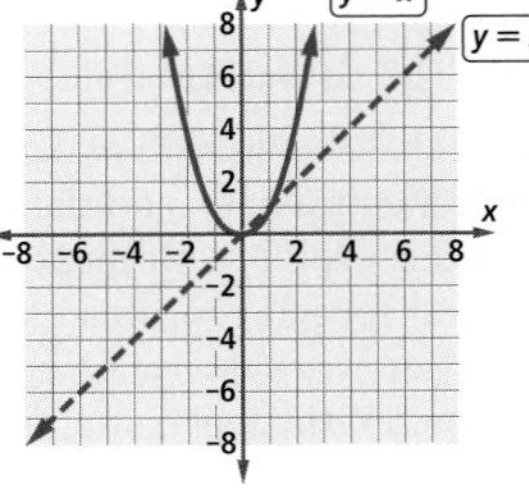

Solution

a. To find an equation for the inverse, switch x and y in the rule for the function. The inverse of the function with equation $y = x^2$ has equation ___?___ = ___?___. x; y^2

b. The graph of ___?___ is the parabola at the right. The graph of its inverse is the reflection image of the parabola over the line with equation ___?___. Copy the graph and add a graph of the inverse to it.

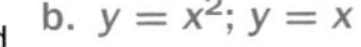
b. $y = x^2$; $y = x$

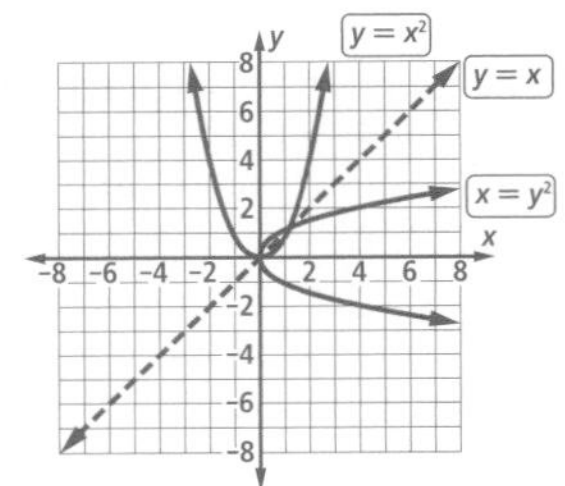

c. Graphs of functions in rectangular coordinates do not include two points with the same first coordinate. The inverse (is/is not) a function because ___?___.
is not; Answers vary. Sample: the graph of the inverse contains the points (1, 1) and (1, -1), which have the same first coordinate.

Accommodating the Learner

Ask students to complete the following steps.

1. Write an equation for the line through (2, 1) and (4, 3). $y = x - 1$
2. Find two additional ordered pairs by switching the x and y values of the points given above. (1, 2), (3, 4)
3. Find an equation for the line through those two points. $y = x + 1$
4. Verify that the two lines represent inverse functions. Rewrite $y = x - 1$ by switching the x and y values and solving for y: $x = y - 1$, so $y = x + 1$; the two functions are inverses.

In a function, no two points have the same first coordinate. So, if the inverse of a function is a function, no two points of the original function can have the same *second* coordinate. This idea implies that if any horizontal line intersects the graph of a function on a rectangular grid at more than one point, then the function's inverse is not a function. This is called the **horizontal-line test** to check whether the inverse of a function is a function. Notice that the graphs of the functions in Examples 1 and 2 do not pass the horizontal-line test.

Example 3

Two functions are graphed.

i.

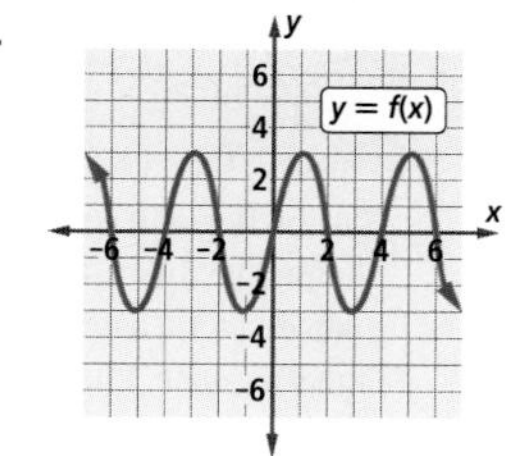

ii.

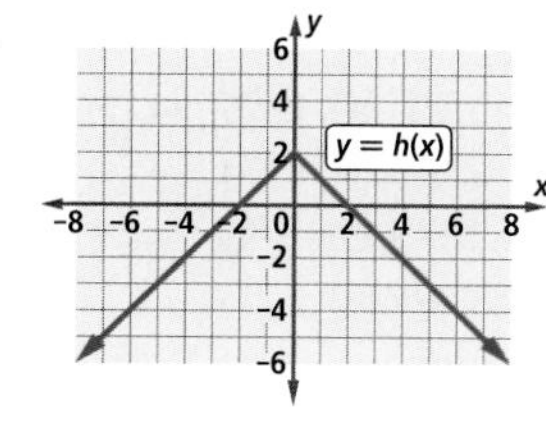

a. Tell whether the inverses of the graphed functions are functions. Explain your reasoning.

b. State the domain and range of each function.

c. State the domain and range of each inverse.

Solution

a. Apply the horizontal-line test. For each function, there is a horizontal line that intersects the graph of the function more than once. Neither the inverse of f nor the inverse of h is a function. Both graphs fail the horizontal-line test.

b. Refer to the graphs above. The domain of f is the set of all real numbers. The range is $\{y \mid -3 \le y \le 3\}$. The domain of h is the set of all real numbers. The range is $\{y \mid y \le 2\}$.

c. Use the Inverse-Relation Theorem. The domain of the inverse of f is the range of f, or $\{x \mid -3 \le x \le 3\}$; the range is the domain of f, or the set of all real numbers. The domain of the inverse of h is $\{x \mid x \le 2\}$;the range is the set of all real numbers.

Accommodating the Learner

Ask students to find an equation for the inverse of the ratio of two functions f and g if $f(x) = ax + b$ and $g(x) = px + q$. $\frac{f(x)}{g(x)} = \frac{ax + b}{px + q}$, so to find an equation for the inverse, solve $x = \frac{ay + b}{py + q}$ for y.

$$ay + b = xpy + xq$$

$$ay - xpy = xq - b$$

$$y(a - xp) = xq - b$$

$$y = \frac{xq - b}{a - xp}$$

Notes on the Lesson

Some students will need to see several examples of finding the inverse from an equation for a function or other relation. Point out that after finding an equation for the inverse, it may help to solve the equation for y before trying to graph it. Here is a simple example: If a function is represented by $y = -2x$, then its inverse is represented by $x = -2y$. To graph the inverse, it is helpful to solve this equation for y: $y = -\frac{1}{2}x$. Point out that when graphed, the lines $y = -2x$ and $y = -\frac{1}{2}x$ are reflection images of each other over the line $y = x$.

Additional Example

Example 3 Two functions are graphed.

I.

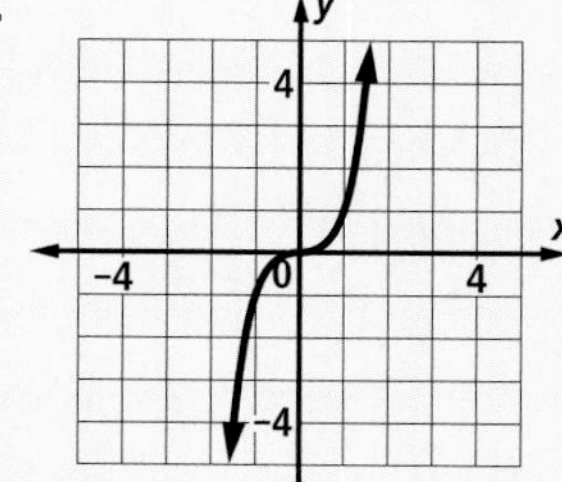

II.

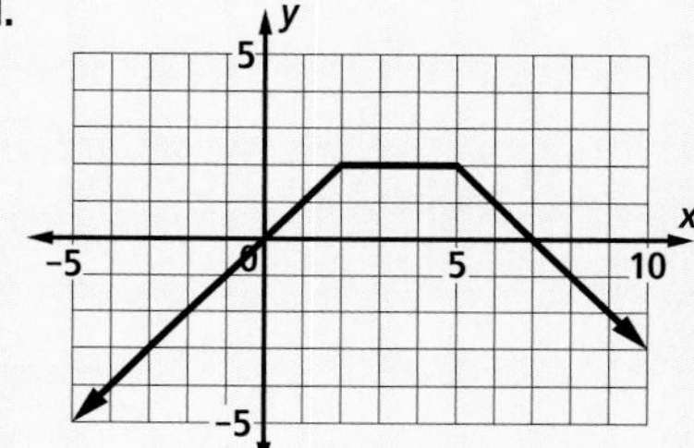

a. Is the inverse of each function a function? Explain your reasoning. Graph I passes the horizontal-line test, so its inverse is a function. Graph II fails the horizontal-line test, so its inverse is not a function.

b. State the domain and range of each function. I: The domain is all real numbers, and the range is all real numbers. II: The domain is all real numbers, and the range is $\{y \mid y \le 2\}$.

c. State the domain and range of each inverse. I: The domain is all real numbers, and the range is all real numbers. II. The domain is $\{x \mid x \le 2\}$, and the range is all real numbers.

3 Assignment

Recommended Assignment

- Questions 1–23
- Question 24 (extra credit)
- Reading Lesson 8-3
- Covering the Ideas 8-3

Additional Answers

3a. $g = \{(-9, -4), (-7, -3), (-1, 0), (5, 3), (7, 4), (11, 6)\}$

3b.

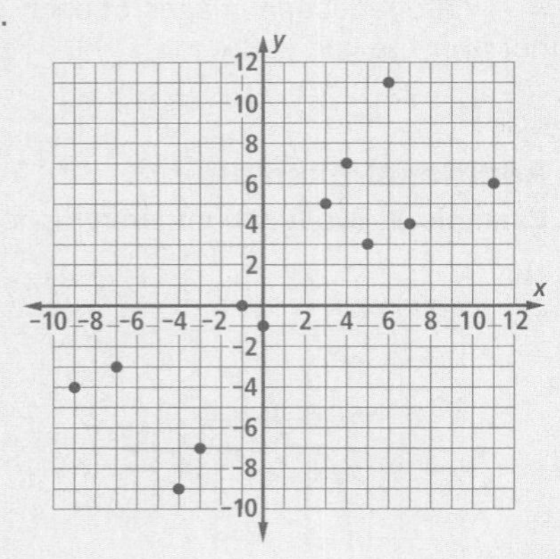

Questions

COVERING THE IDEAS

1. How can the inverse of a relation be found from the coordinates of the points in the relation? by switching the coordinates of the points in the relation

2. Refer to the functions relating distance and speed at the beginning of the lesson.
   a. At what distance away from us is a galaxy moving at roughly 5000 km/sec? about 71.43 Mpc
   b. The photograph at the right shows the disk galaxy NGC 5866 as it appears from Earth, edge-on. NGC 5866 is about 44 million light years, or 13.5 megaparsecs, from the Milky Way. How fast is NGC 5866 receding? about 945 km/sec

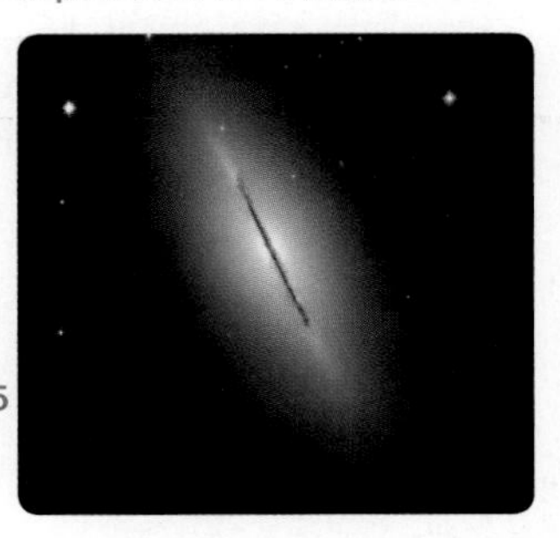

This photograph was taken by the Hubble Space Telescope (named in the astronomer's honor) in June, 2006.

In 3 and 4, let $f = \{(-4,-9), (-3, -7), (0, -1), (3, 5), (4, 7), (6, 11)\}$.

3. a. Find the inverse of *f*. 3a–b. See margin.
   b. Graph *f* and its inverse on the same set of axes.
   c. How are the two graphs related?
   d. Write an equation for the function *f*. $f(x) = 2x - 1$
   e. Write an equation for the inverse of *f*. $g(x) = \frac{x+1}{2}$

4. Give the elements of each set.
   a. the domain of *f* $\{-4, -3, 0, 3, 4, 6\}$
   b. the range of *f* $\{-9, -7, -1, 5, 7, 11\}$
   c. the domain of the inverse of *f* $\{-9, -7, -1, 5, 7, 11\}$
   d. the range of the inverse of *f* $\{-4, -3, 0, 3, 4, 6\}$

5. Explain how the graphs of any relation *f*, its inverse, and the line with equation $y = x$ are related.

In 6 and 7, give an equation for the inverse of the relation.

6. $y = 3x$ $y = \frac{x}{3}$

7. $y = \frac{1}{5}x - 2$ $y = 5x + 10$

8. Refer to Example 2.
   a. Write an equation for the inverse of $y = x^2$. $x = y^2$
   b. Find two points other than those mentioned in the lesson that show the inverse is not a function.

9. The graph of function *q* is given at the right. Explain if there is a way to tell in advance whether the inverse of *q* is a function.
   The inverse of *q* is not a function because the graph of *q* does not pass the horizontal-line test.

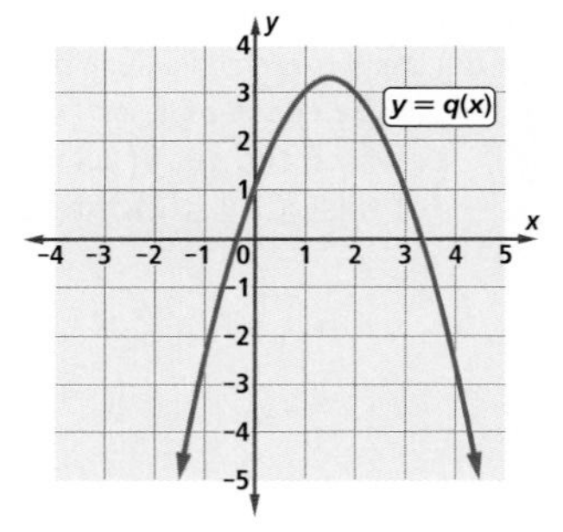

3c. The graph of the inverse is the graph of *f* reflected over the line with equation $y = x$.

5. The graph of the inverse of any relation *f* is the reflection of the graph of *f* over the line with equation $y = x$.

8b. Answers vary. Sample: (4, 2) and (4, -2)

Extension

Ask students to explore the inverse of the composite of two functions. If $f(x) = ax + b$, $g(x) = px + q$, and $h(x) = f \circ g(x)$, what is an equation for the inverse of h? $h(x) = f(g(x)) = f(px + q) = a(px + q) + b = apx + aq + b$. So an equation for the inverse is obtained by solving $x = apy + aq + b$ for y: $y = \frac{x - aq - b}{ap}$.

8-2A Lesson Master

Questions on SPUR Objectives
See Student Edition pages 574–577 for objectives.

SKILLS Objective B

In 1 and 2, give the inverse of the relation.

1. $\{(1, 2), (3, 4), (5, 6)\}$ $\{(2, 1), (4, 3), (6, 5)\}$
2. $\{(14, 2), (7, 7), (2, 14)\}$ $\{(2, 14), (7, 7), (14, 2)\}$

In 3 and 4, give an equation for the inverse of a function.

3. $y = 4.7x^2 - \frac{12}{x}$ $x = 4.7y^2 - \frac{12}{y}$
4. $Ax + By = C$ $Ay + Bx = C$
5. The function $I = 2.54C$ converts lengths from centimeters to inches. Explain what the inverse does.
   The inverse converts lengths from inches to centimeters.

PROPERTIES Objective F

6. Suppose *f* is a function with domain $\{x \mid x \geq -2\}$ and range $\{y \mid 0 \leq y \leq 5\}$. Also suppose *g* is the inverse of *f*. Find the domain and range of *g*.
   a. Domain: $\{x \mid 0 \leq x \leq 5\}$
   b. Range: $\{y \mid y \geq -2\}$
7. Explain why the inverse of the quadratic function $y = ax^2 + bx + c$ is not a function. Answers vary. Sample: The graph of the function $y = ax^2 + bx + c$ is a parabola and does not pass the horizontal line test.

REPRESENTATIONS Objective J

8. If the point (a, v) is on the graph of a function, what point must be on the graph of the inverse? (v, a)

In 9 and 10, graph the function and its inverse on the same axes below each question using two different colors. Determine whether the inverse is a function.

9. $\{(3, 1), (5, -2), (2, 7), (8, 1)\}$
   The inverse is not a function.
10. $y = x^3 - 3$
   The inverse is a function.

Advanced Algebra 465

In 10–12, is the inverse of the graphed function a function? Explain.

10.

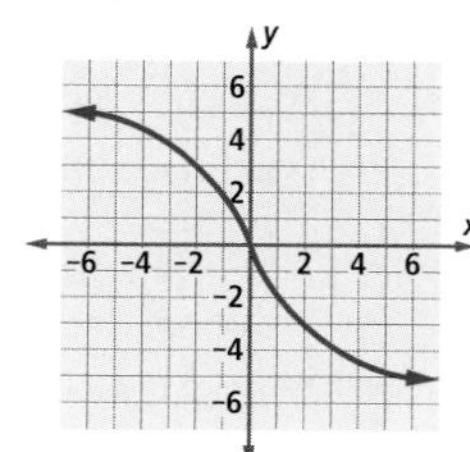

11.

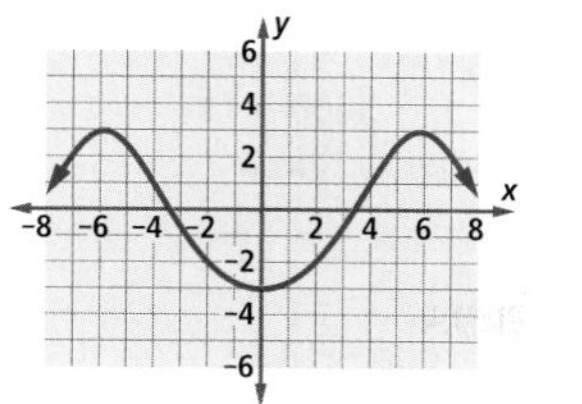

12.

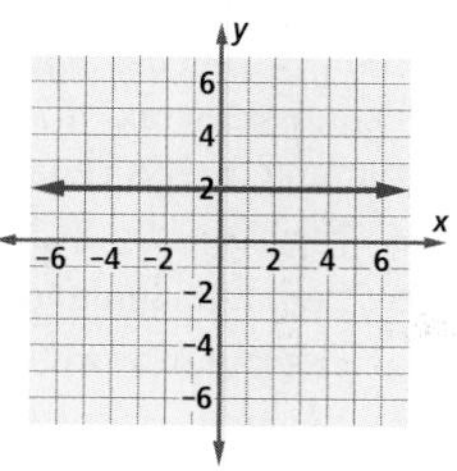

APPLYING THE MATHEMATICS

13. Describe the inverse of the doubling function $D: x \rightarrow 2x$. $H: x \rightarrow \frac{x}{2}$

14. Consider the function f with equation $f(x) = -3$.
 a. Give 5 ordered pairs in f.
 b. Find 5 ordered pairs in the inverse of f.
 c. Draw graphs of f and its inverse on the same set of axes.
 d. What transformation maps the graph of f onto the graph of its inverse?

15. a. Draw the graph of $y = 3x + 7$. 15a, c–e. See margin.
 b. Find an equation for its inverse and solve it for y. $y = \frac{x-7}{3}$
 c. Graph the inverse on the same set of axes.
 d. Is the inverse a function? Explain your answer.
 e. How are the slopes of the graphs of the function and its inverse related?

16. a. Graph the inverse of the absolute-value function $y = |x|$.
 b. Is the inverse a function? Explain why or why not.
 16a–b. See margin.

17. In 2008, one U.S. dollar ($) was worth about 0.64 euros (€). An item costing $1 cost €0.64. Let U be the cost of an item in U.S. dollars and let E be the cost of an item in euros.
 a. Write an equation for U in terms of E. $U = \frac{25}{16}E$
 b. Write an equation for E in terms of U. $E = 0.64U$
 c. Are the two functions you found in Parts a and b inverses of each other? Explain your answer.

10. Yes; the graph of the function passes the horizontal-line test.

11. No; the graph of the function does not pass the horizontal-line test.

12. No; the graph of the function does not pass the horizontal-line test.

14a. Answers vary. Sample: (1, –3), (2, –3), (3, –3), (4, –3), (5, –3)

14b. Answers vary. Sample: (–3, 1), (–3, 2), (–3, 3), (–3, 4), (–3, 5)

14c. See margin.

14d. reflection over the line with equation $y = x$

17c. Yes; the points in the first function are of the form (price in euros, price in dollars), and the points in the second function are of the form (price in dollars, price in euros).

Notes on the Questions

Question 15 Discussing this question carefully will cover many of the topics of the lesson.

Question 17 This is a difficult question for many students. There are only two reasonable answers ($U = 0.64E$ and $E = 0.64U$), so if half your class gets the problem right, it is possible that everyone guessed!

Additional Answers

14c. Answers vary. Sample:

15a,c.

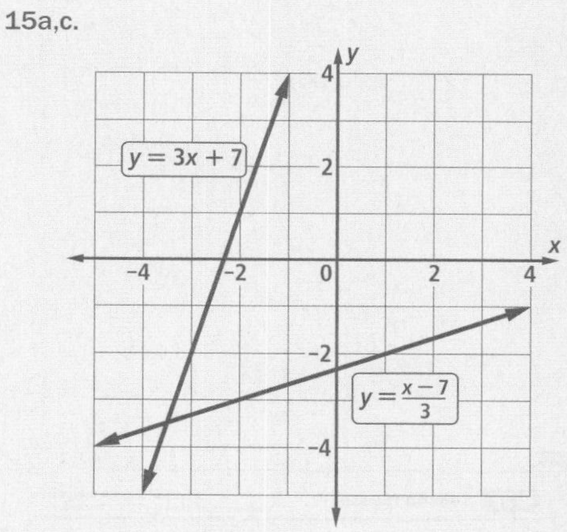

15d. Yes; the graph of the inverse satisfies the vertical-line test.

15e. The slope of the inverse function is the reciprocal of the slope of the function.

Additional Answers

16a.

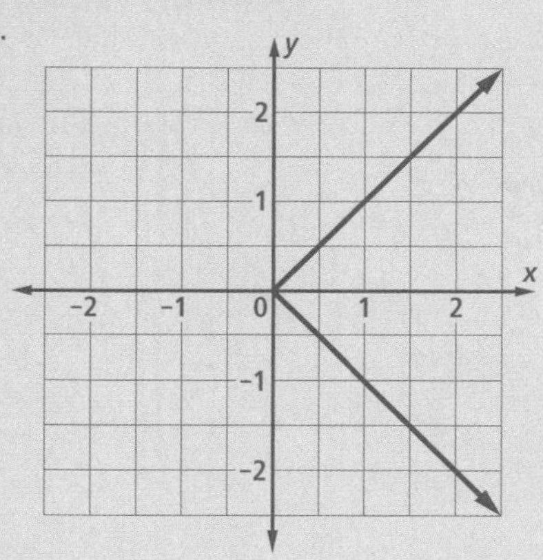

16b. No; Answers vary. Sample: the graph of the inverse function contains the points (1, 1) and (1, –1), which have the same first coordinate.

Notes on the Questions

Question 19 It is very important to discuss this question; it foreshadows the Inverse Functions Theorem in Lesson 8-3. The function in Parts c and d (the identity function) is also a direct-variation function with constant of variation 1 and a power function.

4 Wrap-Up

Ongoing Assessment

Show students the following four sets of ordered pairs and ask them to match each set with its inverse.

1. {(4, 7), (5, -4), (3, 1), (2, -1)}
2. {(4, -7), (5, 4), (3, -1), (2, 1)}
3. {(4, 5), (-7, 4), (1, 2), (-1, 3)}
4. {(-4, 5), (1, 3), (-1, 2), (7, 4)}

1 and 4; 2 and 3

8-2B page 2

11.

8-2B Lesson Master

Questions on SPUR Objectives
See Student Edition pages 574–577 for objectives.

VOCABULARY

1. What is the *inverse of a relation*?
   Answers vary. Sample: The relation obtained by switching the coordinates of each ordered pair in the relation.

12.

SKILLS Objective B

13.

2. The function $M = \frac{F}{5280}$ converts lengths from feet to miles. Write the inverse function and explain what the inverse does.
   $F = 5280M$; The inverse converts lengths from miles to feet.
3. The function $P = 0.0625O$ converts weights from ounces to pounds. Write the inverse function and explain what the inverse does.
   $O = 16P$; The inverse converts weights from pounds to ounces.

In 4–9, a function is defined. a. Write the inverse of the function. b. Tell if the inverse is a function.

14.

4. $f(x) = \{(2, 8), (6, -1), (-4, 4), (0, -1)\}$
   a. {(8, 2), (-1, 6), (4, -4), (-1, 0)}
   b. no
5. $y = 5x$
   a. $y = \frac{1}{5}x$
   b. yes
6. $y = 9x - 2$
   a. $y = \frac{x + 2}{9}$
   b. yes
7. $y = x^2 + 5x + 4$
   a. $y = \frac{-5 + \sqrt{4x + 9}}{2}$ or $y = \frac{-5 - \sqrt{4x + 9}}{2}$
   b. no

15.

8. $y = |x| + 1$
   a. $y = x - 1$ or $y = -x + 1$
   b. no
9. $y = -x^3$
   a. $y = -x^{\frac{1}{3}}$
   b. yes

PROPERTIES Objective F

10. **Fill in the Blank** According to the horizontal-line test for inverses, if no horizontal line intersects the graph of a function f in more than one point, then the inverse of f is a function.

466 *Advanced Algebra*

REVIEW

18. Let c = the cost of a new car. Then $t(c) = 1.07c$ is the cost after a state sales tax of 7%, and $r(c) = c - 3000$ is the cost after a manufacturer's rebate of \$3000. **(Lesson 8-1)**
    a. Evaluate $t(r(29{,}350))$. \$28,194.50
    b. Find a formula for $t(r(c))$. $t(r(c)) = 1.07c - 3210$
    c. Explain in words what $t(r(c))$ represents.
    d. Evaluate $r(t(29{,}350))$. \$28,404.50
    e. Find a formula for $r(t(c))$. $r(t(c)) = 1.07c - 3000$
    f. Explain in words what $r(t(c))$ represents.
    g. If you were the State Treasurer, which would you prefer, $t(r(c))$ or $r(t(c))$, and why?

19. Let $f(x) = 5x - 7$, $g(x) = \frac{1}{5}(x + 12)$, and $h(x) = \frac{1}{5}(x + 7)$. **(Lesson 8-1)**
    a. Find $f \circ g(3)$. 8
    b. Find $g \circ f(3)$. 4
    c. Find $f \circ h(x)$. x
    d. What is another name for the function $f \circ h$? the identity function

20. Given $r(x) = 2x^2 - 1$ and $s(x) = x^2 + 3$, find $r \circ s(x)$. **(Lesson 8-1)**

21. **True or False** For all real numbers x, $|-3x| = 3x$. Justify your answer. **(Lesson 6-2)** False; $|-3(-1)| = 3$, but $3(-1) = -3$.

22. **True or False** Two matrices A and B are inverses if $AB = \begin{bmatrix} 1 & 0 \\ 0 & 1 \end{bmatrix}$. Explain why or why not. **(Lesson 5-5)**

23. In this figure, $\triangle ADB \sim \triangle AEC$. If $DE = 12$, find BC and CE. **(Previous Course)** $BC = 9$; $CE = 8$

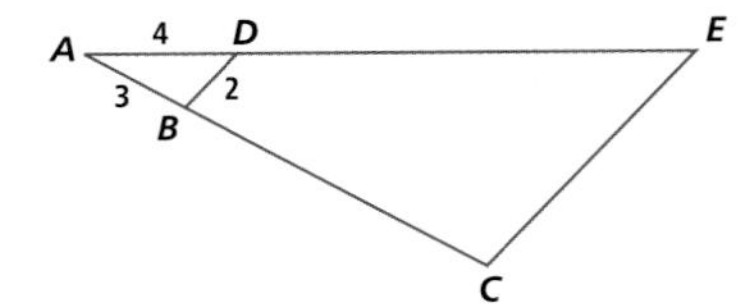

18c. $t(r(c))$ represents the price of a car if the state sales tax is calculated after the manufacturer's rebate is applied.

18f. $r(t(c))$ represents the price of a car if the state sales tax is calculated before the manufacturer's rebate is applied.

18g. The State Treasurer would prefer $r(t(c))$ because the tax is applied to a greater number than in $t(r(c))$.

20. $r \circ s(x) = 2x^4 + 12x^2 + 17$

22. False; Answers vary. Sample: If $A = \begin{bmatrix} 1 & 0 & 1 \\ 0 & 1 & 0 \end{bmatrix}$ and $B = \begin{bmatrix} 1 & 0 \\ 0 & 1 \\ 0 & 0 \end{bmatrix}$, then $AB = \begin{bmatrix} 1 & 0 \\ 0 & 1 \end{bmatrix}$, but A and B are not inverses because $BA = \begin{bmatrix} 1 & 0 & 1 \\ 0 & 1 & 0 \\ 0 & 0 & 0 \end{bmatrix}$.

EXPLORATION

24. Some functions are their own inverses. One such function has the equation $y = \frac{1}{x}$. 24a. Answers vary. Sample: the function with equation $y = -x$
    a. Find at least one more function that is its own inverse.
    b. Graph $y = \frac{1}{x}$ and your answer(s) to Part a. What property do the graphs share? See margin.

Additional Answers

24b. Answers vary. Sample:

$y = -x$

$y = \frac{1}{x}$

Both graphs are symmetric to the line $y = x$.

Lesson 8-3 Properties of Inverse Functions

Vocabulary

inverse function, f^{-1}

▶ **BIG IDEA** When a function has an inverse, the composite of the function and its inverse in either order is the identity function.

Using an Inverse Function to Decode a Message

In Chapter 5, you used matrices to code and decode messages. You can use functions to do this too. For instance, suppose you and your friend have agreed on a key that pairs numbers with the letters they stand for and an encoding function $f(x) = 3x + 11$. This means that your friend began with a number code for a letter (the input), multiplied that number by 3, and then added 11 to get the output. For example, if $A = 65$ it is encoded as $3 \cdot 65 + 11 = 206$. Suppose your friend now sends you this coded message:

212 248 215 218 260 107 206 257 218 107 212 248 248 239

To decode the message, you "undo" your friend's coding; subtract 11 and divide the result by 3 to get the original input: $\frac{206 - 11}{3} = 65$. This "undoing" function is the **inverse function** of f. In Question 13, you will use this inverse function to decode the above message.

Mental Math

Give an equation for the graph of the parabola $y = -2x^2$ under the given translation.

a. $T_{1,3}$

b. $T_{-2,-2}$

c. $T_{0.3,5.4}$

a. $y - 3 = -2(x - 1)^2$

b. $y + 2 = -2(x + 2)^2$

c. $y - 5.4 = -2(x - 0.3)^2$

Formulas for Inverses Using $f(x)$ Notation

There are many ways to obtain a formula for the decoding (inverse) function described above. Here is one way.

Start with the original function equation.	$f(x) = 3x + 11$
Replace $f(x)$ with y.	$y = 3x + 11$
Use the Inverse-Relation Theorem and switch x and y in the equation for f. This represents the decoding function in which y is the input from your friend and x is the output.	$x = 3y + 11$
Solve for y. For a given output x from your friend's encoding function, you can use this function to calculate the original input y.	$y = \frac{x - 11}{3}$
Substitute $g(x)$ for y. This describes the inverse, g.	$g(x) = \frac{x - 11}{3}$

Background

Using an inverse function to decode a message When decoding messages with functions, the list or spreadsheet application on a graphing calculator or a CAS is useful. In one list or column, enter all the numbers from the coded message. In the next list, enter the inverse function as a formula in terms of the first list or column. For example, if the coded message is in L1, then enter "L2 = (L1 − 11)/3" at the top or bottom (depending on the model of your calculator) of L2, where $f^{-1}(x) = (x - 11)/3$ is an equation for the inverse function. This method will give a decoded list of all the numbers.

Notation for inverse functions We could have used the symbol f^{-1} for the inverse of any function. But only when the inverse is a function can we use the symbol $f^{-1}(x)$; otherwise that symbol would be ambiguous. So we restrict the use of f^{-1} to situations in which both f and its inverse are functions.

(continued on next page)

Lesson 8-3

GOAL

Examine situations in which the inverse of a function is also a function. Use the Inverse Functions Theorem to determine if two functions are inverses.

SPUR Objectives

B Find the inverse of a function.

F Apply properties of the inverse of a function.

J Make and interpret graphs of inverses of relations and functions.

Materials/Resources

- Lesson Masters 8-3A and 8-3B
- Resource Masters 140 and 141
- Quiz 1
- CAS

HOMEWORK

Suggestions for Assignment

- Questions 1–25
- Question 26 (extra credit)
- Reading Lesson 8-4
- Covering the Ideas 8-4

Local Standards

1 Warm-Up

In 1–4, what is the inverse of each object under the given operation?

1. multiplicative inverse of -7 $-\frac{1}{7}$

2. additive inverse of 0.625 -0.625

3. multiplicative inverse of

$\begin{bmatrix} 3 & 5 \\ -2 & -4 \end{bmatrix}$ $\begin{bmatrix} 2 & 2.5 \\ -1 & -1.5 \end{bmatrix}$

4. inverse under composition of the translation $T_{3,4}$ $T_{-3,-4}$

2 Teaching

Notes on the Lesson

Other than the Inverse Functions Theorem, there is very little new material in this lesson. However, because of the heavy use of symbols on page 529, you may want to spend part of the class period reading and discussing that page. Point out that the Inverse Functions Theorem provides an *algebraic test* for determining if two functions are inverses. A *geometric test* that f and g are inverse functions is that one of them passes the horizontal-line test and they are reflection images of each other over the line $y = x$.

Question 19 from the previous lesson, in which students show that $f \circ h(x) = x$, is a good lead-in to this lesson. Now have students graph $y = f(x)$ and $y = h(x)$ on the same axes. They will observe that the graphs of f and h are reflection images of each other over the line $y = x$. This confirms that f and h are inverses of each other.

Composites of a Function and Its Inverse

Activity 1

MATERIALS CAS

Work with a partner to complete the following steps. One of you should work with $f(x) = 12x - 4$, the other with $f(x) = \frac{1}{3} + \frac{x}{12}$.

Step 1 Using the method described on the previous page, find the inverse of your function. Call your inverse g and write a formula for it. $g(x) = 12x - 4$; $g(x) = \frac{1}{3} + \frac{x}{12}$

Step 2 On your CAS, define your functions f and g. Evaluate $f(g(x))$ and $g(f(x))$. $f(g(x)) = x$; -4; $g(f(x)) = x$

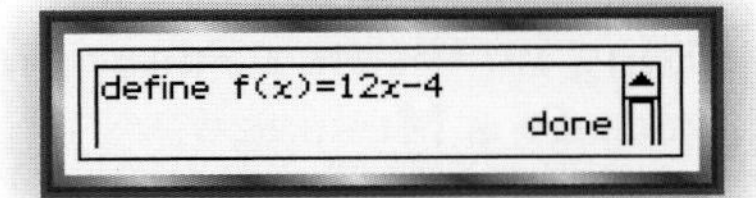

Step 3 Compare your results with those of your partner. The results are the same.

Your results for $f(g(x))$ and $g(f(x))$ in Activity 1 hold for any functions f and g that are inverses. The converse is also true. Both are summarized in the following theorem.

Inverse Functions Theorem

Two functions f and g are inverse functions if and only if:

(1) For all x in the domain of f, $g(f(x)) = x$, and

(2) for all x in the domain of g, $f(g(x)) = x$.

Proof We must prove a statement and its converse. So the proof has two parts.

(I) *The "only if" part:* Suppose f and g are inverse functions. Let (a, b) be any ordered pair in the function f. Then $f(a) = b$. By the definition of inverse, the ordered pairs in g are the reverse of those in f, so (b, a) is an ordered pair in the function g. Thus $g(b) = a$. Now take the composites.

For any number a in the domain of f: $g(f(a)) = g(b) = a$.

For any number b in the domain of g: $f(g(b)) = f(a) = b$.

(II) *The "if" part:* Suppose (1) and (2) in the statement of the theorem are true. Again let (a, b) be any point on the function f. Then $f(a) = b$, and so $g(f(a)) = g(b)$. But using (1), $g(f(a)) = a$, so, by transitivity, $g(b) = a$. This means that (b, a) is in the function g. So g contains all the points obtained by reversing the coordinates in f.

By the same reasoning we can show that f contains all points obtained by reversing the coordinates of g. Thus, f and g are inverse functions.

STOP QY1

QY1

If $f(x) = 2x + 6$ and $g(x) = \frac{1}{2}x - 6$, are f and g inverses of each other?

Multiplication and division are sometimes called "inverse operations." Technically, they are not; the actual inverses are "multiplying by k" and "dividing by k." These are the descriptions of the actions of the functions with equations $y = kx$ and $y = \frac{x}{k}$. Similarly "adding k" and "subtracting k" describe the inverse functions with equations $y = x + k$ and $y = x - k$. Squaring and taking the square root are inverse functions only if the domain is restricted, as the Power Function Inverse Theorem shows.

Inverse functions and the identity function I are related in analogous ways to inverses and the identity for other operations. Here is an example:

Addition	Functions
0 is the additive identity element ($a + 0 = 0 + a = a$).	I is the identity function ($f \circ I = I \circ f = f$).
a and b are additive inverses if and only if $a + b = b + a = 0$, the additive identity element.	f and g are inverses if and only if $f \circ g = g \circ f = I$, the identity function.

Notation for Inverse Functions

Recall that an *identity function* is a function that maps each object in its domain onto itself. Another way of stating the Inverse Functions Theorem is to say that the composite of two functions that are inverses of each other is the identity function I with equation $I(x) = x$.

When an operation on two elements of a set yields an identity element for that operation, then we call the elements *inverses*. For example, 2 and $\frac{1}{2}$ are multiplicative inverses because $2 \cdot \frac{1}{2} = 1$, the identity element for multiplication. This is the reason that we call g the inverse of f, and f the inverse of g: $f(g(x)) = g(f(x)) = I(x)$, the identity function.

The multiplicative inverse of a number x is designated by x^{-1}. Similarly, when a function f has an inverse, we designate the **inverse function** by the symbol $\mathbf{f^{-1}}$, read "f inverse." For instance, for the functions in Activity 1 you showed that for all x, $f(f^{-1}(x)) = f^{-1}(f(x)) = x$, which is read "$f$ of f inverse of x equals f inverse of f of x equals x."

GUIDED

Example

Let $h : x \rightarrow \frac{8(x-2)+5}{3}$. Find a rule for h^{-1}.

Solution Use a process like that shown for the function f at the beginning of the lesson. From the given information,

$$h(x) = \frac{8(x-2)+5}{3}.$$

Simplify. $= \frac{? - ?}{3}$ 8x; 11

Substitute y for $h(x)$.

$y =$ ___?___ $\frac{8x-11}{3}$

An equation for the inverse is found by switching x and y.

$x =$ ___?___ $\frac{8y-11}{3}$

Solve this equation for y.

$3x =$ ___?___ $-$ ___?___ 8y; 11

$3x +$ ___?___ $=$ ___?___ 11; 8y

$y =$ ___?___ $\frac{3x+11}{8}$

So $h^{-1}(x) =$ ___?___. $\frac{3x+11}{8}$

STOP QY2

▶ **QY2**

"Halving" is an inverse for the "doubling" function. What is an inverse for the squaring function?

Additional Example

Example Let $h : x \rightarrow \frac{4(x+7)-3}{2}$. Find a rule for h^{-1}.

Solution $h(x) = \frac{4(x+7)-3}{2} = \frac{? + ?}{2}$ 4x; 25 Substitute y for $h(x)$: $y =$ ___?___. $\frac{4x+25}{2}$ Switching x and y, an equation for the inverse h^{-1} is $x =$ ___?___. $\frac{4y+25}{2}$ Solve this equation for y: $2x =$ ___?___ $+$ ___?___ and $2x -$ ___?___ $=$ ___?___; $y =$ ___?___. 4y; 25; 25; 4y; $\frac{1}{2}x - \frac{25}{4}$

So $h^{-1}(x) =$ ___?___. $\frac{1}{2}x - \frac{25}{4}$.

Accommodating the Learner

Ask students to explain how they can use inverse functions to calculate the area of a circle if they know its circumference. Answers vary. Sample: For a circle with circumference C and radius r, $C = 2\pi r$. The inverse of the function represented by this equation would give the radius for a given circumference. Solve the original equation for r to find an equation for the inverse: $r = \frac{C}{2\pi}$. Then substitute this expression for r into the function with equation $A = \pi r^2$ to get $A = \pi\left(\frac{C}{2\pi}\right)^2 = \frac{C^2}{4\pi}$. Thus, to find the area of a circle from its circumference, square the circumference and divide the result by 4π.

Notes on the Lesson

Power Function Inverse Theorem We expect students to be able to determine whether two functions are inverses, given their equations. So plan to discuss the steps in the proof of this theorem.

Note-Taking Tips

Encourage students to enter in their notes how the symbol "-1" has different meanings in different contexts. For example, on a number line, it is a location. As an exponent, it refers to a reciprocal (or multiplicative inverse): $5^{-1} = \frac{1}{5}$; $x^{-1} = \frac{1}{x}$. Used with a matrix or a function, it refers to an inverse: M^{-1} is the inverse of matrix M; f^{-1} is the inverse of the function f.

In earlier lessons, you worked with the functions with equations $y = x^n$, "taking the nth power," and $y = x^{\frac{1}{n}}$, "taking the nth root." For all $x \geq 0$, it is reasonably easy to show that these functions are inverse functions.

Power Function Inverse Theorem

If $f(x) = x^n$ and $g(x) = x^{\frac{1}{n}}$ and the domains of f and g are the set of *nonnegative* real numbers, then f and g are inverse functions.

Proof First, show that $f \circ g(x) = x$ for all x in the domain of g.

Substitute. $f \circ g(x) = f\left(x^{\frac{1}{n}}\right)$ Definition of g

Because x is a nonnegative number, $x^{\frac{1}{n}}$ is always defined and you can apply f.

$= \left(x^{\frac{1}{n}}\right)^n$ Definition of f

$= x^1 = x$ Power of a Power Postulate

Now you need to show that $g \circ f(x) = x$ for all x in the domain of f. You are asked to do this in Question 12.

An instance of the Power Function Inverse Theorem is illustrated by the graphs of $f(x) = x^6$ and $f^{-1}(x) = x^{\frac{1}{6}}$ at the left below. The graphs are reflection images of each other over the line with equation $y = x$. Notice also that the domain of these functions is the set of nonnegative real numbers.

The function $h(x) = x^6$ with domain the set of *all* real numbers is graphed at the right below. Its inverse is not a function. Notice that the graph of h does not pass the horizontal-line test.

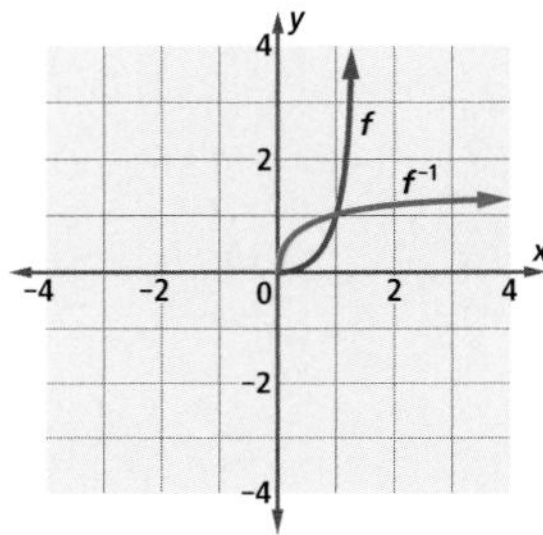

$f(x) = x^6$
Domain of f:
set of nonnegative real numbers
$f^{-1}(x) = x^{\frac{1}{6}}$
Domain of f^{-1}:
set of nonnegative real numbers

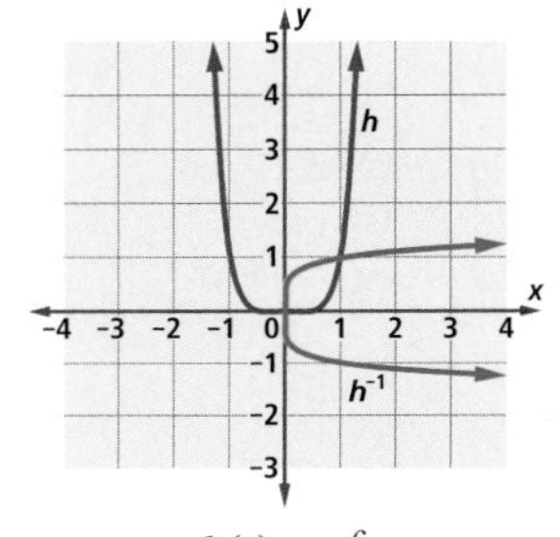

$h(x) = x^6$
Domain of h:
set of real numbers

The inverse of h is not a function.

Accommodating the Learner

Ask students to find a rule for g, the inverse of f, if $f(x) = 4x - 7$. Then ask them to verify their answer by evaluating $f \circ g(x)$ and $g \circ f(x)$. $g(x) = \frac{x + 7}{4}$; $f \circ g(x) = f(g(x)) = f\left(\frac{x+7}{4}\right) = 4\left(\frac{x+7}{4}\right) - 7 = (x + 7) - 7 = x$; $g \circ f(x) = g(f(x)) = g(4x - 7) = \frac{(4x - 7) + 7}{4} = \frac{4x}{4} = x$.

ENGLISH LEARNERS

Vocabulary Development

Many students do not completely understand the meaning of "only if" in the phrase *if and only if.* Explain that, for the Inverse Functions Theorem, the "if" statement is "if the two statements about the domain and range are true, then f and g are inverse functions." The converse of that statement is the "only if" part: "If f and g are inverse functions, then the two statements about the domain and range are true."

A CAS can help you find equations for inverse relations and to limit domains of functions so that their inverses are also functions.

Activity 2

MATERIALS CAS

Use a CAS to find an equation for the inverse of $y = f(x) = x^6$.

Step 1 Clear all variables in a CAS. Define $f(x) = x^6$.

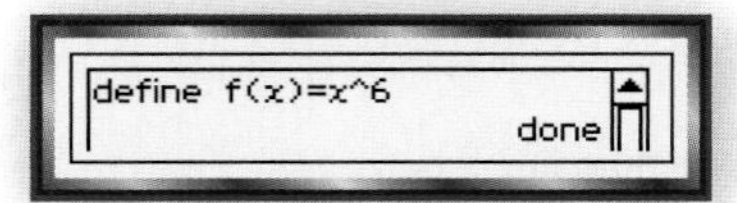

Step 2 Switch x and y and solve $x = f(y)$ for y. See margin.

Step 3 Your display should show an equation for the inverse of f. Is this inverse a function? If not, on what domain of f is f^{-1} a function?
f^{-1} is a function if the domain of f is $x \geq 0$, or the domain of f is $x \leq 0$.

Questions

COVERING THE IDEAS

1. Suppose f is a function. What does the symbol f^{-1} represent, and how is it read? the inverse of f; f inverse
2. Refer to Activity 1. Show that $f(g(2)) = g(f(2))$.
3. Let $f(x) = 5 - 2x$ and $g(x) = \frac{x-5}{-2}$. Are f and g inverses of each other? Justify your answer.
4. The function $h : x \to 5x + 7$ has an inverse h^{-1} which is a function.
   a. Find a formula for $h^{-1}(x)$. $h^{-1}(x) = \frac{x-7}{5}$
   b. Check your answer to Part a by finding $h \circ h^{-1}(x)$ and $h^{-1} \circ h(x)$.
5. Consider the "adding 15" function. Call it A.
   a. What is a formula for $A(x)$? $A(x) = x + 15$
   b. Give a formula for $A^{-1}(x)$. $A^{-1}(x) = x - 15$
   c. What is an appropriate name for A^{-1}? subtracting 15
   d. What is $A^{-1} \circ A(63)$? 63

In 6 and 7, an equation for a function f is given. The domain of f is the set of real numbers. Is the inverse of f a function? If it is, find a rule for f^{-1}. If not, explain why not.

6. $f(x) = 21x$ Yes; $f^{-1}(x) = \frac{x}{21}$
7. $f(x) = 21$

2. $f(g(2)) = f\left(\frac{1}{3} + \frac{2}{12}\right) = f\left(\frac{1}{2}\right) = 12\left(\frac{1}{2}\right) - 4 = 6 - 4 = 2;$
$g(f(2)) = g(12(2) - 4) = g(20) = \frac{1}{3} + \frac{20}{12} = 2$

3. Yes; $f(g(x)) = 5 - 2\left(\frac{x-5}{-2}\right) = 5 + x - 5 = x;$
$g(f(x)) = \frac{(5-2x)-5}{-2} = \frac{-2x}{-2} = x$

4b. $h \circ h^{-1}(x) = x$ and $h^{-1} \circ h(x) = x$

7. No; an equation for the inverse would be $x = 21$, which does not represent a function.

3 Assignment

Recommended Assignment

- Questions 1–25
- Question 26 (extra credit)
- Reading Lesson 8-4
- Covering the Ideas 8-4

Extension

Ask students to look up the formula for the sum of the first n positive integers. $S = \frac{n(n+1)}{2}$ Then ask students to express and explain the inverse of the function represented by that formula.
$n = \frac{-1 + \sqrt{1 + 8S}}{2}$; if S is the sum of the first n positive integers, then this function lets you calculate the value of n.

8-3A Lesson Master

Questions on SPUR Objectives
See Student Edition pages 574–577 for objectives.

SKILLS Objective B

In 1–3, find an equation for f^{-1}.

1. $f(x) = 3 - 5x$ $f^{-1}(x) = \frac{3-x}{5}$
2. $f(x) = mx + b$ $f^{-1}(x) = \frac{x-b}{m}$
3. $f(x) = x^{\frac{5}{7}}, x \geq 0$ $f^{-1}(x) = x^{\frac{7}{5}}$

PROPERTIES Objective F

4. **Fill in the Blank** If $f(21.6) = 3.71$, then $f^{-1}(3.71) =$ 21.6.
5. **Fill in the Blank** If a function b has an inverse b^{-1}, then $b(b^{-1}(n)) =$ n.
6. Let $g(x) = \frac{7}{3}x + 5$ and $h(x) = \frac{3}{7}x - 5$.
   a. $g(h(x)) =$ $x - \frac{20}{3}$
   b. $h(g(x)) =$ $x - \frac{20}{7}$
   c. Are g and h inverses? Explain.
   No; Explanations vary. Sample: Neither $g(h(x))$ nor $h(g(x))$ is equal to x.

REPRESENTATIONS Objective J

In 7 and 8, a function is graphed below each question. Write a restriction of the domain so that the inverse is also a function. Then draw the inverse on the same graph.

7. $f(x) = (x-2)^2 - 3$ Answers vary. Sample: $x \geq 2$
8. $g(x) = \frac{x^4}{4}$ Answers vary. Sample: $x \geq 0$

468 Advanced Algebra

Notes on the Questions

Question 11b There are infinitely many ways of restricting the domain of this function so that its inverse is a function.

8. **Fill in the Blank** For any function f that has an inverse, if x is in the range of f, then $f \circ f^{-1}(x) = \underline{\ ?\ }$. x

9. If $f(x) = x^7$ with domain the set of nonnegative real numbers, give a formula for $f^{-1}(x)$. $f^{-1}(x) = x^{\frac{1}{7}}$

10. Let $m(x) = \frac{x}{5}$. This function could be named "dividing by 5."
    a. Find an equation for m^{-1}. $m^{-1}(x) = 5x$
    b. Give an appropriate name to m^{-1}. multiplying by 5

11. a. Use a CAS to find an equation for the inverse of $f(x) = -\frac{(x+12)^3}{2}$. $f^{-1}(x) = -12 - (2x)^{\frac{1}{3}}$
    b. Is the inverse of f a function? If so, what is its domain? If not, over what domain of f is the inverse a function? yes; all real numbers

12. Prove the second part of the Power Function Inverse Theorem in this lesson. See margin.

13. Recall the code your friend sent you at the beginning of the lesson. Use the following table to decode the message. A space is represented by 32. CODES ARE COOL

Code	65	66	67	68	69	70	71	72	73	74	75	76	77
Letter	A	B	C	D	E	F	G	H	I	J	K	L	M
Code	78	79	80	81	82	83	84	85	86	87	88	89	90
Letter	N	O	P	Q	R	S	T	U	V	W	X	Y	Z

APPLYING THE MATHEMATICS

14. The function S with $S(n) = (n - 2) \cdot 180°$ maps the number of sides of a convex polygon onto the sum of the measures of its interior angles.
    a. Find a formula for $S^{-1}(n)$. $S^{-1}(n) = \frac{n}{180} + 2$
    b. Use the formula to determine the number of sides of a polygon when the sum of the interior angle measures of the polygon is 3780. 23

15. Let $g(x) = x^{\frac{2}{3}}$ and $h(x) = x^{\frac{3}{2}}$ with $x \geq 0$.
    a. Graph g and h on the same set of axes.
    b. Describe how the graphs are related.
    c. Find $h(g(x))$ and $g(h(x))$. Each is equal to x.
    d. **Fill in the Blank** The answer to Part c means that since $64^{\frac{3}{2}} = 512$, $\underline{\ ?\ }$. $64 = 512^{\frac{2}{3}}$
    e. Are g and h inverses? Why or why not?

15a.

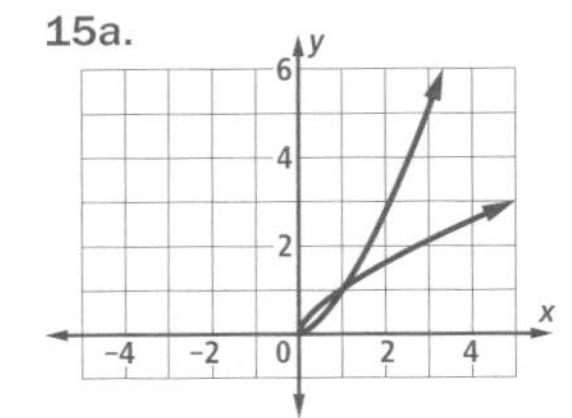

15b. The graph of h is the graph of g reflected over the line with equation $y = x$.

15e. Yes, over the restricted domain $x \geq 0$, they are inverses because the graph of g is the reflection image of the graph of h over the line with equation $y = x$.

Additional Answers

12. $g \circ f(x) = g(x^n)$ Definition of f
$= g(x^n)^{\frac{1}{n}}$ Definition of g
$= x^1 = x$ Power of a Power Postulate

In 16–18, find an equation for the inverse of the function with the given equation in the form $y =$ ___?___.

16. $y = \frac{1}{x}$ $y = \frac{1}{x}$
17. $y = \frac{1}{2}x + 7$
18. $y = x^3 - 2$

17. $y = 2x - 14$
18. $y = (x + 2)^{\frac{1}{3}}$

19. If f is any function that has an inverse, what is $(f^{-1})^{-1}$? Explain your answer in your own words. See margin.

20. a. Explain why the inverse of $g(x) = x^2$ is not a function when the domain of g is the set of all real numbers. 20a–b. See margin.
    b. Split the graph of $g(x) = x^2$ along its line of symmetry. For each half,
       i. State the domain and the corresponding range.
       ii. Give a formula for the inverse of that half.

21. **Multiple Choice** Consider the absolute-value function $y = |x| - 1$ graphed below. Which of the following domains gives a function whose inverse is also a function? B

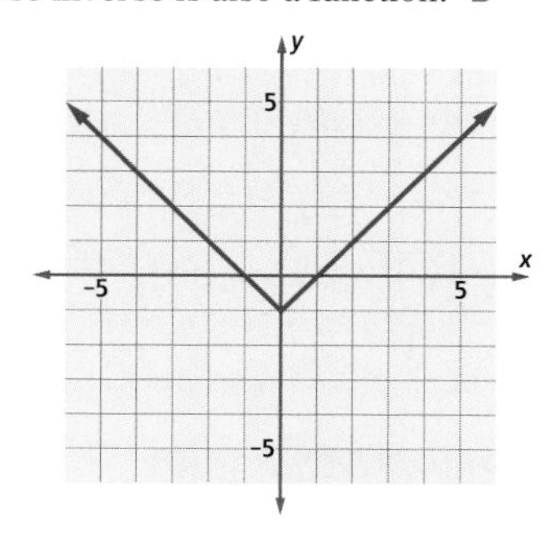

A $\{x \mid -2 \le x \le 5\}$ B $\{x \mid x \ge 1\}$ C $\{x \mid x \ge -4.5\}$

REVIEW

22. Sandy makes \$32,000 per year plus \$24 per hour for each hour over 2000 hours that she works per year. An equation for her total income $I(h)$ when she works h hours is $I(h) = 32{,}000 + 24(h - 2000)$, for $h > 2000$. (Lesson 8-2)
    a. Find a rule for the inverse of I. $I^{-1}(h) = \frac{h + 16{,}000}{24}$
    b. What does the inverse represent? the number of hours she worked given her salary

23. **Fill in the Blanks** Suppose $f: x \rightarrow 2x + 5$ and $g: x \rightarrow x^{-2}$. (Lessons 8-2, 8-1)
    a. $f \circ g(-2) =$ ___?___ $\frac{11}{2}$
    b. $g \circ f(-2) =$ ___?___ 1
    c. $f(g(x)) =$ ___?___ $2x^{-2} + 5$
    d. $g(f(x)) =$ ___?___ $(2x + 5)^{-2}$

Notes on the Questions

Question 19 This question provides an opportunity to stress that the inverse of the inverse of a function is the function itself. Point out that this is a general property of inverses. For instance, the opposite of the opposite of a number n is n itself; the reciprocal of the reciprocal of a number m is m itself.

Question 22 This question is important for showing the practical significance of the inverse as reversing the independent and dependent variables in a situation.

Additional Answers

19. f; the inverse of the inverse of a function is the original function.

20a. Numbers have two square roots. For instance, $(-3)^2$ and 3^2 both equal 9, so the inverse function would give values of -3 and 3 for an input of 9.

20b. i. For $x > 0$, the domain is $x > 0$, and the range is all positive numbers. For $x < 0$, the domain is $x < 0$, and the range is all positive numbers.

20b. ii. For $x > 0$, $g^{-1}(x) = \sqrt{x}$; for $x < 0$, $g^{-1}(x) = -\sqrt{x}$.

4 Wrap-Up

Ongoing Assessment

Ask students to explain how to find a specific rule for the inverse of the function with the equation given.

a. $f(x) = 3x - 5$ Write $x = 3y - 5$; add 5 to each side to get $3y = x + 5$; divide each side by 3 to get $y = \frac{x+5}{3}$.

b. $g(x) = \frac{x+7}{15}$ Write $x = \frac{y+7}{15}$; multiply each side by 15 to get $y + 7 = 15x$; subtract 7 from each side to get $y = 15x - 7$.

c. $h(x) = 5x^3$ Write $x = 5y^3$; divide each side by 5 to get $y^3 = \frac{x}{5}$; take the cube root of each side to get $y = \sqrt[3]{\frac{x}{5}}$.

Administer Quiz 1 (or a quiz of your own) after students complete this lesson.

Project Update

Project 2, *Caesar Cipher,* on page 568 relates to the content of this lesson.

8-3B page 2

16. f(
a.
b.
c.
REI
18. C
a.
b.
c.
d.
e.
19. M
fo
a
A
B
C
470

8-3B Lesson Master

Questions on SPUR Objectives
See Student Edition pages 574–577 for objectives.

SKILLS Objective B

In 1–10, write an equation for f^{-1}.

1. $f(x) = 8x$ $f^{-1}(x) = \frac{1}{8}x$
2. $f(x) = x + 9$ $f^{-1}(x) = x - 9$
3. $f(x) = 2x - 7$ $f^{-1}(x) = \frac{1}{2}(x + 7)$
4. $f(x) = -4x + 3$ $f^{-1}(x) = -\frac{1}{4}(x - 3)$
5. $f(x) = \frac{7}{x}$ $f^{-1}(x) = \frac{7}{x}$
6. $f(x) = \frac{x-5}{2}$ $f^{-1}(x) = 2x + 5$
7. $f(x) = -5(x + 10)$ $f^{-1}(x) = -\frac{1}{5}(x + 50)$
8. $f(x) = \frac{1}{2}x^2$, when $x \geq 0$ $f^{-1}(x) = \sqrt{2x}$
9. $f(x) = x^7$, when $x \geq 0$ $f^{-1}(x) = x^{\frac{1}{7}}$
10. $f(x) = x^{\frac{1}{8}}$, when $x \geq 0$ $f^{-1}(x) = x^8$

PROPERTIES Objective F

11. Consider the function f defined by $f(x) = -5x + 12$.
    a. Write a rule for $f^{-1}(x)$. $f^{-1}(x) = -\frac{1}{5}(x - 12)$
    b. Find $f \circ f^{-1}(x)$. x
    c. Find $f^{-1} \circ f(x)$. x
12. **Fill in the Blank** If $f(6) = 78$, then $f^{-1}(78) =$ 6.
13. **Fill in the Blank** If $t^{-1}(0) = 8$, then $t(8) =$ 0.

In 14–17, two functions f and g are defined over the domain $x \geq 0$. a. Find $f(g(x))$. b. Find $g(f(x))$. c. Tell if f and g are inverses and explain why or why not. Explanations vary. Samples are given.

14. $f(x) = x + 4$ and $g(x) = \frac{1}{4}x$
    a. $\frac{1}{4}x + 4$
    b. $\frac{1}{4}(x + 4) = \frac{1}{4}x + 1$
    c. No; $f(g(x)) \neq g(f(x)) \neq x$
15. $f(x) = x^{\frac{4}{7}}$ and $g(x) = x^{\frac{7}{4}}$
    a. x
    b. x
    c. Yes; $f(g(x)) = g(f(x)) = x$

Advanced Algebra 469

24. When a beam of light in air strikes the surface of water it is *refracted*, or bent. Below are the earliest known data (translated into modern units) on the relation between i, the measure of the angle of incidence in degrees, and r, the measure of the angle of refraction in degrees. The measurements are recorded in *Optics* by Ptolemy, a Greek scientist who lived in the second century BCE. (Lessons 6-6, 3-5)

i
water
r

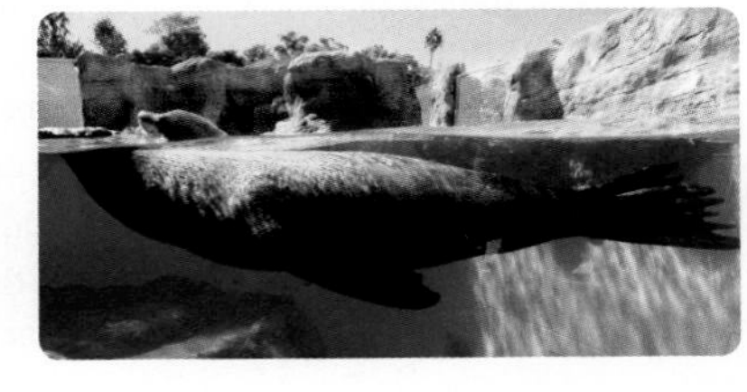

i	10°	20°	30°	40°	50°	60°	70°	80°
r	8°	15.5°	22.5°	29°	35°	40.5°	44.5°	50°

a. Draw a scatterplot of these data. See margin.

b. Fit a quadratic model to these data. $y \approx -0.0026x^2 + 0.824x + 0.054$

c. Fit a linear model to these data. $y \approx 0.594x + 3.89$

d. Which model seems more appropriate? Explain your decision.

25. Line ℓ is parallel to the line with equation $y = \frac{1}{4}x + 7$. (Lesson 3-1)

a. What is the slope of ℓ? $\frac{1}{4}$

b. What numbers are possible y-intercepts of ℓ? all real numbers

24d. Answers vary. Sample: The quadratic model; the data points don't seem to lie on a straight line.

EXPLORATION

26. The *Shoe and Sock Theorem*: Let g be the function with the rule "put your sock on the input." Let f be the function with the rule "put your shoe on the input."

a. Explain in words how to find the output of $f \circ g$ (your foot).

b. What are the rules for g^{-1} and f^{-1}?

c. What is the result of applying $f \circ g$ followed by $(f \circ g)^{-1}$ to your foot? having a bare foot

d. What two steps must be taken to apply $(f \circ g)^{-1}$ to your foot? In what order must the steps be taken?

e. Translate your answer to Part d into symbols: $(f \circ g)^{-1} =$ __?__. $g^{-1} \circ f^{-1}$

f. Now let $f(x) = x^5$ and $g(x) = 7x - 19$. Find formulas for $f^{-1}(x)$ and $g^{-1}(x)$ and use them to find a formula for $(f \circ g)^{-1}(x)$.

$f^{-1}(x) = x^{\frac{1}{5}}$; $g^{-1}(x) = \frac{x + 19}{7}$; $(f \circ g)^{-1}(x) = g^{-1} \circ f^{-1}(x) = \frac{x^{\frac{1}{5}} + 19}{7}$

26a. First put your sock on your foot, then put your shoe on your socked foot.

26b. g^{-1} is "take off your sock," and f^{-1} is "take off your shoe."

26d. Take off your shoe, then take off your sock.

QY ANSWERS

1. No; $f(g(x)) = f\left(\frac{1}{2}x - 6\right) = 2\left(\frac{1}{2}x - 6\right) + 6 = x - 12 + 6 = x - 6 \neq x$
2. the square root function

Additional Answers

24a.

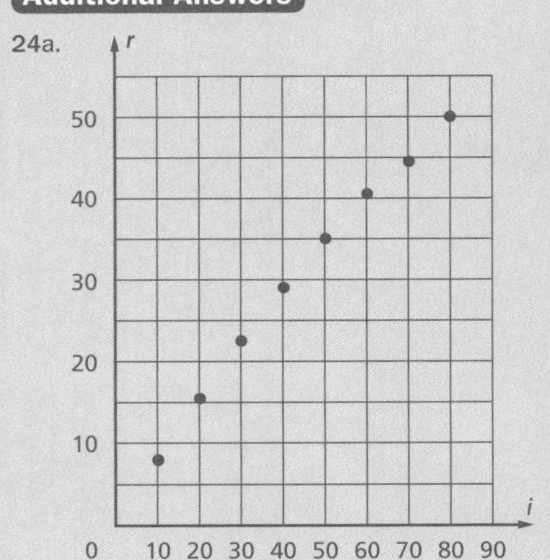

Lesson

8-4 Radical Notation for nth Roots

Vocabulary

radical sign, $\sqrt{}$

$\sqrt[n]{x}$ when $x \geq 0$

geometric mean

▸ **BIG IDEA** For any integer n, the largest real nth root of x can be represented either by $x^{\frac{1}{n}}$ or by $\sqrt[n]{x}$.

As you have learned, the positive nth root of a positive number x can be written as a power of x, namely as $x^{\frac{1}{n}}$. This notation allows all the properties of powers to be used with these nth roots. Another notation, using the **radical sign** $\sqrt{}$, can be used to represent all of the positive nth roots and some other numbers. However, it is more difficult to see the properties of powers with this notation.

Recall that when x is positive, $\sqrt{x}$ stands for the positive square root of x. Because $x^{\frac{1}{2}}$ also stands for this square root when x is positive, $\sqrt{x} = x^{\frac{1}{2}}$. Similarly the nth root of a positive number can be written in two ways.

Definition of $\sqrt[n]{x}$ when $x \geq 0$

When x is nonnegative and n is an integer ≥ 2, then $\sqrt[n]{x} = x^{\frac{1}{n}}$.

Thus, when x is positive, $\sqrt[n]{x}$ is the positive nth root of x. When $n = 2$, we do not write $\sqrt[2]{x}$, but use the more familiar symbol $\sqrt{x}$.

QY1

$\sqrt[n]{x}$ is used to calculate a type of average called a *geometric mean*.

The Geometric Mean

You know several ways to describe a set of values with a single statistic such as an average test score or a median housing price. Such values are called *measures of center,* or *measures of central tendency.*

Suppose a data set has n values. If you add the values and divide by n, you have calculated the *arithmetic mean* of the set. This is commonly called *the average* of the set, but there are other averages. If, instead of adding, you *multiply* the numbers in the set, and instead of dividing you *take the nth root* of the product of the items in the list, you obtain the **geometric mean**.

Mental Math

Vanessa runs an apple orchard. She sells apples for $1.50 per pound, rounded to the nearest half pound.

a. How much does she charge for 3.2 pounds of apples? $4.50

b. How much does she charge for 4.6 pounds of apples? $6.75

c. Suppose one apple weighs about a third of a pound. About how many apples can you buy for $6? 12

d. About how many apples can you buy for $10? 20

▸ **QY1**

Solve for x: $\sqrt[7]{78{,}125} = 78{,}125^x$.

Background

Many students will already be familiar with the cube root symbol $\sqrt[3]{}$. Using the symbol $\sqrt[n]{}$ to denote the nth root is a natural extension.

In some books, the skills explored in Lessons 8-4 through 8-7 are grouped under the designation "simplifying radicals." We use the word *simplify* sparingly because if "simple" is related to the number of operations indicated or the number of keystrokes needed to input an expression, the alternate form that results is often no "simpler" than the original. For example, consider $\sqrt[4]{81x^4y^{11}} = 3|x|(y^2)\sqrt[4]{y^3}$. The expression on the right-hand side is not any simpler than the one on the left-hand side; in fact, it could be considered more complex.

(continued on next page)

Lesson

8-4

GOAL

Begin a two-lesson exploration of rewriting radicals by applying the Root of a Power Theorem (this lesson) and the Root of a Product Theorem (Lesson 8-5); apply all the properties of powers (from Chapter 7) to expressions with nonnegative bases.

SPUR Objectives

C Evaluate radicals.

G Apply properties of radicals and nth root functions.

I Solve real-world problems that can be modeled by equations with radicals.

Materials/Resources

- Lesson Masters 8-4A and 8-4B
- Resource Masters 142–144

HOMEWORK

Suggestions for Assignment

- Questions 1–32
- Question 33 (extra credit)
- Reading Lesson 8-5
- Covering the Ideas 8-5

Local Standards

1 Warm-Up

1. Pick any number between 1 and 100. Enter the number into your calculator and repeatedly press the square root key. Describe what happens. The displayed values get closer and closer to 1 while remaining greater than 1.
2. Repeat Warm-Up 1 with a number between 0 and 1. Describe what happens. The displayed values get closer and closer to 1 while remaining less than 1.
3. Repeat Warm-Up 1 but use the $-\frac{1}{2}$ power. Describe what happens. The displayed values get closer and closer to 1 but alternate being greater than or less than 1.

2 Teaching

Notes on the Lesson

Stress the definition of the radical notation for *n*th roots: $\sqrt[n]{x} = x^{\frac{1}{n}}$. Note that the definition in this lesson is for nonnegative bases only. Thus, we can apply it for any integer value of $n \geq 2$. The *n*th root of a negative number is defined in Lesson 8-7, but then *n* is restricted to an odd integer greater than or equal to 3.

Make sure students know how to use their calculators to find *n*th roots. On some calculators, the $\sqrt[x]{\ }$ key is a second function key. On others, it is found in a menu. On still others, students must use the powering key to enter $x^{\frac{1}{n}}$, as they did in Chapter 7. You may want to use Examples 1 and 2 and QY2 to see if any students have trouble finding roots on their calculators.

Additional Example

Example 1 The following chart shows the population for eight 1-square-mile regions in the United States.

Sample	Population
1	47
2	68
3	159
4	2,215
5	8,715
6	10,512
7	12,130
8	45,312

Use the geometric mean to compute an average population density. about 1656 people per mi^2

The geometric mean may be used when numbers are quite dispersed, to keep one very large number from disproportionately affecting the measure of center. For this reason, the geometric mean is the standard measure of center for data about pollutants and contaminants. The geometric mean is also used to compute an overall rate of percent increase or decrease, as you will see in the Questions.

Example 1

In a water-quality survey, 8 samples give the following levels of *E. coli* bacteria.

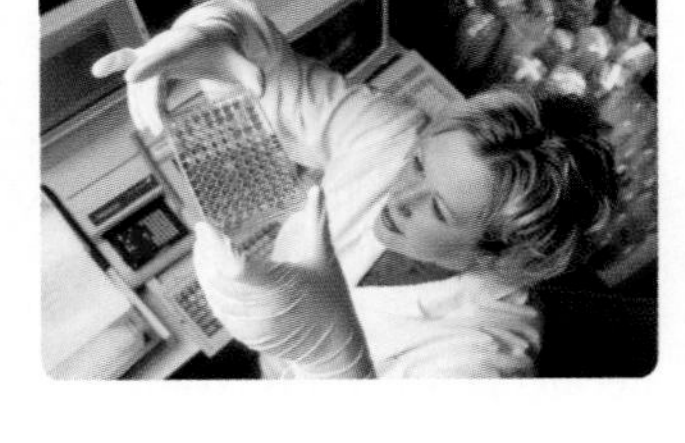

Sample	1	2	3	4	5	6	7	8
Count (per 100 mL)	2	54	145	38	597	1152	344	87

Use the geometric mean to compute an average level of bacteria.

Solution Because there are eight numbers, the geometric mean is the 8th root of their product.

$$\sqrt[8]{2 \cdot 54 \cdot 145 \cdot 38 \cdot 597 \cdot 1152 \cdot 344 \cdot 87} \approx 102.6.$$

A typical sample has about 103 bacteria per 100 mL.

 QY2

> **QY2**
> A ninth sample is taken with an *E. coli* count of 436 per 100 mL. Estimate the average number of bacteria across all nine samples.

Which *n*th Root Does $\sqrt[n]{x}$ Represent?

The symbol $\sqrt[n]{x}$, like $x^{\frac{1}{n}}$, does not represent all *n*th roots of *x*. When *x* is positive and *n* is even, *x* has two real *n*th roots, but only the *positive* real root is denoted by $\sqrt[n]{x}$. Thus, although 3, -3, $3i$, and $-3i$ are all fourth roots of 81, $\sqrt[4]{81} = 81^{\frac{1}{4}} = 3$ only. The negative real fourth root can be written $-81^{\frac{1}{4}}$ or $-\sqrt[4]{81}$, both of which equal -3. Note that the four complex solutions to $x^4 = 81$ are $\pm\sqrt[4]{81}$ and $\pm\sqrt[4]{-81}$, that is, ±3 and $\pm3i$.

GUIDED

Example 2

a. **Set a CAS to real-number mode. Evaluate $\sqrt[4]{6561}$ and explain its meaning.**

b. **Set a CAS to complex-number mode. Find all fourth roots of 6561.**

Geometric mean The geometric mean is related to geometric sequences in the same way that the arithmetic mean is related to arithmetic sequences: In any odd number of consecutive terms in any geometric sequence, the middle term is the geometric mean of the others. Logarithms can reveal additional properties of geometric and arithmetic means: The logarithm of the geometric mean of a set of numbers is the arithmetic mean of the logarithms of the numbers. That is, when numbers are graphed on a logarithmic scale, their geometric mean acts geometrically as an arithmetic mean.

Food for thought: The words *radish* and *radical* have the same origin, from the Latin word *radix,* meaning root.

Solution

a. $\sqrt[4]{6561} = \underline{\ ?\ }^{\frac{1}{4}}$ represents the (positive/negative) number whose $\underline{\ ?\ }$ power is 6561. $(6561)^{\frac{1}{4}} = \underline{\ ?\ }$ because $\underline{\ ?\ }^{4} = 6561$. So, $\sqrt[4]{6561} = \underline{\ ?\ }$.

b. On a CAS, solve the equation $\underline{\ ?\ }$ in complex-number mode. The solutions are $\underline{\ ?\ }$, $\underline{\ ?\ }$, $\underline{\ ?\ }$, $\underline{\ ?\ }$. These solutions are all the $\underline{\ ?\ }$ roots of 6561.

$\sqrt[4]{6561}$	9

a. 6561; positive; 4th; 9; 9; 9

b. $x^4 = 6561$; 9; -9; $9i$; $-9i$; 4th

An early form of the $\sqrt{\ }$ symbol (which looked like a check mark) first appeared in the 1500s, and René Descartes modified it in the early 1600s into the form we use today. The origin of the word *radical* is the Latin word *radix*, which means "root."

Albert Girard suggested the symbol $\sqrt[n]{\ }$, and it first appeared in print in 1690. As you know from Chapter 7, most graphing calculators let you enter the rational power form x^(1/n) to find $\sqrt[n]{x} = x^{\frac{1}{n}}$. Some graphing calculators also let you enter radical forms of roots as shown in Example 2.

Radicals for Roots of Powers

Because radicals are powers, all properties of powers listed in Chapter 7 apply to radicals. In particular, because $\sqrt[n]{x} = x^{\frac{1}{n}}$ for $x > 0$, the mth powers of these numbers are equal. That is, $(\sqrt[n]{x})^m = \left(x^{\frac{1}{n}}\right)^m$, which equals $x^{\frac{m}{n}}$. If x is replaced by x^m in the definition of $\sqrt[n]{x}$, the result is $\sqrt[n]{x^m} = (x^m)^{\frac{1}{n}}$, which also equals $x^{\frac{m}{n}}$. Thus, there are two radical expressions equal to $x^{\frac{m}{n}}$.

Root of a Power Theorem

For all positive integers $m \geq 2$ and $n \geq 2$,

$$\sqrt[n]{x^m} = (\sqrt[n]{x})^m = x^{\frac{m}{n}} \text{ when } x \geq 0.$$

 QY3

Notice that $x \geq 0$ in both the Root of a Power Theorem and QY3. This is because the Root of a Power Theorem only applies to positive bases.

 QY4

▸ QY3

Suppose $x \geq 0$. Use the Root of a Power Theorem to write $\sqrt[6]{x^{18}}$ in two different ways.

▸ QY4

Show that $\sqrt[6]{x^{18}} \neq x^3$ when $x = -2$.

Additional Example

Example 2

a. Set a CAS to real-number mode. Evaluate $\sqrt[4]{2401}$ and explain its meaning.

b. Set a CAS to complex-number mode. Find all the fourth roots of 2401.

Solution

a.

$\sqrt[4]{2401}$	7

$\sqrt[4]{2401} = (\underline{\ ?\ })^{\frac{1}{4}}$ represents the $\underline{\ ?\ }$ number whose $\underline{\ ?\ }$ power is 2401. 2401; positive real; fourth

$(2401)^{\frac{1}{4}} = \underline{\ ?\ }$ because $(\underline{\ ?\ })^4 = 2401$. 7; 7;

So $\sqrt[4]{2401} = \underline{\ ?\ }$. 7

b. Solve the equation $\underline{\ ?\ }$ in complex-number mode. $x^4 = 2401$ The solutions are $\underline{\ ?\ }$, $\underline{\ ?\ }$, $\underline{\ ?\ }$, and $\underline{\ ?\ }$. 7, -7, $7i$, $-7i$ These solutions are all the $\underline{\ ?\ }$ roots of 2401. fourth

Accommodating the Learner

Ask students to write expressions for the arithmetic mean and the geometric mean of two numbers a and b. Then ask them to justify the statement that if $a + b > 0$, then the arithmetic mean is always greater than or equal to the geometric mean. (*Note:* A geometric illustration of this property appears in Lesson 8-5, Question 27.)

The arithmetic mean is $\frac{a+b}{2}$, and the geometric mean is $\sqrt{ab}$. One justification begins with the statement that $(a - b)^2 \geq 0$ for all values of a and b.

$$a^2 - 2ab + b^2 \geq 0$$

$$a^2 + 2ab + b^2 \geq 4ab$$

$$\frac{(a+b)^2}{4} \geq ab$$

Taking the square root of each side gives $\frac{a+b}{2} \geq \sqrt{ab}$.

Notes on the Lesson

Example 3 This example may surprise some students; they may never have thought that various *n*th roots of a number could be so easily related. You might note that the result is an application of the general property that $((x^a)^a)^a = x^{(a^3)}$, with $a = \frac{1}{2}$.

Additional Example

Example 3 Rewrite $\sqrt{\sqrt{\sqrt{\sqrt{10}}}}$ using rational exponents. Is this expression an *n*th root of 10? Justify your answer. $10^{\frac{1}{16}}$; yes; $10^{\frac{1}{16}}$ is a 16th root of 10 because $\left(10^{\frac{1}{16}}\right)^{16} = 10^1 = 10$.

Note-Taking Tips

Ask students to compare the arithmetic mean and the geometric mean by entering the following descriptions in their notes: To find the (arithmetic/geometric) mean, find the (sum/product) of the *n* values. Then (multiply/raise) that value (by/to) the value $\frac{1}{n}$.

Roots of Roots

Consider the sequence 625, 25, 5, $\sqrt{5}$, ... in which each number is the square root of the preceding number. You can define this sequence recursively.

$$\begin{cases} s_1 = 625 \\ s_n = \sqrt{s_{n-1}}, \text{ for integers } n \geq 2 \end{cases}$$

So,
$$s_2 = \sqrt{625} = 25$$
$$s_3 = \sqrt{\sqrt{625}} = \sqrt{25} = 5$$
$$s_4 = \sqrt{\sqrt{\sqrt{625}}} = \sqrt{\sqrt{25}} = \sqrt{5} \approx 2.24$$

STOP QY5

Rewriting the radicals as rational exponents provides a way to deal with roots of roots.

QY5

Is this a geometric sequence? Why or why not?

Example 3

Rewrite $\sqrt{\sqrt{\sqrt{6}}}$ using rational exponents. Is this expression an *n*th root of 6? Justify your answer.

Solution $\sqrt{\sqrt{\sqrt{6}}} = \left(\left(6^{\frac{1}{2}}\right)^{\frac{1}{2}}\right)^{\frac{1}{2}} = \left(6^{\frac{1}{2}}\right)^{\frac{1}{4}} = 6^{\frac{1}{8}}$ by the Power of a Power Postulate. So, by the definition of nth root, $\sqrt{\sqrt{\sqrt{6}}}$ is the positive 8th root of 6.

Check Enter $\sqrt{\sqrt{\sqrt{6}}}$ on a calculator to see that $\sqrt{\sqrt{\sqrt{6}}} = 6^{\frac{1}{8}}$.

In general, when $x > 0$, it is more common to write $x^{\frac{1}{8}}$ as the single radical $\sqrt[8]{x}$, rather than as $\sqrt{\sqrt{\sqrt{x}}}$. But if you only have a square root key on your calculator, then it is nice to know you can calculate 8th roots.

ENGLISH LEARNERS
Vocabulary Development

Discuss with students how the conditions on a variable can be expressed in words or as an inequality. Some examples are as follows:

- a variable is positive: $x > 0$
- a variable is nonnegative: $x \geq 0$
- two variables have the same sign: $xy > 0$
- two variables have different signs: $xy < 0$
- two variables are not both zero: $x^2 + y^2 > 0$

Accommodating the Learner

Ask students to describe different keystroke sequences to calculate $\sqrt[3]{5^2}$, $(\sqrt[3]{5})^2$, and $5^{\frac{2}{3}}$ Answers vary. Check students' work.

Questions

COVERING THE IDEAS

1. Who is credited with first using the radical symbol in its current form? René Descartes

2. Who is credited with first using the symbol $\sqrt[n]{\ }$? Albert Girard

3. **True or False** $\sqrt[n]{x} = (x)^{\frac{1}{n}}$ for all x. false

4. a. How is the geometric mean of n numbers calculated?
   b. Identify a situation in which the geometric mean is the preferred measure of center.

4a. For a data set with n values, multiply the numbers in the set and then take the nth root of their product.

4b. Answers vary. Sample: The geometric mean is useful in computing the overall rate of percent increase or decrease.

5. The table at the right gives the masses of the eight major planets as a ratio with Earth's mass. Find the geometric mean of these masses. about 3.77

Planet	Planet's Mass / Earth's Mass
Mercury	0.06
Venus	0.82
Earth	1
Mars	0.11
Jupiter	318
Saturn	95
Uranus	14.5
Neptune	17.2

The Mars rover Spirit took this photo from the eastern edge of the plateau called "Home Plate."

6. Evaluate without a calculator.
   a. $\sqrt{64}$ 8
   b. $\sqrt[3]{64}$ 4
   c. $\sqrt[6]{64}$ 2
   d. $\sqrt[10]{64^{10}}$

In 7 and 8, use a calculator to approximate to the nearest hundredth.

7. $\sqrt[17]{7845}$ 1.69

8. $\sqrt[8]{1 \cdot 2 \cdot 3 \cdot 4 \cdot 5 \cdot 6 \cdot 7 \cdot 8}$ 3.76

9. **Fill in the Blank** Complete the following statement of the Root of a Power Theorem. For all positive integers m and n with $m \geq 2$ and $n \geq 2$, when $x \geq 0$, $x^{\frac{m}{n}} =$ __?__. $\sqrt[n]{x^m} = (\sqrt[n]{x})^m$

10. Refer to Example 2. Write all the complex fourth roots of 625. 5, –5, 5i, –5i

11. a. Find all the complex fourth roots of 14,641. 11, –11, 11i, –11i
    b. Which root in Part a is $\sqrt[4]{14{,}641}$? 11

In 12–14, write as a single power using a rational exponent. Assume all variables are positive.

12. $\sqrt[6]{z^{10}}$ $z^{\frac{5}{3}}$

13. $\sqrt[5]{c^{15}}$ c^3

14. $\left(\sqrt[14]{t}\right)^7$ $t^{\frac{1}{2}}$

15. Rewrite $\sqrt{\sqrt{\sqrt{\sqrt{x}}}}$ with a rational exponent, for $x \geq 0$. $x^{\frac{1}{16}}$

16. Rewrite $\sqrt{\sqrt{\sqrt{\sqrt{81}}}}$ using a single radical sign. $\sqrt[16]{81}$

3 Assignment

Recommended Assignment

- Questions 1–32
- Question 33 (extra credit)
- Reading Lesson 8-5
- Covering the Ideas 8-5

Notes on the Questions

Question 5 You might ask why the geometric mean is more reasonable as an "average planet mass" than the arithmetic mean. Answers vary. Sample: The values are so far apart that Jupiter would disproportionately affect the arithmetic mean; the spread has less effect on the geometric mean.

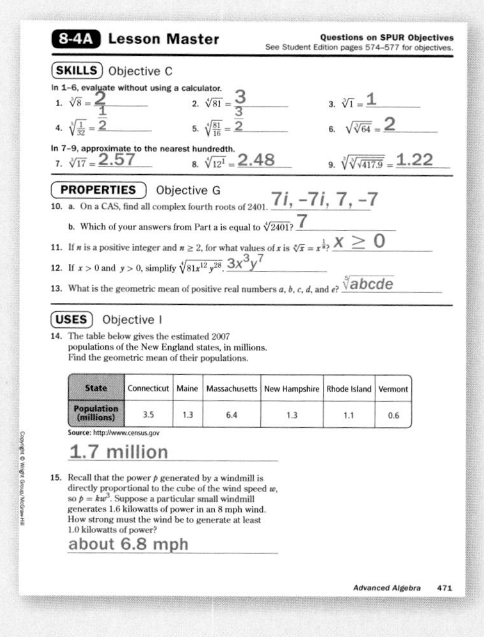

8-4A Lesson Master

Questions on SPUR Objectives
See Student Edition pages 574–577 for objectives.

SKILLS Objective C

In 1–6, evaluate without using a calculator.

1. $\sqrt[3]{8} =$ 2
2. $\sqrt[4]{81} =$ 3
3. $\sqrt[3]{1} =$ 1
4. $\sqrt[5]{\frac{1}{32}} =$ $\frac{1}{2}$
5. $\sqrt[4]{\frac{81}{16}} =$ $\frac{3}{2}$
6. $\sqrt{\sqrt[3]{64}} =$ 2

In 7–9, approximate to the nearest hundredth.

7. $\sqrt[3]{17} =$ 2.57
8. $\sqrt[4]{12^1} =$ 2.48
9. $\sqrt[3]{\sqrt[5]{\sqrt{417.9}}} =$ 1.22

PROPERTIES Objective G

10. a. On a CAS, find all complex fourth roots of 2401. 7i, –7i, 7, –7
    b. Which of your answers from Part a is equal to $\sqrt[4]{2401}$? 7
11. If n is a positive integer and $n \geq 2$, for what values of x is $\sqrt[n]{x} = x^{\frac{1}{n}}$? $x \geq 0$
12. If $x > 0$ and $y > 0$, simplify $\sqrt[4]{81x^{12}y^{28}}$. $3x^3y^7$
13. What is the geometric mean of positive real numbers a, b, c, d, and e? $\sqrt[5]{abcde}$

USES Objective I

14. The table below gives the estimated 2007 populations of the New England states, in millions. Find the geometric mean of their populations.

State	Connecticut	Maine	Massachusetts	New Hampshire	Rhode Island	Vermont
Population (millions)	3.5	1.3	6.4	1.3	1.1	0.6

Source: http://www.census.gov

1.7 million

15. Recall that the power p generated by a windmill is directly proportional to the cube of the wind speed w, so $p = kw^3$. Suppose a particular small windmill generates 1.6 kilowatts of power in an 8 mph wind. How strong must the wind be to generate at least 1.0 kilowatts of power?

about 6.8 mph

Advanced Algebra 471

Notes on the Questions

Questions 17 and 18 These questions are useful for discussing equivalent forms of expressions. In Question 18, you might ask students to see how their CAS deals with these forms.

Question 19 This question relates to the data on page 514. It provides a way for students to answer a question that is often raised by homeowners: How much has the value of my home increased (or decreased), on average, since I bought it?

APPLYING THE MATHEMATICS

Multiple Choice In 17 and 18, which of the expressions is not equivalent to the other two?

17. A $6^{\frac{12}{36}}$ B $\sqrt[12]{6^2}$ C $\sqrt[12]{36}$ A

18. A $p^{\frac{3}{2}}$ B $\left(\sqrt[4]{p^2}\right)^6$ C $\left(\sqrt{\sqrt{p}}\right)^6$ B

19. From the data on page 514, you can compute that the unadjusted median home value in the United States in 2000 was more than 40 times the median value in 1940. The decade-to-decade percentage increase in housing values is summarized in the table below.

Years	1940–1950	1950–1960	1960–1970	1970–1980	1980–1990	1990–2000
% Increase (rounded)	150	62	43	178	68	51
Size-change factor	2.50	? 1.62	? 1.43	? 2.78	? 1.68	? 1.51

a. Fill in the table by converting each percent into a size-change factor.

b. Compute the geometric mean of the size-change factors you found in Part a, and determine the average percentage increase per decade in home values from 1940 to 2000. about 1.856; about 85.6%

20. Recall from Chapter 7 the Baravelle spiral, in which squares are created by connecting midpoints of sides of larger squares. In the Baravelle spiral shown below, the leg length of right triangle A_1 is 1 unit.

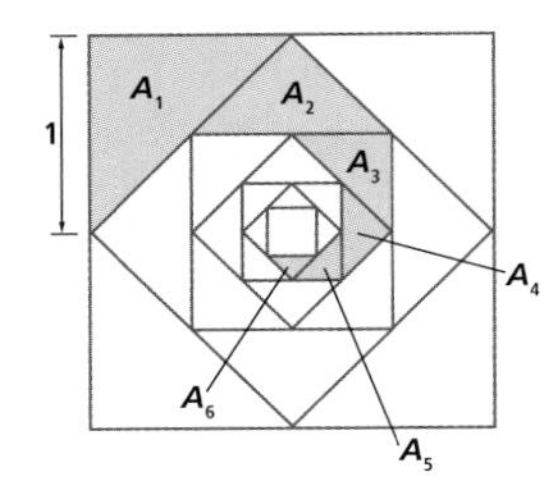

a. What are the lengths of the hypotenuses of right triangles A_1, A_2, and A_3? $\sqrt{2}$; 1; $\frac{\sqrt{2}}{2}$

b. The lengths of the hypotenuses $L_1, L_2, L_3, \ldots$ are a geometric sequence. Write an explicit formula for L_n, the sequence of hypotenuse lengths in this Baravelle spiral. $L_n = \sqrt{2} \cdot \left(\frac{\sqrt{2}}{2}\right)^{n-1}$

21. A sphere has volume V in^3, where $V = \frac{4}{3}\pi r^3$. Express the length of the radius in terms of the volume
   a. using radical notation.
   b. using a rational exponent.

21a. $r = \sqrt[3]{\frac{3}{4\pi}V}$

21b. $r = \left(\frac{3}{4\pi}V\right)^{\frac{1}{3}}$

22. Consider the formula $m = 1.23x^3b$ where m, x, and b are all positive. Solve the formula for x using radical notation. $x = \sqrt[3]{\frac{m}{1.23b}}$

23. Use the expression $\sqrt[4]{\sqrt[4]{43{,}046{,}721z^{48}}}$.
   a. Rewrite the expression with a rational exponent. $(43{,}046{,}721z^{48})^{\frac{1}{16}}$
   b. Rewrite the expression as one radical. $\sqrt[16]{43{,}046{,}721z^{48}}$
   c. Evaluate the expression when $z = 2$. 24

In 24 and 25, write each expression in simplest radical form using no fraction exponents. Assume all variables are positive.

24. $\sqrt{\sqrt{\frac{1}{y^4}}}$ $\sqrt[16]{y}$

25. $\frac{\sqrt{k^{\frac{1}{2}}}}{\sqrt{\sqrt{k}}}$ $\frac{\sqrt[4]{k}}{\sqrt[4]{k}} = 1$

REVIEW

26. Let $h(x) = x^2$ and $k(x) = x^{-\frac{1}{2}}$. (Lessons 8-3, 8-1, 7-8, 7-2)
   a. Find $h \circ k(x)$. $\frac{1}{x}$
   b. Are h and k inverses of each other? How can you tell? No; $h \circ k(x) \neq x$.

27. The height of a baseball that has been hit is described by the parabola $h(x) = -0.00132x^2 + 0.545x + 4$, where x is the distance in feet from home plate. The effect of a 15-mph wind in the direction the ball is traveling is given by $w(x) = 0.9x$. (Lessons 8-1, 6-4)
   a. Which of $w(h(x))$ or $h(w(x))$ represents this situation? (*Hint:* The wind is blowing before the ball is pitched and hit.) $h(w(x))$
   b. Write a formula for your answer to Part a. $h(w(x)) = -0.0010692x^2 + 0.4905x + 4$
   c. How far from home plate will the ball land if there is no wind? about 420.1 ft
   d. How far from home plate will the ball land if there is a 15-mph wind in the direction of travel? about 466.8 ft

In 28 and 29, write without an exponent. Do not use a calculator. (Lesson 7-8)

28. $9^{-\frac{3}{2}}$ $\frac{1}{27}$

29. $-\frac{1}{5}^{-3}$ -125

Extension

Question 22 asks students to solve the formula $m = 1.23x^3b$ for x. Ask students to solve the formula $a = xy^z + w$ for each of the letters x, y, and w. Students should describe any necessary conditions on the variables. $x = \frac{a - w}{y^z}$ $(y \neq 0)$; $y = \sqrt[z]{\frac{a - w}{x}}$ ($a - w$ and x have the same sign, z is a positive integer, $x \neq 0$); $w = a - xy^z$ (no conditions).

4 Wrap-Up

Ongoing Assessment

Ask students to show each expression in three forms by completing the following table. Assume that the bases are positive.

$\sqrt[n]{x^m}$	$(\sqrt[n]{x})^m$	$x^{\frac{m}{n}}$
$\sqrt[5]{p^{20}}$	$(\sqrt[5]{p})^{20}$	$p^{\frac{20}{5}} = p^4$
$\sqrt[3]{q^{17}}$	$(\sqrt[3]{q})^{17}$	$q^{\frac{17}{3}}$
$\sqrt[4]{r^{12}}$	$(\sqrt[4]{r})^{12}$	$r^{\frac{12}{4}} = r^3$

Project Update

Project 1, *Roots and Surds*, on page 568 and Project 5, *Square Roots of Matrices,* on page 569 relate to the content of this lesson.

30. Write the reciprocal of $3 + 2i$ in $a + bi$ form. **(Lesson 6-9)** $\frac{3}{13} - \frac{2}{13}i$

31. If $g(t) = \dfrac{\frac{t-4}{t+3}}{\frac{t-2}{t+1}}$, what values of t are not in the domain of g? **(Lesson 1-4)** t = -1, 2, and -3 are not in the domain of g.

32. A math text from 1887 gives the following apothecary weights: 3 scruples = 1 dram, 8 drams = 1 ounce. How many scruples are in two and a half ounces? **(Previous Course)** 60 scruples

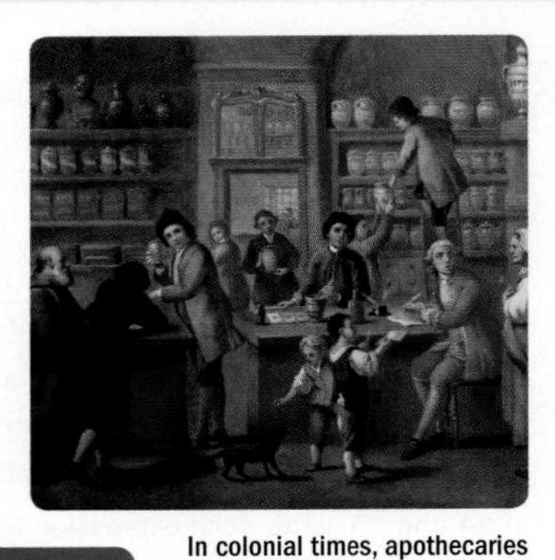

In colonial times, apothecaries provided medical treatment, prescribed medicine, and even performed surgery.

EXPLORATION

33. In Parts a–c, use a calculator to estimate to the nearest hundredth.
    a. $\sqrt{1 + \sqrt{1 + \sqrt{1}}}$ 1.55
    b. $\sqrt{1 + \sqrt{1 + \sqrt{1 + \sqrt{1}}}}$ 1.60
    c. $\sqrt{1 + \sqrt{1 + \sqrt{1 + \sqrt{1 + \sqrt{1}}}}}$ 1.61
    d. Use a CAS to solve the equation $x = \sqrt{1 + x}$ such that $x \geq 0$. $\frac{\sqrt{5} + 1}{2}$
    e. Approximate your solution in Part d to the nearest hundredth, and compare it to your answers in Parts a, b, and c. What do you think is happening?
    Answers vary. Sample: As the approximations of $\sqrt{1 + \sqrt{1 + \ldots}}$ get more exact, they get closer to $\frac{\sqrt{5} + 1}{2}$.

QY ANSWERS

1. $x = \frac{1}{7}$
2. about 120 bacteria per 100 mL
3. $(\sqrt[6]{x})^{18}$ and x^3
4. When $x = -2$, $\sqrt[6]{x^{18}} = \sqrt[6]{(-2)^{18}} = \sqrt[6]{2^{18}}$, a positive number, but $x^3 = -8$, a negative number.
5. No; the ratio between consecutive terms is not constant.

8-4B page 2

8-4B Lesson Master

Questions on SPUR Objectives
See Student Edition pages 574–577 for objectives.

SKILLS Objective C

In 1–12, evaluate without using a calculator.

1. $\sqrt[3]{0.216}$ 0.6
2. $\sqrt[6]{64}$ 2
3. $\sqrt[4]{6561}$ 9
4. $\sqrt[3]{343}$ 3
5. $\sqrt[5]{0.03125}$ 0.5
6. $\sqrt[5]{\frac{243}{32}}$ $\frac{3}{2}$
7. $\sqrt[3]{512}$ 8
8. $\sqrt{169}$ 13
9. $\sqrt[4]{10{,}000}$ 10
10. $\sqrt[3]{0.008}$ 0.2
11. $\sqrt[6]{\frac{64}{729}}$ $\frac{2}{3}$
12. $\sqrt[4]{50{,}625}$ 15

In 13–18, estimate to the nearest hundredth.

13. $\sqrt[4]{16 + 81}$ 3.14
14. $\sqrt[5]{28}$ 1.95
15. $\sqrt[9]{100}$ 1.67
16. $\sqrt[8]{8}$ 1.30
17. $\sqrt[4]{716{,}448}$ 29.09
18. $\sqrt[3]{0.00029}$ 0.07

PROPERTIES Objective G

19. a. On a CAS, find all complex fourth roots of 6561. $9i, -9i, 9, -9$
    b. Which of your answers from Part a is equal to $\sqrt[4]{6561}$? 9
20. Give a counterexample to the statement: For all h, $\sqrt[4]{h^4} = h$.
    Answers vary. Sample: If $h = -2$, $\sqrt[4]{(-2)^4} = 2 \neq -2$
21. Consider the statement $\sqrt[5]{m^5} = m$. For which values of m is the statement true? all real numbers
22. For the radical expression $\sqrt[m]{n}$, what are the possible values
    a. of m? integers ≥ 2
    b. of n? nonnegative real numbers
23. **Multiple Choice** When $x \geq 0$, $\sqrt[9]{x^4}$ equals which of the following? A
    A $x^{\frac{4}{9}}$ B $x^{\frac{9}{4}}$ C $x^{-\frac{4}{9}}$ D $\frac{1}{9}x^4$

472 Advanced Algebra

Lesson

8-5 Products with Radicals

▶ **BIG IDEA** The product of the nth roots of nonnegative numbers is the nth root of the product of the numbers.

Activity

MATERIALS CAS

Clear variables a and b and set the CAS to real-number mode.

Step 1 Enter the following expressions, with $a > 0$ and $b > 0$, into the CAS and record the results.

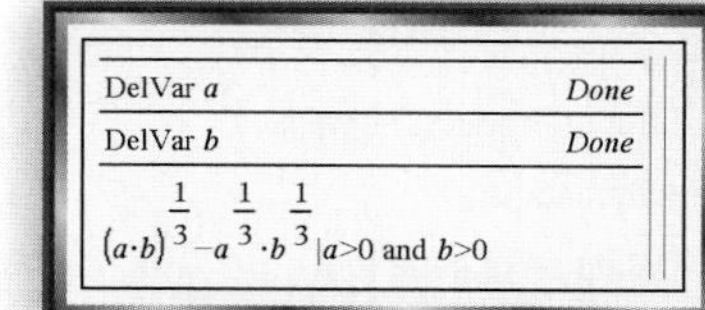

a. $(a \cdot b)^{\frac{1}{3}} - a^{\frac{1}{3}} \cdot b^{\frac{1}{3}}$

b. $(a \cdot b)^{\frac{1}{12}} - a^{\frac{1}{12}} \cdot b^{\frac{1}{12}}$

c. $a^{\frac{1}{4}} \cdot b^{\frac{1}{4}} - (a \cdot b)^{\frac{1}{4}}$

d. $a^{\frac{1}{7}} \cdot b^{\frac{1}{7}} - (a \cdot b)^{\frac{1}{7}}$ See margin.

Step 2 Based on the results from Step 1, make a conjecture: $(a \cdot b)^{\frac{1}{n}} - a^{\frac{1}{n}} \cdot b^{\frac{1}{n}} =$ __?__. 0

Step 3 Based on your conjecture in Step 2, make another conjecture: $(a \cdot b)^{\frac{1}{n}} =$ __?__. $a^{\frac{1}{n}} \cdot b^{\frac{1}{n}}$

The results of the Activity suggest a property of nth roots. This property can also be derived another way. Recall that for all nonnegative numbers a and b,

$$\sqrt{ab} = \sqrt{a} \cdot \sqrt{b}.$$

Rewriting the above equation with rational powers instead of radicals you can see that this property of radicals is a special case of the Power of a Product Postulate, $(ab)^m = a^m \cdot b^m$.

$$(ab)^{\frac{1}{2}} = a^{\frac{1}{2}} \cdot b^{\frac{1}{2}}$$

If you now let $m = \frac{1}{n}$ in the Power of a Product Postulate, you obtain a theorem about the product of nth roots.

Mental Math

Simplify.

a. $\frac{w^{17}}{w^{12}}$ w^5

b. $\frac{x^3}{x^6} \cdot x^5$ x^2

c. $4y\left(\frac{3y}{y^4}\right)^2$ $\frac{36}{y^5}$ or $36y^{-5}$

d. $\left(8wz^2 + \frac{z^3}{2w^2}\right)w^3$ $8w^4z^2 + \frac{wz^3}{2}$

Background

Multiplying radicals Most students will have seen the Root of a Product Theorem in previous mathematics courses. That earlier exposure, however, was probably restricted to square roots, so they may not have realized that the Root of a Product Theorem, when applied to square roots, is just a special case of the Power of a Product Postulate when the exponent is $\frac{1}{2}$. This is a classic example of how different notations can cause closely related concepts to be treated quite differently.

Simplifying radicals Consider the fraction $\frac{m}{n}$, where m and n are integers with no common factors and $m > n$. By the Division Algorithm, there exists a unique integer quotient q and an integer remainder r, with $0 < r < n$, such that $m = nq + r$. So $\frac{m}{n} = \frac{nq + r}{n} = q + \frac{r}{n}$, and since $r < n$, q is the integer part of the mixed number equal to $\frac{m}{n}$. This is the process that students use (though not with variables) when they take

(continued on next page)

Lesson

8-5

GOAL

Apply the Root of a Product Theorem to rewrite products of roots or to calculate a geometric mean.

SPUR Objectives

D Rewrite or simplify expressions with radicals.

G Apply properties of radicals and nth root functions.

Materials/Resources

- Lesson Masters 8-5A and 8-5B
- Resource Masters 145 and 146
- CAS

HOMEWORK

Suggestions for Assignment

- Questions 1–26
- Question 27 (extra credit)
- Reading Lesson 8-6
- Covering the Ideas 8-6

Local Standards

1 Warm-Up

In 1 and 2, a circle contains the four vertices of a rectangle with dimensions 2 units by 5 units.

1. What is the exact area of the circle? 7.25π sq. units
2. What is the circumference of the circle, to the nearest thousandth of a unit? $\pi \cdot \sqrt{29} \approx 16.918$ units

(*Note:* In Warm-Up 1, students must square a square root that likely will be in radical form. In Warm-Up 2, students are multiplying two irrational numbers, which is done in this lesson.)

2 Teaching

Notes on the Lesson

Activity The Activity demonstrates a powerful method of using a CAS to show that two expressions are equivalent: Subtract one from the other. If the difference is 0, then the expressions are equivalent. We have noted that some CASs leave the product $x^{\frac{1}{n}} \cdot y^{\frac{1}{n}}$ as is, while others will rewrite it as $(xy)^{\frac{1}{n}}$. Some may do just the reverse. Some CASs cannot rewrite $x^{\frac{1}{n}} \cdot y^{\frac{1}{n}} - (xy)^{\frac{1}{n}}$; others will display 0. So, the method here works with some but not all CASs.

This may be an appropriate lesson for emphasizing the purpose of examples. Ask your students what they think is the purpose of each example in the lesson. Answers vary. Samples: Example 1 applies the Root of a Product Theorem to numerical expressions and shows that the product of two irrational numbers can be rational. Example 2 applies the Root of a Product Theorem to algebraic expressions. Example 3 applies the Root of a Product Theorem in the other direction, breaking up a product into factors and then rewriting the result. Example 4 is similar to Example 3, except the simplified form is not so simple. Note that Example 4 does not give the direction "simplify" because the expression given in the problem seems much simpler than the answer.

Note-Taking Tips

Students' notes on the Root of a Product Theorem should emphasize that a condition for applying the theorem is that a single root or power is involved; that is, the same nth root, or the same $\frac{1}{n}$th power, must appear in both factors of a multiplication.

Root of a Product Theorem

For any nonnegative real numbers x and y, and any integer $n \geq 2$,

$(xy)^{\frac{1}{n}} = x^{\frac{1}{n}} \cdot y^{\frac{1}{n}}$. power form

$\sqrt[n]{xy} = \sqrt[n]{x} \cdot \sqrt[n]{y}$. radical form

Multiplying Radicals

You can use the Root of a Product Theorem to multiply nth roots.

Example 1

Calculate $\sqrt[3]{50} \cdot \sqrt[3]{20}$ without a calculator.

Solution Rewrite the given expression using the Root of a Product Theorem.

$\sqrt[3]{50} \cdot \sqrt[3]{20} = \sqrt[3]{50 \cdot 20}$ Root of Product Theorem

$= \sqrt[3]{1000}$ Arithmetic

$= 10$ Definition of cube root

Check Use a calculator to find 3-place decimal approximations for $\sqrt[3]{50}$ and $\sqrt[3]{20}$.

$\sqrt[3]{50} \approx 3.684$ $\sqrt[3]{20} \approx 2.714$

Multiply the decimals.

$3.684 \cdot 2.714 = 9.998376$, close enough given the estimates.

GUIDED

Example 2

Assume that $x \geq 0$. Perform the multiplication: $\sqrt[4]{5x} \cdot \sqrt[4]{125x^3}$.

Solution 1 Rewrite using the Root of a Product Theorem.

$\sqrt[4]{5x} \cdot \sqrt[4]{125x^3} = \sqrt[4]{\underline{\ ?\ }}$ $625x^4$

Now use the Root of a Product Theorem to rewrite again.

$= \sqrt[4]{\underline{\ ?\ }} \cdot \sqrt[4]{\underline{\ ?\ }}$ 625; x^4

$= \underline{\ ?\ }$ $5x$

an improper fraction and convert it to a mixed number. Now consider the radical expression $\sqrt[n]{x^m}$ with the same conditions on m and n. It is equivalent to the $\frac{m}{n}$th power of x, where $\frac{m}{n}$ is an improper fraction. Again, $\frac{m}{n} = \frac{nq + r}{n} = q + \frac{r}{n}$, so $\sqrt[n]{x^m} = x^{\frac{m}{n}} = x^{q + \frac{r}{n}} = x^q \cdot x^{\frac{r}{n}} = (x^q)\sqrt[n]{x^r}$. It looks formidable with variables, but if you point out the analogy with mixed numbers, most students easily follow these steps.

Solution 2 Convert to rational exponents.

$$\sqrt[4]{5x} \cdot \sqrt[4]{125x^3} = (5x)^{\frac{1}{4}} \cdot (\underline{\ ?\ })^{\frac{1}{4}} \quad 125x^3$$
$$= (\underline{\ ?\ })^{\frac{1}{4}} \quad 625x^4$$
$$= 625^{\frac{1}{4}} \cdot (\underline{\ ?\ })^{\frac{1}{4}} \quad x^4$$
$$= 5x$$

Simplifying Radicals

In Example 2, you used the Root of a Product Theorem to rewrite an nth root as a product. For instance, $\sqrt[3]{240}$ can be rewritten several ways:

$$\sqrt[3]{240} = \sqrt[3]{2 \cdot 120} = \sqrt[3]{2} \cdot \sqrt[3]{120};$$
$$\sqrt[3]{240} = \sqrt[3]{8 \cdot 30} = \sqrt[3]{8} \cdot \sqrt[3]{30};$$
$$\sqrt[3]{240} = \sqrt[3]{16 \cdot 15} = \sqrt[3]{16} \cdot \sqrt[3]{15}.$$

Because 8 is a perfect cube, the second form shows that $\sqrt[3]{240} = 2\sqrt[3]{30}$. Some people call $2\sqrt[3]{30}$ the ***simplified form*** of $\sqrt[3]{240}$. In general, to simplify an nth root, rewrite the expression under the radical sign as a product of perfect nth powers and other factors. Then apply the Root of a Product Theorem.

Example 3

Suppose $r \geq 0$ and $s \geq 0$. Simplify the expression $\sqrt[3]{64r^6s^{15}}$.

Solution 1 Because it is a third root, identify perfect third powers in the expression under the radical.

$64 = 4^3$, $r^6 = (r^2)^3$, and $s^{15} = (s^5)^3$

Rewrite and simplify.

$\sqrt[3]{64r^6s^{15}} = \sqrt[3]{4^3(r^2)^3(s^5)^3}$	Power of a Power Property
$= \sqrt[3]{4^3} \cdot \sqrt[3]{(r^2)^3} \cdot \sqrt[3]{(s^5)^3}$	Root of a Product Theorem
$= 4r^2s^5$	Root of a Power Theorem

Solution 2 Rewrite using rational exponents.

$\sqrt[3]{64r^6s^{15}} = (64r^6s^{15})^{\frac{1}{3}}$	Definition of $\sqrt[n]{x}$
$= 64^{\frac{1}{3}} \cdot r^{\frac{6}{3}} \cdot s^{\frac{15}{3}}$	Power of a Product and Power of a Power Postulates
$= 4r^2s^5$	Arithmetic

STOP QY1

▸ **QY1**

Suppose $a \geq 0$ and $b \geq 0$. Simplify $\sqrt{16a^4b^{10}}$.

Notes on the Lesson

Encourage students to use fractions or decimals as exponents when rewriting roots, as in Solution 2 for Example 3. Students should move toward doing the second and third steps mentally, while continuing to work for accuracy.

Additional Examples

Example 1 Calculate $\sqrt[3]{320} \cdot \sqrt[3]{25}$ without a calculator. $\sqrt[3]{320} \cdot \sqrt[3]{25} = \sqrt[3]{320 \cdot 25} = \sqrt[3]{8000} = 20$

Example 2 Assume that $x \geq 0$. Perform the multiplication $\sqrt[5]{8x^2} \cdot \sqrt[5]{4x^8}$.

Solution Rewrite using the Root of a Product Theorem.

$$\sqrt[5]{8x^2} \cdot \sqrt[5]{4x^8} = \sqrt[5]{\underline{\ ?\ }} \quad \sqrt[5]{32x^{10}}$$
$$= \sqrt[5]{\underline{\ ?\ }} \cdot \sqrt[5]{\underline{\ ?\ }} \quad 32;\ x^{10}$$
$$= \underline{\ ?\ } \quad 2x^2$$

Example 3 Suppose $a \geq 0$ and $b \geq 0$. Simplify $\sqrt[3]{125a^{12}b^{27}}$. $5a^4b^9$

Additional Answers

Activity

Step 1.

a.

$(a\cdot b)^{\frac{1}{3}} - a^{\frac{1}{3}}\cdot b^{\frac{1}{3}}\ |a>0 \text{ and } b>0 \quad 0$

b.

$(a\cdot b)^{\frac{1}{12}} - a^{\frac{1}{12}}\cdot b^{\frac{1}{12}}\ |a>0 \text{ and } b>0 \quad 0$

c.

$a^{\frac{1}{4}}\cdot b^{\frac{1}{4}} - (a\cdot b)^{\frac{1}{4}}\ |a>0 \text{ and } b>0 \quad 0$

d.

$a^{\frac{1}{7}}\cdot b^{\frac{1}{7}} - (a\cdot b)^{\frac{1}{7}}\ |a>0 \text{ and } b>0 \quad 0$

Accommodating the Learner

After students answer Question 15, ask them to solve each of the following inequalities. Students should assume each variable is always greater than 1.

a. Solve $\sqrt[n]{a} + \sqrt[n]{a} < \sqrt[n]{b}$ for b.
$\sqrt[n]{a} + \sqrt[n]{a} = 2 \cdot \sqrt[n]{a}$. If $2 \cdot \sqrt[n]{a} < \sqrt[n]{b}$, then $(2 \cdot \sqrt[n]{a})^n < (\sqrt[n]{b})^n$, so $b > a \cdot 2^n$.

b. Solve $c \cdot \sqrt[n]{a} + d \cdot \sqrt[n]{a} < \sqrt[n]{g}$ for g.
$c \cdot \sqrt[n]{a} + d \cdot \sqrt[n]{a} = (c + d) \cdot \sqrt[n]{a}$.
If $(c + d) \cdot \sqrt[n]{a} < \sqrt[n]{g}$, then $((c + d) \cdot \sqrt[n]{a})^n < (\sqrt[n]{g})^n$, so $g > a \cdot (c + d)^n$.

(*Note*: If students ask why g is used in Part b when e is the next letter, point out that e has a specific meaning when dealing with roots and powers. It represents a constant that is the base of natural logarithms. Also, f is commonly used in $f(x)$ notations, and so it is not used here.)

Additional Example

Example 4 Suppose $y \geq 0$.
Rewrite $\sqrt[5]{96y^{11}}$ with a smaller power of y inside the radical. $(2y^2)\sqrt[5]{3y}$

3 Assignment

Recommended Assignment

- Questions 1–26
- Question 27 (extra credit)
- Reading Lesson 8-6
- Covering the Ideas 8-6

Sometimes when you try to simplify a radical, some irreducible portions remain, as in Example 4. Then the new expression may be more complicated than the given expression.

Example 4

Suppose $x \geq 0$. Rewrite $\sqrt[3]{120x^4}$ with a smaller power of x inside the radical.

Solution 1 Keep as a radical.

$$\sqrt[3]{120x^4} = \sqrt[3]{2^3 \cdot 15 \cdot x^3 \cdot x}$$
$$= \sqrt[3]{2^3 \cdot x^3} \cdot \sqrt[3]{15x}$$
$$= 2x\sqrt[3]{15x}$$

Solution 2 Convert to rational exponents.

$$\sqrt[3]{120x^4} = (120x^4)^{\frac{1}{3}}$$
$$= 120^{\frac{1}{3}} \cdot x^{\frac{4}{3}}$$
$$= 8^{\frac{1}{3}} \cdot 15^{\frac{1}{3}} \cdot x \cdot x^{\frac{1}{3}}$$
$$= 2x(15x)^{\frac{1}{3}}$$

 QY2

▸ **QY2**
Suppose $w \geq 0$.
Rewrite $\sqrt[5]{w^{17}}$ with a smaller power of w inside the radical.

Questions

COVERING THE IDEAS

1. State the Root of a Product Theorem.
2. **True or False** $\sqrt{50} \cdot \sqrt{3} = \sqrt{15} \cdot \sqrt{10}$ true

In 3 and 4, multiply and simplify.

3. $\sqrt[4]{1000} \cdot \sqrt[4]{100{,}000}$ 100
4. $\sqrt[3]{9} \cdot \sqrt[3]{81}$ 9
5. Write three different expressions equal to $\sqrt[3]{250}$.

In 6 and 7, find a and b. Assume $a > 0$ and $b > 0$.

6. $\sqrt{360} = \sqrt{a} \cdot \sqrt{10} = b\sqrt{10}$
7. $\sqrt[3]{297} = \sqrt[3]{a} \cdot \sqrt[3]{11} = b\sqrt[3]{11}$

In 8 and 9, simplify the radicals.

8. $\sqrt[3]{1250}$ $5\sqrt[3]{10}$
9. $\sqrt{98} \cdot \sqrt{14}$ $14\sqrt{7}$

1. For any nonnegative real numbers x and y, and any integer $n \geq 2$, $(xy)^{\frac{1}{n}} = x^{\frac{1}{n}} \cdot y^{\frac{1}{n}}$.
5. Answers vary. Sample: $\sqrt[3]{25} \cdot \sqrt[3]{10}$; $\sqrt[3]{50} \cdot \sqrt[3]{5}$; $\sqrt[3]{125} \cdot \sqrt[3]{2}$
6. $a = 36$, $b = 6$
7. $a = 27$, $b = 3$

Accommodating the Learner

Ask students to use the properties that $\sqrt[n]{a^n} = a$ and $\sqrt[n]{xy} = \sqrt[n]{x} \cdot \sqrt[n]{y}$ to rewrite the following expressions. Students should assume that a and b are always nonnegative.

1. $\sqrt[n]{a^{2n}}$ a^2
2. $\sqrt[2n]{a^n}$ $\sqrt{a}$
3. $\sqrt[n]{a^n b^n}$ ab
4. $\sqrt[n]{a^{2n}b^{2n}}$ a^2b^2

ENGLISH LEARNERS

Vocabulary Development

In a paragraph prior to the Root of a Product Theorem (see page 545), the term *special case* appears. Help students understand the meaning of this important phrase by illustrating this special case in detail:

Power of a Product Postulate:
$(ab)^m = a^m \cdot b^m$

Special case: $m = \frac{1}{2}$: (1) The power form of the special case uses exponents: $(ab)^{\frac{1}{2}} = a^{\frac{1}{2}} \cdot b^{\frac{1}{2}}$. (2) The radical form of the special case uses radicals: $\sqrt{ab} = \sqrt{a} \cdot \sqrt{b}$.

8-5A Lesson Master

Questions on SPUR Objectives
See Student Edition pages 574–577 for objectives.

SKILLS Objective D

In 1–4, simplify the radical expression. Do as much work as you can by hand.

1. $\sqrt[3]{16}$ $2\sqrt[3]{2}$
2. $\sqrt[4]{1600}$ $2\sqrt[4]{100}$
3. $\sqrt{14} \cdot \sqrt{21}$ $7\sqrt{6}$
4. $\sqrt[3]{81} \cdot \sqrt[3]{3}$ $3\sqrt[3]{9}$
5. Solve for b: $\sqrt[3]{12} \cdot \sqrt[3]{b} = \sqrt[3]{72}$. 6
6. Write three different expressions equivalent to $\sqrt[4]{320}$.
Answers vary. Sample: $\sqrt[4]{32} \cdot \sqrt[4]{10}$, $\sqrt[4]{16} \cdot \sqrt[4]{20}$, $\sqrt[4]{64} \cdot \sqrt[4]{5}$

In 7–12, simplify or rewrite with smaller powers of the variables inside the radical. Assume all variables are nonnegative.

7. $\sqrt[3]{8a^6b^{12}}$ $2a^2b^4$
8. $\sqrt{12x^8}$ $2x^4\sqrt{3}$
9. $\sqrt[5]{320p^{12}}$ $2p^2\sqrt[5]{10p^2}$
10. $\sqrt[4]{160{,}000n^{12}}$ $20n^3$
11. $\sqrt[4]{12x^5} \cdot \sqrt[4]{20x^{10}}$ $2x^3\sqrt[4]{15x^3}$
12. $\sqrt{17a^{12}b^3} \cdot \sqrt{5a^3b^{10}}$ $a^7b^6\sqrt{85ab}$

PROPERTIES Objective G

13. For what values of x is $\sqrt[8]{x^8} = x$? $x \geq 0$
14. Give a counterexample to show that $\sqrt[4]{a} \cdot \sqrt[4]{b} \neq \sqrt[4]{ab}$.
Answers vary. Sample: when $a = -1$ and $b = -16$, $\sqrt[4]{ab} = \sqrt[4]{16} = 2$, but $\sqrt[4]{a} \cdot \sqrt[4]{b}$ is not defined.
15. Chris says that $6\sqrt[3]{3} = \sqrt[6]{6}$. Pat says that $\sqrt[3]{3} = \sqrt[6]{9}$. Who is correct? Explain.
Pat is correct. Explanations vary. Sample: $\sqrt[6]{9} = \sqrt[6]{3^2} = 3^{\frac{2}{6}} = 3^{\frac{1}{3}} = \sqrt[3]{3}$.

474 Advanced Algebra

In 10–12, assume all variables are nonnegative. Simplify or rewrite with a smaller power of the variable inside the radical.

10. a. $\sqrt{144x^4}$ $12x^2$ b. $\sqrt{144x^5}$ $12x^2\sqrt{x}$

11. a. $\sqrt[3]{64y^{18}}$ $4y^6$ b. $\sqrt[3]{\frac{y^{25}}{8}}$ $\frac{y^8}{2}\sqrt[3]{y}$

12. $\sqrt[4]{1250y^3p^{17}}$ $5p^4\sqrt[4]{2y^3p}$

APPLYING THE MATHEMATICS

In 13 and 14, simplify the expression.

13. $\sqrt[3]{12} \cdot \sqrt[3]{18}$ 6

14. $\sqrt[4]{144 \cdot 10^3} \cdot \sqrt[4]{9 \cdot 10^5}$ 600

In 15 and 16, identify which expression is greater.

15. $\sqrt[3]{5} + \sqrt[3]{5}$ or $\sqrt[3]{10}$ $\sqrt[3]{5} + \sqrt[3]{5}$

16. $\sqrt[3]{600{,}000}$ or 100 100

17. Ali Baster simplifies $\sqrt[3]{4} \cdot \sqrt[6]{5}$ to $\sqrt[6]{20}$.
   a. Why is Ali's result incorrect?
   b. Solve $\sqrt[3]{4} \cdot \sqrt[6]{5} = \sqrt[6]{n}$ for n. $n = 80$

17a. The Root of a Product Theorem does not apply when multiplying two different nth roots.

In 18 and 19, assume all variables are positive. Rewrite with a simpler expression inside the radical.

18. $\sqrt[3]{640x^{12}y^{11}}$ $4x^4y^3\sqrt[3]{10y^2}$

19. $\sqrt{4x^2 + 4y^2}$ $2\sqrt{x^2 + y^2}$

REVIEW

20. Since 2000, the price of gasoline has been quite volatile. Here are the changes in average price for the years 2000–2006. Follow the steps to find the average annual price increase.

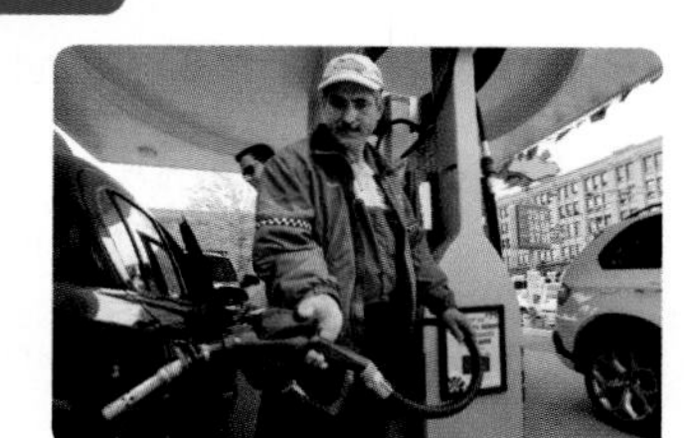

Year	Percent Increase From Preceding Year	Size-Change Factor
2000	28.5	? 1.285
2001	-3.6	? 0.964
2002	-6.5	? 0.935
2003	16.5	? 1.165
2004	18.2	? 1.182
2005	21.9	? 1.219
2006	12.9	? 1.129

   a. Fill in the table above by converting each percent into a size-change factor. **(Previous Course)**
   b. Compute the geometric mean of the factors you found in Part a to determine the average annual percentage increase. **(Lesson 8-4)** 11.9%

Notes on the Questions

Questions 10 and 11 In each question, Part a simplifies nicely, while Part b is more complicated.

Question 15 Many students *incorrectly* assume that $\sqrt[n]{a} + \sqrt[n]{b} = \sqrt[n]{a + b}$. They are generalizing the Root of a Product Theorem inappropriately. Stress that two addends in a sum such as $\sqrt[3]{2} + \sqrt[3]{3}$ cannot usually be combined algebraically, and the Root of a Product Theorem can be used only on a *product* of radicals, not a sum or difference of radicals. You might want to ask why the addends in the sum $\sqrt[3]{3} + \sqrt[3]{24}$ can be combined, and what their sum is. $\sqrt[3]{24} = 2\sqrt[3]{3}$, so $\sqrt[3]{3} + \sqrt[3]{24} = \sqrt[3]{3} + 2\sqrt[3]{3} = 3\sqrt[3]{3}$. This can be checked with a calculator.

Question 20 You might want to ask students to update this question with current price information.

Extension

Ask students to extend Question 17b: If $\sqrt[n]{a} \cdot \sqrt[2n]{b} = \sqrt[2n]{c}$, solve for c. $\sqrt[2n]{a^2} \cdot \sqrt[2n]{b} = \sqrt[2n]{a^2b} = \sqrt[2n]{c}$, so $c = a^2b$.

Then ask students to solve $\sqrt[n]{a} \cdot \sqrt[m]{b} = \sqrt[mn]{c}$ for c. $\sqrt[mn]{a^m} \cdot \sqrt[mn]{b^n} = \sqrt[mn]{a^mb^n} = \sqrt[mn]{c}$, so $c = a^mb^n$.

8-5

4 Wrap-Up

Ongoing Assessment

Ask students to explain how to rewrite the expressions $\sqrt[3]{13.5} \cdot \sqrt[3]{2}$ and $\sqrt[4]{81a^4b^{11}}$. Answers vary. Sample: Rewrite $\sqrt[3]{13.5} \cdot \sqrt[3]{2}$ as $\sqrt[3]{27}$, which is 3; rewrite $\sqrt[4]{81a^4b^{11}}$ as $\sqrt[4]{81} \cdot \sqrt[4]{a^4} \cdot \sqrt[4]{b^8} \cdot \sqrt[4]{b^3}$ or $3ab^2\sqrt[4]{b^3}$

Project Update

Project 3, *Properties of Irrational Numbers*, on page 568 relates to the content of this lesson.

21. Suppose $f(x) = \sqrt[4]{x}$. **(Lesson 8-4)**
    a. If x increases from 1 to 2, by how much does $f(x)$ increase? about 0.189
    b. If x increases from 11 to 12, by how much does $f(x)$ increase? about 0.040

22. **True or False** The inverse of the power function f with $f(x) = x^a$ is $f^{-1}(x) = x^{-a}$. Explain your reasoning. **(Lesson 8-3)**

23. a. Find an equation for the inverse of the linear function L defined by $L(x) = mx + b$. $L^{-1}(x) = \frac{x-b}{m}$
    b. How are the slopes of the function and its inverse related?
    c. When is the inverse of L not a function? **(Lessons 8-2, 3-1)**

24. Solve for real values of y and check: $\frac{y^{-3}}{y} = \frac{1}{81}$. **(Lesson 7-3)** $y = \pm 3$

25. Write $\frac{2+3i}{7-6i}$ in $a + bi$ form. **(Lesson 6-9)** $-\frac{4}{85} + \frac{33}{85}i$

26. a. Multiply $(2 - \sqrt{5}) \cdot (20 + 10\sqrt{5})$. **(Lesson 6-1)** -10
    b. Your answer to Part a should be an integer. Tell how you could know that in advance.

22. False; to find the inverse, switch x and y and solve for y. The result is $f^{-1}(x) = x^{\frac{1}{a}}$.

23b. They are reciprocals.

23c. when $m = 0$

26b. Answers vary. Sample: For $a = 10$, $b = 2$, and $c = 5$, the product can be rewritten as $a(b - \sqrt{c})(b + \sqrt{c}) = a(b^2 - c)$, and for integers a, b, c, the product is an integer.

EXPLORATION

27. The diagram at the right can be used to compare the arithmetic mean and geometric mean of two positive numbers. Suppose that $AC = x$ and $BC = y$.

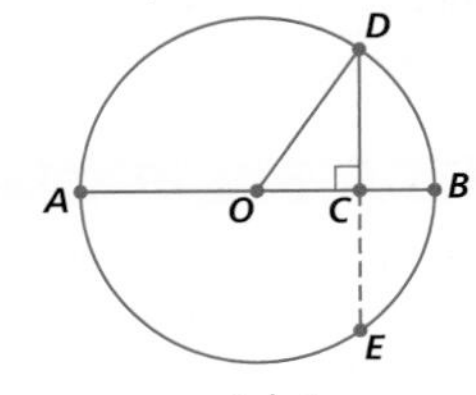

    a. Find the length of the radius of circle O in terms of x and y.
    b. Find CD in terms of x and y. Recall from geometry the Secant Length Theorem: $AC \cdot CB = CD \cdot CE$. In this situation, $CE = CD$. $CD = \sqrt{xy}$
    c. In $\triangle OCD$, which side corresponds to the arithmetic mean of x and y? $\overline{OD}$
    d. In $\triangle OCD$, which side corresponds to the geometric mean of x and y? $\overline{CD}$
    e. Which of the segments you named in Parts c and d must be longer, and why? $\overline{OD}$; It is the hypotenuse of a right triangle in which $\overline{CD}$ is a leg.
    f. In what situation can the two means be equal? when $x = y$

27a. $r = \frac{x+y}{2}$

QY ANSWERS

1. $4a^2b^5$
2. $w^3\sqrt[5]{w^2}$

8-5B page 2

8-5B Lesson Master

Questions on SPUR Objectives
See Student Edition pages 574–577 for objectives.

SKILLS Objective D

1. Find e and f.
   a. $\sqrt{600} = \sqrt{e} \cdot \sqrt{6} = f\sqrt{6}$ $e =$ 100 $f =$ 10
   b. $\sqrt[3]{1600} = \sqrt[3]{e} \cdot \sqrt[3]{25} = f\sqrt[3]{25}$ $e =$ 64 $f =$ 4

Multiple Choice In 2–4, identify the expression that is *not* equivalent to the given expression.

2. $\sqrt[3]{96}$ C
   A $\sqrt[3]{48} \cdot \sqrt[3]{2}$ B $\sqrt[3]{12} \cdot \sqrt[3]{8}$ C $8\sqrt[3]{12}$
   D $2\sqrt[3]{12}$ E $\sqrt[3]{16} \cdot \sqrt[3]{6}$ F $\sqrt[3]{4} \cdot \sqrt[3]{24}$
3. $\sqrt[4]{5} \cdot \sqrt[4]{250}$ B
   A $\sqrt[4]{5} \cdot \sqrt[4]{125} \cdot \sqrt[4]{2}$ B $2\sqrt[4]{5}$ C $\sqrt[4]{5^4} \cdot \sqrt[4]{2}$
   D $\sqrt[4]{1250}$ E $\sqrt[4]{50} \cdot \sqrt[4]{25}$ F $5\sqrt[4]{2}$
4. $\sqrt[6]{128y^{14}}$ D
   A $\sqrt[6]{128} \cdot \sqrt[6]{y^{12}} \cdot \sqrt[6]{y^2}$ B $\sqrt[6]{2^6 \cdot 2 \cdot y^6 \cdot y^6 \cdot y^2}$ C $\sqrt[6]{2^7} \cdot \sqrt[6]{y^{14}}$
   D $64y^{12} \cdot \sqrt[6]{2y^2}$ E $\sqrt[6]{128} \cdot \sqrt[6]{y^{14}}$ F $2y^2\sqrt[6]{2y^2}$

In 5–20, simplify or rewrite with smaller powers of the variables inside the radical. Assume all variables are nonnegative.

5. $\sqrt[3]{250}$ $5\sqrt[3]{2}$
6. $\sqrt[4]{48}$ $2\sqrt[4]{3}$
7. $\sqrt[4]{50{,}000x^7}$ $10x\sqrt[4]{5x^3}$
8. $\sqrt[3]{27x^6y^4}$ $3x^2y\sqrt[3]{y}$
9. $\sqrt[6]{x^{12}y^6}$ x^2y
10. $\sqrt[4]{81m^5}$ $3m\sqrt[4]{m}$
11. $\sqrt[4]{5} \cdot \sqrt[4]{125}$ 5
12. $\sqrt[3]{9} \cdot \sqrt[3]{48}$ $6\sqrt[3]{2}$
13. $\sqrt[3]{2u^7} \cdot \sqrt[3]{4u^2}$ $2u^3$
14. $\sqrt[5]{3^3x} \cdot \sqrt[5]{3^4x^8}$ $3x\sqrt[5]{9x^4}$
15. $\sqrt[3]{54x^8}$ $3x^2\sqrt[3]{2x^2}$
16. $\sqrt[5]{32y^9}$ $2y\sqrt[5]{y^4}$
17. $\sqrt[7]{z^{21}w^{14}}$ z^3w^2
18. $\sqrt[9]{2^{12}x^{14}y^{10}}$ $2xy\sqrt[9]{2^3x^5y}$
19. $\sqrt[3]{4x^2} \cdot \sqrt[3]{2x}$ $2x$
20. $\sqrt[4]{3^6w^7} \cdot \sqrt[4]{3^2w^2}$ $9w^2\sqrt[4]{w}$

476

Advanced Algebra 475

Lesson 8-6 Quotients with Radicals

Vocabulary

rationalizing the denominator

conjugate

BIG IDEA A fraction with a denominator of the form $a + b\sqrt{c}$ can be rewritten without any square root in the denominator.

In the book *The Phantom Tollbooth* (Juster, 1961), Milo and his traveling companions Humbug and Tock encounter the sign below, which gives the distance to the land of Digitopolis.

DIGITOPOLIS	
5	Miles
1,600	Rods
8,800	Yards
26,400	Feet
316,800	Inches
633,600	Half Inches
AND THEN SOME	

The characters argue about which distance to travel. Humbug wants to use miles because he believes the distance is shorter, while Milo wants to travel by half inches because he thinks it will be quicker.

The joke is that all the distances are the same. For example, 1 rod (a measure used in surveying) is equal to 16.5 ft, so $\frac{26{,}400 \text{ ft}}{16.5 \frac{\text{ft}}{\text{rod}}} = 1600$ rods. The point is that there are many ways to express one quantity or one number. You saw this when simplifying radicals in the previous lesson. Now we apply this idea to find different ways of writing quotients with radicals.

Mental Math

At a certain time of day, a tree casts an 18 ft shadow.

a. A nearby 8 ft light pole casts a 12 ft long shadow. How tall is the tree? 12 ft

b. How long is the shadow cast by the nearby 3 ft mailbox? 4.5 ft

c. When Trey gets the mail, his shadow is twice as long as the mailbox's shadow. How tall is he? 6 ft

Rationalizing When the Denominator Is a Radical

Think about how you might approximate the value of $\frac{1}{\sqrt{2}}$ without a calculator. Using long division is no help because dividing 1 by $\sqrt{2}$ requires you to calculate $1.414213\ldots\overline{)1.00}$, which cannot be done by hand. Instead, a process called **rationalizing the denominator** is used to write an equivalent form of the number without a radical in the denominator. *Rationalizing* means rewriting the fraction so that its denominator is a rational number.

Background

Rewriting expressions in particular forms is actually more complicated than solving equations. Equations can be solved by successive approximations and by simple graphical interpretation, but both of those procedures are unavailable for rewriting expressions.

In this lesson, two related kinds of rewriting are discussed: rewriting a fraction that has $\sqrt{x}$ in its denominator (Example 1) and the more general question of rewriting a fraction whose denominator has the form $a + b\sqrt{x}$ (Example 2). The first of these is a useful skill for trigonometry; the second is closely related to the division of complex numbers. These two skills help students to develop understandings of the relationships of square roots to each other and to multiplication and division. They also help in dealing with the variety of forms in which expressions involving radicals may be written.

Lesson 8-6

GOAL

Discuss the traditional skill of rewriting a fraction with a radical sign in its denominator as a fraction with a rational denominator.

SPUR Objectives

D Rewrite or simplify expressions with radicals.

Materials/Resources

- Lesson Masters 8-6A and 8-6B
- Resource Master 147
- Quiz 2
- CAS

HOMEWORK

Suggestions for Assignment

- Questions 1–29
- Question 30 (extra credit)
- Reading Lesson 8-7
- Covering the Ideas 8-7

Local Standards

1 Warm-Up

In 1–3, write in $a + bi$ form.

1. $2i \cdot 3i$ $-6 + 0i$
2. $(9 + 16\sqrt{-1})(9 - 16\sqrt{-1})$ $337 + 0i$
3. $\frac{2i - 6}{3 + i}$ $-1.6 + 1.2i$

2 Teaching

Notes on the Lesson

Activity The type of CAS being used may affect the output. For example, the Casio ClassPad requires that the decimal calculation setting be turned off to rationalize numerical denominators.

Point out that the Activity and Examples 1 and 2 rely on the Equal Fractions Property: The numerator and the denominator of a fraction can be multiplied by the same nonzero number without changing the value of the fraction. Here the equal fractions look quite different, which is why the technique is important.

Example 1 You might ask students how Example 1 could be checked. One way is to substitute a specific value for x. For instance, suppose $x = 2$. Is $\frac{3}{\sqrt{12x}}$ equal to $\frac{\sqrt{3x}}{2x}$? A calculator shows that each is about 0.612; it checks. Another check relies on the Means-Extremes Property: When $x \neq 0$, $\frac{3}{\sqrt{12x}} = \frac{\sqrt{3x}}{2x}$ if and only if $\sqrt{12x} \cdot \sqrt{3x}$ (the product of the means) equals $3 \cdot 2x$ (the product of the extremes). This is the case, since $x \geq 0$, each is equal to $6x$.

Note-Taking Tips

Encourage students to include a comment explicitly describing the conjugate of an expression when they rationalize a denominator. For example, when they rationalize $\frac{3}{4 + \sqrt{7}}$ in Example 2, they should include the statement "the conjugate of $4 + \sqrt{7}$ is $4 - \sqrt{7}$."

Activity

MATERIALS CAS

Step 1 Enter the following expressions into a CAS and record the results. Do not use decimal approximations.

a. $\frac{1}{\sqrt{2}}$ $\frac{\sqrt{2}}{2}$ b. $\frac{3}{\sqrt{5}}$ $\frac{3\sqrt{5}}{5}$ c. $-\frac{13}{\sqrt{7}}$ $-\frac{13\sqrt{7}}{7}$

Step 2 Approximate each original expression in Step 1 and the resulting CAS expression to 3 decimal places. Do the pairs of numbers appear to be equal? yes

Step 3 Rewrite $\frac{1}{\sqrt{a}}$ ($a > 0$) without a radical in the denominator. $\frac{\sqrt{a}}{a}$

The results of the Activity suggest a method for rationalizing denominators of fractions whose denominators are square roots. In general, $\frac{a}{\sqrt{x}} = \frac{a}{\sqrt{x}} \cdot \frac{\sqrt{x}}{\sqrt{x}} = \frac{a\sqrt{x}}{x}$ for $x > 0$. This works because $\frac{\sqrt{x}}{\sqrt{x}} = 1$ and $\sqrt{x} \cdot \sqrt{x} = x$ for all real numbers x.

 QY

> **QY**
> Rewrite $\frac{26}{\sqrt{13}}$ by rationalizing the denominator.

Because of technology, rationalizing denominators to obtain close approximations of quotients is no longer necessary. However, rationalizing denominators is still a useful process because not all technologies put results with radicals in the same form. You can expect to see different but equivalent forms of rationalized expressions depending upon the technology you use.

You can also rationalize denominators involving variable expressions.

GUIDED

Example 1

Rationalize the denominator of $\frac{3}{\sqrt{12x}}$, where $x > 0$.

Solution 1 Simplify the denominator first, then rationalize.

$\frac{3}{\sqrt{12x}} = \frac{3}{\sqrt{3 \cdot 4 \cdot x}} = \frac{3}{\sqrt{3} \cdot \sqrt{?} \cdot \sqrt{?}} = \frac{3}{? \cdot \sqrt{?}} \cdot \frac{?}{?} = \frac{?}{?}$ $\sqrt{3x}$; $\sqrt{3x}$ 4; x; 2; $3x$; $\sqrt{3x}$; $2x$

Solution 2 Rationalize first, then simplify.

$\frac{3}{\sqrt{12x}} \cdot \frac{?}{?} = \frac{?}{12x} = \frac{?}{?}$ $\sqrt{12x}$; $3\sqrt{12x}$; $\sqrt{3x}$ $\sqrt{12x}$; $2x$

Accommodating the Learner

Ask students to show the steps of rationalizing the denominator of $\frac{1}{a + b\sqrt{c}}$. Then ask them if there is a quick way to use their result to rationalize the denominator of $\frac{1}{a - b\sqrt{c}}$. $\frac{1}{a + b\sqrt{c}} \cdot \frac{a - b\sqrt{c}}{a - b\sqrt{c}} = \frac{a - b\sqrt{c}}{a^2 - b^2c}$; to rationalize the denominator for $\frac{1}{a - b\sqrt{c}}$, replace b with $-b$ in that result: $\frac{a - (-b)\sqrt{c}}{a^2 - (-b)^2c} = \frac{a + b\sqrt{c}}{a^2 - b^2c}$.

Rationalizing When the Denominator Is a Sum Containing a Radical

Now consider a fraction $\frac{n}{a + \sqrt{b}}$, in which a radical in the denominator is added to another term. In this form you cannot easily separate the rational and irrational parts. However, to rationalize the denominator, you can use a technique similar to the one you used in Lesson 6-9 to divide complex numbers. Recall that to write $\frac{1}{5 + 2i}$ in $a + bi$ form, you multiply both numerator and denominator by the complex conjugate of the denominator, $5 - 2i$. To rationalize a fraction with a denominator of the form $a + \sqrt{b}$, multiply both numerator and denominator by the **conjugate** $a - \sqrt{b}$. The product has a denominator with no radical terms, because $(x + y)(x - y) = x^2 - y^2$.

> **▸ READING MATH**
> The word *conjugate* comes from the Latin prefix *co-* meaning "together with," and the Latin verb *jugare*, meaning "to join" or "to connect." In algebra, two complex numbers or radical expressions that are conjugates are joined together as a pair.

Example 2

Write $\frac{3}{4 + \sqrt{7}}$ in $a + b\sqrt{c}$ form.

Solution 1 The conjugate of $4 + \sqrt{7}$ is $4 - \sqrt{7}$.

$$\frac{3}{4 + \sqrt{7}} \cdot \frac{4 - \sqrt{7}}{4 - \sqrt{7}} = \frac{3(4 - \sqrt{7})}{4^2 - \sqrt{7}^2} = \frac{3(4 - \sqrt{7})}{16 - 7} = \frac{3(4 - \sqrt{7})}{9} = \frac{4 - \sqrt{7}}{3}$$
$$= \frac{4}{3} - \frac{\sqrt{7}}{3}$$

Solution 2 Use a calculator to multiply the numerator and denominator by the conjugate. The result can be rewritten in $a + b\sqrt{c}$ form as $\frac{4}{3} - \frac{\sqrt{7}}{3}$.

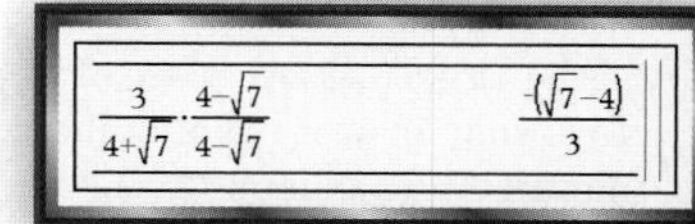

Check Estimate the original and final expressions with decimals.

$\frac{3}{4 + \sqrt{7}} \approx 0.45142$

$\frac{4}{3} - \frac{\sqrt{7}}{3} \approx 0.45142$

It checks.

Questions

COVERING THE IDEAS

1. Verify that the indicated numbers on the DIGITOPOLIS sign are equivalent.
   a. the number of inches and the number of yards
   b. the number of yards and the number of miles
2. Why is it impossible to do long division with $\sqrt{73}$ as a divisor?

1a. $316{,}800 \text{ in.} \cdot \frac{1 \text{ ft}}{12 \text{ in.}} \cdot \frac{1 \text{ yd}}{3 \text{ft}} = 8800 \text{ yd}$

1b. $8800 \text{ yd} \cdot \frac{1 \text{ mi}}{1760 \text{ yd}} = 5 \text{ mi}$

2. It is impossible to use an irrational number as a divisor in long division.

Additional Examples

Example 1 Assume $x > 0$. Rationalize the denominator of $\frac{5}{\sqrt{45x}}$.

Solution 1 Simplify the denominator and then rationalize: $\frac{5}{\sqrt{45x}} = \frac{5}{\sqrt{5 \cdot 9 \cdot x}} = \frac{5}{\sqrt{5} \cdot \sqrt{?} \cdot \sqrt{?}} = \frac{5}{? \sqrt{?}} \cdot \frac{?}{?} = \frac{?}{?}$ 9; x; 3; $5x$; $\sqrt{5x}$; $\sqrt{5x}$; $\sqrt{5x}$; $3x$

Solution 2 Rationalize and then simplify: $\frac{5}{\sqrt{45x}} \cdot \frac{?}{?} = \frac{?}{45x} = \frac{?}{?} = \frac{?}{?}$ $\sqrt{45x}$; $\sqrt{45x}$; $5\sqrt{9}\sqrt{5x}$; $\frac{15\sqrt{5x}}{45x}$; $\frac{\sqrt{5x}}{3x}$

Example 2 Write $\frac{2}{3 - \sqrt{5}}$ in $a + b\sqrt{c}$ form. $\frac{3}{2} + \frac{1}{2}\sqrt{5}$

3 Assignment

Recommended Assignment

- Questions 1–29
- Question 30 (extra credit)
- Reading Lesson 8-7
- Covering the Ideas 8-7

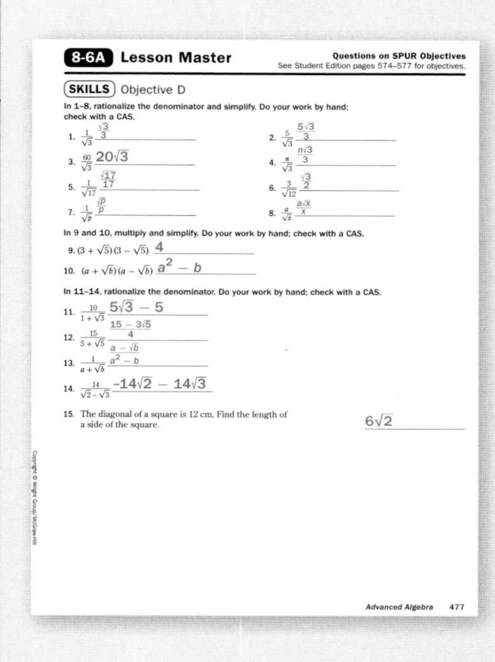

8-6A Lesson Master

Questions on SPUR Objectives
See Student Edition pages 574–577 for objectives.

SKILLS Objective D

In 1–8, rationalize the denominator and simplify. Do your work by hand; check with a CAS.

1. $\frac{1}{\sqrt{3}}$ $\frac{\sqrt{3}}{3}$
2. $\frac{5}{\sqrt{3}}$ $\frac{5\sqrt{3}}{3}$
3. $\frac{60}{\sqrt{3}}$ $20\sqrt{3}$
4. $\frac{n}{\sqrt{3}}$ $\frac{n\sqrt{3}}{3}$
5. $\frac{1}{\sqrt{17}}$ $\frac{\sqrt{17}}{17}$
6. $\frac{3}{\sqrt{12}}$ $\frac{\sqrt{3}}{2}$
7. $\frac{1}{\sqrt{p}}$ $\frac{\sqrt{p}}{p}$
8. $\frac{a}{\sqrt{x}}$ $\frac{a\sqrt{x}}{x}$

In 9 and 10, multiply and simplify. Do your work by hand; check with a CAS.

9. $(3 + \sqrt{5})(3 - \sqrt{5})$ 4
10. $(a + \sqrt{b})(a - \sqrt{b})$ $a^2 - b$

In 11–14, rationalize the denominator. Do your work by hand; check with a CAS.

11. $\frac{10}{1 + \sqrt{3}}$ $5\sqrt{3} - 5$
12. $\frac{15}{5 + \sqrt{5}}$ $\frac{15 - 3\sqrt{5}}{4}$
13. $\frac{1}{a + \sqrt{b}}$ $\frac{a - \sqrt{b}}{a^2 - b}$
14. $\frac{14}{\sqrt{2} - \sqrt{3}}$ $-14\sqrt{2} - 14\sqrt{3}$

15. The diagonal of a square is 12 cm. Find the length of a side of the square. $6\sqrt{2}$

Advanced Algebra 477

Accommodating the Learner

After students complete the Activity, ask them what they think the phrase *rationalize the numerator* might mean. Answers vary. Sample: If a fraction has a radical in the numerator, then rewrite it as an equivalent fraction without a radical in the numerator. (Some students may be interested to know that this process is used in calculus to find the limit of some rational expressions that have a radical in the numerator.) Then ask students to rationalize the numerator for these fractions, showing the steps of their work.

1. $\frac{\sqrt{p}}{\sqrt{q}}$ $\frac{\sqrt{p}}{\sqrt{q}} = \frac{\sqrt{p}}{\sqrt{q}} \cdot \frac{\sqrt{p}}{\sqrt{p}} = \frac{p}{\sqrt{pq}}$

2. $\sqrt{5}$ $\sqrt{5} = \frac{\sqrt{5}}{1} = \frac{\sqrt{5}}{1} \cdot \frac{\sqrt{5}}{\sqrt{5}} = \frac{5}{\sqrt{5}}$

3. $\frac{\sqrt{2} - 5}{\sqrt{2} + 5}$ $\frac{\sqrt{2} - 5}{\sqrt{2} + 5} = \frac{\sqrt{2} - 5}{\sqrt{2} + 5} \cdot \frac{\sqrt{2} + 5}{\sqrt{2} + 5} = \frac{2 - 25}{2 + 2 \cdot 5\sqrt{2} + 25} = \frac{-23}{27 + 10\sqrt{2}}$

Notes on the Questions

Question 3 Students will see this expression when they study trigonometry because $\sin 45° = \cos 45° = \frac{\sqrt{2}}{2}$. This value also equals $\sqrt{\frac{1}{2}}$.

Questions 7 and 8 Students can check their answers by using decimals to approximate the given expression and their rationalized expression.

3. Estimate the value of $\frac{\sqrt{2}}{2}$ to the nearest tenth. 0.7
4. What does the term *rationalize the denominator* mean?
5. If $a > 0$, rewrite $\frac{b}{\sqrt{a}}$ without a radical in the denominator. $\frac{b\sqrt{a}}{a}$
6. Are $\frac{2}{\sqrt{17}}$ and $\frac{2\sqrt{17}}{17}$ equal? Justify your answer.

In 7 and 8, rationalize the denominator.

7. $\frac{11}{\sqrt{3}}$ $\frac{11\sqrt{3}}{3}$
8. $\frac{4}{\sqrt{34}}$ $\frac{2\sqrt{34}}{17}$

In 9 and 10, a fraction is given.

a. Tell what you would multiply the fraction by to rationalize the denominator.

b. Rationalize the denominator and write the result in $a + b\sqrt{c}$ form.

9. $\frac{7}{3 - \sqrt{5}}$
10. $\frac{16}{\sqrt{12t} + 8}$

APPLYING THE MATHEMATICS

In 11–15, rationalize the denominator of each expression. Assume all variables are positive.

11. $\frac{3}{2\sqrt{3}}$ $\frac{\sqrt{3}}{2}$
12. $\frac{47}{\sqrt{47}}$ $\sqrt{47}$
13. $\frac{3x}{\sqrt{9x^5}}$ $\frac{\sqrt{x}}{x^2}$
14. $\frac{5 - \sqrt{12}}{5 + \sqrt{12}}$
15. $\frac{4}{\sqrt{n} - 6}$

16. As pictured at the right, the largest square piece of wood that can be cut out of a circular log with diameter d has a side of length $\frac{d}{\sqrt{2}}$. If the radius of a log is 17 in., what is the side length of the largest square piece of wood that can be cut from it? Give your answer in both rationalized form and to the nearest hundredth of an inch. $17\sqrt{2}$ in.; 24.04 in.

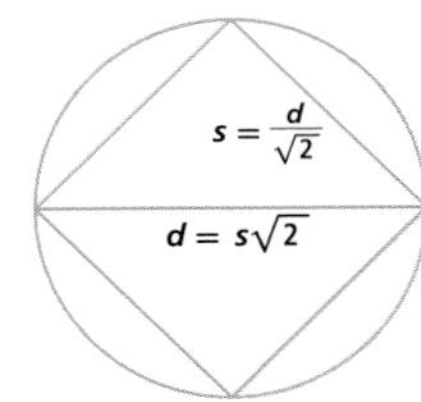

17. Recall from geometry the ratio of the sides of a 30-60-90 triangle as shown in the diagram at the right.
    a. If the length of the longer leg of the triangle is 8, find the length of the hypotenuse in rationalized form. $\frac{16\sqrt{3}}{3}$
    b. If the length of the longer leg of the triangle is a, write rationalized expressions for the lengths of the other two sides of the triangle in terms of a. $\frac{a\sqrt{3}}{3}$; $\frac{2a\sqrt{3}}{3}$
    c. What is the missing x-coordinate of the point on the circle at the far right? Rationalize the denominator of your answer. $\frac{5\sqrt{3}}{3}$

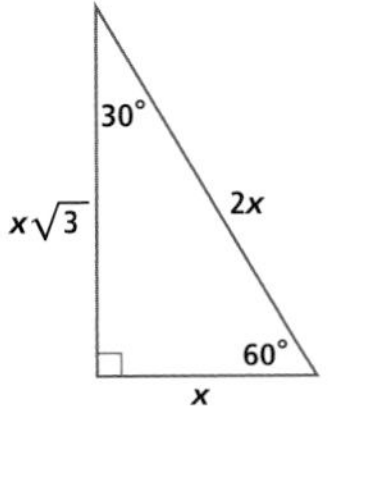

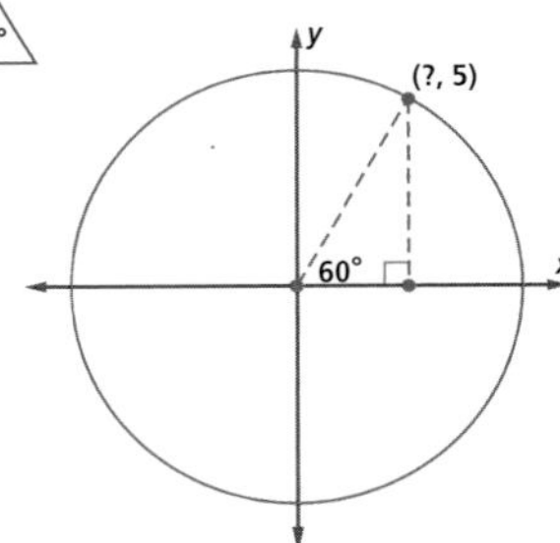

4. It means to write an equivalent form of a fraction that does not have radicals in the denominator.

6. Yes; $\frac{2}{\sqrt{17}} = \frac{2}{\sqrt{17}} \cdot \frac{\sqrt{17}}{\sqrt{17}} = \frac{2\sqrt{17}}{17}$.

9a. $\frac{3 + \sqrt{5}}{3 + \sqrt{5}}$

9b. $\frac{21}{4} + \frac{7\sqrt{5}}{4}$

10a. $\frac{\sqrt{12t} - 8}{\sqrt{12t} - 8}$

10b. $\frac{8\sqrt{3t}}{3t - 16} - \frac{32}{3t - 16}$

14. $\frac{37 - 20\sqrt{3}}{13}$

15. $\frac{4\sqrt{n} + 24}{n - 36}$

ENGLISH LEARNERS

Vocabulary Development

Some students may ask if the math term *rationalize* is related to the term *rationalization* (which refers to finding reasons to support an existing conclusion). The term *rationalization* is related to *rationale,* a noun referring to the basis of a statement, whereas *rationalize* is more closely related to *rational number* because the denominator is being written as a rational number.

18. In the equilateral triangle at the right, find the ratio of s to h. Write your answer with a rationalized denominator. $\frac{2\sqrt{3}}{3}$

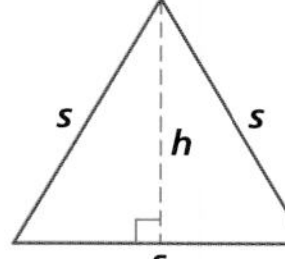

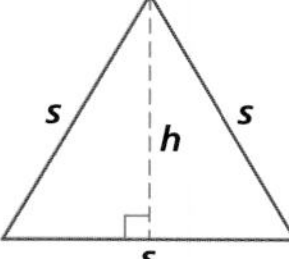

REVIEW

In 19 and 20, simplify the expression. Assume a and b are nonnegative real numbers. (Lesson 8-5)

19. $\sqrt[3]{54a^7}$ $3a^2\sqrt[3]{2a}$

20. $\sqrt[4]{64a^3b^2}\sqrt{8a^6b}$ $8a^3b\sqrt[4]{a^3}$

True or False In 21 and 22, assume all variables are positive. Justify your answer. (Lesson 8-4)

21. $\sqrt{xy^{\frac{1}{4}}} = \sqrt[8]{x^4y}$

22. $\sqrt[3]{m^{\frac{1}{4}}n} = \sqrt[36]{m^3n^{12}}$

23. Suppose $g: x \to x^{\frac{1}{3}}$, and $x > 0$. (Lessons 8-3, 8-2, 8-1)
    a. Find an equation for g^{-1}. $g^{-1}(x) = x^3$
    b. If $h: x \to 2x$, find $g \circ h(x)$. $(2x)^{\frac{1}{3}}$

24. Explain why the inverse of $f: x \to 7x^{38}$ is not a function. (Lessons 8-2, 7-1)

25. Let f be a function defined by the table below. Is the inverse of f a function? Why or why not? (Lesson 8-2)

x	1	3	4	8	11	12
$f(x)$	3	5	13	5	-2	4

In 26 and 27, assume p and q are positive numbers. Write each expression without negative exponents. (Lesson 7-8)

26. $p^{-\frac{1}{5}}q^{\frac{3}{8}}$ $\frac{q^{\frac{3}{8}}}{p^{\frac{1}{5}}}$

27. $\frac{p^{-\frac{2}{3}}}{p}$ $\frac{1}{p^{\frac{5}{3}}}$

In 28 and 29, write an expression to describe the situation. (Lesson 1-1)

28. Kim collects teacups. She now has 14 teacups and buys one new teacup per month. How many teacups will she have after m months? $14 + m$

29. You buy G granola bars at d dollars per bar. How much did you spend? Gd

EXPLORATION

30. A friend tries to rationalize $\frac{1}{\sqrt[3]{x}}$ by performing the following multiplication:
$\frac{1}{\sqrt[3]{x}} \cdot \frac{\sqrt[3]{x}}{\sqrt[3]{x}}$.
    a. Explain why this method will not work.
    b. Devise a method to rationalize the denominator of $\frac{1}{\sqrt[3]{x}}$.
    c. Rewrite $\frac{1}{\sqrt[3]{x}}$ as a rational power of x. $x^{-\frac{1}{3}}$

21. True; by the Power of a Power Postulate, each side is equivalent to $x^{\frac{1}{2}}y^{\frac{1}{8}}$.

22. True; by the Power of a Power Postulate, each side is equivalent to $m^{\frac{1}{12}}n^{\frac{1}{3}}$.

24. The graph of $y = x^{38}$ does not pass the horizontal-line test.

25. No; the inverse contains two points, (5, 3) and (5, 8), with the same first coordinates.

30a. The multiplication gives $\frac{3\sqrt{x}}{(\sqrt[3]{x})^2}$, which does not have a rational denominator.

30b. Multiply the numerator and denominator by $(\sqrt[3]{x})^2$.

QY ANSWER

$\frac{26}{\sqrt{13}} = \frac{26}{\sqrt{13}} \cdot \frac{\sqrt{13}}{\sqrt{13}} = \frac{26\sqrt{13}}{13}$
$= 2\sqrt{13}$

Notes on the Questions

Questions 21 and 22 These questions lead into the ideas of Lesson 8-7.

Question 30 There is no single method for rationalizing denominators with cube roots in them, but here a student could multiply both the numerator and the denominator by $\sqrt[3]{x^2}$.

4 Wrap-Up

Ongoing Assessment

Ask students to work in groups. Two students should select integers a and b and each write an expression of the form $a + b\sqrt{5}$. Then all members of the group should write the same ratio of those two expressions, rationalize the denominator of the ratio, and check each other's work. Answers vary. Check students' work.

Administer Quiz 2 (or a quiz of your own) after students complete this lesson.

Extension

Ask students to extend Question 30 by rationalizing the denominator of $\frac{1}{1 - \sqrt[4]{a}}$.

Answers vary. Sample: $\frac{1}{1 - \sqrt[4]{a}} =$

$$\frac{1}{1 - \sqrt[4]{a}} \cdot \frac{1 + \sqrt[4]{a}}{1 + \sqrt[4]{a}} = \frac{1 + \sqrt[4]{a}}{1 - \sqrt[4]{a^2}} = \frac{1 + \sqrt[4]{a}}{1 - \sqrt{a}} =$$

$$\frac{1 + \sqrt[4]{a}}{1 - \sqrt{a}} \cdot \frac{1 + \sqrt[4]{a^2}}{1 + \sqrt{a}} = \frac{1 + \sqrt[4]{a} + \sqrt[4]{a^2} + \sqrt[4]{a^3}}{1 - a}.$$

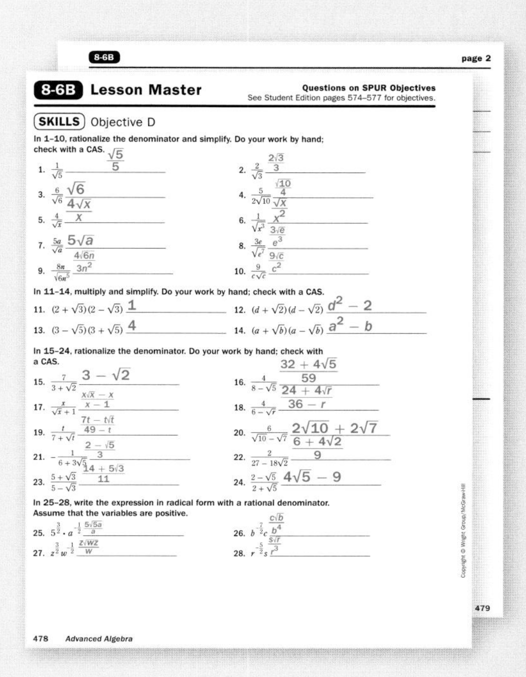

8-6B page 2

8-6B Lesson Master Questions on SPUR Objectives
See Student Edition pages 574–577 for objectives.

SKILLS Objective D

In 1–10, rationalize the denominator and simplify. Do your work by hand; check with a CAS.

1. $\frac{1}{\sqrt{5}}$ $\frac{\sqrt{5}}{5}$
2. $\frac{2}{\sqrt{3}}$ $\frac{2\sqrt{3}}{3}$
3. $\frac{6}{\sqrt{6}}$ $\sqrt{6}$
4. $\frac{5}{2\sqrt{10}}$ $\frac{\sqrt{10}}{4}$
5. $\frac{4}{\sqrt{x}}$ $\frac{4\sqrt{x}}{x}$
6. $\frac{1}{\sqrt{x^3}}$ $\frac{\sqrt{x}}{x^2}$
7. $\frac{5a}{\sqrt{a}}$ $5\sqrt{a}$
8. $\frac{3e}{\sqrt{e^7}}$ $\frac{3\sqrt{e}}{e^3}$
9. $\frac{8n}{\sqrt{6n^5}}$ $\frac{4\sqrt{6n}}{3n^2}$
10. $\frac{9}{c\sqrt{c}}$ $\frac{9\sqrt{c}}{c^2}$

In 11–14, multiply and simplify. Do your work by hand; check with a CAS.

11. $(2 + \sqrt{3})(2 - \sqrt{3})$ 1
12. $(d + \sqrt{2})(d - \sqrt{2})$ $d^2 - 2$
13. $(3 - \sqrt{5})(3 + \sqrt{5})$ 4
14. $(a + \sqrt{b})(a - \sqrt{b})$ $a^2 - b$

In 15–24, rationalize the denominator. Do your work by hand; check with a CAS.

15. $\frac{7}{3 + \sqrt{2}}$ $3 - \sqrt{2}$
16. $\frac{4}{8 - \sqrt{5}}$ $\frac{32 + 4\sqrt{5}}{59}$
17. $\frac{x}{\sqrt{x} + 1}$ $\frac{x\sqrt{x} - x}{x - 1}$
18. $\frac{4}{6 - \sqrt{r}}$ $\frac{24 + 4\sqrt{r}}{36 - r}$
19. $\frac{t}{7 + \sqrt{t}}$ $\frac{7t - t\sqrt{t}}{49 - t}$
20. $\frac{6}{\sqrt{10} - \sqrt{7}}$ $2\sqrt{10} + 2\sqrt{7}$
21. $-\frac{1}{6 + 3\sqrt{5}}$ $\frac{2 - \sqrt{5}}{3}$
22. $\frac{2}{27 - 18\sqrt{2}}$ $\frac{6 + 4\sqrt{2}}{9}$
23. $\frac{5 + \sqrt{3}}{5 - \sqrt{3}}$ $\frac{14 + 5\sqrt{3}}{11}$
24. $\frac{2 - \sqrt{5}}{2 + \sqrt{5}}$ $4\sqrt{5} - 9$

In 25–28, write the expression in radical form with a rational denominator. Assume that the variables are positive.

25. $5^{\frac{3}{2}} \cdot a^{-\frac{1}{2}}$ $\frac{5\sqrt{5a}}{a}$
26. $b^{-\frac{7}{2}}c$ $\frac{c\sqrt{b}}{b^4}$
27. $z^{\frac{3}{2}}w^{-\frac{1}{2}}$ $\frac{z\sqrt{wz}}{w}$
28. $r^{-\frac{5}{2}}s$ $\frac{s\sqrt{r}}{r^3}$

Copyright © Wright Group/McGraw-Hill

479

478 Advanced Algebra

Lesson 8-7

GOAL

Extend the definitions and properties of previous lessons to define $\sqrt[n]{x}$ when n is odd and x is negative.

SPUR Objectives

C Evaluate radicals.

D Rewrite or simplify expressions with radicals.

G Apply properties of radicals and nth root functions.

Materials/Resources

- Lesson Masters 8-7A and 8-7B
- Resource Masters 148 and 149

HOMEWORK

Suggestions for Assignment

- Questions 1–28
- Question 29 (extra credit)
- Reading Lesson 8-8
- Covering the Ideas 8-8

Local Standards

1 Warm-Up

In 1–4, consider the geometric sequence $g_n = x^n$. Identify whether the successive terms of this sequence *always increase, always decrease,* or *sometimes increase and sometimes decrease* as n increases and for the given value of x.

1. $x = 5$ always increase
2. $x = -5$ sometimes increase and sometimes decrease
3. $x = \frac{2}{3}$ always decrease
4. $x = -\frac{2}{3}$ sometimes increase and sometimes decrease
5. In which of the sequences in Warm-Ups 1–4 does the value of g_n approach a limit as $n \to \infty$? Sequences 3 and 4 both approach 0 as a limit.

Lesson 8-7 Powers and Roots of Negative Numbers

Vocabulary

$\sqrt[n]{x}$ when $x < 0$

BIG IDEA Great care must be taken when dealing with nth roots of negative numbers. When the nth roots are not real, then the Root of a Product Theorem may not be true.

You have already calculated some powers and some square roots of negative numbers. First we review the powers.

Integer Powers of Negative Numbers

Activity

Work in pairs. Assign one pair of functions to each partner.

a. $y = (-2)^x$
$y = (-7)^x$

b. $y = (-6)^x$
$y = (-5)^x$

Step 1 Enter your functions into a calculator and generate a table of values starting at $x = 2$ with an increment of 2.

Step 2 Scroll through the table of values. Compare the results for all four functions with your partner. Describe any patterns you see.

Step 3 Generate a table of values starting at $x = 1$ with an increment of 2. Scroll through the table of values. Compare the results for all four functions with your partner. Describe any patterns you see.

See the Additional Answers section at the back of the book.

Step 4 Complete the following generalization, choosing the correct words: __?__ (Even/Odd) integer exponents with negative bases produce __?__ (positive/negative) powers, while __?__ (even/odd) integer exponents with negative bases produce __?__ (positive/negative) powers.

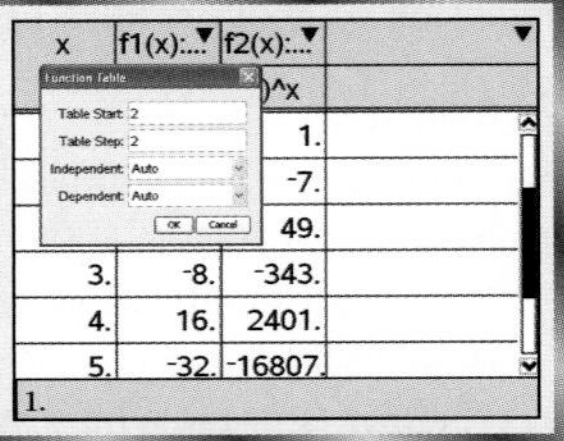

The Activity shows that positive integer powers of negative numbers alternate between positive and negative numbers. Even exponents produce positive numbers, while odd exponents produce negative numbers. The same is true if zero and negative powers are considered, because $(-x)^{-n}$ is the reciprocal of $(-x)^n$.

Mental Math

Miguel is training to run a 3-mile race. In how much time must he run each mile on average if he wants to finish the race in

a. 30 minutes? 10 min

b. 28 minutes? 9 min, 20 sec

c. 26 minutes? 8 min, 40 sec

Step 1. See the Additional Answers section at the back of the book.

Step 2.
Answers vary. Sample: Every even power of a negative number is positive; every even power of an even number is even; every even power of an odd number is odd.

Step 4.
Even; positive; odd; negative

Background

One source of error in working with roots and powers results when a theorem is applied even though its hypothesis is not satisfied. With radicals, the danger is that students will treat negative bases as they do positive ones. However, students knew before beginning this chapter that $\sqrt{x}\sqrt{y} \neq \sqrt{xy}$ when x and y are negative, the powers and roots that are not defined have been carefully discussed, and the restrictions on bases and powers that satisfy the theorems have been emphasized. We hope these things lessen the chance that students will misapply the theorems.

Despite the strong reasons for restricting $\sqrt[n]{x}$ and $x^{\frac{1}{n}}$ to certain values of n and x—namely, if x is negative, then some properties are violated—some calculators and CASs are preprogrammed to give values of these expressions where we have not defined them. For instance, some calculators graph $y = x^{\frac{1}{5}}$ using *all* real numbers as the domain, where we would restrict the domain to nonnegative values.

Integer powers of negative numbers satisfy the order of operations. For example, $-6^4 = -1296$ because the power is calculated before taking the opposite. However, $(-6)^4 = 1296$, so $-6^4 \neq (-6)^4$. All the properties of ***integer*** powers of positive bases that you studied in Chapter 7 also apply to integer powers of negative bases.

GUIDED

Example 1

Write without exponents: $(-3)^5(-3)^{-2}$.

Solution Use the Product of Powers Postulate.

$(-3)^5(-3)^{-2} = (-3)^{\underline{?} + \underline{?}} = (-3)^{\underline{?}} = \underline{?}$ 5; -2, 3, -27

Are There Noninteger Powers of Negative Numbers?

Many times in this course, you have seen that powers and roots of negative numbers do not have the same properties that powers and roots of positive numbers do. Here are some of the properties that are different.

(1) When x is positive, $\sqrt{x}$ is a real number, but $\sqrt{-x}$ is a pure imaginary number.

(2) If both x and y are negative, $\sqrt{x} \cdot \sqrt{y} \neq \sqrt{xy}$. The left side is the product of two imaginary numbers and is negative; the right side is positive. For example, $\sqrt{-3} \cdot \sqrt{-2} \neq \sqrt{(-3)(-2)}$ because $i\sqrt{3} \cdot i\sqrt{2} = -\sqrt{6}$ and $\sqrt{(-3)(-2)} = \sqrt{6}$.

(3) If x is negative, then $x^n \neq \sqrt{x^{2n}}$ for positive integers n. Again, the left side is negative and the right side is positive. For example, $(-2)^3 \neq \sqrt{(-2)^6}$ because $(-2)^3 = -8$ and $\sqrt{(-2)^6} = \sqrt{64} = 8$.

These examples indicate that powers and roots of negative numbers have to be dealt with very carefully. For this reason, we do not define x^m when x is negative and m is not an integer. *Noninteger powers of negative numbers are not defined in this book.* That is, an expression such as $(-3)^{\frac{1}{2}}$ is not defined. However, we allow square roots of negative numbers to be represented by a radical.

QY

▸ **QY**

Explain why $\sqrt{-5} \cdot \sqrt{-11} \neq \sqrt{-55}$.

These calculators treat $x^{\frac{1}{5}}$ as if it is identical to $\sqrt[5]{x}$. As we have seen, to define $x^{\frac{1}{5}}$ when x is negative means that $x^{\frac{1}{5}}$ and $x^{\frac{2}{10}}$ do not necessarily have the same value. This would cause a particular problem for the interpretation of $x^{\cdot 2}$ and for logarithms.

2 Teaching

Notes on the Lesson

Students are already familiar with square roots of negatives, so they should realize that there are some differences in the properties of nth roots of positive and negative numbers. However, they may not be ready for the special interpretation of the notation $\sqrt[n]{x}$ when x is negative, a notation that has meaning only when n is an odd number.

Throughout class discussion, be careful to emphasize the difference between an nth root of a number x (there may be n of these) and $\sqrt[n]{x}$. If x has a real nth root, then the *largest* of these can be denoted by $\sqrt[n]{x}$. However, x does not have a real nth root when x is negative and n is even. If x is negative and n is even, the radical notation is used for square roots only, which represent imaginary numbers.

Addtional Answers can be found in the back of the book.

Additional Example

Example 1 Write $(-5)^{-4}(-5)^7$ without exponents.

Solution Use the Product of Powers Postulate: $(-5)^{-4}(-5)^7 = (-5)^{\underline{?} + \underline{?}} = (-5)^{\underline{?}} = \underline{?}$
-4; 7; 3; -125

Notes on the Lesson

Some calculators will not calculate powers with negative bases. To test for this capability, have students try to calculate $(-2.1)^5$. If an error message appears, that particular calculator will not allow the input of a negative base. Students using such a calculator can use the property that $(-2.1)^5 = (-1)^5 \cdot (2.1)^5$, and then calculate $(-1)^5$ mentally.

It might be helpful to create tables similar to the ones shown below. These tables show uses of these equivalent forms.

Integer Power Forms

Exponential Form	Words
$2^8 = 256$	2 is an 8th root of 256.
$(-2)^8 = 256$	-2 is an 8th root of 256.
$(-6)^3 = -216$	-6 is a cube root of -216.

Root Forms

Radical Form	Fractional Exponent Form
$2 = \sqrt[8]{256}$	$2 = (256)^{\frac{1}{8}}$
But $-2 \neq \sqrt[8]{256}$	$-2 \neq (256)^{\frac{1}{8}}$
$-6 = \sqrt[3]{-216}$	$(-216)^{\frac{1}{3}}$ is not defined

Emphasize that $-2 \neq \sqrt[8]{256}$ because we wish every symbol to stand for only one number. For the same reason, $(256)^{\frac{1}{8}} \neq -2$. Also, $(-216)^{\frac{1}{3}}$ is not defined because the symbol $x^{\frac{1}{n}}$ is defined only for positive values of x.

Additional Example

Example 2 Evaluate $\sqrt[5]{-32}$. -2

The Expression $\sqrt[n]{x}$ When x Is Negative and n Is Odd

When x is positive, the radical symbol $\sqrt[n]{x}$ stands for its unique positive nth root. It would be nice to use the same symbol for an nth root of a negative number. This can be done for odd roots of negative numbers. If a number is negative, then it has exactly one real odd root. For instance, -27 has one real cube root, namely -3. Consequently, it is customary to use the symbol $\sqrt[n]{x}$ when x is negative, provided n is odd.

Definition of $\sqrt[n]{x}$ when $x < 0$

When x is negative and n is an odd integer > 2, $\sqrt[n]{x}$ stands for the real nth root of x.

For instance, because $(-5)^3 = -125$, $\sqrt[3]{-125} = -5$.
Because $-100{,}000 = (-10)^5$, you can write $\sqrt[5]{-100{,}000} = -10$.

To evaluate nth roots of negative numbers without a calculator, you can use numerical or graphical methods.

Example 2

Evaluate $\sqrt[3]{-64}$.

Solution 1 $\sqrt[3]{-64}$ represents the real 3rd root of −64, so you can solve $x^3 = -64$. Because $(-4)^3 = -64$, $\sqrt[3]{-64} = -4$.

Solution 2 Graph $y = x^3$ and $y = -64$. The x-coordinate of the point of intersection is the real 3rd root of −64, as shown at the right. So, $\sqrt[3]{-64} = -4$.

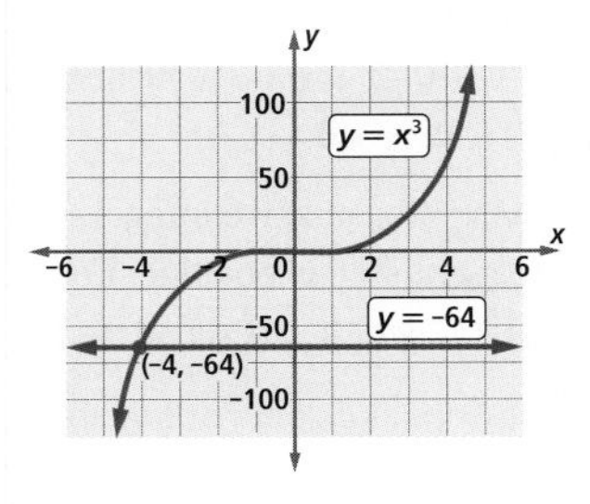

Notice that the graph of the function f with equation $y = x^3$ or $f(x) = x^3$ verifies that every real number has exactly one real 3rd root, because any horizontal line intersects the graph only once. Therefore, -4 is the only real 3rd root of -64.

Accommodating the Learner ↑

Ask students to express y in terms of a, n, and x if $\sqrt[n]{x} = \sqrt[m]{y}$, where $m = an$.

If $\sqrt[n]{x} = \sqrt[an]{y}$, then $(\sqrt[n]{x})^{an} = (\sqrt[an]{y})^{an}$ or $x^{\frac{an}{n}} = y$. So $y = x^{\frac{an}{n}}$ or $y = x^a$.

Accommodating the Learner ↓

Ask students to rewrite each expression without parentheses.

1. $(-3)^n$ if n is even 3^n
2. $(-3)^n$ if n is odd -3^n

The Expression $\sqrt[n]{x}$ When x Is Negative and n Is Even

Square roots of negative numbers are not real numbers, and they do not satisfy all the properties of square roots of positive numbers. However, the radical form $\sqrt{x}$ is used when $x < 0$. When x is negative, $\sqrt{x} = i\sqrt{-x}$. For example, $\sqrt{-7} = i\sqrt{7}$. Other even roots of negative numbers (4th roots, 6th roots, 8th roots, and so on) are also not real, but they are not written using radicals. So, the nth-root expression $\sqrt[n]{x}$ is not defined when x is negative and n is an even integer greater than 2.

Here is a summary of our use of the $\sqrt[n]{}$ symbol when $n > 2$:

(1) When $x \ge 0$, $\sqrt[n]{x}$ is defined for any integer $n > 2$. It equals the positive real nth root of x.

(2) When $x < 0$, $\sqrt[n]{x}$ is defined only for odd integers $n \ge 3$. It equals the negative real nth root of x.

This summary may seem unnecessarily detailed, but it allows you to handle expressions with radical signs in much the same way that square roots are handled, as long as the expressions stand for real numbers.

*n*th Root of a Product Theorem

When $\sqrt[n]{x}$ and $\sqrt[n]{y}$ are defined and are real numbers, then $\sqrt[n]{xy}$ is also defined and $\sqrt[n]{xy} = \sqrt[n]{x} \cdot \sqrt[n]{y}$.

Example 3

Simplify $\sqrt[5]{-640}$. Leave your answer in radical form.

Solution Look for a perfect fifth power that is a factor of –640.

$-640 = -32 \cdot 20 = (-2)^5 \cdot 20$

So, $\sqrt[5]{-640} = \sqrt[5]{-32} \cdot \sqrt[5]{20}$

$= -2 \cdot \sqrt[5]{20}$.

Questions

COVERING THE IDEAS

1. Let $f(x) = (-9)^x$.
   a. Give three values of x that produce a positive value of $f(x)$.
   b. Give three values of x that produce a negative value of $f(x)$.

1a. Answers vary. Sample: 2, 4, 6

1b. Answers vary. Sample: 1, 3, 5

Additional Example

Example 3 Simplify $\sqrt[3]{-1250}$. Write your answer in radical form.

$\sqrt[3]{-1250} = \sqrt[3]{-125} \cdot \sqrt[3]{10} = -5\sqrt[3]{10}$

Note-Taking Tips

Encourage students to record the examples that follow Example 1, such as $\sqrt{-3} \cdot \sqrt{-2} \ne \sqrt{(-3)(-2)}$, $(-2)^3 \ne \sqrt{(-2)^6}$, and other examples of their own, to emphasize the statement that in this text, *noninteger powers of negative numbers are not defined.*

3 Assignment

Recommended Assignment

- Questions 1–28
- Question 29 (extra credit)
- Reading Lesson 8-8
- Covering the Ideas 8-8

ENGLISH LEARNERS
Vocabulary Development

You may want to discuss the phrase *radical form* in Example 3. Although most students understand that the phrase means they should write their answer using a radical, they may not understand that an answer in radical form is an *exact answer,* while a calculator value for that answer might be an *approximation.*

Extension

Ask students to extend their study of roots and negative numbers by rewriting the following expressions as directed.

1. Rewrite $10^{-\frac{1}{3}}$ in radical form and rationalize the denominator.
   $10^{-\frac{1}{3}} = \frac{1}{10^{\frac{1}{3}}} = \frac{1}{\sqrt[3]{10}} \cdot \frac{\sqrt[3]{100}}{\sqrt[3]{100}} = \frac{\sqrt[3]{100}}{\sqrt[3]{1000}} = \frac{\sqrt[3]{100}}{10}$
2. Rewrite $(-5)^{\frac{1}{2}}$ in $a + bi$ form.
   $(-5)^{\frac{1}{2}} = \sqrt{-5} = i\sqrt{5} = 0 + \sqrt{5}i$

8-7A Lesson Master

Questions on SPUR Objectives
See Student Edition pages 574–577 for objectives.

SKILLS Objective C

In 1–6, evaluate each radical expression, if possible. Work by hand; check with a CAS.

1. $\sqrt[3]{-1}$ -1
2. $\sqrt[4]{-16}$ undefined
3. $\sqrt[4]{(-2)^4}$ 2
4. $\sqrt[3]{-\frac{1}{125}}$ $-\frac{1}{5}$
5. $\sqrt[5]{(-10)^{15}}$ -1000
6. $\sqrt[7]{\left(-\frac{3}{5}\right)^{14}}$ $\frac{9}{25}$

In 7–9, evaluate to the nearest thousandth, if possible.

7. $\sqrt[3]{-128.4}$ -5.045
8. $\sqrt[9]{-0.0314}$ -0.681
9. $\sqrt[8]{-1.616}$ undefined

SKILLS Objective D

In 10–13, simplify or rewrite with a smaller power of the variable inside the radical.

10. $\sqrt[3]{-27a^{12}}$ $-3a^4$
11. $\sqrt[4]{48n^{15}}$ $2n^3\sqrt[4]{3n^3}$
12. $\sqrt[5]{-\frac{12}{x^5}} \cdot \sqrt[5]{-\frac{40}{x^{10}}}$ $\frac{2\sqrt[5]{15}}{x^3}$
13. $\sqrt[3]{14p^6r^3} \cdot \sqrt[3]{-28p^2r^9}$ $-2p^2r^4\sqrt[3]{49p^2}$

PROPERTIES Objective G

In 14–19, tell without calculating whether the number is *positive, negative,* or *undefined.*

14. $(-3)^5$ negative
15. $(3)^{-5}$ positive
16. $(-2)^{14}$ positive
17. $\sqrt[3]{-5}$ negative
18. $\sqrt[4]{-12}$ undefined
19. $\sqrt[5]{(-312.7)^2}$ positive
20. Enter each expression into a CAS and write the result.
    a. `solve (x^(1/3)=(x^3)^(1/9),x)` true
    b. `solve (x^(1/3)=(x^2)^(1/6),x)` $x \ge 0$
    c. Explain why the answers are different. Answers vary. Sample: Part a involves only odd powers and roots, so both sides of the equation are the same for all values of x. Part b squares the number first so the right side can only be positive.

480 *Advanced Algebra*

Notes on the Questions

Question 7 The order of operations is important here. The radical sign acts as parentheses (the horizontal bar at the top of the radical sign is a *vinculum,* which is a grouping symbol). So students must work within parentheses and evaluate the negative square roots first, then multiply them together.

2. Calculate $(-8)^n$ for all integer values of n from -3 to 3.
3. Tell whether the number is positive or negative.
   a. $(-3)^4$ positive b. -3^4 negative c. $(-4)^{-3}$ negative d. $(-4)^3$ negative
4. **True or False**
   a. $(-x)^{10} = -x^{10}$ false b. $(-x)^9 = -x^9$ true

In 5 and 6, write as a single power.

5. $(-2)^6(-2)^{-3}$ $(-2)^3$
6. $((-4)^5)^6$ $(-4)^{30}$
7. Calculate $\sqrt{-4} \cdot \sqrt{-9}$. -6

In 8–10, evaluate.

8. $\sqrt[3]{-125x^9}$ $-5x^3$
9. $\sqrt[11]{-1}$ -1
10. $\sqrt[9]{-512 \cdot 10^{27}}$ -2000

In 11–13, simplify.

11. $\sqrt[3]{-\frac{64y^{27}}{27}}$ $-\frac{4}{3}y^9$
12. $\sqrt[9]{-10^{63}}$ -10,000,000
13. $\sqrt[7]{1280q^{23}}$ $2q^3\sqrt[7]{10q^2}$
14. What are the domain and the range of the real function with equation $y = \sqrt[6]{x}$? $x \ge 0$; $y \ge 0$
15. The graphs of $y_1 = x^3$ and $y_2 = -27$ are shown below. What is the significance of the point of intersection of y_1 and y_2?

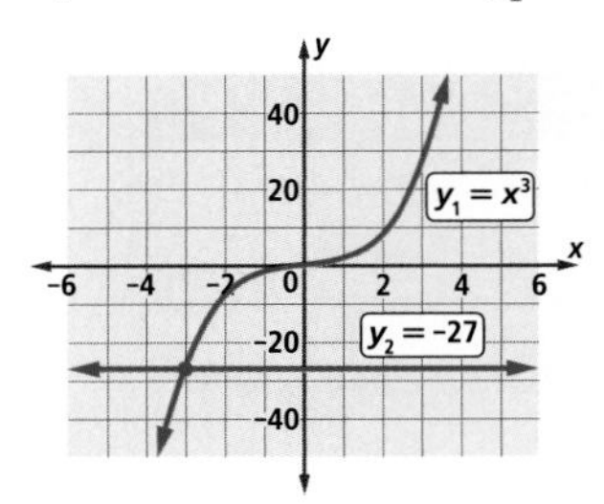

APPLYING THE MATHEMATICS

16. Simplify.
   a. $\sqrt[5]{-32} + \sqrt[4]{16}$ 0
   b. $\sqrt[5]{-32p^{10}} + \sqrt[4]{16p^{16}}$ $-2p^2 + 2p^4$
17. Explain why the graphs of $y = \sqrt[3]{x}$ and $y = \sqrt[18]{x^6}$ are not the same.
18. Let $f: x \to \sqrt[5]{x}$ and $g: x \to \sqrt[15]{x}$. Find $f \circ g(x)$. $\sqrt[75]{x}$
19. a. Show that $2 + 2i$ is a 4th root of -64.
   b. Show that $-2 - 2i$ is a 4th root of -64.
   c. Show that $2 - 2i$ is a 4th root of -64.
   d. Find the one other 4th root of —64 and verify your finding.
   e. How are Parts a–d related to the fact that $\sqrt[4]{-64}$ is not defined?

2. $(-8)^{-3} = -\frac{1}{512}$; $(-8)^{-2} = \frac{1}{64}$; $(-8)^{-1} = -\frac{1}{8}$; $(-8)^0 = 1$; $(-8)^1 = -8$; $(-8)^2 = 64$; $(-8)^3 = -512$

15. The intersection point is (-3, -27). This shows that $(-3)^3 = -27$, or $\sqrt[3]{-27} = -3$.

17. Answers vary. Sample: If $x < 0$, then $\sqrt[18]{x^6} = -\sqrt[3]{x}$.

19a. $(2 + 2i)^4 = (2(1 + i))^4 = 2^4((1 + i)^2)^2 = 2^4 \cdot (2i)^2 = 16 \cdot (-4) = -64$

19b. $(-2 - 2i)^4 = (-(2 + 2i))^4 = (-1)^4(2 + 2i)^4 = 1(-64) = -64$

19c. $(2 - 2i)^4 = (2(1 - i))^4 = 2^4((1 - i)^2)^2 = 2^4 \cdot (-2i)^2 = 16 \cdot (-4) = -64$

19d. The other fourth root is $-2 + 2i$. $(-2 + 2i)^4 = (-(2 - 2i))^4 = (-1)^4(2 - 2i)^4 = 1(-64) = -64$

19e. $\sqrt[4]{-64}$ is not defined because none of the 4th roots of -64 are real numbers.

REVIEW

In 20 and 21, rationalize the denominator and simplify. (Lesson 8-6)

20. $\frac{5}{\sqrt{7}}$ $\frac{5\sqrt{7}}{7}$

21. $\frac{2-\sqrt{3}}{2+\sqrt{3}}$ $7 - 4\sqrt{3}$

22. a. Find the geometric mean of 2, 4, 8, 16, and 32. 8

    b. Generalize Part a. (Lesson 8-4)

23. Evaluate $\sqrt[3]{\sqrt{4096}}$. (Lesson 8-4) 4

24. a. Simplify without using a calculator: $(\sqrt{7}-\sqrt{13})(\sqrt{7}+\sqrt{13})$. -6

    b. Check by approximating $\sqrt{7}$ and $\sqrt{13}$ by decimals with a calculator and multiplying the decimals. (Lessons 8-5, 6-2)

25. Solve $r^{-\frac{2}{3}} = 64^{-1}$ for r. (Lesson 7-8) $r = 512$

26. A rectangle has vertices at (2, 0), (6, 4), (4, 6), and (0, 2). What is its area? (Previous Course) 16

22b. The geometric mean of the first n powers of 2 is

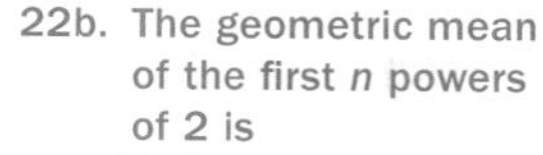

$\sqrt[n]{2^1 \cdot 2^2 \cdot 2^3 \cdot \ldots \cdot 2^n} = \left(2^{\frac{n^2+n}{2}}\right)^{\frac{1}{n}} = 2^{\frac{n+1}{2}}$.

24b. $(2.6458 - 3.6056) \cdot (2.6458 + 3.6056) \approx -6$

In 27 and 28, use the fact that the population in the United States was about 2.96×10^8 in 2005. (Lesson 7-2)

27. With a land area of about 3.5×10^6 mi², what was the average number of people per square mile? 85

28. In 2005, people in the U.S. consumed about 2.78×10^{10} pounds of beef. About how much beef was consumed per person in the U.S. in 2005? 93.9 lb

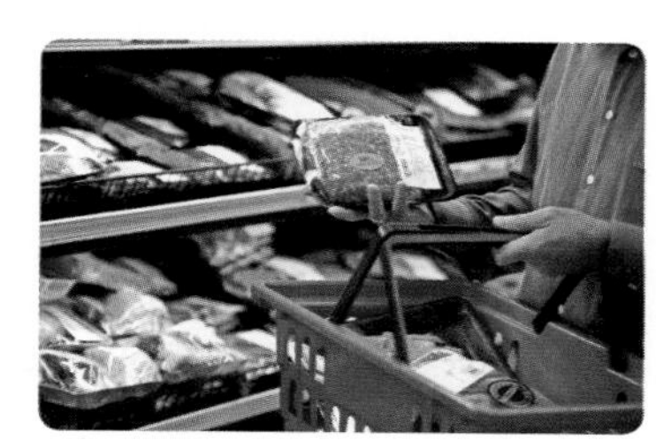

EXPLORATION

29. Use your results from Part a to answer the other parts.

    a. Sketch the graphs of $y = \sqrt[3]{x^3}$, $y = \sqrt[4]{x^4}$, $y = \sqrt[5]{x^5}$, and $y = \sqrt[6]{x^6}$. See margin.

    b. For what values of n does $\sqrt[n]{x^n} = x$ for every real number x? 29b. n odd

    c. For what values of n does $\sqrt[n]{x^n} = |x|$ for every real number x? 29c. n even

    d. Does $y = \sqrt{x^2}$ follow the pattern of other nth root of nth power functions? Yes; this is the case for $n = 2$: $y = \sqrt{x^2} = |x|$.

QY ANSWER

$\sqrt{-5} \cdot \sqrt{-11}$ is a negative number, but $\sqrt{-55}$ is an imaginary number.

Notes on the Questions

Question 23 A rewritten form of the root in this question may be illuminating but is not necessary for the calculation. In general, a cube root of a square root of a number is a sixth root of that number because $\frac{1}{3} \cdot \frac{1}{2} = \frac{1}{6}$.

Question 29 You may find that calculators differ because they allow domains we do not allow. You also may wish to replace the nth roots in each case by the $\frac{1}{n}$ power to see if the same graphs occur. (Because of differences in the domain of rational powers and radical notation, the graphs often do not coincide.)

4 Wrap-Up

Ongoing Assessment

Ask students to evaluate each pair of expressions.

1. $\sqrt{-100} \cdot \sqrt{-64}$; $\sqrt{(-100)(-64)}$
   $10i \cdot 8i = 80i^2 = -80$; $\sqrt{6400} = 80$

2. $(-3)^3$; $\sqrt{(-3)^6}$ -27; $\sqrt{729} = 27$

Project Update

Project 4, *Square Roots of Pure Imaginary Numbers*, on page 569 relates to the content of this lesson.

Additional Answers

29a. $y = \sqrt[4]{x^4}$ and $y = \sqrt[6]{x^6}$

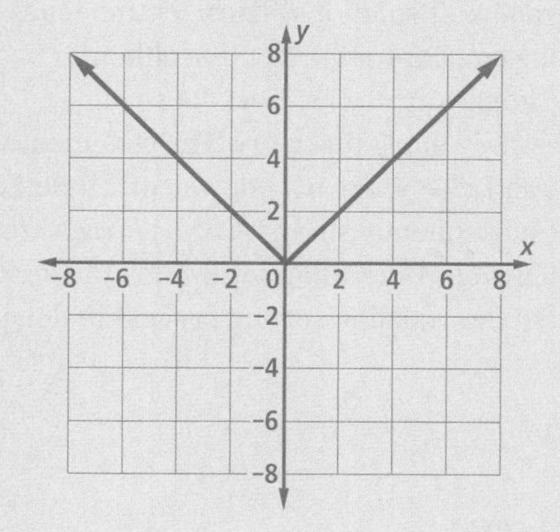

$y = \sqrt[3]{x^3}$ and $y = \sqrt[5]{x^5}$

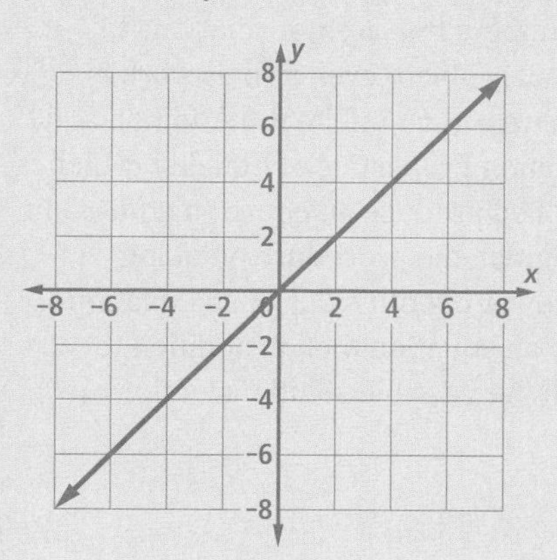

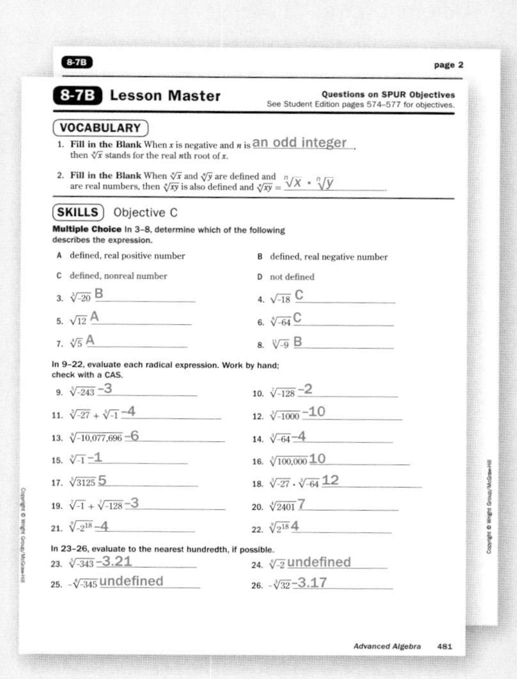

8-7B page 2

8-7B Lesson Master — Questions on SPUR Objectives. See Student Edition pages 574–577 for objectives.

VOCABULARY

1. **Fill in the Blank** When x is negative and n is an odd integer, then $\sqrt[n]{x}$ stands for the real nth root of x.

2. **Fill in the Blank** When $\sqrt[n]{x}$ and $\sqrt[n]{y}$ are defined and are real numbers, then $\sqrt[n]{xy}$ is also defined and $\sqrt[n]{xy} =$ $\sqrt[n]{x} \cdot \sqrt[n]{y}$.

SKILLS Objective C

Multiple Choice In 3–8, determine which of the following describes the expression.

A defined, real positive number
B defined, real negative number
C defined, nonreal number
D not defined

3. $\sqrt[3]{-20}$ B
4. $\sqrt{-18}$ C
5. $\sqrt{12}$ A
6. $\sqrt[6]{-64}$ C
7. $\sqrt[4]{5}$ A
8. $\sqrt[11]{-9}$ B

In 9–22, evaluate each radical expression. Work by hand; check with a CAS.

9. $\sqrt[5]{-243}$ -3
10. $\sqrt[7]{-128}$ -2
11. $\sqrt[3]{-27} + \sqrt[5]{-1}$ -4
12. $\sqrt[3]{-1000}$ -10
13. $\sqrt[9]{-10{,}077{,}696}$ -6
14. $\sqrt[3]{-64}$ -4
15. $\sqrt[9]{-1}$ -1
16. $\sqrt[5]{100{,}000}$ 10
17. $\sqrt[5]{3125}$ 5
18. $\sqrt[3]{-27} \cdot \sqrt[3]{-64}$ 12
19. $\sqrt[7]{-1} + \sqrt[7]{-128}$ -3
20. $\sqrt[4]{2401}$ 7
21. $\sqrt[9]{-2^{18}}$ -4
22. $\sqrt[9]{2^{18}}$ 4

In 23–26, evaluate to the nearest hundredth, if possible.

23. $\sqrt[5]{-343}$ -3.21
24. $\sqrt[6]{-2}$ undefined
25. $-\sqrt[8]{-345}$ undefined
26. $-\sqrt[3]{32}$ -3.17

Advanced Algebra 481

Lesson 8-8

GOAL

Solve equations equivalent to $a\sqrt[n]{x} = b$; discuss why and how to check for extraneous solutions.

SPUR Objectives

E Solve equations with radicals.

I Solve real-world problems that can be modeled by equations with radicals.

Materials/Resources

- Lesson Masters 8-8A and 8-8B
- Resource Masters 150 and 151

HOMEWORK

Suggestions for Assignment

- Questions 1–26
- Question 27 (extra credit)
- Self-Test

Local Standards

1 Warm-Up

Find all the real solutions to $x^{\frac{2}{3}} = 5$ to the nearest hundredth in at least three different ways. Answers vary. Sample: The only real solution, $x \approx 11.18$, can be found by (1) graphing $y = x^{\frac{2}{3}}$ and $y = 5$ and looking at the first coordinate of the point of intersection; (2) estimating $x^{\frac{2}{3}}$ to the nearest hundredth for values of x between the solution to $x^1 = 5$ (which is 5) and $x^{\frac{1}{2}} = 5$ (which is 25); (3) raising each side of the equation to the 1.5 power, obtaining $x = 5^{1.5}$.

Lesson 8-8 Solving Equations with Radicals

Vocabulary

extraneous solution

BIG IDEA To solve an equation of the form $x^{\frac{m}{n}} = k$, where m and n are integers, take the nth power of both sides. But be careful that you do not change the number of solutions to the equation in the process.

Remember that to solve an equation with a single rational power, such as $x^{\frac{4}{5}} = 10$, you can raise both sides to the power of the reciprocal of that exponent.

$$\left(x^{\frac{4}{5}}\right)^{\frac{5}{4}} = 10^{\frac{5}{4}}$$

So $x = 10^{\frac{5}{4}} \approx 17.78$. This checks because $17.78^{\frac{4}{5}} \approx 10$.

Mental Math

Find an equation for the inverse of the function and tell whether the inverse is a function.

a. $y = 7x$ $y = \frac{1}{7}x$; yes

b. $3x + y = 4.5$ $x + 3y = 4.5$; yes

c. $y = 13$ $x = 13$; no

Solving an Equation with a Single Radical

Similarly, because the radical $\sqrt[n]{\ }$ involves an nth root, you can solve an equation containing only this single radical by raising both sides to the nth power.

Example 1

Imagine spinning a ball on a string around in a circle. If the string breaks, the ball will follow a straight-line path in the direction it was traveling at the time of the break as shown below.

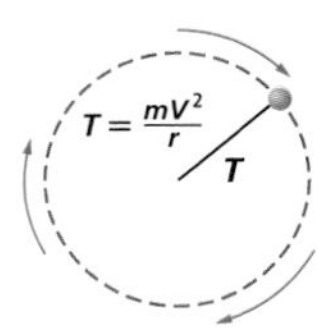

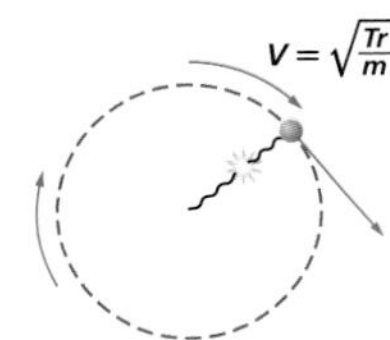

The ball will travel at a velocity V given by the formula $V = \sqrt{\frac{Tr}{m}}$, where T is the tension on the string (in newtons), m is the mass of the ball (in kilograms), and r is the length of the string (in meters). What tension is needed to allow a 5-kilogram ball on a 2-meter string to achieve a velocity of 10 $\frac{\text{meters}}{\text{second}}$?

Background

Students may be surprised that they can obtain numbers that are not solutions to the original problem even if their work is correct. Stress that, unlike the Addition and Multiplication Properties of Equality, which, when applied produce an equation equivalent to the original, the procedure of taking the nth power of both sides of an equation produces an equation that, in addition to having all the possible solutions of the original, may also have some additional (extraneous) solutions. These extraneous results come from the fact that although $x = y$ implies $x^n = y^n$, $x^n = y^n$ does not necessarily imply that $x = y$. The statements $x = y$ and $x^n = y^n$ are *not* equivalent. Students who subsequently study UCSMP *Precalculus and Discrete Mathematics* will study the logic behind the equation-solving process in detail.

Solution Here, $V = 10\ \frac{\text{m}}{\text{s}}$, $m = 5$ kg, and $r = 2$ meters. Substitute the given values into the formula and use a CAS to solve for T.

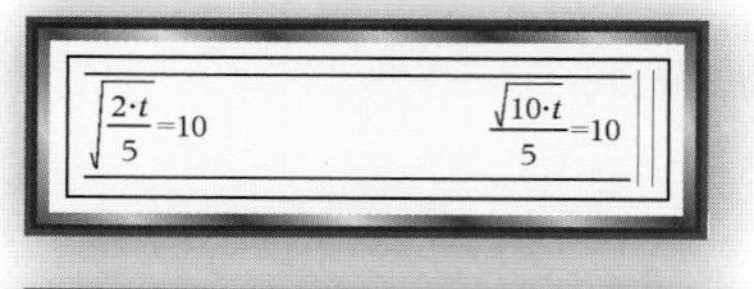

Enter the equation.

Square both sides.

Multiply each side by 5.

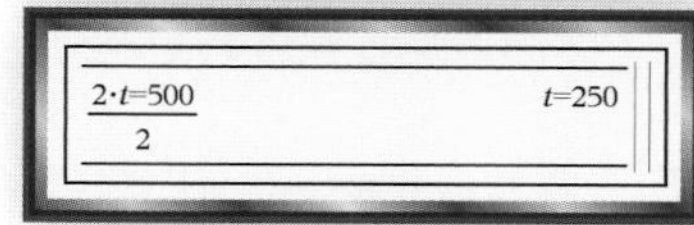

Divide each side by 2.

The string tension needs to be 250 newtons.

Check Use the solve command. It checks.

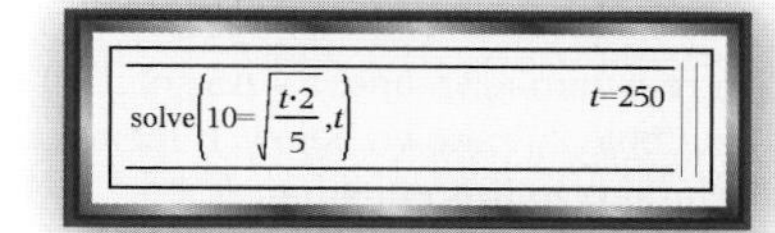

 QY

Extraneous Solutions

There is a major difficulty that may occur when taking an nth power to solve equations with radicals. The new equation may have more solutions than the original equation does. So you must be careful to check each solution in the original equation. If a solution to a later equation does not check in the original equation, it is called an **extraneous solution**, and it is not a solution to the original equation.

▶ QY

A 5-kilogram ball traveling 5 meters per second was attached to a string with a tension of 250 newtons when the string broke. How long was the string?

In this lesson, as in previous ones, it is important to stress that radical notation is not equivalent to rational powers. For instance, because of the restriction of the base in x^n to positive numbers, an equation such as $x^{\frac{2}{5}} = 4$ has only the solution $x = 32$, while the related equation $\sqrt[5]{x^2} = 4$ has the two solutions $x = \pm 32$. Students should understand this important distinction.

2 Teaching

Notes on the Lesson

If students make many computational errors when trying to solve the types of problems given in this lesson, they may be using their calculators incorrectly. You may want to do some calculator drills on the key sequences necessary to solve these types of problems. Also, consider pairing calculator experts with those who are having trouble.

Example 1 Students should be able to solve an equation like this without a CAS. In this example, it may seem that the units do not agree, but 1 newton is the force needed to give 1 kilogram of mass an acceleration of 1 meter per second squared $\left(1\text{ N} = \frac{1\text{m} \cdot \text{kg}}{\text{s}^2}\right)$. Consequently, the equation to be solved is $\sqrt{\frac{2\text{ meters} \cdot T\text{ newtons}}{5\text{ kilograms}}} = 10\ \frac{\text{meters}}{\text{second}}$, or $\sqrt{\frac{2\text{ meters} \cdot T\ \frac{\text{meters} \cdot \text{kilograms}}{\text{seconds}^2}}{5\text{ kilograms}}} = 10\ \frac{\text{meters}}{\text{second}}$. You can see that the unit under the radical is $\left(\frac{\text{meters}}{\text{second}}\right)^2$, which is what is needed.

Additional Example

Example 1 Use the formula $V = \sqrt{\frac{Tr}{m}}$ from Example 1, where T is the tension on the string (in newtons), m is the mass of the ball (in kilograms), and r is the length of the string (in meters). What tension is needed to allow a 4-kilogram ball on a 2.5-meter string to achieve a velocity of 12 $\frac{\text{meters}}{\text{second}}$? 230.4 N

Additional Example

Example 2 The two methods of solving the equation $12 - \sqrt[4]{x} = 20$ given below show that the equation has no real solutions. Complete each method.

Solution 1

$\underline{?} = 8$ Add $\underline{?}$ to both sides. $-\sqrt[4]{x}$; -12

$(\underline{?})^4 = 8^4$ Raise both sides to the 4th power. $-\sqrt[4]{x}$

$x = \underline{?}$ def. of $\underline{?}$ power, arithmetic 4096; *n*th

Check: Substitute $x = \underline{?}$ into the original equation. 4096 Does $12 - \underline{?} = 20$? $\sqrt[4]{4096}$ No. So $\underline{?}$ is not a solution. 4096 It is extraneous. The equation $12 - \sqrt[4]{x} = 20$ has $\underline{?}$ real solutions. no

Solution 2

$-\sqrt[4]{x} = 8$ Add $\underline{?}$ to both sides. -12

The left side of the equation is always a negative number because $\underline{?}$. $\sqrt[4]{x} > 0$, so $-\sqrt[4]{x} < 0$ Therefore, the left side cannot equal positive 8. Thus there are $\underline{?}$ real solutions. no

Example 3 Find coordinates for the two points on the line with equation $x = 3$ that are 10 units away from the point (-4, -2).

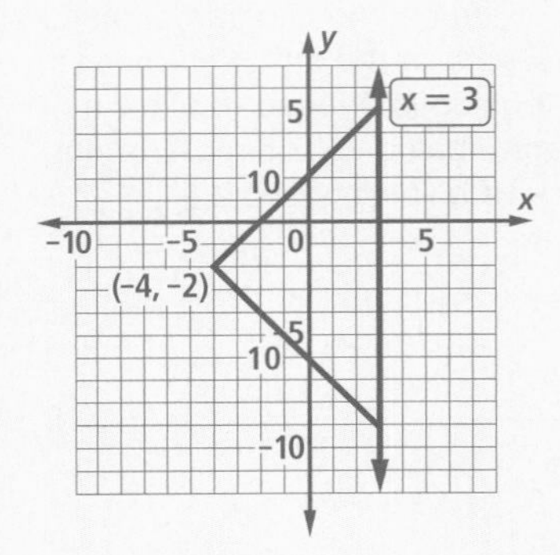

$\sqrt{(3 - (-4))^2 + (y - (-2))^2} = 10$; $(y + 2)^2 = 51$; $y = -2 \pm \sqrt{51}$; $y \approx 5.14$ or $y \approx -9.14$; the points are approximately (3, 5.14) and (3, -9.14).

GUIDED

Example 2

Greg and Terrance both solve the equation $5 - \sqrt[6]{x} = 8$, and each one concludes that there are no real solutions. Complete Solution 1 to see Terrance's approach and Solution 2 to see Greg's.

Solution 1 Solve $5 - \sqrt[6]{x} = 8$.

$\underline{?} = 3$ Add $\underline{?}$ to both sides. $-\sqrt[6]{x}$; -5

$(\underline{?})^6 = (3)^6$ Raise both sides to 6th power. $-\sqrt[6]{x}$

$x = \underline{?}$ Definition of $\underline{?}$ power, arithmetic 729; 6th

Check Substitute $x = \underline{?}$ into the original equation. 729

Does $5 - \sqrt[6]{\underline{?}} = 8$? 729

$5 - \underline{?} = 8$? No. 3

So, $\underline{?}$ is not a solution. It is extraneous. $x = 729$

The sentence $5 - \sqrt[6]{x} = 8$ has $\underline{?}$ real solutions. no

Solution 2 Solve $5 - \sqrt[6]{x} = 8$.

$-\sqrt[6]{x} = 3$ Add –5 to both sides.

The left side of the equation is always a negative number because $\underline{?}$. Therefore, the left side cannot equal positive 3. Thus, there are $\underline{?}$ real solutions. $\sqrt[6]{x} \geq 0$ no

In real-number mode, a CAS solution to the equation in Example 2 is shown below. It means that there are no real solutions to this equation.

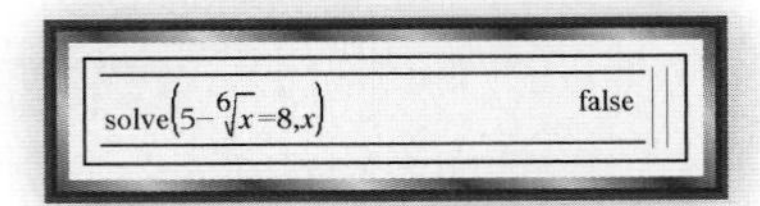

Equations from the Distance Formula

The Pythagorean Distance Formula $d = \sqrt{(x_1 - x_2)^2 + (y_1 - y_2)^2}$ can lead to equations involving square roots. Although the equations may look quite complicated, they can be solved with the same approaches as simpler equations.

ENGLISH LEARNERS

Vocabulary Development

When discussing the term *extraneous solution,* emphasize that the check of whether a solution is extraneous always uses the original equation. Extraneous solutions are introduced by transforming an equation so that the resulting equation is not equivalent to the original equation. Because each step of solving an equation transforms the previous equation, each transformed equation must be suspect. Therefore, the solution must be checked in the original equation, not a transformed one.

Accommodating the Learner

Ask students to show how to solve each of these equations.

a. $\sqrt{2x + 1} = 4$ $2x + 1 = 16$, $2x = 15$, $x = 7.5$

b. $\sqrt{(2x + 1)^2} = 4$ $|2x + 1| = 4$ so $2x + 1 = 4$, $2x = 3$, $x = 1.5$ or $2x + 1 = -4$, $2x = -5$, $x = -2.5$

c. $\sqrt[3]{2x + 1} = 4$ $2x + 1 = 64$, $2x = 63$, $x = 31.5$

d. $\sqrt[4]{2x + 1} = 4$ $2x + 1 = 256$, $2x = 255$, $x = 127.5$

Example 3

Find coordinates for the two points on the line with equation $y = 7$ that are 9 units away from the point (-3, 2).

Solution Draw a picture like the one at the right. Let $(x, 7)$ be one of the points you want.

Because the distance from $(x, 7)$ to $(-3, 2)$ is 9,

$$\sqrt{(x - (-3))^2 + (7 - 2)^2} = 9.$$

Simplify. $\sqrt{(x + 3)^2 + 25} = 9$

Now square both sides. $(x + 3)^2 + 25 = 81$

Subtract 25 from both sides. $(x + 3)^2 = 56$

Take the square root of both sides. $|x + 3| = \sqrt{56}$

So, $x + 3 = \sqrt{56}$ or $x + 3 = -\sqrt{56}$

$x = \sqrt{56} - 3$ or $x = -\sqrt{56} - 3$

$x \approx 4.5$ or $x \approx -10.5$.

The two points are exactly $(\sqrt{56} - 3, 7)$ and $(-\sqrt{56} - 3, 7)$, or approximately $(4.5, 7)$ and $(-10.5, 7)$.

Questions

COVERING THE IDEAS

1. Refer to Example 1. A 2-kilogram ball traveling at $8\frac{m}{s}$ is attached to a string with a tension of 100 newtons. How long is the string? 1.28 m

In 2–5, find all real solutions.

2. $\sqrt[3]{d} = 8$ $d = 512$
3. $12 = 2\sqrt[4]{m}$ $m = 1296$
4. $25 + \sqrt[5]{g} = 10$ $g = -759{,}375$
5. $3 - \frac{1}{2}\sqrt[6]{w} = -5$ $w = 16{,}777{,}216$
6. What is an extraneous solution to an equation?

In 7 and 8, find all real solutions.

7. $\sqrt{8x - 3} = 4$ $x = 2.375$
8. $12 - \sqrt[8]{3x - 1} = 15$ no real solutions
9. Find the two points on the line with equation $y = -2$ that are 4 units away from the point (1, -1). $(1 - \sqrt{15}, -2)$, $(1 + \sqrt{15}, -2)$
10. Find the two points on the line with equation $y = x$ that are 3 units away from the point (5, 7).

6. An extraneous solution is a solution to an equation that has been derived while solving but does not check in the original equation being solved.

10. $(6 + \frac{1}{2}\sqrt{14}, 6 + \frac{1}{2}\sqrt{14})$, $(6 - \frac{1}{2}\sqrt{14}, 6 - \frac{1}{2}\sqrt{14})$

Accommodating the Learner

Ask students to describe two ways to find the coordinates for the two points on the line $y = x$ that are 10 units from the point $A = (10, 0)$. Answers vary. Sample: (1) Because the two points we want are on the line $y = x$, they have coordinates of the form (x, x). Since the distance from (x, x) to $(10, 0)$ is 10, $\sqrt{(x - 10)^2 + (x - 0)^2} = 10$. So $(x - 10)^2 + x^2 = 100$, and $2x^2 - 20x = 0$. Solving this equation for x gives $x = 0$ or $x = 10$. So the two points are $(0, 0)$ and $(10, 10)$. (2) Sketch the line $y = x$. Because $(10, 0)$ is 10 units from $(0, 0)$ and $y = x$ contains $(0, 0)$, one of the needed points must be $(0, 0)$. Sketching a vertical line from $(10, 0)$ to the line $y = x$ shows that the other needed point is $(10, 10)$.

Notes on the Lesson

In Example 3, the solutions can be checked by noting that the two points are symmetric to the line $x = -3$. Furthermore, they are $2\sqrt{56}$ units apart. The altitude from (-3, 2) to the horizontal side of the triangle shown has length 5 and splits the given triangle into two congruent right triangles. Because each triangle has hypotenuse 9 and leg 5, the other leg in each triangle has length $\sqrt{56}$. It checks.

Note-Taking Tips

Encourage students to label each solution to a radical equation with one of the following two sentences: "This is an extraneous solution" or "This is not an extraneous solution." This practice of using such labels can remind students to check each solution to find out if it is extraneous.

3 Assignment

Recommended Assignment

- Questions 1–26
- Question 27 (extra credit)
- Self-Test

Notes on the Questions

Question 8 If students can discern, after adding -12 to both sides, that the left side is negative and the right side is positive, they can immediately state that fact and stop the solution process.

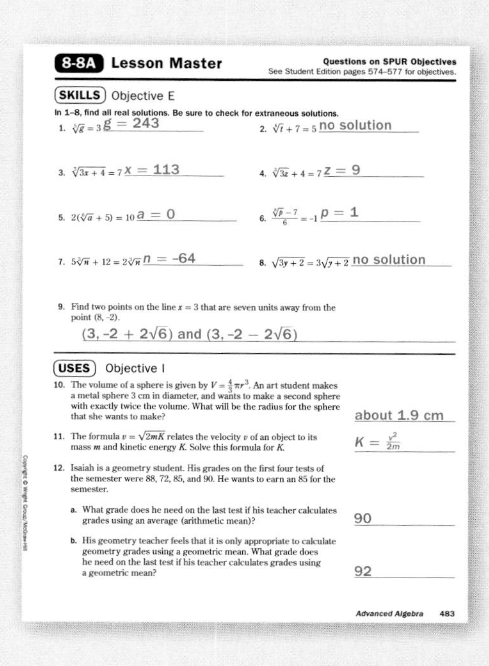

8-8A Lesson Master

Questions on SPUR Objectives
See Student Edition pages 574–577 for objectives.

SKILLS Objective E

In 1–8, find all real solutions. Be sure to check for extraneous solutions.

1. $\sqrt[5]{g} = 3$ $g = 243$
2. $\sqrt[4]{t} + 7 = 5$ no solution
3. $\sqrt[3]{3x + 4} = 7$ $x = 113$
4. $\sqrt[3]{3z} + 4 = 7$ $z = 9$
5. $2(\sqrt[6]{a} + 5) = 10$ $a = 0$
6. $\frac{\sqrt[4]{p} - 7}{6} = -1$ $p = 1$
7. $5\sqrt[3]{n} + 12 = 2\sqrt[3]{n}$ $n = -64$
8. $\sqrt{3y + 2} = 3\sqrt{y + 2}$ no solution
9. Find two points on the line $x = 3$ that are seven units away from the point (8, -2).
   $(3, -2 + 2\sqrt{6})$ and $(3, -2 - 2\sqrt{6})$

USES Objective I

10. The volume of a sphere is given by $V = \frac{4}{3}\pi r^3$. An art student makes a metal sphere 3 cm in diameter, and wants to make a second sphere with exactly twice the volume. What will be the radius for the sphere that she wants to make? about 1.9 cm
11. The formula $v = \sqrt{2mK}$ relates the velocity v of an object to its mass m and kinetic energy K. Solve this formula for K. $K = \frac{v^2}{2m}$
12. Isaiah is a geometry student. His grades on the first four tests of the semester were 88, 72, 85, and 90. He wants to earn an 85 for the semester.
    a. What grade does he need on the last test if his teacher calculates grades using an average (arithmetic mean)? 90
    b. His geometry teacher feels that it is only appropriate to calculate geometry grades using a geometric mean. What grade does he need on the last test if his teacher calculates grades using a geometric mean? 92

Advanced Algebra 483

Notes on the Questions

Question 14 This is one of the few real-world formulas that involves a 7th root.

APPLYING THE MATHEMATICS

11. Patty Packer is designing rectangular boxes like the one at the right, with square bases and a surface area of 18.2 square feet. The formula $s = -h + \sqrt{h^2 + 9.1}$ gives the base-side length s in terms of height h.
    a. Find s when $h = 2$ feet. about 1.62 ft
    b. Find h when $s = 2$ feet. 1.275 ft
    c. Derive the formula.

11c. $18.2 = 4hs + 2s^2$
$18.2 = 2(2hs + s^2)$
$9.1 = 2hs + s^2$
$9.1 + h^2 = 2hs + s^2 + h^2$
$\sqrt{9.1 + h^2} = s + h$
$s = -h + \sqrt{9.1 + h^2}$

12. A sphere has a radius of r centimeters. A new sphere is created with a diameter 3 centimeters less than the original. If the new sphere has a volume of 1500 cm^3, what is the radius of the original sphere? about 10.1 cm

13. Recall the U.S. median home values from page 514. Below is a similar table with home-value data for the state of Texas from 1950 to 2000.

Year	1950	1960	1970	1980	1990	2000
Median Home Value (unadjusted dollars)	5805	8800	12,000	39,100	59,600	82,500

    a. Calculate decade-to-decade percentage growth and the size-change factor for each of the five decades and record your results in a table as shown below. The first decade is done for you.

Years	1950–1960	1960–1970	1970–1980	1980–1990	1990–2000
% Increase	52	? 36	? 226	? 52	? 38
Size-change Factor	1.52	? 1.36	? 3.26	? 1.52	? 1.38

    b. Compute the geometric mean of the size-change factors in Part a, and determine the average increase per decade, expressed as a whole percent, in Texas home values from 1950 to 2000.
    c. The decade-to-decade percentage growth in Texas home values from 1940 to 2000 is ≈ 91%. If this continues, estimate the median Texas home value in 2010. about $157,575

13b. The geometric mean of the size-change factors is about 1.70, indicating an average increase of about 70% per decade.

14. When traveling at a fast rate, a ship's speed s (in knots) varies directly as the seventh root of the power p (in horsepower) generated by the engine. Suppose the equation $s = 6.5\sqrt[7]{p}$ describes the situation for a particular ship. If the ship is traveling at a speed of 15 knots, about how much horsepower is the engine generating? about 349 horsepower

Ken Warby holds the world water speed record. His boat, the *Spirit of Australia*, traveled at 317.6 mph on October 8, 1978.

Extension

Ask students to find an equation for line ℓ if ℓ is the perpendicular bisector of the segment that connects $A = (2, -6)$ and $B = (4, -4)$. Then ask them to identify three points on line ℓ and show that each point is equidistant from points A and B. An equation of the line that contains $\overline{AB}$ is $y = x - 8$, and the midpoint of $\overline{AB}$ is (3, -5). So an equation for ℓ is $y = -x - 2$. A sample of three points on ℓ are $C = (0, -2)$, $D = (-2, 0)$, and $E = (2, -4)$; $CA = \sqrt{4 + 16} = 2\sqrt{5}$, $CB = \sqrt{16 + 4} = 2\sqrt{5}$; $DA = \sqrt{16 + 36} = 2\sqrt{13}$, $DB = \sqrt{36 + 16} = 2\sqrt{13}$; $EA = \sqrt{0 + 4} = 2$, $EB = \sqrt{4 + 0} = 2$.

In 15 and 16, find all real solutions.

15. $5\sqrt[3]{x} - 8 = 13\sqrt[3]{x}$ $x = -1$

16. $\sqrt{y^2 - 9} = 2\sqrt{y - 3}$ $y = 1$, or $y = 3$

REVIEW

In 17 and 18, simplify each expression. Assume variables are nonnegative. (Lessons 8-7, 8-5)

17. $\sqrt[5]{-32y^{15}}$ $-2y^3$

18. $\sqrt{45a^5}\,\sqrt{5b^8}$ $15a^2b^4\sqrt{a}$

19. Give a counterexample to the statement $(x^4)^{\frac{1}{4}} = x$.

True or False In 20 and 21, assume $t > 0$. Justify your answer. (Lesson 8-6)

20. $\frac{1}{\sqrt{t}} = \frac{\sqrt{t}}{t}$

21. $\frac{\sqrt{3t}}{\sqrt{t}} = \frac{3\sqrt{t}}{\sqrt{3t}}$

22. **Multiple Choice** If a and k are positive, which of the following values for x is a solution to $a(x + h)^n = k$? (Lesson 8-6) B

A $\left(\frac{a+h}{k}\right)^{-\frac{1}{n}}$

B $\sqrt[n]{\frac{k}{a}} - h$

C $\sqrt[n]{\frac{k-a}{h}}$

D $\sqrt[n]{\frac{k}{a}} + h$

23. Let $u(x) = \sqrt[3]{x}$ and $v(x) = x^6$. (Lessons 8-4, 8-1)

a. Find an equation for $u \circ v$. What is the domain of $u \circ v$?

b. Find an equation for $v \circ u$. What is the domain of $v \circ u$?

24. Explain why the inverse of the function $f: x \rightarrow x(x + 2)$ is not a function. (Lessons 8-3, 8-2)

25. Write a system of inequalities whose solution is the shaded region graphed at the right. (Lesson 5-8)

26. In 2000, one estimate of known oil reserves worldwide was 1.017×10^{12} barrels (1020 gigabarrels) while annual consumption was estimated to be 2.80×10^{10} barrels. If oil consumption remains constant, how many years after 2000 will known oil reserves last? (Lesson 7-2) about 36 yr

EXPLORATION

27. If you flip a fair coin n times, the expected difference between the number of heads and tails is the integer closest to $\sqrt{\frac{2n}{\pi}}$.

a. How many times would you have to flip a coin to get an expected difference of 8? 89 times

b. Test this formula by using a spreadsheet to simulate flipping a coin the number of times you calculated in Part a. Do multiple simulations and create a bar chart. Does the formula appear to work for your value of n? See margin.

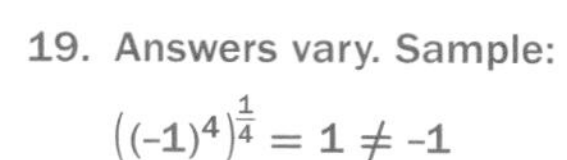

19. Answers vary. Sample: $((-1)^4)^{\frac{1}{4}} = 1 \neq -1$

20. true; $\frac{1}{\sqrt{t}} = \frac{1}{\sqrt{t}} \cdot \frac{\sqrt{t}}{\sqrt{t}} = \frac{\sqrt{t}}{t}$

21. true; $\frac{\sqrt{3t}}{\sqrt{t}} = \frac{\sqrt{3t}}{\sqrt{t}} \cdot \frac{\sqrt{3}}{\sqrt{3}} = \frac{3\sqrt{t}}{\sqrt{3t}}$

23a. $u(v(x)) = \sqrt[3]{x^6} = x^2$; domain: all real numbers

23b. $v(u(x)) = \left(\sqrt[3]{x}\right)^6 = x^2$; domain: all real numbers

24. Answers vary. Sample: The points (-2, 0) and (0, 0) are on the graph of the function, so it does not pass the horizontal-line test and its inverse is not a function.

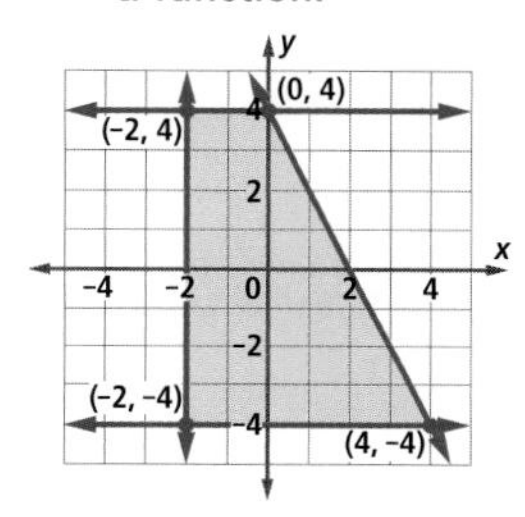

25. $\begin{cases} x \geq -2 \\ y \geq -4 \\ y \leq 4 \\ y \leq 4 - 2x \end{cases}$

QY ANSWER

$\frac{1}{2}$ m

Notes on the Questions

Question 26 If the world usage of petroleum continues to increase, the answer to this question may be more optimistic than realistic.

4 Wrap-Up

Ongoing Assessment

Ask students to describe what an extraneous solution is. How can they determine if a root is extraneous? Answers vary. Sample: An extraneous solution is a value, obtained when solving an equation, that does not satisfy the original equation. To determine if a root is extraneous, see if it checks in the original equation.

Project Update

Project 6, *America's Cup Yachts,* on page 569 relates to the content of this lesson.

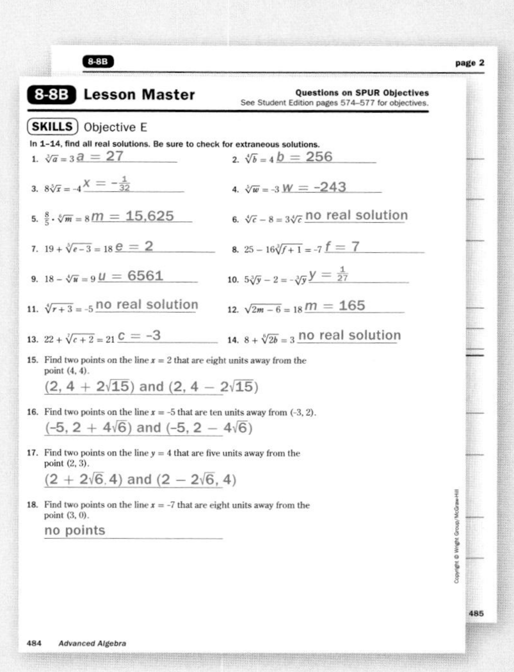

8-8B Lesson Master — Questions on SPUR Objectives (See Student Edition pages 574–577 for objectives.)

SKILLS Objective E

In 1–14, find all real solutions. Be sure to check for extraneous solutions.

1. $\sqrt[3]{a} = 3$ $a = 27$
2. $\sqrt[4]{b} = 4$ $b = 256$
3. $8\sqrt[5]{x} = -4$ $x = -\frac{1}{32}$
4. $\sqrt[5]{w} = -3$ $w = -243$
5. $\frac{8}{5} \cdot \sqrt[3]{m} = 8$ $m = 15{,}625$
6. $\sqrt[4]{c} - 8 = 3\sqrt[4]{c}$ no real solution
7. $19 + \sqrt[3]{e - 3} = 18$ $e = 2$
8. $25 - 16\sqrt[3]{f + 1} = -7$ $f = 7$
9. $18 - \sqrt[4]{u} = 9$ $u = 6561$
10. $5\sqrt[3]{y} - 2 = -\sqrt[3]{y}$ $y = \frac{1}{27}$
11. $\sqrt{r + 3} = -5$ no real solution
12. $\sqrt{2m - 6} = 18$ $m = 165$
13. $22 + \sqrt[3]{c + 2} = 21$ $c = -3$
14. $8 + \sqrt[4]{2b} = 3$ no real solution
15. Find two points on the line $x = 2$ that are eight units away from the point (4, 4). $(2, 4 + 2\sqrt{15})$ and $(2, 4 - 2\sqrt{15})$
16. Find two points on the line $x = -5$ that are ten units away from (-3, 2). $(-5, 2 + 4\sqrt{6})$ and $(-5, 2 - 4\sqrt{6})$
17. Find two points on the line $y = 4$ that are five units away from the point (2, 3). $(2 + 2\sqrt{6}, 4)$ and $(2 - 2\sqrt{6}, 4)$
18. Find two points on the line $x = -7$ that are eight units away from the point (3, 0). no points

484 Advanced Algebra

Additional Answers

27b. The chart indicates that the average difference between the number of heads and tails when tossing 89 coins is $\frac{1 + 1 + 3 + 3 + 5 + 5 + 7 + 7 + 17 + 27}{10} = 7.6 \approx 8$, as expected.

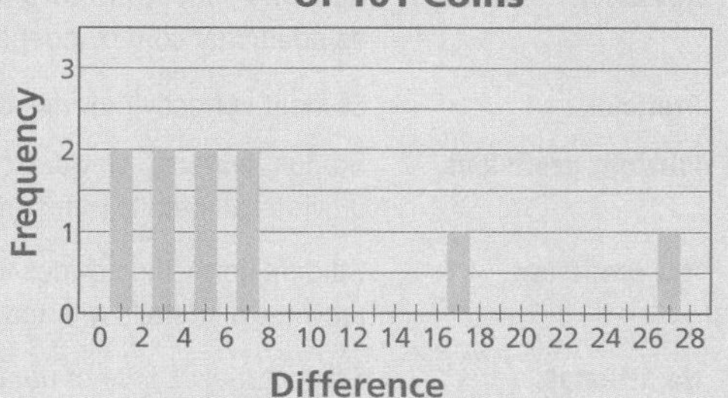

Chapter 8

The projects relate to the content of the lessons of this chapter as follows:

Project	Lesson
1	8-4
2	8-3
3	8-5
4	8-7
5	8-4
6	8-8

1 Roots and Surds
Students may be interested to learn that one of the mathematicians who applied the term *surd* to a root that cannot be expressed as a rational number was Fibonacci.

2 Caesar Cipher
As an extension, you way want to ask students to develop ciphers for digits. Besides a Caesar-type code of adding a number to each digit, another simple code is to imagine the digits 1 through 9 on a telephone keypad and "reflect" each digit over 5 to obtain the coded digit (or the decoded digit). The digits 0 and 5 can be their own codes or encode each other.

3 Properties of Irrational Numbers
To help students begin, ask: Does the closure property hold for addition of the irrational numbers $\sqrt{2}$ and $-\sqrt{2}$?
No; $\sqrt{2} + (-\sqrt{2}) = 0$; because 0 is not an irrational number, the closure property of addition does not hold for the set of irrational numbers.

Chapter 8 Projects

1 Roots and Surds

Some graphing utilities produce a graph like the top one below for $y = x^{\frac{1}{3}}$, while others produce a graph like the bottom one below.

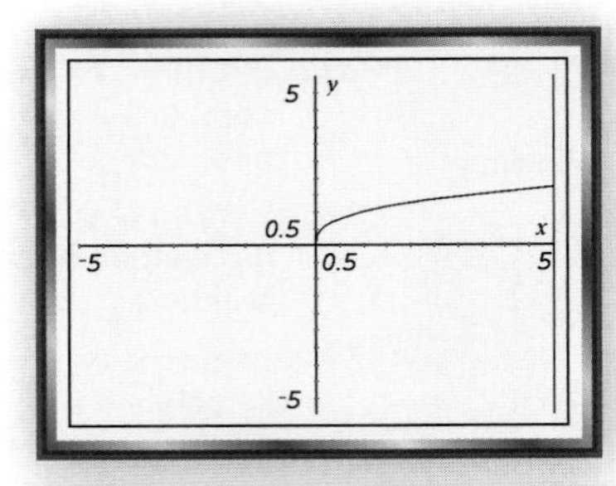

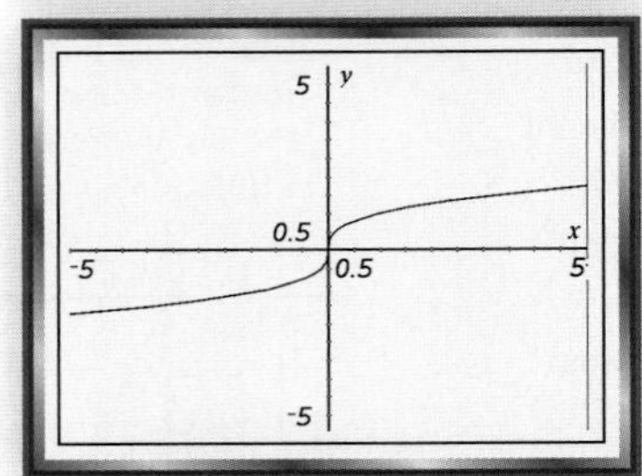

a. Check which graph your CAS or graphing utility creates for this function. Can both graphs be correct? Why or why not?

b. Investigate the term *surd* and how it relates to these graphs. Summarize your findings, explaining the contexts in which both graphs can be correct.

2 Caesar Cipher

Early methods of encoding messages relied on simple or shift ciphers. Research the Caesar cipher. How is the Caesar cipher different from the type of shift cipher you used in this chapter? How does the security of messages encoded with a Caesar cipher compare to the security of the messages used in this chapter?

3 Properties of Irrational Numbers

On page S1, at the back of the book, the field properties of real numbers are listed. Investigate which of these properties apply to the set of irrational numbers. Include examples and counterexamples to illustrate your conclusions.

Project Rubric

Advanced	Student correctly provides all of the details asked for in the project as well as additional correct independent conclusions.
Proficient	Student correctly provides all of the details asked for in the project.
Partially proficient	Student correctly provides some of the details asked for in the project or provides all details with some inaccuracies.
Not proficient	Student correctly provides few of the details asked for in the project or provides all details with many inaccuracies.
No attempt	Student makes little or no attempt to complete the project.

4 Square Roots of Pure Imaginary Numbers

a. Find a square root of i, and hence a fourth root of -1, by solving the equation $i = (a + bi)^2$ for a and b. It will help to remember that $i = 0 + i$, and that two complex numbers are equal if and only if their real parts are equal and their imaginary parts are equal. This allows you to set up a system to solve for a and b. Write the square root of i in radical form.

b. We know that 4 has another square root besides the one denoted $\sqrt{4}$. Similarly, i has another square root. Use what you know about the other square root of 4 to hypothesize about the other square root of i. Check your hypothesis by squaring your result.

c. Find the square roots of some other nonreal numbers.

5 Square Roots of Matrices

For 2×2 matrices A and B, we say that A is a square root of B if $A^2 = B$.

a. Show that $\begin{bmatrix} 1 & 2 \\ 0 & -1 \end{bmatrix}$ and $\begin{bmatrix} -1 & 7 \\ 0 & 1 \end{bmatrix}$ are square roots of $\begin{bmatrix} 1 & 0 \\ 0 & 1 \end{bmatrix}$.

b. If X is an invertible 2×2 matrix, use the associative property of matrix multiplication to show that for any 2×2 matrix A, $(XAX^{-1})(XAX^{-1}) = XA^2X^{-1}$.

c. Use Part b to find several other square roots of $\begin{bmatrix} 1 & 0 \\ 0 & 1 \end{bmatrix}$. How many do you think there are?

6 America's Cup Yachts

One of the most prestigious international sailing competitions is the America's Cup. In order to compete, yachts must adhere to the International America's Cup Class (IACC) yacht design rules. In 2003, one of the rules was that the yacht length L (in meters), sail area S (in square meters), and displacement D (in cubic meters) had to satisfy the inequality

$$\frac{L + 1.25\sqrt{S} - 9.8\sqrt[3]{D}}{0.686} \leq 24.000 \text{ meters}$$

The displacement D is the volume of water displaced by the yacht. It is calculated by taking the mass (in kilograms) of the yacht and dividing it by 1025. The mass of the yacht must be no greater than 24,000 kg, rounded to the nearest 20 kg. The boats have evolved over the years and now tend toward the maximum allowable displacement.

a. Assuming the maximum displacement, solve the inequality for L in terms of S and graph the function mapping S onto the maximum value of L that would be allowed.

b. Using your answer to Part a, find some pairs of dimensions of the length and sail area that would allow a boat to abide by the formula given the maximum displacement.

c. Research the dimensions of various boats (perhaps winners) in the competition to verify that they complied with the formula.

4 Square Roots of Pure Imaginary Numbers

You may want to ask students to include graphs, in the complex plane, of their square roots. Those graphs can provide a geometric interpretation of the square roots.

5 Square Roots of Matrices

To start students on this project, ask: Is there a restriction on the kind of matrix that can have a square root? The matrix must be a square matrix.

6 America's Cup Yachts

In Part a, most students will use 24,000 kg as the maximum mass when calculating the maximum displacement. However, some students may use 24,009 kg because this is the maximum weight that rounds to 24,000 kg when rounded to the nearest 20 kg. This is also a correct answer. Encourage students that use this maximum weight to explain their thinking to the class.

Sample answers for projects are in the Solution Manual in the Electronic Teacher's Edition.

Notes

Chapter 8

Summary and Vocabulary

The Summary gives an overview of the entire chapter and provides an opportunity for students to consider the material as a whole. Thus, the Summary can be used to help students relate and unify the concepts presented in the chapter.

Vocabulary words and symbols are listed by lesson to provide a checklist of concepts that students must know. Emphasize to students that they should read the vocabulary list carefully before starting the Self-Test on pages 572–573. If students do not understand the meaning of a vocabulary word, they should refer back to the indicated lesson.

Theorems and Properties covered in the chapter are listed below the Summary with page references included to lead students back to the location in the chapter where the theorem or property is stated.

Chapter 8 Summary and Vocabulary

- Every relation has an **inverse** that can be found by switching the coordinates of its ordered pairs. The graphs of any relation and its inverse are reflection images of each other over the line $y = x$.

- Inverses of some functions are themselves functions. A real function graphed on the coordinate plane has an inverse if and only if no horizontal line intersects the function's graph in more than one point. In general, two functions f and g are inverses of each other if and only if $f \circ g$ and $g \circ f$ are defined, $f(g(x)) = x$ for all values of x in the domain of g, and $g(f(x)) = x$ for all values of x in the domain of f.

- Consider the function f with domain the set of all real numbers and equation of the form $y = f(x) = x^n$. If n is an odd integer ≥ 3, its inverse is the nth root function with equation $x = y^n$ or $y = \sqrt[n]{x}$. These two functions are graphed below at the left. When n is an even integer ≥ 2, the inverse of $y = f(x) = x^n$ is not a function. However, if the domain of f is restricted to the set of nonnegative real numbers, the inverse of f is the nth root function with equation $y = \sqrt[n]{x} = x^{\frac{1}{n}}$. The restricted function and its inverse are graphed below at the right.

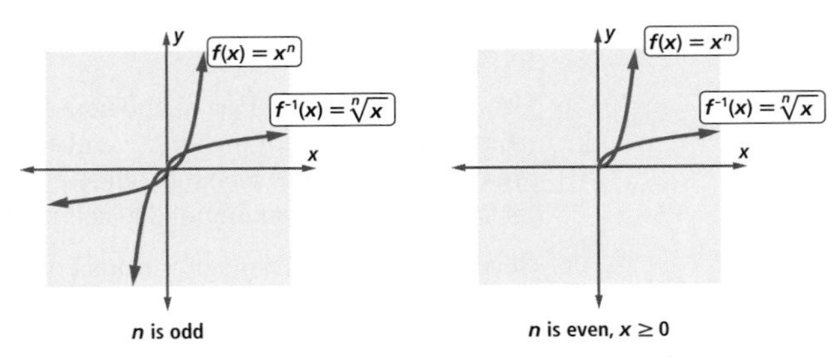

That is,

1. When $x \geq 0$, $\sqrt[n]{x}$ is defined for any integer $n > 2$. It equals the positive nth root of x.
2. When $x < 0$, $\sqrt[n]{x}$ is defined only for odd integers $n \geq 3$. It equals the real nth root of x, a negative number.

Vocabulary

Lesson 8-1
composite, $g \circ f$
*function composition, composition

Lesson 8-2
inverse of a relation
horizontal-line test

Lesson 8-3
*inverse function, f^{-1}

Lesson 8-4
radical sign, $\sqrt{\ }$
$\sqrt[n]{x}$ when $x \geq 0$
geometric mean

Lesson 8-6
rationalizing the denominator
conjugate

Lesson 8-7
$\sqrt[n]{x}$ when $x < 0$

Lesson 8-8
extraneous solution

- All properties of powers listed in Chapter 7 apply to radicals when they stand for real numbers. They lead to the following theorems for any real numbers x and y and integers m and n for which the symbols are defined and stand for real numbers.

  Root of a Power Theorem: $x^{\frac{m}{n}} = \sqrt[n]{x^m} = (\sqrt[n]{x})^m$

  Root of a Product Theorem: $\sqrt[n]{xy} = \sqrt[n]{x} \cdot \sqrt[n]{y}$

- These properties are helpful in simplifying radical expressions and in solving equations with radicals. To solve an equation involving an nth root, you need to raise each side to the nth power. When you do this, you may gain **extraneous solutions**. Always check every possible answer in the original equation to make sure that extraneous solutions have not been included.

- Radicals appear in many formulas. For example, the nth root of the product of n numbers is the geometric mean of the numbers. When a radical appears in the denominator of a fraction, multiplying both the numerator and denominator by a well chosen number can make the new denominator rational. To **rationalize** a fraction with a denominator of the form $a + \sqrt{b}$, multiply both numerator and denominator by the **conjugate** $a - \sqrt{b}$.

Theorems

Inverse-Relation Theorem (p. 524)
Inverse Functions Theorem (p. 530)
Power Function Inverse Theorem (p. 532)
Root of a Power Theorem (p. 539)
Root of a Product Theorem (p. 546)
*n*th Root of a Product Theorem (p. 559)

Summary and Vocabulary 571

Self-Test

For the development of mathematical competence, feedback and correction, along with the opportunity for practice, are necessary. The Self-Test provides the opportunity for feedback and correction; the Chapter Review provides additional opportunities for practice. We cannot overemphasize the importance of these end-of-chapter materials. It is at this point that the material gels for many students, allowing them to solidify skills and understanding. In general, student performance should improve after these pages.

Assign the Self-Test as a one-night assignment. Worked-out solutions for all questions are in the Selected Answers section of the student book. Encourage students to take the Self-Test honestly, grade themselves, and then be prepared to discuss the test in class.

Advise students to pay special attention to those Chapter Review questions (pages 574–577) that correspond to the questions they missed on the Self-Test.

Chapter 8 Self-Test

Take this test as you would take a test in class. You will need a calculator and graph paper. Then use the Selected Answers section in the back of the book to check your work.

In 1–4, let $f(x) = 4 - x^2$ and $g(x) = 3x + 7$.

1. **Fill in the Blank** $f \circ g: -1 \rightarrow$ __?__.
2. Write a formula for $f(g(x))$.
3. Write an equation for $g \circ f$.
4. Are f and g inverses? Justify your answer.
5. a. Find an equation for the inverse of the function r defined by $r(x) = \frac{1}{2}x + 3$.
   b. Is the inverse a function? Justify your answer. Yes; Answers vary. Sample: It is a line in slope-intercept form.

In 6 and 7, refer to the function graphed below.

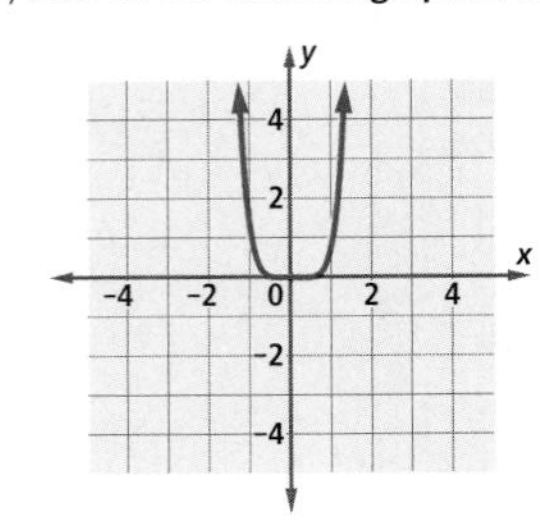

6. Graph the inverse of the function.
7. How can you restrict the domain of the original function so that the inverse is also a function?
8. **True or False** $\sqrt[4]{16} = -2$. Justify your answer.
9. The formula $r = \sqrt{\frac{S}{4\pi}}$ gives the radius r of a sphere with surface area S. What is the surface area, to the nearest square centimeter, of a spherical balloon with radius 12 cm?
   Substitute $r = 12$ into the formula and solve for s:
   $12 = \sqrt{\frac{S}{4\pi}}$; $144 = \frac{S}{4\pi}$; $S = 1810$ cm^2.

In 10–12, simplify and rationalize all denominators. Assume $x > 0$ and $y > 0$.

10. $\sqrt[3]{-216x^{12}y^3}$
11. $\sqrt[4]{\frac{32x^{12}}{x^4}}$
12. $\frac{3x^2}{\sqrt{81x}}$ $\quad \frac{3x^2}{\sqrt{81x}} = \frac{3x^2}{9\sqrt{x}} \cdot \frac{\sqrt{x}}{\sqrt{x}} = \frac{3x^2\sqrt{x}}{9x} = \frac{x^2\sqrt{x}}{3}$
13. The top of a 15-foot ladder rests against a window ledge on the side of a building. The height h of the window ledge above the ground is equal to the distance from the bottom of the ladder to the base of the building. On a test, students were asked to find h. Three students' answers are below:

    Deon: $h = \sqrt{\frac{225}{2}}$

    Tia: $h = \frac{15}{2}$

    Carmen: $h = \frac{15\sqrt{2}}{2}$

    Which answer(s) is (are) correct? Justify your answer.
14. Rewrite $\sqrt[5]{\sqrt[3]{13}}$ as a power with a simple fraction exponent in lowest terms.
15. Rationalize the denominator and simplify $\frac{24}{8 - 2\sqrt{3}}$.
    $\frac{24}{8 - 2\sqrt{3}} \cdot \frac{8 + 2\sqrt{3}}{8 + 2\sqrt{3}} = \frac{192 + 48\sqrt{3}}{52} = \frac{48 + 12\sqrt{3}}{13}$

1. $4 - (3(-1) + 7)^2 = 4 - 16 = -12$
2. $f(g(x)) = 4 - (3x + 7)^2 = -9x^2 - 42x - 45$
3. $g \circ f(x) = 3(4 - x^2) + 7 = 19 - 3x^2$
4. no; from Question 3 $g(f(x)) = 19 - 3x^2 \neq x$

16. Use the formula $r = \sqrt[3]{\frac{3V}{4\pi}}$ to approximate the radius r of a sphere with volume $V = 268$ cubic inches to the nearest hundredth. $r = \sqrt[3]{\frac{3(268)}{4\pi}} = \sqrt[3]{\frac{201}{\pi}} \approx 4.00$ in.

In 17 and 18, solve for x.

17. $25 = 4\sqrt{7x}$

18. $17 + \sqrt[3]{2x + 7} = 20$

19. For what values of n is the inverse of the function f with equation $y = f(x) = x^n$ also a function? odd integers

20. Give the domain and range of the function $y = \sqrt[6]{x}$, if x and y are real numbers.
domain: $x \geq 0$; range: $y \geq 0$

21. Six samples taken in a water quality survey have the following levels of *E. coli* bacteria.

Sample	1	2	3	4	5	6
Count (per 100 mL)	27	32	144	46	597	1092

Use the geometric mean to compute an average level of bacteria across the samples.

22. Eddie is buying a new pair of eyeglasses. He has a store coupon for \$45 off a new pair of glasses. The glasses he chooses have a starting price of P dollars, but they are on sale for 30% off. For what values of P will Eddie get a better deal if he can use the coupon before the discount is taken?
None; The price when the coupon is used first is $0.7(P - 45) = 0.7P - 31.5$, and the price when the discount is taken first is $0.7P - 45$. For all P, $0.7P - 31.5 > 0.7P - 45$.

5a.
$$x = \frac{1}{2}y + 3$$
$$x - 3 = \frac{1}{2}y$$
$$y = 2x - 6$$

6.

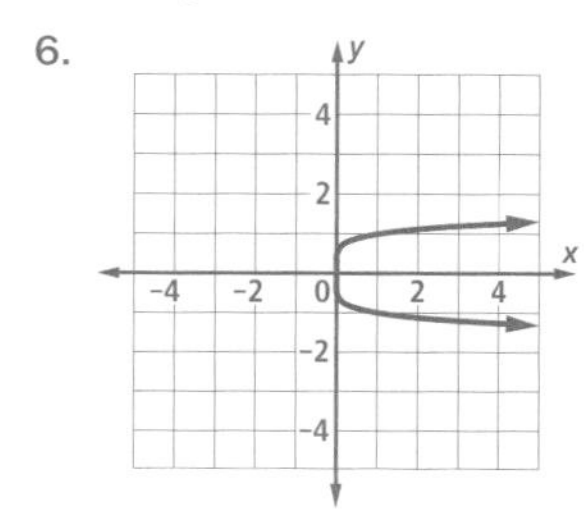

7. Restrict it to either only positive numbers or only negative numbers. That way, the graph of the original function will pass the horizontal-line test.

8. False; While $(-2)^4 = 16$, the use of the radical symbol indicates the positive real 4th root of 16, which is 2.

10. $\sqrt[3]{-216x^{12}y^3} = \sqrt[3]{-216} \cdot \sqrt[3]{x^{12}} \cdot \sqrt[3]{y^3} = -6x^4y$

11. $\sqrt[4]{\frac{32x^{12}}{x^4}} = \frac{\sqrt[4]{16} \cdot \sqrt[4]{2} \cdot \sqrt[4]{x^{12}}}{\sqrt[4]{x^4}} = \frac{2x^3\sqrt[4]{2}}{x} = 2x^2\sqrt[4]{2}$

13. Deon and Carmen; Construct an isosceles right triangle with legs of length h and a hypotenuse of length 15. By the Pythagorean Theorem, $2h^2 = 15^2$. So, $h = \sqrt{\frac{225}{2}} = \frac{15\sqrt{2}}{2}$.

14. $\sqrt[5]{\sqrt[3]{13}} = \left(13^{\frac{1}{3}}\right)^{\frac{1}{5}} = 13^{\frac{1}{15}}$

17.
$$25 = 4\sqrt{7x}$$
$$\left(\frac{25}{4}\right)^2 = 7x$$
$$x = \frac{625}{112}$$

18.
$$17 + \sqrt[3]{2x + 7} = 20$$
$$\sqrt[3]{2x + 7} = 3$$
$$2x + 7 = 27$$
$$x = 10$$

21. $\sqrt[6]{1092 \cdot 597 \cdot 46 \cdot 144 \cdot 32 \cdot 27} \approx 125$ bacteria per mL

Self-Test 573

Chapter Review

The main objectives for the chapter are organized in the Chapter Review under the four types of understanding this book promotes: Skills, Properties, Uses, and Representations.

Whereas end-of-chapter material may be considered optional in some texts, in UCSMP *Advanced Algebra* we have selected these objectives and questions with the expectation that they will be covered. Students should be able to answer these questions with about 85% accuracy after studying the chapter.

You may assign these questions over a single night to help students prepare for a test the next day or you may assign the questions over a two-day period. If you work the questions over two days, we recommend assigning the evens for homework the first night so that students get feedback in class the next day, and then assigning the odds the night before the test because the answers are provided to the odd-numbered questions in the Selected Answers section at the back of the book.

It is effective to ask students which questions they still do not understand and use the day as a total class discussion of the material that the class finds most difficult.

Resources

- Assessment Resources: Chapter 8 Test Forms A–D; Chapter 8 Test, Cumulative Form

Technology Resources

Teacher's Assessment Assistant, Ch. 8
Electronic Teacher's Edition, Ch. 8

Chapter 8 Chapter Review

SKILLS
PROPERTIES
USES
REPRESENTATIONS

SKILLS Procedures used to get answers

OBJECTIVE A Find values and rules for composites of functions. (Lesson 8-1)

1. When applying $f \circ g$, which function is applied last? f

In 2–4, let $p(x) = x^2 + x + 1$ and $q(x) = x - 6$.

2. a. Find $p(q(5))$. 1
   b. Find $p(q(x))$. $x^2 - 11x + 31$
3. a. Find $q(p(5))$. 25
   b. Find $q(p(x))$. $x^2 + x - 5$
4. The function $p \circ q$ maps -10 onto what number? 241

In 5 and 6, rules for functions f and g are given. Does $f \circ g = g \circ f$? Justify your response. 5–6. See margin.

5. $f: x \rightarrow -\frac{3}{8}x$; $g: x \rightarrow -\frac{8}{3}x$
6. $f(x) = 3\sqrt{x}$; $g(x) = \frac{9}{x}$, $x > 0$
7. If $h(x) = x^{\frac{2}{3}}$, find an expression for $h(h(x))$. $h(h(x)) = x^{\frac{4}{9}}$
8. If $r(x) = \frac{2x+1}{x}$, find an expression for $r(r(x))$. $r(r(x)) = \frac{5x+2}{2x+1}$

OBJECTIVE B Find the inverse of a function. (Lessons 8-2, 8-3)

9. A function has equation $y = 6x - 3$. Write an equation for its inverse in slope-intercept form. $y = \frac{1}{6}x + \frac{1}{2}$
10. A function has equation $y = \sqrt{x^2}$. What is an equation for its inverse? $y = x$, for $x \geq 0$
11. **Fill in the Blank** If $f: x \rightarrow 7x + 13$, then $f^{-1}: x \rightarrow$ __?__. $\frac{x-13}{7}$
12. Show that $f: x \rightarrow 3x + 2$ and $g: x \rightarrow \frac{1}{3}x - 2$ are not inverse functions. See margin.
13. **Fill in the Blank** If $g(t) = -t^2$ for $t \leq 0$, then $g^{-1}(t) =$ __?__. $-\sqrt{-t}$
14. **Multiple Choice** Suppose $f(x) = x^5$. Then $f^{-1}(x) = x^k$, where $k =$ B
    A -5.
    B $\frac{1}{5}$.
    C $-\frac{1}{5}$.
    D 5.

OBJECTIVE C Evaluate radicals. (Lessons 8-4, 8-7)

In 15–18, write as a whole number or simple fraction.

15. $\sqrt[5]{243}$ 3
16. $\sqrt[3]{-27}$ -3
17. $\sqrt[3]{\left(\frac{64}{343}\right)^2}$ $\frac{16}{49}$
18. $(\sqrt{15} + \sqrt{13})(\sqrt{15} - \sqrt{13})$ 2

In 19–22, approximate to the nearest hundredth.

19. $\sqrt[3]{3}$ 1.44
20. $\sqrt[4]{81 + 16}$ 3.14
21. $4\sqrt[3]{-75}$ -16.87
22. $\sqrt[9]{\sqrt{365}}$ 1.39

Additional Answers

5. yes; $f \circ g(x) = x = g \circ f(x)$
6. no; $f \circ g(x) = \frac{9}{\sqrt{x}} \neq \frac{3}{\sqrt{x}} = g \circ f(x)$
12. $f(g(x)) = x - 4 \neq x$

OBJECTIVE D Rewrite or simplify expressions with radicals. (Lessons 8-5, 8-6, 8-7)

In 23–30, simplify. Assume that all variables are positive.

23. $\sqrt{b^8}$ b^4
24. $\sqrt[3]{57r^3}$ $r\sqrt[3]{57}$
25. $\sqrt[6]{8} \cdot \sqrt[6]{8}$ 2
26. $\sqrt[3]{-60n^{12}}$ $-n^4\sqrt[3]{60}$
27. $\sqrt[7]{-u^{14}v^{28}}$ $-u^2v^4$
28. $\sqrt{3x^3} \cdot \sqrt{6x}$ $3x^2\sqrt{2}$
29. $\sqrt{\sqrt{\sqrt{k}}}$ $\sqrt[8]{k}$
30. $\sqrt{N} \cdot \sqrt[3]{N} \cdot \sqrt[6]{N}$ N

In 31–34, rationalize the denominator and simplify, if possible.

31. $\frac{13}{\sqrt{13}}$ $\sqrt{13}$
32. $\frac{8}{\sqrt{2}}$ $4\sqrt{2}$
33. $\frac{7}{\sqrt{3}-1}$ $\frac{7\sqrt{3}+7}{2}$
34. $\frac{p}{p+\sqrt{q}}$ $(p > 0, q > 0)$ $\frac{p^2 - p\sqrt{q}}{p^2 - q}$

OBJECTIVE E Solve equations with radicals. (Lesson 8-8)

In 35–40, find all real solutions. Round answers to the nearest hundredth where necessary.

35. $\sqrt[3]{y} = 2.5$ $y = 15.625$
36. $13 = 11\sqrt[4]{f}$ $f \approx 1.95$
37. $12 = \frac{1}{4}\sqrt{16-y}$ $y = -2288$
38. $\sqrt[3]{x-1} - 9 = 27$ $x = 46{,}657$
39. $18 + \sqrt[6]{64n} = 12$ no solution
40. $\sqrt{6x} + 3\sqrt{6x} = 12$ $x = 1.5$

43. domain: $\{x \mid x \geq -6\}$; range: $\{y \mid y \leq 0\}$
45. The range of f is the set of all positive integers.
48. The equation does not hold for $a < 0$ because noninteger powers of negative numbers are not defined.
49. all real numbers

PROPERTIES Principles behind the mathematics

OBJECTIVE F Apply properties of the inverse of a function. (Lessons 8-2, 8-3)

In 41 and 42, state whether the statement is true or false.

41. If functions f and g are inverses of each other, then $f \circ g(x) = g \circ f(x)$ for all x for which these functions are defined. true
42. When the domain of f is the set of positive real numbers, then the inverse of $y = x^6$ has equation $y = \sqrt[6]{x}$. true
43. Suppose the domain of a linear function L is $\{x \mid x \leq 0\}$ and the range is $\{y \mid y \geq -6\}$. What are the domain and range of L^{-1}?

In 44 and 45, suppose f and g are inverses of each other.

44. If (ℓ, m) is a point on the graph of f, what point must be on the graph of g? (m, ℓ)
45. If the domain of g is the set of all positive integers, what can you conclude about the domain or range of f?

OBJECTIVE G Apply properties of radicals and nth root functions. (Lessons 8-4, 8-5, 8-7)

46. If x is negative, for what values of n is $\sqrt[n]{x}$ a real number? odd integers
47. **Multiple Choice** Which expression is not defined? D
    A $\sqrt[3]{625}$ B $\sqrt[3]{-625}$
    C $\sqrt[4]{625}$ D $\sqrt[4]{-625}$
48. Explain why the statement $\sqrt[7]{a} = a^{\frac{1}{7}}$ is not true for all real numbers a.
49. For what values of x is $\sqrt[5]{x^5} = x$?
50. Give a counterexample to this statement: For all real numbers x, $\sqrt[8]{x^8} = x$. See margin.

Additional Answers

50. Answers vary. Sample: for $x = -5$, $\sqrt[8]{x^8} = \sqrt[8]{(-5)^8} = 5 \neq x$

Additional Answers

51. False; the Root of a Product Theorem does not hold for negative a and b and even n.

52. True; for $a, b < 0$, the nth root is defined for odd n, and thus $\sqrt[n]{a} \cdot \sqrt[n]{b} = \sqrt[n]{ab}$.

53c. The deal is the same because both the discount and the sales tax involve multiplication, which is commutative.

54c. Since $g(b) > f(b)$, the waiter gets a bigger tip, and one he or she is entitled to, by receiving a tip on the full amount before the discount is applied.

58a. 1.028; 1.016; 1.023; 1.027; 1.034; 1.032; 1.028

59. the diameter of the first balloon is about 1.91 times larger

61a.

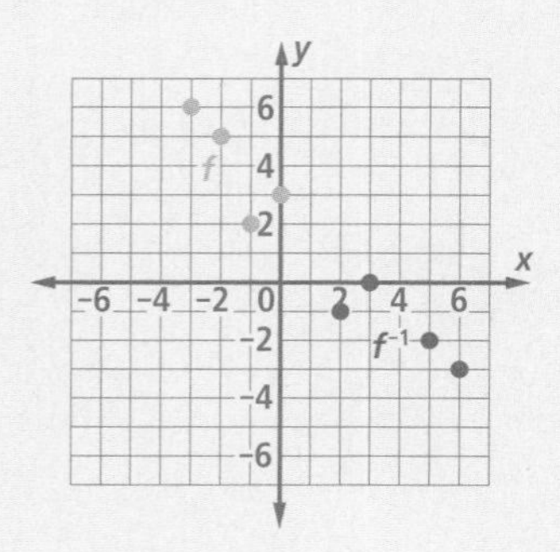

62.

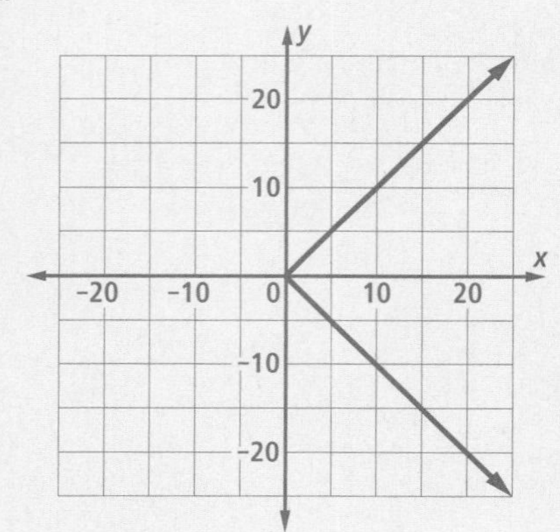

In 51 and 52, tell whether the statement $\sqrt[n]{a} \cdot \sqrt[n]{b} = \sqrt[n]{ab}$ is true for given conditions. Justify your answer. 51–52. See margin.

51. a and b are negative, $n = 2$

52. a and b are negative, $n = 3$

USES Applications of mathematics in real-world situations

OBJECTIVE H Solve real-world problems that can be modeled by composite functions. (Lesson 8-1)

53. An electronics store is having a 25%-off sale on flat-screen televisions. The television Amber wants to buy has a sticker price of \$1200, and the sales tax in the state is 9%.
    - a. How much will Amber pay for the television if the discount is taken before the tax is calculated? \$981
    - b. How much will she pay if the tax is calculated first? \$981
    - c. Would Amber get a better deal if the tax was calculated first or if the discount was taken first? Explain your answer. See margin.

54. A group goes to a restaurant with a \$15-off coupon. The restaurant bill comes to b dollars before the tip and before using the coupon. The group wants to tip the server 20%.
    - a. Find an expression for $f(b)$, the total cost if the coupon is used before the tip is calculated. $f(b) = 1.2(b - 15)$
    - b. Find an expression for $g(b)$, the total cost if the tip is calculated before the coupon is used. $g(b) = 1.2b - 15$
    - c. Restaurants typically urge patrons to tip on the full bill before any discount is applied. Why do you think restaurants do this? See margin.

OBJECTIVE I Solve real-world problems that can be modeled by equations with radicals. (Lessons 8-4, 8-8)

55. The maximum distance d you can see from the top of a building with height h is approximated by the formula $d = k\sqrt{h}$. Apartment buildings A and B are 9 and 16 stories high, respectively. If these two apartment buildings have the same height per floor, about how many times farther can you see from the top of apartment B than the top of apartment A? about 1.33 times farther

In 56 and 57, use the following information: To find the speed s (in mph) that a certain car was traveling on a typical dry road, suppose that police use the formula $s = 2\sqrt{5L}$, where L is the length of the skid marks in feet.

56. The car skidded 35 feet before stopping. According to the formula, how fast was the car going? about 26.5 mph

57. About how far would this car be expected to travel if it skids from 55 mph to a stop? 151.25 ft

58. The U.S. Consumer Price Index (CPI) estimates the price of goods and services over time. In the table below, y is the percent change in the CPI from the previous year to the indicated year.

Year	2001	2002	2003	2004	2005	2006	2007
y (percent)	2.8	1.6	2.3	2.7	3.4	3.2	2.8

    - a. Add a third row to the table in which you convert each percent to a size-change factor. For example, the factor for 2001 is 1.028. See margin.
    - b. Compute the geometric mean of the size-change factors you found in Part a, and determine the average CPI percentage increase over this seven-year time frame. about 1.027; 2.7%

Additional Answers

63a.

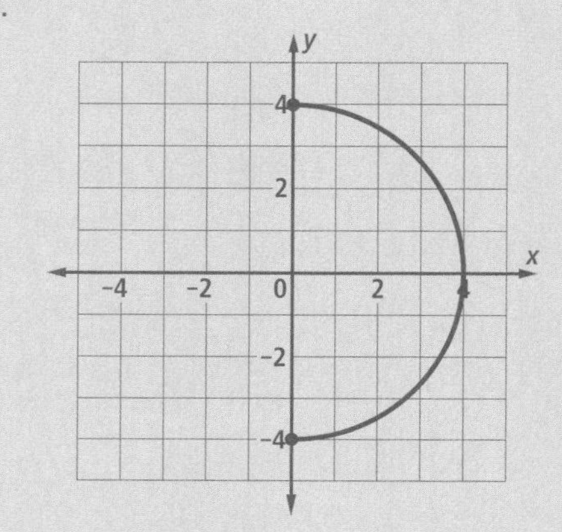

64. Answers vary. Sample:

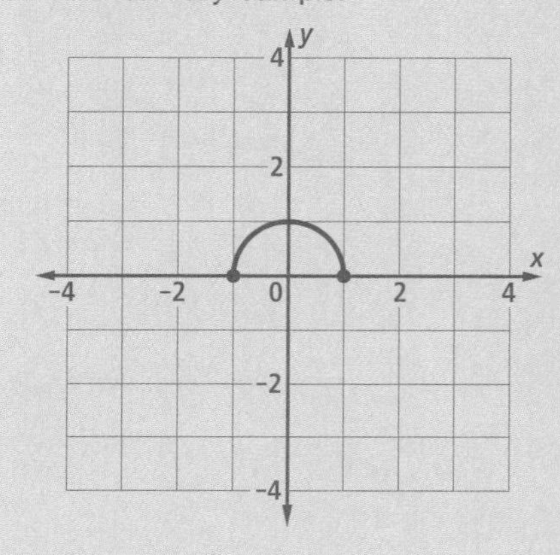

59. The diameter of a spherical balloon varies directly as the cube root of its volume. If one balloon holds 7 times as much air as a second balloon, how do their diameters compare? See margin.

REPRESENTATIONS Pictures, graphs, or objects that illustrate concepts

OBJECTIVE J Make and interpret graphs of inverses of relations and functions. (Lessons 8-2, 8-3)

60. Use the graphs below.

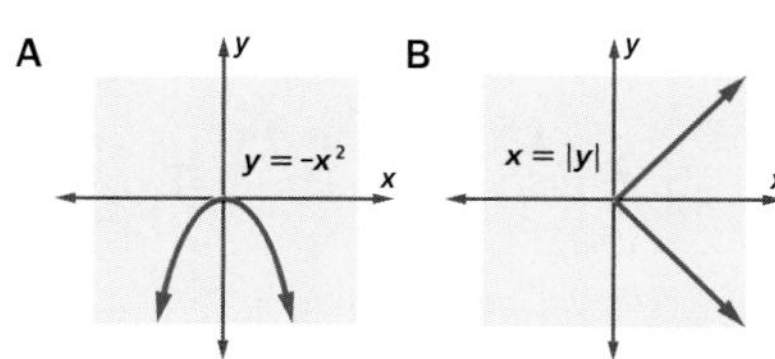

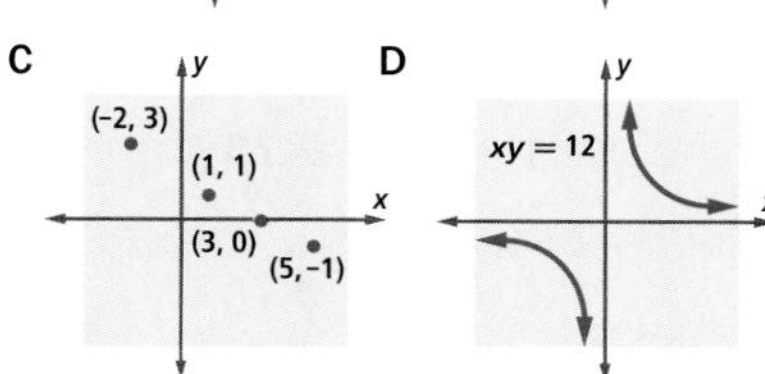

a. **Multiple Choice** Which is the graph of a function whose inverse is not a function? A

b. How can you restrict the domain of the function in your answer to Part a so that its inverse is a function?
Answers vary. Sample: $\{x \mid x < 0\}$

61. Let $f = \{(-3, 6), (-2, 5), (-1, 2), (0, 3)\}$

a. Graph f^{-1}. See margin.

b. What transformation maps f onto f^{-1}?
reflection over the line with equation $y = x$

62. Graph the inverse of the function with equation $y = \sqrt{x^2}$. See margin.

63. a. Graph the inverse of the function graphed below. See margin.

b. Is the inverse a function? Why or why not?

64. Draw a graph of a function with domain $\{x \mid -1 < x < 1\}$ that has an inverse which is not a function. See margin.

65. Let $g(x) = x^3$.

a. Graph $y = g(x)$ and $y = g^{-1}(x)$. See margin.

b. What is the domain of g^{-1}?
the set of all real numbers

In 66 and 67, an equation for a function is given.

a. Graph the function.

b. State the domain and range of the function.

66. $h(x) = \sqrt[6]{x}$ 67. $f(x) = \sqrt[7]{x}$

66–67. See the Additioinal Answers section at the back of the book.

63b. No. Explanations vary. Sample: The graph of the original function does not pass the horizontal-line test.

Assessment

Evaluation The *Assessment Resources* provide four forms of the Chapter 8 Test. Forms A and B present parallel versions of a short-answer format. Form C consists of four to six short-response questions that cover the SPUR objectives from Chapter 8. Form D offers performance assessment that covers a subset (or even just one) of the SPUR objectives for the chapter. The fifth type of test is a Chapter 8 Test, Cumulative Form. About 50% of this test covers Chapter 8, and the remaining 50% covers the previous chapters evenly.

Feedback After students have taken the test for Chapter 8 and you have scored the results, return the tests to students for discussion. Class discussion on the questions that caused trouble for most students can be very effective in identifying and clarifying misunderstandings. You might want to have them note the items they missed and work either in groups or at home to correct them. It is important for students to receive feedback on every chapter test, and we recommend that students see and correct their mistakes before proceeding too far into the next chapter.

Suggestions for Assignment Assign Lesson 9-1 for homework the evening of the test. It gives students work to do after they have completed the test and keeps the class moving. If you do not do this, you may cover one less chapter over the course of the year.

Additional Answers

66–67. See the Additional Answers section at the back of the book.

Additional Answers

65a.

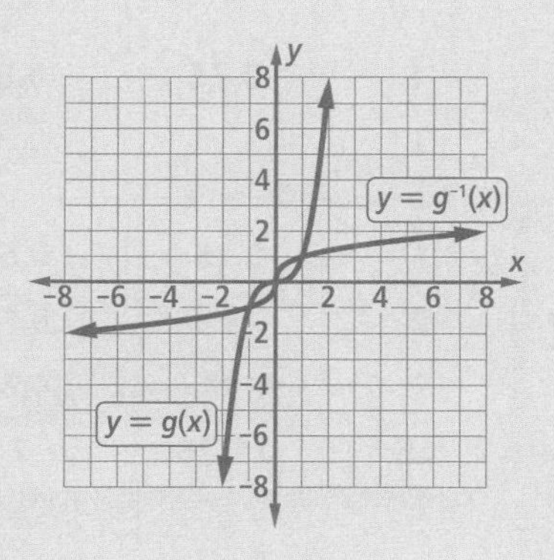

Chapter 9 Exponential and Logarithmic Functions

Chapter Overview

	Chapter Overview	Local Standards	Pacing (in days) Average	Advanced	Block
9-1	**Exponential Growth** **D** Recognize properties of exponential functions. **G** Create and apply exponential growth and decay models. **J** Graph exponential functions.		1	0.75	0.5
9-2	**Exponential Decay** **D, G, J** See 9-1.		1	0.75	0.5
9-3	**Continuous Compounding** **D, G** See 9-1.		1	0.75	0.5
9-4	**Fitting Exponential Models to Data** **H** Fit an exponential model to data.		1	0.75	0.5
	QUIZ 1		0.5	0.5	0.25
9-5	**Common Logarithms** **A** Determine values of logarithms. **C** Solve logarithmic equations. **E** Recognize properties of logarithmic functions. **K** Graph logarithmic curves.		1	0.75	0.5
9-6	**Logarithmic Scales** **C** Solve logarithmic equations. **I** Apply logarithmic scales, models, and formulas.		1	0.75	0.5
9-7	**Logarithms to Bases Other Than 10** **A, C, E, K** See 9-5.		1	0.75	0.5
9-8	**Natural Logarithms** **A** Determine values of logarithms. **E** Recognize properties of logarithmic functions. **I** Apply logarithmic scales, models, and formulas.		1	0.75	0.5
	QUIZ 2		0.5	0.5	0.25
9-9	**Properties of Logarithms** **C** Solve logarithmic equations. **F** Apply properties of logarithms.		1	0.75	0.5
9-10	**Using Logarithms to Solve Exponential Equations** **A** Determine values of logarithms. **B** Use logarithms to solve exponential equations. **F** Apply properties of logarithms. **G** Create and apply exponential growth and decay models.		1	0.75	0.5
		Self-Test	1	0.75	0.5
		Chapter Review	2	1	0.5
		Test	1	1	0.5
		TOTAL	15	11.25	7

Technology Resources

Teacher's Assessment Assistant, Ch. 9
Electronic Teacher's Edition, Ch. 9

Differentiated Options  Universal Access

	Accommodating the Learner	Vocabulary Development	Ongoing Assessment	Materials
9-1	pp. 583, 584	p. 582	group, p. 586	
9-2	pp. 588, 593	p. 589	written, p. 594	dynamic graphing application or graphing utility
9-3	pp. 596, 601	p. 596	written, p. 601	
9-4	pp. 603, 604		written, p. 607	
9-5	pp. 609, 612	p. 610	written, p. 614	graph paper
9-6	pp. 618, 620	p. 616	oral, p. 621	
9-7	pp. 624, 625	p. 623	written, p. 628	
9-8	pp. 631, 633	p. 630	group, p. 634	
9-9	pp. 636, 639		written, p. 642	CAS
9-10	pp. 645, 648		written, p. 649	

Objectives

	Lessons	Self-Test Questions	Chapter Review Questions
Skills			
A Determine values of logarithms.	9-5, 9-7, 9-8, 9-10	5–7, 16, 18a	1–14
B Use logarithms to solve exponential equations.	9-10	11, 21	15–22
C Solve logarithmic equations.	9-5, 9-6, 9-7, 9-9	10, 12	23-30
Properties			
D Recognize properties of exponential functions.	9-1, 9-2, 9-3	3c, 4	31-36
E Recognize properties of logarithmic functions.	9-5, 9-7, 9-8	1, 14, 18b, 18d	37–40
F Apply properties of logarithms.	9-9, 9-10	8, 13, 17	41-56
Uses			
G Create and apply exponential growth and decay models.	9-1, 9-2, 9-3, 9-10	2, 9, 20	57-63
H Fit an exponential model to data.	9-4	22	64-66
I Apply logarithmic scales, models, and formulas.	9-6, 9-8	15	67-71
Representations			
J Graph exponential functions.	9-1, 9-2	3, 18e, 19	72-76
K Graph logarithmic curves.	9-5, 9-7	18c	77-81

Resource Masters Chapter 9

None of the generic Resource Masters apply to this chapter.

Resource Master 153 Lesson 9-1

Resource Master 152 Lesson 9-1

Warm-Up

1. Graph $y = 3^x$, using positive integers for values of x.
2. Add other points to the graph using the zero and negative integer exponents.
3. Add even more points to the graph using at least four noninteger rational exponents.
4. Compare and contrast the graph of this exponential function with that of the numbers of U.S. cellphone subscribers given on page 578.

Additional Example

1. A certain type of bacteria doubles in population every hour. Suppose an experiment began with 300 of these bacteria. Use a CAS and the equation $f(t) = 300(2)^t$, where $f(t)$ is the number of bacteria after t hours.
   a. Estimate the number of bacteria after 3.5 hours.
   b. Estimate to the nearest 0.01 hour when there will be 10,000 bacteria.
   c. Use a graph of f to estimate $f\left(-\frac{1}{2}\right)$.

Resource Masters for Lesson 9-1

Resource Master 155 Lesson 9-2

Resource Master 154 Lesson 9-1

Types of Exponential Functions

	Geometric Sequence	Compound Interest	Exponential Function
Formula	$g_n = g_1 r^{n-1}$	$A = P(1 + r)^t$	$y = ab^x$
Independent Variable	n	t	x
Dependent Variable	g_n	A	y
Starting Value	g_0 or g_1 = first term	P = principal	a = y-intercept
Growth Factor	r	$1 + r$	b

Resource Masters for Lessons 9-1 and 9-2

Resource Master 157 Lesson 9-2

Resource Master 156 Lesson 9-2

Additional Examples

2. Strontium 90 (^{90}Sr) has a half-life of 29 years. This means that in each 29-year period, half of the ^{90}Sr decays and half remains. Suppose you have 1000 grams of ^{90}Sr.
   a. How many grams of ^{90}Sr remain after 6 half-life periods?
   b. How many years is 6 half-life periods?
   c. Write a recursive formula for a_n, the number of grams of ^{90}Sr that remain after n half-life periods.
   d. Write an explicit formula for a_n.
   e. Write a formula for the amount of ^{90}Sr remaining after any real number of half-life periods x.
3. Suppose a sample begins with 80% pure carbon-14. Use the information in Example 2 on pages 588–589.
   a. Write an equation for the percent of carbon-14 remaining in the original sample after x half-life periods.
   b. Graph your equation in Part a and use it to find the age to the nearest century of the sample containing 60% of its original carbon-14.

   Solution
   a. Use the exponential function $f(x) = ab^x$. Rewrite the initial amount as a decimal: a = ____% = ____. Let $f(x)$ be the amount of carbon-14 remaining in the sample after x half-life periods. Then $f(x)$ = ____ • ____.
   b. Graph f on a graphing utility. Trace on the graph where $y \approx$ ____ and record the value of x: $x \approx$ ____. So the sample is about ____ • 5730 ≈ ____ years old to the nearest century.

Resource Masters for Lesson 9-2

Resource Master 159 Lesson 9-3

Resource Master 158 Lesson 9-3

Warm-Up

Use your calculator to verify the calculations in the table at the bottom of page 596. Your calculator may display more decimal places than those given.

Additional Examples

1. Mona invested \$8218.16 in a zero-coupon bond paying 4.5% compounded semiannually. After 25 years, the value of the bond will be about \$25,000. How much would Mona's investment have been worth after 25 years if interest were compounded continuously instead of twice per year?
2. The amount L of a certain radioactive substance remaining after t years decreases according to the formula $L = Be^{-0.0001t}$, where B is the initial amount of radioactive substance. If 2000 grams are left after 6000 years, how many grams were present initially?

   Solution We need to find B, which is the initial amount present. When t = 6000, L = ________. Substitute these values and solve for B.

   $L = Be^{(\_\_\_\_)t}$
   ____ $= Be^{(\_\_\_\_)\cdot(\_\_\_\_)}$
   ____ $\approx B($____$)$
   ____ $\approx B$

   Initially, there were about ____ grams of the radioactive substance.

Resource Masters for Lesson 9-3

Resource Master 161 Lesson 9-4

Resource Master 160 Lesson 9-4

Warm-Up

Mathia and Scientia are the only two countries on the planet of Logicia. The population of Mathia grows at a rate of 10% per year. The population of Logicia decreases at a rate of 10% per year. Assuming that the two countries have the same population, what is the growth rate of Scientia?

Additional Example

1. The table below gives the percent of sunlight present at various depths in a part of an ocean. Find an exponential model to fit the data using the initial condition and one other point in the table.

Depth (meters)	Percent of Sunlight
0	100
10	10.7
20	1.15
30	0.12
40	0.01
50	0.001

Resource Masters for Lesson 9-4

Resource Master 163 Lesson 9-5

Resource Master 162 Lesson 9-4

Question 7

Drop Number	Number of Tails
1	1891
2	
3	470
4	229
5	118
6	
7	27

Resource Masters for Lessons 9-4 and 9-5

Resource Master 165 Lesson 9-5

Resource Master 164 Lesson 9-5

Exponential Form vs. Logarithmic Form (Base 10)

Exponential Form	Logarithmic Form
$10^7 = 10{,}000{,}000$	$\log_{10} 10{,}000{,}000 = 7$
$10^{-3} = 0.001$	$\log_{10} 0.001 = -3$
$10^{\frac{1}{2}} = \sqrt{10}$	$\log_{10}\sqrt{10} = \frac{1}{2}$
$10^{-\frac{1}{4}} = \frac{1}{\sqrt[4]{10}}$	$\log_{10}\frac{1}{\sqrt[4]{10}} = -\frac{1}{4}$
$10^a = b$	$\log_{10} b = a$

Activity

x	y
-2	
-1	
-0.75	
-0.5	
-0.25	
0	
0.25	
0.5	
0.75	
1	
2	

Resource Masters for Lesson 9-5

Resource Master 167 Lesson 9-6

Resource Master 166 Lesson 9-6

Warm-Up

In May 2008, a devastating earthquake hit the Sichuan province in China. It measured 7.9 on the Richter scale. Every increase of 0.1 on this scale corresponds to a growth factor of $10^{0.1}$ in intensity.

1. This earthquake was how many times as intense as the 1994 earthquake centered in Northridge, California, that measured 6.7 on the Richter scale?
2. The earthquake that hit Anchorage, Alaska, in 1964 measured 8.5 on the Richter scale. This earthquake was how many times as intense as the Sichuan earthquake?
3. In 1999, this Alaskan earthquake's intensity was revised to be 9.2 on the Richter scale. If this is an accurate measure, how many times as intense was it compared to the Sichuan earthquake?

Additional Examples

1. Music played at 125 decibels is how many times as intense as music played at 105 decibels?
2. Find the relative intensity in decibels of the sound of a muted conversation in which the sound intensity is $3.16 \cdot 10^{-8}$ watts per square meter.

Resource Masters for Lesson 9-6

Resource Master 169 Lesson 9-6

Resource Master 168 Lesson 9-6

Decibel Scale

Sound Intensity (watts/square meter)		Relative Intensity (decibels)
10^2		140
10^1	jack hammer	130
10^0	rock concert	120
10^{-1}	ambulance siren	110
10^{-2}	school dance	100
10^{-3}	electric drill	90
10^{-4}	lawn mower	80
10^{-5}	hair dryer	70
10^{-6}	normal conversation	60
10^{-7}	refrigerator	50
10^{-8}	library	40
10^{-9}		30
10^{-10}	whisper at 5 ft	20
10^{-11}	normal breathing	10
10^{-12}	barely audible	0

Earthquake Magnitude Scale

Richter Magnitude	Possible Effects
1–2	Usually not felt except by instruments
3	May be felt but rarely causes damage
4	Like vibrations from heavy traffic
5	Strong enough to wake sleepers
6	Walls crack, chimneys fall
7	Ground cracks, houses collapse
8	Few buildings survive, landslides

Resource Masters for Lesson 9-6

Resource Master 171 Lesson 9-7

Resource Master 170 Lesson 9-7

Warm-Up

In 1–4, solve the equation.

1. $0.5^x = 2$
2. $7^y = \sqrt[3]{49}$
3. $50^z = 1$
4. $9^w = 243$

Additional Example

1. Write the equation $P = 12(0.359)^x$ in logarithmic form.

Exponential Form vs. Logarithmic Form (Base 3)

Exponential Form	Logarithmic Form
$3^4 = 81$	$\log_3 81 = 4$
$3^3 = 27$	$\log_3 27 = 3$
$3^2 = 9$	$\log_3 9 = 2$
$3^1 = 3$	$\log_3 3 = 1$
$3^{0.5} = \sqrt{3}$	$\log_3\sqrt{3} = 0.5$
$3^0 = 1$	$\log_3 1 = 0$
$3^{-1} = \frac{1}{3}$	$\log_3\left(\frac{1}{3}\right) = -1$
$3^{-2} = \frac{1}{9}$	$\log_3\left(\frac{1}{9}\right) = -2$
$3^y = x$	$\log_3 x = y$

Resource Masters for Lesson 9-7

Resource Master 173 Lesson 9-8

Resource Master 172 Lesson 9-7

Activity

b	
Domain	
Range	
x-intercepts	
y-intercepts	
Asymptotes	

Questions 22 and 23, Electromagnetic Spectrum

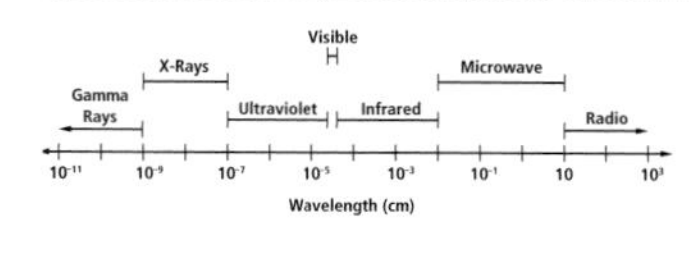

Resource Masters for Lessons 9-7 and 9-8

Resource Master 175 Lesson 9-9

Resource Master 174 Lesson 9-8

Additional Example

3. Under certain geographic conditions, the wind velocity v at a height h centimeters above the ground is given by $v = k \ln\left(\frac{h}{h_0}\right)$, where k is a positive constant that depends on air density, average wind velocity, and other factors, and h_0 is a "roughness" value, depending on the roughness of the vegetation on the ground.
   a. Suppose that $h_0 = 0.7$ centimeter, a value that applies to a lawn 3 centimeters high. If the wind velocity is 435 centimeters per second, what is the value of k?
   b. At what height above the ground is the wind velocity 1500 centimeters per second?

Resource Masters for Lessons 9-8 and 9-9

Resource Master 177 Lesson 9-9 and Lesson 9-10

Resource Master 176 Lesson 9-9

Additional Examples

3. Use the Logarithm of a Quotient Theorem to show that $\log_b\left(\frac{1}{N}\right) = -\log_b N$.
   Solution By the Logarithm of a Quotient Theorem, $\log_b\left(\frac{1}{N}\right) = \log_b$ ____ $- \log_b$ ____ $=$ ____ $- \log_b$ ____ $=$ ____.
4. Solve for d: $\log d = 3\log 2 + \log 7 - \log 4$.

Activity 2

A	$\log(3 \cdot 2)$	
	$\log 3 + \log 2$	
B	$\log\left(\frac{1}{6} \cdot 216\right)$	
	$\log\frac{1}{6} + \log 216$	
C	$\log_5\left(7 \cdot \frac{25}{7}\right)$	
	$\log_5 7 + \log_5 \frac{25}{7}$	
D	$\ln(4 \cdot 32)$	
	$\ln 4 + \ln 32$	

Resource Masters for Lessons 9-9 and 9-10

Resource Master 178 Lesson 9-9

Question 22

Justify each step in the following proof of the Logarithm of a Quotient Theorem.

Let $x = b^m$, $y = b^n$, and $z = \frac{x}{y}$.

a. $\log_b x = m$ and $\log_b y = n$ a. ____________

b. $\log_b\left(\frac{x}{y}\right) = \log_b\left(\frac{b^m}{b^n}\right)$ b. ____________

c. $= \log_b$ ____   c. ____________

d. $= m - n$ d. ____________

e. $\log_b\left(\frac{x}{y}\right) = \log_b x - \log_b y$ e. ____________

Resource Master for Lesson 9-9

Resource Master 180 Lesson 9-10

Resource Master 179 Lesson 9-10

Warm-Up

In 1–3, solve the equation.

1. $m \cdot \log 100 = \log 1000$
2. $p \cdot \ln 100 = \ln 1000$
3. $2^4 \cdot 3^2 \cdot 5 \cdot y = 2^5 \cdot 3 \cdot 5$

Additional Example

1. Recall that the formula for interest compounded continuously is $A = P = (e^r)^t$. At what rate of interest, compounded continuously, do you have to invest your money so that it will triple in 20 years?

Resource Masters for Lesson 9-10

Chapter 9

Pacing

Each lesson in this chapter is designed to be covered in 1 day. At the end of the chapter, you should plan to spend 1 day to review the Self-Test, 1 to 2 days for the Chapter Review, and 1 day for a test. You may wish to spend a day on projects and possibly a day is needed for quizzes. This chapter should therefore take 13 to 16 days. We strongly advise you not to spend more than 18 days on this chapter.

Overview

The bar graph on page 578, displaying the number of cellphone subscribers in the United States from 1985 to 2007, cannot be approximated by a single exponential function because the growth rates have changed over the years. A piecewise definition, using three exponential functions, is given on page 579.

Because the population of the United States was about 304,000,000 in December 2007, when these data were collected, and there are about 4 million children born each year, in 2007 there was 1 cell phone *subscriber* for every person in the country over the age of 12.

Using Pages 578–579

The three bases for the exponential functions—1.547, 1.239, and 1.129—correspond to yearly growth rates of 54.7%, 23.9%, and 12.9%. These show that the yearly growth rate of U.S. cell phone subscribers has generally been declining over time but is still very large.

Students may wonder how these rates and equations were obtained. First, we calculated the yearly growth factors by dividing the number of subscribers in each year by the number of subscribers in the previous year. Then we looked to see where these factors changed and determined that these changes were most significant in 1997 and 2002. Then we used technology to calculate an exponential curve of best fit for each interval, as will be done in Lesson 9-4.

Chapter 9

Exponential and Logarithmic Functions

Contents

Commercial portable cell phones were first produced in 1984. The table at the left below gives the estimated number of cell phone subscribers in the United States from 1985 to 2007. These data are graphed below.

Year	Subscribers (millions)	Year	Subscribers (millions)
1985	0.3	1997	55.3
1986	0.7	1998	69.2
1987	1.2	1999	86.0
1988	2.1	2000	109.5
1989	3.5	2001	128.4
1990	5.3	2002	140.8
1991	7.6	2003	158.7
1992	11.0	2004	182.1
1993	16.0	2005	207.9
1994	24.1	2006	233.0
1995	33.8	2007	255.4
1996	44.0		

Source: CTIA—The Wireless Association

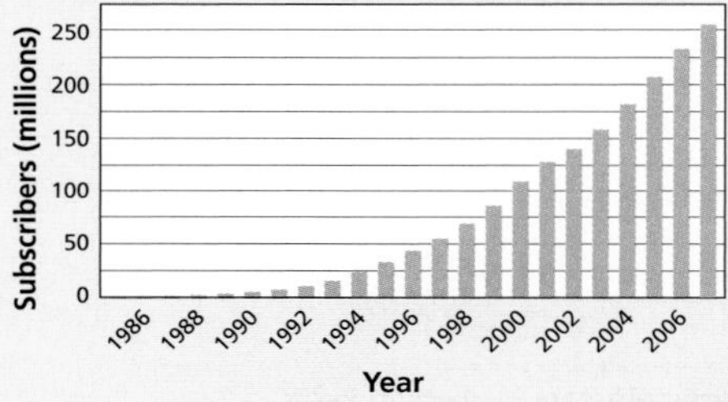

Chapter 9 Overview

Chapter 8 dealt with inverses that were relatively obvious. The functions that comprise the main subject matter of this chapter—logarithmic and exponential functions with the same base—are not immediately seen as inverse functions. Their inverse nature is quite important for their properties, so these functions are more carefully developed.

Lessons 9-1 and 9-2 cover one of the most important classes of applications of exponential functions—growth and decay—and introduce the terminology of exponential functions. Lesson 9-3 extends compound interest to the continuous case, which leads to the important number *e*. Lesson 9-4 discusses how to obtain an exponential function that models real data.

The next three lessons develop meanings for the word *logarithm*. Lesson 9-5 covers logarithms to base 10; Lesson 9-6 introduces logarithmic scales; and Lesson 9-7 presents logarithms to other bases.

The number of subscribers S (in millions) is closely modeled by the piecewise defined function

$$S = \begin{cases} 0.3(1.547)^{t-1984} & \text{for } 1985\text{–}1996 \\ 45.1(1.239)^{t-1996} & \text{for } 1997\text{–}2001, \\ 125.5(1.129)^{t-2001} & \text{for } 2002\text{–}2007 \end{cases}$$

where t is the year. Each equation in the model defines an *exponential function*, so called because the independent variable is in the exponent. Three different equations are needed because the average yearly growth rate of cell phone subscriptions in the United States changed from about 54.7% in the decade following their introduction to about 12.9% after 2002. In Lesson 9-4, you will learn how to find these equations.

Exponential functions have a variety of important applications. They model situations of growth, such as compound interest and population growth. They also model situations of decay, as found in carbon dating and depreciation.

The inverses of exponential functions, the *logarithmic functions*, describe the decibel scale of sound intensity, as well as the pH scale of acidity. They are also useful in solving problems involving exponential functions.

579

Lesson 9-8 introduces e as a base for logarithms. In Lesson 9-9, some important properties about the logarithms of products, powers, and quotients are derived. In Lesson 9-10, students use both common and natural logarithms and the theorems from Lesson 9-9 to solve exponential equations.

This text does not use logarithms for computation. Until the widespread availability of scientific calculators, calculating complicated products, quotients, powers, or roots was the main reason for teaching logarithms. Such content is now obsolete, but logarithms themselves are not obsolete. They are used in many equations that model real-world phenomena, and they are fundamental for solving exponential equations.

You might have students write the three pieces of the piecewise definition given on page 579 as separate equations. Point out that the equations define *exponential functions*. Ask students to suggest how any one of the equations can be used to estimate the number of cellphone subscribers at a particular point in time. Substitute various x-values into the appropriate equations to find the number of subscribers predicted by the model. Note that the predicted value of S almost always differs slightly from the actual value because the growth rate was not exactly constant over any of the three intervals.

Chapter 9 Projects

At the end of each chapter, you will find projects related to the chapter. At this time you might want to have students look over the projects on pages 650 and 651. You might want to have students tentatively select a project on which to work. Then, as students read and progress through the chapter, they can finalize their project choices.

Sometimes students might work alone. At other times, you might let them collaborate with classmates for a presentation and discussion. We recommend that you allow for diversity and encourage students to use their imaginations when presenting their projects. As students work on projects throughout the year, they should see many uses of mathematics in the real world.

Lesson 9-1

GOAL

Learn about exponential functions and their applications to population growth and computer speed.

SPUR Objectives

The SPUR Objectives for all of Chapter 9 are found in the Chapter Review on pages 656–659.

D Recognize properties of exponential functions.

G Create and apply exponential growth models.

J Graph exponential functions.

Materials/Resources

- Lesson Masters 9-1A and 9-1B
- Resource Masters 152–154

HOMEWORK

Suggestions for Assignment

- Questions 1–19
- Question 20 (extra credit)
- Reading Lesson 9-2
- Covering the Ideas 9-2

Local Standards

1 Warm-Up

1. Graph $y = 3^x$, using positive integers for values of x.
Answers vary. Sample:

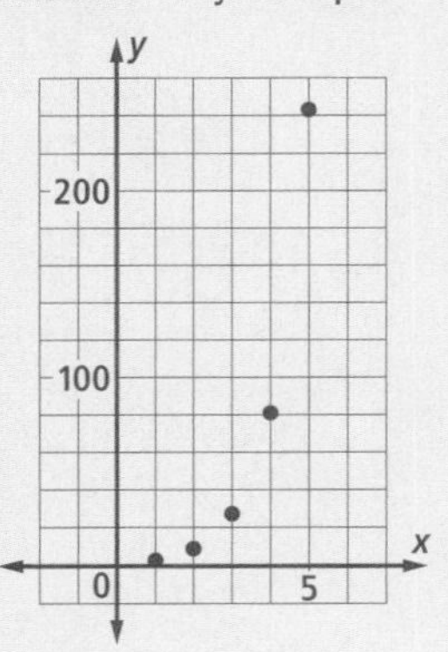

Lesson 9-1 Exponential Growth

Vocabulary

exponential function

exponential curve

growth factor

BIG IDEA Exponential functions model situations of constant growth.

A Situation of Exponential Growth

When a species is introduced to a new environment, it often has no natural predators and multiplies quickly. This situation occurred in Australia in 1859, when a landowner named Thomas Austin released 24 rabbits for hunting. The rabbits reproduced so quickly that within 20 years they were referred to as a "grey carpet" on the continent, and drove many native plant and animal species to extinction. Because a pair of rabbits can produce an average of 7 surviving baby rabbits a year when in a dense environment, you can estimate that the rabbit population multiplied by a factor of $\frac{7}{2}$, or 3.5, each year.

To model this situation, let $r_0 = 24$ be the initial population of rabbits in 1859. This is similar to using h_0 for initial height and v_0 for initial velocity in previous formulas. Then let r_n = the number of rabbits n years after 1859. A recursive formula for a sequence modeling this situation is

$$\begin{cases} r_0 = 24 \\ r_n = 3.5r_{n-1}, \text{ for } n \geq 1 \end{cases}.$$

This is a geometric sequence with starting term 24 and constant ratio 3.5. The table below shows the population r_n predicted by the model for $n = 1, 2, 3, \ldots, 10$ years after 1859, rounded to the nearest whole number of rabbits. The first four ordered pairs are graphed below.

n	r_n	n	r_n
0	24	6	44,118
1	84	7	154,414
2	294	8	540,450
3	1,029	9	1,891,575
4	3,602	10	6,620,514
5	12,605		

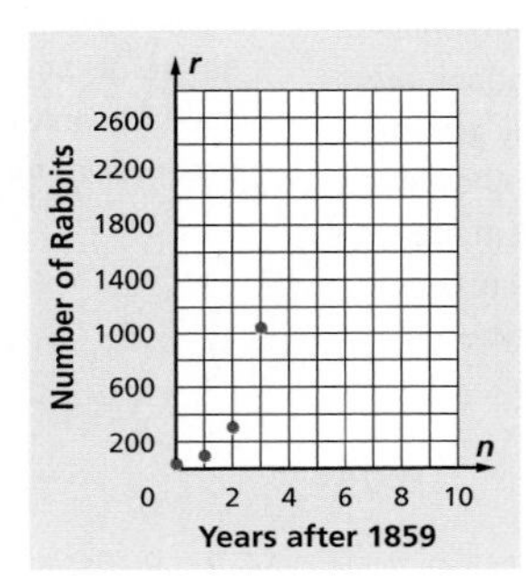

Mental Math

Sahar is preparing for a math test. She plans to study on the four days before the test, and each day she will study $1\frac{1}{2}$ times as long as the day before. On the first day, she studies 24 minutes. How many hours and minutes is she planning to study on the fourth day?
1 hr 21 min

A female rabbit can give birth to several litters in one year, with up to 12 baby rabbits per litter.

Background

Students saw examples of exponential functions in Chapter 7. The formulas $a_n = a_1r^{n-1}$ for the nth term of a geometric sequence and $A = P(1 + r)^t$ for compound interest have the form $y = ab^x$. However, these are discrete functions whose domain is typically limited to integer values of the independent variable. In this chapter, we consider the continuous version of exponential functions.

In both the rabbit-population and computer-speed examples in this lesson, the independent variable is time. This is the most common attribute for the independent variable for an exponential-growth situation. However, in some exponential-growth situations, distance is the independent variable. For example, when light passes through a medium (for example, glass), the intensity of the light typically decreases with the thickness of the medium. If the intensity is decreased by a factor b in every unit thickness of the medium, then $y = ab^x$ describes the intensity after passing through a medium of thickness x.

An explicit formula for this sequence is $r_n = 24(3.5)^n$ for $n \geq 0$. By representing the population as the function f with equation $r = f(t) = 24(3.5)^t$, you can estimate the population r at any real number of years $t \geq 0$.

QY1

In the graph at the left below, $r = 24(3.5)^t$ is plotted for values of t from 0 to 3.75, increasing by 0.25. The middle graph shows values for t from 0 to 3.8, increasing by 0.02.

▶ **QY1**

Using the equation $r = 24(3.5)^t$, estimate the population of rabbits $\frac{1}{2}$ year after their introduction.

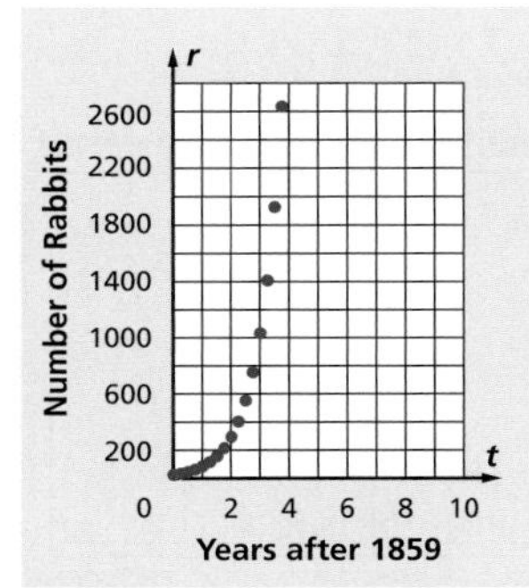

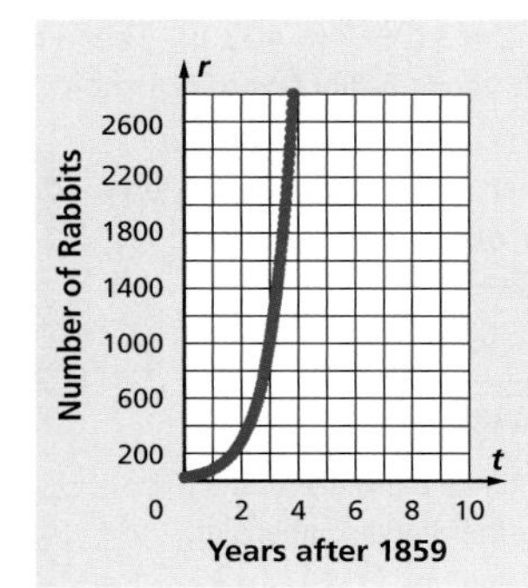

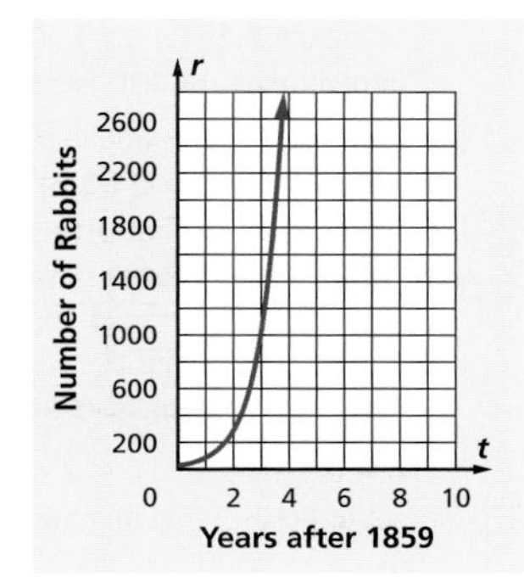

Because time is continuous when measuring population growth, you can think of the function with equation $r = f(t) = 24(3.5)^t$ as being defined for all real nonnegative values of t, as graphed above at the right. However, the equation has meaning for any real number t. Using the set of real numbers as the domain results in the function graphed at the right below.

This graph shows an *exponential curve*. The shape of an exponential curve is different from the shape of a parabola, a hyperbola, or an arc of a circle. The range of the function f is the set of positive real numbers. Its graph never intersects the t-axis, but gets closer and closer to it as t gets smaller and smaller. Thus, the t-axis is a *horizontal asymptote* to the graph. Substituting $t = 0$ into the equation gives an r-intercept of 24. This represents the number of rabbits present when they were first introduced.

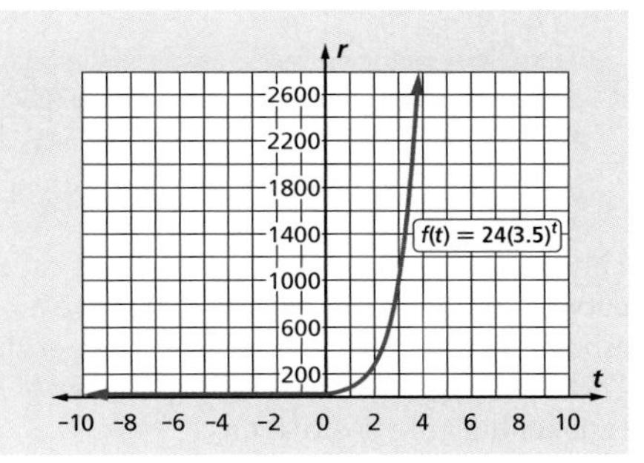

2. Add other points to the graph using zero and negative integers for exponents. Answers vary. Sample:

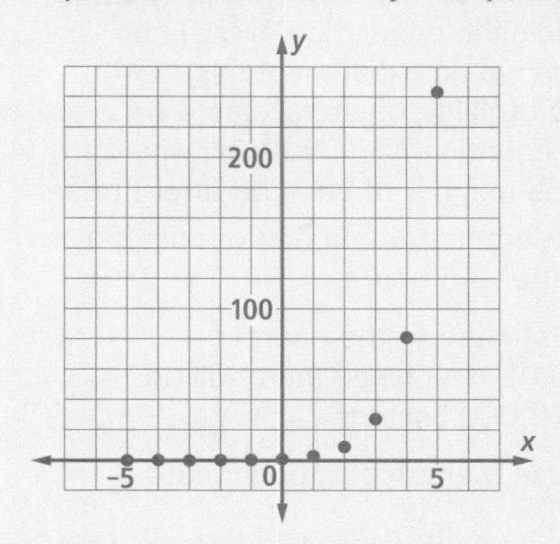

3. Add even more points to the graph using at least four noninteger rational exponents.
Answers vary. Sample:

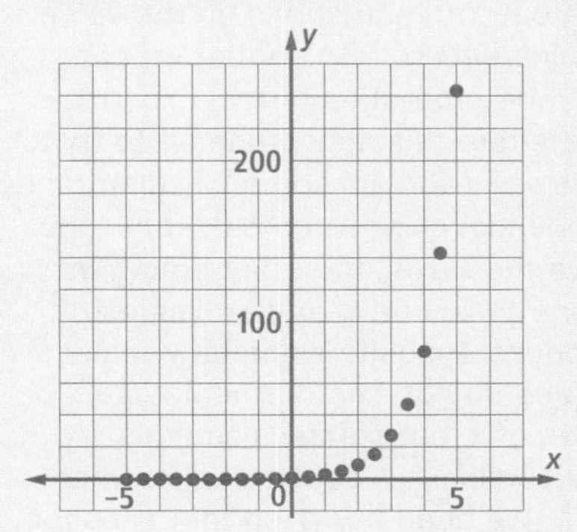

4. Compare and contrast the graph of this exponential function with that of the number of U.S. cellphone subscribers given on page 578.
Answers vary. Sample: Both graphs have about the same shape, going up more quickly as the values of x increase. They differ in their y-intercept.

2 Teaching

Notes on the Lesson

Note that the growth factor of 3.5 for the rabbit situation is a rough estimate, as rabbits can have several litters of 2–8 rabbits per year.

A situation of exponential growth
We generally follow the custom of using subscript notation when working with discrete geometric sequences and function notation when working with continuous models.

Example 2 At this writing, this is the fastest recorded speed. On June 26, 2007, IBM revealed a new computer, the Blue Gene®/P that is predicted to run at 1 *petaflop*. IBM anticipates a computer running at 10 petaflops by 2010, at the earliest. In the metric sequence of prefixes, *peta-* (10^{15}) comes after *kilo-* (10^3), *mega-* (10^6), *giga-* (10^9), and *tera-* (10^{12}).

Students who have studied from UCSMP *Algebra* will have encountered exponential functions. They should be familiar with growth factors and situations of population growth.

Additional Example

Example 1 A certain type of bacteria doubles in population every hour. Suppose an experiment began with 300 of these bacteria. Use a CAS and the equation $f(t) = 300(2)^t$, where $f(t)$ is the number of bacteria after t hours.

a. Estimate the number of bacteria after 3.5 hours. $\approx$3400 bacteria

b. Estimate to the nearest 0.01 hour when there will be 10,000 bacteria. about 5.06 hr

c. Use a graph of f to estimate $f\left(-\frac{1}{2}\right)$. $f\left(-\frac{1}{2}\right) \approx 212.1$

Notes on the Lesson

In a discussion of the equation $y = ab^x$, point out the restrictions on the value of b. We need $b > 0$ so that we can apply the properties of real exponents. To illustrate this, ask students to try to graph $y = (-2)^x$. On some calculators, two exponential curves can be seen—one above the x-axis, the other below. In theory, consecutive integer values of x produce opposite signs on y-values; y-values do not exist for noninteger values of x, but some calculators try to calculate $\sqrt[n]{-2}$ as the y-value when $x = \frac{1}{n}$. We need $b \neq 1$ so that exponential growth is just what the name implies. If b were allowed to equal 1, the equation $y = ab^x$ would become $y = a \cdot 1^x = a$, which is a constant function.

Note-Taking Tips

Have students add to their journals the definition of exponential function, along with an appropriate example.

Example 1

Use a CAS and the equation $f(t) = 24(3.5)^t$.

a. Estimate the number of rabbits after 2 years and 3 months.

b. Estimate the time to the nearest 0.01 year when there were 5000 rabbits.

c. Use a graph of f to estimate $f\left(-\frac{1}{2}\right)$.

Solution

a. Two years and 3 months equals 2.25 years. In the formula for $f(t)$, substitute 2.25 for t: $f(2.25) = 24(3.5)^{2.25} \approx 402.13$. There were approximately 400 rabbits 2 years 3 months after the release.

b. There were 5000 rabbits when $f(t) = 5000$. So, solve the equation $5000 = 24(3.5)^t$ for t on a CAS. The population reaches 5000 rabbits after about 4.26 years.

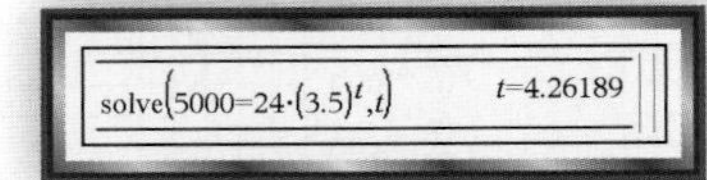

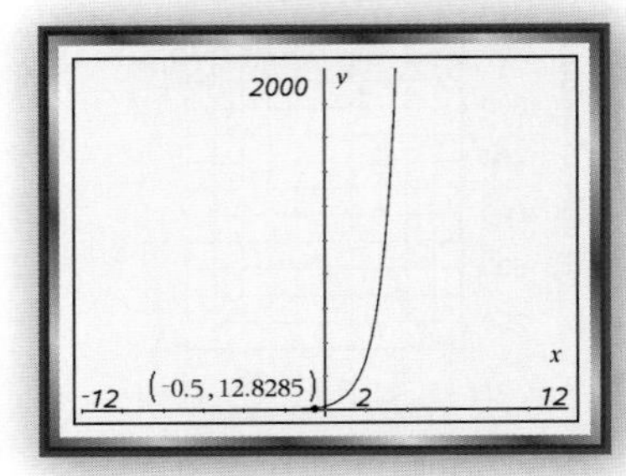

c. Use the window $-12 \leq x \leq 12$. Since the range of f is the set of positive real numbers, use the window dimension $0 \leq y \leq 2000$. Use the TRACE feature. $f\left(-\frac{1}{2}\right) \approx 13$

STOP QY2

▶ **QY2**

According to this model, in what year did the rabbit population reach 21 million, the approximate human population of Australia in 2008?

What Is an Exponential Function?

The equation $f(t) = 24(3.5)^t$ defines a function in which the independent variable t is the exponent, so it is called an *exponential function*.

Definition of Exponential Function

The function f defined by the equation $f(x) = ab^x$ ($a \neq 0$, $b > 0$, $b \neq 1$) is an **exponential function**.

The graph of an exponential function is called an **exponential curve**. This particular exponential curve models *exponential growth*; that is, as time increases, so does the population of rabbits. The accelerating increase in the number of rabbits is typical of exponential growth situations.

In the equation $y = ab^x$, with $a > 0$, b is the **growth factor**; it corresponds to the constant ratio r in a geometric sequence. The rabbit situation involves the growth factor $b = 3.5$. In general, when $b > 1$, exponential growth occurs.

ENGLISH LEARNERS

Vocabulary Development

Review the definition of *exponential function* and have volunteers write examples of exponential functions on the board. Have students use a graphing utility to graph several of the functions and stress that each graph is an *exponential curve*. Explain that the *growth factor* is the base of the power, while the independent variable is the exponent. Discuss with students which of the functions they have graphed show *exponential growth*.

The graphs rise to the right; the y-values increase as the x-values increase.

The compound interest formula $A = P(1 + r)^t$, when P and r are fixed, also defines an exponential function of t. In this case, A is the dependent variable and $1 + r$ is the growth factor. Since $r > 0$, $1 + r$ is greater than one, and compound interest yields exponential growth. The table below shows how geometric sequences and compound interest are modeled by exponential functions.

	Formula	Independent Variable	Dependent Variable	Starting Value	Growth Factor
Geometric Sequence	$g_n = g_1 r^{n-1}$	n	g_n	g_0 or g_1 = first term	r
Compound Interest	$A = P(1 + r)^t$	t	A	P = principal	$1 + r$
Exponential Function	$y = ab^x$	x	y	a = y-intercept	b

GUIDED

Example 2

The speed of a supercomputer is measured in *teraflops*, or trillions of "floating point operations" per second. In 2005, the Blue Gene/L supercomputer recorded a speed of 280.6 teraflops. Over the last 30 years, the speed of the fastest supercomputers has been growing at about 78% per year. Suppose that this growth rate continues, and let $C(x)$ = the speed in teraflops of the fastest supercomputer x years after 2005.

Blue Gene/L at Livermore National Laboratory

a. Write a formula for $C(x)$.

b. Use your formula to predict how long will it take for the fastest supercomputer speed to double the Blue Gene/L record to 561.2 teraflops.

c. Predict how many more years it will take for the fastest supercomputer speed to double again to 1122.4 teraflops.

Solution

a. Model this constant growth situation with an exponential function $C(x) = ab^x$. The initial speed a = __?__. An annual growth rate of 78% means that each year the computer speed is 178% of the previous year's speed, so b = __?__. A model is $C(x)$ = __?__.

b. Solve 561.2 = __?__(__?__)^x on a CAS to get $x \approx$ __?__. It will take about __?__ years for the speed to double.

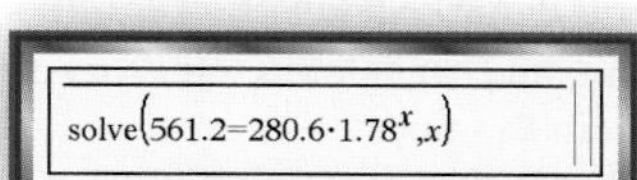

solve$(561.2=280.6\cdot1.78^x,x)$

c. Solve 1122.4 = __?__. So, $x \approx$ __?__. Because __?__ $- 1.2$ = __?__, it will take about __?__ more years for the speed to double a second time.

a. 280.6; 1.78; $280.6(1.78)^x$

b. 280.6; 1.78; 1.2; 1.2

c. $280.6(1.78)^x$; 2.4; 2.4; 1.2; 1.2

Parts b and c of Example 2 demonstrate that, with an exponential growth model, the computing speed doubles in the same amount of time regardless of when you start. This constant doubling time is a general feature of exponential growth.

Notes on the Lesson

Example 2 This example illustrates the problem of determining when an exponential function will have a certain value. To find such an answer algebraically involves solving the exponential equation $y = ab^x$ for x. At this point, solutions can be found by graphing or with a CAS. Students will learn how to solve this type of equation algebraically in Lesson 9-10. Inform them that this is one of the major purposes of logarithms.

Additional Example

Example 2 From 1990 to 2000, the population of California grew by about 1.3% per year. Let $C(x)$ = the California population x years after 2000. In 2000, the population of California was 33,871,648. Suppose that this growth rate continues.

a. Write a formula for $C(x)$.

b. Use your formula to predict how long it would take for the population of California to double.

c. Predict how many more years it would take for the population of California to double again.

Solution

a. Model this constant growth situation with an exponential function: $C(x) = ab^x$. The initial population a = __?__. 33,871,648 An annual growth rate of 1.3% means that each year the population is 101.3% of the previous year's population, so b = __?__. 1.013 A model is $C(x)$ = __?__. $33{,}871{,}648 \cdot 1.013^x$

b. Solve 67,743,296 = __?__ on a CAS to get $x \approx$ __?__. $33{,}871{,}648 \cdot 1.013^x$; 53.6648 It will take about __?__ years for the population to double. 53.7

c. Solve 135,486,592 = __?__. $33{,}871{,}648 \cdot 1.013^x$ So x = __?__. 107.3297 Because __?__ $- 53.7$ = __?__, it will take about __?__ more years for the population to double a second time. 107.3; 53.6; 53.6

Accommodating the Learner

Some students may not understand why there are restrictions on the value of b in $y = ab^x$. Emphasize that b must be greater than 0 so the properties of real exponents can be applied. To convince students of this, have them imagine that there is a function f with $f(x) = (-4)^x$. Ask them to find $f\left(\frac{1}{2}\right)$ and $f\left(\frac{2}{4}\right)$. $f\left(\frac{1}{2}\right) = (-4)^{\frac{1}{2}} = \sqrt{-4} = 2i$; $f\left(\frac{2}{4}\right) = (-4)^{\frac{2}{4}} = \sqrt[4]{(-4)^2} = \sqrt[4]{16} = 2$ Since $\frac{1}{2} = \frac{2}{4}$, f should map $\frac{1}{2}$ and $\frac{2}{4}$ to the same value. Since it does not, f cannot be a function. Remind students that this is why noninteger rational powers of negative numbers are not defined.

In addition, b cannot equal 1, or the equation $y = ab^x$ would be equivalent to $y = a \cdot 1^x = a$, which is a constant function rather than an exponential growth function.

3 Assignment

Recommended Assignment

- Questions 1–19
- Question 20 (extra credit)
- Reading Lesson 9-2
- Covering the Ideas 9-2

Notes on the Questions

Question 5 Students can confirm their choice by graphing each equation.

Additional Answers

7a.

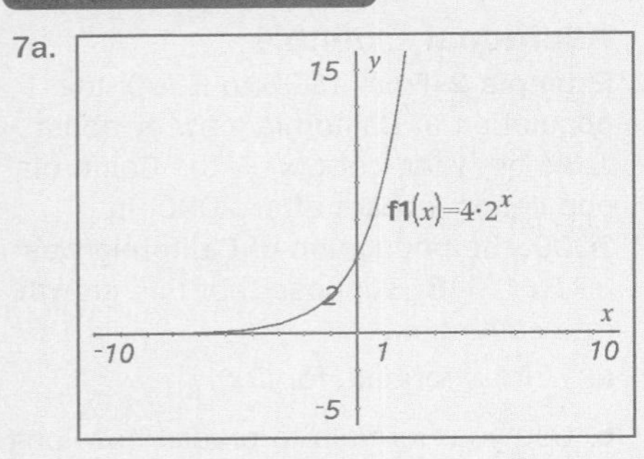

7b. 1.52

7c. True; the function satisfies the definition of an exponential function.

9-1A Lesson Master

Questions on SPUR Objectives
See Student Edition pages 656–659 for objectives.

PROPERTIES Objective D

1. Determine whether each equation is an exponential function.
   a. $y = 3.2^x$ yes
   b. $y = x^{3.2}$ no
   c. $y = 3(2)^x$ yes
2. **Fill in the Blanks** Jillian wants to model a situation with an initial value of 84 and 12% growth.
   a. If she uses $A = P(1 + r)^t$, then $P =$ 84 and $r =$ 0.12.
   b. If she uses $y = a \cdot b^x$, then $a =$ 84 and $b =$ 1.12.

USES Objective G

3. LeBron James was the first NBA draft pick in 2003. In his first season, he earned $4,018,920. Over the next two years, he received about a 7% raise every year.
   a. How much did he make in his third year? about $4,601,262
   b. In his fifth year, he earned $13,041,250. Did the 7% increase continue? no
4. In 2000, about 38.4 million U.S. citizens did not have health insurance. Over the next six years, that number grew at an average rate of 4.1% per year.
   a. Write an equation modeling this situation with y representing the number (in millions) of uninsured U.S. citizens x years after 2000. $y = 38.4(1.041)^x$
   b. If this growth continues at the same rate, estimate the number of U.S. citizens without health insurance in 2010. 57.4 million
   c. If this growth continues at the same rate, in what year will there be 65 million uninsured? ≈ 2013

REPRESENTATIONS Objective J

In 5 and 6, consider the functions f and g with $f(x) = 2^x$ and $g(x) = 5^x$.

5. Fill in the table of values below.

x	$f(x) = 2^x$	$g(x) = 5^x$
-3	0.125	0.008
-2	0.25	0.04
-1	0.5	0.2
0	1	1
1	2	5
2	4	25
3	8	125

6. Carefully graph and label both functions on the same set of axes below.

486 Advanced Algebra

Questions

COVERING THE IDEAS

In 1–3, use the rabbit population model from Example 1.

1. About how many rabbits were there 6.2 years after they were introduced to Australia? 56,680 rabbits
2. After about how many years were 100 million rabbits present? 12.2 yr
3. Suppose that Thomas Austin had released only 10 rabbits for hunting. At the same annual growth factor of 3.5, about how many rabbits would there then have been after 5 years? 5252 rabbits
4. Define *exponential function.* a function f defined by the equation $f(x) = ab^x$ where $a \neq 0$, $b > 0$, $b \neq 1$
5. **Multiple Choice** Which is an equation for an exponential function? C

   A $y = x^{3.04}$ B $y = 3.04x$ C $y = 3.04^x$
6. **Multiple Choice** Which graph below best shows exponential growth? Explain your answer. C; A is a graph of $y = ax^2$, B is a graph of $y = kx$, and D has a horizontal asymptote above $y = 0$.

A
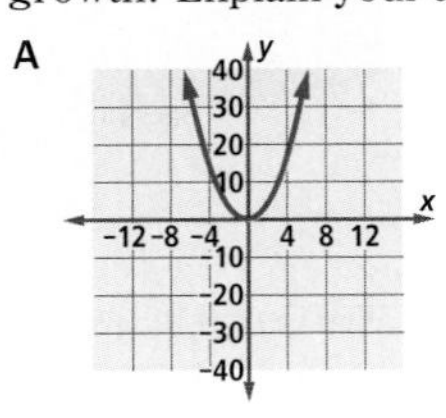

B
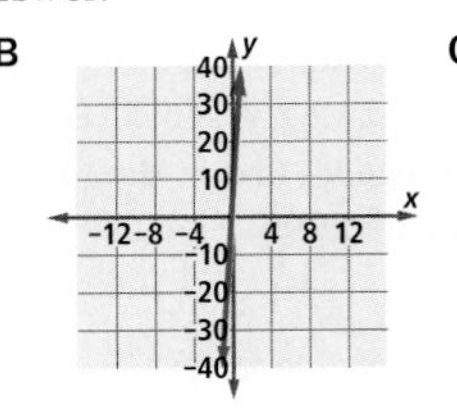

C
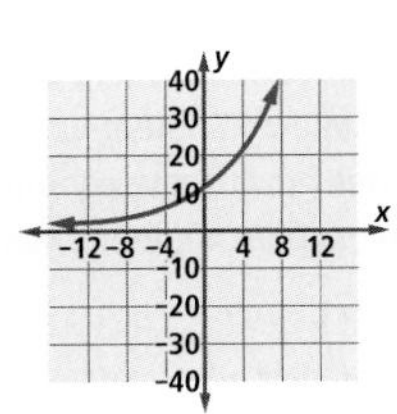

D
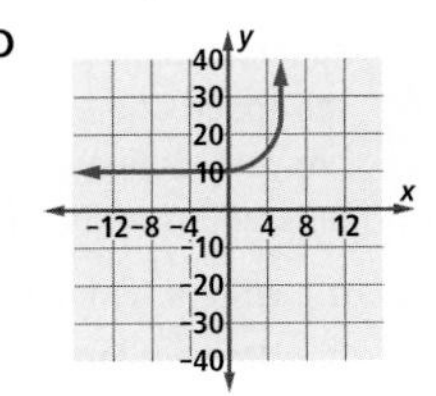

7. Let f be a function with $f(x) = 4 \cdot 2^x$. See margin.
   a. Graph $y = f(x)$.
   b. Approximate $f(-1.4)$.
   c. **True or False** f is an exponential function. Explain.
8. Consider the exponential curve with equation $y = ab^x$, where $b > 1$.
   a. **Fill in the Blank** The y-intercept is __?__. a
   b. **Fill in the Blank** The constant growth factor is __?__. b
   c. Which line is an asymptote to the graph? $y = 0$

In 9 and 10, refer to the situation and function $C(x) = 280.6(1.78)^x$ from Example 2.

9. a. Find $C(-10)$. 0.88
   b. In terms of the situation, what does $C(-10)$ represent? 9b. the speed in teraflops of the fastest computer in 1995
10. a. Use the model to estimate the computing speed of the fastest supercomputer in the year 2010. 5014.04 teraflops
    b. Some researchers believe that a supercomputer capable of 10^4 teraflops could simulate the human brain. If current trends continue, when would such computers be possible? in 2011

Accommodating the Learner

After reading the chapter opener on pages 578 and 579 and completing this lesson, have students find the population of their town, some other city, or their state for each decade that U.S. census information is available. Have students graph the data and determine if the graph approximates an exponential curve. Have students share their graphs with the class.

11. Consider the exponential function with equation $A = P(1 + r)^t$.
   a. Name the independent and dependent variables. 11a. independent: t; dependent: A
   b. What is the growth factor? $(1 + r)$

APPLYING THE MATHEMATICS

12. Refer to the function $C(x) = 280.6(1.78)^x$.
   a. Find the average rate of change between $x = -4$ and $x = -2$. 30.3
   b. Find the average rate of change between $x = 2$ and $x = 4$. 963.9
   c. What conclusions can you draw from your answers in Parts a and b? Answers vary. Sample: The function is not linear because the rate of change is not constant.

13. In 2000, the population of Canada was about 31.1 million people, and the population of Morocco was about 30.2 million people. Over the period 1950–2000, the population of Canada grew at an average rate of about 1.16% annually, while the population of Morocco grew at an average rate of about 2.38% annually. Let the function C with equation $C(x) = a \cdot b^x$ represent the population of Canada x years after 2000, in millions, and let the function M with $M(x) = c \cdot d^x$ represent the population of Morocco x years after 2000, in millions.

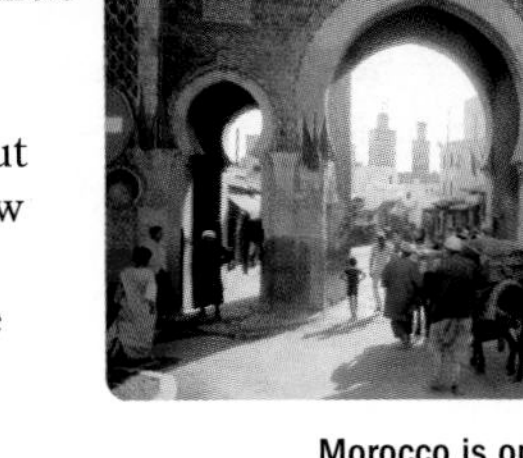

Morocco is on the northwest side of Africa and is slightly larger than California.

   a. Determine the values of a, b, c, and d and write formulas for $C(x)$ and $M(x)$.
   b. Use your formulas from Part a to estimate the populations of Canada and Morocco in 1995. 29.36 million; 26.85 million
   c. Graph $y = C(x)$ and $y = M(x)$ on the same set of axes for $0 \le x \le 50$. See margin.
   d. Make a prediction comparing the future populations of Canada and Morocco if current trends continue.

13a. $a = 31.1$, $b = 1.0116$, $c = 30.2$, $d = 1.0238$; $C(x) = 31.1(1.0116)^x$, $M(x) = 30.2(1.0238)^x$

13d. Answers vary. Sample: Morocco's population will outgrow Canada's population in the long run.

14. In September of 2004, the online user-edited encyclopedia *Wikipedia* contained about 1,000,000 articles. In January of 2001, the month it was launched, it contained 617 articles. This means it has grown on average about 18% per month since its launch date. Let $f(x) = ab^x$ represent the number of articles on *Wikipedia* x months after January of 2001 ($x = 0$ represents January of 2001).
   a. From the given information, find the values of a and b. 14a. $a = 617$, $b = 1.18$
   b. According to this model, how many articles were there in September of 2004? Explain why the answer is not exactly 1,000,000. 14b. 897,622 articles; The answer is not exactly 1,000,000 because the rate of 18% is not exact.
   c. According to this model, how many months did it take for the number of *Wikipedia* articles to double from 1,000,000 to 2,000,000? 14c. 4.19 months

Notes on the Questions

Question 13 Population growth cannot be exponential with the same base over a long period of time, but going back into time one can calculate the average growth rate by using the geometric mean. That is how the annual growth rates of 1.16% and 2.38% for Canada and Morocco were calculated. By using negative values of x, students can estimate populations of these countries in years before 2000.

Question 14c Because the growth rate of 18% is a rounded value, students will get a different final answer if they use September 2004 as the date for 1,000,000 articles than if they calculate the date for 1,000,000 articles using their models.

Additional Answers

13c.

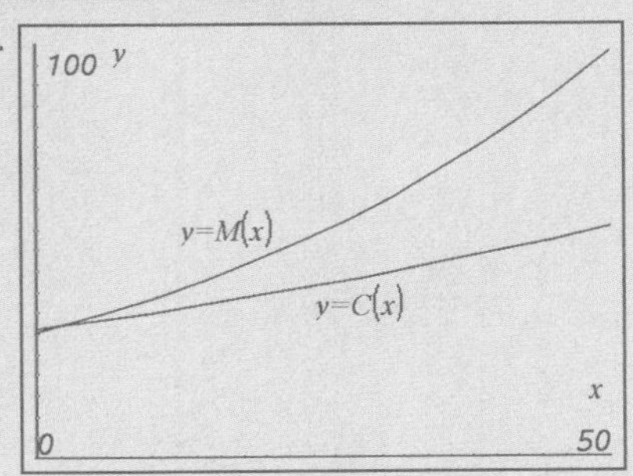

Notes on the Questions

Question 15b To answer this question, students are expected to use trial and error or the zoom or rescale features on a graphing utility. In Lesson 9-10, they will learn how to find b by solving an equation.

Question 19 This question contains ideas that appear in Lesson 9-2 and should be discussed.

Question 20 The key point to stress here is that, for a fixed growth rate, the population at a given time varies directly as the original population.

4 Wrap-Up

Ongoing Assessment

Have students work in small groups. Have each student write an exponential equation of the form $y = ab^x$, with $b > 1$. Have group members exchange papers. Each student should identify the growth factor and use a graphing utility to graph the equation he or she was given. Students should provide exponential equations of the type requested, correctly identify the growth factor of such an equation, and correctly graph the equation.

Project Update

Project 2, *Non-Native Species,* on page 650 relates to the content of this lesson.

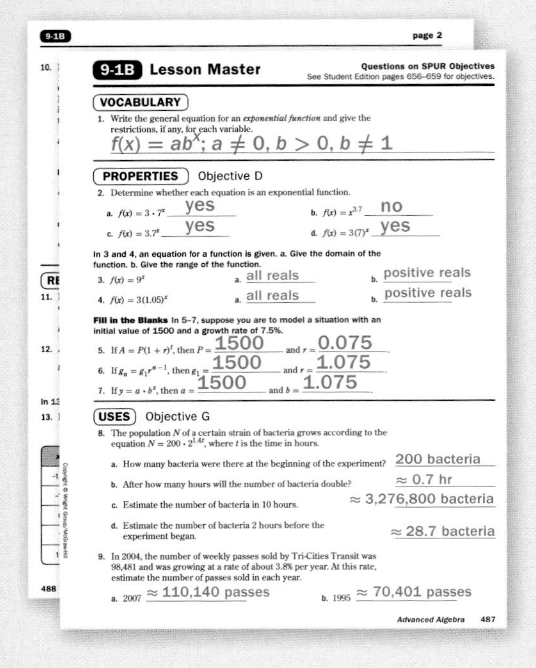

9-1B page 2

9-1B Lesson Master

Questions on SPUR Objectives
See Student Edition pages 656–659 for objectives.

VOCABULARY

1. Write the general equation for an *exponential function* and give the restrictions, if any, for each variable. $f(x) = ab^x;\ a \neq 0,\ b > 0,\ b \neq 1$

PROPERTIES Objective D

2. Determine whether each equation is an exponential function.
   a. $f(x) = 3 \cdot 7^x$ yes
   b. $f(x) = x^{3.7}$ no
   c. $f(x) = 3.7^x$ yes
   d. $f(x) = 3(7)^x$ yes

In 3 and 4, an equation for a function is given. a. Give the domain of the function. b. Give the range of the function.

3. $f(x) = 9^x$ a. all reals b. positive reals
4. $f(x) = 3(1.05)^x$ a. all reals b. positive reals

Fill in the Blanks In 5–7, suppose you are to model a situation with an initial value of 1500 and a growth rate of 7.5%.

5. If $A = P(1 + r)^t$, then $P =$ 1500 and $r =$ 0.075.
6. If $g_n = g_1 r^{n-1}$, then $g_1 =$ 1500 and $r =$ 1.075.
7. If $y = a \cdot b^x$, then $a =$ 1500 and $b =$ 1.075.

USES Objective G

8. The population N of a certain strain of bacteria grows according to the equation $N = 200 \cdot 2^{1.4t}$, where t is the time in hours.
   a. How many bacteria were there at the beginning of the experiment? 200 bacteria
   b. After how many hours will the number of bacteria double? ≈ 0.7 hr
   c. Estimate the number of bacteria in 10 hours. ≈ 3,276,800 bacteria
   d. Estimate the number of bacteria 2 hours before the experiment began. ≈ 28.7 bacteria
9. In 2004, the number of weekly passes sold by Tri-Cities Transit was 98,481 and was growing at a rate of about 3.8% per year. At this rate, estimate the number of passes sold in each year.
   a. 2007 ≈ 110,140 passes
   b. 1995 ≈ 70,401 passes

Advanced Algebra 487

15. In 1993, a sample of fish caught in a Mississippi River pool on the Missouri-Illinois border included 1 bighead carp. In 2000, a same-size sample from the same pool included 102 such fish. Other samples taken during this period support an exponential growth model. Let $f(x) = ab^x$ represent the number of carp caught x years after 1993.
    a. Use the information given to determine the value of a. 1
    b. Find an approximate value for b. 1.94
    c. According to your model, how many bighead carp would be in a similar sample caught in 2014? 1,106,207 bighead carp

Hypophthalmichthys nobilis, **the bighead carp, is an invasive species of fish that was first introduced in 1986.**

REVIEW

16. Suppose $f(x) = 5x - 6$. **(Lessons 8-3, 8-2)**
    a. Find an equation for f^{-1}. $f^{-1}(x) = \frac{x+6}{5}$
    b. Graph $y = f(x)$ and $y = f^{-1}(x)$ on the same axes. See margin.
    c. **True or False** The graphs in Part b are reflection images of each other. true
17. The matrix $\begin{bmatrix} 3 & 3 & -3 \\ -1 & -2 & 3 \end{bmatrix}$ represents triangle TRI. **(Lessons 4-10, 4-1)**
    a. Give the matrix for the image of $\triangle TRI$ under $T_{1,-2}$.
    b. Graph the preimage and image on the same set of axes.
18. Liberty Lumber sells 6-foot long 2-by-4 boards for \$1.70 each, and 8-foot long 2-by-6 boards for \$2.50 each. Last week they sold \$500 worth of these boards. Let x be the number of 2-by-4s sold and y be the number of 2-by-6s sold. **(Lesson 3-2)**
    a. Write an equation relating x and y. $1.70x + 2.50y = 500$
    b. If 200 2-by-4s were sold, how many 2-by-6s were sold? 64
19. Suppose a new car costs \$28,000 in 2009. Find its value one year later, in 2010, if **(Previous Course)**
    a. the car is worth 82% of its purchase price. \$22,960
    b. the car depreciated 20% in value. \$22,400
    c. the value of the car depreciated r%. $\$28{,}000\frac{(100 - r)}{100}$

EXPLORATION

20. The Australian rabbit plague was initiated by introducing 24 rabbits into the country.
    a. Suppose 12 rabbits, not 24, had been introduced in 1859. How, then, would the number of rabbits in later years have been affected?
    b. Answer Part a if 8 rabbits had been introduced.
    c. Generalize Parts a and b.

17a. $\begin{bmatrix} 4 & 4 & -2 \\ -3 & -4 & 1 \end{bmatrix}$

17b. See margin.

20a. There would have been half as many rabbits as there were when 24 were introduced.

20b. There would have been $\frac{1}{3}$ as many rabbits as there were when 24 were introduced.

20c. If n rabbits were introduced in 1859, there would have been $\frac{n}{24}$ times as many rabbits as when 24 were introduced.

QY ANSWERS

1. 45
2. 1869

Additional Answers

16b.

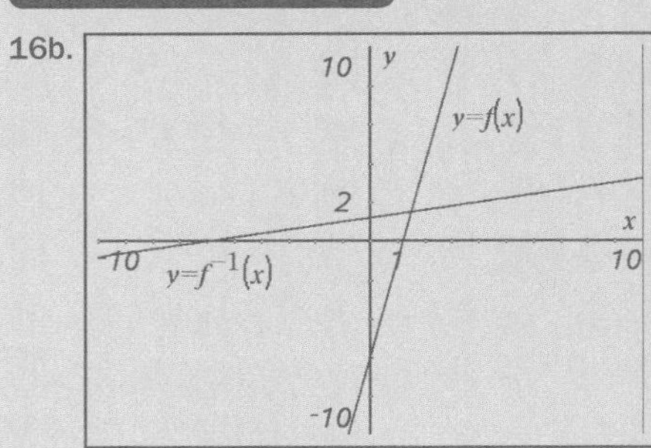

17b.

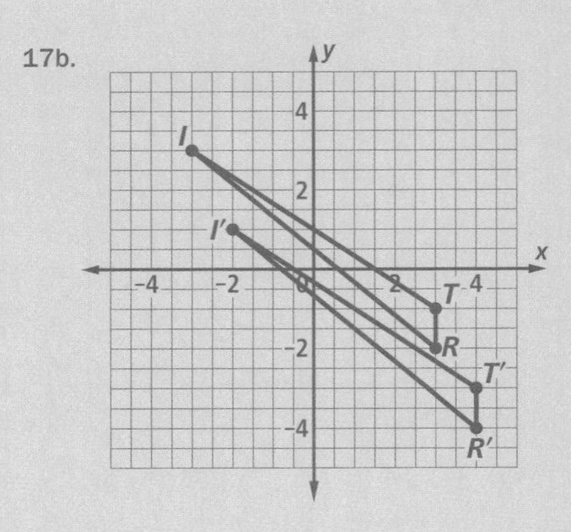

Lesson 9-2 Exponential Decay

Vocabulary

exponential decay
depreciation
half-life

BIG IDEA When the constant growth factor in a situation is between 0 and 1, exponential decay occurs.

In each exponential growth situation in Lesson 9-1, the growth factor b in $f(x) = ab^x$ was greater than 1, so the value of $f(x)$ increased as x increased. When the growth factor b is between 0 and 1, the value of $f(x)$ *decreases* as x increases. The situation then is an instance of **exponential decay**.

Mental Math

Imagine the graph of $y = 0.5x^2$. How many lines

a. are asymptotes to this graph? 0

b. are lines of symmetry of this graph? 1

c. intersect the graph in two points? infinitely many

d. are neither horizontal nor vertical and intersect the graph in exactly one point? infinitely many

e. are horizontal and intersect the graph in exactly one point? 1

Depreciation as an Example of Exponential Decay

Automobiles and other manufactured goods that are used over a number of years often decrease in value. This decrease is called **depreciation**. The function that maps the year onto the value of the car is an example of an exponential decay function.

GUIDED

Example 1

Suppose a new SUV costs $36,025 and depreciates 12% each year.

a. Write an equation that gives the SUV's value when it is t years old.

b. Predict the SUV's value when it is 4 years old.

Solution

a. If the vehicle loses 12% of its value annually, it keeps 100% − 12% = __?__% of its value. Because each year's value is a constant multiple of the previous year's value, the value of the car after t years can be modeled by an exponential function V with equation $V(t) = ab^t$. $V(t)$ is the value of the car when it is t years old. 88

a is the original value, so a = __?__. 36,025

b is the constant multiplier or ratio, so b = __?__. 0.88

So, V(t) = __?__. $36{,}025(0.88)^t$

b. When the car is 4 years old, t = __?__. 4

Substitute. V(__?__) = __?__ • $0.88^{?}$ ≈ __?__. 4; 36,025; 4; 21,604.03

The car's value will be about __?__ after 4 years. $21,604.03

Lesson 9-2

GOAL

Learn about exponential functions in which the base is less than 1 (exponential decay functions) and compare such functions to exponential growth functions.

SPUR Objectives

D Recognize properties of exponential functions.

G Create and apply exponential decay models.

J Graph exponential functions.

Materials/Resources

- Lesson Masters 9-2A and 9-2B
- Resource Masters 155–157
- Dynamic graphing application or graphing utility

HOMEWORK

Suggestions for Assignment

- Questions 1–21
- Questions 22 and 23 (extra credit)
- Reading Lesson 9-3
- Covering the Ideas 9-3

Local Standards

1 Warm-Up

Graph and then compare the graphs of $y = 2x$ and $y = \left(\frac{1}{2}\right)^x$ for $-3 \le x \le 3$. Each graph is the reflection image of the other over the y-axis.

Use this example to compare and contrast growth and decay curves. Answers vary. Sample: Growth curves rise, while decay curves fall.

Background

Two important applications of exponential decay are illustrated in this lesson: depreciation and half-life.

One goal of this lesson is for students to realize that the growth factor determines growth or decay just as the slope of a line determines increase or decrease. Specifically, linear increase (decrease) and exponential growth (decay) are mathematically *isomorphic;* they have the same structure. The former is related to addition, and the latter is related to multiplication. Zero is the pivot in linear increase or decease; a slope greater than 0 means increase, whereas a slope less than 0 means decrease. Similarly, 1 is the pivot in exponential growth or decay; a growth factor greater than 1 means growth, whereas a growth factor less than 1 means decay. Note that the growth factor b must be positive to apply the properties of real exponents.

(continued on next page)

2 Teaching

Notes on the Lesson

Emphasize that $y = ab^x$ models exponential growth when $b > 1$ and exponential decay when $0 < b < 1$. No other values of b are possible in exponential functions because we must have $b > 0$ and $b \neq 1$. These same restrictions will occur later for bases of logarithmic functions.

Some students may have difficulty determining the growth factor when the rate of decay is given as a percent, such as in Example 1. The Accommodating the Learner addresses this issue.

Additional Example

Example 1 Suppose a new piano costs \$8,500 and depreciates 6% each year.

a. Write an equation that gives the piano's value when it is t years old.

b. Predict the piano's value when it is 5 years old.

Solution

a. If the piano loses 6% of its value each year, it keeps 100% − 6% = __?__% of its value. 94 The value of the piano after t years can be modeled by an exponential function V with equation $V(t) = ab^t$. $V(t)$ is the value of the piano when it is t years old; a is the original value, so a = __?__; b is the constant multiplier, or ratio, so b = __?__. \$8500; 0.94 Thus, $V(t)$ = __?__. $8500 \cdot 0.94^t$

b. When the piano is 5 years old, t = __?__. 5 Substitute. $V($__?__$)$ = __?__ $\cdot$ 0.94^__?__ ≈ __?__. 5; 8500; 5; 6238.18 The model predicts that the piano's value will be __?__ after 5 years. about \$6238

Example 2 The term *half-life* is used in subsequent lessons and in later chapters, so it is worth taking some time to discuss Example 2. In Example 1, the growth rate is given per year, but here, the time unit for the growth factor is not a simple unit such as 1 year, 1 day, or 1 month. "Halving every 5730 years" means that the time unit is 5730 years. Thus, in the formula $y = ab^x$, b is $\frac{1}{2}$ and x is the number of 5730-year intervals after the starting point. To obtain the yearly growth factor, one would have to take the 5730th root of $\frac{1}{2}$.

Half-Life and Radioactive Decay

In Lesson 9-1, you saw that when a quantity grows exponentially, its doubling time is constant. If a substance decays exponentially, the amount of time it takes for half of the atoms in this substance to decay into another matter is called its **half-life**. Half-life is an important feature of some chemical processes and of radioactive decay. The half-life of a radioactive substance can be as short as a small fraction of a second, as in the 0.002-second half-life of hassium-265, or as long as billions of years, as in the 4.47 billion-year half-life of uranium-238, a naturally occurring radioactive element.

Example 2

Carbon-14 (sometimes written as ^{14}C) has a half-life of 5730 years. This means that in any 5730-year period, half of the carbon-14 decays and becomes nitrogen-14, and half remains. Suppose that an object contains 100 g of carbon-14. Let a_n be the number of grams of carbon-14 remaining after n half-life periods.

a. How many grams of carbon-14 remain after 4 half-life periods?

b. How many years is 4 half-life periods?

c. Write a recursive formula for a_n.

d. Write an explicit formula for a_n.

e. Write a function for the amount of carbon-14 remaining after any real number of half-life periods x.

Solution

a. Make a table of values of a_n for $n = 0, 1, 2, 3,$ and 4, as at the right. The initial amount of carbon-14 is $a_0 = 100$. Each successive value of a_n is one-half the previous value.

6.25 grams of carbon-14 remain after 4 half-life periods.

n	a_n
0	100
1	50
2	25
3	12.5
4	6.25

b. One half-life period = 5730 years, so,

4 half-life periods = 4 • 5730 = 22,920 years.

c. The amount a_n of carbon-14 remaining after n half-life periods forms a geometric sequence with a constant ratio of $\frac{1}{2}$.

A recursive formula for this sequence is

$$\begin{cases} a_0 = 100 \\ a_n = \frac{1}{2}a_{n-1}, \text{ for integers } n \geq 1. \end{cases}$$

d. Use the Explicit Formula for a Geometric Sequence from Chapter 7.

An explicit formula for this sequence is

$$a_n = 100 \cdot \left(\frac{1}{2}\right)^n \text{ for integers } n \geq 0.$$

Example 2 Note that carbon dating is the context for Example 2. Because carbon dating shows that many things in the world are older than some religions believe the world to be, you may have students who think that carbon dating is not valid.

Accommodating the Learner

Some students may have difficulty determining the growth factor when the rate of decay is given as a percent, as in Example 1. Stress that b always represents the *growth factor,* not the *growth rate.* For a growth rate of 23%, the growth factor is 1.23. In a decay situation, we are interested in what remains after a certain period of time, not what is lost. So, if a certain quantity decays at the rate of 12%, what remains is 100% − 12%, or 88%, and the growth factor is 0.88.

e. Use the equation $f(x) = ab^x$ with $a = 100$ and $b = \frac{1}{2}$.

$$f(x) = 100 \cdot \left(\frac{1}{2}\right)^x$$

During a plant or animal's life, the carbon-14 in its body is naturally replenished from the environment. Once it dies, the amount of carbon-14 decays exponentially as described in Example 2. Archeologists and historians use this fact to estimate the date at which an ancient artifact made of organic material was created.

GUIDED

Example 3

Suppose a sample of a piece of parchment began with 100% pure carbon-14. Use the information about carbon-14 from Example 2.

a. Write an equation for the percent of carbon-14 remaining in the sample after x half-life periods.

b. Graph your equation from Part a and use it to find the age of the sample to the nearest century if it contains 80% of its original carbon-14.

Parchment is an organic material, usually made of animal skin.

Solution

a. Use the exponential equation $f(x) = ab^x$. Rewrite the initial amount as a whole number: $a =$ __?__ % = __?__. 100; 1

Let $f(x)$ be the amount of carbon-14 remaining in the sample after x half-life periods. Then $f(x) =$ __?__ • __?__ ^{x}. 1; $\left(\frac{1}{2}\right)$

b. Graph f on a graphing utility. Trace on the graph where $y \approx$ __?__ 0.8 and record the value of x. $x \approx$ __?__. So, the piece of parchment 0.3 is ≈ __?__ • 5730 ≈ __?__ years old to the nearest century if it 0.3; 1700 contains 80% of its original carbon-14.

Growth versus Decay

The examples of exponential growth from Lesson 9-1 and the examples of exponential decay from this lesson fit a general model called the *Exponential Change Model.*

Exponential Change Model

If a positive quantity a is multiplied by b (with $b > 0$, $b \neq 1$) in each unit period, then after a period of length x, the amount of the quantity is ab^x.

ENGLISH LEARNERS

Vocabulary Development

Explain that one meaning of the term *decay* is "the loss of power, strength, beauty, ..." So *exponential decay* indicates a decrease. Have students note that both *decay* and *decrease* begin with the prefix *de-*. Write equations for several exponential-decay functions, such as $f(x) = 5\left(\frac{1}{3}\right)^x$ and $g(x) = 2\left(\frac{1}{4}\right)^x$, on the board and have students use a graphing utility to graph them. Discuss with students why the functions they have graphed show exponential decay.

The graphs fall to the right; the y-values decrease as the x-values increase.

The term *depreciation* also begins with the prefix *de-*, so it too represents a decrease; in this case, it is a decrease in value. You might contrast depreciation with the term *appreciation,* which means to increase in value.

Additional Examples

Example 2 Strontium 90 (^{90}Sr) has a half-life of 29 years. This means that in each 29-year period, half of the ^{90}Sr decays and half remains. Suppose you have 1000 grams of ^{90}Sr.

a. How many grams of ^{90}Sr remain after 6 half-life periods? 15.625 g

b. How many years is 6 half-life periods? 174 yr

c. Write a recursive formula for a_n, the number of grams of ^{90}Sr that remain after n half-life periods.

$$\begin{cases} a_0 = 1000 \\ a_n = \frac{1}{2}a_{n-1}, \text{ for integers } n \geq 1 \end{cases}$$

d. Write an explicit formula for a_n.

$a_n = 1000 \cdot \left(\frac{1}{2}\right)^n$ for integers $n \geq 0$

e. Write a formula for the amount of ^{90}Sr remaining after any real number of half-life periods x.

$f(x) = 1000 \cdot \left(\frac{1}{2}\right)^x$

Example 3 Suppose a sample began with 80% pure carbon-14. Use the information in Example 2 on pages 588–589.

a. Write an equation for the percent of carbon-14 remaining in the original sample after x half-life periods.

b. Graph your equation in Part a and use it to find the age to the nearest century of the sample when it contains 60% of its original carbon-14.

Solution

a. Use the exponential eqution $f(x) = ab^x$. Rewrite the initial amount as a decimal: $a =$ __?__ % = __?__. 80; 0.8 Let $f(x)$ be the amount of carbon-14 remaining in the sample after x half-life periods. Then $f(x) =$ __?__ · __?__. 0.8; $\left(\frac{1}{2}\right)^x$

b. Graph f on a graphing utility. Trace on the graph where $y \approx$ __?__ and record the value of x: $x \approx$ __?__. 0.6; 0.415 So the sample is about __?__ · 5730 ≈ __?__ years old to the nearest century. 0.415; 2400

Notes on the Lesson

Activity To complete this Activity, students can use a dynamic graphing application that is available on the UCSMP website. The six characteristics of an exponential function in Step 5 not only reinforce what students have learned in this lesson and in Lesson 9-1 but also review vocabulary used in describing functions more generally.

Additional Answers

Activity

Step 1.

a. As b is increases, the steepness of the right side of the graph increases.

b. All of these functions are increasing over their whole domain.

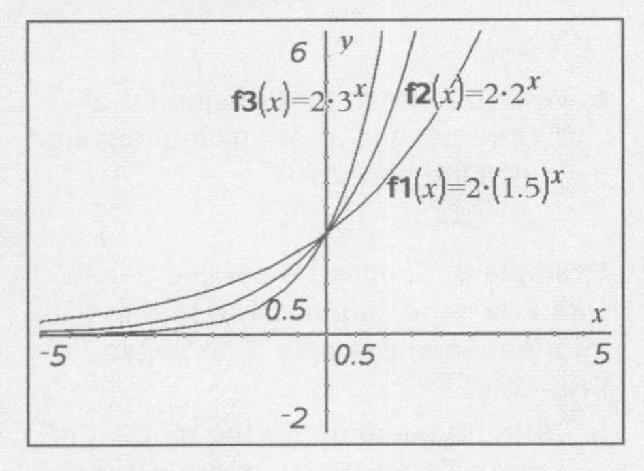

Step 2.

a. As b decreases, the graphs drop more sharply.

b. All of these functions are decreasing over their whole domain.

Step 3. For $0 < b < 1$, the graph decreases for all x; for $b > 1$, the graph increases for all x. The shapes of the two kinds of graphs are reflections of each other over the y-axis.

Step 4. The y-intercept changes with a since $y = a$ at $x = 0$.

Step 5.

Property	Exponential Decay. $a > 0$, $0 < b < 1$	Exponential Growth. $a > 0, b > 1$
Domain	all real numbers	all real numbers
Range	$y > 0$	$y > 0$
y-intercept	a	a
x-intercept	none	none
Horizontal asymptote	$y = 0$	$y = 0$
As x increases, y ...	decreases	increases

Activity Steps 1–6. See margin.

MATERIALS dynamic graphing application or graphing utility

Explore how changing a and b affect the graphs of the family of functions with equations $f(x) = ab^x$. You can use a dynamic graphing application provided by your teacher or graph several instances of the family on a graphing utility.

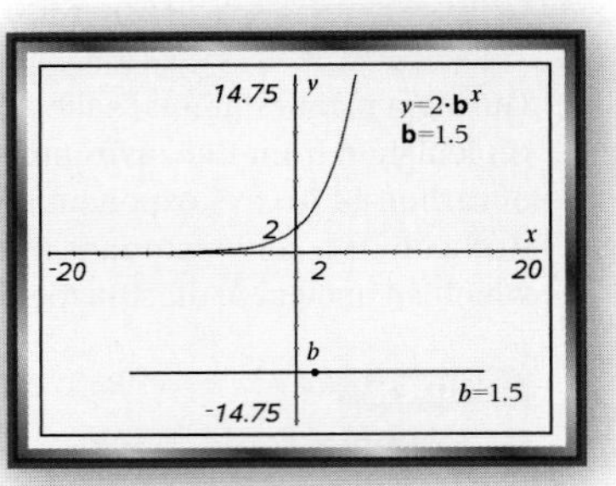

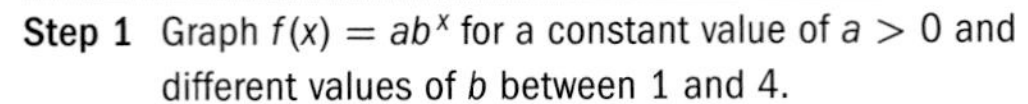

Step 1 Graph $f(x) = ab^x$ for a constant value of $a > 0$ and different values of b between 1 and 4.

a. What features of the graph change as b changes?

b. What features of the graph stay the same? (Hint: Why are these called exponential *growth* functions?)

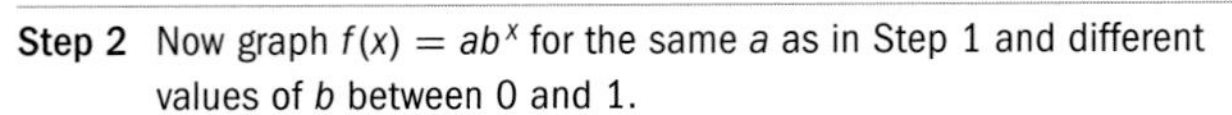

Step 2 Now graph $f(x) = ab^x$ for the same a as in Step 1 and different values of b between 0 and 1.

a. What features of the graph change as b changes?

b. What features of the graph stay the same? (*Hint:* Why are these called exponential *decay* functions?)

Step 2

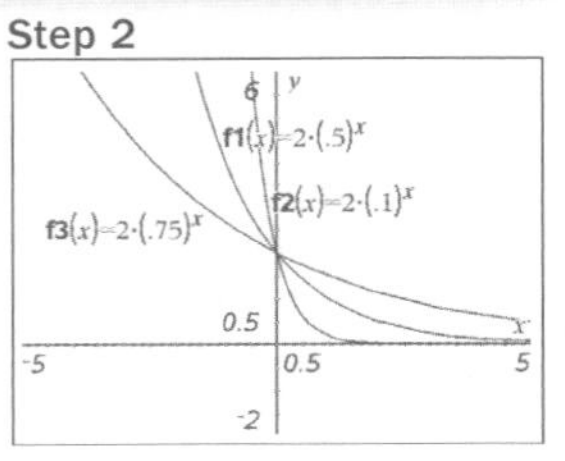

Step 3 How are the graphs, where $0 < b < 1$, different from the graphs where $b > 1$? How are the two kinds of graphs similar?

Step 4 Now graph $f(x) = ab^x$ for a constant value of $b > 0$ and some values of a between 1 and 4. How does a affect the graph of $y = ab^x$?

Step 4

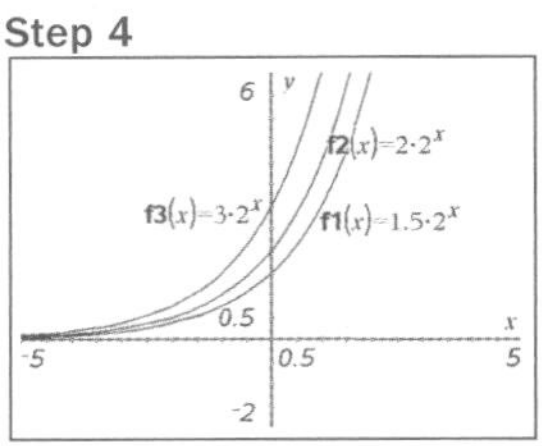

Step 5 Copy and complete the chart below to summarize the features of exponential growth and exponential decay functions.

Property	Exponential Decay $a > 0, 0 < b < 1$	Exponential Growth $a > 0, b > 1$
Domain	set of real numbers	set of real numbers
Range	?	?
y-intercept	?	?
x-intercept	?	?
Horizontal asymptote	?	?
As x increases, y (increases/decreases).	?	?

Step 6 Sketch a graph showing exponential growth and a graph showing exponential decay, labeling $(0, a)$ on both graphs.

Additional Answers

Step 6.

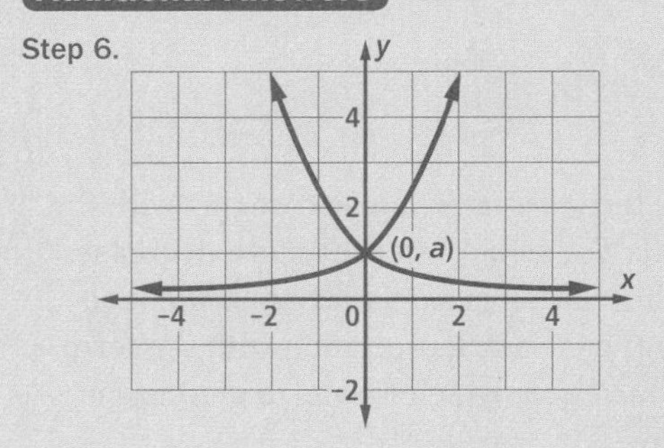

Notice that exponential growth and decay graphs have many features in common. This is not surprising because every exponential growth curve is the reflection image of an exponential decay curve over the y-axis. You are asked about this property in Questions 7 and 14.

Questions

COVERING THE IDEAS

1. Refer to Example 1. If the depreciation model continues to be valid, what would the SUV be worth when it is 10 years old? $10,033.00

2. Suppose a car purchased for $16,000 decreases in value by 8% each year.
   a. What is the yearly growth factor? 0.92
   b. How much is the car worth after 2 years? $13,542.40
   c. How much is the car worth after x years? $16{,}000(0.92)^x$

3. Define *half-life*.

In 4 and 5, refer to Example 3.

4. What percent of an artifact's carbon-14 would remain after 8000 years? 38%

5. In 1996, a human skeleton, nicknamed Kennewick Man, was found in the Columbia River in the state of Washington. Examination showed that the skeleton had about 32% of its original carbon-14 in its bones. In about what year did Kennewick Man die? about 7400 BCE

6. **Fill in the Blank** If $y = ab^x$, $a > 0$, and $0 < b < 1$, then y __?__ as x increases. decreases

7. a. Sketch a graph $y = 4^x$, when $-3 \le x \le 3$. 7a–c. See margin.
   b. Sketch a graph $y = \left(\frac{1}{4}\right)^x$, when $-3 \le x \le 3$.
   c. Explain how the graphs in Parts a and b are related to each other.

8. **True or False** The graph of every exponential function with equation $f(x) = ab^x$ has x-intercept a. Explain your answer.

9. **True or False** The x-axis is an asymptote for the graph of an exponential function. Explain your answer.

3. The *half-life* of a substance is the amount of time it takes for half of the atoms in that substance to decay into other matter.

8. False; the y-intercept of every exponential function is a.

9. True; $ab^x \neq 0$ for all x, when $a \neq 0$ and $b > 0$.

3 Assignment

Recommended Assignment

- Questions 1–21
- Questions 22 and 23 (extra credit)
- Reading Lesson 9-3
- Covering the Ideas 9-3

Additional Answers

7a.

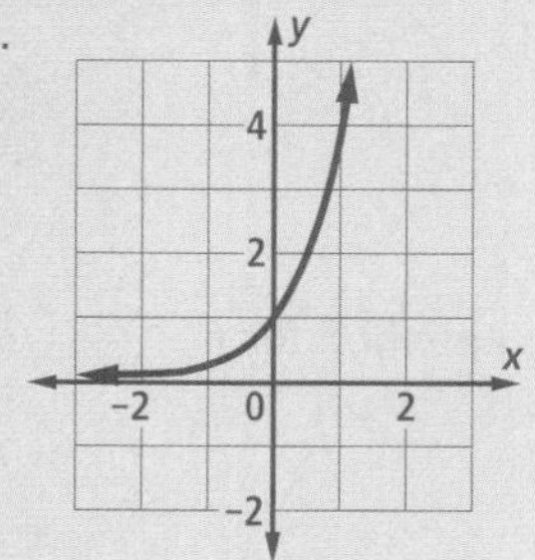

7b.

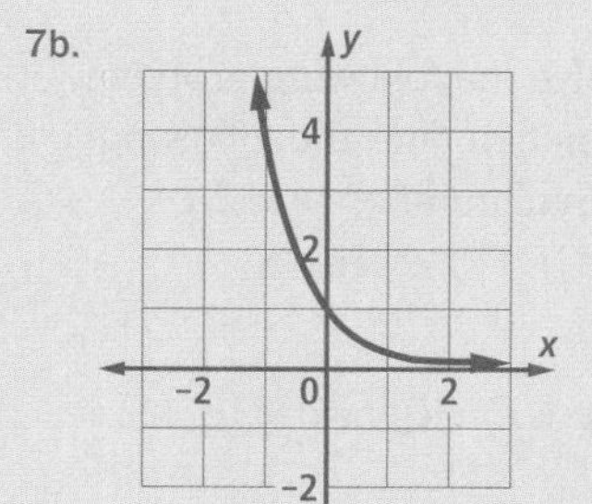

7c. The graph of $y = 4^x$ is the reflection image of the graph of $y = \left(\frac{1}{4}\right)^x$ over the y-axis and vice versa.

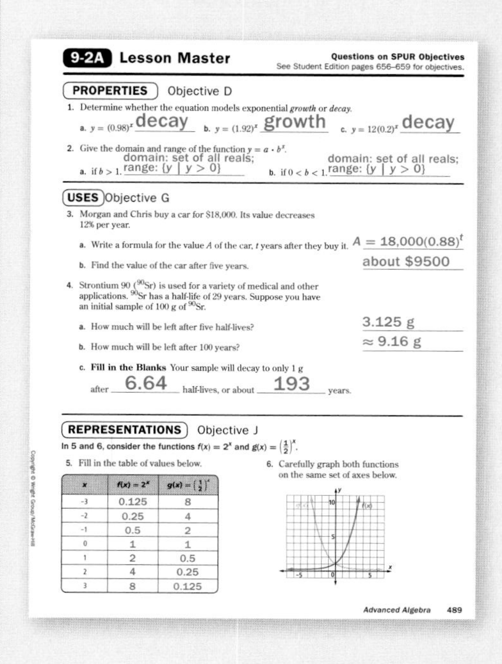

9-2A Lesson Master

Questions on SPUR Objectives
See Student Edition pages 656–659 for objectives.

PROPERTIES Objective D

1. Determine whether the equation models exponential *growth* or *decay*.
   a. $y = (0.98)^x$ decay
   b. $y = (1.92)^x$ growth
   c. $y = 12(0.2)^x$ decay

2. Give the domain and range of the function $y = a \cdot b^x$.
   a. if $b > 1$. domain: set of all reals; range: $\{y \mid y > 0\}$
   b. if $0 < b < 1$. domain: set of all reals; range: $\{y \mid y > 0\}$

USES Objective G

3. Morgan and Chris buy a car for $18,000. Its value decreases 12% per year.
   a. Write a formula for the value A of the car, t years after they buy it. $A = 18{,}000(0.88)^t$
   b. Find the value of the car after five years. about $9500

4. Strontium 90 (^{90}Sr) is used for a variety of medical and other applications. ^{90}Sr has a half-life of 29 years. Suppose you have an initial sample of 100 g of ^{90}Sr.
   a. How much will be left after five half-lives? 3.125 g
   b. How much will be left after 100 years? $\approx$ 9.16 g
   c. **Fill in the Blanks** Your sample will decay to only 1 g after 6.64 half-lives, or about 193 years.

REPRESENTATIONS Objective J

In 5 and 6, consider the functions $f(x) = 2^x$ and $g(x) = \left(\frac{1}{2}\right)^x$.

5. Fill in the table of values below.

x	$f(x) = 2^x$	$g(x) = \left(\frac{1}{2}\right)^x$
-3	0.125	8
-2	0.25	4
-1	0.5	2
0	1	1
1	2	0.5
2	4	0.25
3	8	0.125

6. Carefully graph both functions on the same set of axes below.

Advanced Algebra 489

Notes on the Questions

Questions 10–13 These are rich questions that can each take some time to discuss. You may wish to split students into groups and have each group concentrate on one question and then report to the rest of the class about their answers.

Question 11 You might want to note that the value of the car would become 0 in 10 years under the linear-depreciation model. Yet, practically speaking, the car will always have some value, and this is the case in using an exponential model. However, for tax purposes, linear depreciation is often used.

Additional Answers

10b.

x	J(x)
0	127,433,000
5	121,800,811
10	116,417,549
15	111,272,213
20	106,354,286
25	101,653,718
30	97,160,903
35	92,866,657
40	88,762,206
45	84,839,160

10d. This model differs from the actual value by 0.7%, or approximately 1,000,000 people.

11a.

Year (t)	Value (N)
1	$18,000
2	$16,200
3	$14,580
4	$13,122

11b.

Year (t)	Value (N)
1	$18,000
2	$16,000
3	$14,000
4	$12,000

11c. With the exponential model, $N = 20{,}000(0.9)^t$, so after 6 months, the car is worth $20{,}000(0.9)^{\frac{1}{2}} \approx \$18{,}974$. With the linear model, $N = 20{,}000 - 2{,}000t$, so after 6 months the car is worth $20{,}000 - 2{,}000\left(\frac{1}{2}\right) = \$19{,}000$. Thus, the exponential depreciation model is preferred for this situation.

APPLYING THE MATHEMATICS

10. According to recent estimates, in the future the population of Japan is predicted to *decrease* by 0.9% per year. In 2007, the population of Japan was about 127,433,000 people. Let $J(x)$ be the population (in millions) of Japan x years after 2007. Assume that J is an exponential function with domain $0 \le x \le 45$.
    a. Find a formula for $J(x)$. $J(x) = 127{,}433{,}000(0.991)^x$
    b. Make a table of values of $J(x)$ every 5 years from 2007 until 2052. See margin.
    c. According to this model, in what year would the population of Japan first fall below 110 million people? 2023
    d. Assume the population of Japan in 2008 is about 127,288,000. How well does your model predict this number? Check your model's validity with data for more recent years, if available on the Internet. See margin.

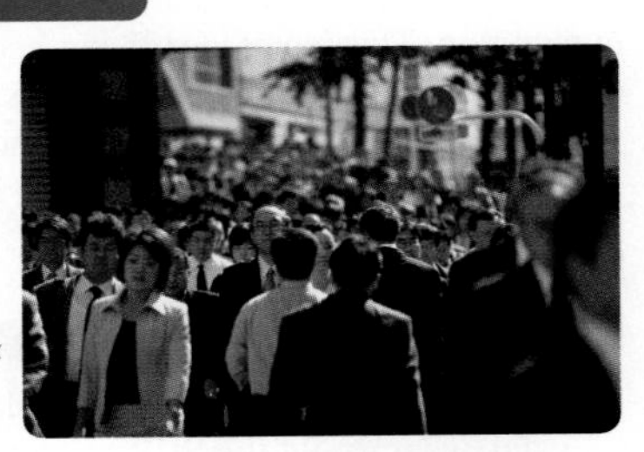

Tokyo, Japan is one of the most densely populated cities in the world.

11. Suppose that a new car costs $20,000 and one year later is worth $18,000. Let N be the value of the car after t years.
    a. Assume the depreciation is exponential. Make a table of values for $t = 1, 2, 3, 4$. 11a–c. See margin.
    b. Repeat Part a if the depreciation is linear.
    c. Suppose you lease this car for 6 months and then decide to buy it (called ***buying out the lease***). The balance to pay for the car is partly based on the car's existing value; that is, a higher value means you pay more for the car. On this basis, do you prefer that the dealer use a linear or exponential depreciation model? Explain your answer.

12. Sam Dunk has a 78% probability of making a free throw on one attempt. Assume that success or failure on one attempt does not affect the probability of success or failure on the next attempt.
    a. Find the probability that Sam makes 2 free throws in a row. 12a. 60.8%
    b. Find the probability that Sam makes 3 free throws in a row. 12b. 47.5%
    c. Let $f(n)$ be the probability that Sam makes n free throws in a row from the beginning of a game. Write a formula for $f(n)$. 12c. $f(n) = (0.78)^n$
    d. Find the smallest positive value of n such that $f(n) < 0.5$. 12d. $n = 3$
    e. What does your answer to Part d mean in the context of Sam Dunk's free throws? 12e. About half of the time, Sam is able to make 3 free throws in a row.

Extension

Have students solve the following problem. A nonconstant function f has the following property: For all real numbers x and y, $f(x + y) = f(x) \cdot f(y)$. For example, $f(5) = f(2) \cdot f(3)$.

1. Prove: $f(0) = 1$. (*Hint:* Consider $f(0 + 0)$.) Given that $f(0 + 0) = f(0) \cdot f(0)$, $f(0) = f(0)^2$. For all real x, if $x = x^2$, then $x = 0$ or $x = 1$, so $f(0) = 0$ or $f(0) = 1$. If $f(0) = 0$, then for all real numbers x, $f(x) = f(x + 0) = f(x) \cdot f(0) = f(x) \cdot 0 = 0$. Then f is a constant function. This contradicts the given condition, so $f(0) = 1$.
2. Find a possible equation for f. Answers vary. Sample: $f(x) = 2^x$

13. In 1965, the computer scientist Gordon Moore first noticed that the size, speed, and cost of computing elements change exponentially over time. In 1981, a 5-megabyte hard drive cost about $1700, or $340 per megabyte. The cost per megabyte has decreased exponentially with a half-life of about 1.2 years since then. Let $P(x)$ be the cost of one megabyte of hard-drive storage x half-life periods after 1981.
    a. Write an equation to for the exponential function P. $P(x) = 340\left(\frac{1}{2}\right)^x$
    b. Copy and fill in the table below.

x	-2	-1	0	1	2	3
P(x)	?	?	?	?	?	?

    c. The year 2020 corresponds to how many half-life periods since 1981? Use your model to predict the cost of hard-drive storage in 2020.
    d. According to your model, when will the cost of hard-drive storage first be less than $0.01 per ***gigabyte***? (1 gigabyte = 1000 megabytes)
    e. Is it realistic that one gigabyte of memory could cost less than a penny? Give a reason for your answer.

14. Suppose $g(x) = ab^x$ is an exponential growth function. Let $h(x) = g(-x)$ for all values of x. Use properties of powers to show that h is an exponential decay function. How are the graphs of h and g related? See margin.

13b. $1360; $680; $340; $170; $85; $42.50

13c. 32.5 half-lives; $P(32.5) \approx \$0.06$ per terabyte (1 terabyte = 1,000,000 megabytes)

13d. after 25 half-lives, that is, in 2011.

13e. Answers vary. Sample: Yes; this just means that a larger quantity of memory, such as the terabyte, would become the basis for the price of memory.

REVIEW

15. Consider the function graphed at the right. **(Lessons 9-1, 1-2)** D
    a. **Multiple Choice** Which could be an equation for the graph?
       A $f(x) = 10^{-x}$
       B $g(x) = 10x$
       C $h(x) = \left(\frac{1}{x}\right)^{10}$
       D $j(x) = 10^x$
    b. What is the domain of the function that answers Part a?
    c. What is the range of the function that answers Part a?

16. In 2005 the population of Dhaka, Bangladesh, was 12,576,000, and the growth rate was 3.6% per year. If that growth rate continues, what will the population of Dhaka be in 2015? **(Lesson 9-1)** 17,911,835

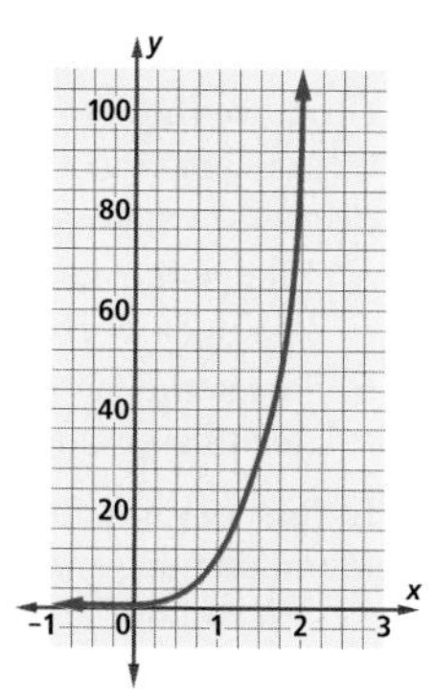

15b. all real numbers

15c. $\{y \mid y > 0\}$

Notes on the Questions

Question 13 Gordon Moore did not predict that this exponential change would occur forever, but it has remained a good estimate for longer than most people thought.

Question 14 Regardless of the function g, if $h(x) = g(-x)$ for all x, then the graph of h is the reflection image of the graph of g over the y-axis.

Question 15 This question provides an opportunity for you to point out that in exponential functions with equations of the form $y = ab^x$, the coefficient a may equal 1 (contrast this with the restriction that $b \neq 1$), and to introduce the exponential function with equation $y = 10^x$ whose inverse is the common logarithm function introduced in Lesson 9-5.

Additional Answers

14. $h(x) = g(-x) = ab^{-x} = a\left(\frac{1}{b}\right)^x = ac^x$ where $0 < c < 1$; thus, h is an exponential decay function. The graph of h is the reflection image of the graph of g over the y-axis.

Accommodating the Learner

Give students newspaper advertisements for cars. Have each student choose a car and predict the value of the car they have chosen after 1 year, 3 years, and 5 years, using the 12% depreciation rate given in Example 1. Answers vary. Check students' work.

4 Wrap-Up

Ongoing Assessment

Have each student write five statements about the properties of exponential functions that are either true or false. Have students exchange statements and identify each statement as either true or false. Students should recognize the properties of exponential functions.

Project Update

Project 3, *Car Values*, on page 650 relates to the content of this lesson.

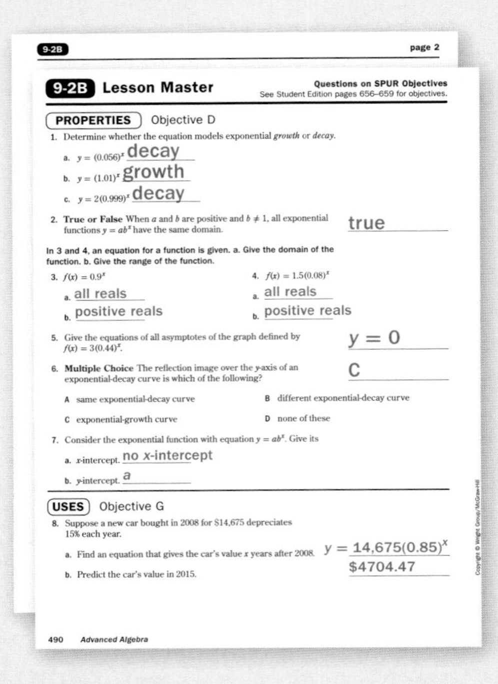

9-2B page 2

9-2B Lesson Master

Questions on SPUR Objectives
See Student Edition pages 656–659 for objectives.

PROPERTIES Objective D

1. Determine whether the equation models exponential *growth* or *decay*.
   a. $y = (0.056)^x$ decay
   b. $y = (1.01)^x$ growth
   c. $y = 2(0.999)^x$ decay

2. **True or False** When a and b are positive and $b \neq 1$, all exponential functions $y = ab^x$ have the same domain. true

In 3 and 4, an equation for a function is given. a. Give the domain of the function. b. Give the range of the function.

3. $f(x) = 0.9^x$
   a. all reals
   b. positive reals

4. $f(x) = 1.5(0.08)^x$
   a. all reals
   b. positive reals

5. Give the equations of all asymptotes of the graph defined by $f(x) = 3(0.44)^x$. $y = 0$

6. **Multiple Choice** The reflection image over the y-axis of an exponential-decay curve is which of the following? C
   A same exponential-decay curve
   B different exponential-decay curve
   C exponential-growth curve
   D none of these

7. Consider the exponential function with equation $y = ab^x$. Give its
   a. x-intercept. no x-intercept
   b. y-intercept. a

USES Objective G

8. Suppose a new car bought in 2008 for $14,675 depreciates 15% each year.
   a. Find an equation that gives the car's value x years after 2008. $y = 14{,}675(0.85)^x$
   b. Predict the car's value in 2015. $4704.47

490 *Advanced Algebra*

17. Shilah is raising guppies, a popular species of freshwater aquarium fish. To raise guppies, it is important to have plenty of aquarium space, ample food, and places for babies to hide (or the guppy mothers may eat them). Shilah began with 12 guppies and the population increased at a biweekly (every two weeks) rate of 33%. **(Lessons 9-1, 7-2)**
    a. How many guppies did Shilah have after 10 weeks? about 50
    b. What is an equation for the number g of guppies after w weeks? $g = 12(1.33)^{\frac{w}{2}}$

18. The inflation rate, a rate at which the average price of goods increases, is reported monthly by the U.S. government. Suppose a monthly rate of 0.3% was reported for January. Assume this rate continues for a year. **(Lessons 9-1, 5-1)**
    a. What is the inflation rate for the year? 3.7%
    b. The value 0.3% has been rounded. The actual value could range from 0.25% up to, but not including, 0.35%. Write an inequality for r, the annual inflation rate, based on those two extreme values. $3.04\% \leq r < 4.28\%$

19. Give the decimal approximation to the nearest tenth. **(Lessons 7-7, 7-2)**
    a. 5^3 125
    b. $5^{\frac{5}{2}}$ 55.9
    c. $5^{\sqrt{7}}$ 70.7

20. Write $\frac{10^{12.7}}{10^{9.3}}$ as a power of ten and as a decimal to the nearest thousandth. **(Lessons 7-2)** $10^{3.4}$; 2511.886

21. Simplify $\frac{tr^{n+1}}{r}$. **(Lesson 7-2)** tr^n

EXPLORATION

22. Often we think of populations as *growing* exponentially, but as Question 10 shows, a country's population may *decrease* exponentially.
    a. Find some countries in the world whose population has been decreasing.
    b. List some factors that would explain their decreasing population.

22a. Answers vary. Sample: Russia, Japan, and Germany

22b. Answers vary. Sample: a high emigration rate, a high mortality rate, a low birth rate

23. In this lesson you have seen several cases in which scientists found an object with a certain percent of its carbon-14 left. Research how scientists find out how much carbon-14 was originally present.
    The ratio of carbon-12 to carbon-14 in the air and in living things is nearly constant; thus, the measured value of this ratio today is the same for all living creatures and would have been nearly the same for ancient animals. Since the amount of carbon-12 in the body remains constant even after an animal dies, a measurement of this ratio for a deceased animal indicates the percentage of carbon-14 lost since death.

Lesson 9-3 Continuous Compounding

Vocabulary

e

compounded continuously

▸ BIG IDEA The more times that a given interest rate is compounded in a year, the larger the amount an account will earn. But there is a limit to the amount earned, and the limit is said to be the result of *continuous compounding*.

Recall the General Compound Interest Formula,

$$A = P\left(1 + \frac{r}{n}\right)^{nt},$$

which gives the amount A that an investment is worth when principal P is invested in an account paying an annual interest rate r and the interest is compounded n times per year for t years.

Suppose you put $1 into a bank account. If the bank were to pay you 100% interest compounded annually, your money would double in one year because the interest would equal the amount in the account. Using the formula with $P = 1$ dollar, $r = 100\% = 1$, $n = 1$, and $t = 1$ year, we have

$$A = 1\left(1 + \frac{1}{1}\right)^1 = 2 \text{ dollars.}$$

Now suppose you put $1 into a bank account and the bank paid 100% compounded ***semiannually***. This means that the bank pays 50% interest twice a year. Now you receive $0.50 in interest after six months, giving a total of $1.50. Then, after another six months you receive $0.75 in interest on the $1.50, giving a total after one year of $2.25. This agrees with what you would compute using the General Compound Interest Formula with $n = 2$. Then,

$$A = \left(1 + \frac{1}{2}\right)^2 = \left(\frac{3}{2}\right)^2 = \frac{9}{4} = 2.25 \text{ dollars.}$$

You are asked to explore what happens as n gets larger in the following Activity.

Mental Math

Consider the largest sphere that will fit in a cube with side length 6.

a. Find the exact volume of the sphere. 36π

b. How many spheres of diameter 3 will fit in the cube without overlapping? 8

Activity

Complete a table like the one on the next page to show the value of $1 at the end of one year ($t = 1$) after an increasing number n of compounding periods per year at a 100% annual rate.

(continued on next page)

Background

The number e is important in mathematics. The exponential function $y = e^x$ has the property that it is equivalent to equals its derivative: The slope of the line tangent to a point on the curve $y = e^x$ equals the second coordinate of the point. This makes it valuable in solving differential equations.

Activity The Activity shows how the number e develops from a real situation. The compound-interest situation gives an instance of the fact that e is the limit of $\left(1 + \frac{1}{n}\right)^n$ as n approaches infinity.

Although it will not be covered in this book, students may be interested in learning that it is possible to take complex powers of numbers. The pure imaginary powers of e are particularly interesting: $e^{ix} = \cos x + i\sin x$. By letting $x = \pi$, $e^{i\pi} = \cos \pi + i\sin \pi = -1 + i \cdot 0 = -1$. This leads to the famous equation, discovered by Leonhard Euler, $e^{i\pi} + 1 = 0$, connecting five of the most important numbers in all of mathematics.

Lesson 9-3

GOAL

Learn about the number *e* and understand that the constant *e* arises from a realistic context, in this case, the Continuously Compounded Interest Formula.

SPUR Objectives

D Recognize properties of exponential functions.

G Create and apply exponential growth and decay models.

Materials/Resources

- Lesson Masters 9-3A and 9-3B
- Resource Masters 158 and 159

HOMEWORK

Suggestions for Assignment

- Questions 1–21
- Question 22 (extra credit)
- Reading Lesson 9-4
- Covering the Ideas 9-4

Local Standards

1 Warm-Up

Use your calculator to verify the calculations in the table at the bottom of page 596. Your calculator may display at the bottom more decimal places than those given.

2 Teaching

Notes on the Lesson

The lesson begins with a natural question about compound interest: How much does a larger number of compoundings benefit the investor? Although compounding more often always increases the yield, it is surprising that the increase does not go to infinity but rather to a fixed value related to the number *e*. Stress that, like π, *e* represents a *constant,* not a variable.

Activity Connect the entries in the table with the everyday situation of a bank. Note that *A* is the amount that \$1 would accrue to and that *A* is directly proportional to (varies directly as) the amount one begins with. The first 50 digits of the decimal expansion of *e* suggest that there might be a pattern, but no pattern is known. *e* is irrational, so its decimal expansion does not terminate or repeat.

Interest compounded continuously Students may wonder why a bank would calculate interest continuously. The reason is that the amounts differ very little from what one gets by compounding daily, and it is much easier to calculate because of the special properties of the number *e.*

Sometimes, the [e^x] key on a calculator requires a second function. If there is no [e^x] key on a calculator, one can use the key sequence 1 [INV] [ln x] to display the calculator's value for *e.*

Additional Answers

Activity

$1\left(\frac{1}{4}\right)^4$; $1\left(1+\frac{1}{12}\right)^{12}$; $1\left(1+\frac{1}{365}\right)^{365}$; $1\left(1+\frac{1}{8760}\right)^{8760}$; $1\left(1+\frac{1}{525{,}600}\right)^{525{,}600}$

Compounding Frequency	n = Number of Compoundings per Year	$P\left(1+\frac{r}{n}\right)^{nt}$	A
Annually	1	$1\left(1+\frac{1}{1}\right)^1$	\$2.00
Semiannually	2	$1\left(1+\frac{1}{2}\right)^2$	\$2.25
Quarterly	4	?	\$2.44141 $1\left(1+\frac{1}{4}\right)^4$
Monthly	?	?	? $12; 1\left(1+\frac{1}{12}\right)^{12}$; \$2.61304
Daily	?	?	? $365; 1\left(1+\frac{1}{365}\right)^{365}$; \$2.71457
Hourly	?	?	? $8760; 1\left(1+\frac{1}{8760}\right)^{8760}$; \$2.71813
By the Minute	?	?	? $525{,}600; 1\left(1+\frac{1}{525{,}600}\right)^{525{,}600}$; \$2.71828

The Activity shows that the more frequently a bank compounds, the more your earnings will be. The sequence of values for the total amount gets closer and closer to the number **e**, which is approximately equal to 2.71828. We say that *e* is the value of \$1 after one year invested at 100% interest **compounded continuously**.

The number *e* is named after Euler, who proved that the sequence of numbers of the form $\left(1+\frac{1}{n}\right)^n$ approaches this particular number as n increases. Like π, *e* is an irrational number that can be expressed as an infinite, nonrepeating decimal. The following are the first 50 digits of the decimal expansion for *e*, and a graph of $y = e^x$ is shown at the right.

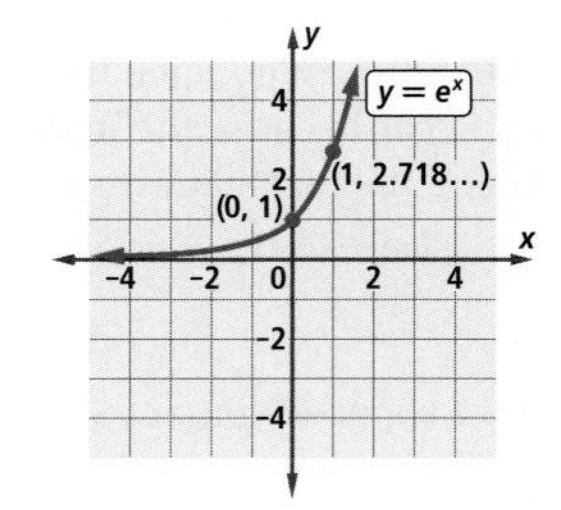

$e \approx 2.71828\,18284\,59045\,23536\,02874\,7135\,2\,66249\,77572\,47093\,69995\ldots$

Like π, an approximation to *e* is stored on virtually every calculator.

QY1

> **QY1**
> What value does your calculator display for *e*? (Hint: Look for a key or menu selection labeled e^x, and evaluate e^1.)

Interest Compounded Continuously

Of course, savings institutions do not pay 100% interest. But the number *e* appears regardless of the interest rate.

Consider an account in which 4% interest is paid on \$1 for one year. The table at the right shows some values of A for different compounding periods. As n increases, the total amount gets closer and closer to \$1.040810..., the decimal value of $e^{0.04}$. Furthermore, in t years of continuous compounding at this rate, the dollar would grow to $(e^{0.04})^t$, or $e^{0.04t}$. So, if an amount P were invested, the amount would grow to $Pe^{0.04t}$.

Compounding Frequency	$P\left(1+\frac{r}{n}\right)^{nt}$	A
Annually	$1\left(1+\frac{0.04}{1}\right)^1$	\$1.04
Quarterly	$1\left(1+\frac{0.04}{4}\right)^4$	\$1.040604
Daily	$1\left(1+\frac{0.04}{365}\right)^{365}$	\$1.040808

Accommodating the Learner

Although most calculators provide an approximation of *e,* many require the student to enter a power of *e* to display it. Some students might not realize that $e = e^1$. Remind them that $x^1 = x$ for all values of x. So, to display the value of *e,* the student may need to key-in a 1 for the exponent.

ENGLISH LEARNERS

Vocabulary Development

Stress that the number *e* is a constant. It is an irrational number like π, never repeating and never terminating. Then define *continuous* as "never ending." This means that the number of times that interest is *compounded continuously* cannot be counted as it can when interest is compounded annually, semiannually, quarterly, and so on.

In general, for situations where interest is compounded continuously, the general Compound Interest Formula can be greatly simplified.

Continuously Compounded Interest Formula

If an amount P is invested in an account paying an annual interest rate r compounded continuously, the amount A in the account after t years is

$$A = Pe^{rt}.$$

 QY2

QY2

What will an account with an initial deposit of $1000 be worth after 3 years if interest is compounded continuously at 5% annual interest rate?

Example 1

Talia invested $3,927.54 in a zero-coupon bond paying 5.5% compounded semiannually. After 30 years the value of the bond will be $20,000. How much would Talia's investment have been worth after 30 years if interest were compounded continuously instead of twice per year?

Solution Use $A = Pe^{rt}$, with $P = 3927.54$, $r = 0.055$, and $t = 30$.

$A = 3927.54e^{0.055(30)}$

$A = 3927.54e^{1.65} \approx 20{,}450.62$

After 30 years, the bond would be worth $20,450.62. This is $450.62 more than a bond with semiannual compounding would earn.

Other Uses of the Number *e*

Many formulas for continuous growth and decay are written using e as the base because the exponential function $y = e^x$ has special properties that make it particularly suitable for applications. We do not study those properties here, but you will learn them if you study calculus. You do not need to know these properties to find values of the function.

GUIDED

Example 2

A *capacitor* is an electrical device capable of storing an electric charge and releasing that charge very quickly. For example, a camera uses a capacitor to provide the energy needed to operate an electronic flash. The percent Q of charge in the capacitor t seconds after a flash begins is given by the formula $Q = Pe^{-10.0055t}$, where P is the initial percent of charge in the capacitor. If 44.8% of the charge is left 0.08 second after a flash begins, to what percent was the capacitor originally charged?

(continued on next page)

Extension

After discussing the Examples, you might explain to students that the function f with equation $f(x) = \frac{1}{\sqrt{2\pi}} e^{\frac{-x^2}{2}}$ is called the "normal density function." Its graph is called the "standard normal curve." Have students estimate $f(-1)$, $f(0)$, and $f(1)$. $f(-1) = f(1) = 0.242$; $f(0) = 0.399$ You may wish to have students graph this curve to see its bell shape. Students will learn more about this curve in Chapter 13.

Notes on the Lesson

You might wish to compare two models for the growth of money in t years, if P dollars are invested at an annual rate r:

- $A = P \cdot (1 + r)^t$ when compounded annually
- $A = P \cdot (e^r)^t$ when compounded continuously

Emphasize that $(1 + r)$ and (e^r) are the growth factors for these two models. To further stress the difference between these models of compounding at an annual rate of r, use the following example.

Suppose $850 is invested at an annual rate of 6%.

- $A = 850 \cdot (1 + .06)^t$ when compounded annually
- $A = 850 \cdot (e^{.06})^t$ when compounded continuously

Point out to students that although continuous compounding yields more interest than annual compounding, the amount that will be earned over a short period of time will be fairly close. This is true because the growth factors $(1 + 0.06) = 1.06$ and $(e^{.06}) \approx 1.0618$ are very close.

Additional Example

Example 1 Mona invested $8218.16 in a zero-coupon bond paying 4.5% compounded semiannually. After 25 years, the value of the bond will be about $25,000. How much would Mona's investment have been worth after 25 years if interest were compounded continuously instead of twice per year? about $25,313.71

Note-Taking Tips

Have students include the Continually Compounded Interest Formula in their journals.

Notes on the Lesson

Example 2 This example may seem contrived. Why have the base *e*? An alternate approach would be to calculate $e^{-10.0055}$, call that number *k*, and make the formula $Q = Pk^t$. This shows that *k* (equivalently, $e^{-10.0055}$) is the growth (decay) factor. However, it is traditional in many fields to use *e* as a base. This tradition has arisen for a powerful mathematical reason beyond the scope of this course: If we ask for a function to describe a situation in which the increase is proportional to the amount, then we are asking for a function *f* whose derivative at each value *x* is proportional to *f*(*x*). That is, we are asking for a function *f* such that $f'(x) = kf(x)$ for all *x*, and the solution to that equation is $f(x) = e^{kx} + c$.

Students may be interested in learning more about capacitors. There are a number of Web sites on the Internet that explain what capacitors do.

Additional Example

Example 2 The amount *L* of a certain radioactive substance remaining after *t* years is given by the formula $L = Be^{-0.0001t}$, where *B* is the initial amount of radioactive substance. If 2000 grams are left after 6000 years, how many grams were present initially?

Solution We need to find *B*, which is the initial amount present. When $t = 6000$, $L =$ __?__. 2000 Substitute these values and solve for *B*.

$L = Be^{(\_?\_)t}$ -0.0001

_?_ $= Be^{(\_?\_)\cdot(\_?\_)}$ 2000; -0.0001; 6000

_?_ $\approx B(\_?\_)$ 2000; 0.54881

_?_ $\approx B$ 3644

Initially, there were about _?_ grams of the radioactive substance. 3644

Solution We need to find *P*. When $t = 0.08$, $Q =$ __?__. 0.448

Substitute these values and solve for *P*.

$Q = Pe^{\_?\_t}$ -10.0055

_?_ $= Pe^{(\_?\_)(\_?\_)}$ 0.448; -10.0055; 0.08

_?_ $\approx P(\_?\_)$ 0.448; 0.449

_?_ $\approx P$ 0.998

The capacitor was originally charged to _?_% of capacity. 99.8

Formulas such as $A = 3000e^{0.05t}$ and $Q = Pe^{-10.0055t}$ model exponential growth and decay, respectively. Models like these are often described using function notation. Let *C* be the initial amount, and let *r* be the growth factor by which this amount continuously grows or decays per unit time *t*. Then *N*(*t*), the amount at time *t*, is given by the equation

$$N(t) = Ce^{rt}.$$

This equation can be rewritten as $N(t) = C(e^r)^t$. So it is an exponential equation of the form

$$y = ab^x,$$

where $a = C$, $x = t$, and the growth factor $b = e^r$. If *r* is positive, then $e^r > 1$ and there is exponential growth. If *r* is negative, then $0 < e^r < 1$ and there is exponential decay.

Questions

COVERING THE IDEAS

1. **Fill in the Blank** Like π, the number *e* is a(n) __?__ number. irrational
2. Approximate *e* to the nearest ten-billionth. 2.7182818284
3. Use the General Compound Interest Formula.
   a. What is the value of $1 invested for one year at 100% interest compounded daily, to the nearest hundredth of a cent? about $2.7146
   b. As *n* increases, the value in Part a becomes closer and closer to what number? *e*
4. Approximate $e^{0.055}$ to the nearest hundred-thousandth. 1.05654

5. Suppose \$1000 is invested at 6% interest compounded continuously.
   a. What is its value at the end of one year? \$1061.83
   b. What is its value at the end of 3.5 years? \$1233.67
6. Suppose \$8000 is invested at an annual interest rate of 4.5% for 15 years.
   a. How much will be in the account if the interest compounds continuously? \$15,712.26
   b. How much will be in the account if the interest compounds annually? \$15,482.26
7. Use the formula $Q = Pe^{-10.005t}$ given in Example 2. What is the initial charge of a capacitor if 30% of its charge remains after 0.1 second? about 81.6%
8. Consider the function N with $N(t) = Ce^{rt}$.
   a. What does C represent? the value of $N(0)$
   b. What does e^r represent? the growth factor
   c. What are the domain and range of N?
   d. How can you determine whether N models exponential growth or exponential decay?

8c. domain: all real numbers; range: all positive real numbers

8d. If $r > 0$, the function models exponential growth, and if $r < 0$, the function models exponential decay.

APPLYING THE MATHEMATICS

9. Equations of three functions are shown below.
   (i) $y_1 = e^x$ (ii) $y_2 = \left(\frac{1}{e}\right)^{-x}$ (iii) $y_3 = e^{-x}$
   a. Determine whether each function is increasing, decreasing, or neither on the set of real numbers.
   b. Check your answer in Part a by graphing each function for $-2 \le x \le 2$. See margin.
   c. Explain why two of the graphs in Part b coincide.
   d. Which of the functions describe(s) exponential growth? i; ii
   e. Which of the functions describe(s) exponential decay? iii

9a. i. increasing; ii. increasing; iii. decreasing

9c. The graphs of y_1 and y_2 coincide because $y_2 = \left(\frac{1}{e}\right)^{-x} = (e^{-1})^{-x} = e^x = y_1$.

10. **Fill in the Blank** Write >, <, or =: π^e __?__ e^π. <
11. A machine used in an industry depreciates so that its value $N(t)$ after t years is given by $N(t) = Ce^{-0.35t}$.
    a. What is the annual rate r of depreciation of the machine? about 29.5%
    b. If the machine is worth \$90,000 after 4 years, what was its original value? about \$364,968
12. The amount L of americium, a radioactive substance, remaining after t years decreases according to the formula $L = Be^{-0.0001t}$. If 5000 micrograms are left after 2500 years, how many micrograms of americium were present initially?

12. about 6420 micrograms

3 Assignment

Recommended Assignment

- Questions 1–21
- Question 22 (extra credit)
- Reading Lesson 9-4
- Covering the Ideas 9-4

Notes on the Questions

Question 9 Students may need to use parentheses when entering the exponent on their calculators.

Question 11b Students may want to solve the equation in this question for C to find $C = N(t)e^{0.35t}$ before substituting for $N(t)$ and t.

Additional Answers

9bi.

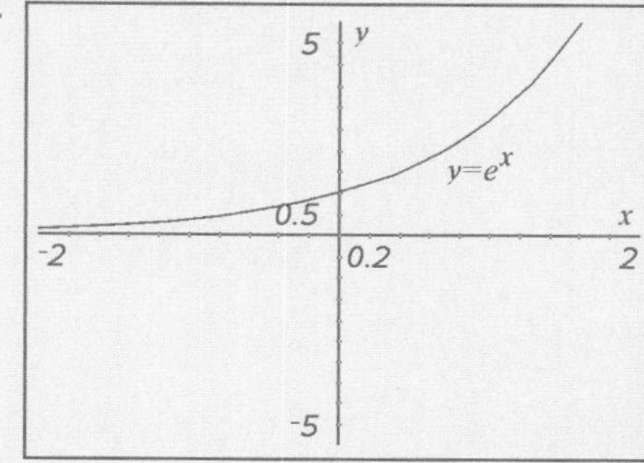

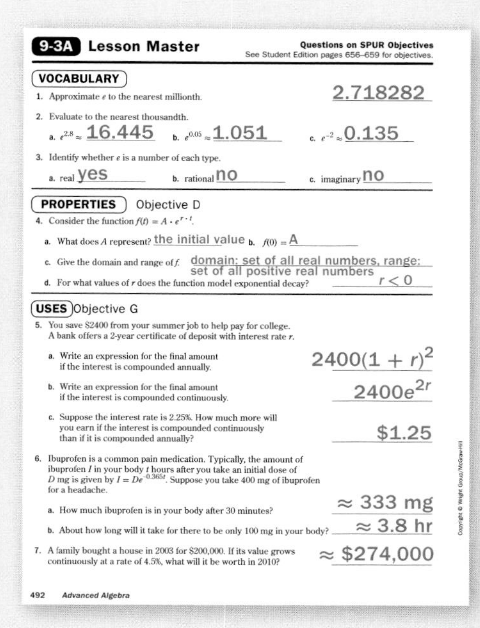

9-3A Lesson Master

Questions on SPUR Objectives
See Student Edition pages 656–659 for objectives.

VOCABULARY

1. Approximate e to the nearest millionth. 2.718282
2. Evaluate to the nearest thousandth.
   a. $e^{2.8} \approx$ 16.445 b. $e^{0.05} \approx$ 1.051 c. $e^{-2} \approx$ 0.135
3. Identify whether e is a number of each type.
   a. real yes b. rational no c. imaginary no

PROPERTIES Objective D

4. Consider the function $f(t) = A \cdot e^{r \cdot t}$.
   a. What does A represent? the initial value b. $f(0) =$ A
   c. Give the domain and range of f. domain: set of all real numbers, range: set of all positive real numbers
   d. For what values of r does the function model exponential decay? $r < 0$

USES Objective G

5. You save \$2400 from your summer job to help pay for college. A bank offers a 2-year certificate of deposit with interest rate r.
   a. Write an expression for the final amount if the interest is compounded annually. $2400(1 + r)^2$
   b. Write an expression for the final amount if the interest is compounded continuously. $2400e^{2r}$
   c. Suppose the interest rate is 2.25%. How much more will you earn if the interest is compounded continuously than if it is compounded annually? \$1.25
6. Ibuprofen is a common pain medication. Typically, the amount of ibuprofen I in your body t hours after you take an initial dose of D mg is given by $I = De^{-0.365t}$. Suppose you take 400 mg of ibuprofen for a headache.
   a. How much ibuprofen is in your body after 30 minutes? ≈ 333 mg
   b. About how long will it take for there to be only 100 mg in your body? ≈ 3.8 hr
7. A family bought a house in 2003 for \$200,000. If its value grows continuously at a rate of 4.5%, what will it be worth in 2010? ≈ \$274,000

492 *Advanced Algebra*

Additional Answers

9b.ii.

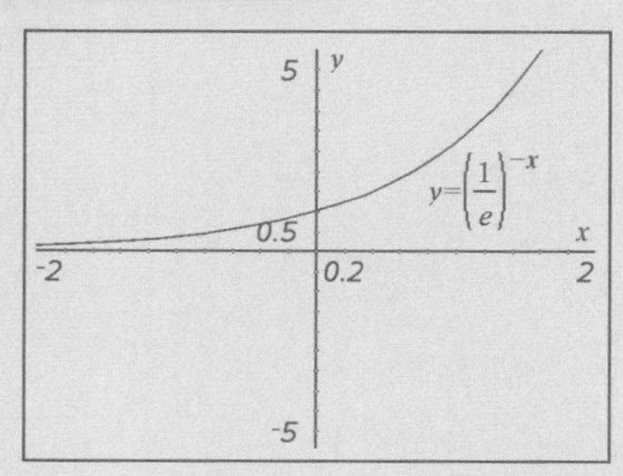

9b.iii.

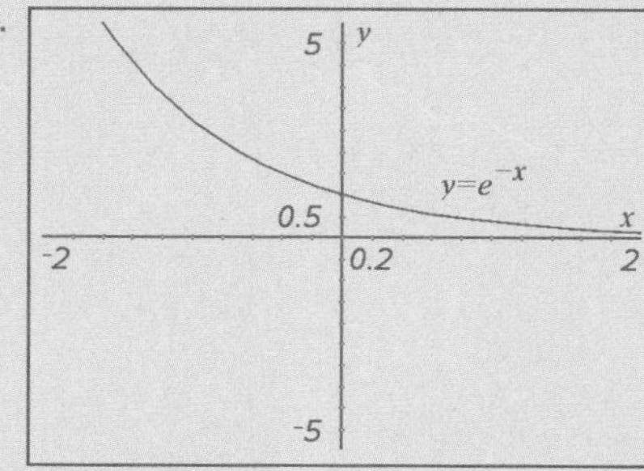

Notes on the Questions

Question 13 You might want to extend this question into an optional project for the chapter. If so, students should graph the functions p and q and compare the populations predicted by the model both in the short run and in the long run.

Question 18 Students who have studied from UCSMP *Geometry* will have seen Varignon's Theorem, which states that the quadrilateral formed by connecting the midpoints of any quadrilateral (even one in space) is a parallelogram.

13. In the 1980s, researchers developed a special "inhibited growth" model to predict the growth of the U.S. population, using data from the 1960s and 1970s. The model predicts the population $p(y)$ (in millions) of the U.S. y years after 1960. An equation for the model is

$$p(y) = \frac{64{,}655.6}{179.3 + 181.3e^{-0.02676y}}.$$

a. According to this model, what is the predicted U.S. population in 2100? about 352.2 million

b. Let y = the number of years since 2000. Then a newer model for the U.S. population is $q(y) = 281.4e^{0.0112y}$. According to this model, what population is predicted for 2100? about 862.4 million

c. Which answer is greater, the answer for Part a or Part b? Can you think of any reason to account for such differences?

d. Research last year's U.S. population and compare it to the values predicted by the two models. See margin.

13c. The answer for Part b; Reasons vary. Sample: The newer model uses a faster rate of population growth.

REVIEW

14. Nobelium was discovered in 1958 and named after Alfred Nobel. Nobelium-255 (^{255}No) has a half-life of 3 minutes. Suppose 100% of nobelium-255 is present initially. **(Lesson 9-2)**

a. Make a table of values showing how much nobelium-255 will be left after 1, 2, 3, 4, and 5 half-life periods. See margin.

b. Write a formula for the percent A of nobelium-255 left after x half-life periods. $A = \left(\frac{1}{2}\right)^x$

c. Write a formula for the percent A of nobelium-255 left after t minutes. $A = \left(\frac{1}{2}\right)^{\frac{t}{3}}$

15. Let $f(x) = 16^x$. **(Lessons 9-1, 8-2, 7-7, 7-3)**

a. Evaluate $f(-3)$, $f(0)$, and $f\left(\frac{3}{2}\right)$. $\frac{1}{4096}$; 1; 64

b. Identify the domain and range of f.

c. Give an equation for the reflection image of the graph of $y = f(x)$ over the line with equation $y = x$. $x = 16^y$

15b. domain: all real numbers; range: all positive real numbers

16. Rationalize the denominator of $\frac{2\sqrt{5}+1}{2\sqrt{5}-1}$. **(Lesson 8-6)** $\frac{21+4\sqrt{5}}{19}$

17. Solve $5k^3 = 27$. **(Lessons 8-4, 7-6)** $k = \frac{3}{\sqrt[3]{5}}$

18. Use the diagram at the right. Midpoints of a 12-by-16 rectangle have been connected to form a rhombus. Then midpoints of the rhombus are connected to form a rectangle, and so on. **(Lesson 7-5, Previous Course)** a. 56, 28, 14, 7, 3.5, 1.75

a. List the perimeters of the first 6 rectangles.

b. What kind of sequence is formed by these perimeters? geometric

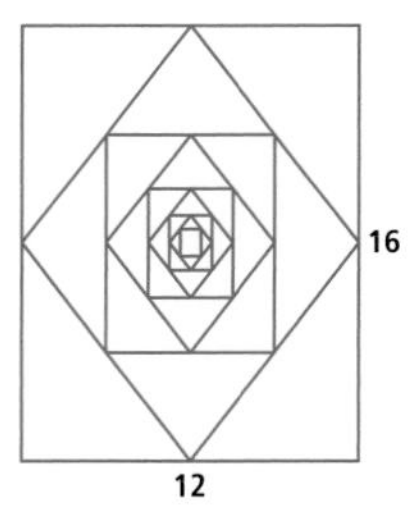

Additional Answers

13d. Answers vary.

14a.

1	2	3	4	5
50%	25%	12.5%	6.25%	3.125%

19. For what values of a does the equation $ax^2 + 8x + 7 = 0$ have no real solutions? **(Lesson 6-10)** $a > \frac{16}{7}$

20. Choose all that apply. What kind of number is $\sqrt{-25}$? **(Lessons 6-8, 6-2)** C

    A rational B irrational C imaginary

21. The table below gives the average height in centimeters for girls of various ages in the U.S. **(Lesson 3-5)**

Age	2	4	6	8	10
Height (cm)	85	101	115	127	138

   a. Let x be age and y be height. Find an equation for the line of best fit for this data set. $y = 6.6x + 73.6$

   b. Use the equation in Part a to predict the height of a girl at age 12. 152.8 cm

EXPLORATION

22. Another way to get an approximate value of e is to evaluate the infinite sum

$$1 + \frac{1}{1!} + \frac{1}{2!} + \frac{1}{3!} + \ldots .$$

(Recall that $n!$ is the product of all integers from 1 to n inclusive.)

   a. Use your calculator to calculate each of the following to the nearest thousandth.

$$1 + \frac{1}{1!} + \frac{1}{2!} + \frac{1}{3!}$$

$$1 + \frac{1}{1!} + \frac{1}{2!} + \frac{1}{3!} + \frac{1}{4!}$$

$$1 + \frac{1}{1!} + \frac{1}{2!} + \frac{1}{3!} + \frac{1}{4!} + \frac{1}{5!}$$ 2.667, 2.708, 2.717

   b. How many terms must you add to approximate $e = 2.71828\ldots$ to the nearest thousandth? What is the last term you need to add to do this? 7 terms; the last term is $\frac{1}{6!}$

QY ANSWERS

1. Answers vary. Sample: 2.71828183

2. $1161.83

Notes on the Questions

Question 22 You might wish to have students work in small groups on this question. As students perform the computations with their calculators, they can compare answers within their groups. Ask one member from each group to summarize the group's results and answer the question about the last term.

4 Wrap-Up

Ongoing Assessment

Have students each write a paragraph describing the amount of money he or she might deposit in a savings account, a realistic interest rate, and the length of time the interest will be compounded continuously. Then have them exchange papers and calculate the amount of money in the account at the end of the indicated time. Students should correctly apply the Continuously Compounding Interest Formula.

Accommodating the Learner

The formula for e in Question 22 is a special case of a formula for e^x: $e^x = 1 + x + \frac{x^2}{2!} + \frac{x^3}{3!} + \frac{x^4}{4!} + \ldots$. Have students use this formula to estimate $e^{\frac{1}{2}}$ and e^2. Then have them compare these values with the values given on their calculators for $e^{\frac{1}{2}}$ and e^2. $e^{\frac{1}{2}} \approx 1.648721$ and $e^2 \approx 7.389056$

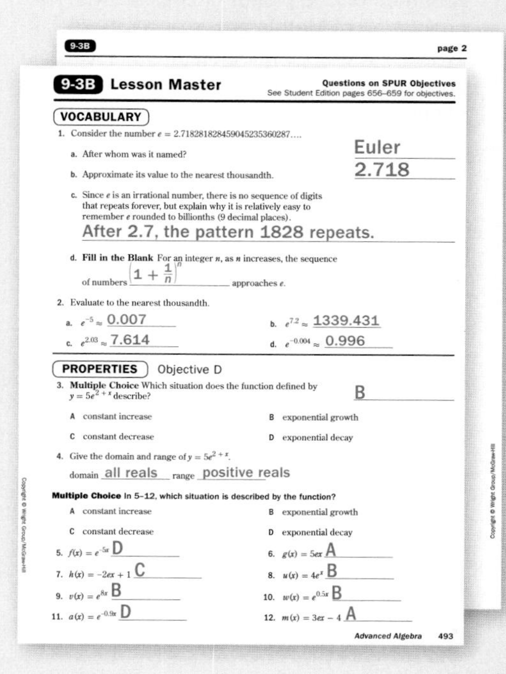

9-3B page 2

9-3B Lesson Master

Questions on SPUR Objectives
See Student Edition pages 656–659 for objectives.

VOCABULARY

1. Consider the number $e = 2.718281828459045235360287\ldots$.

   a. After whom was it named? Euler

   b. Approximate its value to the nearest thousandth. 2.718

   c. Since e is an irrational number, there is no sequence of digits that repeats forever, but explain why it is relatively easy to remember e rounded to billionths (9 decimal places). After 2.7, the pattern 1828 repeats.

   d. **Fill in the Blank** For an integer n, as n increases, the sequence of numbers $\left(1 + \frac{1}{n}\right)^n$ approaches e.

2. Evaluate to the nearest thousandth.

   a. $e^{-5} \approx$ 0.007 b. $e^{7.2} \approx$ 1339.431

   c. $e^{2.03} \approx$ 7.614 d. $e^{-0.004} \approx$ 0.996

PROPERTIES Objective D

3. **Multiple Choice** Which situation does the function defined by $y = 5e^{2+x}$ describe? B

   A constant increase B exponential growth

   C constant decrease D exponential decay

4. Give the domain and range of $y = 5e^{2+x}$.

   domain all reals range positive reals

Multiple Choice In 5–12, which situation is described by the function?

   A constant increase B exponential growth

   C constant decrease D exponential decay

5. $f(x) = e^{-5x}$ D 6. $g(x) = 5ex$ A

7. $h(x) = -2ex + 1$ C 8. $u(x) = 4e^x$ B

9. $v(x) = e^{8x}$ B 10. $w(x) = e^{0.5x}$ B

11. $a(x) = e^{-0.9x}$ D 12. $m(x) = 3ex - 4$ A

Advanced Algebra 493

Lesson 9-4

GOAL

Fit exponential models to two kinds of data: data known to be exponential and data that might be exponential.

SPUR Objectives

H Fit an exponential model to data.

Materials/Resources

- Lesson Masters 9-4A and 9-4B
- Resource Masters 160–162
- Quiz 1

HOMEWORK

Suggestions for Assignment

- Questions 1–16
- Question 17 (extra credit)
- Reading Lesson 9-5
- Covering the Ideas 9-5

Local Standards

1 Warm-Up

Mathia and Scientia are the only two countries on the planet of Logicia. The population of Mathia grows at a rate of 10% per year. The population of Logicia decreases at a rate of 10% per year. Assuming that the two countries have the same population, what is the growth rate of Scientia? Let M be the population of Mathia and S be the population of Scientia. Since the population of Mathia grows at a rate of 10%, after one year the poulation will be $1.1M$. If we let x be the growth factor for Scientia, after one year the population of Scientia will be xS. So, after one year, the population of Logicia will be $1.1M + xS$. But, since Logicia's population decreases by 10% each year, the population after one year will be $0.9(M + S)$. So we will have $1.1M + xS = 0.9(M + S)$. But $M = S$, so we have $1.1M + xM = 0.9(2M)$. Then $(1.1 + x)M = 1.8M$ and $1.1 + x = 1.8$. So $x = 0.7$, and the growth factor for Scientia is 0.7. This means that the population of Scientia is decreasing at a rate of 30% per year.

Lesson 9-4 Fitting Exponential Models to Data

BIG IDEA When a set of data points in a situation seems to be showing exponential growth or decay, exponential regression can fit an exponential function to the data points.

After a person takes medicine, the amount of drug left in the person's body decreases over time. When testing a new drug, a pharmaceutical company develops a mathematical model to quantify this relationship. To find such a model, suppose a dose of 1000 mg of a certain drug is absorbed by a person's bloodstream. Blood samples are taken every five hours, and the amount of drug remaining in the body is calculated.

Possible data from an experiment are shown in the table and scatterplot below. The scatterplot suggests that an exponential model might be appropriate. Exponential models can be fit to data using methods similar to those that you used to find linear and quadratic models in earlier chapters.

Drug Absorption Data

Hours Since Drug was Administered	Amount of Drug in Body (mg)
0	1000
5	550
10	316
15	180
20	85
25	56
30	31

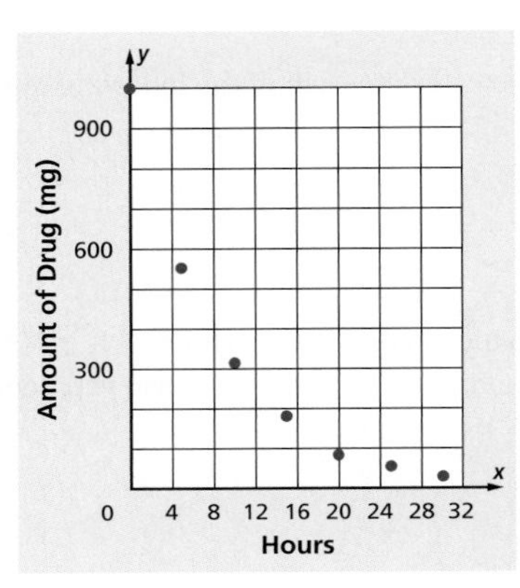

Mental Math

Alberto is putting his books onto a new bookshelf. Each hardcover book is about 2 inches wide and each paperback book is about 1.5 inches wide. Is one 24-inch shelf enough space for his

a. 8 paperback and 4 hardcover mystery novels? yes

b. 3 paperback and 10 hardcover biographies? no

c. 12 paperback and 2 hardcover science fiction books? yes

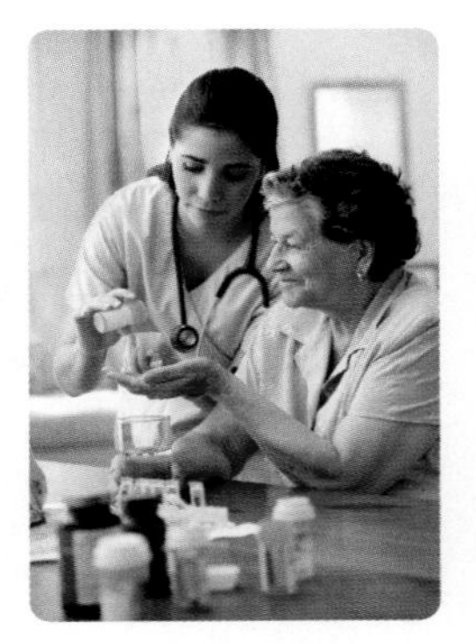

Finding Exponential Models for Data Believed to Be Exponential

As you know, exponential functions have the form $y = ab^x$, where a is the value of y when $x = 0$ and b is the growth factor during each unit period of time.

Background

As we did with the fitting of a linear equation to data, we begin with a situation that fits an exponential model. Students have learned that compound interest fits an exponential model, as do certain growth and decay situations. So do other phenomena, such as the successive heights of a bouncing ball, that lead to geometric sequences.

Example 1 If the initial value is known, then we have the y-intercept of $y = ab^x$, which is the value of a. The value of b can be found by substituting any other known pair (x, y) into the model. This is the process used in the solution to Example 1.

Activity To obtain an exponential equation such as that given on page 603, our calculator uses a program that takes the logarithms of the given y-values, finds the line of best fit to the logarithms of those values, and then translates that line

Example 1

Find an exponential model to fit the drug absorption data using the initial condition and one other point in the table.

Solution You need to find a and b in the equation $y = ab^x$. The initial condition occurs when $x = 0$, so $1000 = ab^0$.
Since $b^0 = 1$, $a = 1000$. So the equation is of the form $y = 1000b^x$.
Choose another point from the table and substitute. We chose (20, 85).

$85 = 1000b^{20}$	Substitute.
$0.085 = b^{20}$	Divide each side by 1000.
$0.884 \approx b$	Take the 20th root of each side (or raise each side to the $\frac{1}{20}$ power).

So, one model for the data is $y = 1000 \cdot (0.884)^x$.

Check Graph this model on a graphing utility. It looks like an exponential decay function with y-intercept 1000, as you would expect from the data.

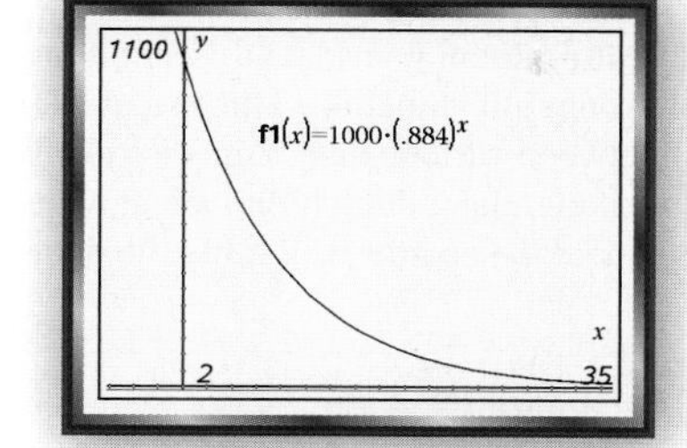

You can also use your graphing utility to find an exponential regression model.

Activity

Step 1 Enter the drug absorption data into your calculator. Apply the exponential regression option to find a and b and then write an equation to model these data.

Step 2 Your calculator probably gives a and b to many digits. The accuracy of the experimental data suggests that a more sensible model rounds a and b to three digits each. Rewrite your equation after rounding.

Step 3 Use your regression model from Step 2 and the two-point model $y = 1000 \cdot (0.884)^x$ from Example 1 to estimate the amount of drug left in a body after 5 hours. Which model better fits the actual 550 mg value from the experiment?

Step 4 Compare the accuracy of the two models by making a table of values for each equation and comparing these values to the actual data. Which model appears to be more accurate overall?
See margin.

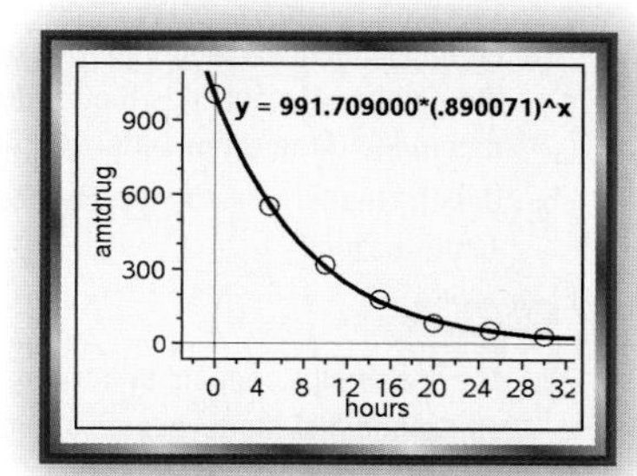

Step 1: $y = 991.709 \cdot (0.890071)^x$

Step 2: $y = 992 \cdot (0.890)^x$

Step 3: The model from Step 2 yields 553.939; the one from Example 1 yields 539.835. Therefore, the Step 2 model fits better.

2 Teaching

Additional Example

Example 1 The table below gives the percent of sunlight present at various depths in a part of an ocean. Find an exponential model to fit the data using the initial condition and one other point in the table.

Depth (meters)	Percentage of Sunlight
0	100
10	10.7
20	1.15
30	0.12
40	0.01
50	0.001

Using (10, 10.7), the model is $y = 100 \cdot (0.80)^x$.

Additional Answers

Activity

Step 4.

Hours Since Administration	Amount of Drug in Body	Example 1	Activity Step 2
0	1000	1000	991.7
5	550	539.8	554.0
10	316	291.4	309.5
15	180	157.3	172.9
20	85	84.93	96.6
25	56	45.85	54.0
30	31	24.75	30.1

The model from Step 2 appears more accurate overall, especially as the number of hours since the drug was taken increases.

back into an exponential equation. That is, it used the points (0, log 1000 = 3), (5, log 550), and so on, to find the linear equation $y \approx -0.050575x + 2.99638$, which it translated back into the exponential equation $y = 991.709000 \cdot (0.890071)^x$.

Accommodating the Learner

Some students may be surprised that the equation for the data in Example 1 is not the same as the equation found in the Activity. Refer these students to the graph of the data on page 602 and stress that all the data points do not exactly fit on the same exponential curve. Point out that each equation fits the data, but neither fits it *exactly.*

Notes on the Lesson

Example 2 This example of decay may surprise students even though it is not uncommon. The exponential model agrees closely with the real-life pattern that box office receipts will diminish slowly after a while and become very close to zero. The basic property is that the ratio of a week's receipts to the previous week's receipts is constant. Similar models of decay are used in situations of memory and the size of a wound that is healing.

Additional Example

Example 2 The amount of a decaying substance that remains after d days is shown in the table below.

Days (d)	Amount (grams)
1	800
2	650
3	512
4	410
5	327
6	260
7	209
8	187
9	134
10	107

a. Fit an exponential model to the data and determine if the exponential model is appropriate. A scatterplot of these data appears to have an exponential shape, so an exponential model seems appropriate.

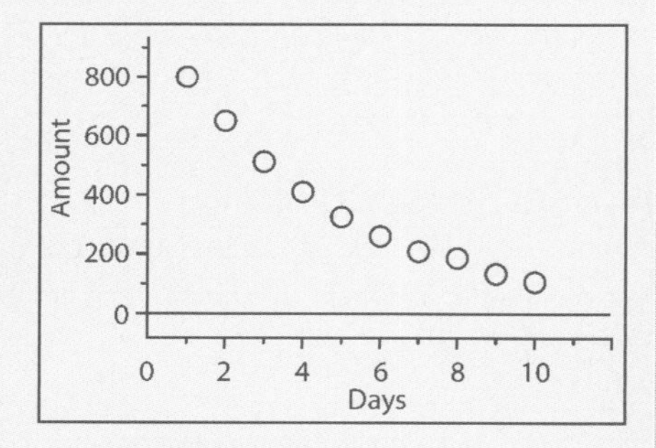

Exponential regression yields $y = 998 \cdot 0.80^x$. The graph of this equation closely follows the data points, so it appears to be a good model.

b. Use the model to estimate the amount of the substance remaining after 20 days. ≈ 11.51 g

Recall that, by design, regression is intended to fit a model as close as possible to ***all*** the data in a set. The Activity shows that a regression model is indeed a better fit to the drug absorption data than a model based on only two points.

Deciding Whether an Exponential Model Is Appropriate

For some data you may not be sure that an exponential model is appropriate. In that case, consider two things. First, look at a scatterplot of your data to see if it has the general shape of an exponential function. This is a quick way to check if the growth factor between various data points is relatively constant. Second, find an exponential model, then look at a table of values or the graph of your model to see how well it fits the data.

Example 2

Below are the U.S. box office gross for the first eleven weekends of the release of the movie *Mission Impossible III* in 2006.

Weekend	1	2	3	4	5	6	7	8	9	10	11
U.S. Box Office Gross (millions of dollars)	47.70	25.00	11.35	7.00	4.68	3.02	1.34	0.72	0.49	0.31	0.20

a. Fit an exponential model for box office gross based on the number of weekends the movie has been out and determine if the exponential model is appropriate.

b. Use the model to estimate the movie's gross in its 12th weekend.

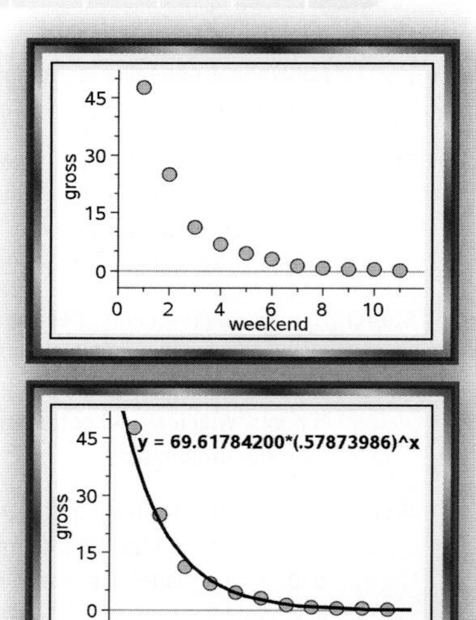

Solution

a. The scatterplot appears to have an exponential shape so an exponential model seems appropriate. Perform exponential regression to obtain

$$y = 69.617842 \cdot (0.57873986)^x.$$

Round a and b based on the actual data's accuracy.

$$y = 69.6 \cdot 0.579^x$$

When it is added to the scatterplot, the graph of the model closely follows the pattern of the data points. It appears to be a good model.

Exponential decay models the data closely, but could a parabola fit the data better?

Accommodating the Learner

If you have not covered Additional Example 1 with students, do so at this time. Then have them use their calculators to find an exponential regression model and compare it with the model found in the example. $y = 107.9(0.794)^x$; Answers vary. Sample: The two models are similar, but the one found by exponential regression seems to be more accurate.

Graph the data together with the graph of a quadratic regression equation.

Exponential decay is a better fit. This makes sense because you know that movie gross earnings typically continues to decrease each successive week after release. Gross earnings do not reach a minimum and then continue to climb indefinitely, so a quadratic model is illogical.

y = .84827506*x^2+-13.676937

b. Substitute $x = 12$ in for x in the model.

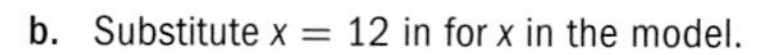

$y = 69.6 \cdot 0.579^{12}$

$y \approx 0.099$

According to this model, the movie grossed about $99,000 in its 12th week.

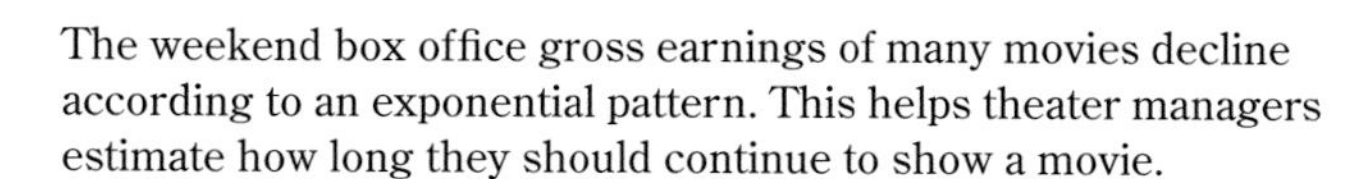

The weekend box office gross earnings of many movies decline according to an exponential pattern. This helps theater managers estimate how long they should continue to show a movie.

Questions

COVERING THE IDEAS

In 1 and 2, refer to the drug absorption data given at the beginning of the lesson.

1. a. Use the point (10, 316) and the method of Example 1 to find an equation to model the data. $y = 1000 \cdot (0.891)^x$
   b. Use your equation from Part a to predict when there will be less than 10 mg of the drug left in the patient's body.
2. Use the model developed in the Activity to predict when the amount of the drug in the patient's body will fall below 10 mg.
3. Can you use the method of Example 1 to find an equation to model the data in Example 2? Why or why not?
4. **Multiple Choice** Which scatterplot(s) below show(s) data that could be reasonably represented by an exponential model? A and C

A

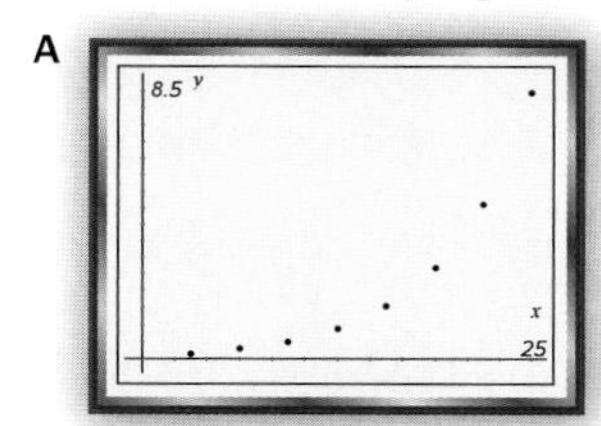

B

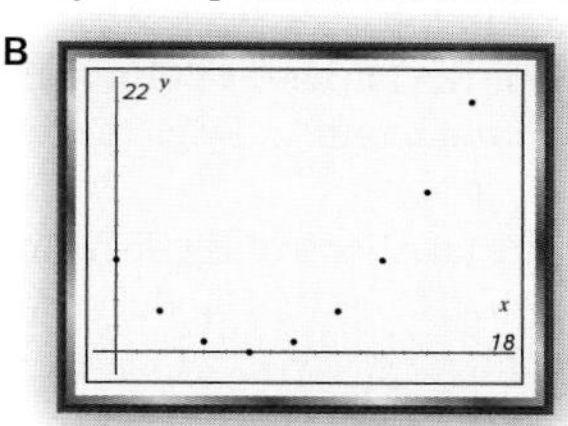

C

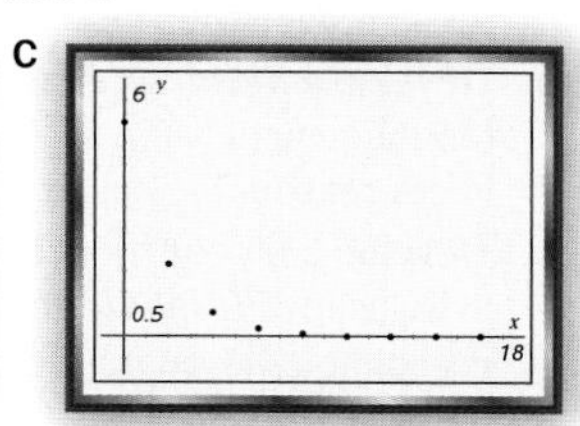

1b. after approximately 39.9 hr

2. after approximately 39.4 hr

3. No; the initial condition is not given.

9-4

3 Assignment

Recommended Assignment

- Questions 1–16
- Question 17 (extra credit)
- Reading Lesson 9-5
- Covering the Ideas 9-5

Notes on the Questions

Questions 1 and 2 The equations are close but not identical. Emphasize that, when using the method of Example 1, the points used should be chosen carefully.

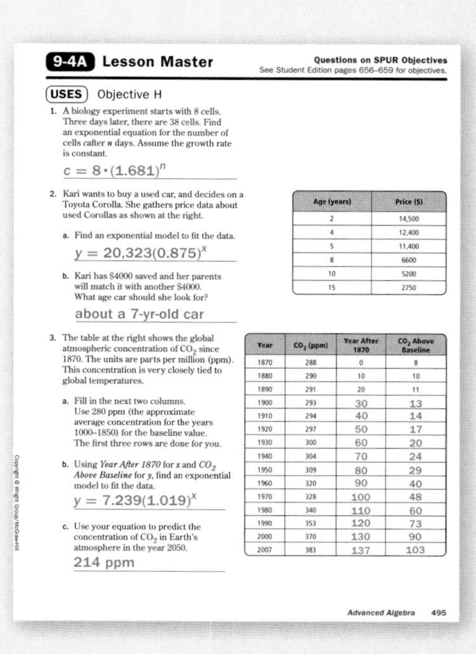

9-4A Lesson Master

Questions on SPUR Objectives
See Student Edition pages 656–659 for objectives.

USES Objective H

1. A biology experiment starts with 8 cells. Three days later, there are 38 cells. Find an exponential equation for the number of cells c after n days. Assume the growth rate is constant.
   $c = 8 \cdot (1.681)^n$
2. Kari wants to buy a used car, and decides on a Toyota Corolla. She gathers price data about used Corollas as shown at the right.

Age (years)	Price ($)
2	14,500
4	12,400
5	11,400
8	6600
10	5200
15	2750

   a. Find an exponential model to fit the data.
   $y = 20{,}323(0.875)^x$
   b. Kari has $4000 saved and her parents will match it with another $4000. What age car should she look for?
   about a 7-yr-old car
3. The table at the right shows the global atmospheric concentration of CO_2 since 1870. The units are parts per million (ppm). This concentration is very closely tied to global temperatures.

Year	CO_2 (ppm)	Year After 1870	CO_2 Above Baseline
1870	288	0	8
1880	290	10	10
1890	291	20	11
1900	293	30	13
1910	294	40	14
1920	297	50	17
1930	300	60	20
1940	304	70	24
1950	309	80	29
1960	320	90	40
1970	328	100	48
1980	340	110	60
1990	353	120	73
2000	370	130	90
2007	383	137	103

   a. Fill in the next two columns. Use 280 ppm (the approximate average concentration for the years 1000–1850) for the baseline value. The first three rows are done for you.
   b. Using *Year After 1870* for x and CO_2 *Above Baseline* for y, find an exponential model to fit the data.
   $y = 7.239(1.019)^x$
   c. Use your equation to predict the concentration of CO_2 in Earth's atmosphere in the year 2050.
   214 ppm

Advanced Algebra 495

Notes on the Questions

Question 8 This question can take time to cover because it forces discussion of all sorts of mathematical approaches to a subject.

Additional Answers

7c. Tyler is correct because approximately half of the coins land heads on every drop.

8a. $y = 479 \cdot 1.0637^x$; the model seems reasonable

8b. $y = 0.945x^2 + 32.2x + 471$; the model seems reasonable

8c. $y = 44.5x + 442$; the model seems reasonable

8d. Answers vary. Sample: For May 2008, the exponential model predicts 5,324,500, the quadratic model predicts 3,164,000, and the linear model predicts 2,216,000. The actual count is around 2,391,000. The linear model gives the best fit.

5. Recall the chart of cell phone subscriptions from the opening of this chapter. The table at the right presents the data for seven years.
   a. Find an exponential model for the growth of cell phone subscriptions. Answers vary. Sample: $y = 126.8 \cdot (1.127)^x$, where x is the number of years after 2001.
   b. Compare cell phone growth and population growth. The population of the United States was 301.1 million in 2007 and growing exponentially at 0.89% per year. In which year does your model first predict that there will be at least one cell phone subscription per person? 2009

Year	Subscribers (millions)
2001	128.4
2002	140.8
2003	158.7
2004	182.1
2005	207.9
2006	233.0
2007	255.4

APPLYING THE MATHEMATICS

6. The gross earnings for the first three weekends of a popular movie are given in the table at the right. 6a. $y \approx 256.2 \cdot (0.509)^x$
   a. Find an exponential model for the decline in weekend gross.
   b. Studio executives want to pull the movie from theaters before its weekend gross drops below $1 million. How many weekends should the studio expect to keep the movie in theaters? 8 weekends

Weekend	Gross earnings (millions of dollars)
1	135
2	62
3	35

7. Deven dropped 3728 pennies on the floor. He picked up all the coins showing heads and set them aside. Then he counted the tails, put them in a container, mixed them up, and dropped them. He repeated this several times and made a table of the results as shown at the right. Unfortunately, he forgot to record a couple of entries.
   a. Create an exponential model of the data using the 5 completed row entries. $y = 3887 \cdot (0.4934)^x$
   b. Use the model to estimate in the missing data. (2, 946), (6, 56)
   c. Deven's brother Tyler said the model looked like a half-life model for radioactive elements. Explain whether Tyler is correct. See margin.

Drop Number	Number of Tails
1	1891
2	?
3	470
4	229
5	118
6	?
7	27

8. The table at the right contains the cumulative monthly English-language article total for the website *Wikipedia*. The timetable ranges from March, 2005 to February, 2006. See margin.
   a. Develop an ***exponential*** model for the number y of English-language articles in *Wikipedia* in month x. Does this model seem reasonable based on the graph?
   b. Develop a ***quadratic*** model for the number y of English-language articles in *Wikipedia* in month x. Does this model seem reasonable based on the graph?
   c. Develop a ***linear*** model for the number y of English-language articles in *Wikipedia* in month x. Does this model seem reasonable based on the graph?
   d. Use each model to predict how many articles will be on *Wikipedia* in the current year. Check your results on the Internet to determine the most accurate model.

Month	Articles (thousands)
1	507
2	539
3	573
4	609
5	655
6	703
7	744
8	791
9	836
10	886
11	942
12	992

REVIEW

9. a. Graph $y = e^{5x}$ for $-2 < x < 2$. Label the coordinates of three points. See margin.
   b. State the domain and range of this function. (Lesson 9-3)

9b. domain: all real numbers; range: all positive real numbers

10. Rumors and fads spread through a population in a process known as *social diffusion*. Social diffusion can be modeled by $N = Ce^{kt}$, where N is the number of people who have heard the rumor after t days. Suppose four friends start a rumor and two weeks later 136,150 people have heard the rumor. (Lesson 9-3)
    a. In this situation, what is the value of C? 4
    b. What is the value of k? about 0.745
    c. Graph the growth of the rumor during the first two weeks. See margin.
    d. How many people heard the rumor after 10 days? about 6879
    e. How long will it take for one million people to have heard the rumor? about 16.7 days

11. Anne put \$4800 in an account with a 3.125% annual interest rate. What will be her balance if she leaves the money untouched for four years compounded
    a. annually? \$5428.71   b. daily? \$5439.08
    c. continuously? (Lessons 9-3, 7-4) \$5439.11

12. Consider the sequence defined by $\begin{cases} h_1 = 8.375 \\ h_n = 0.8h_{n-1}, \text{ for integers } n \geq 2 \end{cases}$. (Lessons 9-2, 9-1, 7-5, 3-1)
    a. List the first five terms of this sequence. 8.375, 6.7, 5.36, 4.288, 3.4304
    b. Which phrase best describes this sequence: *exponential growth, exponential decay, constant increase,* or *constant decrease*? exponential decay

In 13 and 14, simplify without using a calculator. (Lessons 7-8, 7-7, 7-3)

13. $\left(\frac{1}{2}\right)^{-4}$ 16   14. $32^{\frac{6}{5}}$ 64

15. Simplify $(x + y)^2 - (x - y)^2$. (Lesson 6-1) $4xy$

16. Suppose t varies inversely with r, and $t = 24$ when $r = 24$. Find t when $r = 6$. (Lesson 2-2) $t = 96$

EXPLORATION

17. Find weekend box office gross data for a movie that has only been out three or four weeks. Develop a model for its decline in gross and predict the gross for future weekends. Track your predictions to see how accurate your model is. (You may want to update your model as new data comes in.) What factors may cause a movie's weekend gross to not follow an exponential model? See margin.

4 Wrap-Up

Ongoing Assessment

Have students write a paragraph explaining two methods for determining an equation for the drug-absorption data, which are known to be exponential. Students should demonstrate an understanding of how to fit an exponential model to data using exponential regression and using an initial condition and one other data point.

Administer Quiz 1 (or a quiz your own) after students complete this lesson.

Project Update

Project 3, *Car Values,* on page 650 and Project 5, *Predicting Cooling Times,* on page 651 relate to the content of this lesson.

Additional Answers

9a. (–1, 0.0067), (0, 1), (0.25, 3.49)

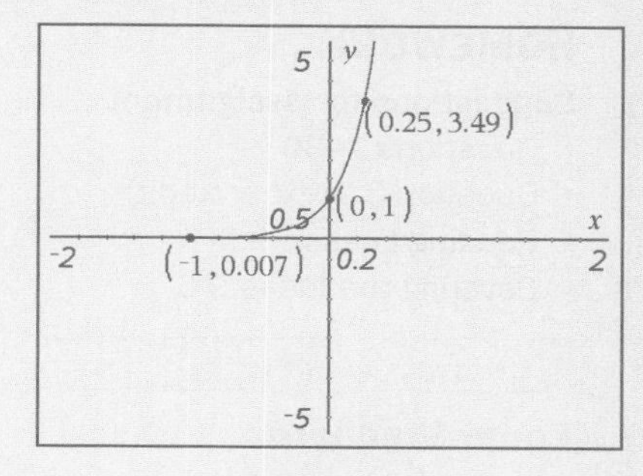

Additional Answers

10c.

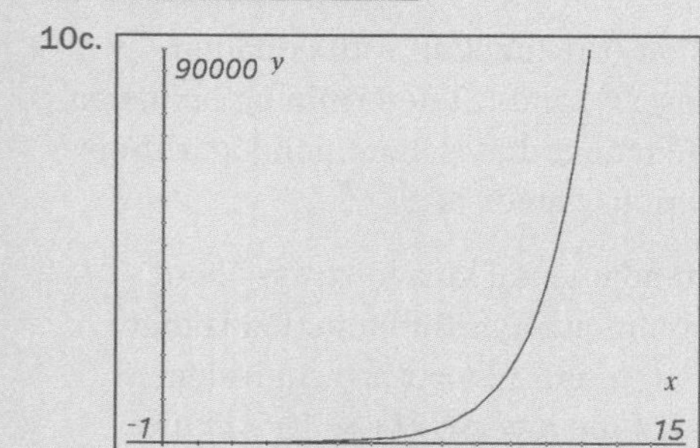

17. Answers may vary. Sample: The gross for one Hollywood movie over the past 3 weeks was \$98,618,668, \$51,190,629, \$31,838,996. An equation that models this decay is $y = 168{,}411{,}000 \cdot 0.568^x$. One factor that may cause a movie not to follow an exponential model is publicity. A movie may gain popularity as it is playing in theaters, thus increasing attendance for a while.

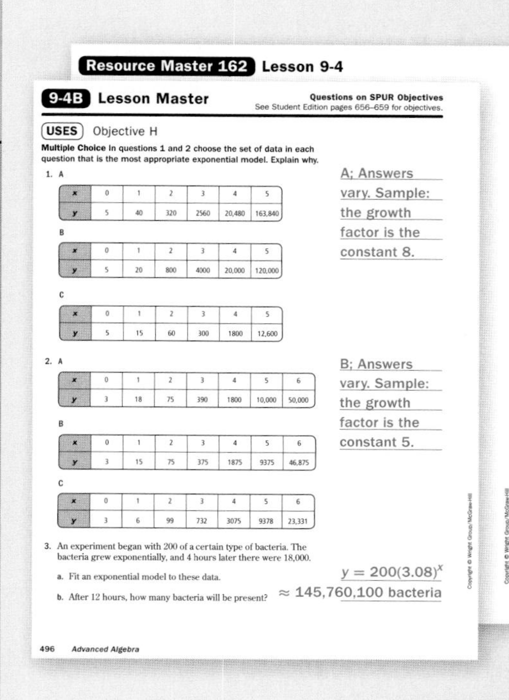

Resource Master 162 Lesson 9-4

9-4B Lesson Master

Questions on SPUR Objectives
See Student Edition pages 656–659 for objectives.

USES Objective H

Multiple Choice In questions 1 and 2 choose the set of data in each question that is the most appropriate exponential model. Explain why.

1. A

x	0	1	2	3	4	5
y	5	40	320	2560	20,480	163,840

B

x	0	1	2	3	4	5
y	5	20	800	4000	20,000	120,000

C

x	0	1	2	3	4	5
y	5	15	60	300	1800	12,600

A; Answers vary. Sample: the growth factor is the constant 8.

2. A

x	0	1	2	3	4	5	6
y	3	18	75	390	1800	10,000	50,000

B

x	0	1	2	3	4	5	6
y	3	15	75	375	1875	9375	46,875

C

x	0	1	2	3	4	5	6
y	3	6	99	732	3075	9378	23,331

B; Answers vary. Sample: the growth factor is the constant 5.

3. An experiment began with 200 of a certain type of bacteria. The bacteria grew exponentially, and 4 hours later there were 18,000.
   a. Fit an exponential model to these data. $y = 200(3.08)^x$
   b. After 12 hours, how many bacteria will be present? ≈ 145,760,100 bacteria

496 Advanced Algebra

Lesson 9-5

GOAL

Obtain common logarithms for numbers with and without calculators.

SPUR Objectives

A Determine values of logarithms.

C Solve logarithmic equations.

E Recognize properties of logarithmic functions.

K Graph logarithmic curves.

Materials/Resources

- Lesson Masters 9-5A and 9-5B
- Resource Masters 163–165
- Graph paper

HOMEWORK

Suggestions for Assignment

- Questions 1–30
- Question 31 (extra credit)
- Reading Lesson 9-6
- Covering the Ideas 9-6

Local Standards

1 Warm-Up

In 1–6, write each power of 10 as a decimal or in radical form.

1. 10^8 100,000,000
2. $10^{0.5}$ $\sqrt{10}$
3. $10^{-0.5}$ $\frac{1}{\sqrt{10}}$ or $\frac{\sqrt{10}}{10}$
4. 10^0 1
5. $10^{5.13}$ $100{,}000 \cdot \sqrt[100]{10^{13}}$
6. 10^{-3} 0.001

(*Note:* Each of these gives a point on the graph of the common logarithm function. For example, the 0.5 power gives the point $(\sqrt{10}, 0.5)$).

Lesson 9-5 Common Logarithms

Vocabulary

logarithm of x to the base 10, log of x to the base 10, log base 10 of x

common logarithm, common log

logarithm function to the base 10, common logarithm function

▸ **BIG IDEA** When a number is written as a power of 10, the exponent in the expression is the logarithm of the number to the base 10.

Whenever there is a situation described by an equation of the form $y = b^x$, you may know the values of y and b, and want to find x. For instance, people may want to know when a population will reach a certain level, or people may want to know the age of an ancient Egyptian mummy. Recall that an equation for the inverse of a function can be found by switching x and y. So, $x = b^y$ is an equation for the inverse of the exponential function. You can use this equation and what you know about exponential functions to solve exponential equations.

Mental Math

Find the exact geometric mean of the arithmetic mean, median, and mode of the data set {1, 1, 2, 3, 5}. $\sqrt[3]{4.8}$

Logarithms to the Base 10

Consider the equation $x = b^y$ when $b = 10$. Then $x = 10^y$, and we say that y is the *logarithm of x to the base 10*.

Definition of Logarithm of x to the Base 10

y is the **logarithm of x to the base 10**, or the **log of x to the base 10**, or the **log base 10 of x**, written $y = \log_{10} x$, if and only if $10^y = x$.

For example, $2 = \log_{10} 100$, because $10^2 = 100$. In the table below are some other powers of 10 and the related logs to the base 10.

Exponential Form	Logarithmic Form
$10^7 = 10{,}000{,}000$	$\log_{10} 10{,}000{,}000 = 7$
$10^{-3} = 0.001$	$\log_{10} 0.001 = -3$
$10^{\frac{1}{2}} = \sqrt{10}$	$\log_{10} \sqrt{10} = \frac{1}{2}$
$10^{-\frac{1}{4}} = \frac{1}{\sqrt[4]{10}}$	$\log_{10} \frac{1}{\sqrt[4]{10}} = -\frac{1}{4}$
$10^a = b$	$\log_{10} b = a$

▸ **READING MATH**

The word *logarithm* is derived from the Greek words *logos*, meaning "reckoning," and *arithmos*, meaning "number," which is also the root of the word *arithmetic*. A *logarithm* is literally a "reckoning number." Logarithms were used for hundreds of years for calculating (or "reckoning") before electronic calculators and computers were invented.

Background

Common logarithms are introduced before a general definition of logarithm is given because students have more experience with powers of 10 than with powers of other numbers. The logarithmic scales of Lesson 9-6 demonstrate that logs to the base 10 are often used. This is one reason why most scientific calculators have a key for common logs but not for logs to other integer bases.

There are two basic ideas in this lesson: (1) graphing the common logarithm function (the function with equation $y = \log_{10} x$); and (2) determining points on that function, that is, common logarithms for various values of x.

The fundamental idea to stress about the common logarithm function is that $y = \log_{10} x$ and $10^y = x$ are equivalent forms of the inverse of $y = 10^x$. Thus, every point on the graph of $y = 10^x$ yields a corresponding number and its logarithm—the coordinates of a point on the graph of $y = \log_{10} x$.

Logarithms are exponents. The logarithm of x is the exponent to which the base is raised to get x. Logarithms to the base 10 are called **common logarithms**, or **common logs**. We often write common logs without indicating the base. That is, $\log x$ means $\log_{10} x$.

Evaluating Common Logarithms

Common logarithms of powers of 10 can be found quickly without a calculator.

GUIDED

Example 1

Evaluate.

a. $\log 100$ b. $\log 0.00001$ c. $\log 1$

Solution First write each number as a power of ten. Then apply the definition of a common logarithm. Remember that the logarithm is the exponent.

a. Because $100 = 10^{\underline{?}}$, $\log_{10} 100 = \underline{?}$. 2; 2

b. You need to find n such that $10^n = 0.00001$.
Because $0.00001 = 10^{\underline{?}}$, $\log 0.00001 = \underline{?}$. -5; -5

c. $10^0 = 1$, so $\log \underline{?} = \underline{?}$. 1; 0

 QY1

> ▶ QY1
> a. What is $\log \sqrt{10}$?
> b. What is the common logarithm of 0.001?

You can use the logarithm function in your calculator to evaluate $\log_{10} x$ for any positive number x.

Example 2

Estimate to the nearest hundred-thousandth.

a. $\log \sqrt{2}$ b. $\log 5$

Solution Use your calculator. You will get a display like that at the right. Round to five decimal places.

a. $\log \sqrt{2} \approx 0.15051$

b. $\log 5 \approx 0.69897$

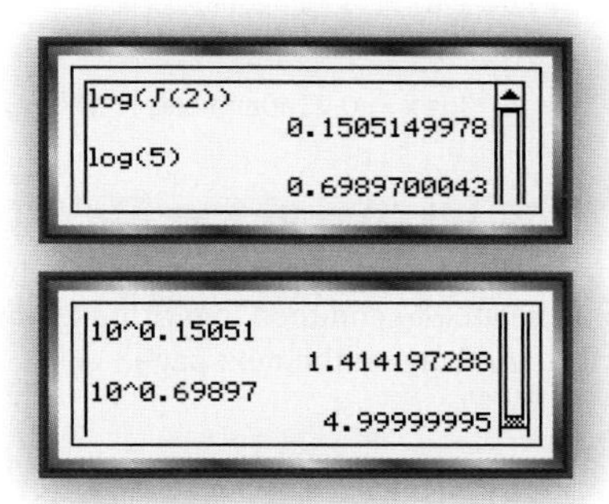

Check Use the definition of logarithm to the base 10: $\log x = y$ if and only if $10^y = x$.

a. Does $10^{0.15051} \approx \sqrt{2}$? Use the power key on your calculator. It checks.

b. Does $10^{0.69897} \approx 5$? Yes, it checks.

2 Teaching

Notes on the Lesson

Go through this lesson slowly and carefully with students. Make certain they complete the Activity so that they see the relationship between the exponential function with base 10 and the common logarithm function. As students work on Examples 1–4, make certain they check their answers.

Additional Examples

Example 1 Evaluate.

a. $\log 10{,}000$

b. $\log 0.001$

c. $\log 10$

Solution Write each number as a power of 10. Then apply the definition of a common logarithm. Remember that the logarithm is the exponent.

a. Because $10{,}000 = 10^{\underline{?}}$, $\log_{10} 10{,}000 = \underline{?}$. 4; 4

b. You need to find n such that $10^n = 0.001$. Because $0.001 = 10^{\underline{?}}$, $\log 0.001 = \underline{?}$. -3; -3

c. $10 = 10^1$, so $\log \underline{?} = \underline{?}$. 10; 1

Example 2 Use your calculator to estimate to the nearest hundred-thousandth.

a. $\log \sqrt{7} \approx 0.42255$

b. $\log 16 \approx 1.20412$

Note-Taking Tips

Have students add the definition of *logarithm of x to the base 10* to their journals, along with an example.

The reflection symmetry of the union of the two curves $y = 10^x$ and $y = \log_{10} x$ helps in determining the domain and range, intercepts, and asymptote of the common logarithm function.

Accommodating the Learner

If students have difficulty understanding that $y = \log_{10} x$ and $10^y = x$ are equivalent forms of the inverse of $y = 10^x$, have them graph $y = 10^x$, $y = \log_{10} x$, and $y = x$ on the same axes on a graphing utility. They will see that the graph of $y = 10^x$ is the reflection image of the graph of $y = \log_{10} x$ over the line $y = x$, and vice versa.

Notes on the Lesson

Point out that the graph of $y = \log_{10} x$ shows that the common logarithm function is an increasing function through its entire domain. This idea is used in Example 3.

Emphasize that the definition of common logarithm must be memorized because it will be used throughout the chapter. Point out how the definition is used in the solutions to Examples 1 and 4. It is worth spending a minute or two during each of the next few days having students read aloud statements such as $\log_{10} 1000 = 3$ ("the log of 1000 to the base 10 is 3").

Many students will not have mastered the content of this lesson by the time they finish the assigned questions. Have faith! There are many review questions in the following lessons and at the end of the chapter. Students will have many opportunities to practice these skills.

Additional Examples

Example 3 Between which two consecutive integers is log 75,981? 75,981 is between $10{,}000 = 10^4$ and $100{,}000 = 10^5$, so log 75,981 is between 4 and 5.

Example 4 Solve for x.

a. $\log x = \frac{3}{4}$ $x \approx 5.623$

b. $\log x = 1.5$ $x \approx 31.623$

STOP QY2

In general, the common logarithm of 10^x is x. That is, $\log_{10}(10^x) = x$. This is why we say a logarithm is an exponent.

The larger a number, the larger its common logarithm. Because of this, you can estimate the common logarithm of a number without a calculator. Either compare the number to integer powers of 10 or write the number in scientific notation to determine between which two consecutive integers the logarithm falls.

▸ QY2

Check your answers to Example 1 using your calculator.

Example 3

Between which two consecutive integers is log 5673?

Solution 1 5673 is between $1000 = 10^3$ and $10{,}000 = 10^4$, so log 5673 is between 3 and 4.

Solution 2 $5673 = 5.673 \cdot 10^3$. This indicates that log 5673 is between 3 and 4.

Check A calculator gives $\log 5673 \approx 3.753...$. It checks.

Solving Logarithmic Equations

You can solve logarithmic equations using the definition of common logarithms.

Example 4

Solve for x.

a. $\log x = \frac{1}{2}$ b. $\log x = 0.71$

Solution

a. $\log x = \frac{1}{2}$ if and only if $10^{\frac{1}{2}} = x$.
So, $x = 10^{\frac{1}{2}} = \sqrt{10} \approx 3.162$.

b. $\log x = 0.71$ if and only if $10^{0.71} = x$. So, $x = 10^{0.71} \approx 5.129$.

The Inverse of $y = 10^x$

The inverse of the exponential function f defined by $f(x) = 10^x$ is related to common logarithms. You will find the inverse in the Activity on the next page.

ENGLISH LEARNERS

Vocabulary Development

Review with students the definition of *logarithm of x to the base 10.* Explain that log is shorthand for logarithm. Then review the terms *base* and *exponent.* Be sure that students relate the definition to the equations $y = \log_{10} x$ and $10^y = x$. They can think of *base* as in *basement,* so the base in the first equation is a subscript, which is lower than the rest of the equation. The first equation is related to the second one in that 10 is the base raised to y power. In the second equation, y is always the exponent.

Stress that logs to the base 10 are called *common logarithms* or *common logs* and that they are often written without indicating the base, 10.

Activity

MATERIALS graph paper See margin.

Step 1 Fill in the y-values in the table when $y = 10^x$.

x	-2	-1	-0.75	-0.5	-0.25	0	0.25	0.5	0.75	1	2
y	?	?	?	?	?	?	?	?	?	?	?

Step 2 Plot the points $(x, 10^x)$ from the table on graph paper. Connect the points with a smooth curve.

Step 3 Plot the points of the inverse of the relation in the table on the same graph as in Step 2. Connect the points with a smooth curve.

Step 4 Graph both $y = 10^x$ and $y = \log x$ on the same set of axes in the window $-2 \le x \le 2$ and $-2 \le y \le 2$ on a graphing utility. Compare them to the graphs you made in Steps 2 and 3.

Your graphs from the Activity should look similar to the one at the right. The graph of $y = 10^x$ passes the horizontal-line test, and so its inverse is a function. This means that $y = \log x$ is an equation for a function, the inverse of the exponential function with equation $y = 10^x$.

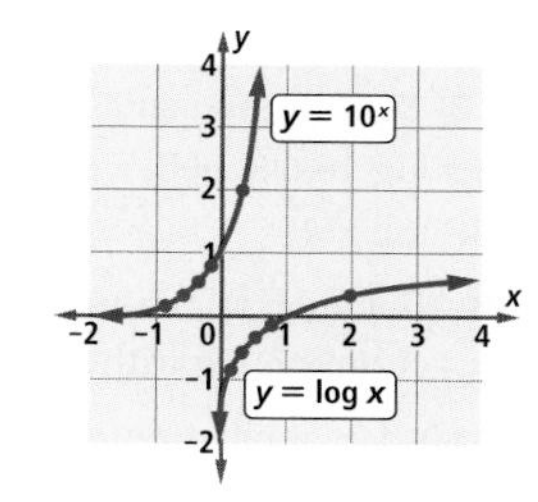

Properties of $y = 10^x$ and $y = \log x$

The inverse of the function f with equation $f(x) = 10^x$ can be described in several ways as shown in the table below.

Ways of Thinking of the Inverse of f with $f(x) = y = 10^x$	Written	Spoken
Switching x and y	$x = 10^y$	"x equals 10 to the yth power."
Using the language of logs	$y = \log_{10} x$ $y = \log x$	"y equals the log of x to the base 10."
Using function notation	$f^{-1}(x) = \log_{10} x$ $f^{-1}(x) = \log x$	"f inverse of x equals the log of x to the base 10."

The curve defined by these equations is called a *logarithmic curve*. As the graph from the Activity above shows, a logarithmic curve is the reflection image of an exponential curve over the line with equation $y = x$.

The function that maps x onto $\log_{10} x$ for all positive numbers x is called the **logarithm function to the base 10**, or the **common logarithm function**.

Additional Answers

Activity

Step 1.

x	$y = 10^x$
-2	0.01
-1	0.1
-0.75	0.178
-0.5	0.316
-0.25	0.562
0	1
0.25	1.778
0.5	3.162
0.75	5.623
1	10
2	100

Step 2.

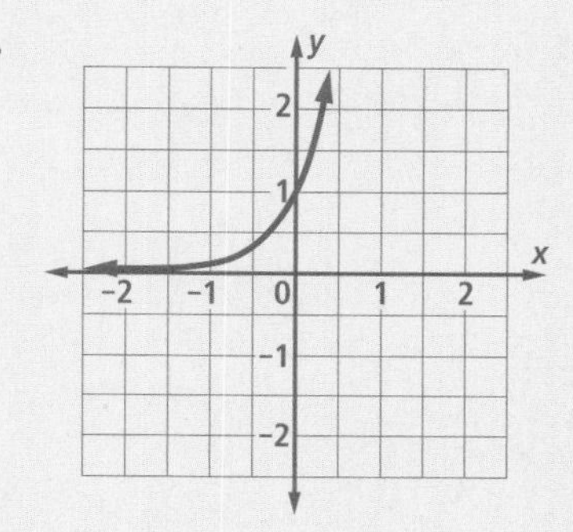

Additional Answers

Activity

Step 3.

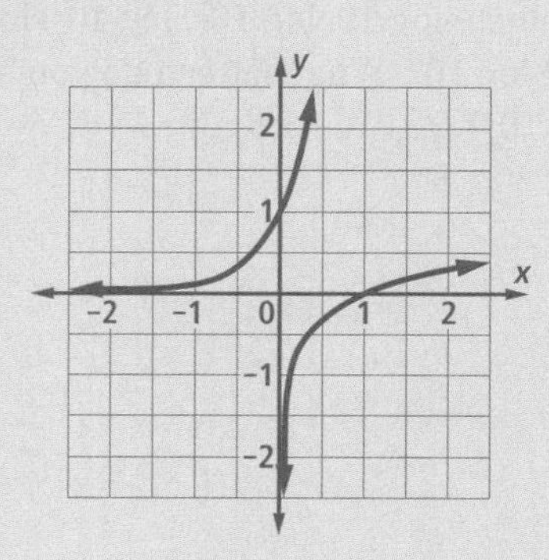

Step 4.

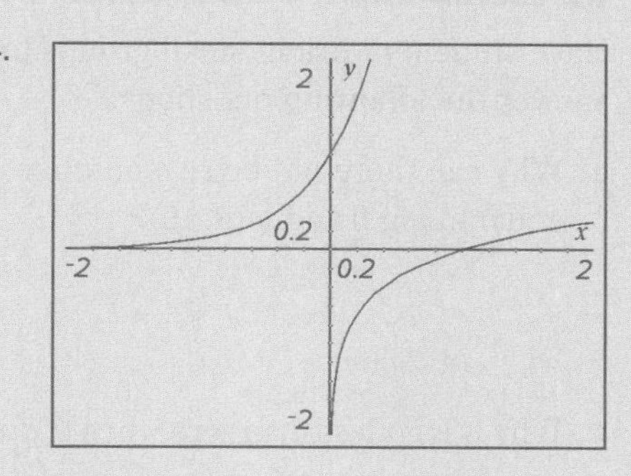

These graphs are the same as those from Steps 2 and 3.

3 Assignment

Recommended Assignment

- Questions 1–30
- Question 31 (extra credit)
- Reading Lesson 9-6
- Covering the Ideas 9-6

Notes on the Questions

Questions 3–8 Students need a way to say what a logarithm means in words. Lead them to say something similar to "the logarithm of x is the exponent of the power of 10 that has the value x."

9-5A Lesson Master

Questions on SPUR Objectives
See Student Edition pages 656–659 for objectives.

VOCABULARY

In 1 and 2, write the exponential equation as a logarithmic equation, or vice-versa.

1. a. $10^{-3} = \frac{1}{1000}$ $\log \frac{1}{1000} = -3$ b. $10^{0.078} \approx 1.197$ $\log(1.197) \approx 0.078$ c. $10^m = n$ $\log n = m$
2. a. $\log 1 = 0$ $10^0 = 1$ b. $\log 390 \approx 2.591$ $10^{2.591} \approx 390$ c. $\log c = t$ $10^t = c$

SKILLS Objective A

Fill in the Blanks In 3 and 4, a. determine in your head what consecutive integers the logarithm is between. b. Check by finding the logarithm to the nearest thousandth with a calculator.

3. a. log 4239 is between 3 and 4. b. $\log 4239 \approx$ 3.627.
4. a. log 0.023 is between -2 and -1. b. $\log 0.023 \approx$ -1.638.

SKILLS Objective C

In 5 and 6, write the equivalent exponential equation; use it to solve the logarithmic equation.

5. $\log n = 3$ $10^3 = n$; $n = 1000$
6. $\log a = -2.86$ $10^{-2.86} = a$; $a \approx 0.00138$
7. Solve $3 \log(2x) = 6$ for x. $x = 50$

PROPERTIES Objective E

8. If $f(x) = \log x$ for $x > 0$, then $f^{-1}(x) =$ 10^x.
9. Explain why $\log 10^n = n$ for all real numbers n. Answers vary. Sample: $f(x) = \log x$ and $g(x) = 10^x$ are inverse functions.

REPRESENTATIONS Objective K

In 13–15, consider the graphs of $f(x) = 10^x$ and $g(x) = \log x$.

10. Graph each function at the right. Label three points on the graph of f with their coordinates, and the corresponding points on the graph of g. Sample points are labeled.
11. Give the domain and range of each function. $f(x)$: Domain: set of all reals, Range: $\{y \mid y > 0\}$; $g(x)$: Domain: $\{x \mid x > 0\}$, Range: set of all reals.
12. Give the x- and y-intercepts of each function, if they exist. $f(x)$: no x-intercept, y-intercept = 1; $g(x)$: x-intercept = 1, no y-intercept

498 *Advanced Algebra*

Because they are inverses, each property of the exponential function defined by $y = 10^x$ corresponds to a property of its inverse, the common logarithm function defined by $y = \log x$.

Function	Domain	Range	Asymptote	Intercepts
$y = 10^x$	set of real numbers	set of positive real numbers	x-axis ($y = 0$)	y-intercept = 1
$y = \log x$	set of positive real numbers	set of real numbers	y-axis ($x = 0$)	x-intercept = 1

Questions

COVERING THE IDEAS

1. If $m = \log_{10} n$, what other relationship exists between m, 10, and n? $10^m = n$
2. a. Write in words how to read the expression $\log_{10} 8$. log base 10 of 8
   b. Evaluate $\log_{10} 8$ to the nearest ten-thousandth. 0.9031

In 3–8, evaluate using the definition of common logarithms.

3. log 10,000,000 7
4. $\log 10^5$ 5
5. log 0.0000001 -7
6. $\log \sqrt[3]{10}$ $\frac{1}{3}$
7. $\log \frac{1}{10}$ -1
8. log 10 1
9. Between which two consecutive integers is the value of the common logarithm of 100,000,421? 8 and 9

In 10–12, approximate to the nearest thousandth.

10. log 3 0.477
11. log 0.00309 -2.510
12. log 309,000 5.490

In 13 and 14, solve for x.

13. $\log x = 5$ $x = 100{,}000$
14. $\log x = 1.25$ $x \approx 17.783$
15. Consider the graph of $y = \log_{10} x$.
    a. Name its x- and y-intercepts, if they exist.
    b. Name three points on the graph.
    c. Name the three corresponding points on the graph of $y = 10^x$.
16. What are the domain and range of the common logarithm function?
17. **Fill in the Blank** The functions f and g, with equations $f(x) = 10^x$ and $g(x) =$ __?__, are inverses of each other. $\log_{10} x$

15a. x-intercept: 1; there is no y-intercept.

15b. Answers vary. Sample: (1, 0), (10, 1), (100, 2)

15c. Answers vary. Sample: (0, 1), (1, 10), (2, 100)

16. domain: all positive real numbers; range: all real numbers

Accommodating the Learner

Have students work in small groups to answer the following questions.

1. Why can there not be real numbers equal to log 0 and log(-10)? If $y = \log 0$, then $10^y = 0$, which is not possible. If $y = \log(-10)$, then $10^y = -10$, which is not possible.
2. Why is $\log x$ less than zero when $0 < x < 1$? If $y = \log x$, then $10^y = x$, and if $0 < x < 1$, then y must be a negative exponent. So, $y = \log x < 0$.
3. Evaluate log 10, $\log 10^2$, $\log 10^3$, $\log 10^4$, and $\log 10^5$. What pattern do you see for $\log 10^x$? 1, 2, 3, 4, 5; $\log 10^x = x$

APPLYING THE MATHEMATICS

18. If $5 \log v = 2$, what is the value of v? $10^{\frac{2}{5}} \approx 2.512$
19. If a number is between 10 and 100, its common logarithm is between which two consecutive integers? 1 and 2
20. The common logarithm of a number is -5. What is the number?
21. Evaluate $10^{\log 3.765}$. 3.765
22. Explain why for all positive numbers a, $10^{\log a} = a$.
23. If $f(x) = 10^x$ and $g(x) = \log_{10} x$, what is $f \circ g(x)$? Explain your answer.

20. $\frac{1}{100{,}000}$

22. $f(x) = 10^x$ and $g(x) = \log x$ are inverse functions, so the composition $f(g(a)) = 10^{\log a} = a$.

23. x; f and g are inverse functions.

In 24 and 25, use this information: Most of today's languages are thought to be descended from a few common ancestral languages. The longer the time lapse since a language split from the ancestral language, the fewer common words exist in the descendant language. Let c = the number of centuries since two languages split from an ancestral language. Let w = the fraction of words from the ancestral language that are common to the two descendent languages. In linguistics, the equation $\frac{10}{c} = \frac{2 \log r}{\log w}$ (in which $r = 0.86$ is the index of retention) has been used to relate c and w.

English and Spanish descended from the Indo-European language family. Chinese descended from the Sino-Tibetan family.

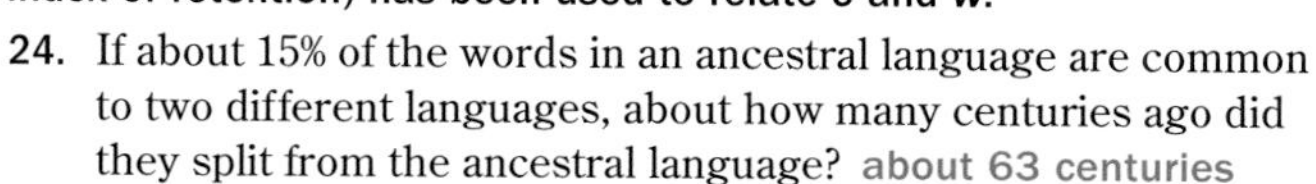

24. If about 15% of the words in an ancestral language are common to two different languages, about how many centuries ago did they split from the ancestral language? about 63 centuries
25. If it is known that two languages split from an ancestral language about 1500 years ago, about what percentage of the words in the ancestral language are common to the two languages? about 64%

REVIEW

26. Find an equation of the form $y = ab^x$ that passes through the points (0, 3) and (4, 48). **(Lesson 9-4)** $y = 3 \cdot 2^x$
27. A tool and die machine used in a metal working factory depreciates so that its value after t years is given by $N(t) = Ce^{-0.143t}$, where C is its initial value. If after 4 years the machine is worth \$921,650, what was its original value? **(Lesson 9-3)** \$1,632,986

Notes on the Questions

Questions 24 and 25 Latin is known to be the ancestral language of French, Spanish, Italian, Portuguese, and Romanian, all of which developed in the past 2000 years. But some ancestral languages are only theorized because no written evidence of them is known.

Extension

Ask students to explain why the answer to Question 12 is eight greater than the answer to Question 11. That is, why is log 0.00309 eight greater than log 309,000? If $10^x = 0.00309$, then $10^{x+8} = 10^x \cdot 10^8 = 0.00309 \cdot 10^8 = 309{,}000$ and x and $x + 8$ are the desired logarithms.

Notes on the Questions

Questions 29 and 30 These questions review some properties of powers that are used in Lesson 9-9.

Question 31 Although the research that produced this genetic sequence information took place at institutions around the world, all the information was collected and compiled at these three public repositories. The creators of these repositories sought to make every nucleotide sequence freely available to the scientific community, and this has advanced the research of molecular biologists world wide.

4 Wrap-Up

Ongoing Assessment

Have students list six powers of 10 and their corresponding whole-number or decimal values. Have them include at least two negative-integer exponents, as well as some decimal exponents. Then have them write a corresponding logarithmic equation for each statement. Students should correctly write powers of 10 and the logarithmic equations for each power.

Project Update

Project 4, *How Many Digits Are in That Number?*, on page 650 relates to the content of this lesson.

9-5B Lesson Master

Questions on SPUR Objectives
See Student Edition pages 656–659 for objectives.

VOCABULARY

1. a. Write the following sentence as an equation. y is the logarithm of x to the base 10. $y = \log x$ or $y = \log_{10} x$
   b. **Fill in the Blank** y is the common logarithm of x if and only if $10^y = x$.
2. Write the exponential equation as a logarithmic equation, or vice-versa.
   a. $\log 10 = 1$ $10^1 = 10$
   b. $10^{2.635} \approx 432$ $\log 432 \approx 2.635$
   c. $10^r = s$ $\log s = r$

SKILLS Objective A

In 3–5, evaluate in your head. You may check with a calculator.

3. a. $\log 10^{18} =$ 18 b. $\log 0.001 =$ −3 c. $\log \sqrt[6]{10} = \frac{1}{6}$
4. a. $\log 100 =$ 2 b. $\log 10^{-35} =$ −35 c. $\log \sqrt{100} =$ 1
5. a. $\log 10^{\frac{3}{2}} = \frac{3}{2}$ b. $\log 10{,}000 =$ 4 c. $\log \sqrt[4]{10^6} = \frac{3}{2}$

Fill in the Blanks In 6 and 7, a. Determine in your head what consecutive integers the logarithm is between. b. Check by finding the logarithm to the nearest thousandth with a calculator.

6. a. log 316 is between 2 and 3. b. $\log 316 \approx 2.500$.
7. a. log 0.000069 is between −5 and −4. b. $\log 0.000069 \approx -4.161$.

SKILLS Objective C

In 8–13, write the equivalent exponential equation; use it to solve the logarithmic equation. Round to 5 decimal places when appropriate.

8. $\log n = 0$ $n = 10^0$; $n = 1$
9. $\log a = -4$ $a = 10^{-4}$; $a = 0.0001$
10. $\log x = \frac{1}{3}$ $x = 10^{\frac{1}{3}}$; $x \approx 2.15443$
11. $\log w = 2.9$ $w = 10^{2.9}$; $w = 794.32823$
12. $\log p = -3.55$ $p = 10^{-3.55}$; $p \approx 0.00028$
13. $\log y = 4$ $y = 10^4$; $y = 10{,}000$
14. Solve $2 \log(x) = 6$ for x. $x = 1000$

Advanced Algebra 499

28. Refer to the graph at the right of the cubing function f defined by $f(x) = x^3$. (Lessons 8-3, 7-6, 7-1)

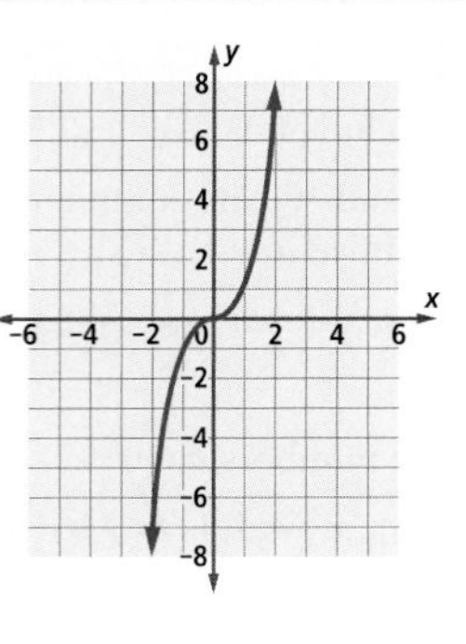

   a. What are the domain and range of this function?
   b. Graph the inverse. See margin.
   c. Is the inverse a function? Why or why not?
   d. What name is usually given to the inverse function? the cube root function

28a. domain: all real numbers, range: all real numbers

28c. Yes; the graph of f passes the horizontal-line test.

In 29 and 30, simplify without using a calculator. (Lessons 7-6, 7-3, 7-2)

29. $(13^3 \cdot 13^{-6})^2$ 13^{-6}

30. $\sqrt[5]{8^{15}}$ 512

EXPLORATION

31. In 2005, the three leading international public repositories for DNA and RNA sequence information reached over 100 gigabases (100,000,000,000 bases) of sequence. For perspective, the human genome is about 3 gigabases. The table below presents the approximate size of the international databases in each year from 2000-2005.

Year	2000	2001	2002	2003	2004	2005
Gigabases	11	18	37	53	81	104

   a. Write an equation to predict the number n of bases stored t years after 2000. Answers vary. Sample: $n \approx 12.2 \cdot (1.58)^t$
   b. What is the growth rate of sequence mapping? about 58%
   c. Use your equation in Part a to predict the year that the international databases will hold the amount of information equal to the information contained in the genomes of 1000 people. 2012

QY ANSWERS

1. a. $\frac{1}{2}$ b. −3

2.

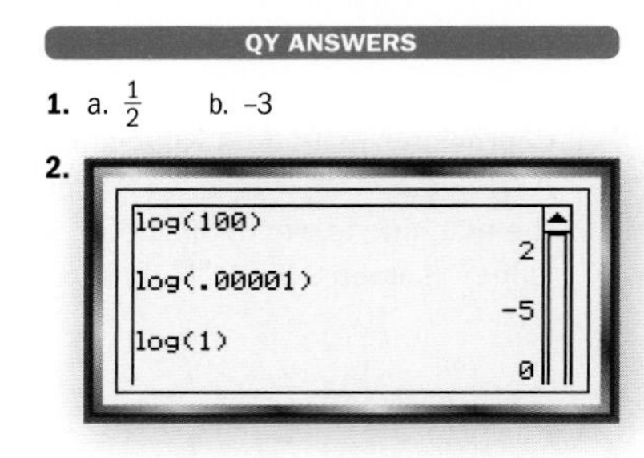

Additional Answers

28b.

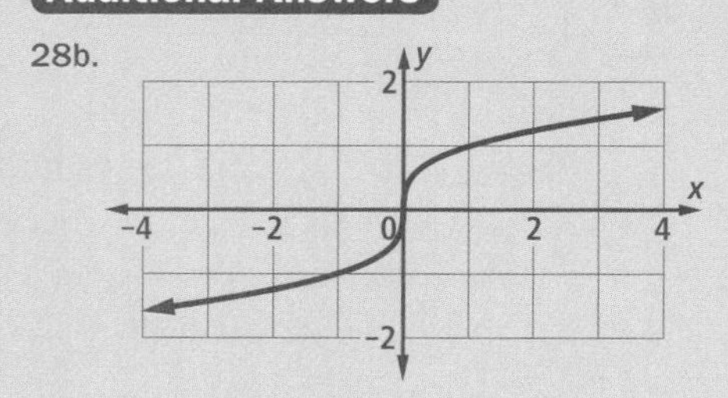

Lesson 9-6 Logarithmic Scales

Vocabulary

logarithmic scale

decibel, dB

▶ **BIG IDEA** A **logarithmic scale** is one in which the numbers are written as the powers of a fixed number, and the exponents of the powers are used as the scale values.

Logarithmic scales are used when all the measures of an attribute are positive and cover a wide range of values from small to very large. Two logarithmic scales you may have heard of are the *decibel scale* that measures relative sound intensity and the *Richter magnitude scale* that measures the intensity of earthquakes.

Mental Math

Simplify.

a. $\frac{10^6}{10^2}$ 10^4 or 10,000

b. $\frac{4.3 \cdot 10^4}{4.3 \cdot 10^{-7}}$ 10^{11}

c. $\frac{2.42 \cdot 10^{12}}{1.21 \cdot 10^3}$ $2 \cdot 10^9$

d. $\frac{a \cdot 10^m}{b \cdot 10^n}$ $\frac{a}{b} \cdot 10^{m-n}$

The Decibel Scale

The decibel scale is based on *watts*. The watt is a measure of power. The quietest sound that a human ear can pick up has an intensity of about 10^{-12} watts per square meter $\left(\frac{\text{w}}{\text{m}^2}\right)$. The human ear can also hear sounds with an intensity as large as $10^2 \frac{\text{w}}{\text{m}^2}$. Because the range from 10^{-12} to 10^2 is so large, it is convenient to use a measure that is based on the exponents of 10 in the intensity. This measure of relative sound intensity is the **decibel**, abbreviated **dB**. Because it is based on a ratio of units, the decibel is a dimensionless unit, like angle measure. A formula that relates the sound intensity N in $\frac{\text{w}}{\text{m}^2}$ to its relative intensity D in decibels is

$$D = 10 \log\left(\frac{N}{10^{-12}}\right).$$

The chart at the right gives the sound intensity in $\frac{\text{w}}{\text{m}^2}$ and the corresponding decibel values for some common sounds.

Notice that as the decibel values in the right column increase by 10, corresponding intensities in the left column are multiplied by 10. Thus, if the number of decibels increases by 20, the sound intensity multiplies by $10 \cdot 10$ or 10^2. If you increase the number of decibels by 40, you multiply the watts per square meter by $10 \cdot 10 \cdot 10 \cdot 10$, or 10^4.

Sound Intensity (watts/square meter)		Relative Intensity (decibels)
10^2		140
10^1	jack hammer	130
10^0	rock concert	120
10^{-1}	ambulance siren	110
10^{-2}	school dance	100
10^{-3}	electric drill	90
10^{-4}	lawn mower	80
10^{-5}	hair dryer	70
10^{-6}	normal conversation	60
10^{-7}	refrigerator	50
10^{-8}	library	40
10^{-9}		30
10^{-10}	whisper at 5 ft	20
10^{-11}	normal breathing	10
10^{-12}	barely audible	0

Background

A logarithmic scale is one in which equal differences between values on the scale (or equal distances, if the values are graphed) correspond to equal ratios of the quantities being scaled.

The logarithmic scales (decibel, pH, Richter) that are part of this and subsequent lessons are so common that familiarity with these uses of mathematics is an objective for this chapter. Students are generally quite interested in knowing about these scales. Despite what seems to be a great deal of reading, this is not a difficult lesson for most students.

Lesson 9-6

GOAL

Understand why logarithmic scales are used and learn how to read and interpret the decibel and Richter scales.

SPUR Objectives

C Solve logarithmic equations.

I Apply logarithmic scales, models, and formulas.

Materials/Resources

- Lesson Masters 9-6A and 9-6B
- Resource Masters 166–169

HOMEWORK

Suggestions for Assignment

- Questions 1–28
- Question 29 (extra credit)
- Reading Lesson 9-7
- Covering the Ideas 9-7

Local Standards

1 Warm-Up

In May 2008, a devastating earthquake hit the Sichuan province in China. It measured 7.9 on the Richter scale. Every increase of 0.1 on this scale corresponds to a growth factor of $10^{0.1}$ in intensity.

1. This earthquake was how many times as intense as the 1994 earthquake centered in Northridge, California, that measured 6.7 on the Richter scale? $10^{1.2}$, or about 15.85 times as intense
2. The earthquake that hit Anchorage, Alaska, in 1964 measured 8.5 on the Richter scale. This earthquake was how many times as intense as the Sichuan earthquake? $10^{0.6}$, or about 4 times as intense
3. In 1999, this Alaskan earthquake's intensity was revised to be 9.2 on the Richter scale. If this is an accurate measure, how many times more intense was it compared to the Sichuan earthquake? $10^{1.3}$, or about 20 times as intense

2 Teaching

Notes on the Lesson

You might begin by explaining why the decibel scale is called a logarithmic scale. Look at the decibel table on page 615. The numbers in the left column form an exponential (geometric) sequence. The numbers in the right column form a linear (arithmetic) sequence. Although the decibel values are not strictly the common logarithms of the sound intensities, they are a linear function of the logarithms of those sound intensities. Thus, decibels are very closely related to the logarithms of the sound intensities—by the formula $D = 10\log\left(\frac{N}{10^{-12}}\right)$—and we call the decibel scale a *logarithmic scale.* Questions 13–16 discuss a similar scale, the pH scale.

Additional Examples

Example 1 Music played at 125 decibels is how many times as intense as music played at 105 decibels?

100 times as intense

Example 2 Find the relative intensity in decibels of a muted conversation in which the sound intensity is $3.16 \cdot 10^{-8}$ watts per square meter.

45 dB

In general, an increase of n dB multiplies the sound intensity by $10^{\frac{n}{10}}$.

 QY

> **QY**
> How many times as intense is a sound of 90 decibels as a sound of 60 decibels?

Example 1

Due to a law in France, manufacturers had to limit the sound intensity of their MP3 players to 100 decibels. How many times as intense is a particular MP3 player's maximum 115-decibel intensity than the limited intensity imposed in France?

Solution Use the generalization above. An increase of n dB multiplies the sound intensity by $10^{\frac{n}{10}}$. The difference in the decibel level is $115 - 100 = 15$ dB. So, the maximum sound intensity is $10^{\frac{15}{10}} = 10^{1.5} \approx 32$ times as intense as the limit imposed in France.

A decibel is $\frac{1}{10}$ of a bel, a unit named after Alexander Graham Bell (1847–1922), the inventor of the telephone.

Experiments have shown that people perceive a sound that is 10 decibels louder than another sound as only twice as loud. That is, the ear perceives a sound of 80 decibels as only sixteen times as loud as one of 40 decibels, even though in fact the sound is 10^4 times as intense. Even if a person does not feel pain, long or repeated exposure to sounds at or above 85 decibels can cause permanent hearing loss.

Using the formula on the previous page, if you know the intensity of a sound, you can find its relative intensity in decibels.

Example 2

Grunting while hitting the ball has become a controversial issue in professional tennis. Some people are concerned that such loud sounds are unfair distractions to the opposing player. Serena Williams's grunts have been measured at a sound intensity of $6.31 \cdot 10^{-4}\ \frac{\text{w}}{\text{m}^2}$. Find the relative intensity of the sound in decibels.

Solution Substitute $6.31 \cdot 10^{-4}$ for N in the formula $D = 10\log\frac{N}{10^{-12}}$.

$D = 10\log\left(\frac{6.31 \cdot 10^{-4}}{10^{-12}}\right) = 10\log 631{,}000{,}000 \approx 88$

The relative intensity of the grunting is about 88 dB.

Check Refer to the chart on the previous page.
Notice that $10^{-4} < 6.31 \cdot 10^{-4} < 10^{-3}$, and the relative intensity of 88 dB falls between 80 and 90 dB. It checks.

To convert from the decibel scale to the $\frac{\text{w}}{\text{m}^2}$ scale, you can solve a logarithmic equation.

ENGLISH LEARNERS

Vocabulary Development

Review the meaning of *bel, decibel,* and the abbreviation *dB.* Have students note that the term *decibel* has the prefix deci-, meaning one-tenth, so a decibel is one-tenth of a bel.

Example 3

The maximum sound intensity of Melody's MP3 player is 115 dB. What is the maximum sound intensity in watts per square meter?

Solution 1

$115 = 10 \log\left(\frac{N}{10^{-12}}\right)$ Substitute 115 for D in the formula.

$11.5 = \log\left(\frac{N}{10^{-12}}\right)$ Divide each side by 10.

$10^{11.5} = \frac{N}{10^{-12}}$ Definition of common logarithm

$10^{11.5} \cdot 10^{-12} = N$ Multiply each side by 10^{-12}.

$10^{-0.5} = N$ Product of Powers Postulate

$10^{-0.5} \approx 0.316$. So, the maximum sound intensity of the MP3 player is about 0.316 $\frac{W}{m^2}$.

Check Solve on a CAS. It checks as shown on the calculator display at the right.

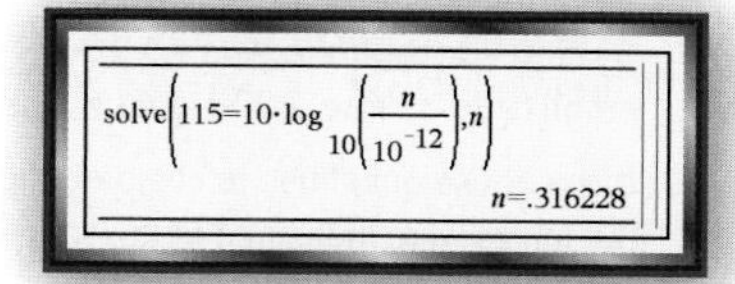

Earthquake Magnitude Scales

The most popular scale used by the media for describing the magnitudes of earthquakes is the Richter scale, designed by Charles Richter in 1935. Like the decibel scale, the Richter scale is a logarithmic scale. A value x on the Richter scale corresponds to a measured force, or amplitude, of $k \cdot 10^x$, where the constant k depends on the units being used to measure the quake. Consequently, each increase of 1 on the Richter scale corresponds to a factor of 10 change in the amplitude. The table below gives a brief description of the effects of earthquakes of different magnitudes.

Richter Magnitute	Possible Effects
1–2	Usually not felt except by instruments
3	May be felt but rarely causes damage
4	Like vibrations from heavy traffic
5	Strong enough to wake sleepers
6	Walls crack, chimneys fall
7	Ground cracks, houses collapse
8	Few buildings survive, landslides

When $k = 1$, the Richter magnitude is the common logarithm of the force, because x is the common logarithm of 10^x.

Notes on the Lesson

You may find it helpful to bring in a radio with a dial (a nondigital model). On the AM scale, compare the distance between 600 and 800 with the distance between 1200 and 1400. You will find that they are not equal. The radio scale is not linear. Note, however, that the distance between 600 and 800 and the distance between 1200 and 1600 *are* equal. The radio scale is an example of a logarithmic scale $\left(\frac{800}{600} = \frac{4}{3} = \frac{1600}{1200}\right)$.

Alternately, or in addition to a brief discussion of the radio scale, show a transparency of the decibel or pH scales. You might also consider showing that large slide rule that may be gathering dust in a storeroom.

Additional Example

Example 3 A very loud rock band plays at a relative intensity of 125 decibels. What is the sound intensity in watts per square meter? about 3.16 $\frac{W}{m^2}$

Additional Example

Example 4 On May 12, 2008, the Sichuan province in China was hit by an earthquake that registered 7.9 on the Richter scale. The deadly tsunami that struck 12 Indian Ocean nations in December 2004 was triggered by an earthquake that measured 9.3 on the Richter scale. The force of the 2004 quake was how many times the force of the 2008 quake?

Solution The amplitude of the 2008 quake was $k \cdot 10^{\underline{\ ?\ }}$. The amplitude of the 2004 quake was $k \cdot 10^{\underline{\ ?\ }}$. 7.9; 9.3 Divide these quantities to compare the amplitudes:

$$\frac{k \cdot 10^{\underline{\ ?\ }}}{k \cdot 10^{\underline{\ ?\ }}} = 10^{\underline{\ ?\ }}.$$ 9.3; 7.9; 1.4

As a decimal, $10^{\underline{\ ?\ }} \approx$ __?__, indicating that the 2004 quake had about __?__ times the force of the __?__ quake. 1.4; 25.11; 25; 2008

3 Assignment

Recommended Assignment

- Questions 1–28
- Question 29 (extra credit)
- Reading Lesson 9-7
- Covering the Ideas 9-7

9-6A Lesson Master — Questions on SPUR Objectives
See Student Edition pages 656–659 for objectives.

SKILLS Objective C

In 1 and 2, use this information. The pH scale measures the strength of acids and bases. Its formula is $pH = -\log(H^+)$ where H^+ is the concentration of hydrogen ions, measured in moles per liter.

1. A type of hand soap has a concentration of hydrogen ions of 3.16×10^{-9} moles per liter. Find its pH. ≈ 8.5
2. The pH of lemon juice is 2.4. Find the concentration of hydrogen ions. $\approx 3.98 \times 10^{-3}\ \frac{\text{moles}}{\text{L}}$

In 3 and 4, use this information. The decibel scale of relative sound intensity is based on watts. The watt is a measure of power. The formula $D = 10 \log\left(\frac{N}{10^{-12}}\right)$ relates sound intensity N in watts per square meter to its relative intensity D in decibels.

3. A school lunchroom has a noise level of 1.58×10^{-4} watts per square meter. Find the decibel level in the lunchroom. ≈ 82 dB
4. A car horn is rated at 110 decibels. Find its power in watts per square meter. $\frac{1}{10}\ \frac{\text{W}}{\text{m}^2}$

USES Objective I

5. The table at the right shows the pH values of common beverages.

Beverage	pH
Cola	2.5
Orange Juice	3.5
Tomato Juice	4.0
Milk	6.0

   a. Which is the most acidic? cola
   b. How many times as acidic as tomato juice is orange juice? $\approx$ 3 times
   c. How many times as acidic as milk is cola? $\approx$ about 3162 times

6. Two companies manufacture lawnmowers. Company A's model is rated at 89 decibels. Company B advertises their model as "half as loud as the competition." How loud is Company B's lawnmower, in decibels? ≈ 86 dB
7. Recall that the scales for measuring earthquakes are logarithmic, so that an increase of 1.0 in intensity corresponds to a ten-fold increase in the earthquake's power. In 2005, an earthquake of magnitude 7.6 struck Pakistan. In 2008, a magnitude 7.9 earthquake struck Sichuan, China. How many times as strong as the 2005 earthquake was the 2008 one? about twice as strong

Advanced Algebra 501

GUIDED

Example 4

Just before a 1989 World Series game in San Francisco, California there was an earthquake in the nearby Santa Cruz Mountains that registered 6.9 on the Richter scale. The tsunami that hit twelve Indian Ocean nations in December 2004 was triggered by an earthquake that measured 9.3 on the Richter scale. The force of the 2004 earthquake was how many times the force of the 1989 quake?

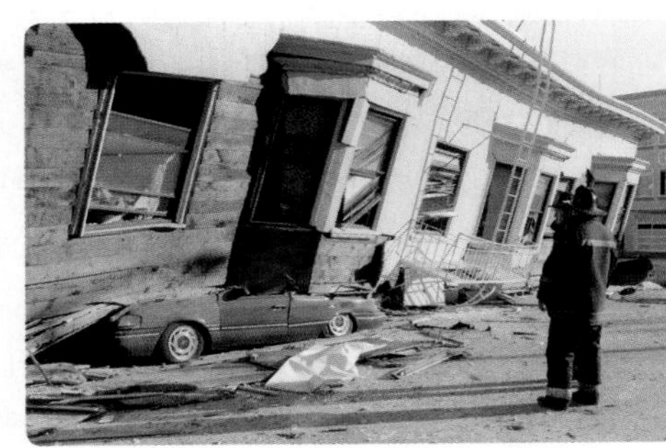

The 1989 earthquake in San Francisco caused the third floor of this apartment building to collapse onto this car.

Solution The amplitude of the 1989 World Series earthquake was $k \cdot 10^{\underline{\ ?\ }}$. The amplitude of the 2004 quake was $k \cdot 10^{\underline{\ ?\ }}$. 6.9; 9.3

Divide these quantities to compare the amplitudes. Since we are assuming the forces were measured in the same units, the two k-values are the same.

$$\frac{k \cdot 10^{\underline{\ ?\ }}}{k \cdot 10^{\underline{\ ?\ }}} = 10^{\underline{\ ?\ }}.$$ 9.3; 6.9; 2.4

As a decimal, $10^{\underline{\ ?\ }} \approx$ __?__, indicating that the 2004 earthquake had about __?__ times as much force as the __?__ earthquake. 2.4; 251.189 251; 1989

Some other examples of logarithmic scales include the pH scale for measuring the acidity or alkalinity of a substance, the scales used on radio dials, and the scale for measuring the magnitude (brightness) of stars.

Questions

COVERING THE IDEAS

In 1 and 2, use the formula $D = 10 \log\left(\frac{N}{10^{-12}}\right)$ that relates relative intensity D in dB of sound to sound intensity N in $\frac{\text{W}}{\text{m}^2}$.

1. Find the relative intensity in decibels of an explosion that has a sound intensity of $2.45 \cdot 10^{-5}$. 73.89 dB
2. Find the intensity in $\frac{\text{W}}{\text{m}^2}$ of a sound that has a relative intensity of 78 decibels. $6.31 \times 10^{-5}\ \frac{\text{W}}{\text{m}^2}$

Accommodating the Learner

Some students may have difficulty interpreting logarithmic scales. Show them the diagram below.

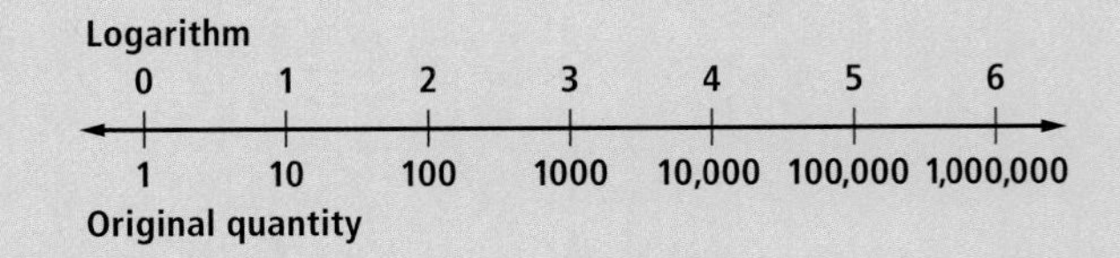

Have students compare the numbers above and below the line and note that the logarithms represent a linear scale; that is, *subtracting* one unit from the next produces a constant difference. In contrast, for the original quantities, *dividing* one unit by the other produces a constant ratio.

In 3–5, refer to the chart of sound intensity levels from the beginning of this lesson.

3. In Example 2, we found that Serena Williams's grunts reach an intensity of 88 decibels. Between which two powers of 10 is the equivalent sound intensity?
4. If you are near a refrigerator, how many times as intense would the sound have to be in order for it to reach the level emitted by a jackhammer?
5. How many times as intense is a whisper than a noise that is barely audible? 100 times as intense

Serena Williams

6. Lester Noyes is deciding between two dishwashers for purchase. One dishwasher's rating is 56 decibels (dB) and the other is 59 dB. The salesman says the sound intensity of the 59 dB dishwasher is only 5% more than the other one, and this difference is insignificant. Do you agree? Explain.

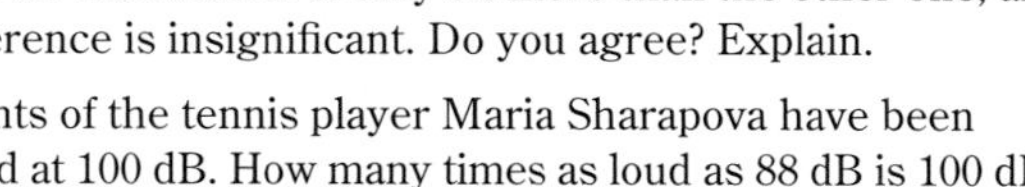

7. The grunts of the tennis player Maria Sharapova have been measured at 100 dB. How many times as loud as 88 dB is 100 dB?
8. An earthquake measuring 6.5 on the Richter scale carries how many times as much force as one measuring 5.5? 10 times as much force
9. An earthquake measuring 8.2 on the Richter scale carries how many times as much force as one measuring 6.7?
10. If one earthquake's Richter value is 0.4 higher than another, how many times as much force is in the more powerful earthquake?

3. between 10^{-4} and 10^{-3}
4. 100,000,000 times as intense
6. No; $10^{\frac{3}{10}} \approx 2$, so the sound intensity of the louder dishwasher is actually twice as intense.
7. about 15.8 times as loud
9. 31.6 times as much force
10. about 2.5 times as much force

APPLYING THE MATHEMATICS

In 11 and 12, use this information. In 1979, seismologists introduced the *moment magnitude scale* based on the formula $M_w = \frac{\log M_0}{1.5} - 10.7$ for moment magnitude M_w. Seismic moment M_0 is a measure of the size of the earthquake. Its units are dyne-cm. (One dyne is the force required to accelerate a mass of 1 gram at a rate of 1 centimeter per second squared.)

11. An earthquake had a seismic moment of 3.86×10^{27} dyne-cm. Find its moment magnitude M_w. 7.69
12. If the moment magnitude of one earthquake is 1 higher than that of another, how do their seismic moments differ? by a factor of 31.62

9-6

Notes on the Questions

Questions 13–16 Here is another logarithmic scale, perhaps easier to understand than the decibel scale. The pH numbers are the opposites of the common logarithms of the concentration of hydrogen ions in a substance.

Questions 17 and 18 The star magnitude scale is the fourth and last of the logarithmic scales to be discussed in this lesson. Other examples can be found on the Internet by searching under "logarithmic scale." Rigel is the brightest star within 3000 light-years of Earth. Because it is only about 800 light-years from Earth, it is by far the brightest star in our vicinity. It has 40,000 times the luminosity of the Sun.

In 13–16, use the pH scale for measuring acidity or alkalinity of a substance shown at the right. Its formula is $pH = -\log(H^+)$, where H^+ is the concentration of hydrogen ions in $\frac{\text{moles}}{\text{liter}}$ of the substance.

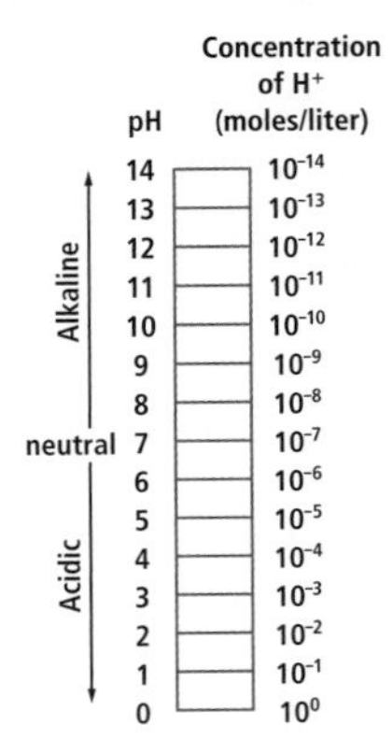

13. The pH of normal rain is 5.6 and the pH of acidic rain is 4.3. The concentration of hydrogen ions in acid rain is how many times the concentration of hydrogen ions in normal rain? 19.95

14. For a healthy individual, human saliva has an average pH of 6.4.
    a. Is saliva acidic or alkaline? acidic
    b. What is the concentration of hydrogen ions in human saliva? 3.98×10^{-7}

15. The concentration of hydrogen ions in a typical piece of white bread is $3.16 \times 10^{-6} \frac{\text{mol}}{\text{liter}}$. What is the pH of white bread? 5.5

16. The Felix Clean Company manufactures soap. In one advertisement the company claimed that its soap has a tenth of the pH of the competing brand.
    a. What range of values could the pH of the soap have if this were true? $0 \le pH \le 1.4$
    b. What would happen if the soap did indeed have a pH as claimed in the advertisement?
    c. What did the advertiser probably mean?

16b. The soap would be extremely acidic.

16c. Answers vary. Samle: They probably meant that the soap has a pH of 1 more than the competing brand (thus a tenth of the concentration of hydrogen ions).

In 17 and 18, use this information: In astronomy, the *magnitude* (brightness) m of a star is measured not by the energy I meeting the eye, but by its logarithm. In this scale, if one star has radiation energy I_1 and absolute magnitude m_1, and another star has energy I_2 and absolute magnitude m_2, then $m_1 - m_2 = -2.5 \log\left(\frac{I_1}{I_2}\right)$.

17. The star Rigel in the constellation Orion radiates about 150,000 times as much energy as the Sun. The Sun has absolute magnitude 4.8. If the ratio of intensities is 150,000, find the absolute magnitude of Rigel. -8.14

18. Suppose the difference $m_1 - m_2$ in absolute magnitudes of two stars is 5. Find $\frac{I_1}{I_2}$, the ratio of the energies they radiate. 0.01

REVIEW

In 19 and 20, explain how to evaluate without using a calculator. (Lesson 9-5)

19. $\log_{10} 1{,}000{,}000$

20. $\log_{10} 10^{-5}$

In 21 and 22, solve. (Lesson 9-5)

21. $\log x = 7$ $x = 10{,}000{,}000$

22. $\log 7 = x$ $x \approx 0.845$

19. $1{,}000{,}000 = 10^6$; thus, $\log_{10} 1{,}000{,}000 = 6$.

20. The logarithm is the exponent, so $\log_{10} 10^{-5} = -5$

Accommodating the Learner

After completing the lesson, have students find a reasonable range of values for the pH scale. Then have them find examples of foods that have pHs that are acidic and alkaline. Ask them to describe how they think acidity affects the taste of foods.

$0 \le pH \le 14$. Answers vary. Sample: A tangerine is acidic but tofu is alkaline. Foods that are sour seem to be more acidic.

23. Give two equations for the inverse of the function with the equation $y = 10^x$. **(Lesson 9-5)** $y = \log x$, $x = 10^y$

24. The *Haugh unit* is a measure of egg quality that was introduced in 1937 in the *U.S. Egg and Poultry Magazine*. The number U of Haugh units of an egg is given by the formula

$$U = 100 \log\left[H - \frac{1}{100}\sqrt{32.2}(30W^{0.37} - 100) + 1.9\right],$$

where W is the weight of the egg in grams, and H is the height of the albumen in millimeters when the egg is broken on a flat surface. Find the number of Haugh units of an egg that weighs 58.8 g and for which $H = 6.3$ mm. **(Lesson 9-5)** 79.156

25. Is $y = 2^{-x}$ the equation for a function of exponential growth or exponential decay? Explain how you can tell. **(Lesson 9-2)**

25. exponential decay; Answers vary. Sample: y will decrease as x increases.

26. Consider the graph of the function g at the right. Give the domain and range of g^{-1}. **(Lesson 8-2)** domain: $x \geq 0$, range: $y \leq 0$

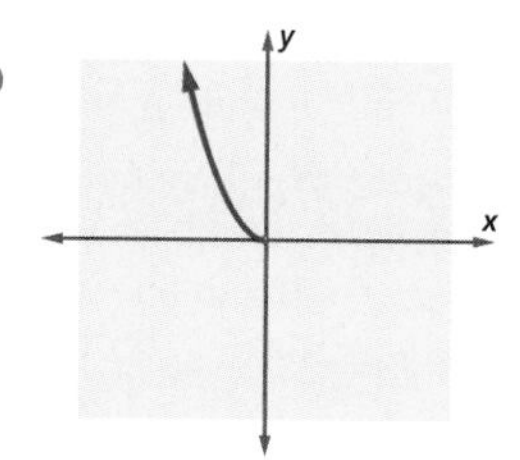

In 27 and 28, assume all variables represent positive real numbers. Simplify. (Lessons 7-7, 7-2)

27. $\dfrac{p^5q^4}{(pm)^3}$ $\dfrac{p^2q^4}{m^3}$

28. $(r^2)^{\frac{1}{4}}(t^{10})^{\frac{3}{5}}$ $r^{\frac{1}{2}}t^6$

EXPLORATION

29. The mathematician L.F. Richardson classified conflicts according to their magnitude, the base-10 logarithm of the total number of deaths. For example, a war in which there were 10,000 deaths would have a magnitude of 4 because $10^4 = 10{,}000$. A gang fight with 10 casualties would have a magnitude of 1 because $10^1 = 1$. Use Richardson's scale to classify the Revolutionary War, the Civil War, World War I, World War II, the Vietnam War, and the Persian Gulf War. Comment on the effectiveness of Richardson's scale in comparing the number of deaths in the wars.

Answers vary. Sample: One estimate gives the following magnitudes for the wars: Revolutionary War: 4.5, Civil War: 5.8, World War I: 7.6, World War II: 7.8, Vietnam War: 6.5, Persian Gulf War: 4.5. One problem with scaling wars in this way is in comparing different wars. For example, the difference between World Wars I and II is 0.2 on Richardson's scale but around 20 million lives, whereas the difference between the Revolutionary War and the Civil War is 1.3 on the scale but about 600,000 lives.

QY ANSWER

$10^3 = 1000$ times as intense

Notes on the Questions

Question 24 The formula looks foreboding, but with a calculator this is not a difficult question. Remind students, however, that when this formula was introduced, there were no hand-held calculators.

Question 29 There are no correct or incorrect answers to this question.

4 Wrap-Up

Ongoing Assessment

Have students choose two different categories from the decibel chart on page 615, for example, *refrigerator* and *jack hammer.* Have students determine how many times as intense the louder sound is than the softer sound. Students should correctly apply logarithmic scales. For the example given above, the jack hammer sound is $10^8 = 100{,}000{,}000$ times as intense as the refrigerator sound.

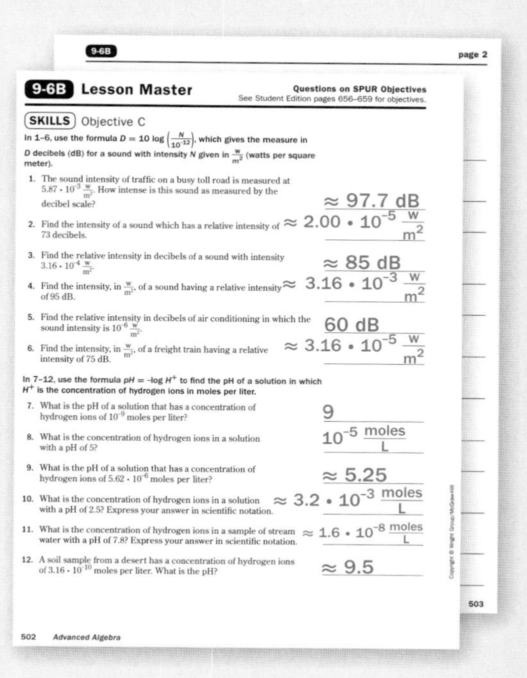
9-6B page 2

9-6B Lesson Master

Questions on SPUR Objectives
See Student Edition pages 656–659 for objectives.

SKILLS Objective C

In 1–6, use the formula $D = 10 \log\left(\frac{N}{10^{-12}}\right)$, which gives the measure in D decibels (dB) for a sound with intensity N given in $\frac{w}{m^2}$ (watts per square meter).

1. The sound intensity of traffic on a busy toll road is measured at $5.87 \cdot 10^{-3}\ \frac{w}{m^2}$. How intense is this sound as measured by the decibel scale? ≈ 97.7 dB
2. Find the intensity of a sound which has a relative intensity of 73 decibels. $\approx 2.00 \cdot 10^{-5}\ \frac{w}{m^2}$
3. Find the relative intensity in decibels of a sound with intensity $3.16 \cdot 10^{-4}\ \frac{w}{m^2}$. ≈ 85 dB
4. Find the intensity, in $\frac{w}{m^2}$, of a sound having a relative intensity of 95 dB. $\approx 3.16 \cdot 10^{-3}\ \frac{w}{m^2}$
5. Find the relative intensity in decibels of air conditioning in which the sound intensity is $10^{-6}\ \frac{w}{m^2}$. 60 dB
6. Find the intensity, in $\frac{w}{m^2}$, of a freight train having a relative intensity of 75 dB. $\approx 3.16 \cdot 10^{-5}\ \frac{w}{m^2}$

In 7–12, use the formula $pH = -\log H^+$ to find the pH of a solution in which H^+ is the concentration of hydrogen ions in moles per liter.

7. What is the pH of a solution that has a concentration of hydrogen ions of 10^{-9} moles per liter? 9
8. What is the concentration of hydrogen ions in a solution with a pH of 5? $10^{-5}\ \frac{\text{moles}}{\text{L}}$
9. What is the pH of a solution that has a concentration of hydrogen ions of $5.62 \cdot 10^{-6}$ moles per liter? ≈ 5.25
10. What is the concentration of hydrogen ions in a solution with a pH of 2.5? Express your answer in scientific notation. $\approx 3.2 \cdot 10^{-3}\ \frac{\text{moles}}{\text{L}}$
11. What is the concentration of hydrogen ions in a sample of stream water with a pH of 7.8? Express your answer in scientific notation. $\approx 1.6 \cdot 10^{-8}\ \frac{\text{moles}}{\text{L}}$
12. A soil sample from a desert has a concentration of hydrogen ions of $3.16 \cdot 10^{-10}$ moles per liter. What is the pH? ≈ 9.5

502 Advanced Algebra 503

Lesson **9-7**

GOAL

Obtain common logarithms to any integer base for numbers with and without calculators.

SPUR Objectives

A Determine values of logarithms.

C Solve logarithmic equations.

E Recognize properties of logarithmic functions.

K Graph logarithmic curves.

Materials/Resources

- Lesson Masters 9-7A and 9-7B
- Resource Masters 170–172

HOMEWORK

Suggestions for Assignment

- Questions 1–29
- Question 30 (extra credit)
- Reading Lesson 9-8
- Covering the Ideas 9-8

Local Standards

1 Warm-Up

In 1–4, solve the equation.

1. $0.5^x = 2$ $x = -1$
2. $7^y = \sqrt[3]{49}$ $y = \frac{2}{3}$
3. $50^z = 1$ $z = 0$
4. $9^w = 243$ $w = 2.5$

Lesson 9-7 Logarithms to Bases Other Than 10

Vocabulary

logarithm of *a* to the base *b*

logarithm function with base *b*

BIG IDEA When a number is written as a power of *b*, the exponent in the expression is the *logarithm of the number to the base b*.

In Lesson 9-5, you learned about the common logarithm, which allows you to solve for x when $10^x = a$. But how do you solve $b^x = a$ when b is any positive value other than 1? The same question was considered by Leonhard Euler in the 18th century. It led him to the following definition of a logarithm to any positive base other than 1.

Mental Math

Let $P = (3, 5)$. Give the coordinates of the image of P under the given transformation.

a. r_y (–3, 5)

b. S_3 (9, 15)

c. $S_{-2,-1}$ (–6, –5)

d. $T_{-2,-1}$ (1, 4)

Definition of Logarithm of *a* to the Base *b*

Let $b > 0$ and $b \neq 1$. Then x is the **logarithm of *a* to the base *b***, written $x = \log_b a$, if and only if $b^x = a$.

For example, because $3^5 = 243$, you can write $5 = \log_3 243$. This is read "5 is the logarithm of 243 with base 3" or "5 is log 243 to the base 3" or "5 is the log base 3 of 243." At the right are some other powers of 3 and the related logs to the base 3.

Exponential Form	Logarithmic Form
$3^4 = 81$	$\log_3 81 = 4$
$3^3 = 27$	$\log_3 27 = 3$
$3^2 = 9$	$\log_3 9 = 2$
$3^1 = 3$	$\log_3 3 = 1$
$3^{0.5} = \sqrt{3}$	$\log_3 \sqrt{3} = 0.5$
$3^0 = 1$	$\log_3 1 = 0$
$3^{-1} = \frac{1}{3}$	$\log_3\left(\frac{1}{3}\right) = -1$
$3^{-2} = \frac{1}{9}$	$\log_3\left(\frac{1}{9}\right) = -2$
$3^y = x$	$\log_3 x = y$

STOP QY1

QY1

Rewrite $7^4 = 2401$ in logarithmic form.

Example 1

Write the equation $P = 9(1.028)^x$ in logarithmic form.

Solution First rewrite the equation in $b^n = m$ form. Divide both sides by 9.

$$1.028^x = \frac{P}{9}$$

Background

Although any positive number other than 1 can be the base for a logarithm function, the questions in this book use only base e or integer bases greater than 1. We do this because, in practice, the use of other bases is rare. Bases other than base 10 (common logarithms), base 2 (sometimes used in describing the time that it takes for computers to perform certain operations), and base e (natural logarithms, to be introduced in Lesson 9-8) are seldom used. However, the properties of logarithms hold for any base, and so it is just as easy to introduce all bases other than base 10 as it would be to focus on special cases. Also, having all bases provides an alternate approach to the solving of equations of the form $a^x = b$ in Lesson 9-10.

Apply the definition of logarithm. The base is 1.028.

$\log_{1.028}\left(\frac{P}{9}\right) = x$

Evaluating Logarithms to Bases Other Than 10

The methods of evaluating logs and solving equations of logs with bases other than 10 are very similar to the methods used with common logarithms. For example, when a is a known power of the base b, $\log_b a$ can be quickly found without a calculator.

GUIDED

Example 2

Evaluate the following.

a. $\log_7 49$ b. $\log_8 2$ c. $\log_4\left(\frac{1}{64}\right)$

Solution

a. Let $\log_7 49 = x$.

$7^x = 49$ Definition of logarithm

$7^x = 7^2$ Rewrite 49 as a power of 7.

$x = \underline{?}$ Equate the exponents. 2

So, $\log_7 49 = \underline{?}$. Transitive Property of Equality 2

b. Let $\log_8 2 = x$.

$8^x = 2$ $\underline{?}$ definition of logarithm

$(2^3)^x = 2^{\underline{?}}$ Rewrite both sides as powers of 2. 1

$2^{\underline{?}} = 2^{\underline{?}}$ Power of a Power Postulate $3x$; 1

$\underline{?} = \underline{?}$ Equate the exponents. $3x$; 1

$x = \underline{?}$ $\underline{?}$ $\frac{1}{3}$; Division Property of Equality

So, $\log_8 2 = \underline{?}$. $\frac{1}{3}$

c. Let $\log_4\left(\frac{1}{64}\right) = x$.

$\underline{?} = \frac{1}{64}$ 4^x

$\underline{?} = 4^{\underline{?}}$ 4^x; -3

$\underline{?} = \underline{?}$ x; -3

So, $\log_4\left(\frac{1}{64}\right) = \underline{?}$. -3

In each part of Example 2 you moved from an expression of the form $b^m = b^n$ to one of the form $m = n$. We call this "equating the exponents." When $b \neq 1$ and b is positive, this is a valid process because the exponential function with base b takes on a unique value for each exponent.

ENGLISH LEARNERS

Vocabulary Development

Relate the definition of *logarithm of a to the base b* to the definition of *logarithm of x to the base 10* given in Lesson 9-5. The difference is that in this lesson, the base can be a number other than 10. Have students refer to the table of exponential and logarithmic forms following the definition on page 622 to help them clarify the definition in this lesson. Discuss the graphs of the exponential function $y = 3^x$ and the logarithmic equation $y = \log_3 x$ as graphed on page 624. Have students note that both $y = \log_3 x$ and $10^y = x$ describe the inverse of the exponential function $y = 3^x$.

2 Teaching

Notes on the Lesson

It is useful to have students read aloud logarithmic expressions and equations to ensure that they are using the correct terminology.

Point out that because exponential functions exist with any positive base other than 1, the logarithm to any positive base (except 1) can be defined. In theory, students should be able to evaluate expressions of the form $\log_b m$ for any $b > 0$, $b \neq 1$. In practice, we use only whole numbers for b and typically only small whole numbers. The problems tend to involve bases that are products of powers of 2, 3, or 5 because simple rational powers with these bases can be easily evaluated.

Example 1 After you have explained the definition of logarithm of a to the base b and discussed Example 1, ask students to translate the Warm-Up equations into logarithmic form. (1) $x = \log_{0.5} 2$; (2) $y = \log_7 \sqrt[3]{49}$; (3) $z = \log_{50} 1$; (4) $w = \log_9 243$

Additional Examples

Example 1 Write the equation $P = 12(0.359)^x$ in logarithmic form. $\log_{0.359}\left(\frac{P}{12}\right) = x$

Example 2 Evaluate the following.

a. $\log_2 16$

b. $\log_6 \sqrt{6}$

c. $\log_3\left(\frac{1}{81}\right)$

Solution

a. Let $\log_2 16 = x$.

$2^x = 16$

$2^x = 2^4$

$x = \underline{?}$ 4

So, $\log_2 16 = \underline{?}$. 4

b. Let $\log_6 \sqrt{6} = x$.

$6^x = \underline{?}$ $\sqrt{6}$

$6^x = \underline{?}$ $6^{\frac{1}{2}}$

$\underline{?} = \underline{?}$ x; $\frac{1}{2}$

So, $\log_6 \sqrt{6} = \underline{?}$. $\frac{1}{2}$

c. Let $\log_3\left(\frac{1}{81}\right) = x$.

$\underline{?} = \frac{1}{81}$ 3^x

$\underline{?} = 3^{\underline{?}}$ 3^x; 3^{-4}

$\underline{?} = \underline{?}$ x; -4

So, $\log_3\left(\frac{1}{81}\right) = \underline{?}$. 4

Note-Taking Tips

Have students add to their journals the definition of logarithm of a to the base b given in this lesson, as well as the properties of the function with an equation of the form $y = \log_b x$ given on page 625.

When a is not an integer power of b, a CAS can be used to find $\log_b a$. Some CAS allow you to enter any base b when you press the logarithm key. The template used for logs on one CAS is shown at the left below. The CAS response to $\log_2 3.5$ is shown at the right below.

In addition, any CAS may be used to find x when $\log_b a = x$. Simply rewrite the equation in exponential form and solve for x. This method is used to find $\log_2 3.5$ as shown at the right.

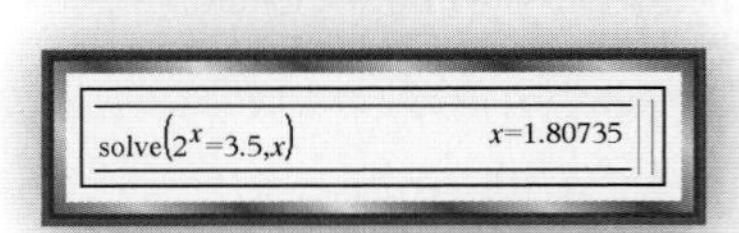

QY2

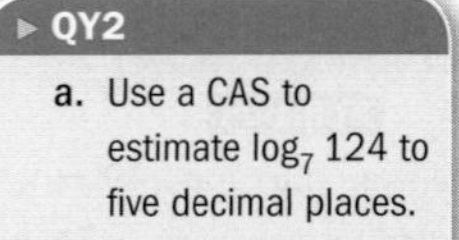

QY2

a. Use a CAS to estimate $\log_7 124$ to five decimal places.

b. To what exponential equation is the result of Part a an estimated solution?

Graphs of Logarithm Functions

Both the exponential equation $3^y = x$ and the logarithmic equation $y = \log_3 x$ describe the *inverse* of the function with equation $y = 3^x$. These functions are graphed at the right. In general, the **logarithm function with base b**, $g(x) = \log_b x$, is the inverse of the exponential function with base b, $f(x) = b^x$.

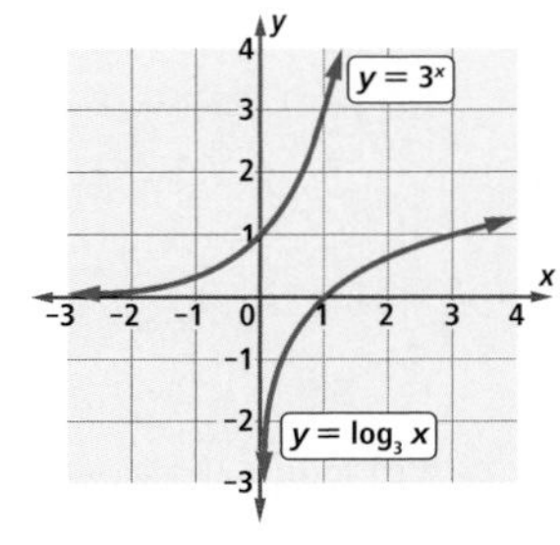

Recall that the domain of the exponential function with equation $y = 3^x$ is the set of all real numbers. Consequently, the range of the logarithm function with equation $y = \log_3 x$ is also the set of all real numbers. So logarithms to the base 3 can be negative. However, the range of the exponential function $y = 3^x$ and the domain of the corresponding logarithm function is the set of positive real numbers. This means that in the set of real numbers there is no logarithm of a nonpositive number.

Activity

Work with a partner and use a graphing utility. See margin.

Step 1 Each partner should choose a different value of b, with $b > 0$ and $b \neq 1$, and graph $y = \log_b x$. An example is shown at the right.

Step 2 Fill in a chart like the one on the next page to record the domain, range, intercepts, and asymptotes of the graph for your value of b. Then have your partner fill in another row of the chart for his or her value of b.

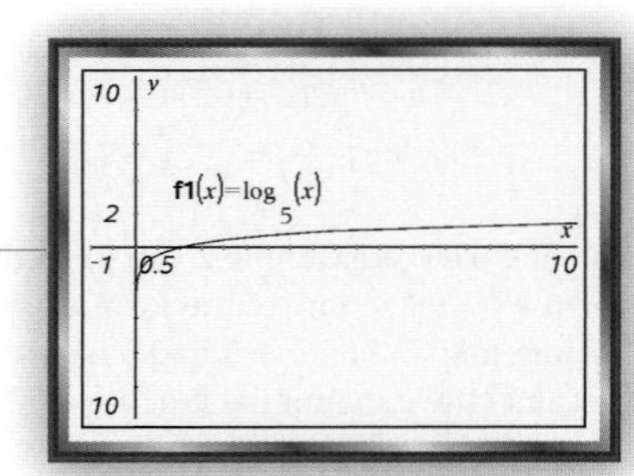

Accommodating the Learner

Some students may not understand why the base in a logarithmic function must be a positive number. One convincing demonstration is to have students use a calculator to try to find the logarithm of a number to a negative base. For example, they could try to evaluate $\log_{-2}(8)$. Most calculators will respond with an ERROR message.

b	Domain	Range	*x*-intercepts	*y*-intercepts	Asymptotes
?	?	?	?	?	?

Step 3 Set the window on your graphing utility to square. Each partner should graph $y = b^x$ on the same set of axes as in Step 1. What is the relationship between the graph of $y = \log_b x$ and the graph of $y = b^x$?

Step 4 Both partners should repeat Steps 1–3 for two additional values of *b*. Choose values that are different from your partner's values, and be sure to choose some noninteger values for *b*.

Step 5 Summarize your results. What properties do these functions seem to share?

The Activity shows that there are properties shared by all logarithm functions, regardless of their base. Every function with an equation of the form $y = \log_b x$, where $b > 0$ and $b \neq 1$, has the following properties.

1. Its domain is the set of positive real numbers.
2. Its range is the set of all real numbers.
3. Its *x*-intercept is 1, and there is no *y*-intercept.
4. The *y*-axis ($x = 0$) is an asymptote to the graph.
5. Its graph is the reflection image over $y = x$ of the graph of $y = b^x$.

You may wonder why *b* cannot equal 1 in the definition of the logarithm of *a* with base *b*. It is because the inverse of the function with equation $y = 1^x$ is not a function.

QY3

▶ QY3

Why can the base *b* of logarithms never be negative?

Solving Logarithmic Equations

To solve a logarithmic equation, it often helps to use the definition of logarithm to rewrite the equation in exponential form.

Example 3

Solve for *h*: $\log_4 h = \frac{3}{2}$.

Solution

$4^{\frac{3}{2}} = h$ definition of logarithm

$8 = h$ Rational Exponent Theorem

9-7

Additional Example

Example 3 Solve for *a*: $\log_{81} a = \frac{5}{4}$.
$a = 243$

Additional Answers

Activity

Step 1. Answers vary. Sample: $b = 2$;

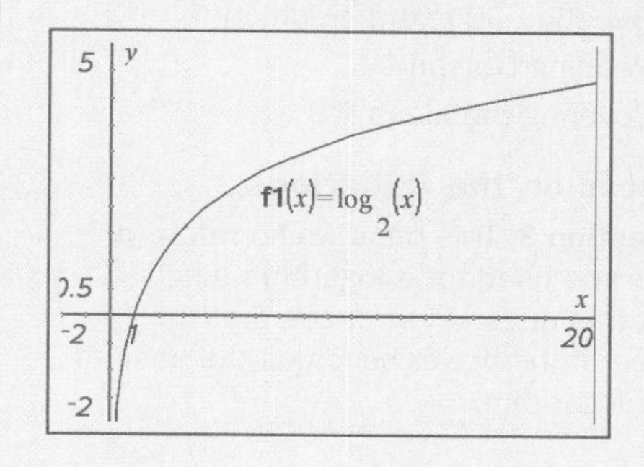

Step 2.

b	Domain	Range	x-ints.	y-ints.	Asymptotes
2	all positive real numbers	all real numbers	1	none	$x = 0$

Step 3.

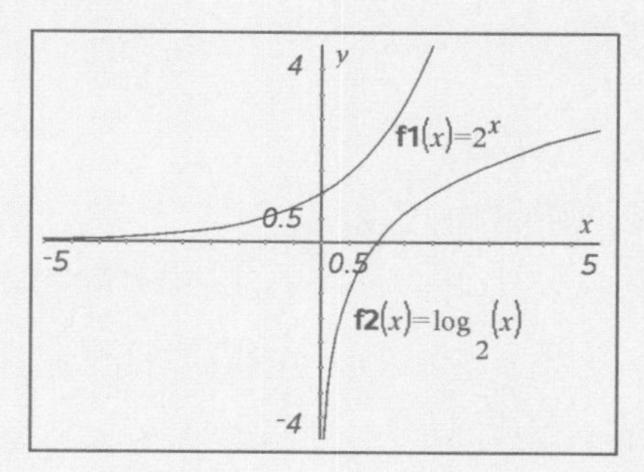

They are reflection images of one another over the line $y = x$.

Step 4. Answers vary.

Step 5. Answers vary. Sample: The functions all have an *x*-intercept of 1 and an asymptote of $x = 0$. They all have the same domain and range.

Accommodating the Learner

Have students work in pairs to graph each function and tell how each graph is related to the graph of $y = \log_3 x$.

1. $y = \log_3 x + 1$
2. $y = \log_3 (x + 1)$
3. $y = \log_3 |x|$

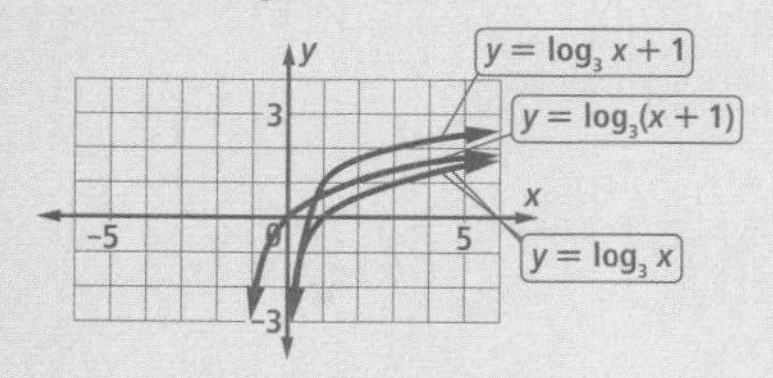

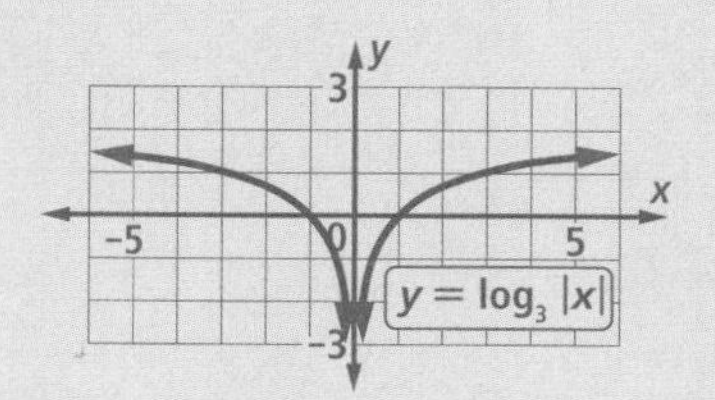

Graphs 1 and 2 are translation images of the graph of $y = \log_3 x$. Graph 3 is the union of the graph of $y = \log_3 x$ and its reflection image over the *y*-axis.

Additional Example

Example 4 Find z if $\log_z 8 = \frac{3}{4}$. $z = 16$

3 Assignment

Recommended Assignment

- Questions 1–29
- Question 30 (extra credit)
- Reading Lesson 9-8
- Covering the Ideas 9-8

Notes on the Questions

Question 3 This base would rarely (if ever) be used for a logarithm function, but this question stresses that the base of the power becomes the base of the logarithm.

9-7A Lesson Master

Questions on SPUR Objectives
See Student Edition pages 656–659 for objectives.

VOCABULARY

In 1 and 2, write the exponential equation as a logarithmic equation, or vice-versa.

1. a. $6^{-3} = \frac{1}{216}$ $\log_6 \frac{1}{216} = -3$ b. $8^{\frac{2}{3}} = 4$ $\log_8 4 = \frac{2}{3}$ c. $b^n = p$ $\log_b p = n$
2. a. $\log_3 81 = 4$ $3^4 = 81$ b. $\log_2 10 \approx 3.322$ $2^{3.322} \approx 10$ c. $\log_b c = d$ $b^d = c$

SKILLS Objective A

In 3–5, evaluate in your head. You may check with a calculator.

3. $\log_5 25 =$ 2
4. $\log_2 \frac{1}{16} =$ -4
5. $\log_7 \sqrt{7} =$ $\frac{1}{2}$
6. Evaluate to the nearest thousandth.
   a. $\log_2 41.3 \approx$ 5.368 b. $\log_{0.6} 0.9 \approx$ 0.206 c. $\log_{12} 8.29 \approx$ 0.851

SKILLS Objective C

In 7–10, write the equivalent exponential equation; use it to solve the logarithmic equation. Do as much work as you can in your head.

7. $\log_5 x = 3$ $5^3 = x$; $x = 125$
8. $\log_4 x = \frac{5}{2}$ $4^{\frac{5}{2}} = x$; $x = 32$
9. $\log_b 64 = 6$ $b^6 = 64$; $b = 2$
10. $\log_x \left(\frac{1}{8}\right) = -\frac{3}{4}$ $x^{-\frac{3}{4}} = \frac{1}{8}$; $x = 16$
11. Solve $3 \log_5 x + 2 = 8$ for x. $x = 25$

PROPERTIES Objective E

12. Give the restrictions on b and n in the expression $\log_b n$. $b > 0, b \neq 1, n > 0$
13. **Fill in the Blank** If $f(x) = \log_{42} x$ when $x > 0$, then $f^{-1}(x) =$ 42^x.

REPRESENTATIONS Objective K

In 14 and 15, consider the graphs of $f(x) = 3^x$ and $g(x) = \log_3 x$.

14. Graph each function at the right. Label three points on the graph of f with their coordinates, and the corresponding points on the graph of g. Answers vary. Sample: f: $\left(-2, \frac{1}{9}\right)$, $(0, 1)$, $(1, 3)$ and g: $\left(\frac{1}{9}, -2\right)$, $(1, 0)$, $(3, 1)$
15. Name the asymptotes of each function.
    f: $y = 0$ (the x-axis); g: $x = 0$ (the y-axis)

504 *Advanced Algebra*

To solve for the base in a logarithmic equation, apply the techniques you learned in Chapters 7 and 8 for solving equations with nth powers.

Example 4

Find w if $\log_w 1024 = 10$.

Solution

$w^{10} = 1024$	definition of logarithm
$(w^{10})^{\frac{1}{10}} = (1024)^{\frac{1}{10}}$	Raise both sides to the $\frac{1}{10}$ power.
$w = 2$	Power of a Power Postulate

Check Does $\log_2 1024 = 10$? Does $2^{10} = 1024$? Yes, it checks.

Questions

COVERING THE IDEAS

1. Logarithms to the base b arose from Euler's attempt to describe the solution(s) to what equation?
2. **Fill in the Blank** Suppose $b > 0$ and $b \neq 1$. When $b^n = m$, $n = \underline{\ ?\ }$. $\log_b m$
3. Write the equivalent logarithmic form for $(6\sqrt{3})^8 = 136{,}048{,}896$.

In 4 and 5, write the equivalent exponential form for the sentence.

4. $\log_4 0.0625 = -2$ $4^{-2} = 0.0625$
5. $\log_b a = c$ $b^c = a$
6. Write the inverse of the function with equation $y = 2^x$ as
   a. an exponential equation.
   b. a logarithmic equation.
7. State the domain and range of the function defined by $y = \log_3 x$.
8. Write an equation for the asymptote to the graph of $y = \log_b x$, where $b > 0$ and $b \neq 1$. $x = 0$
9. Sketch the graph of $y = \log_4 x$. See margin.

In 10–12, write the corresponding exponential form of each logarithmic equation, then solve for the exponent on a CAS.

10. $\log_{121} 1331 = x$
11. $\log_{\frac{1}{4}}\left(\frac{1}{64}\right) = y$
12. $\log_{\sqrt{5}} 625 = z$

In 13–17, write the corresponding exponential form of each logarithmic equation. Then, solve for the given variable.

13. $\log_a 8 = \frac{1}{3}$
14. $\log_7 c = 4$
15. $\log_{47} d = -0.2$
16. $\log_t\left(\frac{1}{6}\right) = -\frac{1}{3}$ $t^{-\frac{1}{3}} = \frac{1}{6}$; $t = 216$
17. $\log_w w = 1$ $w^1 = w$; $w > 0$, $w \neq 1$

1. $b^x = a$ when b is any positive value other than 1
3. $\log_{6\sqrt{3}} 136{,}048{,}896 = 8$

6a. $x = 2^y$

6b. $\log_2 x = y$

7. domain: $x > 0$; range: all real numbers

10. $121^x = 1331$; $x = \frac{3}{2}$
11. $\left(\frac{1}{4}\right)^y = \frac{1}{64}$; $y = 3$
12. $\left(\sqrt{5}\right)^z = 625$; $z = 8$
13. $a^{\frac{1}{3}} = 8$; $a = 512$
14. $7^4 = c$; $c = 2401$
15. $47^{-0.2} = d$; $d \approx 0.463$

Additional Answers

9.

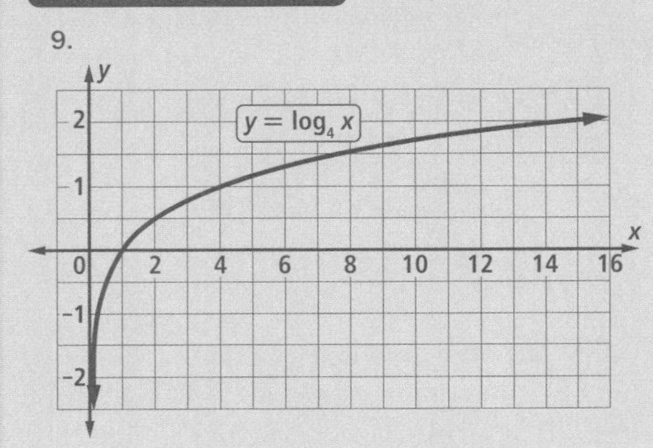

APPLYING THE MATHEMATICS

18. a. Make a table of values for $y = 2^x$ with $x = -2, -1, 0, 1, 2$ and a corresponding table of values for $y = \log_2 x$.
    b. Graph $y = 2^x$ and $y = \log_2 x$ on the same set of axes. 18a–b. See margin.
    c. **True or False** The domain of $y = 2^x$ is the range of $y = \log_2 x$. true
19. *Self-information* I is a measure (in bits) of how the knowledge gained about a certain event adds to your overall knowledge. A formula for self-information is $I = \log_2\left(\frac{1}{x}\right)$, where x is the probability of a certain event occurring.
    a. When flipping a coin, the probability of it landing on tails is 0.5. Find the number of bits this adds to your self-information. 1
    b. The probability of drawing a card with a diamond on it from a standard deck of cards is 0.25. Find the number of bits this adds to your self-information. 2
    c. If the self-information added is 2.3 bits, what was the probability of the event? about 0.203
20. The depreciation of a certain automobile that initially costs \$25,000 is given by the formula $N = 25{,}000(0.85)^t$, where N is the current value after t years.
    a. Write this equation in logarithmic form. $\log_{0.85}\left(\frac{N}{25{,}000}\right) = t$
    b. How old is a car that has a current value of \$9500? about 6 yr
21. a. Evaluate $\log_6 216$ and $\log_{216} 6$. $3; \frac{1}{3}$
    b. Evaluate $\log_7 49$ and $\log_{49} 7$. $2; \frac{1}{2}$
    c. Generalize the results of Parts a and b. $\log_a b = \frac{1}{\log_b a}$

REVIEW

In 22 and 23, refer to the representation of the electromagnetic spectrum below. (Lesson 9-6)

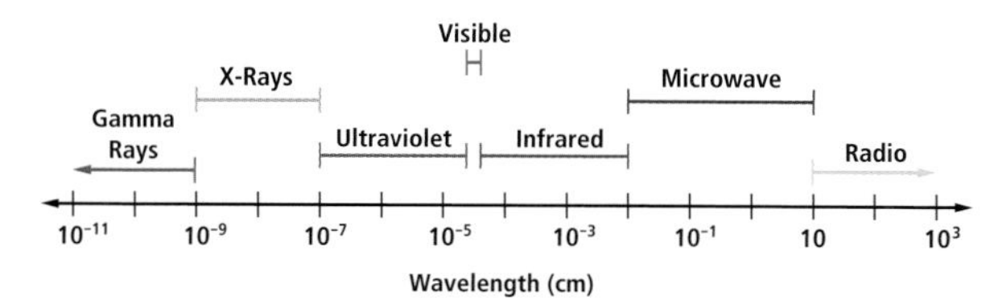

22. What kind of scale is used to depict the wavelengths for the electromagnetic spectrum? logarithmic
23. The shortest radio wave is how many times the length of the longest gamma ray wave? 10^{10}

Extension

Have students rewrite one of the exponential models they found for the drug absorption data in Lesson 9-4 as a logarithmic equation. Ask them to explain what each of the variables represents in the equation and to describe a situation in which the logarithmic form of the equation might be used.

Answers vary. Sample: $\log_{0.884}\left(\frac{y}{1000}\right) = x$, where y is the amount of drug in a person's system and x is the amount of time since the person took the drug. A doctor might use the logarithmic form of the equation to find out how long ago a patient took a drug based on the results of a blood test.

Notes on the Questions

Question 21 The generalization is a useful property for calculating some logarithms without a calculator.

Questions 22 and 23 Notice that units on the number-line representation of the various wavelengths are not spaced by their actual lengths but as an exponent of the power of 10 describing the length. That exponent is the logarithm, and that is why this is a logarithmic scale.

Additional Answers

18a.

x	$y = 2^x$
-2	$\frac{1}{4}$
-1	$\frac{1}{2}$
0	1
1	2
2	4

x	$y = \log_2 x$
$\frac{1}{4}$	-2
$\frac{1}{2}$	-1
1	0
2	1
4	2

18b.

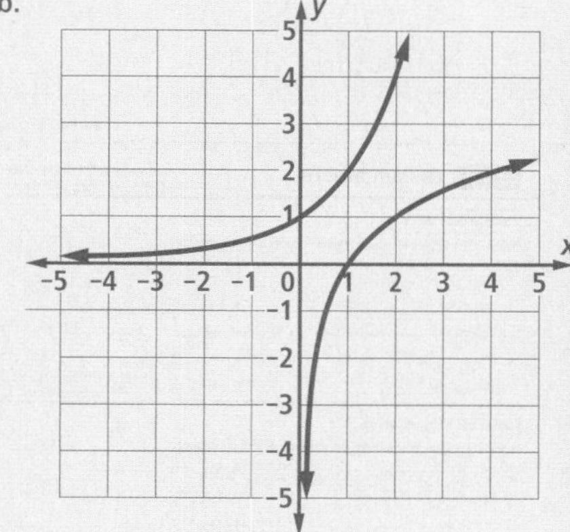

Notes on the Questions

Questions 24 and 25 Although the probability of an impact with a near-Earth object is low, the catastrophe that would occur might be so great that it could destroy a great deal of the planet. Consequently, space agencies have been considering ways of diverting any object that looks as if it might collide with Earth.

Question 29 Properties of exponents are reviewed in preparation for studying properties of logarithms in Lesson 9-9.

4 Wrap-Up

Ongoing Assessment

Have students, with their books closed, list properties they know to be true for every function with an equation of the form $y = \log_b x$. Then have them compare their list to the list of properties given on page 625 and make any changes or additions that are necessary. Students should be able to identify the properties of logarithmic equations.

Project Update

Project 6, *Finding when* $a^x = \log_a x$, on page 651 relates to the content of this lesson.

9-7B Lesson Master — page 2

Questions on SPUR Objectives
See Student Edition pages 656–659 for objectives.

VOCABULARY

In 1–4, write the logarithmic equation as an exponential equation.

1. $\log_7 \frac{1}{343} = -3$ $7^{-3} = \frac{1}{343}$
2. $\log_9 27 = \frac{3}{2}$ $9^{\frac{3}{2}} = 27$
3. $\log_4 16{,}384 = 7$ $4^7 = 16{,}384$
4. $\log_{16} 64 = \frac{3}{2}$ $16^{\frac{3}{2}} = 64$

In 5–8, write the exponential equation as a logarithmic equation.

5. $6^8 = 1{,}679{,}616$ $\log_6 1{,}679{,}616 = 8$
6. $x^y = z$ $\log_x z = y$
7. $12^4 = 20{,}736$ $\log_{12} 20{,}736 = 4$
8. $25^{3.5} = 78{,}125$ $\log_{25} 78{,}125 = 3.5$

SKILLS Objective A

In 9–18, evaluate in your head. You may check with a calculator.

9. $\log_4 \frac{1}{4}$ -1
10. $\log_{26} 26$ 1
11. $\log_{16} 4$ $\frac{1}{2}$
12. $\log_2 8$ 3
13. $\log_{39} 1$ 0
14. $\log_{52} 52^4$ 4
15. $\log_8 4$ $\frac{2}{3}$
16. $\log_6 7776$ 5
17. $\log_5 25$ 2
18. $\log_{12} \sqrt[4]{12^5}$ $\frac{5}{4}$
19. Evaluate to the nearest thousandth.
   a. $\log_2 403 \approx 8.655$ b. $\log_{0.6} 9 \approx -4.301$ c. $\log_{15} 1.06 \approx 0.022$

SKILLS Objective C

In 20–23, write the equivalent exponential equation; use it to solve the logarithmic equation. Do as much work as you can in your head.

20. $\log_7 x = 3$ $7^3 = x; x = 343$
21. $\log_{16} x = -\frac{3}{2}$ $16^{-\frac{3}{2}} = x; x = \frac{1}{64}$
22. $\log_b 27 = 3$ $b^3 = 27; b = 3$
23. $\log_x 8 = -\frac{3}{4}$ $x^{-\frac{3}{4}} = 8; x = \frac{1}{16}$
24. Solve $5 \log_5 x + 2 = 12$ for x. $x = 25$

PROPERTIES Objective E

25. **True or False** If the expression $\log_b n$ is defined,
   a. $b = 1$. false b. $n > 0$. true c. $b < 0$. false
26. Write the equivalent logarithmic form for $p^r = s$. $\log_p s = r$

Advanced Algebra 505

In 24 and 25, consider the Palermo Technical Impact Hazard Scale, a logarithmic scale used by astronomers to rate the potential hazard of impact of near-Earth objects (NEO) such as asteroids, comets, and large meteoroids. A Palermo value P is given by the formula $P = \log\left(\frac{p_i}{f_B T}\right)$, where p_i = the event's probability, T = the time in years until the event, and $f_B = 0.03E^{-0.8}$ is the annual probability of an impact event with energy E (in megatons of TNT) at least as large as the event in question. (Lesson 9-6)

While most meteor showers are caused by comet debris, the Geminid meteor showers are caused by asteroid 3200 Phaethon.

24. NASA keeps a database of all near-Earth objects. Discovered in 2008, the asteroid 2008 HJ is expected to approach Earth in 2077. For that year, it has an impact probability of $1.3 \cdot 10^{-6}$ and an expected impact energy of 0.408 megaton. Calculate the 2020 Palermo value for 2008 HJ. -6.43
25. 2002 RB182 is an asteroid with a 2005 Palermo value of -7.17. If it were to collide with Earth in 2044, it would have an expected energy of 35.6 megatons. What is the probability that it will impact Earth in 2044? 4.5×10^{-9}

In 26 and 27, evaluate using powers of 10. (Lesson 9-5)

26. $\log 10^7$ 7
27. $\log 0.0001$ -4
28. Thorium-232 (^{232}Th) has a half-life of 1.41×10^{10} years. (Lesson 9-2)
   a. Write an equation giving the percent p of thorium-232 in a substance after n years. $p = 100\left(\frac{1}{2}\right)^{\frac{n}{1.41 \cdot 10^{10}}}$
   b. Sketch a graph of your equation from Part a. See margin.
   c. Calculate the number of years needed for 99% of the original thorium to be present. about $2.04 \cdot 10^8$ yr
29. Simplify each expression. (Lessons 8-4, 7-2)
   a. $x^3 \cdot x^9$ x^{12} b. $\frac{x^3}{x^9}$ x^{-6} c. $(x^3)^9$ x^{27} d. $\sqrt[3]{x^9}$ x^3

EXPLORATION

30. Logarithms were invented by English mathematician John Napier (1550–1617), in the early 1600s. Henry Briggs, also from England, first used common logarithms around 1620. In England even today logs to the base 10 are sometimes called Briggsian logarithms. Find more information about one of these mathematicians.
   Answers vary. Sample: Henry Briggs is best known for calculating thousands of common logarithms and for the original discovery of the binomial theorem.

QY ANSWERS

1. $\log_7 2401 = 4$
2. a. 2.47713
   b. $7^x = 124$
3. Exponential functions are not defined for negative bases.

Additional Answers

28b.

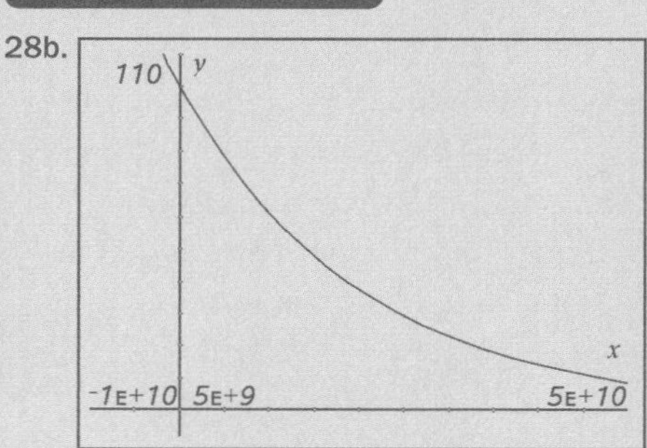

Lesson 9-8 Natural Logarithms

Vocabulary

natural logarithm of m, $\ln m$

▶ **BIG IDEA** When a number is written as a power of the irrational number e, the exponent in the expression is the natural logarithm of the number.

What Are Natural Logarithms?

Any positive number except 1 can be the base of a logarithm. The number e that you studied in Lesson 9-3 is frequently used as a logarithm base in real-world applications.

Logarithms to the base e are called *natural logarithms*. Just as $\log x$ (without any base named) is shorthand for $\log_{10} x$, $\ln x$ is shorthand for $\log_e x$.

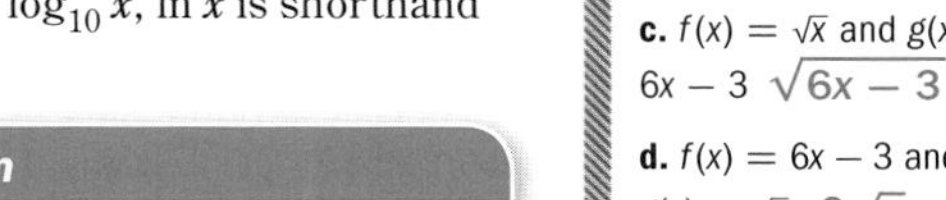

Definition of Natural Logarithm of m

n is the **natural logarithm of m**, written $n = \ln m$, if and only if $m = e^n$.

Mental Math

Find an expression for $f \circ g(x)$ if

a. $f(x) = x^2$ and $g(x) = x^4$ x^8

b. $f(x) = x^4$ and $g(x) = x^2$ x^8

c. $f(x) = \sqrt{x}$ and $g(x) = 6x - 3$ $\sqrt{6x-3}$

d. $f(x) = 6x - 3$ and $g(x) = \sqrt{x}$ $6\sqrt{x} - 3$

The symbol $\ln x$ is usually read "natural log of x".

Natural logarithms of powers of e can be determined in your head from the definition.

$\ln 1 = \log_e 1 = 0$ because $1 = e^0$.

$\ln e = \log_e e = 1$ because $e = e^1$.
That is, $\ln 2.718 \approx 1$ because $e^1 \approx 2.718$.

$\ln e^3 = \log_e e^3 = 3$ because $e^3 = e^3$.
That is, $\ln 20.086 \approx 3$ because $e^3 \approx 20.086$.

In general, $\ln(e^x) = x$.

 QY1

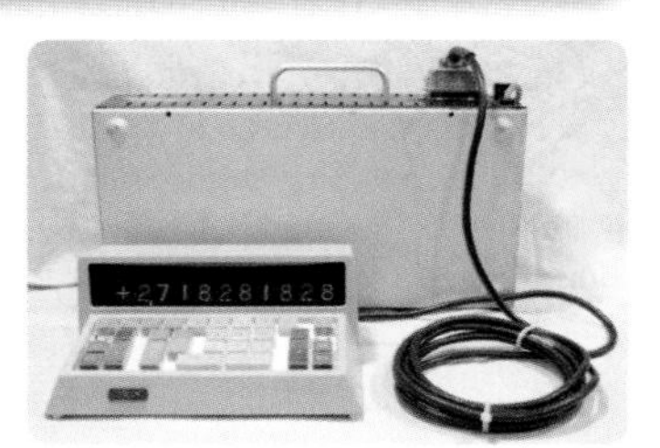

The Wang Model 360E calculator, first developed in 1964, was one of the first calculators capable of computing logarithms.

▶ **QY1**

What is the value of $\ln\left(\frac{1}{e}\right)$?

Lesson 9-8

GOAL

Learn about e as a base of logarithms and learn the definition of natural logarithms.

SPUR Objectives

A Determine values of logarithms.

E Recognize properties of logarithmic functions.

I Apply logarithmic scales, models, and formulas.

Materials/Resources

- Lesson Masters 9-8A and 9-8B
- Resource Masters 173 and 174
- Quiz 2

HOMEWORK

Suggestions for Assignment

- Questions 1–26
- Question 27 (extra credit)
- Reading Lesson 9-9
- Covering the Ideas 9-9

Local Standards

1 Warm-Up

In 1–3, write each expression as an integer or as the power of a single number or variable.

1. $\frac{x^a \cdot x^b}{x^c}$ x^{a+b-c}
2. $((((-2)^{-1})^0)^1)^2$ 1
3. $(5)(5)^2(5)^3$ 5^6

Background

Much of the content of this lesson parallels what students have seen with logarithms to other bases. Students should realize that natural logarithms are simply a specific kind of logarithm, so they can use what they have learned about logarithms in general to solve problems involving natural logarithms.

Base e logarithms have many useful properties that are important in higher mathematics. For example, the area in the region bounded by the hyperbola $y = \frac{1}{x}$, the x-axis, $x = 1$, and $x = p$ (where p is any positive number) equals $\ln p$. Another property is that natural logarithms are easily calculated using the infinite series shown in Question 22 of Lesson 9-3. Yet another property is the relationship between natural logarithms and the distribution of primes. The constant e, embedded in all these properties, is overtly found in the equation of the normal distribution curve studied in Lesson 13-9.

(continued on next page)

2 Teaching

Notes on the Lesson

You may want to introduce the topic of natural logarithms in a manner similar to that used for common logarithms. Have students make a table of values and graph $y = e^x$ and then graph its inverse by reversing the ordered pairs. Students should recognize the inverse as a logarithm function. Introduce the definition of natural logarithm and show students how to use the natural logarithm key on a calculator.

Additional Example

Example 1 Estimate the following to the nearest thousandth using a calculator.

a. ln 325 ≈ 5.784

b. ln 8 ≈ 2.079

Note-Taking Tips

Have students add to their journals the definition of natural logarithm given in this lesson.

Evaluating Natural Logarithms

Example 1

Estimate the following to the nearest thousandth using a calculator.

a. ln 100

b. ln 5

Solution Enter as shown at the right.

ln(100)	4.60517
ln(5)	1.60944

a. ln 100 $\approx$ 4.605

b. ln 5 $\approx$ 1.609

QY2

Caution! In many computer languages, the natural logarithm function is denoted as log(x). This can be confusing because in most other places, including on calculators, log(x) means the common log, with base 10.

QY2

Check your answers to Example 1 using powers of e.

The Graph of $y = \ln x$

The function with equation $y = \ln x$ is the inverse of the function with equation $y = e^x$, just as $y = \log x$ is the inverse of $y = 10^x$ and $y = \log_2 x$ is the inverse of $y = 2^x$. The inverse relationship of $y = e^x$ and $y = \ln x$ is displayed in the tables and graphs below. The graph of each function is the reflection image of the other over the line with equation $y = x$.

x	$y = e^x$
-1	0.37
0	1.00
1	e ≈ 2.72
1.6	4.95

x	$y = \ln x$
0.37	-1
1.00	0
e ≈ 2.72	1
4.95	1.6

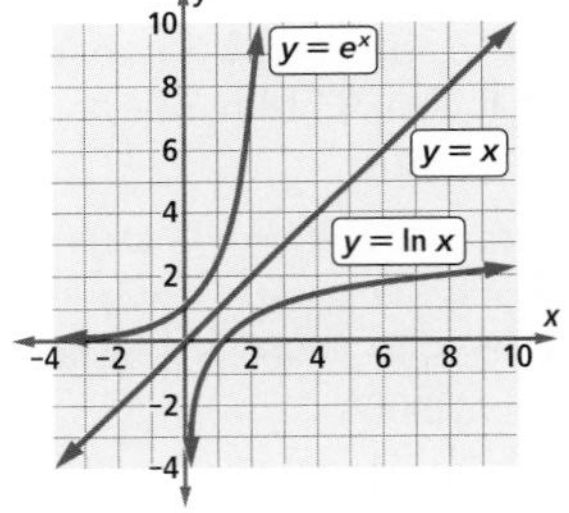

The function f with equation $f(x) = \ln x$ has all the properties held by all other logarithmic functions. In particular, the domain of the natural logarithm function is the set of positive real numbers, and its range is the set of all real numbers.

It is also overtly found in the solutions to many ordinary differential equations because the continuous function that equals its derivative at all values of x has the equation $y = e^x$.

ENGLISH LEARNERS

Vocabulary Development

Have students read the definition of *natural logarithm* and compare it with the definitions of *common logarithm* and *logarithm of a to the base b* in previous lessons. Students should be able to distinguish between *log* and *ln*. Spend some time discussing the material following the definition to make sure that students understand the concept.

Applications of Natural Logarithms

Natural logarithms are frequently used in formulas.

GUIDED

Example 2

According to the Beer-Lambert law, if you shine a 10-lumen light into a lake, the light intensity I (in lumens) at a depth of d feet under water is given by $d = -k \cdot \ln\left(\frac{I}{10}\right)$, where k is a measure of the light absorbance of the water. For a lake where $k = 34$, at what depth is the light intensity 6 lumens?

Solution Substitute the known values of k and I and solve for d.

$k = 34$ and $I =$ __?__ 6

So, $d =$ __?__ $\cdot \ln\left(\frac{?}{10}\right)$ -34; 6

$d \approx$ __?__ 17.4

The light intensity is 6 lumens at about __?__ feet. 17.4

Example 3

Let O_1 and O_2 be the temperatures of a cooling object before and after taking t minutes to cool, and let S_1 and S_2 be the temperatures of the surrounding environment before and after those t minutes. Newton's Law of Cooling says that t varies directly as the natural log of the ratio of the differences in temperature between the object and the surrounding area, or $t = k \ln\left(\frac{O_2 - S_2}{O_1 - S_1}\right)$.

The constant of variation k depends on the temperature scale (Celsius or Fahrenheit), the type of container the object is in, the altitude, and other environmental conditions.

a. After bringing it to a boil (212°F), Laura let her soup cool for 15 minutes to 140°F. Use the data to find a value of k if Laura is making her soup in an 80°F kitchen.

b. Suppose Laura heats a pot of vegetable soup to boiling, and lets it cool 15 minutes before serving. What is the serving temperature of the soup if the kitchen is 70°F?

(continued on next page)

Additional Examples

Example 2 Ignoring the force of gravity, the maximum velocity v of a rocket is given by the formula $v = c \cdot \ln R$, where c is the velocity of the exhaust and R is the ratio of the mass of the rocket with fuel to its mass without fuel. With a small payload, a solid-propellant rocket could have a mass ratio of about 19. A typical exhaust velocity for such a rocket might be about 2.4 kilometers per second. Find the maximum velocity of the rocket.

Solution Substitute the known values of c and R and solve for v: $c = 2.4$ and $R =$ __?__, so $v = 2.4 \cdot \ln($__?__$) = 2.4 \cdot$ __?__ $=$ __?__. 19; 19; 2.944; 7.067 The maximum velocity is about __?__ kilometers per second. 7.1

Example 3 Under certain geographic conditions, the wind velocity v at a height h centimeters above the ground is given by $v = k \ln\left(\frac{h}{h_0}\right)$, where k is a positive constant that depends on air density, average wind velocity, and other factors and h_0 is a "roughness" value, depending on the roughness of the vegetation on the ground.

a. Suppose that $h_0 = 0.7$ centimeter, a value that applies to a lawn 3 centimeters high. If the wind velocity is 435 centimeters per second, what is the value of k? Substitute values for v, h, and h_0 into the equation and solve for k: $k \approx 299$.

b. At what height above the ground is the wind velocity 1500 centimeters per second? Substitute values for v, k, and h_0 into the equation and solve for h. The velocity is 1500 cm/sec at a height of about 106 cm.

Accommodating the Learner

Have students work in groups to order $\log_3 27$, $\log_{\frac{1}{3}} 27$, $\ln 3$, and $\ln \frac{1}{3}$ from least to greatest without using a calculator. Have group members discuss their reasoning. $\ln \frac{1}{3} < \ln 3$ because the natural logarithm is an increasing function. Since $e < 3 < e^2$, $1 < \ln 3 < 2$. But $\log_3 27 = 3$, so $\ln 3 < \log_3 27$. Since $\ln \frac{1}{3}$ is positive but $\log_{\frac{1}{3}} 27 = \log_{\frac{1}{3}}\left(\frac{1}{3}\right)^{-3} = -3$, $\log_{\frac{1}{3}} 27 < \ln \frac{1}{3}$. So the order from least to greatest is $\log_{\frac{1}{3}} 27$, $\ln \frac{1}{3}$, $\ln 3$, and $\log_3 27$.

3 Assignment

Recommended Assignment

- Questions 1–26
- Question 27 (extra credit)
- Reading Lesson 9-9
- Covering the Ideas 9-9

Solution

a. Substitute values for O_1, O_2, S_1, S_2, and t into the equation to solve for k. Note that because the kitchen temperatures did not change, $S_1 = S_2 = 80$. Enter the equation into a CAS as shown below. This CAS simplifies the fraction automatically.

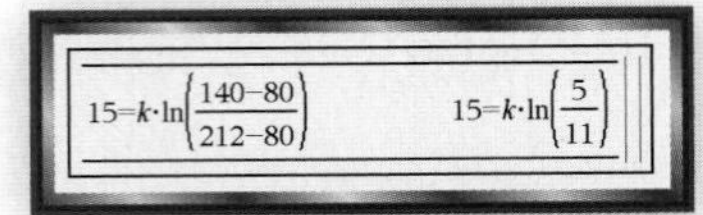

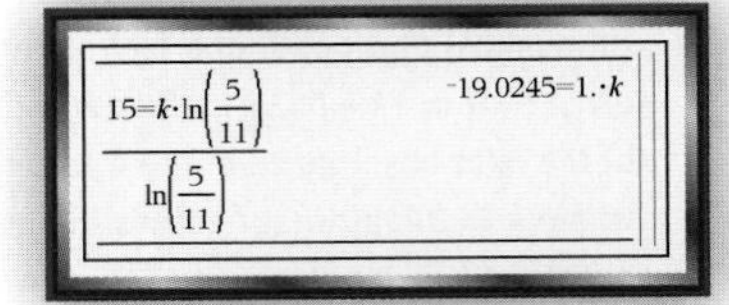

Divide both sides by $\ln\left(\frac{5}{11}\right)$, as shown at the right.

So, $k \approx -19$.

b. From Part a, $T = -19 \ln\left(\frac{O_2 - S_2}{O_1 - S_1}\right)$. Substitute values for O_1, S_1, S_2, and t into the equation from Part a and divide both sides by -19.

$$15 = -19 \ln\left(\frac{O_2 - 70}{212 - 70}\right)$$

$$-\frac{15}{19} = \ln\left(\frac{O_2 - 70}{142}\right)$$

Use the definition of natural logarithm to rewrite the equation.

$$e^{-\frac{15}{19}} = \frac{O_2 - 70}{142}$$

Calculate $e^{-\frac{15}{19}}$ and multiply both sides by 142.

$0.454(142) \approx O_2 - 70$

$134 \approx O_2$

The serving temperature of the soup is about 134°F.

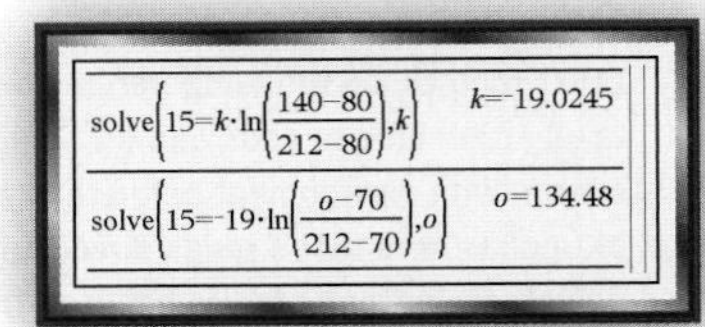

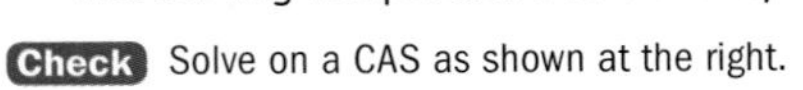

Check Solve on a CAS as shown at the right.

Questions

COVERING THE IDEAS

1. What are logarithms to the base e called? natural logarithms

2. **Multiple Choice** Which of the following is not equivalent to $y = \ln x$? There may be more than one correct answer. A and D

   A $x = \log_e y$ B $e^y = x$ C $y = \log_e x$ D $e^x = y$

In 3 and 4, write an equivalent exponential equation.

3. $\ln 1 = 0$ $e^0 = 1$

4. $\ln 1000 \approx 6.908$ $e^{6.908} \approx 1000$

9-8A Lesson Master

Questions on SPUR Objectives
See Student Edition pages 656–659 for objectives.

VOCABULARY

In 1 and 2, write the exponential equation as a logarithmic equation, or vice-versa.

1. a. $e^3 \approx 20.086$ $\ln 20.086 \approx 3$ b. $e^{-1.5} \approx 0.223$ $\ln 0.223 \approx -1.5$ c. $e^r = a$ $\ln a = r$

2. a. $\ln 0.135 \approx -2$ $e^{-2} \approx 0.135$ b. $\ln 3361 \approx 8.12$ $e^{8.12} \approx 3361$ c. $\ln v = u$ $e^u = v$

SKILLS Objective A

In 3–5, evaluate to the nearest thousandth.

3. $\ln 873.5 \approx$ 6.773 4. $\ln 0.0924 \approx$ −2.382 5. $\ln \sqrt{2} \approx$ 0.347

In 6–8, give an exact answer. Do all work in your head; check with a CAS if necessary.

6. $\ln e =$ 1 7. $\ln e^5 =$ 5 8. $\ln \frac{1}{e^2} =$ −2

PROPERTIES Objective E

9. Give the domain and range of the function f where $f(x) = \ln x$. domain: $\{x \mid x > 0\}$; range: set of all reals

10. Explain why $\ln(e^a) = a$. Answers vary. Sample: This is a logarithmic equation equivalent to the exponential equation $e^a = e^a$.

USES Objective I

11. The median height for girls aged 2 to 16 is approximated by the function h with equation $h(a) = 47.28 + 40.86 \ln(a)$, where $h(a)$ is the median height in centimeters of a girl a years old.

    a. Use the function to approximate the median height of 14-year-old girls. 155 cm

    b. At what age (to the nearest month) is the median height one meter? 3 yrs, 8 mo

    c. Explain why this function would not be appropriate to estimate the median height of 42-year-old women. Answers vary. Sample: The logarithmic function continues to grow, but people do not.

12. For large values of n, the number of prime numbers less than n is approximated by a function P where $P(n) = \frac{n}{\ln(n)}$.

    a. Find $P(100)$, $P(1000)$, and $P(1{,}000{,}000)$. 21.7; 144.8; 72,382.4

    b. There are 25 prime numbers less than 100; 168 less than 1000; and 78,498 less than 1,000,000. For which of these values did $P(n)$ give the best estimate? Explain. Answers vary. Sample: 1,000,000: Percent errors are 13.2%, 13.8%, and 7.8%

In 5 and 6, write in logarithmic form.

5. $e^5 \approx 148.41$ ln 148.41 ≈ 5
6. $e^{0.5} \approx 1.65$ ln 1.65 ≈ 0.5
7. Without using a calculator, tell which is greater, ln 1000 or log 1000. How do you know?
8. Approximate ln 210 to the nearest thousandth. 5.347
9. Refer to Example 2. If the light intensity is 4.5 lumens, at what depth is the light in the lake? about 27.1 ft
10. Does the function with equation $f(x) = \ln x$ have an inverse? If so, what is it? Yes; $f^{-1}(x) = e^x$.

7. ln 1000; because $e < 10$, e must be raised to a greater power to get 1000.

In 11–13, evaluate without using a calculator.

11. $\ln e$ 1
12. $\ln e^4$ 4
13. $\ln e^{-2}$ −2
14. Refer to Part b of Example 3. What will the temperature of Laura's soup be if it cools for 10 minutes instead of 15? about 154°F

16a. Answers vary. Sample: The calculator reports an error: "nonreal answer."

APPLYING THE MATHEMATICS

15. Refer to Example 3. When cooling hot food in a refrigerator or freezer for service at a later time, caterers want to move through the temperature range from 145°F to 45°F as quickly as possible to avoid pathogen growth. How much longer will it take soup to go from 145° to 45° in a 34°F refrigerator than a 5°F freezer? (Assume $k = -19$.) about 20 minutes longer

16. a. What happens when you try to find ln(−5) on a calculator?
    b. Use the graph of $y = \ln(x)$ to explain why the calculator displayed what you saw in Part a.
17. In Lesson 9-6 you saw that the decibel scale is a logarithmic scale used to measure relative power intensity, often for sound. Named after John Napier, the ***neper*** is another measure of relative power intensity based on the natural log scale. A conversion formula between nepers and decibels is 1 neper $= \frac{20}{\ln 10}$ decibels. Find the number of decibels that are equivalent to 3 nepers. about 26 decibels
18. How can you use a graph of $y = e^x$ to find the value of $\ln\left(\frac{2}{3}\right)$?
19. a. What is the y-intercept of the graph of $y = \ln x$? no y-intercept
    b. What is the y-intercept of the graph of $y = \log x$? no y-intercept
    c. Prove a generalization about the y-intercepts of the graphs of all equations of the form $y = \log_b x$.

16b. The domain of the natural log function is $x > 0$, so −5 is not included in the domain.

18. The value of x when $y = \frac{2}{3}$ on a graph of $y = e^x$ is the value of $\ln\left(\frac{2}{3}\right)$.

19c. Graphs of equations of the form $y = \log_b x$ where $b > 0$ and $b \neq 1$ have no y-intercept. This is because $b^y \neq 0$ for all y.

In 20 and 21, suppose $\ln x = 9$, $\ln y = 3$, and $\ln z = 27$. Evaluate.

20. $\ln(xyz)$ 39
21. $\ln \sqrt[y]{\frac{z}{x}}$ 0.896

Accommodating the Learner

For Questions 20 and 21, remind students to evaluate the expressions using the order of operations before they find the natural log. In Lesson 9-9, they will learn properties of logarithms that will provide another method for evaluating these expressions.

4 Wrap-Up

Ongoing Assessment

Have students work in pairs. Have each student use the [e^x] key on their calculators to list five values obtained by raising e to five different powers. Then have students write only the values on a sheet of paper and exchange papers with their partners. Each partner should find the natural logarithm of each value. Students should correctly use calculators to find powers of e and determine the values of natural logarithms.

Administer Quiz 2 (or a quiz of your own) after students complete this lesson.

Project Update

Project 5, *Predicting Cooling Times,* on page 651 relates to the content of this lesson.

9-8B page 2

9-8B Lesson Master

Questions on SPUR Objectives
See Student Edition pages 656–659 for objectives.

VOCABULARY

1. **Fill in the Blank** Logarithms to the base ___e___ are called *natural logarithms.*

In 2–9, write the logarithmic equation as an exponential equation.

2. $\ln 15 \approx 2.708$ $e^{2.708} \approx 15$
3. $\ln 1.5 \approx 0.405$ $e^{0.405} \approx 1.5$
4. $\ln 42 \approx 3.738$ $e^{3.738} \approx 42$
5. $\ln 0.2 \approx -1.609$ $e^{-1.609} \approx 0.2$
6. $\ln 2.4 \approx 0.875$ $e^{0.875} \approx 2.4$
7. $\ln 3{,}000 \approx 8.006$ $e^{8.006} \approx 3000$
8. $\ln 7 \approx 1.95$ $e^{1.95} \approx 7$
9. $\ln 0.01 \approx -4.61$ $e^{-4.61} \approx 0.01$

In 10–15, write the exponential equation as a logarithmic equation.

10. $e^{-1.3} \approx 0.273$ $\ln 0.273 \approx -1.3$
11. $e^{15} \approx 3{,}269{,}017$ $\ln 3{,}269{,}017 \approx 15$
12. $e^{7} \approx 1097$ $\ln 1097 \approx 7$
13. $e^{1.5} \approx 4.482$ $\ln 4.482 \approx 1.5$
14. $e^{-\frac{1}{2}} \approx 0.607$ $\ln 0.607 \approx -\frac{1}{2}$
15. $e^{\frac{7}{4}} \approx 5.755$ $\ln 5.755 \approx \frac{7}{4}$

SKILLS Objective A

In 16–21, evaluate. Round to the nearest hundredth when necessary.

16. $\ln 95$ 4.55
17. $\ln 0.03$ −3.51
18. $\ln 8$ 2.08
19. $\ln 0.44$ −0.82
20. $\ln 5068$ 8.53
21. $\ln 0.05$ −3.00

In 22–35, give an exact answer. Do all work in your head; check with a CAS if necessary.

22. $\ln e^8$ 8
23. $\ln e^{\frac{1}{2}}$ $\frac{1}{2}$
24. $\ln e^{-\frac{2}{5}}$ $-\frac{2}{5}$
25. $\ln e^{14}$ 14
26. $\ln e$ 1
27. $\ln e^0$ 0
28. $\ln e^{\frac{4}{3}}$ $\frac{4}{3}$
29. $5 \ln e^2$ 10
30. $-\ln e^{-0.02}$ 0.02
31. $5 \ln e^{\frac{1}{5}}$ 1
32. $2 \ln e^{-4.2}$ −8.4
33. $3.5 \ln e^{-\frac{3}{7}}$ −1.5
34. $\frac{1}{8} \ln e^{-1}$ $-\frac{1}{8}$
35. $\frac{5}{3} \ln e^3$ 5

508 Advanced Algebra

REVIEW

22. Let $y = 7^x$. Write an equivalent logarithmic equation. (Lesson 9-7) $\log_7 y = x$

23. Solve for x: $\log_x 37 = 2$. (Lesson 9-7) $x = \sqrt{37}$

24. Use the earthquake moment magnitude scale formula $M_w = \log \frac{M_0}{1.5} - 10.7$. Determine the seismic moment M_0 for the earthquake in Chile, May 22, 1960, where $M_w = 9.5$, the largest (as of January 2007) ever recorded with a seismometer. (Lesson 9-6) $2.377 \cdot 10^{20}$

25. **Multiple Choice** Pick the equation for an exponential decay function. Explain your choice. (Lesson 9-2)
    A $f(x) = \frac{1^x}{7}$ B $f(x) = 7^{-x}$ C $f(x) = 7^x$ D $f(x) = \left(\frac{1}{7}\right)^{-x}$
    B; this is equation can be written in the the form $f(x) = ab^x$, where $a = 1$ and $b = \frac{1}{7}$. Since $0 < b < 1$, this equation describes exponential decay.

26. A 1:1000 scale model of the Empire State Building is a little less than $1\frac{1}{2}$ feet tall with a volume of 0.037 cubic foot. From this information, about how many cubic feet does the Empire State Building contain? (Lesson 2-1) 37,000,000 ft^3

EXPLORATION

27. John Napier, the Scottish mathematician who invented logarithms, also invented a calculating device known as *Napier's bones*. Investigate how this device works. Use your findings to simulate and describe Napier's process for any 3-digit-by-2-digit multiplication.
    Napier's bones is an abacus used to calculate the products and quotients of numbers by reducing multiplication to addition operations and division to subtraction operations. This device is explained with examples on many Internet sites.

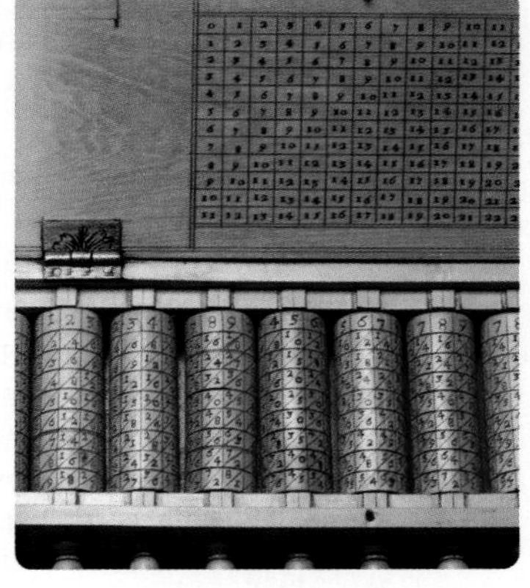

Napier's bones was an early counting device.

QY ANSWERS

1. −1

2a. $e^{4.605} \approx 100$

b. $e^{1.609} \approx 5$

Lesson 9-9 Properties of Logarithms

BIG IDEA Each basic property of powers corresponds to a basic property of logarithms.

The following properties of powers should be familiar both from Chapter 7 and from your work in previous courses. For all positive numbers x and for all real numbers m and n:

Zero Exponent Theorem	$x^0 = 1$
Product of Powers Postulate	$x^m \cdot x^n = x^{m+n}$
Quotient of Powers Theorem	$\frac{x^m}{x^n} = x^{m-n}$
Power of a Power Postulate	$(x^m)^n = x^{mn}$

Because every logarithm in base b is the exponent n of b^n, properties of logarithms can be derived from the properties of powers. In this lesson you will see five theorems, each related to one of the four properties of powers mentioned above.

Mental Math

Put in order from least to greatest.

a. $2 \cdot 10, 2^{10}, 10^2$ $2 \cdot 10, 10^2, 2^{10}$

b. $3^{16}, \pi^{16}, e^{16}$ $e^{16}, 3^{16}, \pi^{16}$

c. $0.5, \sqrt{0.5}, \sqrt[3]{0.5}$ $0.5, \sqrt{0.5}, \sqrt[3]{0.5}$

The Logarithm of a Power of the Base

Recall that the base b of a logarithm can be any positive number other than 1.

Activity 1

Step 1 Evaluate each of the following:

a.	b.	c.
$\log_2 1$ 0	$\log_2 2$ 1	$\log_2 2^{-2}$ −2
$\log_3 1$ 0	$\log_3 3$ 1	$\log_2 2^{-1}$ −1
$\log_4 1$ 0	$\log_4 4$ 1	$\log_2 2^0$ 0
$\ln 1$ 0	$\ln e$ 1	$\log_2 2^1$ 1

Step 2 Describe the pattern or write a generalization for each of the three sets of expressions in Step 1.
For set a, for any base $b > 0, b \neq 1, \log_b 1 = 0$. For set b, for any base $b > 0, b \neq 1, \log_b b = 1$. For set c, for any base $b > 0, b \neq 1$, and any real number n, $\log_b b^n = n$.

Background

When numbers are written as powers of the same number, you can multiply them by adding exponents, divide them by subtracting exponents, and take them to the nth power by multiplying the exponent by n. Logarithms with that number as base are exactly those exponents, which is why one can find the logarithm of a product by adding logs, find the logarithm of a quotient by subtracting logs, and find the logarithm of a power by multiplying a log by the power's exponent. These are three of the five properties of this lesson. The other two come directly from the definition of logarithm.

Lesson 9-9

GOAL

Learn and use five properties of logarithms to assist in obtaining values of logarithm functions and solving equations.

SPUR Objectives

C Solve logarithmic equations.

F Apply properties of logarithms.

Materials/Resources

- Lesson Masters 9-9A and 9-9B
- Resource Masters 175–178
- CAS

HOMEWORK

Suggestions for Assignment

- Questions 1–30
- Question 31 (extra credit)
- Reading Lesson 9-10
- Covering the Ideas 9-10

Local Standards

1 Warm-Up

1. Use a calculator to complete this table. Record logarithms to the nearest thousandth.

x	$\log x$
2	0.301
3	0.477
4	0.602
5	0.699
6	0.778
7	0.845
8	0.903
9	0.954
10	1

2. Find three logarithms such that the sum of two of them is the third. Answers vary. Sample: $\log 2 + \log 3 = \log 6$

(continued on next page)

3. Find three logarithms such that the difference of two of them is the third. Answers vary. Sample: $\log 8 - \log 2 = \log 4$
4. Find two logarithms that are double the values of other logarithms in the table. $\log 9 = 2 \log 3$; $\log 4 = 2 \log 2$

2 Teaching

Notes on the Lesson

To introduce this lesson, begin with the properties of exponents with which students are familiar. Rewrite the properties using the definition of logarithm (see page 622). When written in logarithmic form, $x^0 = 1$ becomes the Logarithm of 1 Theorem. Now let $b^n = x$. Then rewrite the equation as $\log_b x = n$ using the definition of logarithm. Have students substitute b^n for x; the result is the Log_b of b^n Theorem.

Remind students that the theorems proved in this lesson apply to logs with any positive base $b \neq 1$ and thus apply when $b = e$. Consequently, these properties apply to natural logs as well as to common logs. These properties are used in the solutions for Examples 1–4.

The logarithm of a product A proof of the Logarithm of a Product Theorem is given in the lesson; proofs of the Logarithm of a Quotient and Logarithm of a Power Theorems are found in Questions 22 and 23.

These theorems will be applied extensively in Lesson 9-10, so they should be committed to memory as soon as possible.

Steps 1b and 1c of Activity 1 illustrate the following theorem. You already used this theorem in Lessons 9-7 and 9-8 to evaluate logarithms of numbers with various bases.

Log_b of b^n Theorem

For every positive base $b \neq 1$, and any real number n, $\log_b b^n = n$.

Proof
1. Suppose $\log_b b^n = x$.
2. $b^x = b^n$ Definition of logarithm
3. $x = n$ Equate the exponents.
4. $\log_b b^n = n$ Substitution (Steps 1 and 3)

So, if a number can be written as the power of the base, the exponent of the power is its logarithm.

Let $n = 0$ in the Log_b of b^n Theorem. Then $\log_b b^0 = 0$, and because $b^0 = 1$ for $b \neq 0$, $\log_b 1 = 0$. This should agree with what you found in Step 1a of Activity 1.

Logarithm of 1 Theorem

For every positive base $b \neq 1$, $\log_b 1 = 0$.

The Logarithm of 1 Theorem is a special case of the Log_b of b^n Theorem.

The Logarithm of a Product

The Product of Powers Postulate says that in order to multiply two powers with the same base, add their exponents. In particular, for any base b (with $b > 0$, $b \neq 1$) and any real numbers m and n, $b^m \cdot b^n = b^{m+n}$.

The corresponding property of logarithms is about the logarithm of a product of two numbers.

Activity 2

MATERIALS CAS

Step 1 Make a table like the one on the next page.
Use a CAS to evaluate each expression, and then record the result.

Accommodating the Learner

Explain to students that the theorems in this lesson can be remembered in words that correspond to properties of powers. For example, when multiplying two powers of the same number, add exponents. With logarithms, the Logarithm of a Product Theorem indicates that the logarithm of the product is found by adding logarithms of the factors. Similar corresponding sentences exist for the Logarithm of a Quotient and Logarithm of a Power Theorems.

A	$\log(3 \cdot 2)$	?	$\log 6$
	$\log 3 + \log 2$	?	$\log 6$
B	$\log\left(\frac{1}{6} \cdot 216\right)$	?	$2 \log 6$
	$\log \frac{1}{6} + \log 216$	?	$2 \log 6$
C	$\log_5\left(7 \cdot \frac{25}{2}\right)$	?	$\log_5\left(\frac{175}{2}\right)$
	$\log_5 7 + \log_5 \frac{25}{2}$	?	$\log_5\left(\frac{175}{2}\right)$
D	$\ln(4 \cdot 32)$	?	$7 \ln 2$
	$\ln 4 + \ln 32$	?	$7 \ln 2$

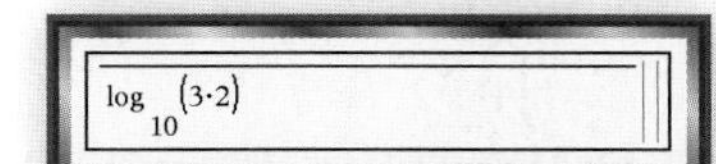

Step 2 Make a conjecture based on the results of Step 1: $\log_b (x \cdot y) =$ __?__ $\log_b x + \log_b y$

Activity 2 shows that the logarithm of a product equals the sum of the logarithms of the factors. We state this result as a theorem and prove it using the Product of Powers Postulate.

Logarithm of a Product Theorem

For any positive base $b \neq 1$ and positive real numbers x and y, $\log_b(xy) = \log_b x + \log_b y$.

Proof Let $x = b^m$ and $y = b^n$, for any $b > 0$, $b \neq 1$. Let $z = xy$.

Then $\log_b x = m$ and $\log_b y = n$.	Definition of logarithm
So $\log_b(xy) = \log_b(b^m \cdot b^n)$	Substitution (Given)
$= \log_b(b^{m+n})$	Product of Powers Postulate
$= m + n$	Log_b of b^n Theorem
$= \log_b x + \log_b y$	Substitution (Step 1)

Example 1

Find $\log_8 128 + \log_8 4$ and check your result.

Solution By the Logarithm of a Product Theorem,

$\log_8 128 + \log_8 4 = \log_8(128 \cdot 4) = \log_8 512$

Because $512 = 8^3$, $\log_8 512 = 3$.

So, $\log_8 128 + \log_8 4 = 3$.

Check Notice that 8, 128, and 4 are all integer powers of 2.

Let $x = \log_8 128$. Then $8^x = 128$, or $2^{3x} = 2^7$. So, $x = \frac{7}{3}$.

Let $y = \log_8 4$. Then $8^y = 4$, or $2^{3y} = 2^2$. So, $y = \frac{2}{3}$.

Consequently, $x + y = \frac{7}{3} + \frac{2}{3} = \frac{9}{3} = 3$. It checks.

Extension

Have students solve this equation:

$\frac{1}{2} \log_b (x + 2) + \frac{1}{2} \log_b (x - 22) = \frac{2}{3} \log_b 27$.

$x = 25$

Notes on the Lesson

Activity 2 When evaluating logarithmic expressions, different CASs may produce different and/or unexpected results. For example, if the expression $\log_b x + \log_b y$ is entered into both a Casio Classpad and a TI-Nspire, the results are equivalent, yet different in form, as shown below.

$\log_b(x) + \log_b(y)$

$\frac{\ln(x)}{\ln(b)} + \frac{\ln(y)}{\ln(b)}$

$\log_b(x) + \log_b(y)$ $\quad$ $\log_b(x) + \log_b(y)$

For reasons such as these, you may want to pair students with the same CAS model together to compare results after completing Activity 2 or when examining Questions 12–17. Or you may want to pair students with different CAS models to exhibit the differences.

Additional Example

Example 1 Find $\log_9 243 + \log_9 3$ and check your result. By the Logarithm of a Product Theorem, $\log_9 243 + \log_9 3 = \log_9(243 \cdot 3) = \log_9 729$. Because $729 = 9^3$, $\log_9 729 = 3$. So $\log_9 243 + \log_9 3 = 3$. Check: Notice that 243, 9, and 3 are all integer powers of 3. Let $x = \log_9 243$. Then $9^x = 243$, or $3^{2x} = 3^5$. So $x = \frac{5}{2}$. Let $y = \log_9 3$. Then $9^y = 3$, or $3^{2y} = 3^1$. So $y = \frac{1}{2}$. Consequently, $x + y = \frac{5}{2} + \frac{1}{2} = \frac{6}{2} = 3$. It checks.

Notes on the Lesson

Example 2 It is natural for students to wonder how they could check this example. An easy way is given in Lesson 9-10, when they encounter the Change of Base Theorem. This enables students to estimate $\log_b a$ with a calculator for any values of a and b for which the logarithm is defined.

Additional Examples

Example 2 Write $\log_6 48$ as the sum of two logarithms. Answers vary. Sample: $\log_6 48 = \log_6(4 \cdot 12) = \log_6 4 + \log_6 12$

Example 3 Use the Logarithm of a Quotient Theorem to show that $\log_b\left(\frac{1}{N}\right) = -\log_b N$.

Solution By the Logarithm of a Quotient Theorem, $\log_b\left(\frac{1}{N}\right) = \log_b \underline{\ ?\ } - \log_b \underline{\ ?\ } = \underline{\ ?\ } - \log_b \underline{\ ?\ } = \underline{\ ?\ }$. 1; N; 0; N; $-\log_b N$

Example 2

Write $\log_7 96$ as the sum of two logarithms.

Solution Find two positive integers whose product is 96.

$\log_7 96 = \log_7(3 \cdot 32)$

$= \log_7 3 + \log_7 32$ Logarithm of a Product Theorem

QY

▸ QY

Write $\log_7 96$ as the sum of a different pair of logarithms than those used in Example 2.

The Logarithm of a Quotient

A Logarithm of a Quotient Theorem follows from the related Quotient of Powers Theorem, $b^m \div b^n = b^{m-n}$.

Logarithm of a Quotient Theorem

For any positive base $b \neq 1$ and for any positive real numbers x and y,

$$\log_b\left(\frac{x}{y}\right) = \log_b x - \log_b y.$$

The proof of the Logarithm of a Quotient Theorem is similar to that of the Logarithm of a Product Theorem. You are asked to complete the proof in Question 22.

GUIDED

Example 3

Recall from Lesson 9-6 that the formula $D = 10 \log\left(\frac{N}{10^{-12}}\right)$ is used to compute the number D of decibels from the sound intensity N measured in watts per square meter. Use the Logarithm of a Quotient Theorem to rewrite this formula without a quotient.

Solution By the Logarithm of a Quotient Theorem,

$\log\left(\frac{N}{10^{-12}}\right) = \log \underline{\ ?\ } - \log \underline{\ ?\ }$ N; 10^{-12}

$= \log \underline{\ ?\ } + \underline{\ ?\ }$, because $\log_{10}(10^x) = x$. N; 12

Thus, $D = 10 \log\left(\frac{N}{10^{-12}}\right)$ is equivalent to

$D = 10(\log \underline{\ ?\ } + \underline{\ ?\ })$. N; 12

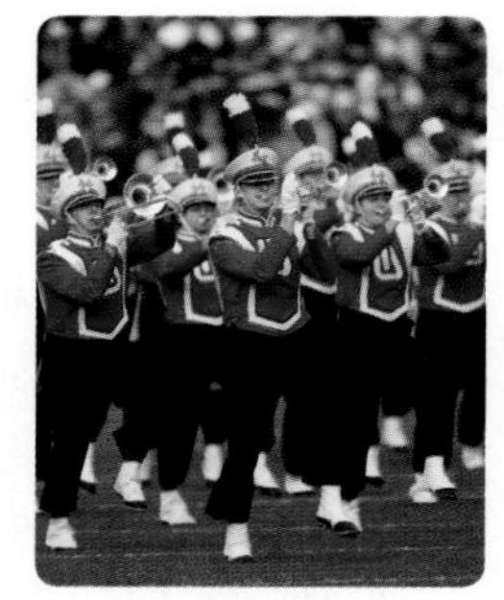

Members of marching bands are encouraged to wear earplugs to prevent hearing loss.

The Logarithm of a Power

Recall that $\log_b b^n = n$. In Activity 3 you will explore $\log_b x^n$, where $x \neq b$.

Activity 3

Step 1 Estimate each logarithm to the nearest thousandth.

a. log 3 0.477 **b.** $\log 3^2$ 0.954
c. $\log 3^3$ 1.431 **d.** $\log 3^4$ 1.908
e. ln 10 2.303 **f.** ln 100 4.605
g. ln 1000 6.908 **h.** ln 10,000 9.210

Step 2 Make a conjecture based on the results of Step 1: $\log_b x^n =$ __?__. $n \cdot \log_b x$

Step 3 In Step 1 you should have found that $\log 3^4 = \log 3 + \log 3 + \log 3 + \log 3 = 4 \log 3$. What property of logarithms supports this conclusion? The Product Property of Logarithms supports this conclusion.

Activity 3 illustrates the following theorem.

Logarithm of a Power Theorem

For any positive base $b \neq 1$ and for any positive real number x and any real number n, $\log_b(x^n) = n \log_b x$.

You are asked to complete the proof of this theorem in Question 23.

You can use the properties of logarithms to solve equations.

Example 4

Solve for k: $\log k = 2 \log 5 + \log 6 - \log 3$.

Solution Use the properties of logarithms.

$\log k = \log 5^2 + \log 6 - \log 3$ Logarithm of a Power Theorem

$\log k = \log(5^2 \cdot 6) - \log 3$ Logarithm of a Product Theorem

$\log k = \log\left(\frac{5^2 \cdot 6}{3}\right) = \log 50$ Logarithm of a Quotient Theorem, arithmetic

$k = 50$

Check Evaluate $2 \log 5 + \log 6 - \log 3$ on a CAS. The result, as shown at the right, is log 50. It checks.

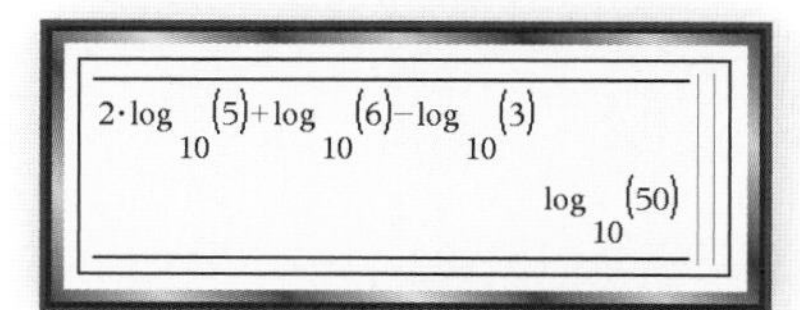

Accommodating the Learner

After discussing the Examples, have students work in small groups to write a question similar to those in Examples 1, 2, and 4. Have them provide three choices for answers, only one of which is correct. Then have students exchange papers and answer the questions. Answers vary. Check students' work.

Notes on the Lesson

Example 4 Not all CAS models will produce log 50 when 2log 5 + log 6 − log 3 is entered. If this is the case for the models your students have, you can have them test the equivalence of the original expression and the answer by subtracting one from the other and seeing if the result is zero.

Additional Example

Example 4 Solve for d: $\log d = 3\log 2 + \log 7 - \log 4$. $d = 14$

Note-Taking Tips

Have students add to their journals the theorems given in this lesson, along with appropriate examples.

3 Assignment

Recommended Assignment

- Questions 1–30
- Question 31 (extra credit)
- Reading Lesson 9-10
- Covering the Ideas 9-10

Notes on the Questions

Questions 12, 14, and 15 These questions are excellent for classroom discussion of the most common errors made when applying the logarithm theorems.

Questions 18 and 19 The solutions to the equations in these questions involve an inference from the statement $\log x = \log y$ to $x = y$. The justification for this inference is as follows: Because the log function has an inverse that is a function, if two values of the function are equal, the arguments that produced them also must be equal.

Questions

COVERING THE IDEAS

In 1–3, simplify.

1. $\log_{5.1} 5.1^{15.4}$ 15.4
2. $\log_r r^n$ n
3. $\log_b 1$ 0
4. Write $\log_7 96$ as the sum of a pair of logarithms different from the pair used in Example 2 and the QY.

In 5–7, an expression is given.

a. Write it as the logarithm of a single number or as a number without a logarithm.

b. Name the property or properties of logarithms that you used.

5. $\log_2 49 - \log_2 7$ a. $\log_2 7$
6. $\log_{64} 3 + \log_{64} 8 - \log_{64} 4$ a. $\log_{64} 6$
7. $3 \log_3 \sqrt{9}$ a. 3
8. Here is the start of a proof to show that $\log x^4 = 4 \log(x)$ without using the Logarithm of a Power Theorem. Begin by realizing $\log x^4 = \log(x \cdot x \cdot x \cdot x)$. Next, use the Logarithm of a Product Theorem. With this hint, complete the rest of the proof.
9. A student enters $\log(64)$ on a CAS and gets $6 \log 2$ as an output. Show that the two expressions are equivalent using the properties of logarithms. $\log(64) = \log(2^6) = 6 \log 2$

In 10 and 11, rewrite the expression as a single logarithm.

10. $\log 14 - 3 \log 4$ $\log\left(\frac{7}{32}\right)$
11. $\log_b x - \log_b y + \frac{1}{2} \log_b z$ $\log_b\left(\frac{x\sqrt{z}}{y}\right)$

True or False In 12–17, if the statement is false, give a counterexample, and then correct the statement to make it true.

12. $\log_b(3x) = 3 \log_b x$
13. $\ln M - \ln N = \ln\left(\frac{M}{N}\right)$ true
14. $\frac{\log p}{\log q} = \log\left(\frac{p}{q}\right)$
15. $\log(M + N) = \log M + \log N$
16. $\log_7\left(\frac{M}{N}\right) = \frac{\log_7 M}{\log_7 N}$
17. $6 \log_2 T = \log_2(T^6)$ true

APPLYING THE MATHEMATICS

In 18 and 19, solve for *y*.

18. $\ln h = \frac{1}{4} \ln x + \ln y$ $y = xk^{-\frac{1}{4}}$
19. $\log w = \log\left(\frac{x}{y^4}\right)$ $y = \left(\frac{x}{w}\right)^{\frac{1}{4}}$

4. Answers vary. Sample: $\log_7 48 + \log_7 2$

5b. Logarithm of a Quotient Theorem

6b. Logarithm of a Product Theorem, Logarithm of a Quotient Theorem

7b. Answers vary. Sample: Logarithm of a Power Theorem

8. $\log(x \cdot x \cdot x \cdot x) = \log x + \log x + \log x + \log x$ (Logarithm of a Product Theorem), $\log x + \log x + \log x + \log x = 4 \log x$ (repeated addition, model of multiplication).

12. false; Answers vary. Sample: For $x = 2$, $\log 6 \neq 3 \log 2$; $\log_b x^3 = 3 \log_b x$.

14. false; Answers vary. Sample: For $p = 3$ and $q = 4$, $\frac{\log 3}{\log 4} \neq \log\left(\frac{3}{4}\right)$; $\log p - \log q = \log\left(\frac{p}{q}\right)$.

15–16. See margin.

Additional Answers

15. false; Answers vary. Sample: For $M = 3$, $N = 7$, $\log(10) \neq \log 3 + \log 7$; $\log(MN) = \log M + \log N$.

16. false; Answers vary. Sample: For $M = 3$, $N = 4$, $\log_7\left(\frac{3}{4}\right) \neq \frac{\log_7 3}{\log_7 4}$; $\log_7\left(\frac{M}{N}\right) = \log_7 M - \log_7 N$.

9-9A Lesson Master

Questions on SPUR Objectives
See Student Edition pages 656–659 for objectives.

SKILLS Objective C

In 1–4, use properties of logarithms to solve the equation in your head.

1. $\log 14 + \log 12 = \log x$ $x = 168$
2. $\log_3 120 - \log_3 6 = \log_3 n$ $n = 20$
3. $5 \log 2 = \log t$ $t = 32$
4. $\ln 40 - \ln n = \ln 5$ $n = 8$
5. Solve for y: $\log x + \log y = \frac{1}{2} \log z$ $y = \frac{\sqrt{z}}{x}$
6. Solve for b: $3 \ln a - 2 \ln b = \ln(c + 5)$ $b = \sqrt{\frac{a^3}{c+5}}$

PROPERTIES Objective F

In 7–12, express as a single logarithm. Use paper and pencil as needed.

7. $\log 12 + \log 9$ $\log 108$
8. $\ln 5 + 2 \ln 3$ $\ln 45$
9. $\log_2 12 + \log_2 3 - \log_2 6$ $\log_2 6$
10. $\ln(4a) - \ln a$ $\ln 4$
11. $\ln a + 3 \ln b - 2 \ln c$ $\ln \frac{ab^3}{c^2}$
12. $3 \log x + \frac{2}{3} \log y + \log z$ $\log x^3 y^{\frac{2}{3}} z$

In 13 and 14, write as an integer. Do all work in your head.

13. $\log 50 + \log 8 - \log 4$ 2
14. $\log_6 28 - \log_6 7 + 2 \log_6 3$ 2
15. Give a counterexample to show that $\log(a + b) \neq \log a + \log b$.
Answers vary. Sample: $a = 1$, $b = 10$
16. Write three different expressions equivalent to log 30. Answers vary. Sample: $\log 3 + \log 10$; $\log 60 - \log 2$; $\log 6 + \log 5$
17. **Multiple Choice** Newton's Law of Cooling states that the time for an object to cool from O_1 degrees to O_2 degrees as the surrounding temperature changes from S_1 degrees to S_2 degrees is given by $t = k \ln \frac{(O_2 - S_2)}{(O_1 - S_1)}$ where k is a constant. Determine which of the following equations is equivalent to this. C

A $t = k \ln \frac{(O_2 + S_2)}{(O_1 + S_1)}$

B $t = k \frac{\ln O_2 - \ln S_2}{\ln O_1 - \ln S_1}$

C $t = k(\ln(O_2 - S_2) - \ln(O_1 - S_1))$

510 *Advanced Algebra*

20. In the formula for the decibel scale $D = 10\log\left(\frac{N}{10^{-12}}\right)$, where N is the sound intensity and D is relative intensity, show that $D = 120 + \log N^{10}$ by using properties of logarithms.

21. Janella used a CAS to expand `log(a*b)`, where a and b are both positive. The display at the right shows her CAS output. Show that this CAS output is equivalent to the original expression.

$$\text{expand}(\log_{10}(a \cdot b) \mid a>0 \text{ and } b>0)$$
$$\frac{\log_{10}(a)}{\log_{10}(5)+\log_{10}(2)} + \frac{\log_{10}(b)}{\log_{10}(5)+\log_{10}(2)}$$

22. **Fill in the Blanks** Justify each step in the following proof of the Logarithm of a Quotient Theorem.

Let $x = b^m$, $y = b^n$, and $z = \frac{x}{y}$.

a. $\log_b x = m$ and $\log_b y = n$ a. __?__ definition of logarithm

b. $\log_b\left(\frac{x}{y}\right) = \log_b\left(\frac{b^m}{b^n}\right)$ b. __?__ substitution

c. $= \log_b(\underline{\ ?\ })$ c. __?__ b^{m-n}; Quotient of Powers Theorem

d. $= m - n$ d. __?__ $\log_b b^n$ Theorem

e. $\log_b\left(\frac{x}{y}\right) = \log_b x - \log_b y$ e. __?__ substitution

23. **Fill in the Blanks** Complete the following proof of the Logarithm of a Power Theorem.

Let $\log_b x = m$.

a. Then, $x = \underline{\ ?\ }$. b^m — definition of logarithm

b. $x^n = \underline{\ ?\ }$ $(b^m)^n$ — Raise both sides to the nth power.

c. $x^n = \underline{\ ?\ }$ b^{mn} — Power of a Power Postulate

d. $x^n = \underline{\ ?\ }$ b^{nm} — Commutative Property of Multiplication

e. $\log_b x^n = \underline{\ ?\ }$ nm — definition of logarithm

$\log_b x^n = n \log_b x$ — substitution

REVIEW

24. Simplify without a calculator. (Lesson 9-7)

a. $\log_{81} 81$ 1 b. $\log_{81} 9$ $\frac{1}{2}$ c. $\log_{81} 3$ $\frac{1}{4}$

d. $\log_{81} 1$ 0 e. $\log_{81}\left(\frac{1}{81}\right)$ -1 f. $\log_{81}\left(\frac{1}{9}\right)$ $-\frac{1}{2}$

In 25 and 26, solve. (Lessons 9-7, 9-5)

25. $\log_x 144 = 2$ $x = 12$

26. a. $\log y = -4$ $y = \frac{1}{10{,}000}$ b. $\log(-4) = z$ no solution

20. $D = 10(\log N - \log 10^{-12})$
$D = 10(\log N - (-12 \log 10))$
$D = 10 \log N + 120$
$D = \log N^{10} + 120$

21. $\log_{10} 5 + \log_{10} 2 = \log_{10}(5 \cdot 2) = \log_{10} 10 = 1$ and $\log_{10}(a \cdot b) = \log_{10} a + \log_{10} b$; therefore, $\frac{\log_{10} a}{\log_{10} 5 + \log_{10} 2} + \frac{\log_{10} b}{\log_{10} 5 + \log_{10} 2} = \frac{\log_{10}(a \cdot b)}{\log_{10} 5 + \log_{10} 2} = \log_{10}(a \cdot b)$

Notes on the Questions

Question 21 The CAS shown here only produces this result when composite bases are used. Students will get different results if they use prime bases or natural logs.

Question 23 An alternate proof for the Logarithm of a Power Theorem, when n is a positive integer, is as follows:

$$\log_b(x^n) = \log_b(\underbrace{x \cdot x \cdot \ldots \cdot x}_{n \text{ factors}}) = \underbrace{\log_b x + \log_b x + \ldots + \log_b x}_{n \text{ addends}} = n\log_b x.$$

Question 24 Stress the general principle of writing the argument as a power of 81. Then the logarithm is the exponent.

Notes on the Questions

Question 27 In 1923, the rate of inflation hit $3.25 \cdot 10^6$ percent per month. This meant prices doubled every two days. When completing Part c, stress that the model should be based on half-year periods after July 1914, so July 1914 corresponds to an *x*-value of 0, January 1919 to an *x*-value of 9, etc.

Question 31 When logarithms were used for computation, students would memorize the common logarithms of 2 and 3 to a few decimal places. It still is occasionally useful to know that $\log 2 \approx 0.3$.

4 Wrap-Up

Ongoing Assessment

Have students write one specific example corresponding to each of the five theorems in this lesson. Students should demonstrate that they understand the theorems by writing a specific instance to illustrate each theorem.

Project Update

Project 1, *Slide Rules,* on page 650 relates to the content of this lesson.

9-9B page 2

9-9B Lesson Master

Questions on SPUR Objectives
See Student Edition pages 656–659 for objectives.

SKILLS Objective C

In 1–14, use properties of logarithms to solve the equation in your head.

1. $\log x = 5 \log 4$ $x = 1024$
2. $\log_5 u = \frac{1}{3}\log_5 64$ $u = 4$
3. $\log m = \log 2 + \log 14$ $m = 28$
4. $\log 28 - \log 7 = \log y$ $y = 4$
5. $\log (4z) = \log 5 + \log 4$ $z = 5$
6. $3 \log_2 4 = \log_2 m$ $m = 64$
7. $\log 6 + \log 10 = \log (5a)$ $a = 12$
8. $4 \log x = \log 32 - \log 2$ $x = 2$
9. $\log p = \log 6 + 3 \log 5$ $p = 750$
10. $\log_4 h = \frac{1}{2}\log_4 49 - \log_4 3$ $h = \frac{7}{3}$
11. $-\frac{1}{2}\log n = \log 1 - 2 \log 9$ $n = 6561$
12. $\log_8\left(\frac{x}{2}\right) = 2 \log_8 5 + 3 \log_8 2$ $x = 400$
13. $\log_5 625 - \log_5 25 = 2 \log_5 h$ $h = 5$
14. $\log_{19}(15y) = \log_{19} 3 + \log_{19} 5$ $y = 1$
15. Solve for *y*: $2 \log x - \log y = \log z$ $y = \frac{x^2}{z}$
16. Solve for *b*: $\frac{1}{3}\ln a + 2 \ln b = \ln (a - 2)$ $b = \sqrt{\frac{a-2}{\sqrt[3]{a}}}$
17. Solve for *x*: $4 \log x - 3 \log 2x = \log t$ $x = 8t$
18. Solve for *m*: $\ln m + 3 \ln m = 2 \ln x$ $m = \sqrt[4]{x^2}$

PROPERTIES Objective F

In 19 and 20, express as a single logarithm. Use paper and pencil as needed.

19. $\log x + 5 \log r$ $\log xr^5$
20. $\log_3 4 + \log_3 x - \frac{1}{2}\log_3 d$ $\log_3 \frac{4x\sqrt{d}}{d}$

In 21–36, evaluate. Do work in your head as much as possible.

21. $\log_{12} 1$ 0
22. $\log_{27} 27^{13}$ 13
23. $\log_8 4 + \log_8 2$ 1
24. $2 \log_9 27$ 3
25. $\log_{18} 18^{20}$ 20
26. $\log_{12} 3 + \log_{12} 4$ 1
27. $4 \log_3 9$ 8
28. $\log_6 72 - \log_6 2$ 2
29. $\log_{25} 7 - \log_{25} 35$ −0.5
30. $\log_8 32{,}768$ 5
31. $7 \log_3 3 - 8 \log_3 3$ −1
32. $\log \sqrt[8]{100}$ 0.25

512

Advanced Algebra 511

27. After World War I, harsh reparation payments imposed on Germany caused the value of the deutschmark to decline against foreign currencies and German wholesale prices to increase rapidly. The table at the right shows the wholesale price index in Germany from 1914 to 1922. **(Lesson 9-4)**
    a. Sketch a scatterplot of these data. See margin.
    b. Why do these data suggest an exponential model?
    c. Find an exponential equation that models these data for semiannual periods after July 1914.
    d. Use Part c to predict the wholesale price index for January 1923. 46.11
    e. The actual wholesale price index for January 1923 was 2785. Does this model over or underpredict the actual wholesale price index? under predicts

Date	Wholesale Price Index
July 1914	1.0
Jan. 1919	2.6
July 1919	3.4
Jan. 1920	12.6
Jan. 1921	14.4
July 1921	14.3
Jan. 1922	36.7
July 1922	100.6

27b. Answers vary. Sample: The data seem to roughly lie on an exponential curve.

27c. Answers vary. Sample: $y \approx 0.533 \bullet 1.30^x$

28. A student borrows \$2000 to go to college. The student loan accrues interest continuously at a rate of 3.75% for four years. What is the total loan balance after four years? **(Lesson 9-3)** \$2323.67

29. a. Find the average rate of change between $x = -3$ and $x = -2$ for the function with equation $y = \frac{1}{3}x^3$. **(Lesson 7-1)** $\frac{19}{3}$
    b. Sketch a graph and use it to explain your answer to Part a.

29b. $\frac{19}{3}$ is the slope of the line segment connecting the points $(-3, -9)$ and $\left(-2, -\frac{8}{3}\right)$.

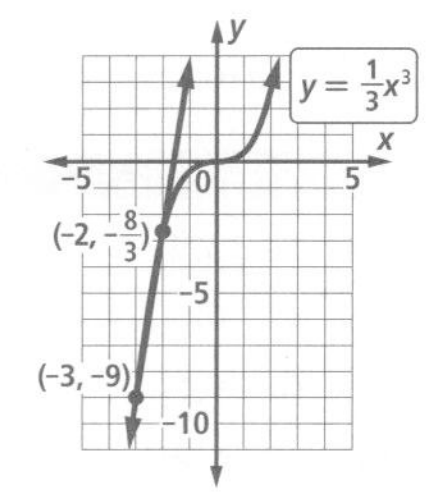

30. **Multiple Choice** A distributor sells old-time movies from the 1940s and 1950s for \$5.99 each plus a shipping and handling charge of \$3.89 per order. As a bonus, every fifth movie ordered is free. Which equation gives the correct charge $f(m)$ for m movies? **(Lesson 3-9)** A
    A $f(m) = 3.89 + 5.99m - 5.99\left\lfloor \frac{m}{5} \right\rfloor$
    B $f(m) = 3.89 + 5.99m - 5.99\left\lfloor 1 - \frac{m}{5} \right\rfloor$
    C $f(m) = \frac{5.99m}{5} + 3.89$
    D $f(m) = 3.89 + 5.99m - \frac{5.99m}{5}$

EXPLORATION

31. What common logarithms of whole numbers from 1 through 20 can you estimate without a calculator using only log 1, $\log 2 \approx 0.301$, $\log 3 \approx 0.477$, and log 10? See margin.

QY ANSWER

Answers vary. Sample: $\log_7 12 + \log_7 8$

Additional Answers

27a.

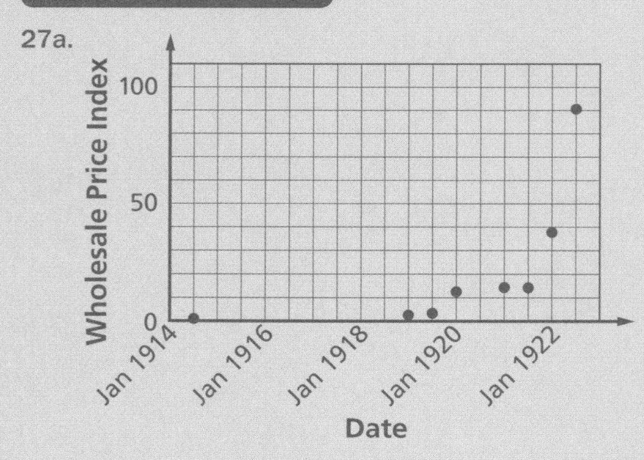

31. $\log 1 = 0$, $\log 2 \approx 0.301$, $\log 3 \approx 0.477$, $\log 4 = 2\log 2 \approx 0.602$, $\log 5 = \log\left(\frac{10}{2}\right) = 1 - \log 2 \approx 0.699$, $\log 6 = \log(3 \cdot 2) = \log 3 + \log 2 \approx 0.778$, $\log 8 = 3\log 2 \approx 0.903$, $\log 9 = 2\log 3 \approx 0.954$, $\log 10 = 1$, $\log 12 = \log(3 \cdot 4) = \log 3 + \log 4 = \log 3 + 2\log 2 \approx 1.079$, $\log 15 = \log(3 \cdot 5) = \log 3 + \log 5 = \log 3 + \log 10 - \log 2 \approx 1.176$, $\log 16 = 4 \log 2 \approx 1.204$, $\log 18 = \log(9 \cdot 2) = 2\log 3 + \log 2 = 1.255$, $\log 20 = \log(10 \cdot 2) = \log 10 + \log 2 = 1.301$

Lesson

9-10 Using Logarithms to Solve Exponential Equations

▸ **BIG IDEA** The solution to the exponential equation $b^x = a$ can be written as $\log_b a$, or it can be written as $\frac{\log a}{\log b}$.

Methods for Solving $b^x = a$

You already know a few ways to solve equations of the form $b^x = a$. When a is an integer power of b, you may solve the equation in your head. For instance, to solve $4^x = 64$, you may know that 3 is a solution, because $4^3 = 64$.

Sometimes you may notice that a and b are powers of the same number. For instance,

$$100^x = \sqrt{10}$$

can be solved by noting that both sides of the equation can be written as powers of 10.

$$100^x = (10^2)^x = 10^{2x} \quad \text{and} \quad \sqrt{10} = 10^{0.5}$$

Substitute into the given equation.

$$10^{2x} = 10^{0.5}$$

Equate the exponents and solve the resulting equation for x.

$$2x = 0.5$$

$$x = 0.25$$

Still another way to solve an equation of the form $b^x = a$ is to graph $y = b^x$ and see where the graph intersects the horizontal line $y = a$.

And, of course, you could use a CAS to solve $b^x = a$ directly.

But what happens if a and b are not easily found powers of the same number and a graphing utility or a CAS is not available? Then you can use logarithms to solve these equations.

Mental Math

Solve.

a. $3^x = 81$ $x = 4$

b. $5^y + 75 = 200$ $y = 3$

c. $4 \cdot 7^z = 196$ $z = 2$

d. $2^{w+2} - 16 = 0$ $w = 2$

Background

When logarithms were first defined by Napier, and even when common logarithms were first invented by Briggs, they were not connected with exponents. At that time, there was no meaning for a general real exponent.

More than 100 years later, Euler attached logarithms to exponents by considering them as the solutions to equations of the form $b^x = a$. He was the first to give the definition of logarithm in common use today, namely that $b^x = a$ if and only if $x = \log_b a$.

In this lesson, we wish to solve equations of the form $b^x = a$. By definition, $x = \log_b a$ is the solution. However, the solution $\log_b a$ to the equation $b^x = a$ begs the question: How do you calculate $\log_b a$? If only the definition is used, the reasoning becomes circular; that is, you cannot calculate $\log_b a$ without solving $b^x = a$.

(continued on next page)

Lesson

9-10

GOAL

Show that the solution to $b^x = a$ can be represented as either $\frac{\log a}{\log b}$ or $\log_b a$.

SPUR Objectives

A Determine values of logarithms.

B Use logarithms to solve exponential equations.

F Apply properties of logarithms.

G Create and apply exponential growth and decay models.

Materials/Resources

- Lesson Masters 9-10A and 9-10B
- Resource Masters 177, 179 and 180

HOMEWORK

Suggestions for Assignment

- Questions 1–27
- Question 28 (extra credit)
- Self-Test

Local Standards

1 Warm-Up

In 1–3, solve the equation.

1. $m \cdot \log 100 = \log 1000$ $m = 1.5$
2. $p \cdot \ln 100 = \ln 1000$ $p = 1.5$
3. $2^4 \cdot 3^2 \cdot 5 \cdot y = 2^5 \cdot 3 \cdot 5$ $y = \frac{2}{3}$

2 Teaching

Notes on the Lesson

You may want to introduce this lesson by asking students to solve (a) $x^2 = 144$ and (b) $2^x = 144$. The first equation is easy to solve and yields the solutions $x = \pm 12$. Solutions to the second equation can be approximated. Because $2^7 = 128$ and $2^8 = 256$, we know that $7 < x < 8$, and x is probably closer to 7 than to 8. To find the exact value of x, have students use the pattern in the solution for Example 3 and find that $x = \frac{\log 144}{\log 2} = \frac{\ln 144}{\ln 2}$ (the exact answer) or $x \approx 7.17$ (an approximation to the nearest hundredth). Have students use a graphing utility to examine the graph of $y = 2^x$ near $x = 7$ and verify that $2^{7.17} \approx 144$.

Note that when solving $b^x = a$, if $b = e$, then the equation can be solved easily by using the definition of natural logarithm. When $b = 10$, it is easiest to solve by using the definition of common logarithm. However, if b is neither e nor 10, then it becomes the solver's choice; the equation can be solved using either common or natural logs or logs to any other base. We pick base 10 or base e because the needed values can be found easily with calculators.

Additional Example

Example 1 Recall that the formula for interest compounded continuously is $A = P \cdot (e^r)^t$. At what rate of interest, compounded continuously, do you have to invest your money so that it will triple in 20 years? 5.49%

Using Logarithms to Solve $b^x = a$

The process is similar to the process you have used to solve many equations where the unknown is on one side of the equation. Instead of adding the same number to both sides or multiplying both sides by the same number, you take the logarithm of both sides. Then apply the Logarithm of a Power Theorem to solve the resulting equation. When the base of the exponential equation is e, use natural logarithms.

Example 1

At what rate of interest, compounded continuously, do you have to invest your money so that it will double in 12 years?

Solution Use the Continuously Compounded Interest Formula $A = Pe^{rt}$. You want to know the rate at which after 12 years A will equal twice P, so substitute $2P$ for A and 12 for t.

$$A = 2P = Pe^{12r}$$

Since P is not zero, you can divide both sides by P.

$$2 = e^{12r}$$

Because the base in the equation is e, it is easiest to take the natural logarithm of each side.

$$\ln 2 = \ln(e^{12r})$$

$$\ln 2 = 12r \qquad \text{Log}_b \text{ of } b^n \text{ Theorem}$$

$$r = \frac{\ln 2}{12} \approx 0.0578 = 5.78\%$$

Check Choose a value for P and substitute the values back into the formula. We use $P = \$500$.

$A = 500 \cdot e^{(0.0578)(12)} \approx 1000$, or twice the investment. It checks.

 QY

QY

Why would it be less efficient to use common logarithms in Example 1?

Decay or depreciation problems modeled by exponential equations with negative exponents can be solved in a similar way.

GUIDED

Example 2

Archie Oligist finds the remains of an ancient wood cooking fire and determines that it has lost about 23.2% of the carbon-14 expected for that kind of wood. Recall that the half-life of carbon-14 is about 5730 years. A radioactive decay model for this situation is $A = Ce^{-\frac{\ln 2}{5730}t}$, where C is the original amount of carbon-14 and A is the amount present after t years. Use the model to estimate the age of the wood.

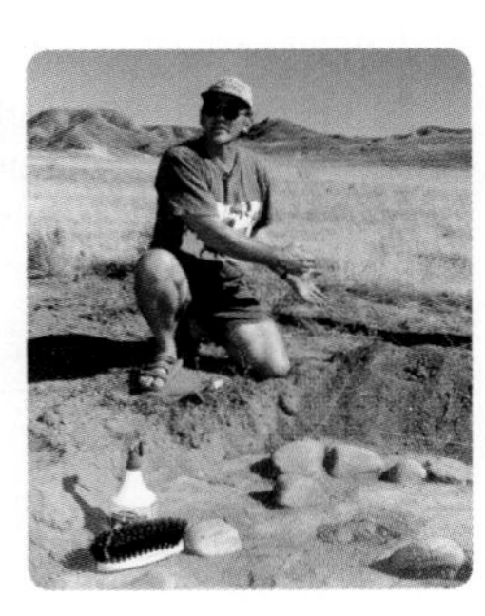

The way out of this dilemma is to use the general properties of logarithms. By taking the logarithm of both sides of the equation $b^x = a$, noting that the left side is a power, we get $x \log b = \log a$, where any base of logs could be used. Thus $x = \frac{\log a}{\log b}$. In order to evaluate this expression, what we have to be able to do is evaluate the logarithms of a and b to one base of our choosing. Thus, by choosing 10 or e as the base we can solve any equation of the form $b^x = a$ by using the common or natural logarithm key on a calculator. These equations can arise from any powering situation, and so solving them is most useful.

Solution Substitute values for the variables into the model. Because 23.2% of the carbon-14 has decayed, 76.8% remains and $A = 0.768C$.

$$A = Ce^{-\frac{\ln 2}{5730}t}$$

$0.768C = \underline{\ ?\ }$	Substitute for A. $Ce^{-\frac{\ln 2}{5730}t}$
$0.768 = \underline{\ ?\ }$	Divide both sides by C. $e^{-\frac{\ln 2}{5730}t}$
$\ln 0.768 = \underline{\ ?\ }$	Take the natural log of both sides. $\ln\left(e^{-\frac{\ln 2}{5730}t}\right)$
$\ln 0.768 = \underline{\ ?\ }$	Log_b of b^n Theorem $-\frac{\ln 2}{5730}t$
$\underline{\ ?\ } \cdot \ln 0.768 = t$	Solve for t. $-\frac{5730}{\ln 2}$
$t \approx \underline{\ ?\ }$ 2182.11	

The wood is about __?__ years old. 2182

Check Solve on a CAS as shown below. It checks.

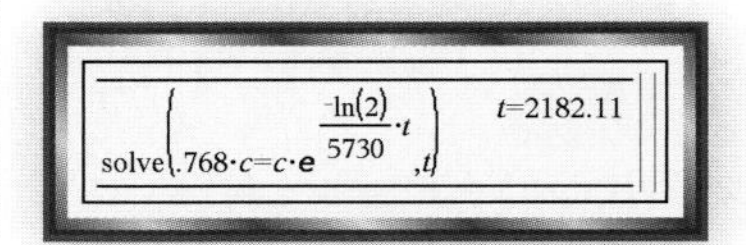

In the previous Examples, exponential equations were solved by taking natural logarithms of both sides because the base in the exponential equation was e. You can use any base of a logarithm to solve an exponential equation.

Example 3

Solve $7^x = 28$ by taking

a. the common logarithm of each side.

b. the natural logarithm of each side.

Solution Solutions for Parts a and b are written side-by-side. First read the solution to Part a (the columns at the left and center). Then read the solution to Part b (the center and right columns). Then reread both solutions by reading across each line.

a.		b.
$7^x = 2$		$7^x = 28$
$\log 7^x = \log 28$	Take the log of each side.	$\ln 7^x = \ln 28$
$x \log 7 = \log 28$	Logarithm of a Power Theorem	$x \ln 7 = \ln 28$
$x = \frac{\log 28}{\log 7}$	Divide both sides by the coefficient of x.	$x = \frac{\ln 28}{\ln 7}$
$x \approx 1.7124$	Evaluate with a calculator.	$x \approx 1.7124$

Accommodating the Learner

Have students solve the following equations for x and check their results.

1. $e^{2x} - 2e^x - 8 = 0$ $x = \ln 4$
2. $e^x - \frac{3}{e^{-x}} = -6$ $x = \ln 3$
3. $e^x = \sqrt{e^x}$ $x = 0$

Additional Examples

Example 2 The amount A of radioactivity from a nuclear explosion is estimated to be modeled by $A = A_0e^{-2t}$, where t is the number of days since the explosion. How long will it take for the radioactivity to reach $\frac{1}{1000}$ of its original intensity?

Solution Substitute the given values for the variables into

$$A = A_0e^{-2t}.$$

$\underline{\ ?\ } = \underline{\ ?\ } \cdot e^{-2t}$ $\frac{1}{1000}$; 1

$\underline{\ ?\ } = e^{-2t}$ $\frac{1}{1000}$

$\ln \frac{1}{1000} = \ln \underline{\ ?\ }$ e^{-2t}

$\ln \frac{1}{1000} = \underline{\ ?\ }$ $-2t$

$\underline{\ ?\ } \cdot \ln \frac{1}{1000} = t$ $-\frac{1}{2}$

$t \approx \underline{\ ?\ }$ 3.5

The radioactivity will reach $\frac{1}{1000}$ of its original intensity in about __?__ days. 3.5

Example 3 Solve $5^x = 32$ by taking

a. the common logarithm of each side. $x \approx 2.1534$

b. the natural logarithm of each side. $x \approx 2.1534$

Note-Taking Tips

Have students add the Change of Base theorem to their journals and include an appropriate example.

Additional Example

Example 4 Approximate $\log_4 24$ to the nearest thousandth. 2.292

Logarithms to bases 10 and e are used in the solutions to Example 3. Any other base for the logarithms could have been used to solve the equation. Because the same results are *always* obtained regardless of the base, you may choose common logarithms, natural logarithms, or logarithms to any other base for a given situation.

Changing the Base of a Logarithm

While most graphing utilities have keys for the natural logarithm [LN] and common logarithm [LOG], some of them do not have a single operation that allows you to find logarithms with bases other than 10 or e. However, with the following theorem you can convert logarithms with any base b, such as $\log_5 18$, to a ratio of either common logarithms or natural logarithms. The proof is a generalization of the process used in Examples 1–3.

Change of Base Theorem

For all positive real numbers a, b, and t, $b \neq 1$ and $t \neq 1$,

$$\log_b a = \frac{\log_t a}{\log_t b}.$$

Proof Suppose $\log_b a = x$.

Definition of logarithm	$b^x = a$
Take the log base t of each side.	$\log_t b^x = \log_t a$
Apply the Logarithm of a Power Theorem.	$x \log_t b = \log_t a$
Divide.	$x = \frac{\log_t a}{\log_t b}$
Transitive Property of Equality	$\log_b a = \frac{\log_t a}{\log_t b}$

The Change of Base Theorem says that the logarithm of a number to any base is the log of the number divided by the log of the base. Notice that the logarithms on the right side of the formula must have the same base.

Example 4

Approximate $\log_5 18$ to the nearest thousandth.

Solution 1 Use the Change of Base Theorem with common logarithms.

$$\log_5 18 = \frac{\log 18}{\log 5} \approx 1.796$$

Extension

Give students the following problem: Suppose 10 grams of highly radioactive material decay to 9 grams in 30 days. Write a function describing y, the amount of material present, as a function of x, the amount of time in days. $y = 10(0.996)^x$ Use logarithms to find the half-life of the material. Check your answer using a graph. Find the x-value when $y = 5$. $5 = 10(0.996)^x$, so $\frac{1}{2} = (0.996)^x$ and $\ln \frac{1}{2} = x \cdot \ln 0.996$. Thus $x \approx 172.94$. The half-life of the material is approximately 173 days. Check: Tracing the graph of $y = 10(0.996)^x$ shows that when $y = 5$, $x \approx 172.94$.

Solution 2 Use the Change of Base Theorem with natural logarithms.

$$\log_5 18 = \frac{\ln 18}{\ln 5} \approx 1.796$$

Check By definition, $\log_5 18 \approx 1.796$ is equivalent to $5^{1.796} \approx 18$. The calculator display at the right shows that $5^{1.796} \approx 18$. It checks.

Questions

COVERING THE IDEAS

1. Solve $3^x = 243$
   a. in your head. 5
   b. by taking common logarithms. 5
   c. by taking natural logarithms. 5
2. Solve $20^r = 30$ to the nearest thousandth by using logarithms. 1.135

In 3 and 4, solve and check.

3. $\log_4 140 = y$
4. $53.75^z = 44$
5. Solve Example 1 using common logarithms.
6. Refer to Example 1. What interest rate, compounded continuously, would it take to triple your money in 12 years? about 9.16%
7. Refer to Example 2. Another artifact found several miles away contains only 48% of its expected carbon-14. About how old is this artifact? about 6067 years old

3. about 3.565; $4^{3.565} \approx 140$
4. about 0.9498; $53.75^{0.9498} \approx 44$
5. $r = \frac{\log 2}{12 \log e} \approx 0.0578$

In 8 and 9, approximate the logarithm to the nearest thousandth and check your answer.

8. $\log_2 30$ 4.907; $2^{4.907} \approx 30$
9. $\log_{0.5} 80$ -6.322; $0.5^{-6.322} \approx 80$
10. Express as a single logarithm: $\frac{\log_8 P}{\log_8 Q}$. $\log_Q P$

APPLYING THE MATHEMATICS

11. Suppose you invest \$250 in a savings account paying 3.25% interest compounded continuously. How long would it take for your account to grow to \$300, assuming that no other deposits or withdrawals are made? about 5.61 yr
12. Suppose a colony of bacteria grows according to $N = Be^{2t}$, where N is the number of bacteria after t hours and B is the initial number in the colony. How long does it take the colony to grow to 10 times its original size? about 1.15 hr

In 13 and 14, solve.

13. $8^{4y} = 1492$ $y \approx 0.879$
14. $\log_{12} 313 = -3x$ $x \approx -0.771$

9-10

3 Assignment

Recommended Assignment

- Questions 1–27
- Question 28 (extra credit)
- Self-Test

Notes on the Questions

Questions 8 and 9 Students could check their answers by using a different base in the calculation, by calculating a relevant power, or by graphing.

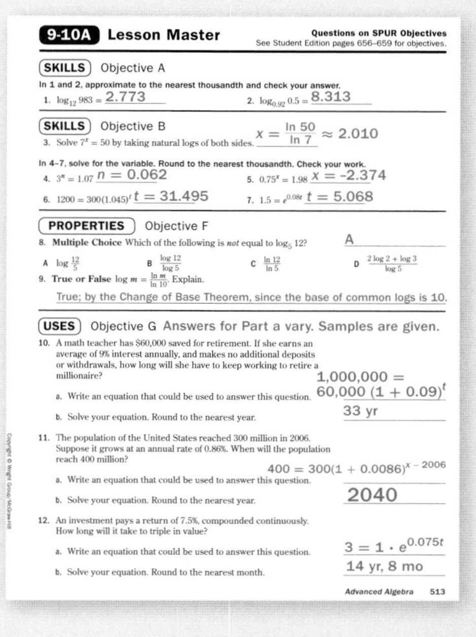

9-10A Lesson Master

Questions on SPUR Objectives
See Student Edition pages 656–659 for objectives.

SKILLS Objective A

In 1 and 2, approximate to the nearest thousandth and check your answer.

1. $\log_{12} 983 =$ 2.773
2. $\log_{0.92} 0.5 =$ 8.313

SKILLS Objective B

3. Solve $7^x = 50$ by taking natural logs of both sides. $x = \frac{\ln 50}{\ln 7} \approx 2.010$

In 4–7, solve for the variable. Round to the nearest thousandth. Check your work.

4. $3^n = 1.07$ $n = 0.062$
5. $0.75^x = 1.98$ $x = -2.374$
6. $1200 = 300(1.045)^t$ $t = 31.495$
7. $1.5 = e^{0.08t}$ $t = 5.068$

PROPERTIES Objective F

8. **Multiple Choice** Which of the following is *not* equal to $\log_5 12$? A
   A $\log \frac{12}{5}$
   B $\frac{\log 12}{\log 5}$
   C $\frac{\ln 12}{\ln 5}$
   D $\frac{2 \log 2 + \log 3}{\log 5}$
9. **True or False** $\log m = \frac{\ln m}{\ln 10}$. Explain.
   True; by the Change of Base Theorem, since the base of common logs is 10.

USES Objective G Answers for Part a vary. Samples are given.

10. A math teacher has \$60,000 saved for retirement. If she earns an average of 9% interest annually, and makes no additional deposits or withdrawals, how long will she have to keep working to retire a millionaire?
    a. Write an equation that could be used to answer this question. $1{,}000{,}000 = 60{,}000(1 + 0.09)^t$
    b. Solve your equation. Round to the nearest year. 33 yr
11. The population of the United States reached 300 million in 2006. Suppose it grows at an annual rate of 0.86%. When will the population reach 400 million?
    a. Write an equation that could be used to answer this question. $400 = 300(1 + 0.0086)^{x - 2006}$
    b. Solve your equation. Round to the nearest year. 2040
12. An investment pays a return of 7.5%, compounded continuously. How long will it take to triple in value?
    a. Write an equation that could be used to answer this question. $3 = 1 \cdot e^{0.075t}$
    b. Solve your equation. Round to the nearest month. 14 yr, 8 mo

Advanced Algebra 513

Notes on the Questions

Question 22 Students may look for an error that directly involves properties of logarithms and, in the process, miss the error due to misapplication of a property of inequalities.

Question 23 You might ask students to use the properties of logarithms to find an equivalent formula that does not contain logarithms: $V = \ln(R_1^{c_1}R_2^{c_2}R_3^{c_3})$, so $e^V = R_1^{c_1}R_2^{c_2}R_3^{c_3}$.

15. In 1999 the world population was estimated to be 5,995,000,000, and in 2000 the estimate was 6,071,000,000.
    a. Calculate the percentage increase between 1999 and 2000.
    b. Assume the percent increase remains the same. In what year will the world population reach 7 billion? Explain your answer.
    c. In what year will the population be double the 2000 population? in 2054
    d. Use the Internet to find the current and previous year's world population, and then calculate the percentage increase. With this growth rate, estimate when the world population will be twice the 2000 population.
16. In the formula $A = C\left(\frac{1}{2}\right)^{\frac{t}{H}}$, A is the amount of carbon left after time t, where C is the initial amount and H is the half-life. In this lesson the formula $A = Ce^{-\frac{\ln 2}{H}t}$ is used. Use the properties of exponents and logarithms to prove that $C\left(\frac{1}{2}\right)^{\frac{t}{H}} = Ce^{-\frac{\ln 2}{H}t}$ for all t.

15a. about 1.27%

15b. in 2011; $5{,}995{,}000{,}000 \cdot (1.0127)^{12.28} \approx 7{,}000{,}000{,}000$

15d. Answers vary. Sample: 2008: 6,706,992,932; 2007: 6,627,548,985; growth rate: 1.20%; in 2057

16. $\frac{1}{2} = e^{\ln\left(\frac{1}{2}\right)} = e^{\ln(2^{-1})} = e^{-\ln 2}$; therefore, $C\left(\frac{1}{2}\right)^{\frac{t}{H}} = C\left(e^{-\ln 2}\right)^{\frac{t}{H}} = Ce^{\frac{-\ln 2}{H}t}$

In 17–19, between which two consecutive whole numbers does each logarithm fall? Answer without using a calculator.

17. $\log_3 21$ 2 and 3
18. $\log_{12} 200$ 2 and 3
19. $\log_7\left(\frac{1}{50}\right)$ -3 and -2

REVIEW

In 20 and 21, solve and check. (Lesson 9-9)

20. $\log w = \frac{3}{2}\log 16 - \log 8$ $w = 8$
21. $\log 125 = x \log 5$ $x = 3$
22. Find the error in the following proof that $3 < 2$. (*Hint:* What is the sign of $\log\left(\frac{1}{3}\right)$?) **(Lessons 9-9, 9-5, 5-1)**

$$\frac{1}{27} < \frac{1}{9}$$
$$\log\left(\frac{1}{27}\right) < \log\left(\frac{1}{9}\right)$$
$$\log\left[\left(\frac{1}{3}\right)^3\right] < \log\left[\left(\frac{1}{3}\right)^2\right]$$
$$3\log\left(\frac{1}{3}\right) < 2\log\left(\frac{1}{3}\right)$$
$$3 < 2$$

22. The error is in the last step: $\log\left(\frac{1}{3}\right)$ is negative, so the inequality sign must be reversed when both sides are divided by $\log\left(\frac{1}{3}\right)$.

23. For a 3-stage model rocket, the formula $V = c_1 \cdot \ln R_1 + c_2 \cdot \ln R_2 + c_3 \cdot \ln R_3$ is used to find the velocity of the rocket at final burnout. If $R_1 = 1.37$, $R_2 = 1.59$, $R_3 = 1.81$, $c_1 = 2185\ \frac{\text{m}}{\text{sec}}$, $c_2 = 2530\ \frac{\text{m}}{\text{sec}}$, and $c_3 = 2610\ \frac{\text{m}}{\text{sec}}$, find V. **(Lesson 9-8)**
    about $3409.7\ \frac{\text{m}}{\text{sec}}$

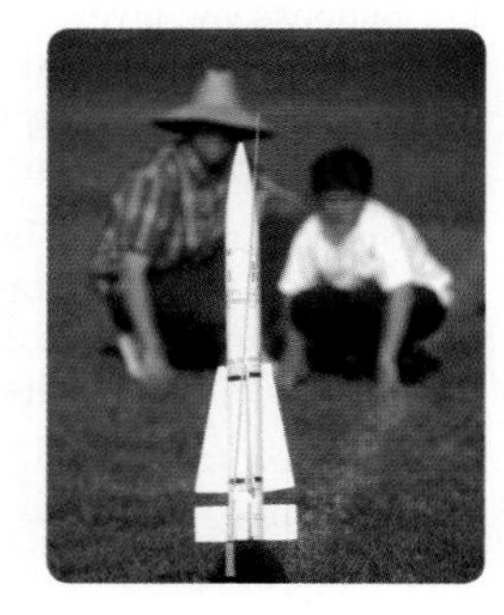

Accommodating the Learner

After completing the lesson, have pairs of students solve the following equations. Have them note that the numbers in the equations are the same, but the variable is in a different place in each equation. Make sure students check each solution.

1. $\log_{\sqrt{3}} a = 6$ $a = 27$
2. $\log_b \sqrt{3} = 6$ $b = \sqrt[12]{3} \approx 1.0959$
3. $\log_{\sqrt{3}} 6 = c$ $c = \frac{\log 6}{\log\sqrt{3}} \approx 3.2619$

24. Recall that the relative intensity of sound is given by $D = 10\log\left(\frac{N}{10^{-12}}\right)$. Find the decibel level of a sound that has an absolute intensity of $3.7 \cdot 10^{-5}$. **(Lesson 9-6)** about 75.68 decibels

In 25 and 26, evaluate, given $g(x) = \log x$. (Lessons 9-5, 8-3)

25. $g(0.01)$ -2

26. $g^{-1}(4)$ 10,000

27. a. Graph the triangle represented by $\begin{bmatrix} -5 & 5 & 0 \\ 0 & 0 & 5 \end{bmatrix}$. **(Lessons 4-5, 4-1)** See margin.
    b. What kind of triangle is this? isosceles
    c. What matrix describes the image of the triangle in Part a under the transformation given by $\begin{bmatrix} 4 & 0 \\ 0 & 1 \end{bmatrix}$? $\begin{bmatrix} -20 & 20 & 0 \\ 0 & 0 & 5 \end{bmatrix}$
    d. Graph the image on the same set of axes as in Part a. See margin.
    e. Are the triangles in Parts a and c similar? no

EXPLORATION

28. The table shows part of the Krumbein *phi* (ϕ) scale. Geologists use this scale to measure the grain size of the individual particles that make up rocks, soils, and other solids. Notice that the sizes in the first column are all powers of 2. Determine a logarithmic relationship between the size range and the ϕ-scale numbers in the second column.

Size Range (mm)	ϕ Scale	Aggregate Name	Other Names
> 256	< -8	Boulder	
64–256	-6 to -8	Cobble	
32–64	-5 to -6	Very coarse gravel	Pebble
16–32	-4 to -5	Coarse gravel	Pebble
8–16	-3 to -4	Medium gravel	Pebble
4–8	-2 to -3	Fine gravel	Pebble
2–4	-1 to -2	Very fine gravel	Granule
1–2	0 to -1	Very coarse sand	
$\frac{1}{2}$–1	1 to 0	Coarse sand	
$\frac{1}{4}$–$\frac{1}{2}$	2 to 1	Medium sand	

28. $\phi = \log_2\left(\frac{1}{s}\right)$, where s is the lower bound on the size range and ϕ is the upper bound and on the ϕ scale, or s is the upper bound on the size range and ϕ is the lower bound on the ϕ scale.

QY ANSWER

Answers vary. Sample: You would be required to solve $\log 2 = 12r \log e$.

4 Wrap-Up

Ongoing Assessment

Have students write two equations of the form $b^x = a$. Then have them write an explanation of how logarithms can be used to solve each equation. Students' explanations should be clear and demonstrate an understanding of how to solve exponential equations.

Additional Answers

27a.

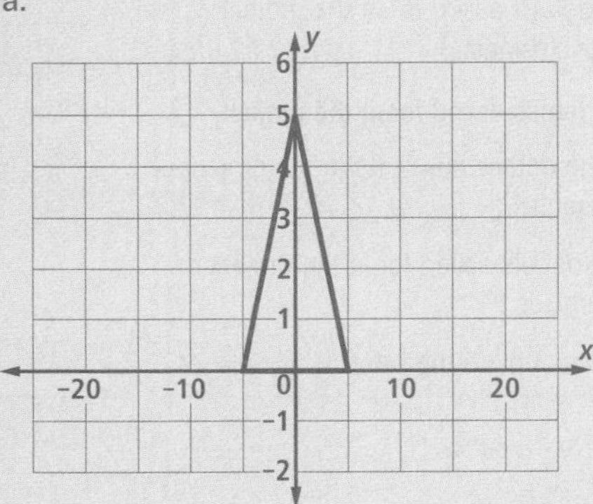

27d.

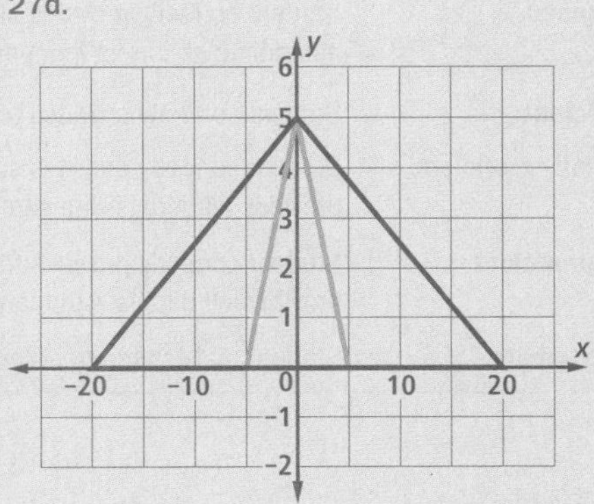

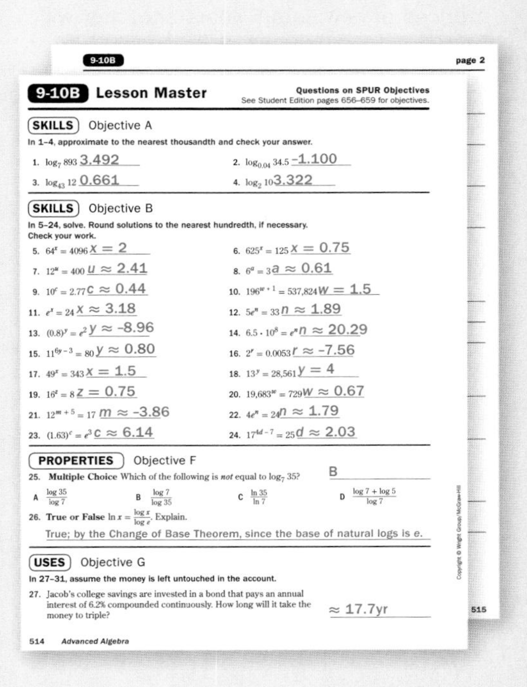

9-10B page 2

9-10B Lesson Master

Questions on SPUR Objectives
See Student Edition pages 656–659 for objectives.

SKILLS Objective A

In 1–4, approximate to the nearest thousandth and check your answer.

1. $\log_7 893$ 3.492
2. $\log_{0.04} 34.5$ -1.100
3. $\log_{43} 12$ 0.661
4. $\log_2 10$ 3.322

SKILLS Objective B

In 5–24, solve. Round solutions to the nearest hundredth, if necessary. Check your work.

5. $64^x = 4096$ $x = 2$
6. $625^x = 125$ $x = 0.75$
7. $12^u = 400$ $u \approx 2.41$
8. $6^a = 3$ $a \approx 0.61$
9. $10^c = 2.77$ $c \approx 0.44$
10. $196^{w+1} = 537{,}824$ $w = 1.5$
11. $e^x = 24$ $x \approx 3.18$
12. $5e^n = 33$ $n \approx 1.89$
13. $(0.8)^y = e^2$ $y \approx -8.96$
14. $6.5 \cdot 10^8 = e^n$ $n \approx 20.29$
15. $11^{6y-3} = 80$ $y \approx 0.80$
16. $2^r = 0.0053$ $r \approx -7.56$
17. $49^x = 343$ $x = 1.5$
18. $13^y = 28{,}561$ $y = 4$
19. $16^z = 8$ $z = 0.75$
20. $19{,}683^w = 729$ $w \approx 0.67$
21. $12^{m+5} = 17$ $m \approx -3.86$
22. $4e^n = 24$ $n \approx 1.79$
23. $(1.63)^c = e^3$ $c \approx 6.14$
24. $17^{4d-7} = 25$ $d \approx 2.03$

PROPERTIES Objective F

25. **Multiple Choice** Which of the following is *not* equal to $\log_7 35$? B
    A $\frac{\log 35}{\log 7}$ B $\frac{\log 7}{\log 35}$ C $\frac{\ln 35}{\ln 7}$ D $\frac{\log 7 + \log 5}{\log 7}$

26. **True or False** $\ln x = \frac{\log x}{\log e}$. Explain.
    True; by the Change of Base Theorem, since the base of natural logs is e.

USES Objective G

In 27–31, assume the money is left untouched in the account.

27. Jacob's college savings are invested in a bond that pays an annual interest of 6.2% compounded continuously. How long will it take the money to triple? ≈ 17.7yr

514 *Advanced Algebra*

515

Chapter 9

The projects relate to the content of the lessons of this chapter as follows:

Project	Lesson
1	9-9
2	9-1
3	9-2, 9-4
4	9-5
5	9-4, 9-8
6	9-7

1 Slide Rules
Students can find information about slide rules on the Internet. You might check if your school has one in a storeroom somewhere.

2 Non-Native Species
Students can find many references to non-native species on the Internet. You might ask them to share their findings with the class.

3 Car Values
In doing their research for Part b, students may have to use several books to track the price data of the particular cars they choose. For example, if they use *Edmund's Used Car Prices* to find the prices of new cars 5 years ago, they will have to use volumes of the book from the past 4 years. They can also research prices on the Internet.

Chapter 9 Projects

1 Slide Rules

Battery operated electronic calculators first became available in the early 1970s. Before that time many engineers and scientists used a slide rule to do calculations involving multiplication, division, exponentiation, finding roots, and so on (but not adding and subtracting). Slide rules are based on the principles of common logarithms. Find out how they work. Summarize your findings in a report and demonstrate a few calculations for the class.

2 Non-Native Species

The Australian rabbit plague shows how introducing a species to a new environment can be catastrophic. Other non-native species whose introductions have had or are having disastrous consequences for environments in the United States include the Asian long-horned Beetle, the emerald ash borer, the zebra mussel, and the fungi causing Dutch elm disease (*Ophiostoma ulmi* and related fungi) and sudden oak death syndrome (*Phytophthora ramorum*). Research one of these foreign species invasions to find out when and how the species was introduced, how quickly it has spread, what the consequences are, and how the species' spread is being controlled (if at all).

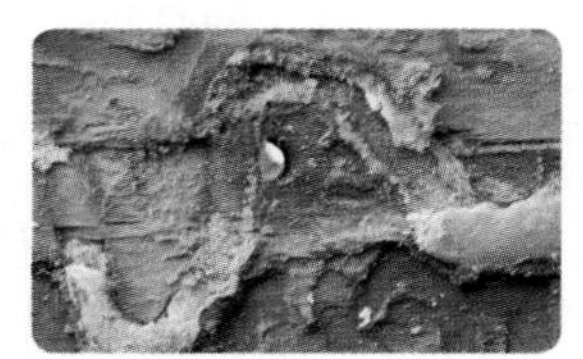

damage from an emerald ash borer

3 Car Values

a. Consult a car dealer, insurance agent, books, magazines, or the Internet to learn how automobile depreciation is typically calculated. Is depreciation typically described by a linear, exponential, or some other type of model?

b. Gather data on the book value of two or three cars that interest you. Include only cars whose values you can determine for at least the past five years. Which book values over time, if any, seem to illustrate exponential decay? Find equations that model the value of these cars over time. Use the equations to predict the value of each car five years from now. In your opinion, how reasonable are these estimates? What are some limitations of your mathematical models?

4 How Many Digits Are in That Number?

Logarithms can be used to determine how many digits a number has. While initially this may not seem useful, consider finding the number of digits in the number 2^{5000} when written in base 10. Most calculators will not calculate the value, let alone help you figure out how many digits it has. However, by using logarithms, you can find that this number has 1506 digits. Research how to perform this process and find out why it works.

Project Rubric

Advanced	Student correctly provides all of the details asked for in the project as well as additional correct independent conclusions.
Proficient	Student correctly provides all of the details asked for in the project.
Partially proficient	Student correctly provides some of the details asked for in the project or provides all details with some inaccuracies.
Not proficient	Student correctly provides few of the details asked for in the project or provides all details with many inaccuracies.
No attempt	Student makes little or no attempt to complete the project.

5 Predicting Cooling Times

You can predict how long it will take a 12-fluid-ounce soft drink to cool to a desired temperature on a particular shelf in your refrigerator using either exponential or logarithmic functions. You will need a thermometer that measures a wide range of temperatures.

a. Measure the temperature T_R in your refrigerator. (Let's say it is 42°F.) Assume T_R is constant. Fill a ceramic cup with very hot tap water. Measure the temperature T_M of the water. (Say it is 135°F.) Place the cup in your refrigerator. Make a table like the one below and record your first measurement.

t (min)	T_M (°F)	$T_M - T_R$ (°F)
Time since cooling began	Measured temperature of water	Difference between measured temperature and refrigerator temperature
0	135	135 − 42 = 93

b. Measure the temperature of the water periodically. At first you will want to take a measurement every 5 minutes. Later you might wait longer between measurements. Record the temperatures in the table. Continue taking measurements for at least 4 hours. Be sure to take the measurements the same way each time.

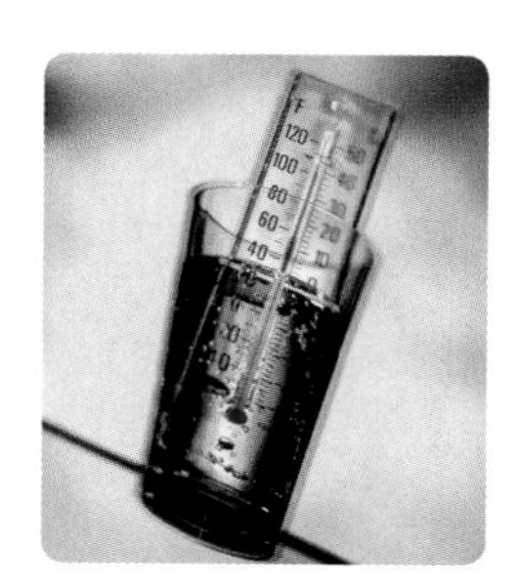

c. Plot the ordered pairs $(t, T_M - T_R)$. Describe the shape of the graph. Use the modeling features on a graphing utility or statistics application to fit a reasonable curve to your data. Explain why you chose the model you did.

d. Use technology to fit a logarithmic model to your data. This time, let $T_M - T_R$ be your independent variable and t be your dependent variable. The statistics application might give you a model such as $t = a + b \cdot \ln(T_M - T_R)$, where a and b are parameters for the model. Is this model equivalent to the one you found in Part c? Why or why not?

e. Use your model(s) from Parts c and d to predict how long it takes for a 12-fluid-ounce can of soft drink in your refrigerator to cool from 70°F (about room temperature) to 48°F (an acceptable drinking temperature). Comment on the answer(s) you get.

6 Finding when $a^x = \log_a x$

a. Use a graphing utility to graph $f(x) = a^x$ and $g(x) = \log_a x$ for several values of a such that $0 < a < 1$.

b. Use a graphing utility to graph $f(x) = a^x$ and $g(x) = \log_a x$ for several values of $a > 1$.

c. Based on the results of Parts a and b, what approximate values of a cause these functions to intersect once? What approximate values of a cause them to intersect twice?

d. Approximate the a-value at which these two functions intersect for the last time.

4 How Many Digits Are in That Number?

As preparation for finding the number of digits in 2^{5000}, ask students to use logarithms to solve the following problem: A college savings account is worth \$15,200. Six years earlier, the account was worth \$10,420. What is the average annual rate of growth for the account? Using r as the annual growth factor, $15{,}200 = 10{,}420 \cdot r^6$, so $r^6 = \frac{15{,}200}{10{,}420} = 1.45873$. So $6 \log r = \log 1.45873$ and $\log r = (\log 1.45873) \div 6 = 0.027329$, so $r = 1.06495$; the average annual rate of growth was about 6.5%.

This type of problem, which requires solving an equation of the form $v^n = a$, where v is a variable and n and a are numbers, can be preparation for solving an equation problem of the form $a^n = b^v$, where v is a variable and a, n, and b are numbers, such as $2^{5000} = 10^n$, which models the question of the number of digits in 2^{5000}.

5 Predicting Cooling Times

If your school's science department has temperature probes that will enable students to obtain the required temperature values, ask a science teacher if your class can borrow the probes for this project.

6 Finding When $a^x = \log_a x$

This project is based on the article "The Where, Why, and How of Solving $a^x = \log_b x$" (M. Lassak and B. Heller; *Mathematics Teacher* 99(9):650–653).

Sample answers for projects are in the Solution Manual in the Electronic Teacher's Edition.

Notes

Chapter 9

Summary and Vocabulary

The Summary gives an overview of the entire chapter and provides an opportunity for students to consider the material as a whole. Thus, the Summary can be used to help students relate and unify the concepts presented in the chapter.

Vocabulary words and symbols are listed by lesson to provide a checklist of concepts that students must know. Emphasize to students that they should read the vocabulary list carefully before starting the Self-Test on pages 654–655. If students do not understand the meaning of a vocabulary word, they should refer back to the indicated lesson.

Theorems and Properties covered in the chapter are listed below the Summary with page references included to lead students back to the location in the chapter where the theorem or property is stated.

Chapter 9 Summary and Vocabulary

- A function with an equation of the form $y = ab^x$, where $b > 0$ and $b \neq 1$, is an **exponential function**. All geometric sequences are also exponential functions. In the formula $A = P\left(1 + \frac{r}{n}\right)^{nt}$, when P, r, and n are given, A is an exponential function of t.
- The exponential function with base b has an equation of the form $f(x) = ab^x$. Some exponential functions represent **exponential growth** or **decay** situations. In an exponential growth situation, the growth factor b is greater than one. In an exponential decay situation, b is between 0 and 1. Over short periods of time, many populations grow exponentially. The value of many items depreciates exponentially. Quantities that grow or decay exponentially have a constant doubling time or **half-life**, respectively. Real data from these and other contexts can be modeled using exponential functions.
- When an initial amount of \$1.00 is continuously compounded at 100% interest, the value of the investment after one year is $e \approx 2.71828$. Like π, the number e is an irrational number. In general, the formula $A = Pe^{rt}$ can be used to calculate the value A of an investment of P dollars at r% interest **compounded continuously** for t years.
- The inverse of the exponential function $f: x \rightarrow b^x$ is $f^{-1}: b^x \rightarrow x$, the **logarithm function with base *b***. Thus, $b^x = a$ if and only if $x = \log_b a$. Because exponential and logarithm functions are inverses, their graphs are reflection images of each other over the line $y = x$. Properties of logarithm functions can be derived from the corresponding properties of exponential functions.

Exponential Growth Function

$y = b^x, b > 1$

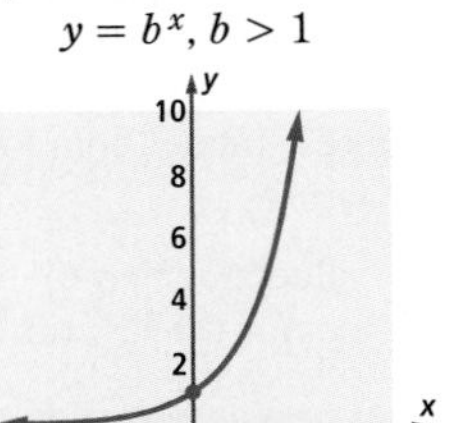

Logarithmic Function

$y = \log_b x, b > 1$

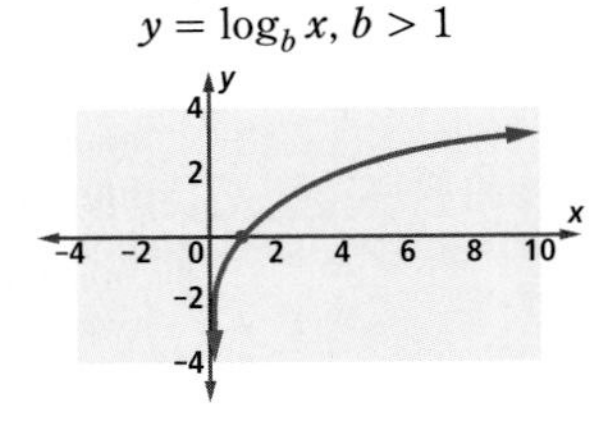

Vocabulary

Lesson 9-1
*exponential function
exponential curve
growth factor

Lesson 9-2
exponential decay
depreciation
half-life

Lesson 9-3
e
compounded continuously

Lesson 9-5
logarithm of *x* to the base 10, log of *x* to the base 10, log base 10 of *x*
common logarithm, common log
logarithmic function to the base 10, common logarithm function

Lesson 9-6
logarithmic scale
decibel, dB

Lesson 9-7
*logarithm of *a* to the base *b*
logarithm function with base *b*

Lesson 9-8
*natural logarithm of *m*, ln *m*

Exponential Growth Function		Logarithmic Function
all real numbers	**Domain**	all positive reals
all positive reals	**Range**	all real numbers
y-intercept is 1, no x-intercept	**Intercepts**	x-intercept is 1, no y-intercept
the x-axis ($y = 0$)	**Asymptotes**	the y-axis ($x = 0$)

- Logarithmic functions are used to scale data having a wide range (for example, **decibel** levels or earthquake magnitudes) and to solve equations of the form $b^x = a$, where b and a are positive and $b \neq 1$. One way to solve equations of this type is to take the logarithm of both sides; the solution is $x = \frac{\log a}{\log b}$.
- The base of a logarithmic function can be any positive real number not equal to 1, but the most commonly used bases are 10 and e. When the base is 10, the values of the log function are called **common logarithms**. When the base is e, the values of the log function are called **natural logarithms**.
- The basic properties of logarithms correspond to properties of powers. Let $x = b^m$ and $y = b^n$, and take the logarithms of both sides of each power property. The result is a logarithm property.

Power Property	Logarithm Property
$b^0 = 1$	$\log_b 1 = 0$
$b^m \cdot b^n = b^{m+n}$	$\log_b(xy) = \log_b x + \log_b y$
$\frac{b^m}{b^n} = b^{m-n}$	$\log_b\left(\frac{x}{y}\right) = \log_b x - \log_b y$
$(b^m)^a = b^{am}$	$\log_b(x^a) = a \log_b x$
$b^x = a$	$\log_b a = \frac{\log_t a}{\log_t b}$

Theorems

Continuously Compounded Interest Formula (p. 597)
Log_b of b^n Theorem (p. 636)
Logarithm of 1 Theorem (p. 636)
Logarithm of a Product Theorem (p. 637)
Logarithm of a Quotient Theorem (p. 638)
Logarithm of a Power Theorem (p. 639)
Change of Base Theorem (p. 646)

Summary and Vocabulary 653

Self-Test

For the development of mathematical competence, feedback and correction, along with the opportunity for practice, are necessary. The Self-Test provides the opportunity for feedback and correction; the Chapter Review provides additional opportunities for practice. We cannot overemphasize the importance of these end-of-chapter materials. It is at this point that the material gels for many students, allowing them to solidify skills and understanding. In general, student performance should improve after these pages.

Assign the Self-Test as a one-night assignment. Worked-out solutions for all questions are in the Selected Answers section of the student book. Encourage students to take the Self-Test honestly, grade themselves, and then be prepared to discuss the test in class.

Advise students to pay special attention to those Chapter Review questions (pages 656–659) that correspond to the questions they missed on the Self-Test.

Additional Answers

2. The fraction of uranium remaining in an artifact after x half-lives is $U(x) = \left(\frac{1}{2}\right)^x$. Since in this case one half-life is about a week, the fraction remaining after three half-lives is $U(3) = 0.125$. So there is 12.5% of the original amount of uranium remaining in an artifact after 3 weeks.

3a.

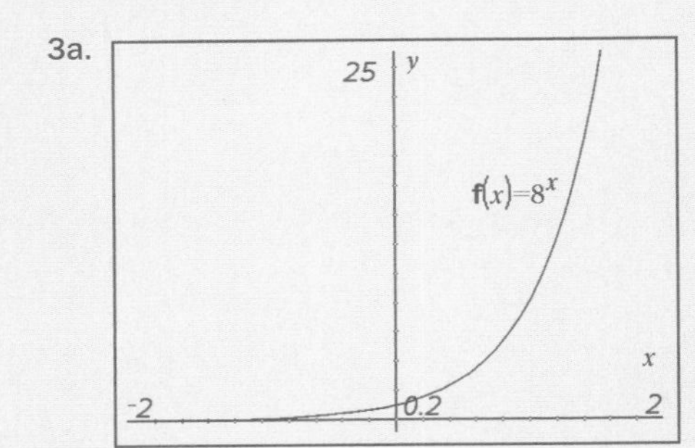

5. $\log(100{,}000{,}000) = \log(10^8) = 8$ by the Log_b of b^n Theorem.

6. $\log_2\left(\frac{1}{16}\right) = \log_2 2^{-4} = -4$ by the Log_b of b^n Theorem.

Chapter 9 Self-Test

Take this test as you would take a test in class. You will need a calculator. Then use the Selected Answers section in the back of the book to check your work.

1. What are the domain and range of the function f defined by $f(x) = \log_{13} x$?
2. The half-life of uranium-237 is about 7 days. What percent of the original amount of uranium will remain in an artifact after three weeks? See margin.
3. Let $f(x) = 8^x$. 3a. See margin.
   a. Graph f on the interval $-2 \le x \le 2$.
   b. Approximate $f(\pi)$ to the nearest tenth.
   c. Does the graph have any asymptotes? If it does, state the equations for all asymptotes. If it does not, explain why not.
4. a. Give a value of b for which the equation $y = ab^x$ models exponential decay.
   b. What are the domain and range of the function in Part a for your value of b?

In 5–7, explain how you would evaluate each expression exactly without using a calculator.

5. $\log 100{,}000{,}000$
6. $\log_2\left(\frac{1}{16}\right)$
7. $\ln e^{-4}$ $\ln e^{-4} = -4$ because $\ln e^x = x$.
8. Rewrite $\log a + 2 \log t - \log s$ as a single logarithm. 5–6, 8–9. See margin.
9. Without natural predators, the number of a certain species of bird will grow each year by 12%. A colony of 50 birds is started in a predator-free area. What is the expected number of birds of this species after 3 years?

1. domain: $x > 0$; range: all real numbers
3b. $f(\pi) = 8^\pi \approx 687.3$
3c. yes; $y = 0$
4a. any b with $0 < b < 1$; example: $b = 0.5$
4b. domain: all real numbers; range: $y > 0$ if $a > 0$; $y < 0$ if $a < 0$

In 10–12, solve. If necessary, round solutions to the nearest hundredth. 10–12. See margin.

10. $\log_x 27 = \frac{3}{4}$
11. $5^y = 40$
12. $\ln(7z) = \ln 3 + \ln 21$
13. **True or False** $\log_5 a + \log_3 b = \log_{15}(ab)$. Justify your answer. See margin.
14. Write an equation for the inverse of the function with equation $y = \log_4 x$.
15. The Henderson-Hasselbalch formula $pH = 6.1 + \log\left(\frac{B}{C}\right)$ can be used to find the pH of a patient's blood as a function of the bicarbonate concentration B and the carbonic-acid concentration C. A patient's blood has a bicarbonate concentration of 23 and a pH reading of 7.3. Find the concentration of carbonic acid. See margin.
16. To the nearest thousandth, what is $\log_{14} 24.72$? $\log_{14} 24.72 = \frac{\log 24.72}{\log 14} \approx 1.215$
17. State the general property used in simplifying the expression $\log_{19} 19^{23}$.
18. Consider the function defined by $y = \log_5 x$. 18a, b, c, e. See margin.
    a. State the coordinates of three points on the graph.
    b. State the domain and range of the function.
    c. Graph the function.
    d. State an equation for its inverse. $y = 5^x$
    e. Graph the inverse on the same axes you used in Part c.

14. The inverse of a logarithmic function is an exponential function with the same base, so an equation for the inverse is $y = 4^x$.
17. $\log_b b^n = n$, $b > 0$, $b \neq 1$

Additional Answers

8. $\log a + 2 \log t - \log s = \log a + \log(t^2) - \log s = \log(at^2) - \log s = \log\left(\frac{at^2}{s}\right)$
9. The initial population is 50 and the yearly growth factor is 1.12, so the number of birds after t years is given by $N(t) = 50(1.12)^t$. $N(3) = 70.2464$; thus, after 3 years, there will be about 70 birds.
10. $\log_x 27 = \frac{3}{4}$; $x^{\frac{3}{4}} = 27$; $x = 27^{\frac{4}{3}}$; $x = 81$
11. $5^y = 40$; $y \log 5 = \log 40$; $y = \frac{\log 40}{\log 5} \approx 2.29$
12. $\ln(7z) = \ln 3 + \ln 21$; $\ln(7z) = \ln(3 \cdot 21) = \ln(63)$; $7z = 63$; $z = 9$
13. False; if $a = 5$ and $b = 3$, $\log_5 a + \log_3 b = 1 + 1 = 2$ but $\log_{15}(ab) = 1$.
14. The inverse of a logarithmic function is an exponential function with the same base, so an equation for the inverse is $y = 4^x$.
15. $7.3 = 6.1 + \log\left(\frac{23}{C}\right)$; $1.2 = \log 23 - \log C$; $\log C = \log 23 - 1.2 \approx 0.162$; $C \approx 10^{0.162} \approx 1.45$.

19. **Multiple Choice** Assume that the value of an investment grows according to the model $y = I(1.075)^x$, where I is the original investment and y is the amount present after x years. Which graph below could represent this situation?

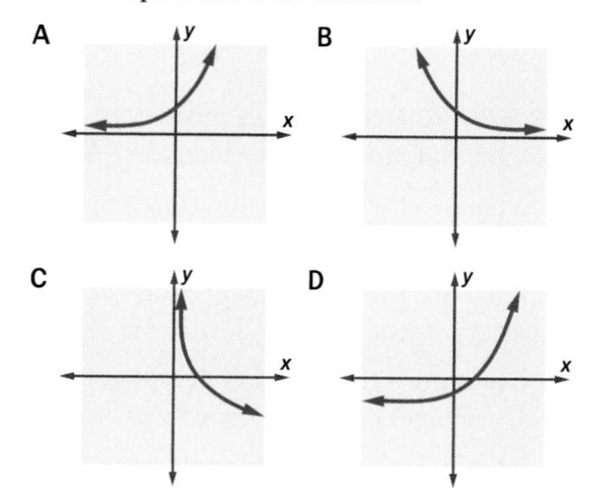

20. The Population Reference Bureau reports the following data about the population P of the United States. See margin.

Population mid-2007	302,200,000
Births per 1000 population	14
Deaths per 1000 population	8
Rate of natural increase/year	0.6% = 0.006
Projected population, mid-2025	349,400,000

Assume the continuous growth model $P = 302{,}200{,}000e^{rt}$, where r is the annual rate of increase and t is the number of years after 2007.

a. Use the model to show that the reported rate of natural increase of 0.6% is *not* the rate leading to the projected population in 2025.

b. Calculate the growth rate to the nearest 0.1% that will give the reported projected population for 2025 of 349,400,000. Show how you arrived at your answer.

21. For the equation $27^x = 14$,

a. find the exact solution.

b. find a decimal solution rounded to the nearest thousandth. $x = 0.801$

22. The table below shows the total number of German-language articles in *Wikipedia* each month from March 2007 to February 2008. See margin.

Month	Articles (thousands)
March 2007	570
April 2007	584
May 2007	599
June 2007	612
July 2007	626
August 2007	640
September 2007	655
October 2007	668
November 2007	681
December 2007	695
January 2008	711
February 2008	726

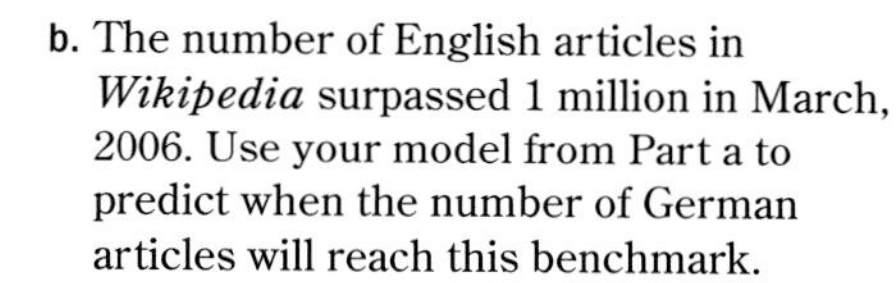

a. Fit an exponential model to these data.

b. The number of English articles in *Wikipedia* surpassed 1 million in March, 2006. Use your model from Part a to predict when the number of German articles will reach this benchmark.

19. A; graphs of exponential growth have this shape and a y-intercept of 1.

21a. $27^x = 14$; $x \cdot \ln 27 = \ln 14$; $x = \frac{\ln 14}{\ln 27}$

Additional Answers

18a. Answers vary. Sample: (1, 0); (5, 1); (25, 2)

18b. Powers of 5 must be positive, so the domain is $x > 0$; all real numbers can be exponents, so the range is all real numbers.

18c.

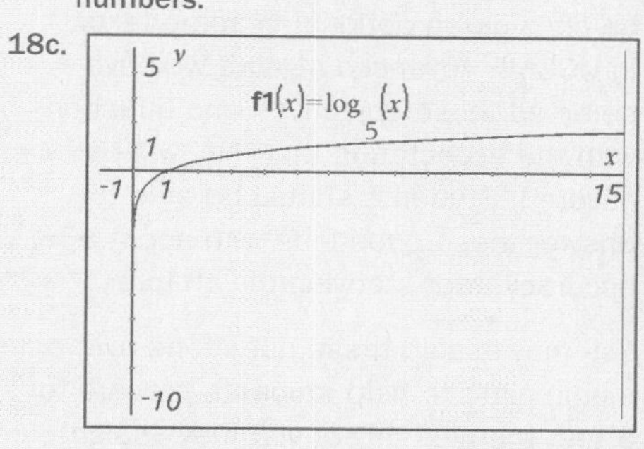

18e.

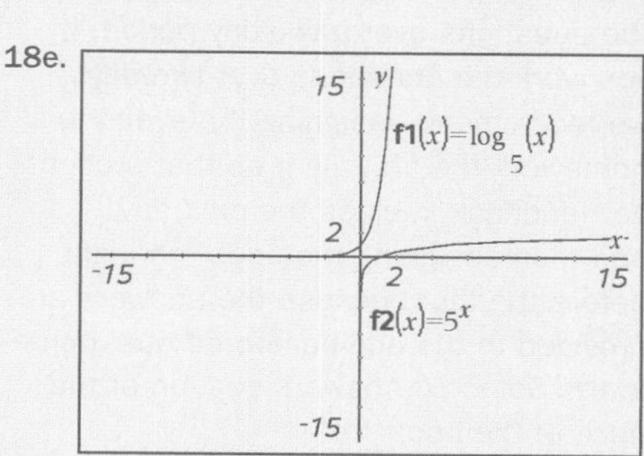

20a. In 2025, $t = 18$, and so $P = 302{,}200{,}000e^{0.006(18)} \approx 336{,}665{,}229 \neq 349{,}400{,}000$

20b. $349{,}400{,}000 = 302{,}200{,}000e^{18r}$; $1.156188 = e^{18r}$; $18r = \ln 1.156188 \approx 0.145128$; $r = 0.00806$. So a growth rate of about 0.8% would give the reported projected population.

22a. Exponential regression shows that an exponential model for these data is $y = 572.6123(1.022)^x$, where x is the number of months after March 2007 and y is the number of articles in thousands.

22b. $1{,}000 = 572.6123(1.022)^x$; $1.74638 = 1.022^x$; $\ln 1.74638 = x\ln 1.022$, $x = \frac{\ln 1.74638}{\ln 1.022} \approx 25.6$. This model predicts that there will be 1 million German Wikipedia articles about 26 months after March 2007, or in April 2009.

Chapter Review

The main objectives for the chapter are organized in the Chapter Review under the four types of understanding this book promotes: Skills, Properties, Uses, and Representations.

Whereas end-of-chapter material may be considered optional in some texts, in UCSMP *Advanced Algebra* we have selected these objectives and questions with the expectation that they will be covered. Students should be able to answer these questions with about 85% accuracy after studying the chapter.

You may assign these questions over a single night to help students prepare for a test the next day or you may assign the questions over a two-day period. If you work the questions over two days, we recommend assigning the evens for homework the first night so that students get feedback in class the next day, and then assigning the odds the night before the test because the answers are provided to the odd-numbered questions in the Selected Answers section at the back of the book.

It is effective to ask students which questions they still do not understand and use the day as a total class discussion of the material that the class finds most difficult.

Resources

- Assessment Resources: Chapter 9 Test Forms A–D; Chapter 9 Test, Cumulative Form; Comprehensive Test, Chapters 1–9

Technology Resources

Teacher's Assessment Assistant, Ch. 9
Electronic Teacher's Edition, Ch. 9

Chapter 9 Chapter Review

SKILLS
PROPERTIES
USES
REPRESENTATIONS

SKILLS Procedures used to get answers

OBJECTIVE A Determine values of logarithms. (Lessons 9-5, 9-7, 9-8, 9-10)

In 1–8, find the exact value of each logarithm without using a calculator.

1. $\log 10{,}000$ 4
2. $\log 0.00001$ -5
3. $\ln e^8$ 8
4. $\log_4 1024$ 5
5. $\log_{13}(13^{15})$ 15
6. $\ln 1$ 0
7. $\log_{\frac{1}{3}} 27$ -3
8. $\log_9 \sqrt[3]{9}$ $\frac{1}{3}$

In 9–14, approximate each logarithm to the nearest hundredth.

9. $\log 98{,}765$ 4.99
10. $\ln 10.95$ 2.39
11. $\ln(-3.7)$ undefined
12. $\log 0.003$ -2.52
13. $\log_7 25$ 1.65
14. $\log_3 12.3$ 2.28

OBJECTIVE B Use logarithms to solve exponential equations. (Lesson 9-10)

In 15–22, solve. If necessary, round to the nearest hundredth. 15–22. See margin.

15. $\log_6 5 = t$
16. $\log_{12} 9900 = s$
17. $2000(1.06)^n = 6000$
18. $13 \cdot 2^x = 1$
19. $e^z = 44$
20. $(0.8)^w = e$
21. $11^{a+1} = 1011$
22. $3^{-2a} = 53$

OBJECTIVE C Solve logarithmic equations. (Lessons 9-5, 9-6, 9-7, 9-9)

In 23–30, solve. If necessary, round to the nearest hundredth. 23–30. See margin.

23. $\log_x 33 = \log_{11} 33$
24. $\ln(4y) = \ln 9 + \ln 12$
25. $\log z = 18$
26. $\log x = 3.71$
27. $3 \ln 5 = \ln x$
28. $\log_8 x = \frac{3}{7}$
29. $\log_x 347 = 3$
30. $\log_x 5 = 10$

PROPERTIES Principles behind the mathematics

OBJECTIVE D Recognize properties of exponential functions. (Lessons 9-1, 9-2, 9-3)

31. What are the domain and range of the function f defined by $f(x) = e^x$? See margin.
32. What are the domain and range of the function g defined by $g(x) = 2^x$? See margin.
33. When does the function $f: x \rightarrow a^x$ describe exponential growth? when $a > 1$
34. What must be true about the value of b in the equation $y = ab^x$, if the equation models exponential decay? $0 < b < 1$
35. Write the equation(s) of the asymptote(s) to the graph of $y = 27(1.017)^x$. $y = 0$
36. **Multiple Choice** Which situation does the equation $y = e^{-x}$ describe? D
   A constant increase
   B constant decrease
   C exponential growth
   D exponential decay

OBJECTIVE E Recognize properties of logarithmic functions. (Lessons 9-5, 9-7, 9-8)

37. What is the inverse of f, when $f(x) = e^{-x}$? $f^{-1}(x) = -\ln x$
38. Give an equation of the form $y = \underline{\ ?\ }$ for the inverse of the function with equation $y = \log_3 x$. $y = 3^x$
39. **True or False** The domain of the log function with base 12 is the range of the exponential function with base 12. true
40. **True or False** Negative numbers are not included in the domain of f when $f(x) = \log_b x$. true

Additional Answers

15. $t = 0.90$
16. $s = 3.70$
17. $n = 18.85$
18. $x = -3.70$
19. $z = 3.78$
20. $w = -4.48$
21. $a = 1.89$
22. $a = -1.81$
23. $x = 11$
24. $y = 27$
25. $z = 10^{18}$
26. $x = 5128.61$
27. $x = 125$
28. $x = 2.44$
29. $x = 7.03$
30. $x = 1.17$
31. domain: all real numbers, range: positive real numbers
32. domain: all real numbers, range: positive real numbers

OBJECTIVE F Apply properties of logarithms. (Lessons 9-9, 9-10)

In 41–44, write in exponential form. 41–44. See margin.

41. $\log_3\left(\frac{1}{243}\right) = -5$
42. $\ln 23.14 \approx \pi$
43. $\log m = n$
44. $\log_b p = q$

In 45–48, write in logarithmic form. 45–48. See margin.

45. $10^{-1.8} \approx 0.01585$
46. $e^5 \approx 148.413$
47. $x^y = z, x > 0, x \neq 1$
48. $4^a = 18$

In 49–56, rewrite the expression as a whole number or a single logarithm and state the theorem or theorems you used. 49–56. See margin.

49. $\ln 17 + \ln 12$
50. $\log 50 - \log 5$
51. $-2 \log_{12} 11$
52. $\ln e$
53. $\log_{107} 107^{79}$
54. $\log_{6.3} 1$
55. $\log a - 3 \log b$
56. $\log u + \log v + 0.7 \log w$

USES Applications of mathematics in real-world situations

OBJECTIVE G Create and apply exponential growth and decay models. (Lessons 9-1, 9-2, 9-3, 9-10)

57. In 2005 the population of the Tokyo-Yokohama region in Japan was about 35.327 million, the largest metropolitan area in the world. The average annual growth rate was 0.43%. Assuming this growth rate continues, find the population of the Tokyo-Yokohama area in 2020. about 37.675 million

58. In 2005 the sixth largest metropolitan area in the world was that of Mumbai, India, with 18.202 million people. Mumbai was growing at an average rate of 1.96% annually. Suppose this rate continues indefinitely.
   a. Find the population of this area in 2020. about 24.354 million
   b. In what year will the population of Mumbai reach 30 million? 2030

65a. See margin.
65b. $p = 2.72(2.06)^h$
65c. about 771,100 bacteria

59. Refer to Questions 57 and 58. Estimate the year in which Mumbai's population will first exceed Tokyo-Yokohama's population. 2048

60. The population of a certain strain of bacteria grows according to $N = C \cdot 3^{0.593t}$, where t is the time in hours. How long will it take for 30 bacteria to increase to 500 bacteria? about 4.3 hr

61. The amount A of radioactivity from a nuclear explosion is given by $A = Ce^{-0.2t}$, where t is measured in days after the explosion. What percent of the original radioactivity is present 9 days after the explosion? 16.53%

62. Strontium-90 (^{90}Sr) has a half-life of 29 years. If there was originally 25 grams of ^{90}Sr,
   a. how much strontium will be left after 87 years? 3.125 grams
   b. how much strontium will be left after t years? $25\left(\frac{1}{2}\right)^{\frac{t}{29}}$ grams

63. A new car costing \$28,000 is predicted to depreciate at a rate of 14% per year. About how much will the car be worth in six years? \$11,327.88

OBJECTIVE H Fit an exponential model to data. (Lesson 9-4)

64. Find an equation for the exponential function $f: x \rightarrow ab^x$ passing through (0, 1.2) and (3, 25). $f(x) = 1.2(2.75)^x$

65. A bacteria population was counted every hour for a day with the following results.

Hour h	1	2	3	4	5	6	7
Population p (hundreds)	5	13	25	49	103	211	423

   a. Construct a scatterplot of these data.
   b. Fit an exponential model to these data.
   c. Use your model to estimate the population at the 11th hour.

Additional Answers

41. $3^{-5} = \frac{1}{243}$
42. $e^\pi \approx 23.14$
43. $10^n = m$
44. $b^q = p$
45. $\log(0.01585) \approx -1.8$
46. $\ln(148.413) \approx 5$
47. $\log_x z = y, x > 0, x \neq 1$
48. $\log_4 18 = a$
49. $\ln(204)$; Logarithm of a Product Theorem
50. 1; Logarithm of a Quotient Theorem, $\log_b$ of b^n Theorem
51. $\log_{12}\left(\frac{1}{121}\right)$; Logarithm of a Power Theorem
52. 1; $\log_b$ of b^n Theorem
53. 79, Logarithm of a Power Theorem, $\log_b$ of b^n Theorem
54. 0; Logarithm of 1 Theorem
55. $\log\left(\frac{a}{b^3}\right)$; Logarithm of a Power Theorem, Logarithm of a Quotient Theorem
56. $\log(uvw^{0.7})$; Logarithm of a Power Theorem, Logarithm of a Product Theorem

Additional Answers

65a.

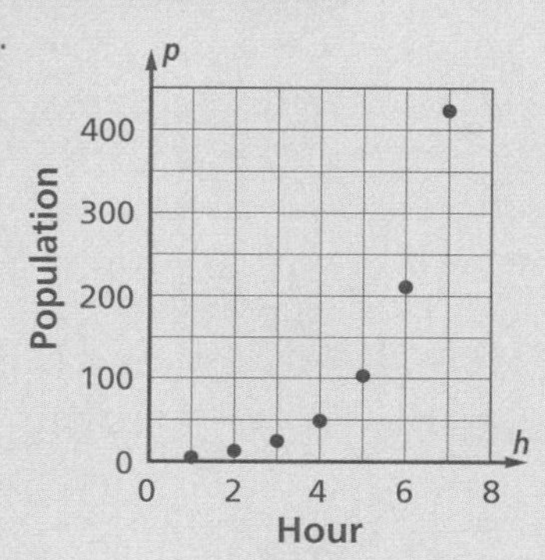

Additional Answers

66a.

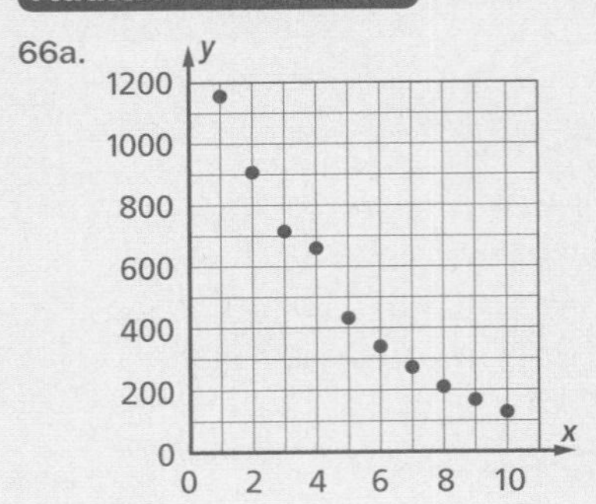

66b. About 4 days; this is the time at which approximately half of the mathium remains.

72.

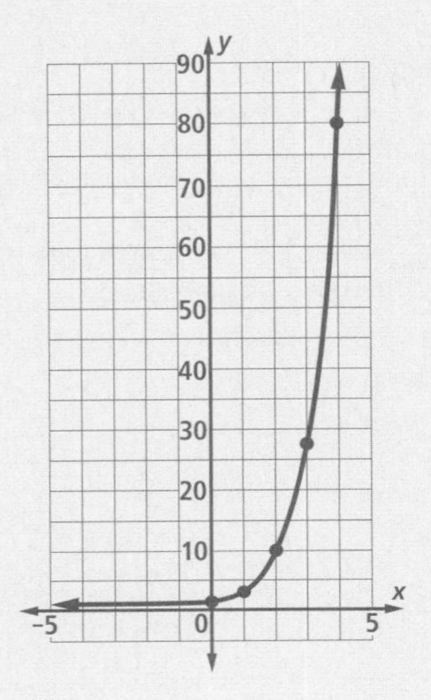

73.

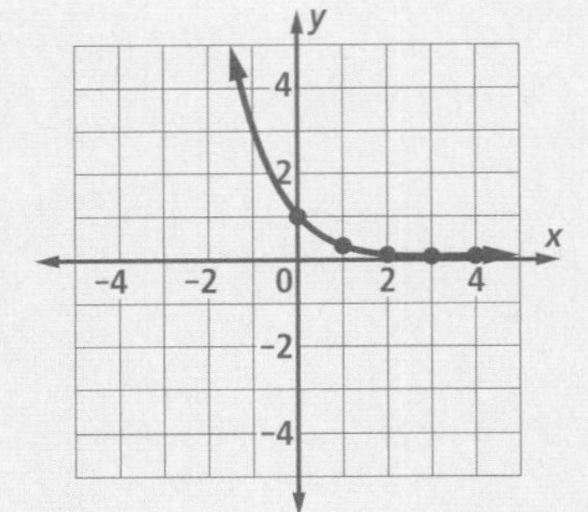

66. A hypothetical new substance, mathium, was manufactured and experiments showed that it decayed at the following rate.

Days	Amount Present (g)
1	1156
2	907
3	715
4	660
5	432
6	340
7	273
8	210
9	168
10	129

a–b. See margin.

a. Construct a scatterplot of these data.

b. From the data in the scatterplot, what is the approximate half-life of this new substance? Explain your answer.

c. Fit an exponential model to these data. $A = 1522.76(0.78)^d$

d. On the 20th day, how much of the substance will be present? about 10.58 grams

OBJECTIVE I Apply logarithmic scales, models, and formulas. (Lessons 9-6, 9-8)

In 67–69, use the formula $D = 10 \log\left(\frac{I}{10^{-12}}\right)$ to convert sound intensity I in $\frac{\text{W}}{\text{m}^2}$ into relative intensity D in decibels.

67. Find D when $I = 3.88 \cdot 10^9$. 215.89 decibels

68. What sound intensity corresponds to a relative intensity of 80 decibels? $10^{-4} \frac{\text{W}}{\text{m}^2}$

69. How many times as intense is a 60 dB sound as a 20 dB sound? 10,000

70. Baking soda has a pH value of 8, while pure water has a pH value of 7. How many times as acidic is water than baking soda? 10 times as acidic

71. The boiling point T of water in degrees Fahrenheit at barometric pressure P in inches Hg (inches of mercury) is given by the model

$$T = 49.161 \cdot \ln P + 44.932.$$

At what temperature does water boil in Colorado if the average barometric pressure is 27 inches Hg? 206.96°F

REPRESENTATIONS Pictures, graphs, or objects that illustrate concepts

OBJECTIVE J Graph exponential functions. (Lessons 9-1, 9-2) 72–73. See margin.

72. Graph $y = 3^x$ using at least five points.

73. Graph $y = \left(\frac{1}{3}\right)^x$ using at least five points.

74. Graph $g(x) = \left(\frac{1}{5}\right)^x$ and $h(x) = \left(\frac{1}{5}\right)^{2x}$ on the same set of axes.

a. Which function has greater values when $x > 0$? g

b. Which function has greater values when $x < 0$? h

75. Below are the graphs of the equations $y = 2^x$ and $y = 3^x$.

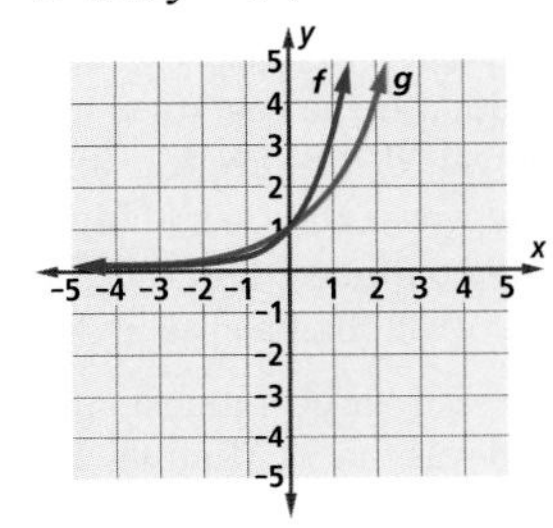

a. Which equation corresponds to the graph of f? $y = 3^x$

b. Which equation corresponds to the graph of g? $y = 2^x$

c. Describe how the graph of $y = e^x$ is related to the graphs of f and g.
The graph of $y = e^x$ shares the same y-intercept and falls between the graphs of f and g for all other values of x.

76. **Multiple Choice** Which graph below represents exponential decay? D

A

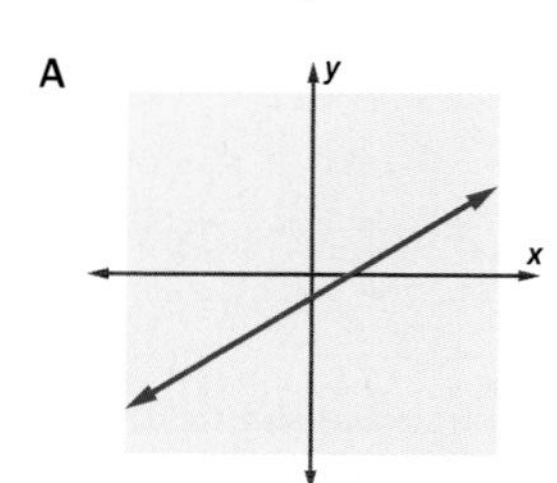

B

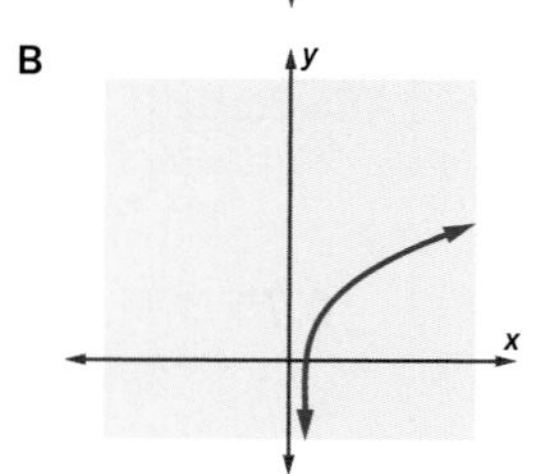

C

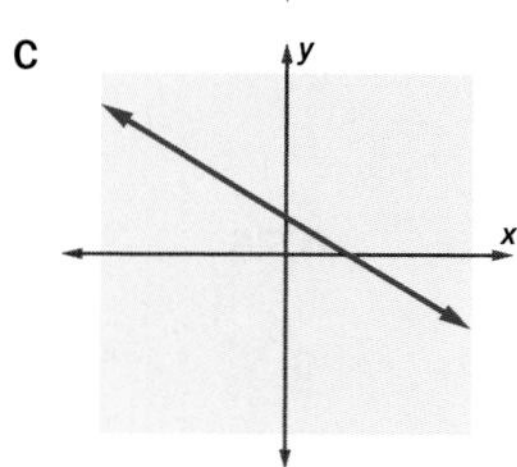

D

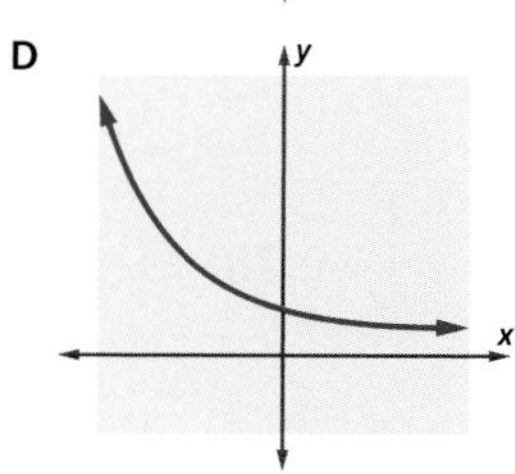

OBJECTIVE K Graph logarithmic curves. (Lessons 9-5, 9-7)

77. a. Graph $y = 4^x$ using at least five points.

b. Use the results of Part a to plot at least five points on the graph of $y = \log_4 x$.
a–b. See margin.

78. a. Plot $y = 10^x$ and $y = \log_{10} x$ on the same set of axes.

b. Identify all intercepts of these curves.

79. a. Graph $y = \ln x$ using at least five points.

b. Give an equation for the inverse of this function. $y = e^x$

80. The graph below has the equation $y = \log_Q x$. Find Q. $Q = 4$

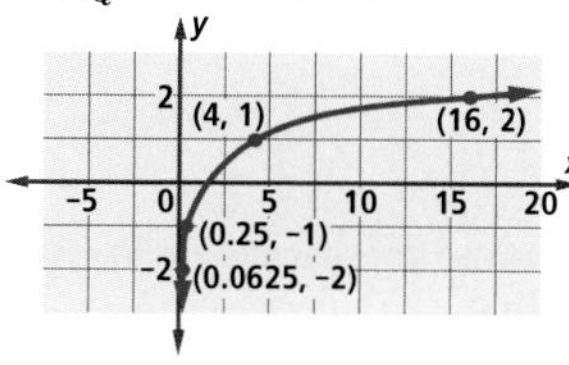

81. What is the x-intercept of the graph of $y = \log_b x$, where $b > 1$? 1

78a.

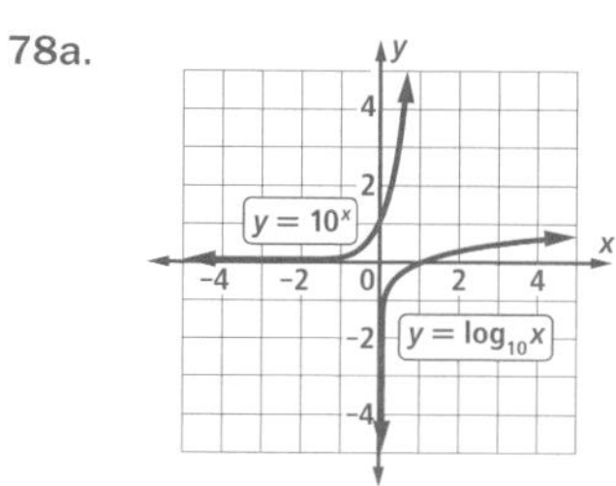

78b. The y-intercept of $y = 10^x$ is 1; the x-intercept of $y = \log_{10} x$ is 1.

79a.

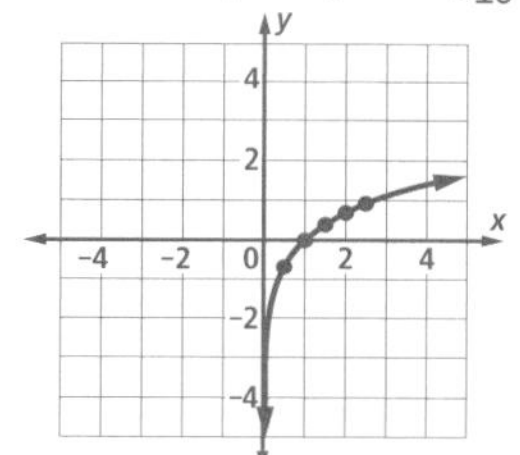

Assessment

Evaluation The *Assessment Resources* provide four forms of the Chapter 9 Test. Forms A and B present parallel versions of a short-answer format. Form C consists of four to six short-response questions that cover the SPUR objectives from Chapter 9. Form D offers performance assessment that covers a subset (or even just one) of the SPUR objectives for the chapter. The fifth type of test is a Chapter 9 Test, Cumulative Form. About 50% of this test covers Chapter 9, and the remaining 50% covers the previous chapters evenly.

Feedback After students have taken the test for Chapter 9 and you have scored the results, return the tests to students for discussion. Class discussion on the questions that caused trouble for most students can be very effective in identifying and clarifying misunderstandings. You might want to have them note the items they missed and work either in groups or at home to correct them. It is important for students to receive feedback on every chapter test, and we recommend that students see and correct their mistakes before proceeding too far into the next chapter.

Suggestions for Assignment Assign Lesson 10-1 for homework the evening of the test. It gives students work to do after they have completed the test and keeps the class moving. If you do not do this, you may cover one less chapter over the course of the year.

Additional Answers

77a.

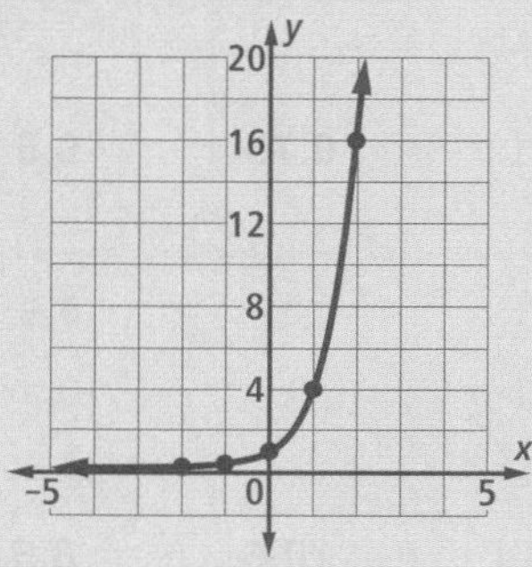

77b.

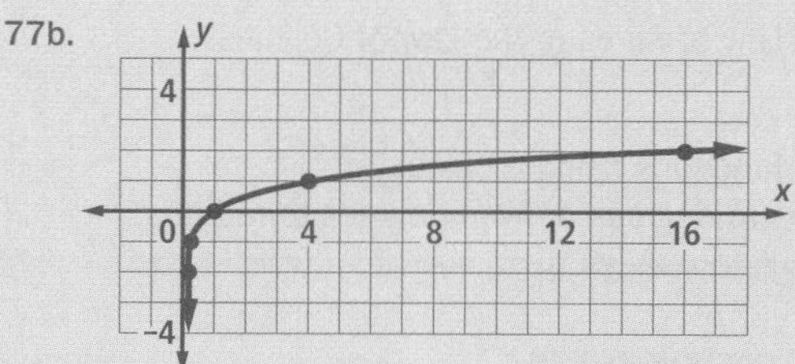

Chapter

10 Basic Ideas of Trigonometry

Chapter Overview

		Local Standards	Pacing *(in days)* Average	Advanced	Block
10-1	**Three Trigonometric Functions** **A** Approximate values of trigonometric functions using a calculator. **E** Identify and use the definitions of sine, cosine, and tangent. **G** Solve real-world problems using the trigonometry of right triangles.		1	0.75	0.5
10-2	**More Right-Triangle Trigonometry** **B** Determine the measure of an angle given its sine, cosine, or tangent. **G** Solve real-world problems using the trigonometry of right triangles.		1	0.75	0.5
10-3	**Trigonometry, Earth, Moon, and Stars** **G** Solve real-world problems using the trigonometry of right triangles.		1	0.75	0.5
	QUIZ 1		0.5	0.5	0.25
10-4	**The Unit-Circle Definition of Cosine and Sine** **E** Identify and use the definitions of sine, cosine, and tangent. **I** Use the properties of a unit circle to find values of trigonometric functions.		1	0.75	0.5
10-5	**Relationships among Sines and Cosines** **E** Identify and use the definitions of sine, cosine, and tangent. **F** Identify and use theorems relating sines and cosines. **I** Use the properties of a unit circle to find values of trigonometric functions.		1	0.75	0.5
10-6	**The Cosine and Sine Functions** **J** Identify properties of the sine and cosine functions using their graphs.		1	0.75	0.5
	QUIZ 2		0.5	0.5	0.25
10-7	**The Law of Sines** **B** Determine the measure of an angle given its sine, cosine, or tangent. **C** Find missing side lengths and angle measures of a triangle using the Law of Sines or the Law of Cosines. **F** Identify and use theorems relating sines and cosines. **H** Solve real-world problems using the Law of Sines or the Law of Cosines.		1	0.75	0.5
10-8	**The Law of Cosines** **C** Find missing side lengths and angle measures of a triangle using the Law of Sines or the Law of Cosines. **H** Solve real-world problems using the Law of Sines or the Law of Cosines.		1	0.75	0.5
10-9	**Radian Measure** **A** Approximate values of trigonometric functions using a calculator. **D** Convert angle measures from radians to degrees or from degrees to radians.		1	0.75	0.5
		Self-Test	1	0.75	0.5
		Chapter Review	2	1	0.5
		Test	1	1	0.5
		TOTAL	14	10.5	6.5

Technology Resources

Teacher's Assessment Assistant, Ch. 10
Electronic Teacher's Edition, Ch. 10

Differentiated Options  Universal Access

	Accommodating the Learner	Vocabulary Development	Ongoing Assessment	Materials
10-1	pp. 663, 664	p. 666	oral, p. 669	ruler and protractor or DGS
10-2	pp. 672, 673	p. 671	group, p. 674	
10-3	pp. 678–679	p. 676	oral, p. 681	whiteboard or butcher paper, ruler, string
10-4	pp. 683, 685	p. 684	written, p. 686	compass, protractor, graph paper
10-5	pp. 688, 689	p. 688	group, p. 692	
10-6	pp. 694, 695	p. 695	oral, p. 699	calculator
10-7	pp. 701, 702	p. 703	written, p. 705	ruler, protractor
10-8	pp. 708, 709	p. 707	written, p. 711	
10-9	pp. 713, 714	p. 713	group, p. 717	

Objectives

	Lessons	Self-Test Questions	Chapter Review Questions
Skills			
A Approximate values of trigonometric functions using a calculator.	10-1, 10-9	1	1-6
B Determine the measure of an angle given its sine, cosine, or tangent.	10-2, 10-7	2	7-10
C Find missing side lengths and angle measures of a triangle using the Law of Sines or the Law of Cosines.	10-7, 10-8	10, 13	11-15
D Convert angle measures from radians to degrees or from degrees to radians.	10-9	15, 16	16-23
Properties			
E Identify and use the definitions of sine, cosine, and tangent.	10-1, 10-4, 10-5	3	24-33
F Identify and use theorems relating sines and cosines.	10-5, 10-7	4, 6	34-37
Uses			
G Solve real-world problems using the trigonometry of right triangles.	10-1, 10-2, 10-3	14-17	38-41
H Solve real-world problems using the Law of Sines or Law of Cosines.	10-7, 10-8	9	42-45
Representations			
I Use the properties of a unit circle to find values of trigonometric functions.	10-4, 10-5	5, 7, 8	46-56
J Identify properties of the sine and cosine functions using their graphs.	10-6	11, 12	57-61

Resource Masters Chapter 10

None of the generic Resource Masters apply to this chapter.

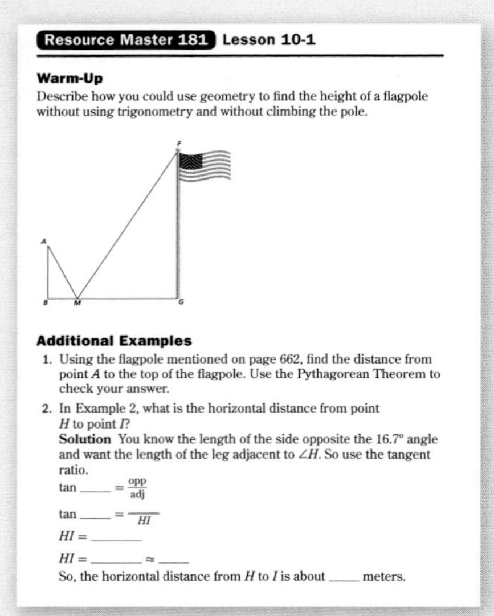

Resource Master 181 Lesson 10-1

Warm-Up

Describe how you could use geometry to find the height of a flagpole without using trigonometry and without climbing the pole.

Additional Examples

1. Using the flagpole mentioned on page 662, find the distance from point A to the top of the flagpole. Use the Pythagorean Theorem to check your answer.
2. In Example 2, what is the horizontal distance from point H to point I?
   Solution You know the length of the side opposite the 16.7° angle and want the length of the leg adjacent to $\angle H$. So use the tangent ratio.
   tan ____ = $\frac{\text{opp}}{\text{adj}}$
   tan ____ = $\frac{\quad}{HI}$
   HI = ______
   HI = ______ ≈ ____
   So, the horizontal distance from H to I is about ____ meters.

Resource Master for Lesson 10-1

Resource Master 183 Lesson 10-1

Resource Master 182 Lesson 10-1

Additional Examples

3. Each edge of the regular pentagon $ABCDE$ is 15.4 inches. Find the length of diagonal $\overline{AC}$.
4. Draw a right triangle with hypotenuse $AB = 10$, leg $AC = 5$, and leg $BC = 5\sqrt{3}$. Use your triangle to find an expression for cos B. Explain how you know the measures of the angles of $\triangle ABC$.

Right-Triangle Definitions of Sine, Cosine, and Tangent

In a right triangle with acute angle θ,

the **sine** of $\theta = \frac{\text{length of leg opposite } \theta}{\text{length of hypotenuse}}$;

the **cosine** of $\theta = \frac{\text{length of leg adjacent to } \theta}{\text{length of hypotenuse}}$;

the **tangent** of $\theta = \frac{\text{length of leg opposite } \theta}{\text{length of leg adjacent to } \theta}$.

hypotenuse
leg opposite θ
leg adjacent to θ

Resource Masters for Lesson 10-1

Resource Master 184 Lesson 10-2

Warm-Up

In $\triangle ABC$, $AB = 20$, $BC = 21$, and $AC = 29$.

1. Explain why $\triangle ABC$ is a right triangle.
2. Calculate sin A, cos A, and tan A.
3. The quotient of two of the answers to Warm-Up 2 equals the third answer. Write out one of the two equations.

Additional Example

1. Consider a right triangle QRS in which hypotenuse $\overline{SQ}$ has length 19 and $SR = 15$. What is m$\angle QSR$?

Resource Master for Lesson 10-2

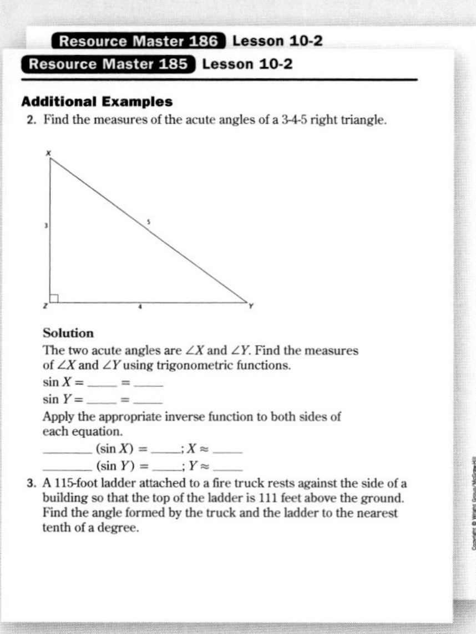

Resource Master 186 Lesson 10-2

Resource Master 185 Lesson 10-2

Additional Examples

2. Find the measures of the acute angles of a 3-4-5 right triangle.

   Solution
   The two acute angles are $\angle X$ and $\angle Y$. Find the measures of $\angle X$ and $\angle Y$ using trigonometric functions.
   sin X = ____ = ____
   sin Y = ____ = ____
   Apply the appropriate inverse function to both sides of each equation.
   ______ (sin X) = ____; X ≈ ____
   ______ (sin Y) = ____; Y ≈ ____
3. A 115-foot ladder attached to a fire truck rests against the side of a building so that the top of the ladder is 111 feet above the ground. Find the angle formed by the truck and the ladder to the nearest tenth of a degree.

Resource Masters for Lesson 10-2

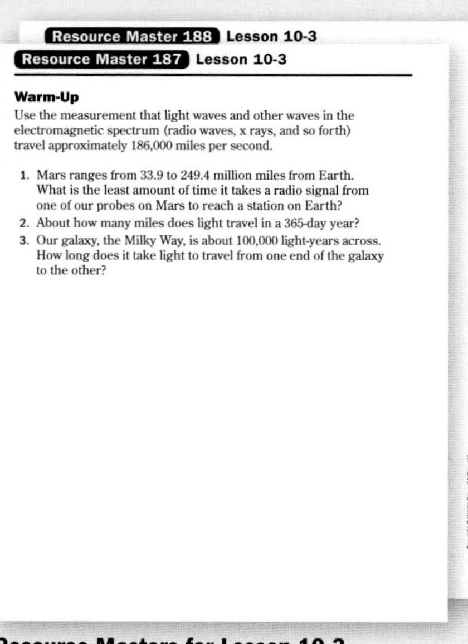

Resource Master 188 Lesson 10-3

Resource Master 187 Lesson 10-3

Warm-Up

Use the measurement that light waves and other waves in the electromagnetic spectrum (radio waves, x rays, and so forth) travel approximately 186,000 miles per second.

1. Mars ranges from 33.9 to 249.4 million miles from Earth. What is the least amount of time it takes a radio signal from one of our probes on Mars to reach a station on Earth?
2. About how many miles does light travel in a 365-day year?
3. Our galaxy, the Milky Way, is about 100,000 light-years across. How long does it take light to travel from one end of the galaxy to the other?

Resource Masters for Lesson 10-3

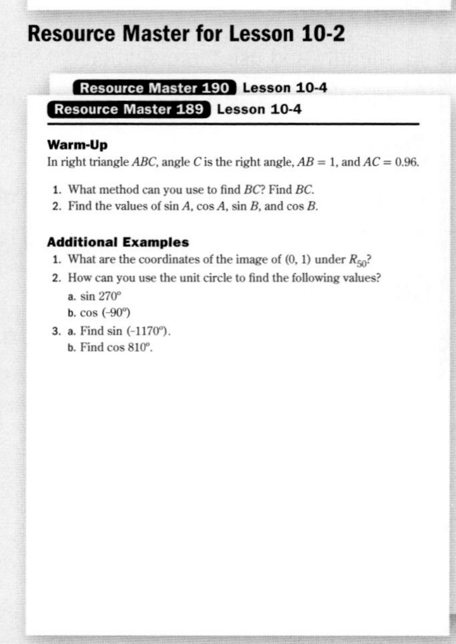

Resource Master 190 Lesson 10-4

Resource Master 189 Lesson 10-4

Warm-Up

In right triangle ABC, angle C is the right angle, $AB = 1$, and $AC = 0.96$.

1. What method can you use to find BC? Find BC.
2. Find the values of sin A, cos A, sin B, and cos B.

Additional Examples

1. What are the coordinates of the image of (0, 1) under R_{50}?
2. How can you use the unit circle to find the following values?
   a. sin 270°
   b. cos (-90°)
3. a. Find sin (-1170°).
   b. Find cos 810°.

Resource Masters for Lesson 10-4

Resource Master 192 Lesson 10-5

Resource Master 191 Lesson 10-5

Warm-Up

In right triangle DEF, D is the right angle, $DE = \sqrt{83}$, and $EF = \sqrt{89}$.

1. Find the exact values of cos E and sin E and show that $\cos^2 E + \sin^2 E = 1$.
2. Estimate cos E and sin E to the nearest millionth and show that with these estimates, $\cos^2 E + \sin^2 E \approx 1$.

Additional Examples

1. In the diagram for Example 1, suppose that the angle formed by the segment and the positive x-axis is 52°.
   a. Approximate the coordinates of point C to the nearest thousandth.
   b. Verify that your coordinates in Part a satisfy the Pythagorean Identity.
2. Show why cos 252° = −cos 72°.

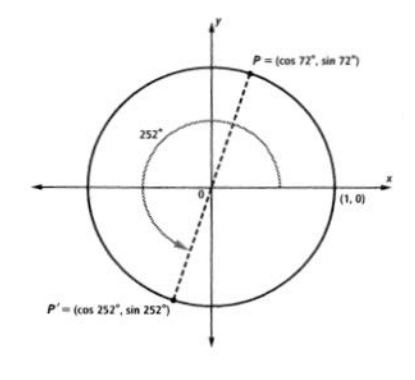

Resource Masters for Lesson 10-5

Resource Master 193 Lesson 10-5

Example 1

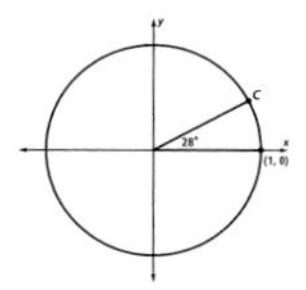

Question 29

θ	sin θ	tan θ	sin θ − tan θ
10°			
5°			
2°			
1°			
0.5°			
0.1°			

Resource Master for Lesson 10-5

Resource Master 194 Lesson 10-6

Warm-Up

Do Activity 1 to graph the cosine function.

Additional Example

Suppose a bird lands on a Ferris wheel basket at the basket's highest position and rides for one complete revolution. If the Ferris wheel has a diameter of 180 feet, the center of rotation is 110 feet above the ground, and the wheel takes 10 minutes to travel one revolution, which sine wave below models the height of the bird t minutes after it lands on the Ferris wheel?

Graph A:

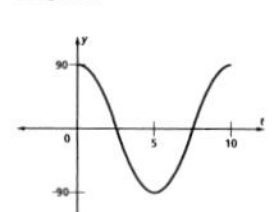

Graph B:

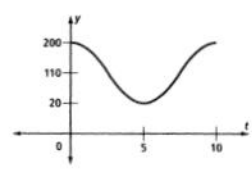

Graph C:

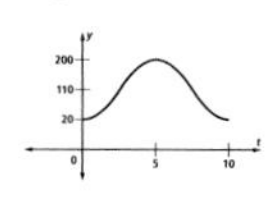

Resource Master for Lesson 10-6

Resource Master 196 Lesson 10-6

Resource Master 195 Lesson 10-6

Activity 1

θ	cos θ
0°	1.00
15°	0.97
30°	0.87
45°	0.71
60°	
75°	
90°	
105°	
120°	
135°	
150°	
165°	
180°	
195°	
210°	
225°	
240°	
255°	
270°	
285°	
300°	
315°	
330°	
345°	
360°	

Resource Masters for Lesson 10-6

Resource Master 198 Lesson 10-7

Resource Master 197 Lesson 10-7

Warm-Up

Do the Activity as a Warm-Up.

Additional Examples

1. Find all solutions to sin θ = 0.528 in the interval 0° < θ < 180°.
2. In Example 2, suppose stations S and T are 18 miles apart, the ranger at S sees a fire at an angle of 42° with $\overrightarrow{ST}$, and the ranger at T sees the fire at an angle of 74° with $\overrightarrow{TS}$ as shown below. Find the distance from station T to the fire.

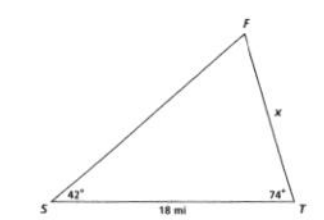

3. In $\triangle TRI$, m∠R = 25°, m∠I = 72°, and r = 13. Find t.
   Solution Sketch the figure.
   Use the Law of Sines: $\frac{\sin R}{r} = \frac{\sin T}{t}$.
   $\frac{\sin \_\_\_}{\_\_\_} = \frac{\sin \_\_\_}{\_\_\_}$
   t = ______

Resource Masters for Lesson 10-7

Resource Master 200 Lesson 10-8

Resource Master 199 Lesson 10-8

Warm-Up

Evaluate the expression $\sqrt{a^2 + b^2 - 2ab(\cos \theta)}$ when $a = 3$, $b = 4$, and θ has the given value.

1. 45°
2. 90°
3. 120°

Additional Examples

1. In Example 1, suppose that the two straight roads meet in Canton at an angle of 38°. Anton is 11 miles down one road, and Banton is 5 miles down the other. How far apart are Anton and Banton?
2. In $\triangle PQR$, r = 10, p = 18, and m∠P = 45°. Find q.

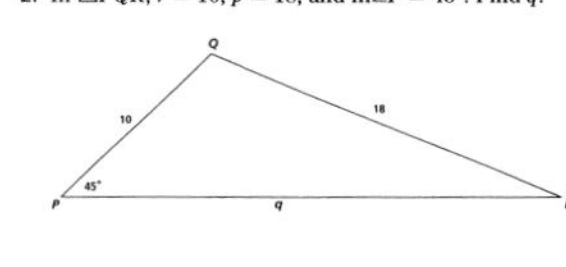

Resource Masters for Lesson 10-8

Resource Master 201 Lesson 10-9

Warm-Up

1. What is the circumference of the unit circle?
2. What is the length of a 20° arc on the unit circle?
3. What is the length of an x° arc on the unit circle?

Additional Examples

1. Convert 1 degree to radians.
2. a. Convert 60° to its exact radian equivalent.
   b. Convert $\frac{5}{6}\pi$ to its exact degree equivalent.
   Solution
   a. 60° • ____ = ____ radians
   60° = ____ radians, exactly.
   b. $\frac{5}{6}\pi$ • ____ = ____
   $\frac{5}{6}\pi$ = ____, exactly.
3. Set your calculator to radian mode.
   a. Evaluate cos 6.
   b. Evaluate tan $\frac{7\pi}{6}$.
   Solution
   a. Enter COS ____. You should find cos ____ ≈ ____.
   b. Enter TAN ____. You should find tan ____ ≈ ____.

Resource Master for Lesson 10-9

Resource Master 202 Lesson 10-9

Equivalences of Radians and Degrees

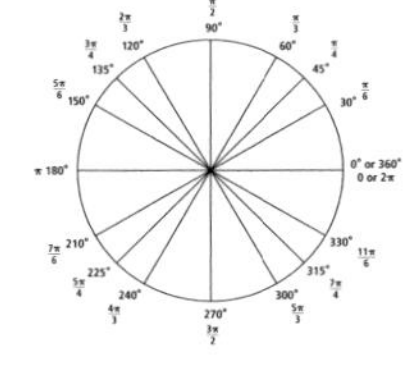

Resource Master for Lesson 10-9

Resource Master 203 Lesson 10-9

Graphs of the Sine and Cosine Functions Using Radians

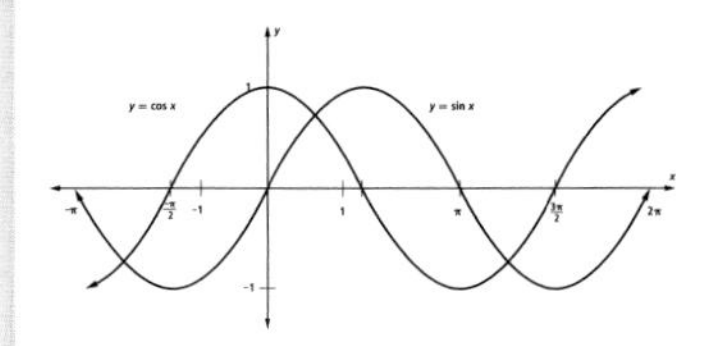

Question 12

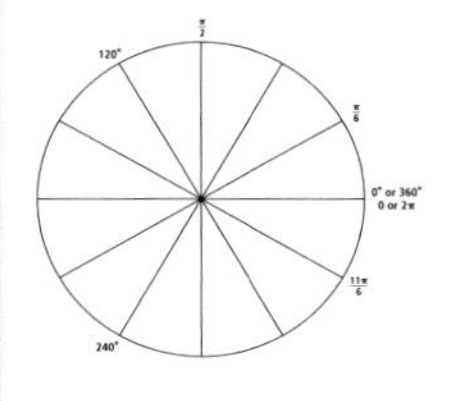

Resource Master for Lesson 10-9

Chapter 10

Pacing

Each lesson in this chapter is designed to be covered in 1 day. If you do all the activities, however, you will need to add 1 to 2 days. At the end of the chapter, you should plan to spend 1 day to review the Self-Test, 1 to 2 days for the Chapter Review, and 1 day for a test. You may wish to spend a day on projects and possibly a day is needed for quizzes. This chapter should therefore take 14 to 17 days. We strongly advise you not to spend more than 18 days on this chapter.

Overview

This chapter is an introduction to trigonometry and presents only the sine, cosine, and tangent ratios. Understanding these ratios provides sufficient mathematical power to solve virtually every trigonometric problem. It is easy to find the [SIN], [COS], and [TAN] commands on most calculators, but it is not so easy to find the [CSC], [SEC], or [COT] commands.

We believe trigonometry should be included in an advanced algebra course because every high school graduate should know something about this branch of mathematics. It is important in engineering, carpentry, electronics, drafting, and metallurgy as well as many other fields.

Your students may have explored and studied sines, cosines, tangents, and other right-triangle trigonometric ideas in their geometry course; trigonometry is found in some introductory algebra texts (e.g., to show that the slope of a line is the tangent of the angle it makes with the positive *x*-axis) and even in some junior high (middle) school math programs. Also, students may have seen trigonometry in a physics class. Before beginning this chapter, we encourage you to find out what your students know.

Chapter 10 Basic Ideas of Trigonometry

Contents

The word *trigonometry* is derived from Greek words meaning "triangle measure," and its study usually begins by examining relationships between sides and angles in right triangles. These ideas originated thousands of years ago. As early as 1500 BCE, the Egyptians had sun clocks. Using their ideas, the ancient Greeks created sundials by erecting a *gnomon*, or staff, in the ground. The shadows and the gnomon created triangles that could be used to measure the angle of the Sun at any time. With these measurements, ancient mathematicians could measure the length of a year by seeing when the angles of the Sun repeated themselves.

Using geometry and trigonometry, the ancient Greeks were also able to measure the circumference of Earth to within 1 percent of its actual value. Additionally, the astronomers Hipparchus and Ptolemy used trigonometry to estimate the distance from Earth to the Moon to be about 250,000 miles, impressively close to the current estimated value of 238,000 miles. To arrive at this estimate, Hipparchus and Ptolemy used observations of *parallax*, the apparent motion of the Moon against the background of the stars when observed from different positions. The same method is still used today. The satellite *Hipparcos*, (the Greek version of the Latin name Hipparchus), collected parallax data from 1989 until 1993 that has established the distances from Earth to over 120,000 stars.

660

Chapter 10 Overview

The chapter naturally splits into three 3-lesson sections. The first three lessons, devoted to right-triangle trigonometry, include solving for the lengths of sides or measures of angles in right triangles. Students are expected to use ideas from geometry to find exact values of trigonometric ratios and to use calculators to find approximations.

In the middle section, Lessons 10-4 and 10-5 extend the definitions of sine and cosine from a domain of angle measures between 0° and 90° to the domain of the set of all real numbers. The sine and cosine functions are graphed in Lesson 10-6.

In the last section, Lessons 10-7 and 10-8 develop and apply the Law of Sines and the Law of Cosines; by the end of Lesson 10-8, students will have had extensive experience with the classical meaning of *trigonometry,* that is, triangle measuring. Finally, the last lesson introduces radians, a unit that is central to the study of trigonometry in later mathematics courses.

Trigonometry is also used to describe wave-like patterns. For instance, when a spacecraft is launched from Cape Canaveral, tracking its position with respect to the equator produces a graph like the curve below. This curve can be described with trigonometric functions.

This chapter introduces the three fundamental trigonometric functions, *sine, cosine,* and *tangent*, as ratios of sides in right triangles. It explores ancient astronomy by recreating the computations of Earth's circumference and the distances to the Moon and to a nearby star. Many real-world uses of trigonometry, including Global Positioning Systems (GPS), are based on solving triangles. Beyond right-triangle relationships, you will study extensions of the sine and cosine functions to the domain of real numbers.

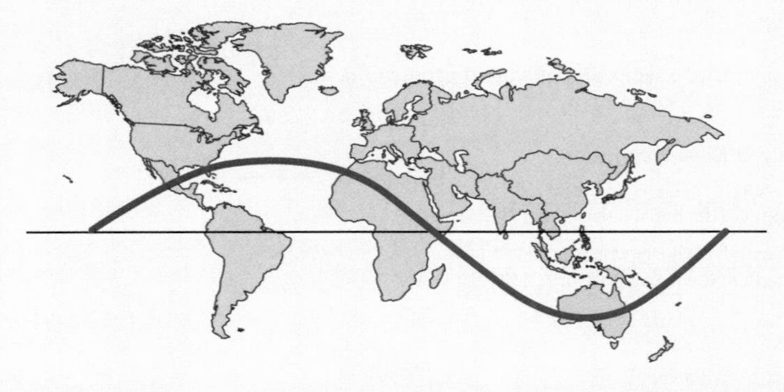

661

Using Pages 660–661

Although trigonometry is one of the oldest branches of mathematics, it is still very useful in solving problems in today's world. This is evident here.

Many of the trigonometric applications mentioned here are found in the chapter. A method that the Egyptians used to measure the height of the Egyptian pyramids is the method used to find the height of the flagpole in Lesson 10-1. Using shadows to measure the angle of the sun is explained in Lesson 10-2. The idea of parallax is found in Lesson 10-3. The path of a spacecraft shown here is similar to that which students will study in Lesson 10-6.

As you start the chapter, and continually throughout, make sure students understand the difference between the homophones "sine" and "sign."

Chapter 10 Projects

At the end of each chapter, you will find projects related to the chapter. At this time you might want to have students look over the projects on pages 718 and 719. You might want to have students tentatively select a project on which to work. Then, as students read and progress through the chapter, they can finalize their project choices.

Sometimes students might work alone. At other times, you might let them collaborate with classmates for a presentation and discussion. We recommend that you allow for diversity and encourage students to use their imaginations when presenting their projects. As students work on projects throughout the year, they should see many uses of mathematics in the real world.

Lesson

10-1

GOAL

Apply the definitions of sine, cosine, and tangent to find the lengths of sides in right triangles.

SPUR Objectives

The SPUR Objectives for all of Chapter 10 are found in the Chapter Review on pages 724–727.

A Approximate values of trigonometric functions using a calculator.

E Identify and use the definitions of sine, cosine, and tangent.

G Solve real-world problems using the trigonometry of right triangles.

Materials/Resources

- Lesson Masters 10-1A and 10-1B
- Resource Masters 181–183
- Ruler and protractor or DGS

HOMEWORK

Suggestions for Assignment

- Questions 1–23
- Question 24 (extra credit)
- Reading Lesson 10-2
- Covering the Ideas 10-2

Local Standards

1 Warm-Up

Describe how you could use geometry to find the height of a flagpole without using trigonometry and without climbing the pole.

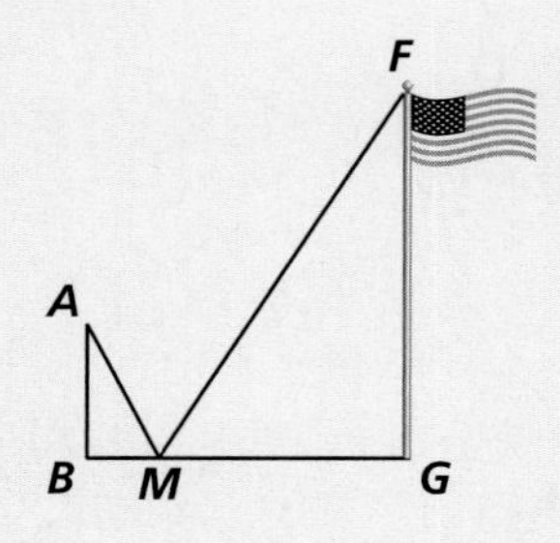

Lesson

10-1 Three Trigonometric Functions

Vocabulary

right-triangle definitions of sine (sin), cosine (cos), and tangent (tan)

sine function

cosine function

tangent function

angle of elevation

BIG IDEA The sine, cosine, and tangent of an acute angle are each a ratio of particular sides of a right triangle with that acute angle.

Mental Math

Picture two similar triangles, $\triangle BOW$ and $\triangle TIE$. Are the following ratios equal?

a. $\frac{BO}{TI}$ and $\frac{OW}{IE}$ yes

b. $\frac{WB}{ET}$ and $\frac{TI}{BO}$ no

c. $\frac{OB - OW}{WB}$ and $\frac{TI - IE}{TE}$ yes

Suppose a flagpole casts a 22-foot shadow when the Sun is at an angle of 39° with the ground. What is the height of the pole?

The height of the pole is determined by the given information because you know the measures of two angles of the right triangle (the 39° angle and the right angle) and the side they include. The ASA Congruence Theorem indicates that all triangles with these measurements are congruent.

Problems like the one above led to the development of *trigonometry*. Consider the two right triangles ABC and $A'B'C'$, with $\angle A \cong \angle A'$.

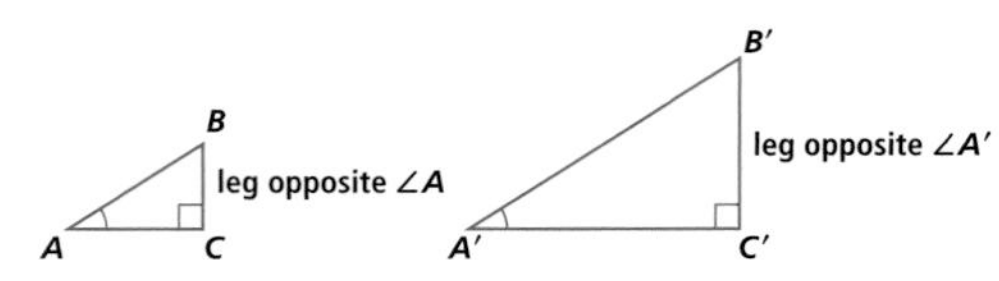

By the AA Similarity Theorem, these triangles are similar, so ratios of the lengths of corresponding sides are equal. In particular,

$$\frac{B'C'}{BC} = \frac{A'B'}{AB}.$$

Exchanging the means produces an equivalent proportion.

$$\frac{B'C'}{A'B'} = \frac{BC}{AB}$$

Look more closely at these two ratios:

$$\frac{B'C'}{A'B'} = \frac{\text{length of the leg opposite } \angle A'}{\text{length of the hypotenuse of } \triangle A'B'C'}$$

and $$\frac{BC}{AB} = \frac{\text{length of the leg opposite } \angle A}{\text{length of the hypotenuse of } \triangle ABC}.$$

Background

The definitions of the trigonometric ratios can be justified by customary arguments based on the properties of similar triangles. Although the Activity (see page 664) asks students to measure lengths to estimate the values of trigonometric functions, calculators are generally used to supply estimates of trigonometric values.

Students may have studied triangle ratios in their science classes or previous math classes, so you may want to check with your students to determine whether they have encountered this material before.

Three trigonometric ratios The other three trigonometric ratios are *cosecant, secant,* and *cotangent,* which are the reciprocals of sine, cosine, and tangent, respectively. These reciprocal functions are not studied in this course.

Thus, in every right triangle with an angle congruent to $\angle A$, the ratio of the length of the leg opposite that angle to the length of the hypotenuse of the triangle is the same.

Three Trigonometric Ratios

In similar right triangles, any other ratio of corresponding sides is also constant. These ratios are called *trigonometric ratios*. There are six possible trigonometric ratios. All six have special names, but three of them are more important and are defined here. The Greek letter θ (theta) is customarily used to refer to an angle or to its measure.

Right-Triangle Definitions of Sine, Cosine, and Tangent

In a right triangle with acute angle θ,

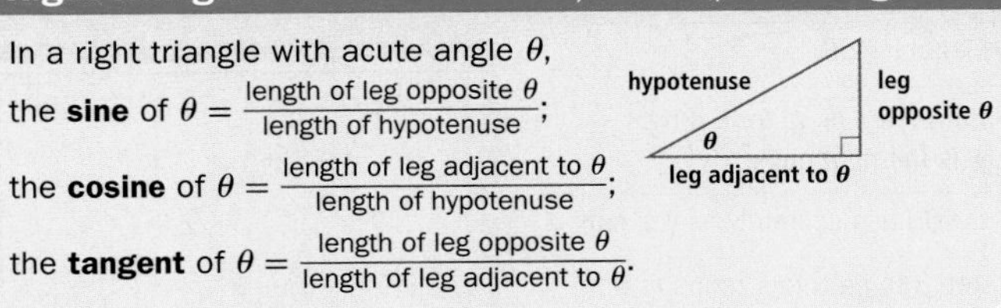

the **sine** of $\theta = \frac{\text{length of leg opposite } \theta}{\text{length of hypotenuse}}$,

the **cosine** of $\theta = \frac{\text{length of leg adjacent to } \theta}{\text{length of hypotenuse}}$,

the **tangent** of $\theta = \frac{\text{length of leg opposite } \theta}{\text{length of leg adjacent to } \theta}$.

▸ READING MATH

Trigonometry, like algebra and geometry, is a branch of mathematics. The word *trigonometry* comes from the Greek words *trigon*, meaning "triangle" and *metron*, meaning "measure," so trigonometry means "triangle measure," that is, measuring the sides and angles of triangles.

Following a practice begun by Euler, we use the abbreviations sin θ, cos θ, and tan θ to stand for these ratios, and abbreviate them as shown below.

$$\sin\theta = \frac{\text{opposite}}{\text{hypotenuse}} = \frac{\text{opp.}}{\text{hyp.}}$$

$$\cos\theta = \frac{\text{adjacent}}{\text{hypotenuse}} = \frac{\text{adj.}}{\text{hyp.}}$$

$$\tan\theta = \frac{\text{opposite}}{\text{adjacent}} = \frac{\text{opp.}}{\text{adj.}}$$

QY

▸ QY

Write the ratios sin θ, cos θ, and tan θ when $\theta = \angle A$ in $\triangle ABC$ on the previous page.

Sine, Cosine, and Tangent Functions

The three correspondences that map an angle measure θ in a right triangle onto each right-triangle ratio above define functions called the **sine**, **cosine**, and **tangent functions**.

sin: $\theta \rightarrow \sin\theta$ *cos*: $\theta \rightarrow \cos\theta$ *tan*: $\theta \rightarrow \tan\theta$

From their right-triangle definitions, the domain of each of these functions is the set of all possible acute angle measures, that is, $\{\theta \mid 0° < \theta < 90°\}$. However, in a later lesson we will extend the domain so that θ can have any degree measure, positive, negative, or zero.

Answers vary. Sample: Method 1: Find the length of the shadow of the pole. Hold a meterstick perpendicular to the ground and find the length of its shadow. Equate the ratios of the lengths of the pole and the meterstick to the lengths of their shadows. Method 2: Lay a mirror on the ground at *M*. Move away from the mirror until the top of the flagpole can be seen in the mirror. Call *B* the point where you are standing and *A* where your eyes are. Then $\triangle ABM \sim \triangle FGM$ by the AA Similarity Theorem (measure of the angle of incidence equals the measure of the angle of reflection, and the triangles have right angles). Measure *BM*, *AB*, and *MG*. Solve $\frac{FG}{AB} = \frac{GM}{BM}$ for *FG*, the height of the flagpole.

2 Teaching

Notes on the Lesson

You may wish to have students measure the sides and angles of $\triangle ABC$ and $\triangle A'B'C'$. Have students calculate selected ratios and remind them that the AA Similarity Theorem guarantees that whenever $m\angle A = m\angle A'$ and $m\angle B = m\angle B'$, the ratios $\frac{BC}{AB}$ and $\frac{B'C'}{A'B'}$ must be equal.

Now have students use their calculators to determine the cosine, sine, and tangent of the angle they found and compare these to the ratios $\frac{AC}{AB}$, $\frac{BC}{AB}$, and $\frac{BC}{AC}$, respectively, from their measurements. This sets up the Activity on page 664.

Some teachers like to use the mnemonic SOH-CAH-TOA (pronounced "so-kah-toe-ah") to help their students remember the three ratios: SOH: $\sin = \frac{\text{opp}}{\text{hyp}}$; CAH: $\cos = \frac{\text{adj}}{\text{hyp}}$; TOA: $\tan = \frac{\text{opp}}{\text{adj}}$. This mnemonic likely arose from a pun on the famous Native American young woman Sacajawea, a Shoshone who helped guide the Lewis and Clark expedition of 1803. (The mnemonic predates the phrase "Sock it to me" made famous on the 1960s television program *Laugh-In*.)

Accommodating the Learner

Ask students to sketch each triangle *ABC*, where *C* is the right angle, and answer each question.

a. If $\sin A = \frac{4}{5}$, find cos *A*, cos *B*, tan *A*, and tan *B*.

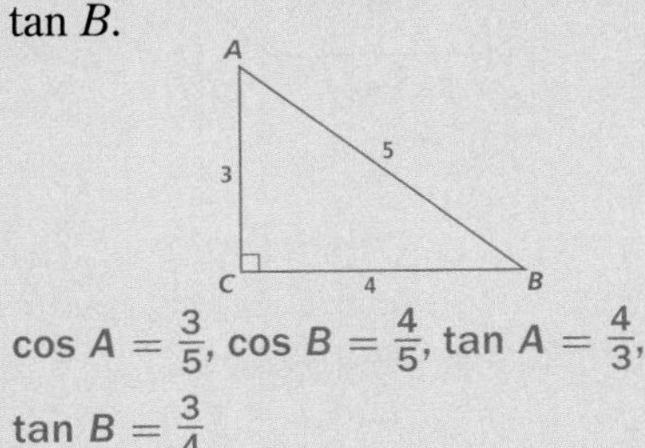

$\cos A = \frac{3}{5}$, $\cos B = \frac{4}{5}$, $\tan A = \frac{4}{3}$, $\tan B = \frac{3}{4}$

b. If $\tan B = 2$, find sin *A*, sin *B*, and tan *A*.

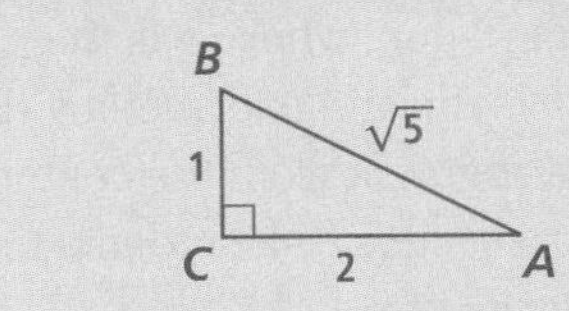

$\sin A = \frac{\sqrt{5}}{5}$, $\sin B = \frac{2\sqrt{5}}{5}$, and $\tan A = \frac{1}{2}$

Notes on the Lesson

Activity Most students will benefit from actually measuring the angles and sides of triangles.

Examples 1 and 2 These examples illustrate how the trigonometric ratios are used to solve problems. It is important that students become familiar with the keys for the trigonometric functions on their calculators. Encourage students to substitute decimals for the trigonometric values only after they have solved equations for the unknowns.

Additional Example

Example 1 Using the flagpole mentioned on page 662, find the distance from point A to the top of the flagpole. Use the Pythagorean Theorem to check your answer.

$\cos 39° = \frac{\text{adj}}{\text{hyp}}$; $0.7771 = \frac{22}{AB}$; $AB = 22 \div 0.7771 \approx 28.3087$, or about 28.3 ft. Check: $AB = \sqrt{22^2 + (17.82)^2} \approx \sqrt{484 + 317.5} = \sqrt{801.5} \approx 28.3$

In the early history of trigonometry, mathematicians calculated values of the sine, cosine, and tangent functions and published the values in tables.

Today, people use calculators to find these values, with built-in programs using formulas derived from calculus. Most calculators allow you to enter angle measures in *degrees* or *radians*. You will learn about radians in Lesson 10-9. For now, make sure that any calculator you use is set to degree mode.

Activity

MATERIALS ruler and protractor or DGS

See how close you can measure sides to obtain values of the trigonometric functions.

Step 1 Draw a 39° angle and label it PQR. Steps 1–2. See margin.

Step 2 Draw a perpendicular from P to $\overrightarrow{QR}$ to form a right triangle PQR, where $\angle R$ is the right angle.

Step 3 Measure the sides of $\triangle PQR$ as accurately as you can.

Step 4 Use the measures in Step 3 to calculate ratios to the nearest thousandth to estimate the sine, cosine, and tangent of 39°.

Step 5 Set your calculator to degree mode. Find sin 39°, cos 39°, and tan 39° to the nearest thousandth.

Step 6 Subtract to calculate the error in each of the estimates you found by measuring. Divide each error by the calculator value to determine the *relative error* of the estimate. Consider yourself to have measured well if your relative error is less than 3%.

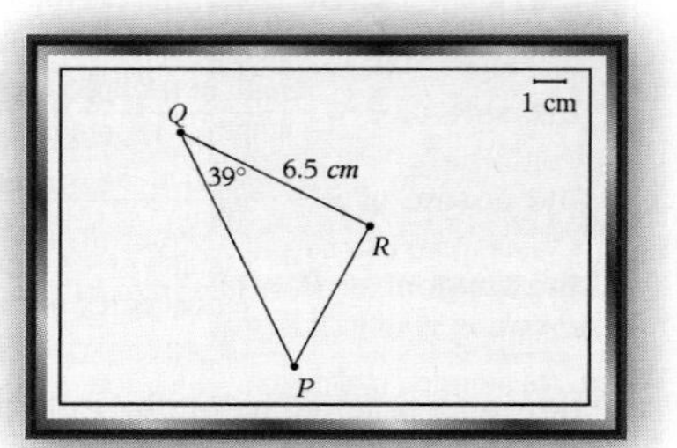

Step 3. Answers vary. Sample: $PQ = 8.4$ cm, $QR = 6.5$ cm, $RP = 5.3$ cm

Step 4. $\sin 39° \approx 0.631$, $\cos 39° \approx 0.774$, $\tan 39° \approx 0.815$

Step 5. $\sin 39° \approx 0.629$, $\cos 39° \approx 0.777$, $\tan 39° \approx 0.810$

Step 6. 0.3%, –0.3%, 0.6%

In this book, we usually give values of the trigonometric functions to the nearest thousandth. But when trigonometric values appear in long calculations, we do not round the calculator values until the end.

Using Trigonometry to Find Sides of Right Triangles

Example 1

Find the height of the flagpole mentioned in the first paragraph of this lesson.

Solution With respect to the 39° angle, the adjacent leg is known and the opposite leg is needed. Use the tangent ratio to set up an equation. Let x be the height of the flagpole.

Accommodating the Learner

Show students the diagram at the right of part of a regular n-gon, where a is the apothem and θ is the angle formed by the apothem and a segment from the center of the polygon to a vertex. Ask students to express θ in terms of n. $2\theta = \frac{360}{n}$; $\theta = \frac{180}{n}$ Then ask students to rewrite the formula for the area of a regular polygon, $A = \frac{1}{2}ap$, in terms of the number of sides n and the length s of each side.

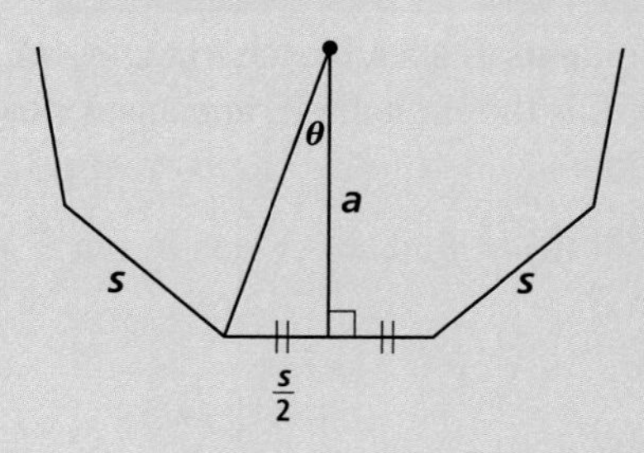

$\tan \theta = \frac{\frac{s}{2}}{a}$, so $a \tan \theta = \frac{s}{2}$ and $a = \frac{s}{2(\tan \theta)}$.

Then $A = \frac{1}{2}ap = \frac{1}{2}\left(\frac{s}{2(\tan \theta)}\right)(ns) = \frac{ns^2}{4(\tan \theta)}$.

Finally, $A = \frac{ns^2}{4\left(\tan \frac{180}{n}\right)}$.

$\tan 39° = \frac{\text{opposite}}{\text{adjacent}}$

$\tan 39° = \frac{x}{22}$

Solve for x.

$x = 22 \cdot \tan 39°$

From the Activity, we know that $\tan 39° \approx 0.810$. Substitute.

$x \approx 22(0.810) = 17.82.$

The flagpole is about 18 feet high.

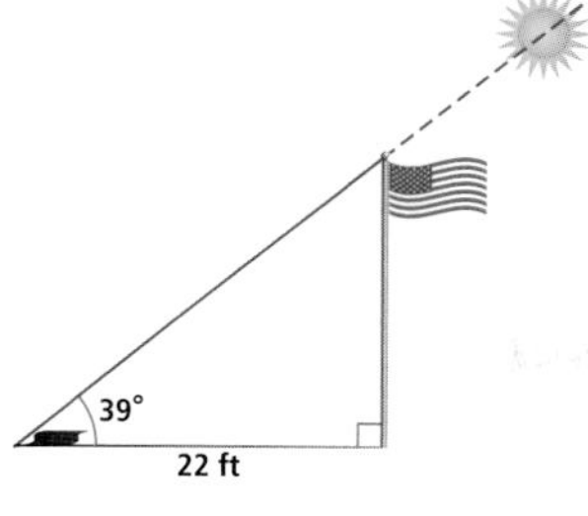

Check Recall from geometry that within a triangle, longer sides are opposite larger angles. We have found that the side opposite the 39° angle is about 18 feet long. The angle opposite the 22-foot side has measure 51°, which is larger than 39°. So the answer makes sense.

The **angle of elevation** of an object, such as the Sun above the horizon or the peak of a mountain from its base, is the angle between the horizontal base of the object and the observer's line of sight to the object. If you know the angle of elevation of an object, you can use trigonometry to find distances that would otherwise be difficult to find.

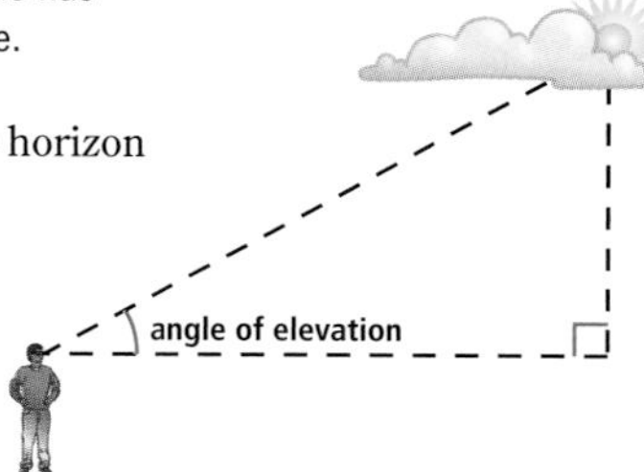

GUIDED

Example 2

The Zephyr Express chair lift in Winter Park, Colorado, has a vertical rise of about 490 meters. Suppose the lift travels at an average 16.7° angle of elevation. How many meters long is the ride?

Solution A diagram of this situation is given below.

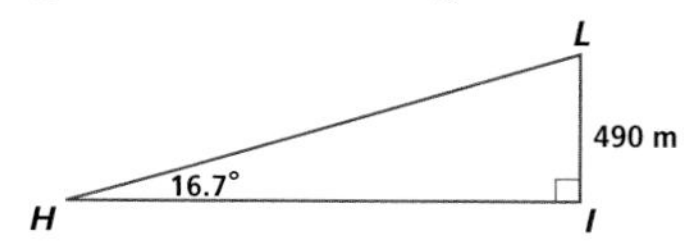

You know the length of the side opposite the 16.7° angle and want to find the length of the hypotenuse LH. So use the sine ratio.

$\sin \underline{\ ?\ } = \frac{\text{opp.}}{\text{hyp.}}$ 16.7°

$= \frac{?}{LH}$ Substitution 490

$LH = \frac{?}{?}$ Solve for LH. 490; sin 16.7°

$LH \approx \underline{\ ?\ }$ Calculate. 1705.2

So, the ride up the chair lift is about __?__ meters long. 1705

Check Use the Pythagorean Theorem to calculate HI.

$HI = \sqrt{\underline{\ ?\ }^2 - \underline{\ ?\ }^2} \approx \underline{\ ?\ }$ meters. Using the known angle, the cosine ratio relates HI and LH. $\cos \underline{\ ?\ } \approx \underline{\ ?\ }$ and $\frac{HI}{LH} \approx \underline{\ ?\ }$. It checks. 1705; 490; 1633 16.7°; 0.958; 0.958

A chair lift travels in a continuous loop, so riders must get on and off while it is moving. Many first-time riders fall on their way off.

Additional Example

Example 2 In Example 2, what is the horizontal distance from point H to point I?

Solution You know the length of the side opposite the 16.7° angle and want the length of the leg adjacent to $\angle H$. So use the tangent ratio.

$\tan \underline{\ ?\ } = \frac{\text{opp}}{\text{adj}}$ 16.7

$\tan \underline{\ ?\ } = \frac{?}{HI}$ 16.7; 490

$HI = \underline{\ ?\ }$ $\frac{490}{\tan 16.7°}$

$HI = \underline{\ ?\ } \approx \underline{\ ?\ }$ $\frac{490}{0.3000}$; 1633

The horizontal distance from H to I is about __?__ meters. 1633

Note-Taking Tips

Help students understand that a trigonometric function such as $\sin \theta$ refers to "the sine of θ," not the product of sine and θ. Encourage students to record in their notes that $\sin \theta$ notation is similar to $f(x)$ notation, where the variable (θ or x) is the argument for the function (sin or f).

Additional Answers

Activity

Step 1 and 2.

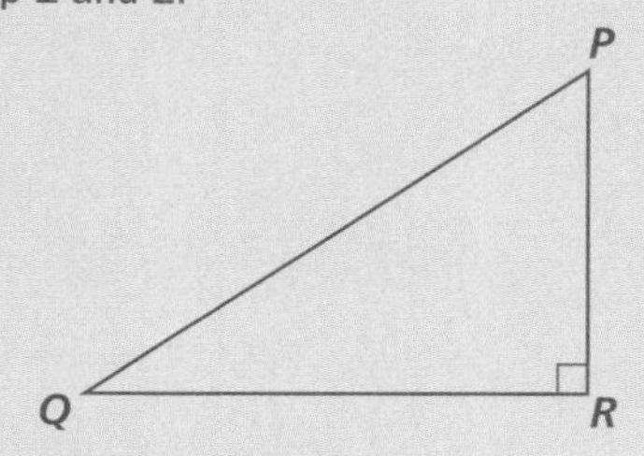

Notes on the Lesson

Example 3 Right-triangle trigonometry can be applied to figures that are not right triangles. You might point out that in a later lesson (Lesson 10-8), students will learn a way to find *VO* without drawing an auxiliary line.

Example 4 The exact value for cos 30° is derived. For some values of θ, the values of sin θ, cos θ, and tan θ can be found without knowing the exact value of any side of the right triangle because the trigonometric expressions refer to the *ratios* of side lengths.

Additional Examples

Example 3 Each edge of the regular pentagon *ABCDE* is 15.4 inches. Find the length of diagonal $\overline{AC}$. about 24.9 in.

Example 4 Draw a right triangle with hypotenuse $AB = 10$, leg $AC = 5$, and leg $BC = 5\sqrt{3}$. Use your triangle to find an expression for cos *B*. Explain how you know the measures of the angles of $\triangle ABC$. $\cos B = \frac{\text{adj}}{\text{hyp}} = \frac{AC}{AB} = \frac{5\sqrt{3}}{10} = \frac{\sqrt{3}}{2}$; $\triangle ABC$ is a 30-60-90 triangle because the sides have the ratio $1:\sqrt{3}:2$, so $m\angle A = 60$, $m\angle B = 30$, and $m\angle C = 90$.

Drawing Auxiliary Lines to Create Right Triangles

When you wish to find the length of a segment and no right triangle is given, you can sometimes draw an auxiliary line to create a right triangle.

Example 3

Each side in the regular pentagon *VIOLA* is 7.8 cm long. Find the length of diagonal $\overline{VO}$.

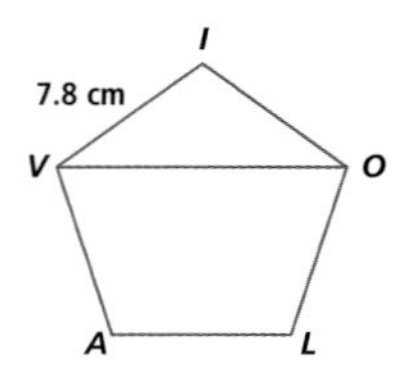

Solution Create a right triangle by drawing the segment perpendicular to $\overline{VO}$ from *I*. Call the intersection point *P*, as in the drawing at the right. Recall that each angle in a regular pentagon has measure

$\frac{180(5-2)}{5} = 108°$. So $m\angle VIO = 108°$.

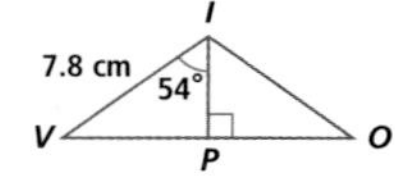

$\overline{IP}$ bisects $\angle VIO$. So $m\angle VIP = 54°$. Since the hypotenuse of $\triangle VIP$ is known and the opposite leg, *VP*, is needed, use the sine ratio.

$$\sin 54° = \frac{\text{opposite}}{\text{hypotenuse}} = \frac{VP}{7.8}$$

$$VP = 7.8 \cdot \sin 54° \approx 6.3$$

The perpendicular $\overline{IP}$ bisects $\overline{VO}$, so the diagonal is about 2(6.3), or 12.6 cm long.

Using Special Right Triangles to Find Sines and Cosines

When θ is 30°, 45°, or 60°, you can use properties of 45-45-90 triangles or 30-60-90 triangles to find exact values of sin θ and cos θ.

Example 4

Use a 30-60-90 triangle to find cos 30°.

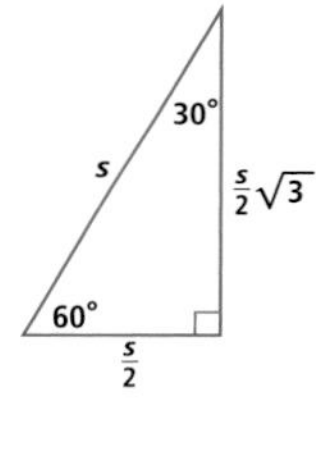

Solution Draw a 30-60-90 triangle. Label the 30° and 60° angles and let the length of the hypotenuse be *s*. Recall from geometry that since a 30-60-90 triangle is half of an equilateral triangle, if the length of the hypotenuse is *s*, the lengths of the legs are $\frac{s}{2}$ and $\frac{s}{2}\sqrt{3}$.

So, the length of the leg opposite the 30° angle is $\frac{s}{2}$, and the length of the leg adjacent to the 30° angle is $\frac{s}{2}\sqrt{3}$.

Then, by the right-triangle definition of cosine, $\cos 30° = \frac{\frac{s}{2}\sqrt{3}}{s} = \frac{\sqrt{3}}{2}$.

ENGLISH LEARNERS

Vocabulary Development

This lesson provides a good opportunity to review the two special right triangles: the 30-60-90 triangle and the 45-45-90 triangle. For each triangle, students should be able to find the length of all three sides given the length of any one side. Also, students should be aware of when those triangles appear in other figures. (The 30-60-90 triangle shows up in equilateral triangles and regular hexagons; the 45-45-90 triangle shows up in squares and regular octagons.)

Using similar methods, you can find all the sine and cosine values below. You will use these special values of sine and cosine often in later mathematics courses.

$$\sin 30° = \frac{1}{2} \quad \sin 60° = \frac{\sqrt{3}}{2} \quad \sin 45° = \frac{\sqrt{2}}{2}$$

$$\cos 30° = \frac{\sqrt{3}}{2} \quad \cos 60° = \frac{1}{2} \quad \cos 45° = \frac{\sqrt{2}}{2}$$

Questions

COVERING THE IDEAS

1. **Multiple Choice** The fact that different angles with the same measure have the same sine value is due to a property of which kinds of triangles? D
   - A congruent triangles
   - B isosceles triangles
   - C right triangles
   - D similar triangles

2. **Fill in the Blanks** Refer to $\triangle JMS$ at the right.
   - a. $\overline{JS}$ is the __?__ of the triangle. hypotenuse
   - b. __?__ is the leg opposite $\angle J$. $\overline{MS}$
   - c. __?__ is the leg adjacent to $\angle J$. $\overline{MJ}$
   - d. $\frac{MJ}{JS} = $ __?__ J cos
   - e. $\frac{MS}{MJ} = $ __?__ J tan
   - f. $\frac{MS}{JS} = $ __?__ J sin

Fill in the Blanks In 3 and 4, use $\triangle ABC$ at the right. Answer with expressions involving a, b, and/or c.

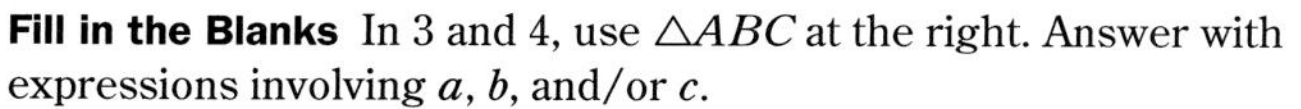

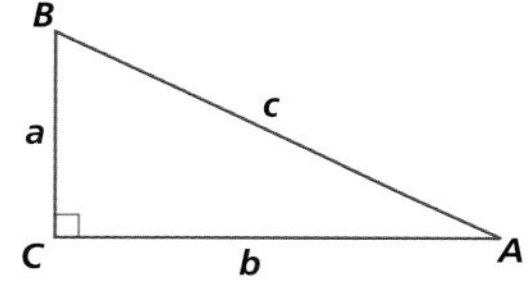

3. a. $\sin A = $ __?__ $\frac{a}{c}$ b. $\cos A = $ __?__ $\frac{b}{c}$ c. $\tan A = $ __?__ $\frac{a}{b}$
4. a. $\sin B = $ __?__ $\frac{b}{c}$ b. $\cos B = $ __?__ $\frac{a}{c}$ c. $\tan B = $ __?__ $\frac{b}{a}$
5. Suppose a construction crane casts a shadow 21 meters long when the Sun is 78° above the horizon. How high is the crane? about 98.9 m
6. Suppose that a tree near your school casts a 32-foot shadow from its base when the Sun is 72° above the horizon. How tall is the tree? about 98.5 ft
7. Refer to Example 3. Use a trigonometric ratio to find IP to the nearest hundredth. 4.58 cm
8. a. Use a 30-60-90 triangle to show that $\cos 60° = \frac{1}{2}$.
   b. Use a 45-45-90 triangle to show that $\sin 45° = \frac{\sqrt{2}}{2}$.
   8a-b. See margin.

3 Assignment

Recommended Assignment

- Questions 1–23
- Question 24 (extra credit)
- Reading Lesson 10-2
- Covering the Ideas 10-2

Notes on the Questions

Questions 2–4 These questions drill students on the definitions of the three trigonometric ratios. Stress that each acute angle in a right triangle has its own adjacent leg and opposite leg.

Additional Answers

8a.

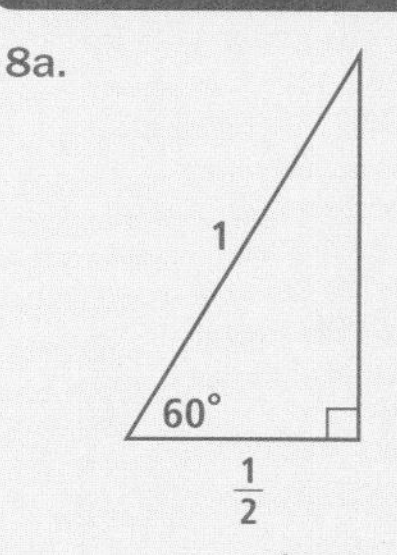

$$\cos 60° = \frac{\frac{1}{2}}{1} = \frac{1}{2}$$

8b.

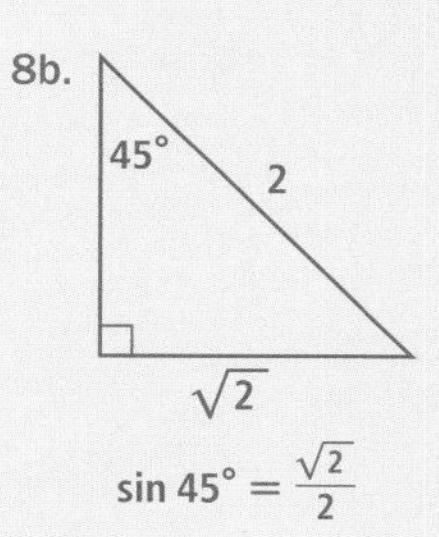

$$\sin 45° = \frac{\sqrt{2}}{2}$$

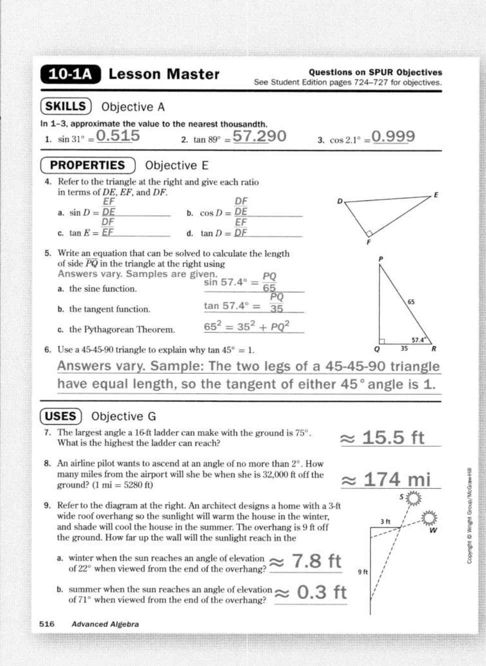

10-1A Lesson Master

Questions on SPUR Objectives
See Student Edition pages 724–727 for objectives.

SKILLS Objective A

In 1–3, approximate the value to the nearest thousandth.

1. $\sin 31° =$ 0.515
2. $\tan 89° =$ 57.290
3. $\cos 2.1° =$ 0.999

PROPERTIES Objective E

4. Refer to the triangle at the right and give each ratio in terms of DE, EF, and DF.
   - a. $\sin D = \frac{EF}{DE}$
   - b. $\cos D = \frac{DF}{DE}$
   - c. $\tan E = \frac{DF}{EF}$
   - d. $\tan D = \frac{EF}{DF}$
5. Write an equation that can be solved to calculate the length of side $\overline{PQ}$ in the triangle at the right using
   Answers vary. Samples are given.
   - a. the sine function. $\sin 57.4° = \frac{PQ}{65}$
   - b. the tangent function. $\tan 57.4° = \frac{PQ}{35}$
   - c. the Pythagorean Theorem. $65^2 = 35^2 + PQ^2$
6. Use a 45-45-90 triangle to explain why $\tan 45° = 1$.
   Answers vary. Sample: The two legs of a 45-45-90 triangle have equal length, so the tangent of either 45° angle is 1.

USES Objective G

7. The largest angle a 16-ft ladder can make with the ground is 75°. What is the highest the ladder can reach? ≈ 15.5 ft
8. An airline pilot wants to ascend at an angle of no more than 2°. How many miles from the airport will she be when she is 32,000 ft off the ground? (1 mi = 5280 ft) ≈ 174 mi
9. Refer to the diagram at the right. An architect designs a home with a 3-ft wide roof overhang so the sunlight will warm the house in the winter, and shade will cool the house in the summer. The overhang is 9 ft off the ground. How far up the wall will the sunlight reach in the
   - a. winter when the sun reaches an angle of elevation of 22° when viewed from the end of the overhang? ≈ 7.8 ft
   - b. summer when the sun reaches an angle of elevation of 71° when viewed from the end of the overhang? ≈ 0.3 ft

516 *Advanced Algebra*

Extension

Ask students to extend Example 3 by answering these questions for a regular pentagon, a regular hexagon, and a regular octagon. Consider all the diagonals in each figure.

1. How many diagonals are there?
2. How many different lengths are represented by the diagonals?
3. If a side of a regular pentagon (hexagon, octagon) is s, what is an expression for the length of each diagonal?

Regular pentagon: (1) 5 diagonals; (2) all have the same length; (3) all have length $2s \cdot \sin 54°$.

Regular hexagon: (1) 9 diagonals; (2) 2 different lengths; (3) 3 have length $2s$, and 6 have length $s\sqrt{3}$.

Regular octagon: (1) 20 diagonals; (2) 3 different lengths; (3) 4 have length $s + s\sqrt{2}$, 8 have length $2s \cdot \sin 67.5°$, and 8 have length $s\sqrt{4 + 2\sqrt{2}}$.

Notes on the Questions

Question 9 This is a very practical problem in any household where a person requires a wheelchair.

Question 11 After discussing this question, point out that the term *cosine* refers to "the complement's sine."

Question 12 An auxiliary altitude must be drawn.

Question 13 Most students will likely give a decimal answer, but you should ask for an exact answer as well as a decimal approximation.

APPLYING THE MATHEMATICS

9. The Americans with Disabilities Act specifies that the angle of elevation of ramps can be no greater than about 4.76°. The door pictured at the right is 2 feet off the ground.
   a. What is the length of the shortest ramp that will meet the code? about 24.1 ft
   b. How far from the building will the ramp in Part a extend?

9b. about 24.0 ft

10. Explain why tan 45° = 1. (*Hint:* Draw a right triangle.)

10. The legs of a 45-45-90 triangle have equal length.

11. a. Fill in the table.
   b. What is the relationship between the angles in each pair?
   c. What is the relationship between the sine and cosine values you calculated in Part a?
   d. Generalize your answers to Parts b and c as a conjecture.
   e. Test your answer to Part d by finding sine and cosine of other angle pairs.

sin 30° = ?	sin 40° = ?
cos 60° = ?	cos 50° = ?
sin 15° = ?	sin 9.3° = ?
cos 75° = ?	cos 80.7° = ?

11a–e. See margin.

12. The Great Pyramid of Giza had a square base with side length 230 meters and a height of 146.6 meters when first built around 2570 BCE. Due to erosion, the pyramid's height has decreased, but its side lengths are still nearly the same. The pyramid casts a 30.5-meter shadow when the Sun is at a 43.3° angle of elevation, as shown below. What is the current height of the pyramid to the nearest meter? 137.1 m

43.3°
230 m
30.5 m

13. A regular octagon has diagonals of three different lengths. What is the length of the shortest diagonal if a side of the regular octagon has length 1 unit? about 1.85 units

Additional Answers

11a.

sin 30° = 0.5	sin 40° = 0.643
cos 60° = 0.5	cos 50° = 0.643
sin 15° = 0.259	sin 90° = 1
cos 75° = 0.259	cos 0° = 1

11b. They are complementary.

11c. They are equal.

11d. The cosine of an angle is equal to the sine of its complement (and, equivalently, the sine of an angle is equal to the cosine of its complement).

11e. Answers vary. Sample: cos 85° = sin 5° ≈ 0.087

14. In $\triangle TRI$ at the right, $m\angle I = 90°$. Let $m\angle R = \theta$.
    a. Find $\sin \theta$, $\cos \theta$, and $\tan \theta$. $\frac{TI}{TR}, \frac{IR}{TR}, \frac{TI}{IR}$
    b. Use your answer from Part a to prove that $\frac{\sin \theta}{\cos \theta} = \tan \theta$.

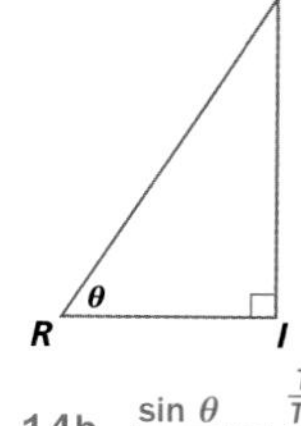

15. Use the figure at the right.
    a. Prove that the area of $\triangle ABC$ is $\frac{1}{2}ab \sin C$. (*Hint:* Find *h*.)
    b. Find the area of $\triangle ABC$ if $m\angle C = 20.3°$, $a = 72$, and $b = 75$. 936.73

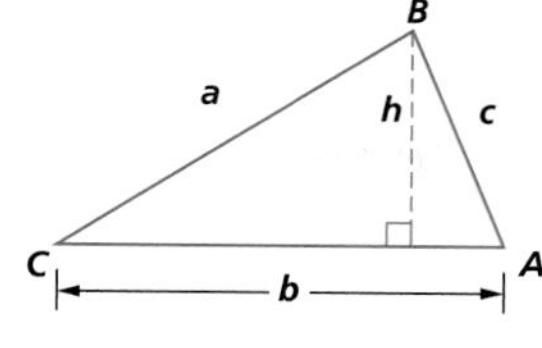

14b. $\frac{\sin \theta}{\cos \theta} = \frac{\frac{TI}{TR}}{\frac{IR}{TR}} = \frac{TI}{IR} = \tan \theta$

15a. $\sin C = \frac{h}{a}$; $h = a \sin C$; $A = \frac{1}{2}bh = \frac{1}{2}ba \sin C$

16. If it takes 34.66 years for an investment to double under continuous compounding, how long would it take to be multiplied by a factor of 2.5? **(Lessons 9-10, 9-3)** about 45.8 yr

17. Solve for z: $9\sqrt[3]{z - 5} = 27$. **(Lesson 8-8)** $z = 32$

18. Write two different expressions equal to $\frac{x^2}{x\sqrt{8}}$, $x \neq 0$. At least one expression should have a rational denominator. **(Lesson 8-6)**

18. Answers vary. Sample: $\frac{x}{\sqrt{8}}, \frac{x\sqrt{8}}{8}$

19. Suppose h is a function with an inverse. Simplify. **(Lesson 8-3)**
    a. $h(h^{-1}(\pi))$ π
    b. $h^{-1}(h(\pi))$ π

20. One group of students ordered 5 hamburgers and 5 veggie burgers and paid \$66.00. Another group ordered 4 hamburgers and 7 veggie burgers and paid \$71.55. At these prices, what was the cost of one hamburger? **(Lesson 5-4)** \$6.95

True or False. In 21 and 22, refer to the figure at the right where $j \parallel k$. Explain your answer. **(Previous Course)**

21. $\angle 1 \cong \angle 7$ false, $\angle 1 \cong \angle 5$

22. $\angle 2 \cong \angle 6$

22. true; they are corresponding angles.

23. In the figure at the right, $m\angle HTC = x°$ and $\overline{TH} \parallel \overline{BC}$. **(Previous Course)**
    a. Find $m\angle BTC$. $(90 - x)°$
    b. Find $m\angle C$. $x°$

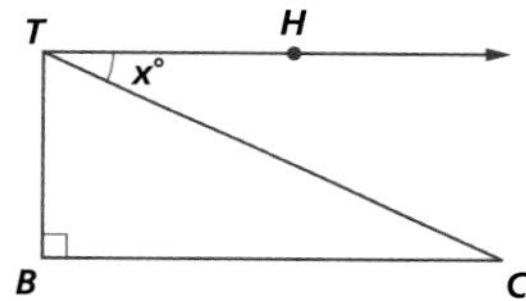

EXPLORATION

24. a. As θ increases from 0° to 90°, what happens to the value of $\sin \theta$? Does it increase? Does it decrease? Does it shift back and forth? Use values obtained from a calculator to find the pattern. Then use a geometrical argument and the definition of $\sin \theta$ to explain why $\sin \theta$ acts as it does.
    b. What happens to the value of $\cos \theta$ over the same interval?
    c. What happens to the value of $\tan \theta$?
    It increases from 0 without bound.

24a. The value of sine increases from 0 to 1 as θ increases from 0° to 90°. This follows from the fact that a larger angle implies a longer opposite side.

24b. It decreases from 1 to 0.

QY ANSWER

$\sin \theta = \frac{BC}{AB}$, $\cos \theta = \frac{AC}{AB}$, $\tan \theta = \frac{BC}{AC}$.

Notes on the Questions

Question 14 We could have defined $\tan \theta$ as $\frac{\sin \theta}{\cos \theta}$ and will do so in Lesson 10-5 when all values of θ are considered, but that is not the customary, right-triangle definition.

Questions 19 and 21–23 These questions preview material needed in Lesson 10-2.

Question 24 This question should be discussed, even though it might be difficult at this time. It requires a kind of thinking that is helpful in understanding the graphs of the cosine and sine functions.

4 Wrap-Up

Ongoing Assessment

Ask students to sketch right triangle *MNP*, with the right angle at vertex *P*.

1. Ask them to describe the ratio $\frac{MP}{MN}$ as the sine of an angle and as the cosine of an angle. sin *N*; cos *M*
2. Ask students to describe the ratio $\frac{NP}{MN}$ as the sine of an angle and as the cosine of an angle. sin *M*; cos *N*
3. Ask students to describe the ratio $\frac{MP}{NP}$ as the tangent of an angle. tan *N*

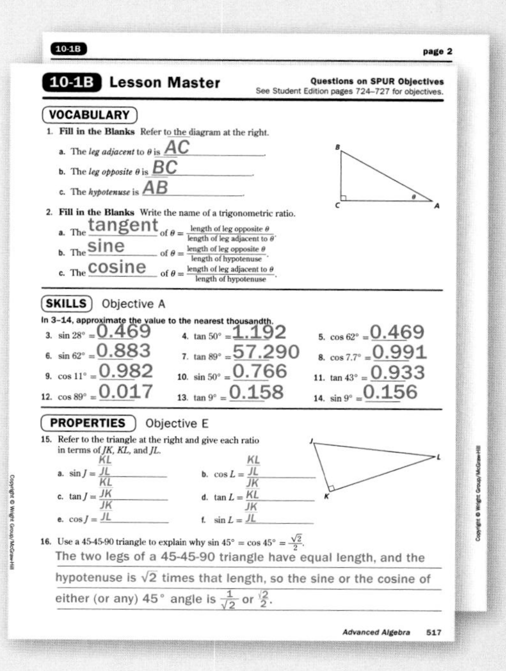

10-1B page 2

10-1B Lesson Master

Questions on SPUR Objectives
See Student Edition pages 724–727 for objectives.

VOCABULARY

1. **Fill in the Blanks** Refer to the diagram at the right.
   a. The *leg adjacent* to θ is AC.
   b. The *leg opposite* θ is BC.
   c. The *hypotenuse* is AB.

2. **Fill in the Blanks** Write the name of a trigonometric ratio.
   a. The tangent of $\theta = \frac{\text{length of leg opposite } \theta}{\text{length of leg adjacent to } \theta}$.
   b. The sine of $\theta = \frac{\text{length of leg opposite } \theta}{\text{length of hypotenuse}}$.
   c. The cosine of $\theta = \frac{\text{length of leg adjacent to } \theta}{\text{length of hypotenuse}}$.

SKILLS Objective A

In 3–14, approximate the value to the nearest thousandth.

3. $\sin 28° =$ 0.469
4. $\tan 50° =$ 1.192
5. $\cos 62° =$ 0.469
6. $\sin 62° =$ 0.883
7. $\tan 89° =$ 57.290
8. $\cos 7.7° =$ 0.991
9. $\cos 11° =$ 0.982
10. $\sin 50° =$ 0.766
11. $\tan 43° =$ 0.933
12. $\cos 89° =$ 0.017
13. $\tan 9° =$ 0.158
14. $\sin 9° =$ 0.156

PROPERTIES Objective E

15. Refer to the triangle at the right and give each ratio in terms of *JK*, *KL*, and *JL*.
    a. $\sin J = \frac{KL}{JL}$
    b. $\cos L = \frac{KL}{JL}$
    c. $\tan J = \frac{KL}{JK}$
    d. $\tan L = \frac{JK}{KL}$
    e. $\cos J = \frac{JK}{JL}$
    f. $\sin L = \frac{JK}{JL}$

16. Use a 45-45-90 triangle to explain why $\sin 45° = \cos 45° = \frac{\sqrt{2}}{2}$.
    The two legs of a 45-45-90 triangle have equal length, and the hypotenuse is $\sqrt{2}$ times that length, so the sine or the cosine of either (or any) 45° angle is $\frac{1}{\sqrt{2}}$ or $\frac{\sqrt{2}}{2}$.

Advanced Algebra 517

Lesson

10-2

GOAL

Use the sine, cosine, and tangent ratios to find angle measures in right triangles; solve problems involving angles of elevation and angles of depression.

SPUR Objectives

B Determine the measure of an angle given its sine, cosine, or tangent.

G Solve real-world problems using the trigonometry of right triangles.

Materials/Resources

- Lesson Masters 10-2A and 10-2B
- Resource Masters 184–186

HOMEWORK

Suggestions for Assignment

- Questions 1–21
- Question 22 (extra credit)
- Reading Lesson 10-3
- Covering the Ideas 10-3

Local Standards

1 Warm-Up

In $\triangle ABC$, $AB = 20$, $BC = 21$, and $AC = 29$.

1. Explain why $\triangle ABC$ is a right triangle. $20^2 + 21^2 = 841 = 29^2$, so by the converse of the Pythagorean Theorem, the triangle is a right triangle.
2. Calculate sin *A*, cos *A*, and tan *A*. $\frac{21}{29}$, $\frac{20}{29}$, and $\frac{21}{20}$
3. The quotient of two of the answers to Warm-Up 2 equals the third answer. Write out one of the two equations. sin *A* ÷ cos *A* = tan *A* or sin *A* ÷ tan *A* = cos *A*

Lesson

10-2 More Right-Triangle Trigonometry

Vocabulary

inverse sine function, $\sin^{-1}$
inverse cosine function, $\cos^{-1}$
inverse tangent function, $\tan^{-1}$
angle of depression

BIG IDEA If you know two sides of a right triangle, you can use inverse trigonometric functions to find the measures of the acute angles.

In the last lesson, you used sines, cosines, and tangents of angles to find lengths of sides in right triangles. In this lesson, you will see how to use these ratios to find the measures of angles in right triangles.

Mental Math

Between which two consecutive whole numbers does each value fall?

a. $\log 15{,}823{,}556$ 7 and 8
b. $\ln e^{8.76}$ 8 and 9
c. $\log_{18} 7$ 0 and 1
d. $\log_5 620 + \log_9 77$ 5 and 6

Finding an Angle from a Trigonometric Ratio

Given an angle measure *x*, you can use a calculator to find its sine, cosine, and tangent. That is, you can find *y* when $y = \sin x$, $y = \cos x$, or $y = \tan x$. Now, instead of knowing the angle, suppose you know its sine, cosine, or tangent. That is, suppose you know *y* in one of these situations. Can you find *x*?

The function that maps sin *x* onto *x* is the *inverse* of the function that maps *x* onto sin *x*. Appropriately, this function is called the **inverse sine function**. On a calculator, this function is denoted by the symbol $\mathbf{sin^{-1}}$. Like the inverse of any function, when composed with the original function, the result is the identity. That is, for any angle θ between 0° and 90°, $\sin^{-1}(\sin \theta) = \theta$.

Example 1

Consider a right triangle *TOP* in which the hypotenuse $\overline{TP}$ has length 25 and $TO = 17$. What is $m\angle TPO$?

Solution Let θ be the unknown angle measure. Draw a figure, as shown at the right. From the figure, notice that $\sin \theta = \frac{\text{opp.}}{\text{hyp.}} = \frac{17}{25} = 0.68$. To solve for θ, apply the inverse sine function to each side of the equation. Make sure that your calculator is in degree mode.

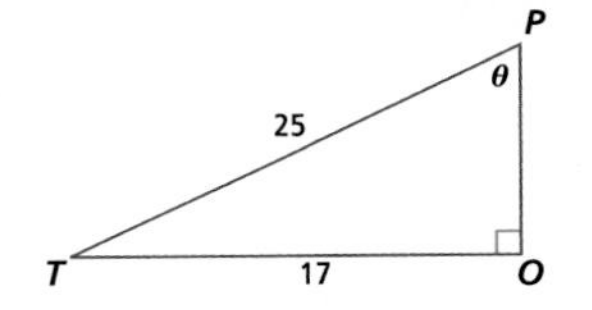

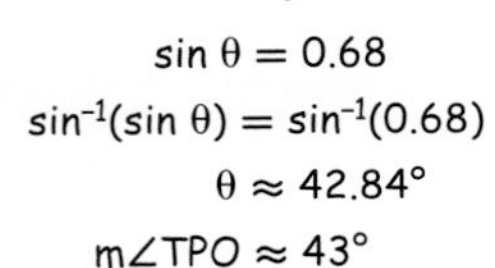

$$\sin \theta = 0.68$$
$$\sin^{-1}(\sin \theta) = \sin^{-1}(0.68)$$
$$\theta \approx 42.84°$$
$$m\angle TPO \approx 43°$$

Background

In Lesson 10-1, the measure of an angle was given, and students used a calculator to find its sine, cosine, or tangent. In the first part of this lesson, students do the reverse: They are given (or compute) the value of a trigonometric ratio for a particular acute angle and then find the measure of the angle.

The conceptual difference between finding an angle measure and finding a side is that for the former, the inverse of a trigonometric function is needed. The inverses of the trigonometric functions of real numbers are not functions because on most intervals these inverses do not pass the horizontal-line test. However, the inverses of the three trigonometric functions for acute angles *are* functions, so at this point there is no ambiguity. In Lesson 10-7, when we encounter $\sin \theta = k$, where θ can be either acute or obtuse, an additional step is needed to find the obtuse value of θ.

The **inverse cosine function** (denoted **cos^{-1}**) and the **inverse tangent function (tan^{-1})** can be used in a similar way.

QY1

GUIDED

Example 2

Find the measures of the acute angles of the 5-12-13 right triangle below at the right.

Solution The two acute angles of this triangle are $\angle B$ and _?_. $\angle A$

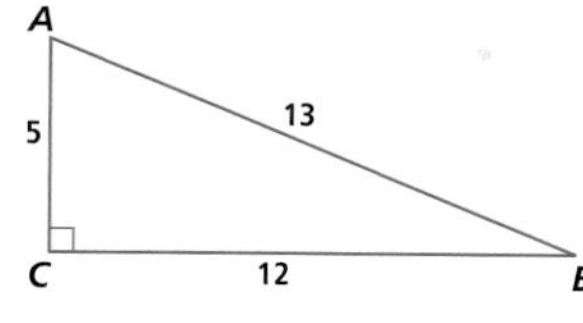

Find the measure of $\angle B$ by using any of the trigonometric ratios.

_?_ B $= \frac{?}{?}$ Answers vary. Sample: sin; 5; 13

Apply the _?_$^{-1}$ function to both sides of the equation. sin

_?_$^{-1}$ (_?_ B) = _?_$^{-1}\left(\frac{?}{?}\right)$ sin; sin; sin; 5; 13

Simplify. $m\angle B \approx$ _?_° 22.62°

To find $m\angle A$ you could use another ratio, but applying the Triangle-Sum Theorem may be quicker.

$m\angle A + m\angle B + m\angle C = 180°$

$m\angle A +$ _?_ $+ 90° \approx 180°$ 22.62°

$m\angle A \approx$ _?_ 67.38°

Check Use another ratio to find $m\angle B$ and see if you get the same answers.

QY2

Finding Angles of Elevation and Depression

One of the most important applications of trigonometry is to find distances and angle measures that are difficult or impossible to measure directly. In the last lesson, you used the trigonometric functions to find distances. The inverse trigonometric functions can be used to find angles.

▸ QY1

Approximate the angle θ between 0° and 90° to the nearest degree.

a. $\sin \theta = 0.324$
b. $\tan \theta = 1.357$
c. $\cos \theta = \frac{4}{7}$

▸ QY2

In Example 2, if you wanted to find $m\angle A$ using the cosine ratio, what fraction should be entered as the argument of $\cos^{-1}(\ )$?

10-2

2 Teaching

Notes on the Lesson

Examples 1 and 2 You might begin by noting that whenever the lengths of two sides of a right triangle are given, the length of the third side can be found by using the Pythagorean Theorem. Trigonometry enables the angle measures to be found as well. In Example 1, we write the measure of the desired angle to only two decimal places. That is certainly more than sufficient accuracy given the numbers used in the question. In Example 2, emphasize that only two sides are needed to find each angle.

Additional Examples

Example 1 Consider a right triangle QRS in which hypotenuse $\overline{SQ}$ has length 19 and $SR = 15$. What is $m\angle QSR$?

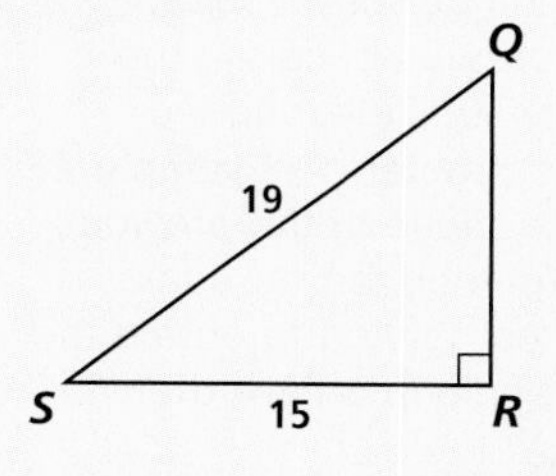

$\cos \theta = \frac{SR}{SQ} = \frac{15}{19} \approx 0.7895$;
$\theta = \cos^{-1}(0.7895) \approx 37.9°$

Example 2 Find the measures of the acute angles of a 3-4-5 right triangle.

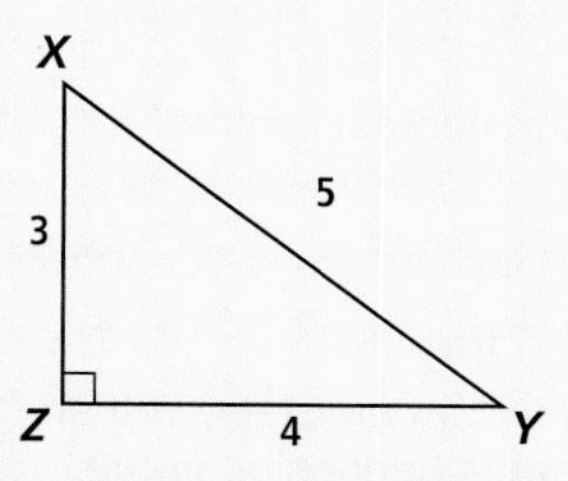

Solution The two acute angles are $\angle X$ and $\angle Y$. Find the measures of $\angle X$ and $\angle Y$ using trigonometric functions.

$\sin X =$ _?_ $=$ _?_ $\frac{4}{5}$; 0.8

$\sin Y =$ _?_ $=$ _?_ $\frac{3}{5}$; 0.6

Apply the appropriate inverse function to both sides of each equation.

_?_(sin X) = _?_; $X \approx$ _?_
sin^{-1}; 0.8; 53.13°

_?_(sin Y) = _?_; $Y \approx$ _?_
sin^{-1}; 0.6; 36.87°

Examples 1 and 2 are straightforward uses of trigonometry to find an angle measure. Example 3 applies this idea to an angle of elevation. Example 4 involves an angle of depression.

ENGLISH LEARNERS

Vocabulary Development

As mentioned in the Notes on the Lesson for Examples 3 and 4, emphasize that both an angle of elevation and an angle of depression are angles measured from a horizontal line. Students should understand that the given angle may not be in a triangle, and they may have to use an alternate interior angle (or perhaps a complementary angle) to identify and set up a trigonometric ratio.

Notes on the Lesson

QY1 An equation such as $\sin \theta = 0.324$ can be solved with a CAS solve command, but we expect the inverse sine function to be used because the CAS solve command will often yield solutions that are too general. For example, when solving $\sin \theta = 0.324$, many CAS models show all possible solutions to this equation and give results such as $x = 18.905... + 360 \cdot n_1$ or $x = 161.095... + 360 \cdot n_1$, where n_1 stands for any positive integer. At this point, such general solutions will be more confusing than helpful.

Examples 3 and 4 Make sure that students realize that one side of an angle of elevation or an angle of depression is horizontal, while the other is directed toward the object being viewed. In Example 3, the screenshot shows 8 decimal places, the written answer shows 3 decimal places, and the final answer is rounded to the nearest whole number of degrees. The answer is rounded because the given information is likely rounded information. The problem in Example 4 is very much like those in the previous lesson. The difference is that some geometry must be applied to obtain the measure of an angle in a right triangle.

Additional Example

Example 3 A 115-foot ladder attached to a fire truck rests against the side of a building so that the top of the ladder is 111 feet above the ground. Find the angle formed by the truck and the ladder to the nearest tenth of a degree. 74.8°

Note-Taking Tips

Encourage students to explain, in their own words, what is happening in the three equations that appear in the solution to Example 1. Help students understand that the first equation uses the given information to write a sine ratio; the second equation applies the inverse sine function to each side; and, in the third equation, the left side shows the result of applying two inverse functions, while the right side shows a numerical result from a calculator.

Example 3

Suppose a cell tower is anchored to the ground by a supporting wire. The wire is attached at a point on the tower 120 feet above the ground and is attached to the level ground 150 feet from the base of the tower. What is the angle of elevation of the wire?

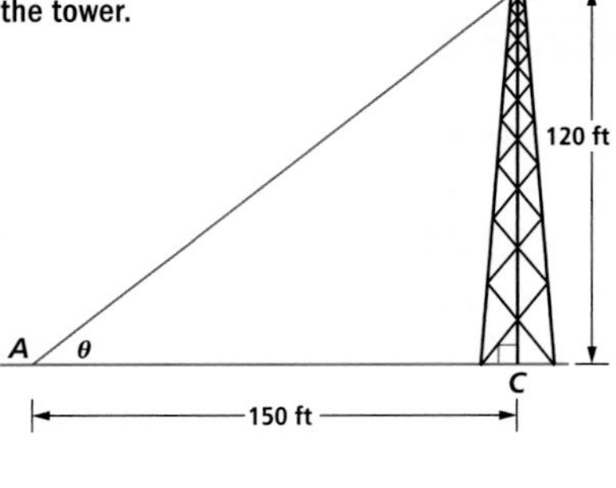

Solution In the drawing, $BC = 120$ feet, $AC = 150$ feet, and $\frac{BC}{AC} = \tan \theta$, where θ is the angle of elevation.

Then, $\tan \theta = \frac{120}{150} = 0.8$ and $\theta = \tan^{-1}(0.8) \approx 38.660$.

So, the angle of elevation of the wire is about 39°.

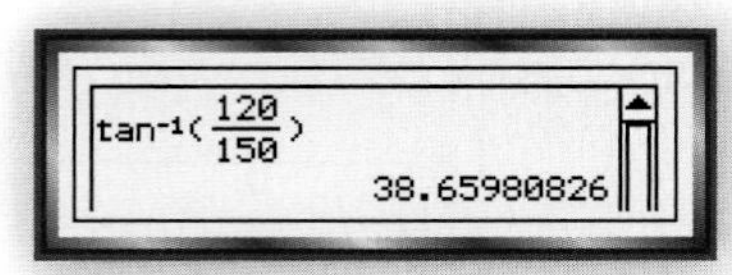

Check Does $\tan 39° = 0.8$? $\tan(39°) \approx 0.8098$. Yes, it checks.

In the figure at the right, β (the Greek letter beta) represents the angle of elevation as person T looks up at person S. If S looks down at T, the angle α (the Greek letter alpha) between S's line of sight and the horizontal is called the **angle of depression**. The line of sight between T and S is a transversal for the parallel horizontal lines. Thus, β and α are alternate interior angles and are congruent. *So, the angle of elevation is equal to the angle of depression.*

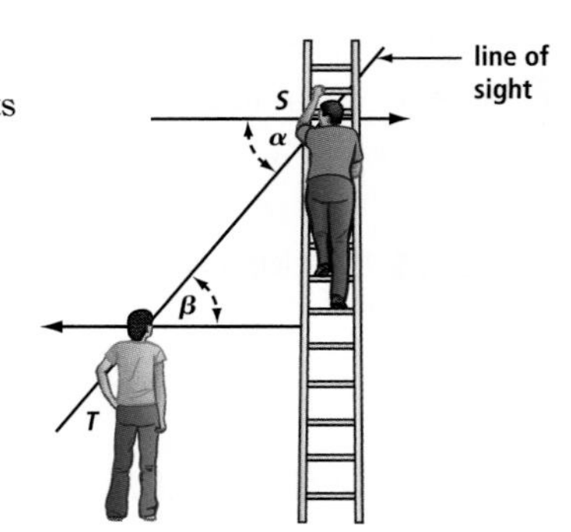

GUIDED

Example 4

A surveyor standing on a bridge points her scope towards an assistant standing on level ground 110.56 feet from the base of the bridge. Her surveying laser measures a direct (slant) distance to the assistant of 125.75 feet. To the nearest hundredth of a degree, find the angle of depression of the scope.

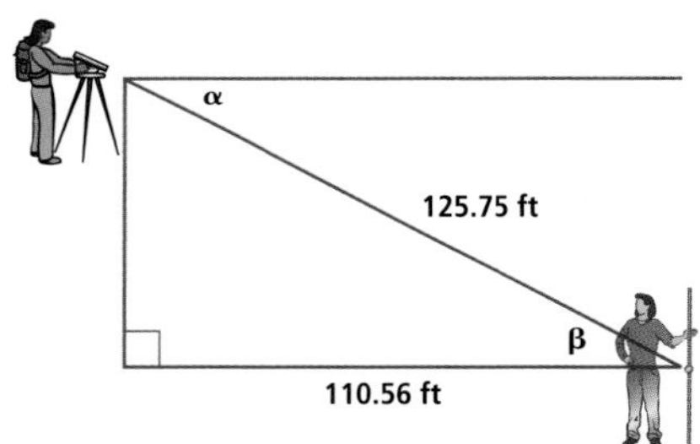

Solution The angle of depression α is not inside the triangle, so you cannot use it directly to set up a trigonometric ratio. However, the angle of depression α is equal to the angle of __?__. So the angle of depression can be found using the __?__ ratio. elevation β; cosine

Accommodating the Learner

Ask students to find an expression for c in terms of A, B, a, and b.

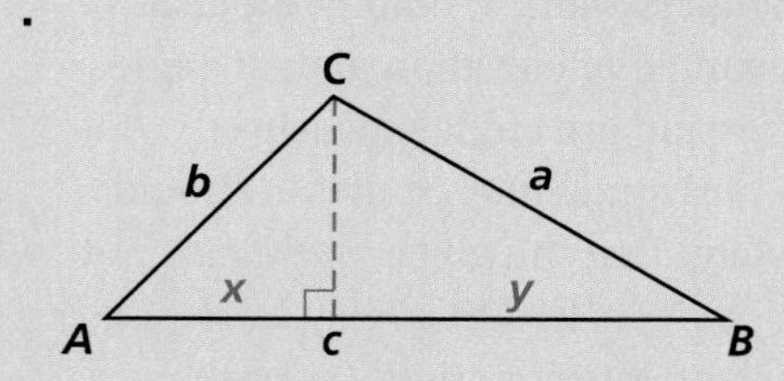

If students need a hint, tell them to draw a perpendicular from C and find the lengths of the two parts of $\overline{AB}$. $\cos A = \frac{x}{b}$, so $x = b \cos A$; $\cos B = \frac{y}{a}$, so $y = a \cos B$. Then $c = x + y = b \cos A + a \cos B$.

$\cos \underline{\ ?\ } = \frac{?}{?}$ definition of cosine β; 110.56; 125.75

$\cos^{-1}(\cos \underline{\ ?\ }) = \cos^{-1} \underline{\ ?\ }$ Apply the inverse cosine function. β; 0.8792

$m\angle\beta \approx \underline{\ ?\ }$ 28.45°

Since $m\angle\alpha = m\angle\beta$, the angle of depression is about ___?___ degrees. 28.45

Questions

COVERING THE IDEAS

1. Write a key sequence for your calculator to find θ if $\sin \theta = 0.475$. See the Additional Answers section at the back of the book.

In 2 and 3, approximate to three decimal places.

2. $\cos^{-1}(0.443)$ 63.705°
3. $\sin^{-1}\left(\frac{\sqrt{2}}{2}\right)$ 45°
4. Refer to $\triangle ABC$ at the right. Find θ to the nearest degree. 34°
5. Refer to Example 2.
   a. Find $m\angle B$ using the tangent ratio. $\tan^{-1}\left(\frac{5}{12}\right) \approx 22.62°$
   b. Find $m\angle A$ using the sine ratio. $\sin^{-1}\left(\frac{12}{13}\right) \approx 67.38°$
6. Find the measures of the acute angles of an 8-15-17 right triangle to the nearest thousandth. 28.072°, 61.928°

B
47
θ
C
39.1
A

7. **Fill in the Blank** The angle of depression is the angle made between the line of sight to an object and the ___?___. horizontal
8. Suppose a statue 15.5 meters high casts a shadow 21 meters long. What is the angle of elevation of the Sun? 36.43°
9. Explain why the angle of depression from a point R to a point S equals the angle of elevation from S to R. See the Additional Answers section at the back of the book.
10. Refer to Example 4. Suppose the assistant stands 75 feet from the base of the bridge and the direct distance between the surveyor and the assistant is 120 feet. What is the angle of depression? about 51.3°

APPLYING THE MATHEMATICS

11. According to one railway company's guidelines, industrial railroad tracks must be built with a 1.5% grade or less. A 1.5% grade means that the track rises 1.5 feet vertically for every 100 feet horizontally.
    a. What is the slope of a line with a 1.5% grade? 0.015
    b. What is the tangent of the angle of elevation of a 1.5% grade? 0.015
    c. What angle does a track with a 1.5% grade make with the horizontal? about 0.86°

This train, on White Pass in Alaska, will rise approximately 3000 feet over just 20 miles.

Additional Example

Example 4 A hawk, cruising at an altitude of 215 feet, spots a prey at a direct (slant) distance of 406 feet. To the nearest hundredth of a degree, find the angle of depression of the prey as seen by the hawk.

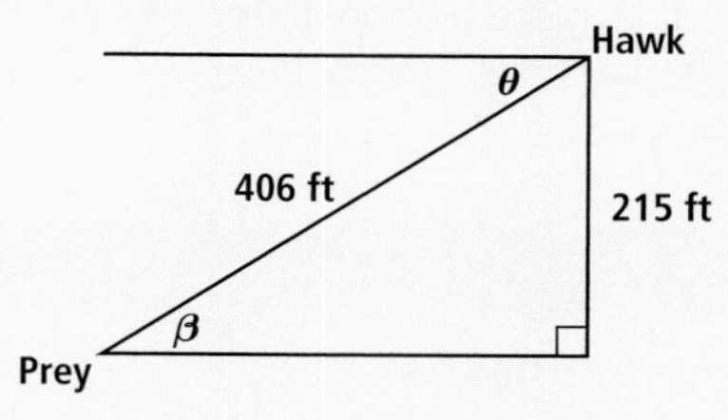

Solution The angle of depression is not inside the triangle, so use the angle of ___?___. elevation Use the ___?___ ratio. sine

$\sin \underline{\ ?\ } = \underline{\ ?\ } \approx \underline{\ ?\ }$ θ; $\frac{215}{406}$; 0.5295567

$\sin^{-1}(\sin \underline{\ ?\ }) = \sin^{-1}(\underline{\ ?\ })$ θ; 0.5295567

$m\angle\beta \approx \underline{\ ?\ }$ 31.97550

The angle of depression is about ___?___ degrees. 31.98

3 Assignment

Recommended Assignment

- Questions 1–21
- Question 22 (extra credit)
- Reading Lesson 10-3
- Covering the Ideas 10-3

10-2A Lesson Master

Questions on SPUR Objectives
See Student Edition pages 724–727 for objectives.

SKILLS Objective B

In 1–3, approximate the angle θ between 0° and 90° to the nearest degree.

1. $\sin \theta = 0.407$ 24°
2. $\cos \theta = 0.987$ 9°
3. $\tan \theta = 2.000$ 63°
4. Find $m\angle A$ in the figure below to the nearest degree.
   $m\angle A =$ 32°

   A 84 C 53 B

5. Find the measures to the nearest degree of the acute angles in a right triangle with one leg 12 cm long and hypotenuse 14 cm long. 31° and 59°

USES Objective G

6. The base of a 24-ft extension ladder is 5 ft from a house. What angle does the ladder make with the ground? Round to the nearest degree. 78°

In 7–9, recall the fact that 1 mile = 5280 feet.

7. The Sears Tower in Chicago is the tallest building in the United States at a height of 1450 ft. If you are standing a mile away from the Sears Tower, at what angle must you look up to see the top? Round to the nearest degree. 15°
8. The Katoomba Scenic Railway in the Blue Mountains of Australia is the steepest railway incline in the world. The track is 415 m long and rises 178 m. What is the track's average angle of elevation? Round to the nearest degree. 25°
9. In 2005, adventurer Steve Fossett flew around the world solo without stopping or refueling his plane, the Global Flyer. He flew at an altitude of 45,000 ft and started his descent for landing when he wasabout 300 mi from the Salina, Kansas, airport, from which he had taken off approximately 67 hours earlier. At what angle did he descend? Round your answer to the nearest tenth of a degree. 1.6°

Advanced Algebra 519

Accommodating the Learner

For each given value of sin A, ask students to **(a)** find $\frac{1}{2}(\sin A)$, $\frac{A}{2}$, and $\sin\left(\frac{A}{2}\right)$; **(b)** tell whether $\frac{1}{2}(\sin A)$ is equal to $\sin\left(\frac{A}{2}\right)$ for these three examples; and **(c)** tell which is greater if the two values are not equal.

1. $\sin A = 0.85$
2. $\sin A = \frac{\sqrt{2}}{2}$
3. $\sin A = \frac{1}{2}$

$\sin A$	$\frac{1}{2}(\sin A)$	$\frac{A}{2}$	$\sin\left(\frac{A}{2}\right)$
0.85	0.425	29.106°	0.486
$\frac{\sqrt{2}}{2}$ or 0.707	0.354	22.5°	0.383
$\frac{1}{2}$ or 0.5	0.25	15°	0.259

For these three values of sin A, $\frac{1}{2}(\sin A)$ is not equal to $\sin\left(\frac{A}{2}\right)$; $\frac{1}{2}(\sin A)$ is less than $\sin\left(\frac{A}{2}\right)$.

10-2

Notes on the Questions

Additional Answers can be found in the back of the book.

Question 18 Only one side measurement is sufficient to solve an isosceles right triangle.

Questions 20–21 Students should recall that the composite of two reflections over intersecting lines is a rotation.

4 Wrap-Up

Ongoing Assessment

With students working in small groups, have each group write several decimal values between 0 and 1, then take turns describing how to find the measures of angles whose sine ratio or cosine ratio is one of the decimals.

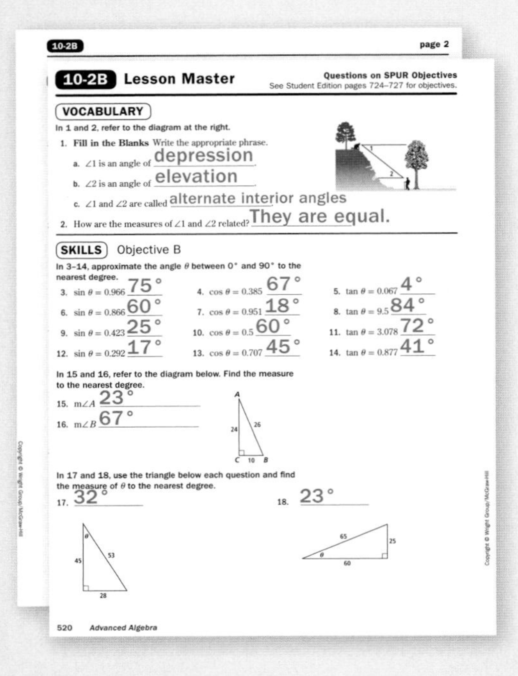

10-2B page 2

10-2B Lesson Master — Questions on SPUR Objectives. See Student Edition pages 724–727 for objectives.

VOCABULARY

In 1 and 2, refer to the diagram at the right.

1. **Fill in the Blanks** Write the appropriate phrase.
   a. $\angle 1$ is an angle of depression.
   b. $\angle 2$ is an angle of elevation.
   c. $\angle 1$ and $\angle 2$ are called alternate interior angles.
2. How are the measures of $\angle 1$ and $\angle 2$ related? They are equal.

SKILLS Objective B

In 3–14, approximate the angle θ between 0° and 90° to the nearest degree.

3. $\sin\theta = 0.966$ 75°
4. $\cos\theta = 0.385$ 67°
5. $\tan\theta = 0.067$ 4°
6. $\sin\theta = 0.866$ 60°
7. $\cos\theta = 0.951$ 18°
8. $\tan\theta = 9.5$ 84°
9. $\sin\theta = 0.423$ 25°
10. $\cos\theta = 0.5$ 60°
11. $\tan\theta = 3.078$ 72°
12. $\sin\theta = 0.292$ 17°
13. $\cos\theta = 0.707$ 45°
14. $\tan\theta = 0.877$ 41°

In 15 and 16, refer to the diagram below. Find the measure to the nearest degree.

15. $m\angle A$ 23°
16. $m\angle B$ 67°

In 17 and 18, use the triangle below each question and find the measure of θ to the nearest degree.

17. 32°
18. 23°

520 Advanced Algebra

12. Consider the line with equation $y = \frac{2}{3}x + b$.
    a. What is the slope of the line? $\frac{2}{3}$
    b. What is the tangent of the acute angle that the line makes with x-axis? $\frac{2}{3}$
    c. What is the measure of the acute angle that the line makes with the x-axis, to the nearest degree? 34°
    d. What is the tangent of the acute angle that the line with equation $y = mx + b$ makes with the x-axis? m

13. Haylee has the plans to build a skateboard launch ramp with dimensions as shown in the drawing at the right. What is the angle of elevation of the ramp? about 23.20°

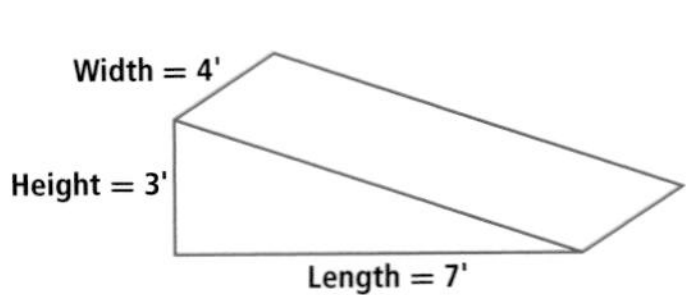

14. Explain why the domain of the inverse sine function cannot include a number greater than 1.

15. Dawn Hillracer, an avid skier, rides 1600 meters on a chair lift to the top of a slope. If the lift has a 450-meter vertical rise, at what average angle of elevation does it ascend the slope? about 16.33°

14. Answers vary. Sample: The range of the sine function is $-1 \le y \le 1$, so the domain of the inverse of sin, or $\sin^{-1}$, is $-1 \le x \le 1$, thus, the domain of $\sin^{-1} x$ cannot include a number greater than 1.

REVIEW

16. Chinese legend tells of a General Han Hsin, who used a kite during battle to work out the distance between his army and a castle so he could dig tunnels under the walls. Suppose the kite's string was 200 meters long and at an angle of 62° with the ground when the kite was above the courtyard of a castle. If the tunnels are dug straight, how long should the tunnels be in this case? Round to the nearest meter. **(Lesson 10-1)** 94 m

17. Rationalize the denominator of $\frac{11}{\sqrt{8}}$. **(Lesson 8-6)** $\frac{11\sqrt{2}}{4}$

18. If an isosceles right triangle has a leg of length z, how long is its hypotenuse? **(Lesson 8-5, Previous Course)** $z\sqrt{2}$

19. Solve for x: $rx^2 + sx + t = 0$. **(Lesson 6-7)** $x = \frac{-s \pm \sqrt{s^2 - 4rt}}{2r}$

In 20 and 21, use triangle *DON* at the right. (Lessons 4-7, 4-6, 4-4)

20. a. Find the coordinates of the vertices of $r_y(\triangle DON)$.
    b. Find the coordinates of the vertices of $r_x \circ r_y(\triangle DON)$.

21. Find DO. $\sqrt{13} \approx 3.606$

20a. $r_y(D) = (-1, 1)$; $r_y(N) = (-1, 4)$; $r_y(O) = (-3, 4)$

20b. $r_x \circ r_y(D) = (-1, -1)$; $r_x \circ r_y(N) = (-1, -4)$; $r_x \circ r_y(O) = (-3, -4)$

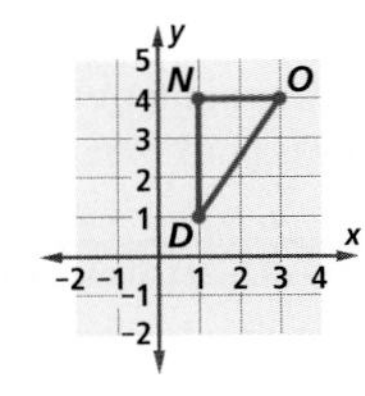

EXPLORATION

22. a. Graph the $\sin^{-1}$ function over the domain $\{x \mid 0 < x < 1\}$. What is the range of the $\sin^{-1}$ function over this domain?
    b. Graph $\sin \circ \sin^{-1}$ over the domain $\{x \mid 0 < x < 1\}$. What is the range of this function over this domain? 22a–b. See the Additional Answers section at the back of the book.

QY ANSWERS

1. a. $\theta \approx 19°$
   b. $\theta \approx 54°$
   c. $\theta \approx 55°$
2. $\frac{5}{13}$

Extension

If $\sin A = x$, what is $\sin\left(\frac{A}{2}\right)$ in terms of x? What are $\cos\left(\frac{A}{2}\right)$ and $\tan\left(\frac{A}{2}\right)$ in terms of y and z if $\cos A = y$ and $\tan A = z$?

If $\sin A = x$, then $A = \sin^{-1}(x)$ and $\left(\frac{A}{2}\right) = \frac{\sin^{-1}(x)}{2}$. So $\sin\left(\frac{A}{2}\right) = \sin\left(\frac{\sin^{-1}(x)}{2}\right)$. Similarly, if $\cos A = y$ and $\tan A = z$, then $\cos\left(\frac{A}{2}\right) = \cos\left(\frac{\cos^{-1}(y)}{2}\right)$ and $\tan\left(\frac{A}{2}\right) = \tan\left(\frac{\tan^{-1}(z)}{2}\right)$.

Lesson 10-3 Trigonometry, Earth, Moon, and Stars

Vocabulary

parallax angle

▸ BIG IDEA Trigonometry has been used to estimate with great accuracy very large distances, such as are found in the solar system and in our galaxy.

Over 2000 years ago the ancient Greeks observed that when a ship arrived in port, the mast was the first part of the ship that could be seen. They concluded that Earth's surface must be curved. Using trigonometry and without modern equipment, the ancient Greeks were able to estimate the circumference of Earth and the distance from Earth to our Moon with remarkable accuracy. Their methods were so powerful that the same ideas are still used today to measure interstellar distances. One of these ideas is that of ***parallax***.

Mental Math

Is the transformation an isometry, a similarity transformation, or neither?

a. $r_{y=x} \circ R_{200}$ isometry

b. $T_{2,16} \circ S_{2,4.5}$ neither

c. $S_{3.5} \circ R_{450} \circ S_{\frac{2}{7}} \circ r_x$ isometry

Activity 1

Work with a partner.

Step 1 Have your partner stand about eight feet in front of you. Extend your arm in front of your face and hold up one thumb. Close your left eye. Then open your left eye and close your right eye.

Your thumb and your partner both appear to jump to new locations. Which jumps more? Does the background behind your partner jump as well? Steps 1–2. See margin.

Take four steps back and repeat the experiment. What moves now?

Step 2 When you switched eyes, you changed the position from which you viewed your thumb and partner by about three inches. As a result, both your thumb and your partner appeared to move across the background behind them. This illusion of motion created by changing viewing positions is called *parallax.*

Copy the parallax diagram at the right. Draw lines from the observation sites *A* and *B* through the star *S* to the row of numbered squares in the background. The line from *A* indicates which square the star appears to obscure when viewed from the left site. That square marks the *apparent position* of the star from site *A*. Record that square, and the square obscured from site *B*.

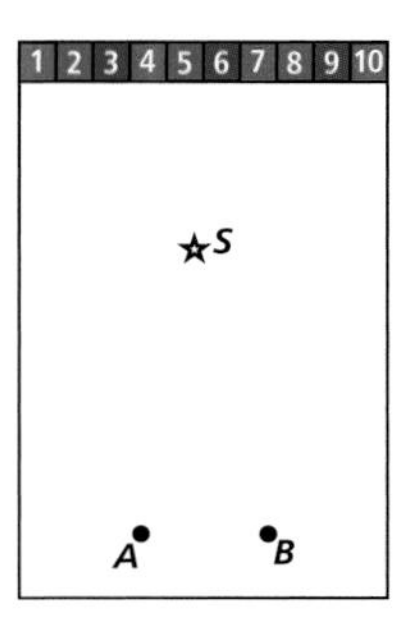

(continued on next page)

Background

Activity 4 61 Cygni is a binary (double) star system that got its name from its location in the constellation Cygnus. It is barely visible to the naked eye, even though at a distance of 11.36 ± 0.06 light-years it is one of the closest stars to our Sun. (Only seven star systems are within 10 light-years of the Sun. Information about these star systems can be found at http://www.solstation.com/stars.htm.)

The circumference of Earth The calculation of the circumference of Earth by the Greek mathematician Eratosthenes is one of the great accomplishments of mathematics. Eratosthenes had access to Euclid's *Elements* (he lived in the same city about 50 years after Euclid), but he did not have trigonometric functions or tables. He had to use similar triangles to determine the equivalents of the trigonometric ratios. The details about Eratosthenes's work in Activity 5 are taken from Karen Loskey's *The Librarian Who Measured the Earth* (Little, Brown & Co., Boston, Mass., 1994).

Lesson 10-3

GOAL

Explore two historically famous applications of trigonometry: (1) using parallax to determine the distance to the Moon and nearby stars and (2) using right-triangle trigonometry to determine the circumference of Earth.

SPUR Objectives

G Solve real-world problems using the trigonometry of right triangles.

Materials/Resources

- Lesson Masters 10-3A and 10-3B
- Resource Masters 187 and 188
- Quiz 1
- Whiteboard or butcher paper, ruler, string

HOMEWORK

Suggestions for Assignment

- Questions 1–13
- Question 14 (extra credit)
- Reading Lesson 10-4
- Covering the Ideas 10-4

Local Standards

1 Warm-Up

Use the measurement that light waves and other waves in the electromagnetic spectrum (radio waves, x rays, and so forth) travel approximately 186,000 miles per second.

1. Mars ranges from 33.9 to 249.4 million miles from Earth. What is the least amount of time it takes a radio signal from one of our probes on Mars to reach a station on Earth? about 182 sec
2. About how many miles does light travel in a 365-day year? about $5.87 \cdot 10^{12}$ mi

(continued on next page)

3. Our galaxy, the Milky Way, is about 100,000 light-years across. How long does it take light to travel from one end of the galaxy to the other? The phrase *100,000 light-years across* means it takes light 100,000 years to cross from one end of the galaxy to the other.

2 Teaching

Notes on the Lesson

This lesson is designed around its five activities: Activities 1 and 2 cover the concept of parallax in a classroom situation. Activities 3 and 4 apply the idea of parallax to estimate distances to the Moon and a nearby star, 61 Cygni. Activity 5 replicates the process that led to the estimation of the circumference of Earth by Eratosthenes over 2200 years ago.

Activities 1 and 2 These activities simulate the idea of parallax. In each case, students are calculating the distance to an object by its change in placement among background fixed objects. In Activity 2, 16 feet is good for Step 1a.

Note-Taking Tips

Encourage students to annotate the diagrams they prepare for each of the activities by identifying the initial point, the interim point, and the background point for each view.

Additional Answers

Activity 1

Step 1. Answers vary. Sample: My thumb moves more than my partner. The background doesn't seem to jump. After stepping back, only my thumb seems to jump.

Step 2. Apparent position of star from *A*: 6; apparent position of star from *B*: 4

Step 3 As you noticed with your partner and your thumb, objects that are closer to the observer appear to move sideways more than objects that are far away. a–b. See margin.

a. On the diagram you copied in Step 2, draw three more stars between the two observation sites and the shaded background.

b. Draw lines to identify each star's apparent position from each site and record the results.

c. For each pair of observations, determine how many squares the star "jumped." How does that number relate to the angle formed by site *A*, the star, and site *B*?

d. Write a sentence explaining why closer objects seem to jump sideways more than more distant objects.

Activity 1

Step 3c. Answers vary. Sample: 3, 5; 8, 9; 2, 10; the larger the jump, the larger the angle.

Step 3d. Close objects seem to jump more than distant objects because the angle between the two segments connecting the object to both eyes is greater when the object is closer.

In Activity 1 you measured the parallax effect by the magnitude of background movement. Another way is to measure $\angle ASB$. The larger the measure of this angle, the closer the star is to A and B. In practice, astronomers use half this angle and call it the **parallax angle**.

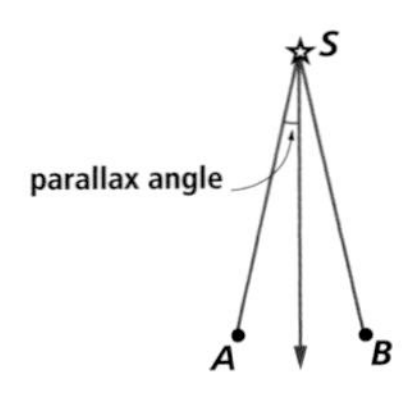

Astronomers measure parallax angles with special equipment, including satellites and telescopes with scales for measuring angles. You and a partner can simulate what they do by making a larger version of the parallax diagram used in Activity 1. One partner takes the place of the star, and the other makes observations from two sites.

Activity 2

MATERIALS whiteboard or butcher paper, ruler, string

Step 1 a. Mark points *A* and *B* on the floor 4 feet apart so that $\overline{AB}$ is parallel to, and several feet from, a whiteboard or wall covered in butcher paper.

b. Draw equally spaced vertical lines on the board. Use a ruler to accurately space the lines 1 inch apart for every foot between $\overline{AB}$ and the board. (For example, if $\overline{AB}$ is 16 feet from the board, the lines should be 16 inches apart.)

Step 2 The star needs to be equidistant from the two observation sites. (In astronomical parallax, the variations in Earth's position are so small compared to the distances being measured that this condition is easy to meet.) Use string to construct the perpendicular bisector $\overleftrightarrow{MS}$ of $\overline{AB}$. Have your partner, the star, stand on $\overleftrightarrow{MS}$ between $\overline{AB}$ and the background. Observe your partner's head from *A* and from *B* by closing one eye and noting with the other eye the line on the board that appears to be closest to your partner's head. Close the same eye each time. Record the number of spaces between the observed board lines. See margin.

ENGLISH LEARNERS

Vocabulary Development

Activity 4 mentions the term *arc-second.* Ask students to look up and explain the unit *arc-second.* A degree can be divided into 60 equal parts called arc-minutes, and each arc-minute can be divided into 60 equal parts called arc-seconds. So 1 arc-second $= \frac{1}{60} \cdot \frac{1}{60} = \frac{1}{3600}$ degree. Ask students to express the measurement in Question 4, 0.38 arc-second, as a decimal part of a degree. $0.38 \cdot \frac{1}{3600} \approx 0.00010556°$

Step 3 Convert your range of spaces to an angle. If *A* and *B* are 16 feet from the board, each space corresponds to an angle of about 5°. So if you observed a 3.5-space difference from the two sites, this corresponds to a $5 \cdot 3.5 = 17.5°$ angle. Half this angle (8.25°) is the parallax angle shown in the diagram at the right. Copy the diagram and write your angle measurement in the "Par ∠" space. If you are not able to do the physical experiment, use the lines in the diagram shown here to estimate a parallax angle. See margin.

Step 4 △*ASB* is isosceles. Use this fact to fill in the measures of all other labeled angles. See margin.

Step 5 Use trigonometry to find *MS*. See margin.

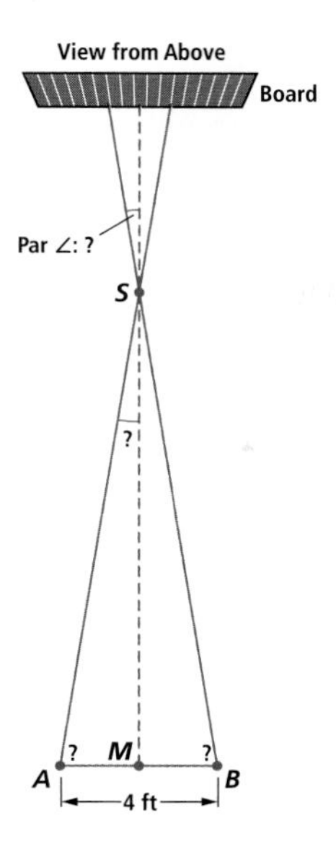

In Activity 2, *MS* is the distance from the observation sites line to the star. Using trigonometry, you were able to determine the distance to this remote object without having to go there and without sending anything to it.

The Distance to the Moon

Since ancient times, astronomers have used parallax to measure distances from Earth to celestial objects: the Moon, the planets, and in the last 200 years, nearby stars. In the second century BCE, Hipparchus used data recorded during a solar eclipse to estimate the distance from Earth to the Moon. Although the books describing his exact procedure have been lost, we know he used estimates of the Moon's parallax angle in his calculations. Now that you have seen how parallax works, you can use trigonometry to make your own estimates of the distance from Earth to the Moon.

Activity 3

Step 1 Data from observers of an eclipse in two Greek cities, Alexandria and Hellespont, led Hipparchus to approximate the Moon's parallax angle as 0.11°. This is the measure of ∠*ANM* in the diagram at the right.

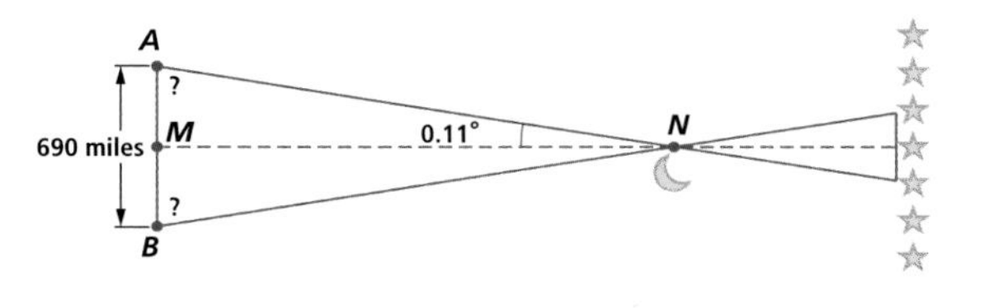

Because the Moon, represented by point *N*, is far away from Earth, $AN \approx BN$, so △*ANB* is isosceles with base $\overline{AB}$. Let *M* be the midpoint of $\overline{AB}$. Approximate the measures of the missing angles. 89.89°, 89.89°

Step 2 Given that $AB = 690$ miles, use trigonometry to compute the distance *MN* from Earth to the Moon. 179,700 mi

Extension

The second paragraph in this lesson refers to seeing a ship's mast appearing at the horizon. Ask students to extend this idea by finding an expression for the distance *d* to the horizon (along the curved surface of Earth) in terms of the radius *r* of Earth and your height *h* above Earth's surface. Answers vary. Sample:

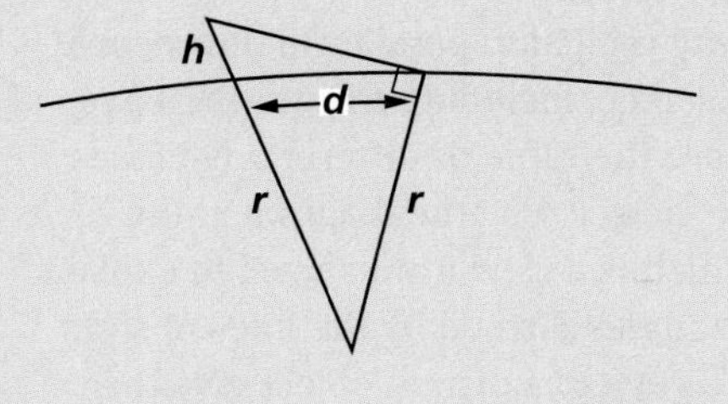

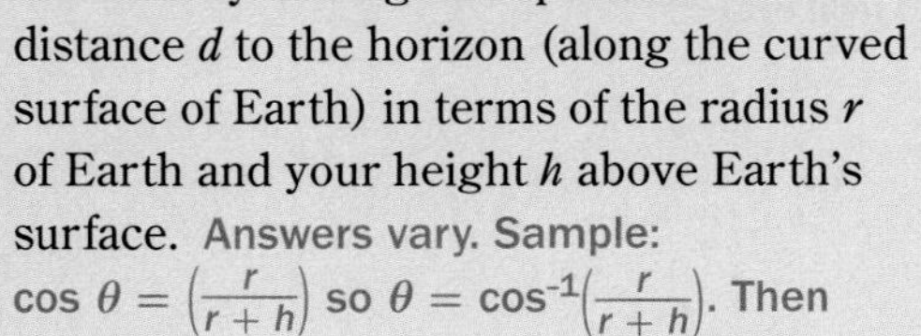

$\cos\theta = \left(\frac{r}{r+h}\right)$ so $\theta = \cos^{-1}\left(\frac{r}{r+h}\right)$. Then

$$d = \frac{\theta}{360} \cdot 2\pi r = \frac{\cos^{-1}\left(\frac{r}{r+h}\right) \cdot \pi r}{180}.$$

Notes on the Lesson

Activities 3 and 4 These activities repeat the kinds of calculations done by Hipparchus and Bessel to determine the distances to the Moon and the star 61 Cygni. Some of your students may not realize that all stars (including our Sun and its solar system) are in motion. The reason that 61 Cygni was identified as possibly being closer to us than other stars was that some years before Bessel's calculation, Giuseppi Piazzi, an Italian astronomer, had called this star (not yet known as a double star) the "Flying Star," due to its change in position relative to other stars in the sky. This suggested that it was a close star, perhaps moving approximately perpendicular to our line of sight to it.

Additional Answers

Activity 1

Step 3a. Answers vary. Sample:

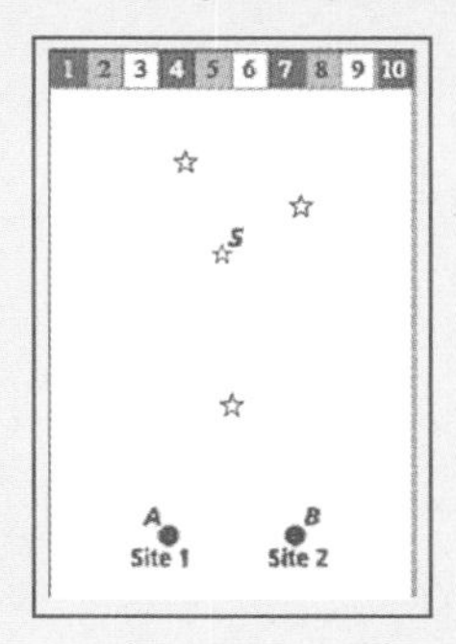

Step 3b.

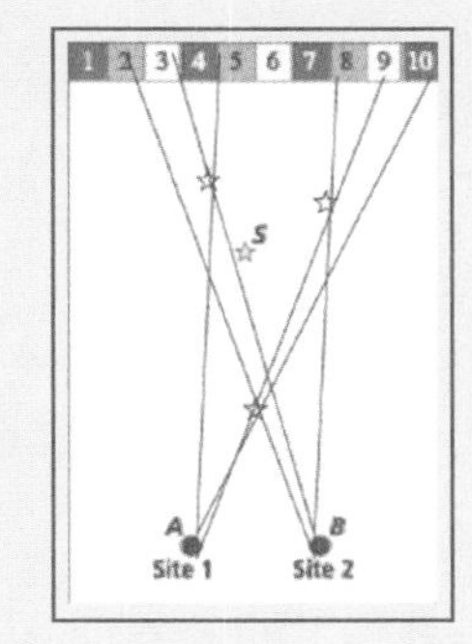

Activity 2

Step 3. Answers vary. Sample: Par ∠: 7.5°

Step 4. Answers vary. Sample: 7.5°, 82.5°, 82.5°

Step 5. Answers vary. Sample: 15.2 ft

The actual distance from Earth to the Moon is about 238,000 miles. The data you used in Activity 3 leads to an underestimate by about 25%, which means that 0.11° is probably not the measure of the parallax angle when the Moon is exactly equidistant from the two cities. When Hipparchus did his calculations without modern trigonometry, he overestimated the distance by about 5%. The inaccuracy of Hipparchus' calculations may be due to the difficulty in verifying the data he worked with, and to the fact that none of the observers of his time had telescopes.

The Distance to a Star

To find distances to stars, you need to use observation sites that are much farther apart than 690 miles, and even then the parallax angles are extremely small. So while the ancient Greeks knew that the stars were extremely far away, they did not have an accurate way to measure those distances.

The first successful attempt to measure the distance to a star was by Friedrich Wilhelm Bessel in 1838, when he used the opposite sides of Earth's orbit around the Sun to measure a parallax angle to the star 61 Cygni. (This technique is called ***annual parallax***.)

Friedrich Wilhelm Bessel has an asteroid named for him, 1552 Bessel.

Activity 4

The angle measured by Bessel was 0.314 arc-second; one arc-second is $\frac{1}{3600}$ degree. Earth's orbit is roughly circular with a diameter of 186,000,000 miles.

Step 1 Draw a diagram and compute the distance from Earth to 61 Cygni.

Step 2 One light-year is the distance light can travel in one Earth year, approximately $5.88 \cdot 10^{12}$ miles. How many light-years away is 61 Cygni? about 10.4 light-years

Step 1.

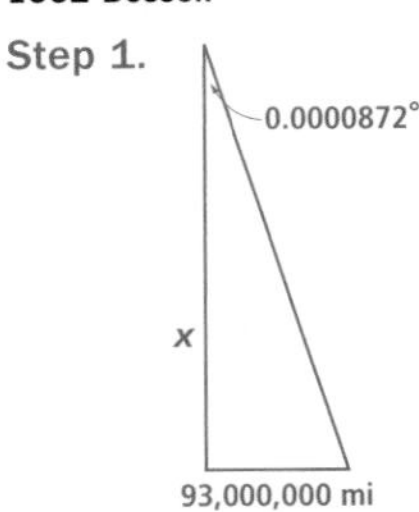

$6.11 \cdot 10^{13}$ mi

The Circumference of Earth

Hipparchus's original parallax computations gave the distance from Earth to the Moon in terms of Earth's radius. The radius of Earth was already known in Hipparchus's time, having been computed by Eratosthenes, a mathematician who lived in the third century BCE. Eratosthenes lived in Alexandria, Egypt, an important location of learning at the time. Eratosthenes found Earth's radius from its circumference. Activity 5 recreates his measurement of Earth's circumference.

Accommodating the Learner

An activity related to parallax is how people judge distance, including telling when two objects are the same or different distances from the viewer. Use the diagram at the right, which is a view from above, to explain how the angles formed by the lines of sight from each eye to a distant object give the viewer information on the distance between the viewer and the object.

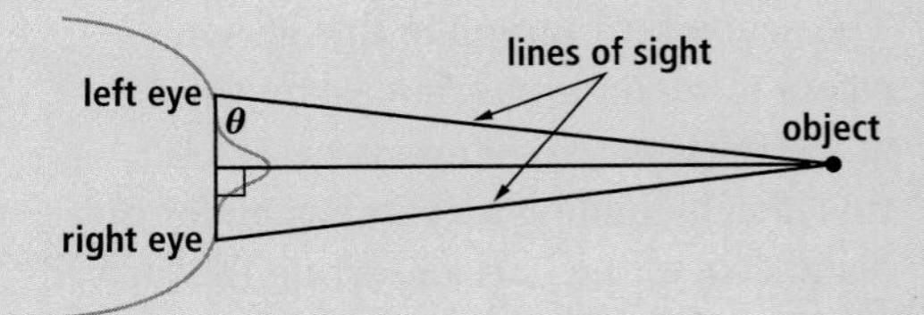

Activity 5

Step 1 Eratosthenes knew that at noon on a particular day each year, in Cyene (an ancient city on the Nile River near what is now Aswan, Egypt), the Sun would shine directly overhead, even reflecting from the water in a deep well. In Alexandria on the same day each year, the Sun at noon was *not* directly overhead. In that city at noon, a 10-meter pole would cast a shadow approximately 1.27 meters long. Copy the diagram at the right, and use trigonometry to compute θ. See margin.

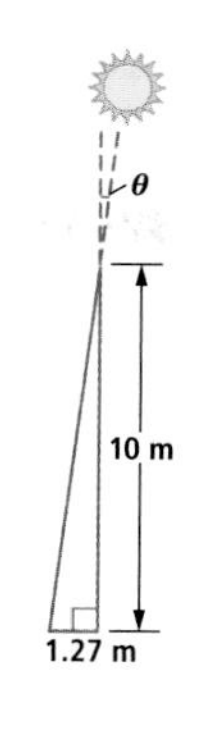

Step 2 Because the Sun is very far away from Earth, the rays reaching Earth are essentially parallel. If the Sun's rays strike Earth at different angles, it can only be because Earth's surface is curved. Copy the diagram at the right, substituting the angle measure θ you found in Step 1 and including the measures of all other angles in the figure. What is the degree measure of $\widehat{AC}$? See margin.

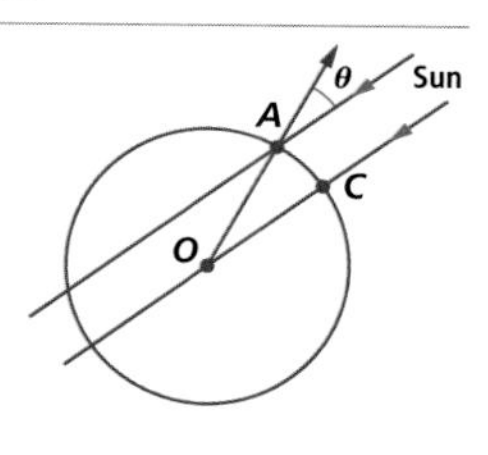

Step 3 Your work in Step 2 shows that the measure of $\widehat{AC}$ is $\frac{\theta}{360}$ of Earth's circumference. From caravans of merchants traveling between the two cities, Eratosthenes knew that Alexandria and Cyene were approximately 5,000 *stadia* apart. Although the exact correspondence is not known, scholars believe that 1 kilometer is approximately 6.27 stadia. Convert 5000 stadia into kilometers. 797.45 km

Step 4 If x is Earth's circumference and d is the distance between Alexandria and Cyene, then $\frac{\theta}{360}x = d$. Solve this equation for x using the values of θ and d that you computed in Steps 1 and 3. $x \approx 39{,}652$ km

The lack of modern technology at the time of Eratosthenes and Hipparchus makes their achievements even more amazing. Without using telescopes, much less calculators and computers, they were able to predict huge distances with incredible precision. The success of their techniques is a testament not just to their persistence but to the brilliance of their work and the power of mathematics in helping us understand the world around us.

The object and the viewer's two eyes are the vertices of an isosceles triangle with base angle θ. Let d be the distance between the viewer's eyes and x be the distance from the viewer to the object. Then as x increases, θ increases; $\tan \theta = \frac{x}{\frac{d}{2}}$, so $x = \frac{d}{2} \cdot \tan \theta$.

Accommodating the Learner

In Activity 3, the text mentions that 0.11° is probably not the parallax angle when the Moon is equidistant from the two cities. Use the actual Earth-to-Moon distance of 238,000 miles to calculate the actual measure of the parallax angle. $\tan \theta = \frac{345}{238{,}000} \approx 0.00144958$, so $\theta \approx 0.083°$.

Additional Answers

Activity 5

Step 1.

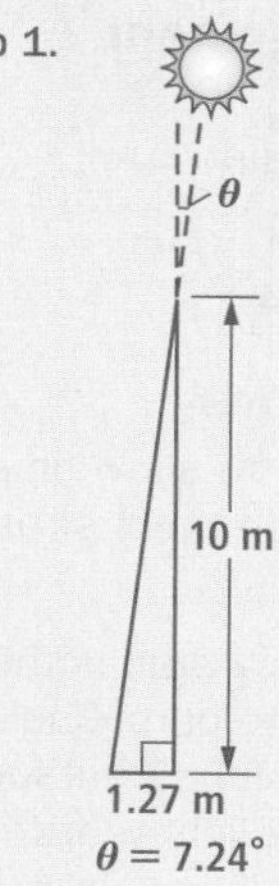

$\theta = 7.24°$

Step 2.

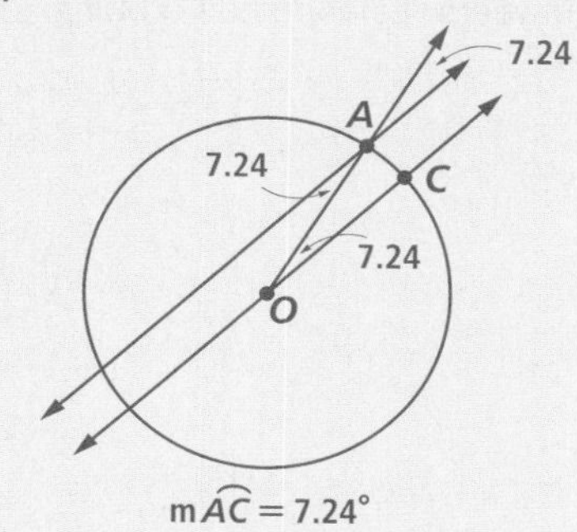

$m\widehat{AC} = 7.24°$

10-3

3 Assignment

Recommended Assignment

- Questions 1–13
- Question 14 (extra credit)
- Reading Lesson 10-4
- Covering the Ideas 10-4

Notes on the Questions

The question set is short to allow time for review and/or a quiz on the first part of the chapter.

Question 4 Sirius, a binary star, is the fifth closest star system to ours. The four closer systems are Alpha Centauri, a triple star system, 4.22 light-years away; Barnard's Star, 6.0 light-years; Wolf 359, 7.8 light-years; and Lalande, 8.3 light-years. Lalande has orbiting planets.

10-3A Lesson Master

Questions on SPUR Objectives
See Student Edition pages 724–727 for objectives.

USES Objective G

1. Refer to the diagram below. If the distance $AB = 3$ ft and the parallax angle $\angle AOM$ measures 12°, find the distance OM. $\approx$ 7 ft

A, M, O, B

2. Suppose points A and B in the diagram above represent your two eyes, and O is an object held in front of you. Explain why the tangent of $\angle AOM$ will get smaller as the distance OM increases.
Answers vary. Sample: As OM gets larger but AM stays the same, the tangent ratio $\frac{AM}{OM}$ gets smaller.

3. An item has a parallax angle of 4.1° from two sites 10 mi apart. How far away is the item? $\approx$ 69.8 mi

4. One evening just after dusk, two friends view the International Space Station. Celia in Prague and Dele in Munich determine that the parallax angle is 23.3°. Prague is 301 km from Munich. What was the altitude of the International Space Station? $\approx$ 349 km

In 5 and 6, use the following information.
- **Parallax angles are measured from opposite sides of Earth's orbit.**
- **Earth's orbit around the sun is approximately a circle with diameter 186,000,000 miles.**
- **One light-year (the distance that light travels in one year) is approximately $5.88 \cdot 10^{12}$ miles.**

5. One of the closest stars to Earth is called Barnard's Star. It has a parallax angle of $(1.52 \cdot 10^{-4})°$. Estimate the distance to Barnard's Star, to the nearest light-year. 6 light-years

6. Polaris, the North Star, is a distance of 431 light-years from Earth. Estimate its parallax angle. Give your answer in scientific notation. $(2.1 \cdot 10^{-6})°$

522 Advanced Algebra

Questions

COVERING THE IDEAS

1. What is meant by *parallax*?

   1. the illusion of motion created by changing viewing positions

2. If an object has a parallax angle of 6.5° from two sites 4 feet apart, about how many feet away is the object? 17.55 ft

3. In recreating Hipparchus's computation of the Moon's distance from Earth, what did we assume about the two observation sites? What justifies this assumption?

   3. We assumed the Moon was equidistant from the two cities. This assumption is justified because the variation is very small compared to the distances being measured.

4. Refer to Activity 4. The ancient Egyptians marked the seasons by the location of the brightest star in the night sky, Sirius. Modern observations show that Sirius has a parallax angle of 0.38 arc-second when measured from opposite ends of Earth's orbit.
   a. Compute the distance from Sirius to Earth in miles.
   b. Use your result from Part a to compute the distance between Earth and Sirius in light-years. (Sirius is one of the closest stars to Earth.) about 8.6 light-years

   4a. $5.05 \cdot 10^{13}$ mi

Hipparchus of Rhodes is considered the Father of Astronomy and was the first person to systematically survey the sky.

APPLYING THE MATHEMATICS

5. Depending on conditions, an unaided human eye can distinguish objects as little as $\frac{1}{60}$ degree apart. For apparent motion, however, the human eye can detect only differences of about 1° or greater. Suppose that when you close one eye and open the other, an object appears to jump 1°, for a parallax angle of 0.5°. If your eyes are 3 inches apart, how many feet away is the object? 14.32 ft

6. The nearest star to Earth is Proxima Centauri, 4.22 light-years away. Using the fact that 1 light-year $= 5.88 \times 10^{12}$ miles, compute the parallax angle you would observe for Proxima Centauri, using the endpoints of Earth's orbit as the two observation sites. about 0.77 arc-second

REVIEW

In 7 and 8, use the following information. The top of the Rock of Gibraltar is 426 meters above sea level. The Strait of Gibraltar, the body of water separating Gibraltar from the African continent, is 14 kilometers wide at its narrowest point. (Lessons 10-2, 10-1)

7. If the captain of the ship HMS Pinafore took a sighting on the Rock of Gibraltar and recorded a 14° angle of elevation, how far was the Pinafore from Gibraltar? 1708.6 m

8. To avoid running into the African shore, what is the minimum angle of elevation possible? 1.743°

9. In the triangle at the right, find each value. **(Lesson 10-1)**
   a. $\sin\theta$ $\frac{s}{5r}$
   b. $\cos\theta$ $\frac{1}{5}$
   c. $\tan\theta$ $\frac{s}{r}$

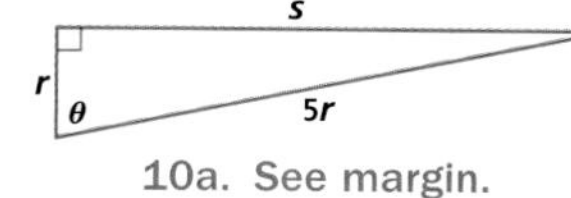

10. a. Solve the system $\begin{cases} y = x^2 - x - 2 \\ y = 3 \end{cases}$ by graphing. 10a. See margin.
    b. Check your work using some other method. **(Lessons 5-3, 5-2)** 10b. See margin.

11. Find the coordinates of each point. **(Lesson 4-8)**
    a. $R_{90}(1, 0)$ (0, 1)
    b. $R_{180}(1, 0)$ (–1, 0)
    c. $R_{270}(1, 0)$ (0, –1)
    d. $R_{-90}(1, 0)$ (0, –1)

12. After an initial 5000-mile break-in period, Mr. Euler changed the oil in his car and, thereafter changed the oil every 3000 miles. **(Lessons 3-8, 3-6, 3-1)**
    a. What did the car's odometer read at the time of the second oil change? 8000 mi
    b. What will the car's odometer read at the nth oil change after the break-in period? $5000 + 3000(n - 1)$ mi
    c. How many times will Mr. Euler have changed his oil when the odometer reads 67,000? 21 times

13. State the Quadrants (I, II, III, or IV) in which (x, y) may be found if
    a. x is negative and y is negative. III
    b. x is negative and y is positive. II
    c. $x = y$ and $xy \neq 0$. **(Previous Course)** I, III

EXPLORATION

14. Let x be is the parallax angle for a star as seen from the endpoints of Earth's orbit, and let d be the star's distance from Earth in light-years.
    a. Write a formula for d in terms of x. $d = \frac{1.58 \cdot 10^{-5}}{\tan x}$
    b. Graph your equation from Part a using values of x between 0° and $\left(\frac{1}{3600}\right)^\circ$. Describe the graph clearly. See margin.
    c. Using a table or a graph, compare the values of $f(x) = \tan x$ and $g(x) = \frac{\pi x}{180}$ for x between 0° and $\left(\frac{1}{3600}\right)^\circ$. 14c. Answers vary. Sample: The values are equal.
    d. Use your observation in Part c to rewrite your formula in Part a. Does your rewritten formula hold for larger values of x, such as 20°?
    $d = \frac{9.05 \cdot 10^{-4}}{x}$; No, the function g approximates the tangent function only for small values of x.

Notes on the Questions

Questions 11 and 13 These questions preview ideas that will be used in Lesson 10-4.

Question 12 Perhaps this question will help students correctly pronounce the name of the famous mathematician Euler as "Oiler."

4 Wrap-Up

Ongoing Assessment

Ask students to explain why objects seem to change position when they use one eye to view the object and then switch eyes. Answers vary. Sample: The key is how the object "lines up" with the background. A line of sight from one eye, through the object, identifies a particular position in the background. The line of sight from the other eye, through the same object, identifies a different position in the background. Switching eyes changes the background position, so the object seems to "jump" from one background position to the other.

Administer Quiz 1 (or a quiz of your own) after students complete this lesson.

Project Update

Project 5, *Benjamin Banneker,* and Project 6, *The Great Trigonometric Survey,* on page 719 relate to the content of this lesson.

Additional Answers

10a. $x = -1.79$ or $x = 2.79$

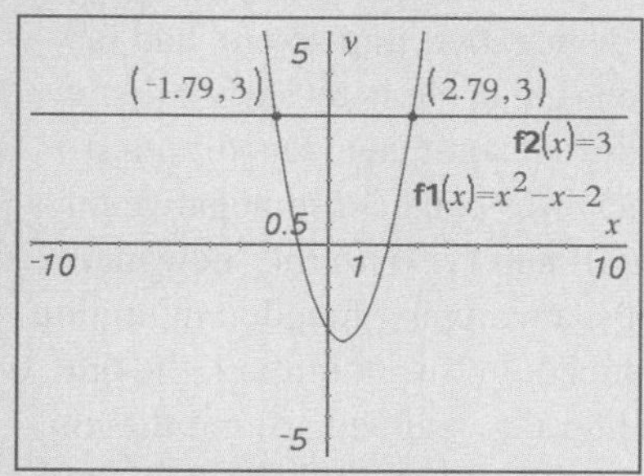

10b. Answers vary. Sample:

$$x = \frac{1 \pm \sqrt{1 - 4(1)(-5)}}{2(1)} = \frac{1 \pm \sqrt{21}}{2}$$

$x = -1.79$ or $x = 2.79$

14b.

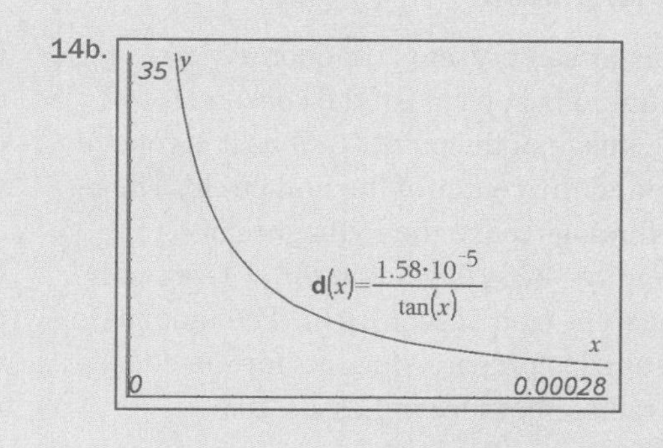

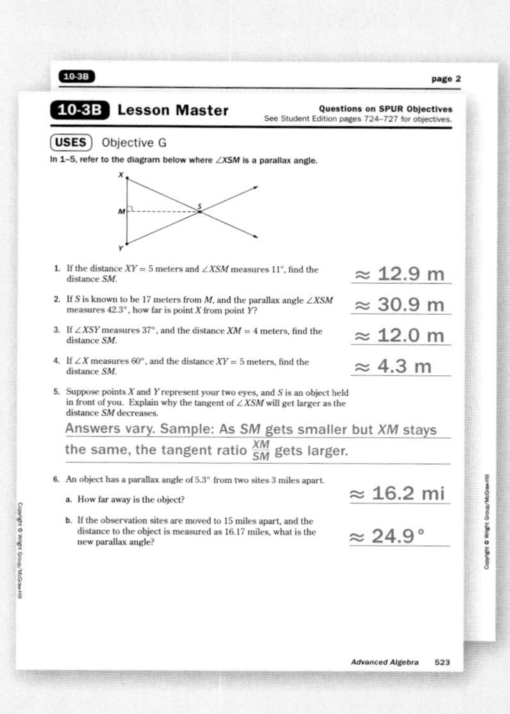
10-3B page 2

10-3B Lesson Master Questions on SPUR Objectives See Student Edition pages 724–727 for objectives.

USES Objective G

In 1–5, refer to the diagram below where ∠XSM is a parallax angle.

1. If the distance XY = 5 meters and ∠XSM measures 11°, find the distance SM. ≈ 12.9 m
2. If S is known to be 17 meters from M, and the parallax angle ∠XSM measures 42.3°, how far is point X from point Y? ≈ 30.9 m
3. If ∠XSY measures 37°, and the distance XM = 4 meters, find the distance SM. ≈ 12.0 m
4. If ∠X measures 60°, and the distance XY = 5 meters, find the distance SM. ≈ 4.3 m
5. Suppose points X and Y represent your two eyes, and S is an object held in front of you. Explain why the tangent of ∠XSM will get larger as the distance SM decreases. Answers vary. Sample: As SM gets smaller but XM stays the same, the tangent ratio $\frac{XM}{SM}$ gets larger.
6. An object has a parallax angle of 5.3° from two sites 3 miles apart.
   a. How far away is the object? ≈ 16.2 mi
   b. If the observation sites are moved to 15 miles apart, and the distance to the object is measured as 16.17 miles, what is the new parallax angle? ≈ 24.9°

Advanced Algebra 523

Lesson 10-4

GOAL

Use the unit circle as a geometric vehicle to define sin *x* and cos *x* for any real value of *x*.

SPUR Objectives

E Identify and use the definitions of sine and cosine.

I Use the properties of a unit circle to find values of trigonometric functions.

Materials/Resources

- Lesson Masters 10-4A and 10-4B
- Resource Masters 189 and 190
- Compass, protractor, graph paper

HOMEWORK

Suggestions for Assignment

- Questions 1–30
- Question 31 (extra credit)
- Reading Lesson 10-5
- Covering the Ideas 10-5

Local Standards

1 Warm-Up

In right triangle *ABC*, angle *C* is the right angle, $AB = 1$, and $AC = 0.96$.

1. What method can you use to find *BC*? Find *BC*. the Pythagorean Theorem; 0.28
2. Find the exact values of sin *A*, cos *A*, sin *B*, and cos *B*. 0.28, 0.96, 0.96, and 0.28

Lesson 10-4 The Unit-Circle Definition of Cosine and Sine

Vocabulary

unit circle

unit-circle definition of cosine and sine

BIG IDEA Every point *P* on the unit circle has coordinates of the form (cos *θ*, sin *θ*), where *θ* is the magnitude of a rotation that maps (1, 0) onto *P*.

In a right triangle, the two angles other than the right angle each have a measure between 0° and 90°. So the definitions of sine, cosine, and tangent given in Lesson 10-1 only apply to measures between 0° and 90°. However, the sine, cosine, and tangent functions can be defined for all real numbers. To define cosines and sines for all real numbers, we use rotations with center (0, 0).

Mental Math

Let *g* be a geometric sequence with the formula $g_n = 120(0.75)^{n-1}$.

a. What is the second term of the sequence? 90

b. If the sequence models the height in inches of a dropped ball after the *n*th bounce, from what height in feet was the ball dropped? 16 ft

c. Could this sequence model the number of people who have heard a rumor? no

Activity

MATERIALS compass, protractor, graph paper

Work with a partner.

Step 1 Draw a set of coordinate axes on a piece of graph paper. Let each side of a square on your coordinate grid have length 0.1 unit. With the origin as the center, use a compass to draw a circle with radius 1. Label the positive *x*-intercept of the circle as A_0. Your circle should look like the one below at the right. Check students' work.

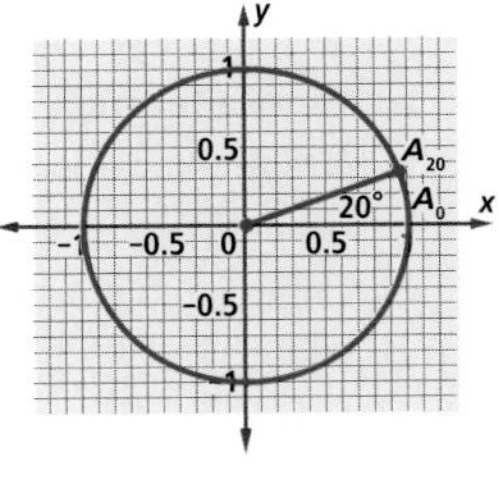

Step 2 **a.** With a protractor, locate the image of $A_0 = (1, 0)$ under R_{20}. Label this point A_{20}.

b. Use the grid to estimate the *x*- and *y*-coordinates of A_{20}.

c. Use a calculator to find cos 20° and sin 20°.

Step 3 **a.** With a protractor, locate $R_{40}(1, 0)$. Label it A_{40}.

b. Use the grid to estimate the *x*- and *y*-coordinates of A_{40}.

c. Use a calculator to find cos 40° and sin 40°.

Step 4 **a.** Locate $R_{75}(1, 0)$. Label it A_{75}.

b. Estimate the *x*- and *y*-coordinates of this point.

c. Use a calculator to evaluate cos 75° and sin 75°.

Steps 2–5. See the Additional Answers section at the back of the book.

Background

This lesson presents trigonometric definitions in terms of the coordinates of the image of the point (1, 0) as it is rotated around the center of the unit circle. These definitions make the Pythagorean Identity—$(\cos \theta)^2 + (\sin \theta)^2 = 1$—readily apparent (see Lesson 10-5). The unit circle also helps prepare students for the concept of radian measure in Lesson 10-9.

Before 1960, sin *θ* and cos *θ* were usually defined separately, using triangles in each quadrant. A problem with these definitions was that if *x* and *y* were lengths, then they could not be negative, and so one had to finesse the issue of signs by saying that *x* was considered negative in Quadrants II and III, and *y* was considered negative in Quadrants III and IV. With the "new math" of the 1960s, a wrapping function definition was introduced. In this definition, the line $x = 1$ was literally wrapped around the unit circle. The point with coordinate *θ* on that line would then be considered to be mapped onto a point on the circle, which was called (cos *θ*, sin *θ*).

Step 5 **a.** Look back at your work for Steps 2–4. What relationship do you see between the *x*- and *y*-coordinates of $R_\theta(1, 0)$, $\cos\theta$, and $\sin\theta$?

b. Use your answer to Step 5 Part a to estimate the values of cos 61° and sin 61° from your figure without a calculator.

c. What is the relative error between your predictions in Step 5 Part b and the actual values of cos 61° and sin 61°? Were you within 3% of the actual values?

The Unit Circle, Sines, and Cosines

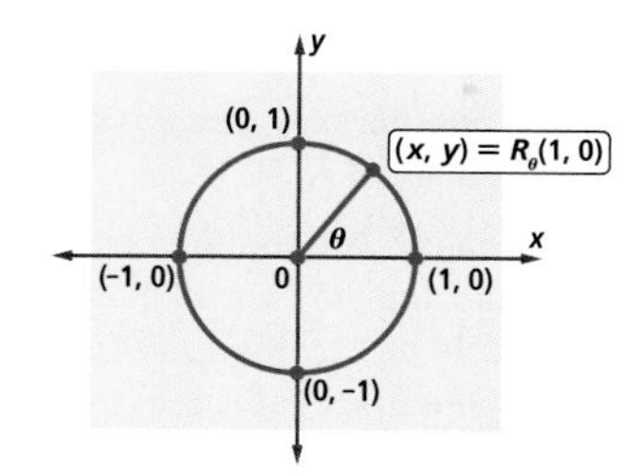

The circle you drew in the Activity is a ***unit circle***. The **unit circle** is the circle with center at the origin and radius 1 unit. If the point (1, 0) on the circle is rotated around the origin with magnitude θ, then the image point (x, y) is also on the circle. The coordinates of the image point can be found using sines and cosines, as you should have discovered in the Activity.

Example 1

What are the coordinates of the image of (1, 0) under R_{70}?

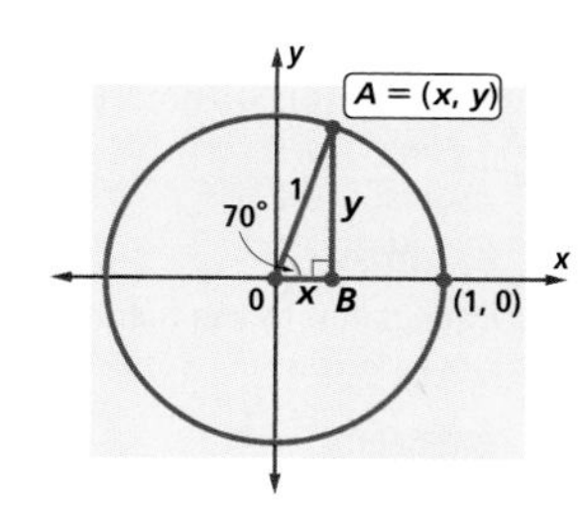

Solution Let $A = (x, y) = R_{70}(1, 0)$. In the figure at the right, $OA = 1$ because the radius of the unit circle is 1. Draw the segment from A to $B = (x, 0)$. $\triangle ABO$ is a right triangle with legs of length x and y, and hypotenuse of length 1. Now use the definitions of sine and cosine.

$$\cos 70° = \frac{\text{adj}}{\text{hyp}} = \frac{x}{1} = x$$

$$\sin 70° = \frac{\text{opp}}{\text{hyp}} = \frac{y}{1} = y$$

The first coordinate is cos 70°, and the second coordinate is sin 70°. Thus, $(x, y) = (\cos 70°, \sin 70°) \approx (0.342, 0.940)$. That is, the image of (1, 0) under R_{70} is (cos 70°, sin 70°), or about (0.342, 0.940).

Check Use the Pythagorean Theorem with cos 70° and sin 70° as the lengths of the legs.

Is $(0.342)^2 + (0.940)^2 \approx 1^2$? $0.117 + 0.884 = 1.001 \approx 1$, so it checks.

The idea of Example 1 can be generalized to define the sine and cosine of any magnitude θ. Since any real number can be the magnitude of a rotation, this definition enlarges the domain of these trigonometric functions to be the set of all real numbers.

The approach given here also utilizes the unit circle, but it does not require anything students have not seen before. Specifically, it does not require wrapping a line about a circle. In later courses, students may use this approach to deduce the formulas for $\cos(x + y)$ and $\sin(x + y)$.

Accommodating the Learner

Ask students to select several values for θ and, for each value, verify that the distance between $(\cos\theta, \sin\theta)$ and the origin is 1. Answers vary. Sample: For $\theta = 25°$, $(\cos 25°, \sin 25°) \approx (0.9063, 0.4226)$, and the distance between (0.9063, 0.4226) and (0, 0) is $\sqrt{0.9063^2 + 0.4226^2} \approx \sqrt{0.8214 + 0.1786} = \sqrt{1} = 1$.

10-4

2 Teaching

Notes on the Lesson

After students complete the Activity, the remainder of this lesson is neither long nor difficult. So this is a reasonable lesson to assign to be read without preliminary discussion. However, if you believe students will need preparation before reading, we suggest you introduce the lesson with a question such as the one in Example 1.

Use the solution of Example 1 as a model. Have students rotate the point (1, 0) by 70° (or pick a different magnitude between 0° and 90°) around the center of the unit circle. Ask them to find the coordinates of the image. Point out that the first coordinate of the image is cos 70° and the second coordinate is sin 70°. Now give the definition of $\cos\theta$ and $\sin\theta$ stated on page 684 and show that when $0° < \theta < 90°$, this new definition is equivalent to the right-triangle definitions in Lesson 10-1.

Explain to students that it is customary to use a rather large unit when drawing the unit circle. The size is necessary to show what is going on. However, its size may give the mistaken impression that sines and cosines can be numbers greater than 1 or less than –1. At least once, draw for students a unit circle using the scale that is customarily used for graphing. (You will see a very small unit circle.)

For students who have difficulty remembering which coordinate (x or y) corresponds to which trigonometric function ($\cos\theta$ or $\sin\theta$), point out that the correspondence follows alphabetical order: c (in cosine) precedes s (in sine) as x precedes y.

Additional Answers can be found in the back of the book.

Additional Example

Example 1 What are the coordinates of the image of (0, 1) under R_{50}? $(\cos 50°, \sin 50°) \approx (0.643, 0.766)$

Additional Example

Example 2 How can you use the unit circle to find the following values?

a. sin 270° sin 270° is the *y*-coordinate of R_{270}. Because $R_{270}(1, 0) = (0, -1)$, then sin 270° = -1.

b. cos (-90°) $R_{-90}(1, 0) = (0, -1)$. Because cos -90° is the *x*-coordinate of R_{-90}, then cos(-90°) = 0.]

Note-Taking Tips

Encourage students to use Pythagorean triples to find the coordinates of points on the unit circle. For example, students can use the Pythagorean triple 6, 8, 10 to find the eight ordered pairs (±0.6, ±0.8) and (±0.8, ±0.6) and show that each one lies on the unit circle.

Unit-Circle Definition of Cosine and Sine

Let R_θ be the rotation with center (0, 0) and magnitude θ. Then, for any θ, the point (cos θ, sin θ) is the image of (1, 0) under R_θ.

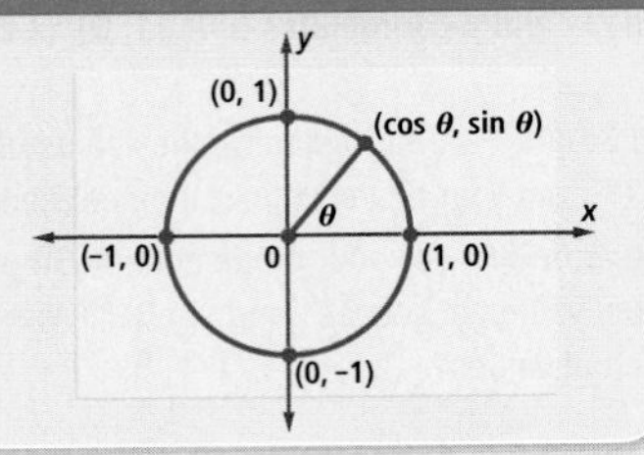

Stated another way, cos θ is the *x*-coordinate of $R_\theta(1, 0)$; sin θ is the *y*-coordinate of $R_\theta(1, 0)$.

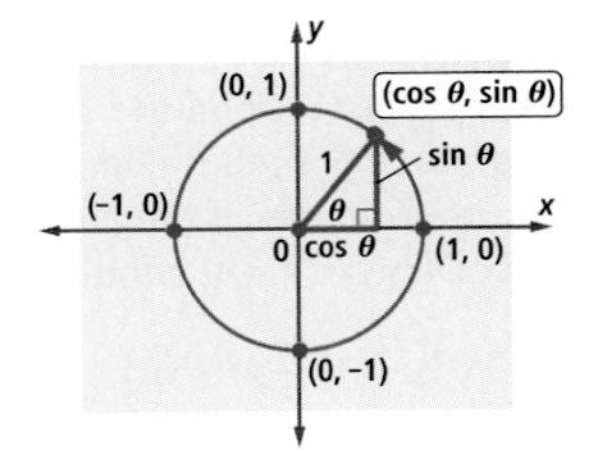

This unit-circle definition agrees with the right-triangle definition of cosine and sine for all magnitudes between 0° and 90°. Since the unit circle has radius 1, cos θ is the ratio of the side adjacent to θ to the hypotenuse, and sin θ is the ratio of the side opposite θ to the hypotenuse.

Cosines and Sines of Multiples of 90°

Sines and cosines of multiples of 90° can be found from the unit-circle definition without using a calculator.

Example 2

Explain how to use the unit circle to find

a. cos 90°. **b. sin (–180°).**

Solution

a. Think: cos 90° is the *x*-coordinate of $R_{90}(1, 0)$. $R_{90}(1, 0) = (0, 1)$. So cos 90° = 0.

b. $R_{-180}(1, 0) = (-1, 0)$. Since sin(–180°) is the *y*-coordinate of this point, sin(–180°) = 0.

Check Check these values on your calculator.

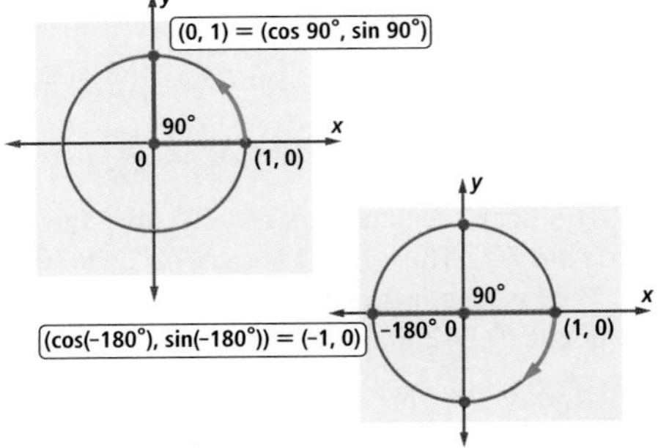

As you saw in your study of geometry and in Chapter 4, if a rotation of magnitude *x* is followed by a rotation of magnitude *y* with the same center, then the composite transformation is a rotation with magnitude *x* + *y*. That is, $R_x \circ R_y = R_{x+y}$. Furthermore, rotations of multiples of 360° are the identity transformation. Consequently, if you add or subtract integer multiples of 360° from the magnitude of a rotation, the rotation is the same. This means that you can add or subtract integer multiples of 360° from the arguments of the sine or cosine functions, and the value remains the same.

ENGLISH LEARNERS

Vocabulary Development

You may want to discuss the term *form* that appears in the Big Idea on page 682. Students should be accustomed to exponents and other symbols in the "form of an expression," such as the Pythagorean Theorem $(a^2 + b^2 = c^2)$ or $2\pi r$ for the circumference of a circle. However, it may not be immediately clear that the form (cos θ, sin θ) refers to an ordered pair whose first coordinate is the cosine of an angle and whose second coordinate is the sine of the same angle.

Extension

Ask students to explain why, for Quadrant I points on the unit circle, $\tan\theta = \frac{\sin\theta}{\cos\theta}$. Answers vary. Sample: $\tan\theta = \frac{y}{x}$, and $\frac{y}{x} = \frac{\sin\theta}{\cos\theta}$. Then ask students to revisit the Activity to find tan 20°, tan 40°, and tan 75°, first using the *x*- and *y*-coordinates from the Activity and then checking their results with a calculator. Check students' work.

Example 3

a. Find sin 630°.

b. Find cos –900°.

Solution Add or subtract multiples of 360° from the argument until you obtain a value from 0° to 360°.

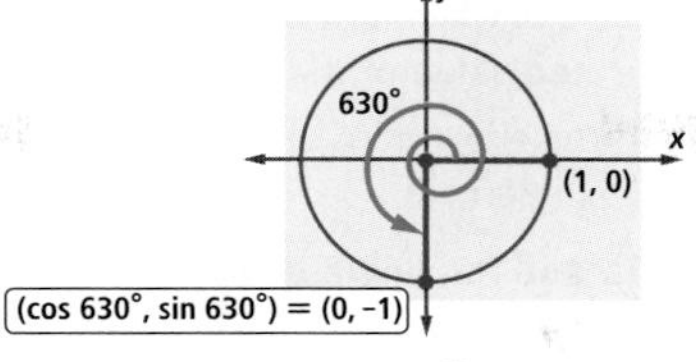

a. $630° - 360° = 270°$. So R_{630} equals one complete revolution followed by a 270° rotation, and R_{630} and R_{270} have the same images. $R_{630}(1, 0) = R_{270}(1, 0) = (0, -1)$. So sin 630° = –1.

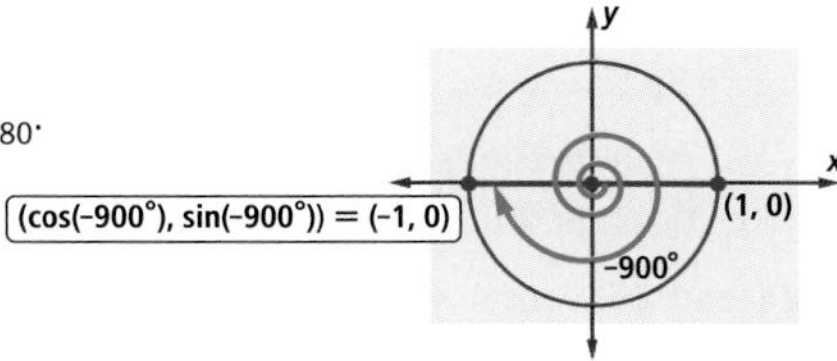

b. Add 3 • 360° to –900° to obtain a magnitude from 0° to 360°. $-900° + 3 \cdot 360° = 180°$. $R_{-900} = R_{180}$. So cos –900° = cos 180° = –1.

Questions

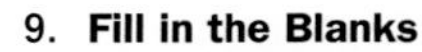

COVERING THE IDEAS

1. **Fill in the Blanks** If (1, 0) is rotated θ degrees around the origin,
   a. cos θ is the __?__-coordinate of its image. *x*
   b. sin θ is the __?__-coordinate of its image. *y*
2. **True or False** The image of (1, 0) under R_{23} is (sin 23°, cos 23°). false
3. **Fill in the Blanks** $R_0(1, 0)$ = __?__, so cos 0° = __?__ and sin 0° = __?__. (1, 0); 1; 0
4. Explain how to use the unit circle to find sin 180°.

4. Answers vary. Sample: $R_{180}(1, 0) = (-1, 0)$. Since sin 180° is the *y*-coordinate of this point, sin 180° = 0.

In 5–7, use the unit circle to find the value.

5. cos 90° 0
6. sin (-90°) -1
7. cos 270° 0
8. If (1, 0) is rotated -42° about the origin, what are the coordinates of its image, to the nearest thousandth? (0.743, -0.669)
9. **Fill in the Blanks**
   a. A rotation of 540° equals a rotation of 360° followed by __?__. a rotation of 180°
   b. The image of (1, 0) under R_{540} is __?__. (-1, 0)
   c. Evaluate sin 540°. 0

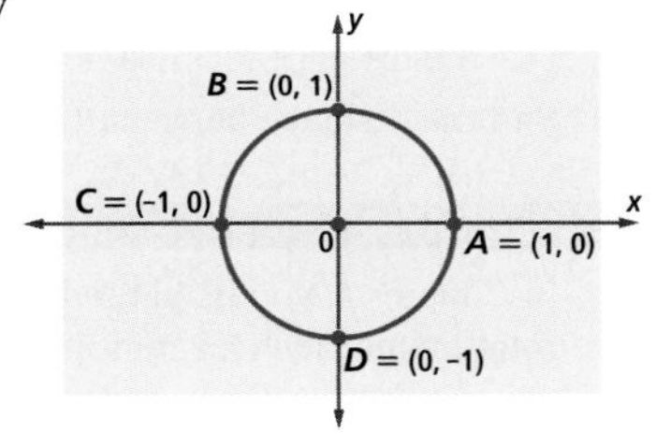

In 10–12, suppose A = (1, 0), B = (0, 1), C = (-1, 0), and D = (0, -1). Which of these points is the image of (1, 0) under the stated rotation?

10. R_{450} *B*
11. R_{540} *C*
12. R_{-720} *A*

Additional Example

Example 3

a. Find sin(–1170°). $-1170 + 4 \cdot 360 = 270$, so sin(–1170°) = sin 270° = –1.

b. Find cos 810°. $810 - 2 \cdot 360 = 90$, so cos 810° = cos 90° = 0.

3 Assignment

Recommended Assignment

- Questions 1–30
- Question 31 (extra credit)
- Reading Lesson 10-5
- Covering the Ideas 10-5

Notes on the Questions

Questions 1, 3, 13 and 14 Notice that cosine appears before sine. As much as possible, try to get students into that habit.

Accommodating the Learner

Ask students to identify any three Pythagorean triples (some examples are 3, 4, 5; 5, 12, 13; 8, 15, 17; and 7, 24, 25). For each triple, ask students to form a new triple by dividing all three numbers by the greatest number in the triple and then show that the first two numbers in the new triple determine an ordered pair that is on the unit circle.

Answers vary. Sample: In general, for the Pythagorean triple *a*, *b*, *c*, we know that $a^2 + b^2 = c^2$. The ordered pair is $\left(\frac{a}{c}, \frac{b}{c}\right)$, and the distance between that point and (0, 0) is $\sqrt{\left(\frac{a}{c} - 0\right)^2 + \left(\frac{b}{c} - 0\right)^2} = \sqrt{\frac{a^2}{c^2} + \frac{b^2}{c^2}} = \sqrt{\frac{c^2}{c^2}}$, so $\left(\frac{a}{c}, \frac{b}{c}\right)$ is on the unit circle.

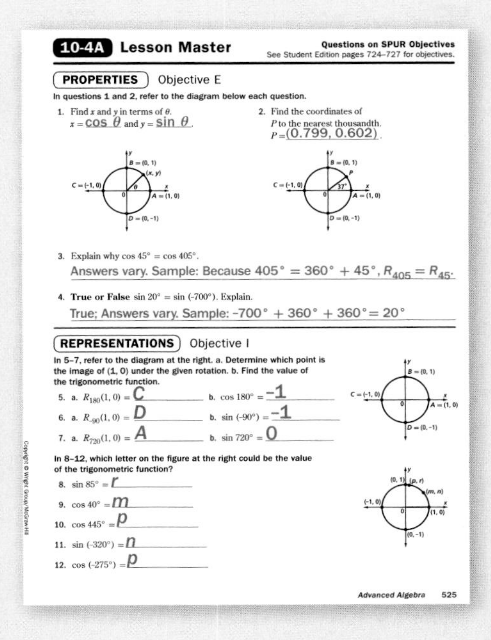

10-4A Lesson Master

Questions on SPUR Objectives
See Student Edition pages 724–727 for objectives.

PROPERTIES Objective E

In questions 1 and 2, refer to the diagram below each question.

1. Find *x* and *y* in terms of θ.
   x = cos θ and y = sin θ.
2. Find the coordinates of *P* to the nearest thousandth.
   P = (0.799, 0.602).

3. Explain why cos 45° = cos 405°.
   Answers vary. Sample: Because 405° = 360° + 45°, $R_{405} = R_{45}$.
4. **True or False** sin 20° = sin (-700°). Explain.
   True; Answers vary. Sample: –700° + 360° + 360° = 20°

REPRESENTATIONS Objective I

In 5–7, refer to the diagram at the right. a. Determine which point is the image of (1, 0) under the given rotation. b. Find the value of the trigonometric function.

5. a. $R_{180}(1, 0)$ = C b. cos 180° = –1
6. a. $R_{-90}(1, 0)$ = D b. sin (-90°) = –1
7. a. $R_{720}(1, 0)$ = A b. sin 720° = 0

In 8–12, which letter on the figure at the right could be the value of the trigonometric function?

8. sin 85° = r
9. cos 40° = m
10. cos 445° = p
11. sin (-320°) = n
12. cos (-275°) = p

Advanced Algebra 525

Notes on the Questions

Question 23 When discussing this question, you may also want to ask students for the smallest possible value of cos θ and the largest possible value of sin θ. This will give the range of the sine and cosine functions.

Questions 24 and 25 These questions give instances of the identities that will be discussed in Lessons 10-5 and 10-7.

Question 31 This is a difficult question, requiring students to realize that the image of (0, 1) under R_θ is the image of (1, 0) under $R_{90+\theta}$.

4 Wrap-Up

Ongoing Assessment

Ask students to find the image of (1, 0) under each rotation:

a. R_{45} $\left(\frac{\sqrt{2}}{2}, \frac{\sqrt{2}}{2}\right)$

b. R_{135} $\left(-\frac{\sqrt{2}}{2}, \frac{\sqrt{2}}{2}\right)$

c. R_{240} $\left(-\frac{1}{2}, -\frac{\sqrt{3}}{2}\right)$

d. R_{330} $\left(\frac{\sqrt{3}}{2}, -\frac{1}{2}\right)$

In 13 and 14, evaluate without using a calculator.

13. cos 450° and sin 450° 0; 1
14. cos(-720°) and sin(-720°) 1; 0

APPLYING THE MATHEMATICS

In 15–20, which letter on the figure at the right could stand for the indicated value of the trigonometric function?

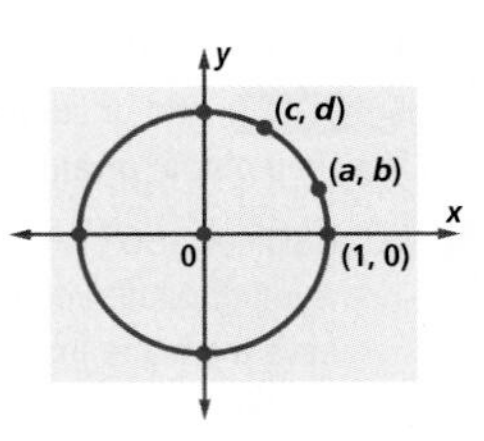

15. cos 80° *c*
16. sin 80° *d*
17. cos(-280°) *c*
18. sin 800° *d*
19. cos 380° *a*
20. sin(-340°) *b*

In 21 and 22, find a solution to the equation between 0° and 360°. Then check your answer by using a calculator to approximate both sides of the equation to the nearest thousandth.

21. cos 392° = cos *x*
22. sin(-440°) = sin *y*

23. a. What is the largest possible value of cos θ? 1
    b. What is the smallest possible value of sin θ? -1

In 24 and 25, verify by substitution that the statement holds for the given value of θ.

24. $(\cos\theta)^2 + (\sin\theta)^2 = 1$; $\theta = 7290°$
25. $\sin\theta = \sin(180° - \theta)$; $\theta = -270°$ sin(-270°) = sin 450° = 1

REVIEW

26. If an object has a parallax angle of 3° from two sites 100 meters apart, about how far away is the object? **(Lesson 10-3)**
27. Why must the observation sites be very far apart to determine the distance to a star by parallax? **(Lesson 10-3)**
28. A private plane flying at an altitude of 5000 feet begins its descent along a straight line to an airport 5 miles away. At what constant angle of depression does it need to descend? **(Lesson 10-2)** about 10.72°
29. A submarine commander took a sighting at sea level of the aircraft carrier USS Enterprise, the tallest ship in the U.S. Navy at 250 feet. He knew that the top of the ship was about 210 feet above sea level, and he noted that the angle of elevation to the top of the mast was 4°. How far from the Enterprise was the submarine? **(Lesson 10-1)**

30. Use the distance formula $d = \sqrt{(x_1 - x_2)^2 + (y_1 - y_2)^2}$ to find the distance between (-2, 3) and (2, -7). **(Lesson 4-4)** $\sqrt{116} \approx 10.77$

EXPLORATION

31. In Chapter 4, you used the Matrix Basis Theorem to develop rotation matrices for multiples of 90°. Use that theorem and the unit circle to produce a rotation matrix for any magnitude θ. See margin.

21. $x = 32°$; cos 392° = cos 32° ≈ 0.848
22. $y = 280°$; sin(-440°) = sin 280° ≈ -0.985
24. cos 7290° = cos 90° = 0, sin 7290° = sin 90° = 1, $0^2 + 1^2 = 1$
26. about 49.93 m away
27. Because stars are extremely far away, you need to use very distant sites in order to have manageable parallax angles.
29. about 3003 ft away

Additional Answers

31. The Matrix Basis Theorem states that for a transformation *A* represented by a 2 × 2 matrix, if *A*: (1, 0) → (x_1, y_1) and (0, 1) → (x_2, y_2), then *A* has the matrix $\begin{bmatrix} x_1 & x_2 \\ y_1 & y_2 \end{bmatrix}$. Therefore, the rotation about the unit circle has the matrix $\begin{bmatrix} \cos\theta & (\cos 90° + \theta) \\ \sin\theta & (\sin 90° + \theta) \end{bmatrix}$.

10-4B page 2

10-4B Lesson Master Questions on SPUR Objectives
See Student Edition pages 724–727 for objectives.

PROPERTIES Objective E

In 1 and 2, use the diagram at the right.

1. Explain why $x = \cos\theta$ and $y = \sin\theta$.
   Since the circle has radius = 1, $\cos\theta = \frac{x}{1} = x$ and $\sin\theta = \frac{y}{1} = y$.
2. Give two rotations that map point *A* to point *D*.
   Answers vary. Samples: R_{270}, R_{-90}

In 3 and 4, use the diagram at the right.

3. Find the coordinates of *P* to the nearest thousandth.
   P = (0.731, 0.682)
4. Give a rotation that maps point *P* to point *B*.
   Answers vary. Sample: R_{47}

In 5–7, use the diagram at the right.

5. Find cos θ. 0.559
6. Find sin θ. 0.829
7. Find θ to the nearest degree. 56°
8. Explain why cos 13° = cos 373°.
   Answers vary. Sample: Because 373° = 360° + 13°, $R_{373} = R_{13}$.
9. Explain why sin 89° = sin 449°.
   Answers vary. Sample: Because 449° = 360° + 89°, $R_{449} = R_{89}$.
10. **True or False** sin (-120°) = sin (600°). Explain.
    True; Answers vary. Sample: -120° + 360° + 360° = 600°
11. **True or False** cos 45° = cos (-315°). Explain.
    True; Answers vary. Sample: 45° + (-360°) = -315°

526 Advanced Algebra

Lesson 10-5 Relationships among Sines and Cosines

Vocabulary

identity

tangent of θ (for all values of θ)

▶ **BIG IDEA** Many properties of sines and cosines follow logically from the definition $(\cos\theta, \sin\theta) = R_\theta(1, 0)$ and properties of the unit circle.

With a calculator, it is easy to determine the values of $\cos\theta$ and $\sin\theta$ for any value of θ. But how can you check that you are correct? If θ is a multiple of 90°, you can find $\cos\theta$ and $\sin\theta$ by visualizing the exact location of $R_\theta(1, 0)$. If $0 < \theta < 90°$, then $R_\theta(1, 0)$ is in the first quadrant and you can estimate the values by drawing a right triangle. For other values of θ, you can use the symmetry of the unit circle.

Determining the Signs of cos θ and sin θ

When θ is not a multiple of 90°, $(\cos\theta, \sin\theta)$ is in one of the four quadrants. As the figure below at the left shows, each quadrant is associated with one-fourth of the interval $0° < \theta < 360°$.

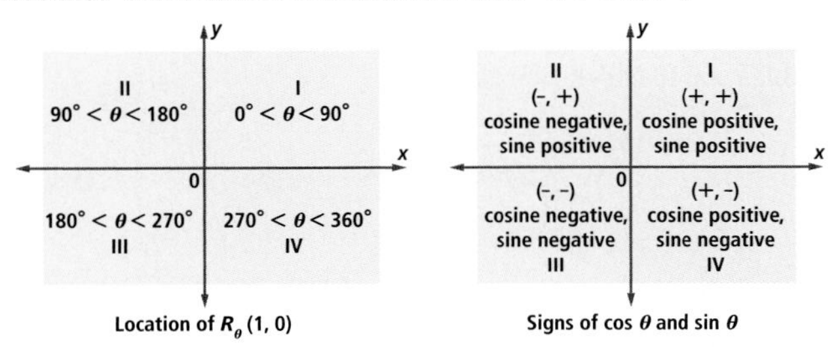

Location of $R_\theta(1, 0)$ Signs of $\cos\theta$ and $\sin\theta$

The quadrants enable you to determine quickly whether $\cos\theta$ and $\sin\theta$ are positive or negative. Refer to the figure above at the right. Because $\cos\theta$ is the first or x-coordinate of the image, it is positive when $R_\theta(1, 0)$ is in Quadrant I or IV and negative when $R_\theta(1, 0)$ is in Quadrant II or III. Because $\sin\theta$ is the second or y-coordinate of $R_\theta(1, 0)$, $\sin\theta$ is positive when $R_\theta(1, 0)$ is in Quadrant I or II and negative when $R_\theta(1, 0)$ is in Quadrant III or IV.

You do *not* need to memorize this information. You can always rely on the definition of $\cos\theta$ and $\sin\theta$ or visualize $R_\theta(1, 0)$ on the unit circle.

 QY

Mental Math

Jamal is packing bulk auto parts into boxes to ship to automotive stores. He can only send full boxes. How many parts will Jamal have left over if he has

a. 672 windshield-wiper blades and 160 fit in a box? 32

b. 223 fan belts and 24 fit in a box? 7

c. 17 fuel pumps and he can use boxes that fit 4 or 5 pumps? 0

▶ **QY**

A value of $\cos\theta$ or $\sin\theta$ is given. Identify the quadrant of $R_\theta(1, 0)$ and tell whether the value is positive or negative.

a. cos 212°

b. sin 212°

c. cos –17°

d. sin –17°

Background

With the definition of $(\cos\theta, \sin\theta)$ based on rotations, it is natural to use reflections and rotations to obtain exact values of sines and cosines for multiples of 30° and 45° that are not in Quadrant I. This method is efficient because it uses reference points, eliminating the need for new terminology, such as reference angles.

There is more than one way to obtain the values of cosines and sines in Quadrants II–IV. Many teachers prefer to think of reflecting points to obtain values in Quadrants II and IV and rotating by 180° to obtain values in Quadrant III. These are the approaches taken on pages 688 and 689.

Of course, a calculator will give approximations for these values regardless of the value of θ. One purpose of this lesson, which follows our general belief that students should always have a way to check their work, is to give students a way to check the answers obtained with their calculators.

Lesson 10-5

GOAL

Discuss the values of cos x and sin x when x is not between 0° and 90°; introduce the tangent function.

SPUR Objectives

E Identify and use the definitions of sine, cosine, and tangent.

F Identify and use theorems relating sines and cosines.

I Use the properties of a unit circle to find trigonometric ratios.

Materials/Resources

- Lesson Masters 10-5A and 10-5B
- Resource Masters 191–193

HOMEWORK

Suggestions for Assignment

- Questions 1–28
- Question 29 (extra credit)
- Reading Lesson 10-6
- Covering the Ideas 10-6

Local Standards

1 Warm-Up

In right triangle DEF, D is the right angle, $DE = \sqrt{83}$, and $EF = \sqrt{89}$.

1. Find the exact values of cos E and sin E and show that $\cos^2 E + \sin^2 E = 1$. $\sqrt{\frac{83}{89}}; \sqrt{\frac{6}{89}}; \left(\sqrt{\frac{83}{89}}\right)^2 + \left(\sqrt{\frac{6}{89}}\right)^2 = \frac{83}{89} + \frac{6}{89} = \frac{89}{89} = 1$
2. Estimate cos E and sin E to the nearest millionth and show that with these estimates, $\cos^2 E + \sin^2 E \approx 1$. 0.965704, 0.259645; $0.932584 + 0.067416 \approx 1$

2 Teaching

Notes on the Lesson

Emphasize that the first step in answering many of the questions in this lesson is to sketch a unit circle.

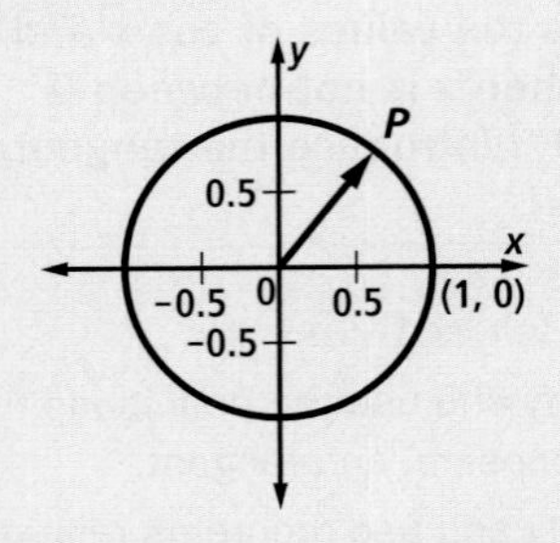

Show students that when you rotate the pointer a fixed amount in either direction from (1, 0), a unique point P on the circle is determined. That point P has unique coordinates.

Determining the signs of cos θ and sin θ Have students determine whether the coordinates of P resulting from a given rotation are positive or negative. For example, $\theta = 120°$ determines P with a negative x-coordinate and a positive y-coordinate. Next, remind students that the x-coordinate is cos θ, and the y-coordinate is sin θ. Have students visually estimate cos θ and sin θ after a given rotation. For instance, rotate the pointer 250° and have students estimate, to the nearest tenth, the x- and y-coordinates of the terminal point P. They might say $x \approx -0.3$, $y \approx -0.9$. Have them use their calculators to evaluate cos 250° ($\approx$-0.342) and sin 250° ($\approx$-0.940) to check their estimates.

Finally, give students either an x-coordinate or a y-coordinate of a point P on the circle. Explain that if neither x nor y is 0 or ± 1, there will be two magnitudes θ between 0° and 360° that result in the given coordinate. Have students estimate that value of θ. For instance, if the y-coordinate of P is 0.4, the diagrams below show two the possible values of θ.

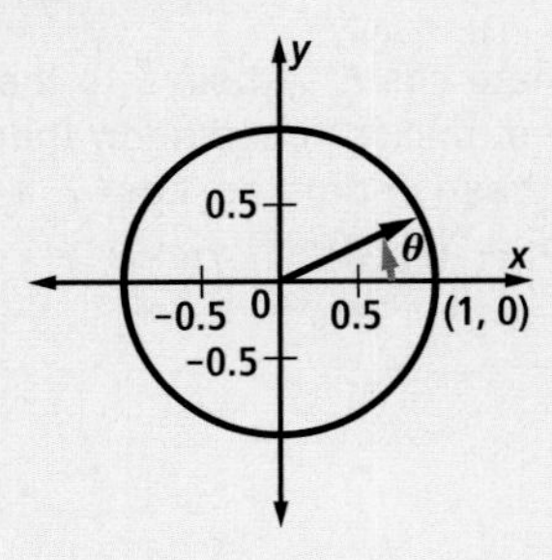

Determining sin θ from cos θ, and Vice Versa

Relationships that are true for all values of variables in a domain are called **identities**. The basic identity relating sin θ and cos θ comes from the Pythagorean Distance Formula. So it is called the *Pythagorean Identity*.

Pythagorean Identity Theorem

For all θ, $(\cos \theta)^2 + (\sin \theta)^2 = 1$.

Proof For any θ, $(\cos \theta, \sin \theta)$ is a point on the unit circle. Let $A = (\cos \theta, \sin \theta)$ and $O = (0, 0)$. By the Pythagorean Distance Formula,

$$OA = \sqrt{(\cos \theta - 0)^2 + (\sin \theta - 0)^2}.$$

But $OA = 1$ for every point A on the circle. Substituting 1 for OA and squaring both sides,

$$(\cos \theta)^2 + (\sin \theta)^2 = 1.$$

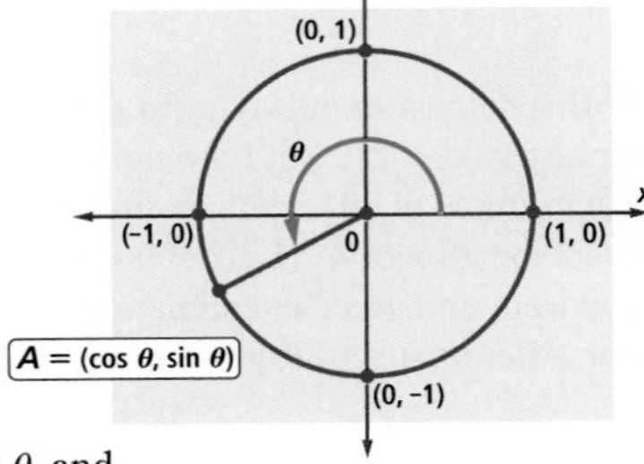

To avoid having to write parentheses, $(\sin \theta)^n$ is written $\sin^n \theta$, and powers of the other trigonometric functions are written similarly. With this notation, the Pythagorean Identity is:

$$\text{For all } \theta,\ \cos^2 \theta + \sin^2 \theta = 1.$$

The Pythagorean Identity enables you to determine sin θ if cos θ is known, and vice versa. It also enables you to check sine and cosine values that you have obtained.

Example 1

Refer to the unit circle at the right.

a. Approximate the coordinates of point C to the nearest thousandth.

b. Verify that your coordinates in Part a satisfy the Pythagorean Identity.

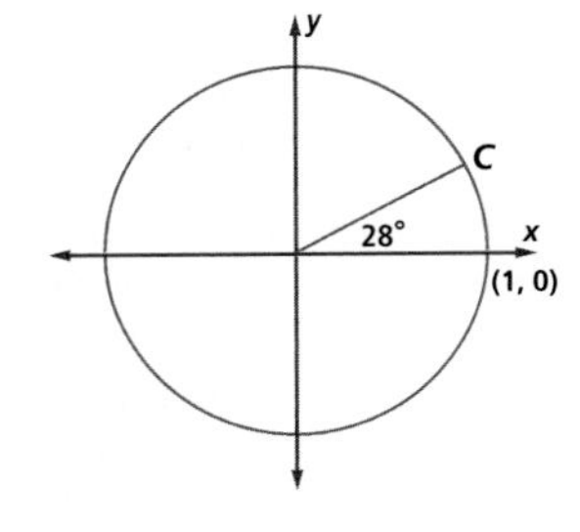

Solution

a. Since $C = R_{28}(1, 0)$, $C = (\cos 28°, \sin 28°) \approx (0.883, 0.469)$.

b. Here $\theta = 28°$.
$\cos^2 28° + \sin^2 28° \approx 0.883^2 + 0.469^2 = 0.99965 \approx 1$

Using Symmetry to Find Sines and Cosines

A circle is reflection-symmetric to any line through its center. For this reason, once you know the coordinates of one point on the circle, you can find the coordinates of many other points.

Accommodating the Learner

Ask students to make a copy of the diagram shown on page 687, that illustrates the quadrants in which cosine and sine are positive and negative. Then, using the definition of tan θ in the direction line for Questions 17–20, ask students to add the sign of the tangent function to each quadrant. Tangent is positive in Quadrants I and III and negative in Quadrants II and IV.

ENGLISH LEARNERS

Vocabulary Development

This lesson provides a natural opportunity to review and apply the meanings of the transformations *rotation* and *reflection*. Students should be able to describe how a rotation by 90°, 180°, or 270° affects a point (x, y) on the unit circle. They should also be able to describe points on the unit circle that are reflection images of each other over either axis.

Second-Quadrant Values

When θ is between 90° and 180°, $R_\theta(1, 0)$ is in Quadrant II. Every point on the unit circle in Quadrant II is the image of a point on the circle in Quadrant I under a reflection over the *y*-axis. For instance, the point (cos 150°, sin 150°) is the reflection image over the *y*-axis of the point (cos 30°, sin 30°), which is in the first quadrant. Notice that the acute angles determined by these two points and the *x*-axis are congruent.

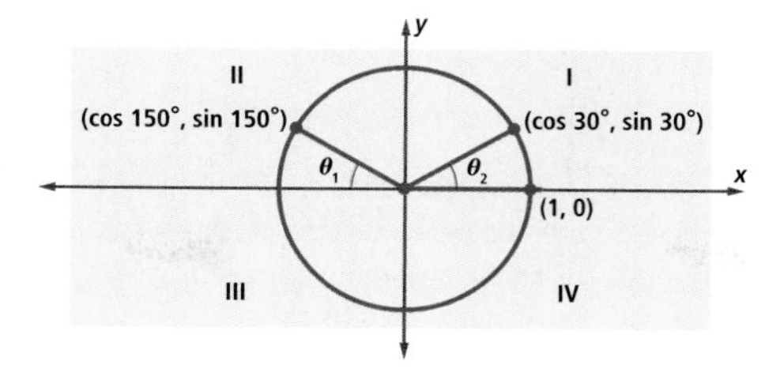

Recall that under r_y, the image of (x, y) is $(-x, y)$. The first coordinates of these points are opposites. Thus, $\cos 150° = -\cos 30° = -\frac{\sqrt{3}}{2}$.

The second coordinates are equal, so $\sin 150° = \sin 30° = \frac{1}{2}$.

Third-Quadrant Values

When a point is in Quadrant I, rotating it 180° gives a point in Quadrant III. Thus, to find sin θ or cos θ when $180° < \theta < 270°$, think of the angle with measure $\theta - 180°$.

Example 2

Show why sin 222° = -sin 42°.

Solution Make a sketch. $P' = (\cos 222°, \sin 222°)$ is the image of $P = (\cos 42°, \sin 42°)$ under R_{180}. Because the image of (x, y) under a rotation of 180° is $(-x, -y)$, P' has coordinates $(-\cos 42°, -\sin 42°)$. Thus, $\sin 222° = -\sin 42°$.

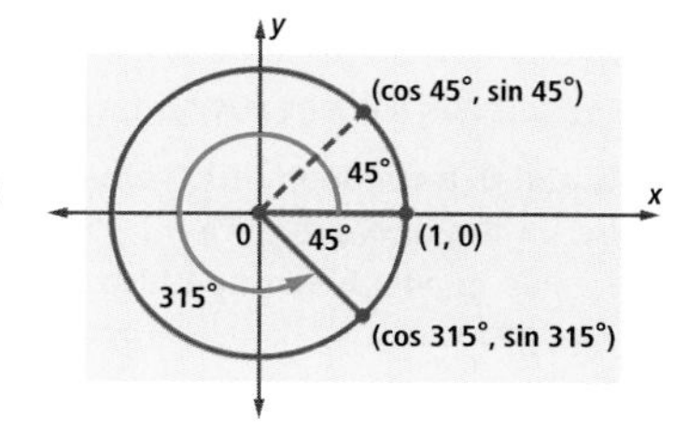

Check Using a calculator, $\sin 222° \approx -0.669$ and $-\sin 42° \approx -0.669$, so it checks.

Fourth-Quadrant Values

Points in Quadrant IV are reflection images over the *x*-axis of points in Quadrant I.

Example 3

Find an exact value for cos 315°.

Solution cos 315° is the first coordinate of a point in Quadrant IV, so the cosine is positive. Reflect (cos 315°, sin 315°) over the x-axis. Since $360° - 315° = 45°$, the image point is (cos 45°, sin 45°). Since the first coordinates of these points are equal, $\cos 315° = \cos 45° = \frac{\sqrt{2}}{2}$.

y
(cos 45°, sin 45°)
45°
x
0
45°
(1, 0)
315°
(cos 315°, sin 315°)

(continued on next page)

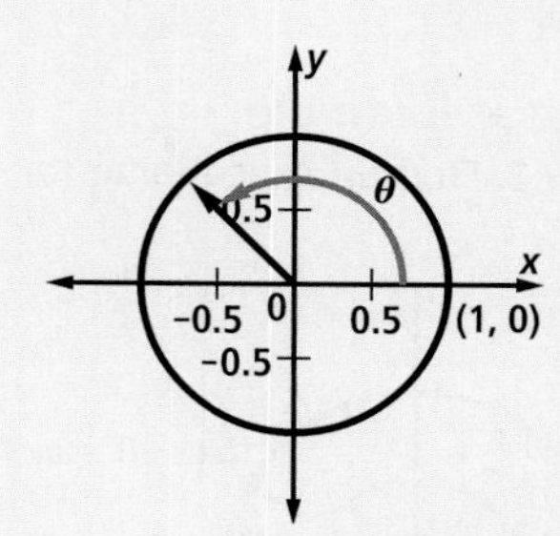

The values are about 25° and 155°. Using a calculator, $\theta \approx 23.6°$; using a symmetry argument, $\theta \approx 180° - 23.6° = 156.4°$ is also possible. This is a good precursor to the solving of $\sin \theta = k$ that occurs in Lesson 10-7.

Additional Examples

Example 1 In the diagram for Example 1, suppose that the angle formed by the segment and the positive *x*-axis is 52°.

a. Approximate the coordinates of point *C* to the nearest thousandth. (0.616, 0.788)

b. Verify that your coordinates in Part a satisfy the Pythagorean Identity. $0.616^2 + 0.788^2 = 0.379456 + 0.620944 = 1.0004 \approx 1$

Example 2 Show why cos 252° = -cos 72°.

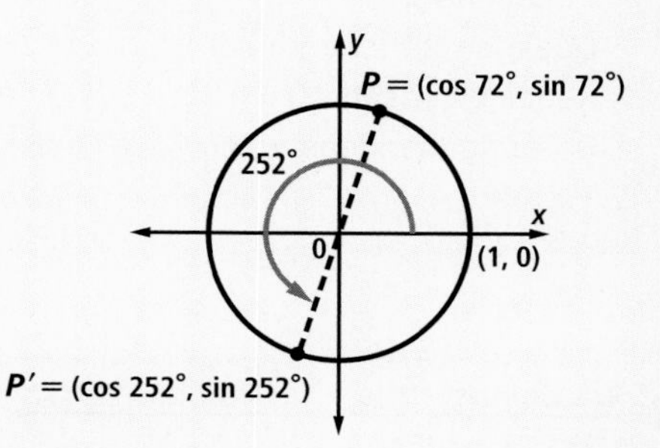

$252 - 180 = 72$, so $P' =$ (cos 252°, sin 252°) is the image of $P =$ (cos 72°, sin 72°) under R_{180}. The image of (x, y) under a rotation of 180° is $(-x, -y)$, so P' has coordinates (-cos 72°, -sin 72°). Thus cos 252° = -cos 72°.

Accommodating the Learner

Ask students to verify the property about reflections over the *y*-axis (described in the section "Second Quadrant Values" on page 689) by answering the following questions.

a. What angle is the reflection, over the *y*-axis, of 10°? of 82°? of $n°$ for $0 < n < 90$? 170°; 98°; $(180 - n)°$

b. How are cos 10° and cos 82° related to the cosines of their reflections over the *y*-axis? How are sin 10° and sin 82° related to the sines of their reflections over the *y*-axis? the cosines are opposites; the sines are equal.

c. Use a calculator and your answers to Part a to check your answer to Part b. $\cos 10° \approx 0.9848$, $\cos 170° \approx -0.9848$; $\cos 82° \approx 0.1392$, $\cos 98° \approx -0.1392$; $\sin 10° \approx 0.1736$, $\sin 170° \approx 0.1736$; $\sin 82° \approx 0.9903$, $\sin 98° \approx 0.9903$; it checks.

Note-Taking Tips

When students record the diagram that shows the signs of cos θ and sin θ, encourage them to add information about cos θ and sin θ for points on the axes. For example, the intersection of the unit circle and the negative *x*-axis is (-1, 0), so the cosine of that angle is -1, and the sine of that angle is 0.

Additional Example

Example 3 Find an exact value for sin 330°.

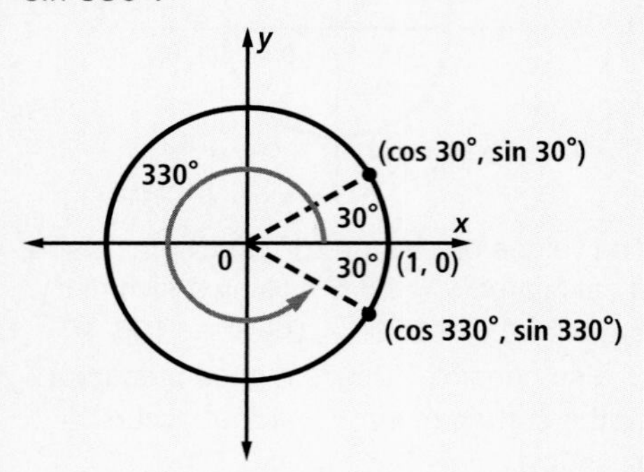

330° is in Quadrant IV, so the sine of 330° is negative. Reflect (cos 330°, sin 330°) over the *x*-axis to get the image point (cos 30°, sin 30°). Because sin 30° $= \frac{1}{2}$, then sin 330° $= -\frac{1}{2}$.

Notes on the Lesson

Additional Answers can be found in the back of the book.

3 Assignment

Recommended Assignment

- Questions 1–28
- Question 29 (extra credit)
- Reading Lesson 10-6
- Covering the Ideas 10-6

10-5A Lesson Master — Questions on SPUR Objectives
See Student Edition pages 724–727 for objectives.

PROPERTIES Objective E

1. a. In which quadrants is the sine positive? I and II
   b. In which quadrants is the cosine positive? I and IV
2. a. If $\cos\theta < 0$ and $\sin\theta < 0$, in which quadrant is θ? III
   b. If $\cos\theta < 0$ and $\sin\theta > 0$, in which quadrant is θ? II
3. a. Use a calculator to find the coordinates of $R_{50}(1, 0)$ and $R_{310}(1, 0)$ to the nearest thousandth. (0.643, 0.766) and (0.643, -0.766)
   b. Explain how your two answers are related. Answers vary. Sample: The two points are reflection images of each other over the *x*-axis.

PROPERTIES Objective F

In 4 and 5, find the *y*-coordinate of *P* in the unit circle at the right using the given method. Round to the nearest tenth.

(Figure: unit circle, $P = (0.8, y)$, θ, 0, x, y)

4. Use the inverse cosine function to find θ; use θ to find the *y*-coordinate. $\theta =$ 36.9°, $y =$ 0.6
5. **Fill in the Blanks** Use the Pythagorean Identity to find *y*. Equation: $y^2 + (0.8)^2 = 1$, $y =$ 0.6
6. If $\sin\theta = 0.951$, find all possible values of θ between 0° and 360° to the nearest degree. 72°, 108°

REPRESENTATIONS Objective I

In 7–10, use the unit circle at the right. a. Mark the point on the unit circle, and b. find the exact value of the trigonometric function.

7. a. $R_{60}(1, 0)$ b. cos 60° = $\frac{1}{2}$
8. a. $R_{135}(1, 0)$ b. sin 135° = $\frac{\sqrt{2}}{2}$
9. a. $R_{210}(1, 0)$ b. cos 210° = $-\frac{\sqrt{3}}{2}$
10. a. $R_{-120}(1, 0)$ b. sin (-120°) = $-\frac{\sqrt{3}}{2}$
11. a. $R_{405}(1, 0)$ b. sin 405° = $\frac{\sqrt{2}}{2}$

528 *Advanced Algebra*

Check A calculator shows cos 315° ≈ 0.707. Since 0.707 is an approximation for $\frac{\sqrt{2}}{2}$, it checks.

Activity

Step 1 Draw a good-sized copy of the figure of Example 1. Reflect *C* over the *y*-axis. Call the image C_2 (since it is in Quadrant II). Using the answer to Example 1, give the coordinates of C_2 to the nearest thousandth. Steps 1, 3, and 5. See the Additional Answers section at the back of the book.

Step 2 Explain why R_{152} maps (1, 0) onto C_2. Estimate cos 152° and sin 152° to the nearest thousandth.

Step 3 Reflect the original point *C* over the *x*-axis. Call the image C_4 (since it is in Quadrant IV). Using the answer to Example 1, give the coordinates of C_4 to the nearest thousandth.

Step 4 What is the magnitude θ of a rotation that maps (1, 0) onto C_4? Use your answer to obtain sin θ and cos θ for this particular θ.

Step 5 Let $C_3 = R_{180}(C)$. Add C_3 to your figure and use it to obtain sin θ and cos θ for another value of θ.

Step 2. The acute angles that *C* and C_2 make with the *x*-axis are congruent, so they both measure 28°. Thus, the magnitude of the rotation that maps (1, 0) onto C_2 is 180° − 28° = 152°. cos 152° ≈ -0.883, sin 152° ≈ 0.469.

Step 4. θ = -28° = 332°; sin 332° ≈ -0.469, cos 332° ≈ 0.883

In Lesson 10-4, you learned that if you know sin *x*, you also know sin $(x + n \cdot 360)$ because you can add or subtract multiples of 360° from the argument without changing the value of the sine. With the techniques in this lesson, if you know sin *x*, you can use the Pythagorean Identity, reflections, and rotations to obtain the sines and cosines of many other arguments between 0° and 360°.

Questions

COVERING THE IDEAS

Fill in the Blank In 1–3, choose one of the following: *is always positive, is always negative,* or *may be positive or negative.*

1. If $R_\theta(1, 0)$ is in Quadrant II, then cos θ __?__. is always negative
2. When $180° < \theta < 360°$, sin θ __?__. is always negative
3. When $0° > \theta > -90°$, cos θ __?__. is always positive
4. When cos θ is negative, in which quadrant(s) can $R_\theta(1, 0)$ be? II or III

In 5 and 6, a trigonometric value is given. Draw the corresponding point on the unit circle. Then, without using a calculator, state whether the value is positive or negative. 5–6. See margin.

5. sin 271°
6. cos 200°

Extension

Ask students to start with the Pythagorean Identity $\cos^2\theta + \sin^2\theta = 1$. Ask them to write two other equations, the first by dividing both sides by $\cos^2\theta$ and the second by dividing both sides by $\sin^2\theta$. Further, ask them to replace $\frac{\sin\theta}{\cos\theta}$ by $\tan\theta$ in their results and to replace $\frac{\cos\theta}{\sin\theta}$ by $\frac{1}{\tan\theta}$. $1 + \frac{\sin^2\theta}{\cos^2\theta} = \frac{1}{\cos^2\theta}$ or $1 + \tan^2\theta = \frac{1}{\cos^2\theta}$; $\frac{\cos^2\theta}{\sin^2\theta} + 1 = \frac{1}{\sin^2\theta}$ or $\frac{1}{\tan^2\theta} + 1 = \frac{1}{\sin^2\theta}$. Finally, ask students to select several values of θ (which yield no zeros in denominators) to check their new trigonometric identities.

7. Suppose $\sin x = \frac{5}{13}$. Use the unit circle to
   a. find the two possible values of $\cos x$. $\frac{12}{13}, -\frac{12}{13}$
   b. explain why $\sin(-x) = -\frac{5}{13}$.

In 8 and 9, the given statement is true. Use the unit circle and transformations to explain why the statement is true. Then, verify the statement with a calculator. 8–9. See margin.

8. $\cos 130° = \cos 230°$
9. $\sin 295° = -\sin 65°$

10. **Fill in the Blanks** Copy and complete with *positive* or *negative*. If $\angle B$ is obtuse, then $\cos B$ is ___?___ and $\sin B$ is ___?___.

APPLYING THE MATHEMATICS

In 11–14, find the exact value without a calculator.

11. $\cos 315°$
12. $\sin 135°$
13. $\sin(-120°)$
14. $\cos 930°$

15. Refer to the unit circle at the right. Find θ to the nearest degree.
16. Given that $0° < x < 180°$ and $\cos x = -0.433$, find x to the nearest hundredth of a degree. 115.66°

In 17–20, use this information. The tangent of θ, $\tan \theta$, is defined for all values of θ as $\frac{\sin \theta}{\cos \theta}$. This agrees with its right-triangle definition when $0° < \theta < 90°$.

17. a. Use your calculator to evaluate $\sin 300°$, $\cos 300°$, and $\tan 300°$.
    b. Verify that $\frac{\sin 300°}{\cos 300°} = \tan 300°$.
18. What is the sign of $\tan \theta$ when $90° < \theta < 180°$? Justify your answer using the definition of $\tan \theta$. See the Additional Answers section.
19. Without a calculator, evaluate $\tan 900°$. 0
20. Without a calculator, give the exact value of $\tan 135°$. -1
21. Use the unit circle to explain why, for all θ, $\sin \theta = \sin(180° - \theta)$. (Hint: What is the image of a point when reflected over the y-axis?) See the Additional Answers section at the back of the book.

REVIEW

22. Without a calculator, evaluate $\sin 90°$ and $\cos 90°$. (Lesson 10-4)
23. **True or False** When measuring an object's distance using the parallax effect, a parallax angle of 110° is possible. (Lesson 10-3)
24. In the picture at the right, a person is standing on a cliff looking down at a boat. Which angle, θ or α, is the angle of depression? (Lesson 10-2) θ

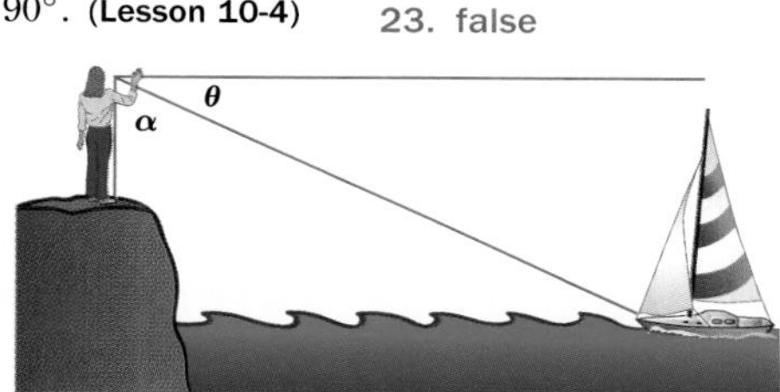

7b. $\sin x$ is the y-coordinate of $R_x(1, 0)$, and $\sin(-x)$ is the y-coordinate of $R_{-x}(1, 0)$. Because $R_{-x}(1, 0)$ is the reflection image of $R_x(1, 0)$ over the x-axis, the y-coordinates of these points are opposites. Therefore, $\sin(-x) = -\frac{5}{13}$.

10. negative; positive

11. $\frac{\sqrt{2}}{2}$
12. $\frac{\sqrt{2}}{2}$
13. $-\frac{\sqrt{3}}{2}$
14. $-\frac{\sqrt{3}}{2}$
15. 233°

17a. $\sin 300° \approx -0.866$, $\cos 300° = 0.5$, $\tan 300° \approx -1.732$

17b. $\frac{-0.866}{0.5} = -1.732$

22. 1; 0

23. false

10-5

Notes on the Questions

Questions 5 and 6 You might have students estimate the values to the nearest tenth and then use their calculators to check their estimates.

Question 8 Make sure students realize that the reason these two cosines have the same value is that one statement is $(180 + 50)°$ and the other statement is $(180 - 50)°$, not because they differ by 100°.

Questions 10 This question involves Quadrant II, which is critical for success in Lesson 10-7.

Questions 17–20 These questions should be discussed in detail so that students realize that the tangent function defined in this way is a generalization of the tangent ratio that they saw in Lesson 10-1.

Question 21 The result of this proof is used in the proof of the Law of Sines in Lesson 10-7 and should be reviewed in detail.

Additional Answers can be found in the back of the book.

Additional Answers

5. negative

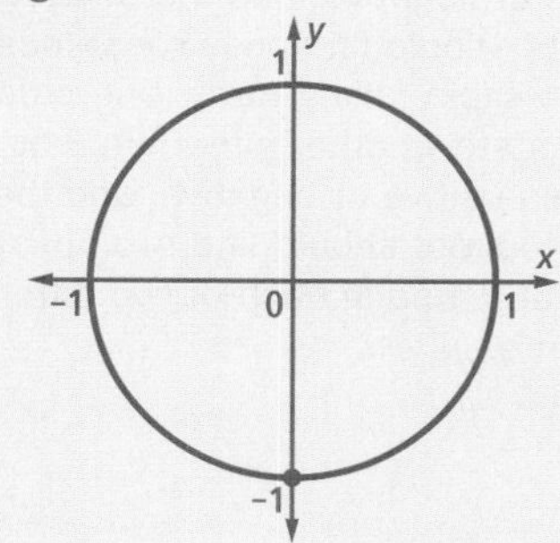

6. negative

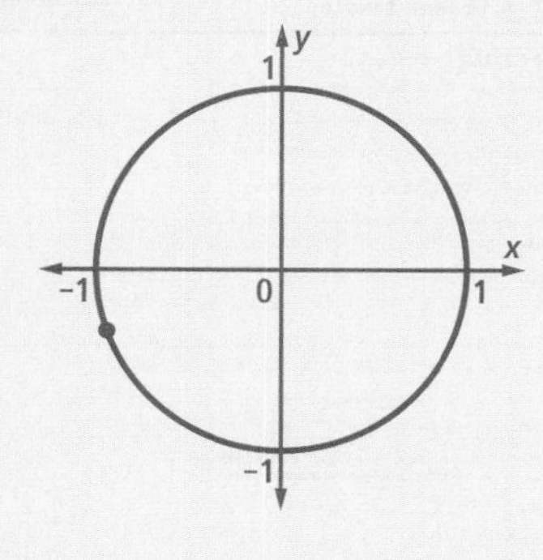

Additional Answers

8.

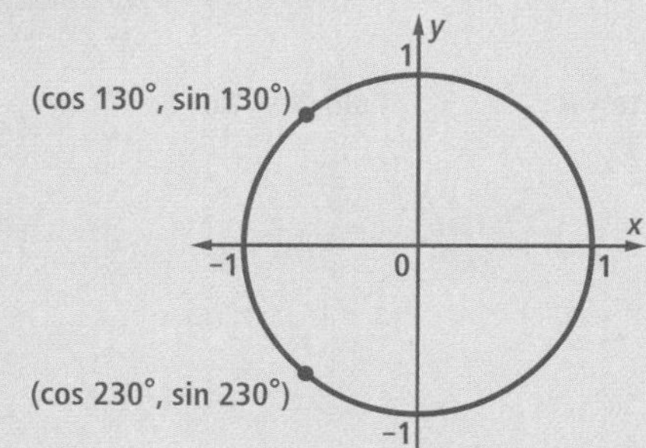

Since (cos 230°, sin 230°) is the image of (cos 130°, sin 130°) reflected over the x-axis, we know $\cos 130° = \cos 230°$. $\cos 130° = \cos 230° \approx -0.643$

9.

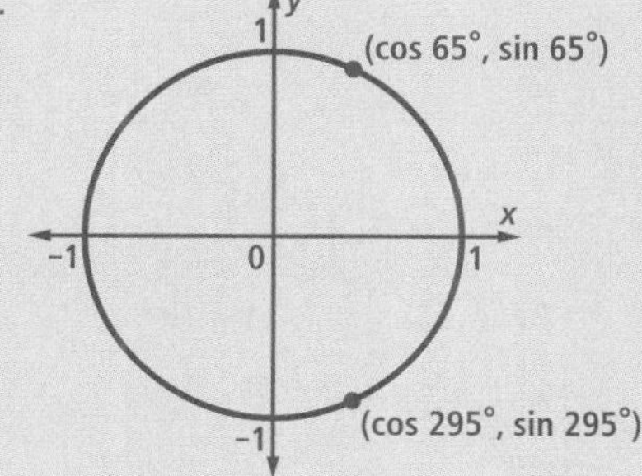

Since (cos 295°, sin 295°) is the image of (cos 65°, sin 65°) reflected over the y-axis, we know $\sin 295° = -\sin 65°$. $\sin 295° = -\sin 65° \approx -0.906$

Notes on the Questions

Question 27 Remind students that a first step in solving the equation in this question could be to divide both sides of the equation by 3.

Question 28 This question reviews notions of triangle congruence that are used in Lessons 10-7 and 10-8. Ask: Which, if any, of these triangles are congruent by SAS? a Are any congruent by AAS? d Are any congruent by SSS? no

Question 29 If students put their calculators in radian mode and then calculate sines and tangents, they will find still another generalization, namely that when x is close to 0, $x \approx \sin x \approx \tan x$. You could use this idea as motivation for the discussion of radians that occurs in Lesson 10-9. (This property is also explored in the Extension in Lesson 10-9 on page 715.)

4 Wrap-Up

Ongoing Assessment

Ask students to work in small groups. Taking turns, one student should state whether each of sin θ and cos θ are positive or negative, and the other students should find possible values for θ. Then, again taking turns, one student should state whether *either* sin θ or cos θ is positive or negative, and the other students should find two possible values of θ, one in each of two different quadrants. Answers vary. Check students' work.

10-5B page 2

10-5B Lesson Master Questions on SPUR Objectives
See Student Edition pages 724–727 for objectives.

PROPERTIES Objective E

1. a. In which quadrants is the sine negative? III and IV
   b. In which quadrants is the cosine negative? II and III
2. a. If $\cos\theta > 0$ and $\sin\theta < 0$, in which quadrant is θ? IV
   b. If $\cos\theta > 0$ and $\sin\theta > 0$, in which quadrant is θ? I
3. a. Use a calculator to find the coordinates of $R_{70}(1, 0)$ and $R_{290}(1, 0)$ to the nearest thousandth. (0.342, 0.940) and (0.342, -0.940)
   b. Explain why your two answers are related. Answers vary. Sample: The two points are reflection images of each other over the x-axis.
4. a. Use a calculator to find the coordinates of $R_{-25}(1, 0)$ and $R_{-335}(1, 0)$ to the nearest thousandth. (0.906, -0.423) and (0.906, 0.423)
   b. Explain how your two answers are related. Answers vary. Sample: The two points are reflection images of each other over the x-axis.

In 5–12, for the indicated point in the unit circle at the right, tell if the value for sin θ or cos θ is *positive, negative,* or *zero.*

5. A, cos θ positive
6. B, sin θ positive
7. C, sin θ positive
8. D, cos θ negative
9. E, cos θ negative
10. F, cos θ negative
11. G, cos θ zero
12. H, sin θ negative

PROPERTIES Objective F

Fill in the Blanks In 13–16, use the unit circle at the right to fill in the blanks.

13. Use the inverse sine function to find α; use α to find the x-coordinate. $\alpha \approx$ 112.9°; $x \approx$ -0.390
14. Use the Pythagorean Identity to find x. Equation: $x^2 + (0.921)^2 = 1$, $x \approx$ -0.390
15. Use the inverse cosine function to find θ; use θ to find the y-coordinate. $\theta \approx$ -104°, $y \approx$ -0.970
16. Use the Pythagorean Identity to find y. Equation: $y^2 + (-0.242)^2 = 1$, $y \approx$ -0.970

Advanced Algebra 529

25. Before 1992, one national building code specified that stairs in homes should be built with an $8\frac{1}{4}$-inch maximum riser height and 9-inch minimum tread. Falls are a leading cause of nonfatal injuries in the United States. In an effort to reduce the number of falls, the building code was changed in 1992 to require a 7-inch maximum riser and an 11-inch minimum tread. **(Lesson 10-2)**

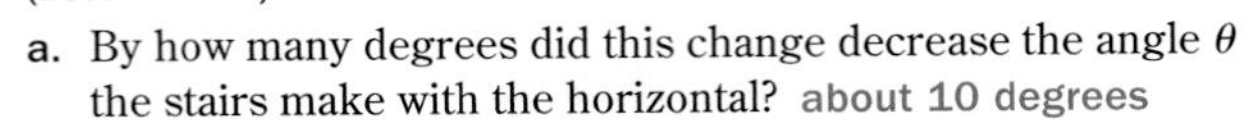

   a. By how many degrees did this change decrease the angle θ the stairs make with the horizontal? about 10 degrees
   b. Why do you think the writers of the code thought the new stairs would be safer? Answers vary. Sample: The stairs will now be less steep.

26. Cierra's grandmother put \$10,000 into a college account at Cierra's birth. The money is invested so she will have \$30,000 on her 18th birthday. **(Lessons 9-10, 9-3, 7-4)**
   a. What rate of interest compounded annually will allow this? 26a. 6.29%
   b. If the interest is compounded continuously, what rate will be required? 6.10%

27. Solve $3(x - 5)^6 = 12{,}288$ for x. **(Lesson 7-6)** $x = 9$ or $x = 1$

28. Determine whether the triangles in each pair are congruent. **(Previous Course)**

a. 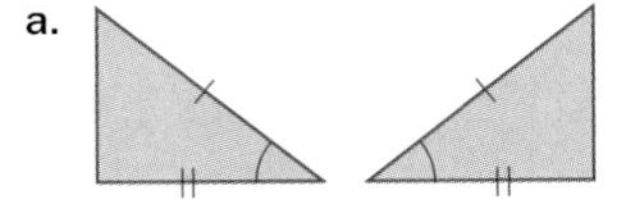

b. 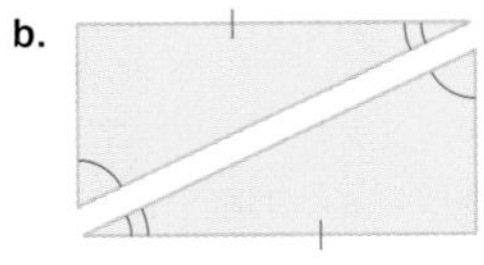

c.

d. 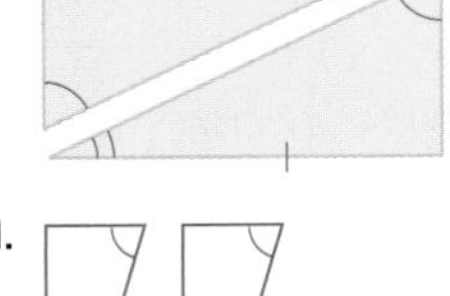

28a. yes
28b. yes
28c. no
28d. yes

QY ANSWERS

a. III; negative
b. III; negative
c. IV; positive
d. IV; negative

EXPLORATION

29. a. Copy and complete the table at the right using a calculator or spreadsheet. Round answers to 6 decimal places. See margin.
   b. You should find that ($\sin\theta - \tan\theta$) gets closer and closer to 0. Explain why this happens.

θ	sin θ	tan θ	sin θ – tan θ
10°	?	?	?
5°	?	?	?
2°	?	?	?
1°	?	?	?
0.5°	?	?	?
0.1°	?	?	?

Additional Answers

29a.

θ	sin θ	tan θ	sin θ – tan θ
10°	0.173648	0.176327	-0.002679
5°	0.087156	0.087489	-0.000333
2°	0.034899	0.034921	-0.000021
1°	0.017452	0.017455	-0.000003
0.5°	0.008727	0.008727	0
0.1°	0.001745	0.001745	0

29b. For very small values of θ, cos θ is very close to 1, so $\tan\theta = \frac{\sin\theta}{\cos\theta} \approx \sin\theta$.

Lesson 10-6 The Cosine and Sine Functions

Vocabulary

periodic function, period

sine wave

sinusoidal

BIG IDEA The graphs of the cosine and sine functions are sine waves with period 2π.

Remember that when (1, 0) is rotated θ degrees around the origin, its image is the point ($\cos\theta$, $\sin\theta$). The correspondence $\theta \to \cos\theta$ is the cosine function, with domain the set of real numbers. The values of this function are the first coordinates of the images of (1, 0) under rotations about the origin.

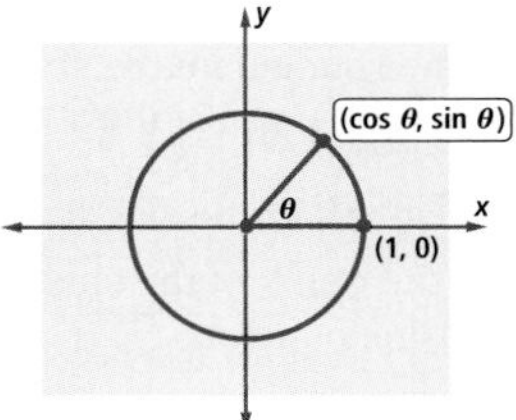

Similarly, the correspondence $\theta \to \sin\theta$ is the sine function. The values of this function are the second coordinates of the images of (1, 0) under R_θ.

Mental Math

Which is longer?

a. the side of a regular octagon or its shortest diagonal the shortest diagonal

b. the leg opposite a 40° angle in a right triangle or the other leg the other leg

c. the diagonal of a square or the diameter of a circle inscribed in it the diagonal

d. the diagonal of a square or the diameter of a circle circumscribed around it They are the same length.

A Graph of the Cosine Function

To imagine the graph of $y = \cos\theta$ as θ increases from 0, think of a point moving around the unit circle counterclockwise from (1, 0). As the point moves halfway around the circle, its first coordinate decreases from 1 to -1. As the point continues to move around the circle, its first coordinate increases from -1 to 1. The Activity provides more detail.

Activity

MATERIALS calculator

Set a calculator to degree mode.

Steps 1–4. See the Additional Answers section at the back of the book.

Step 1 Make a table of values of $\cos\theta$ for values of θ in the interval $0° \le \theta \le 360°$, in increments of 15°. You will need 25 rows, not 10 as shown at the right. Round the cosines to the nearest hundredth. The first few pairs in the table are shown.

Step 2 Graph the points you found in Step 1. Plot θ on the horizontal axis and $\cos\theta$ on the vertical axis. Connect the points with a smooth curve.

Step 3 Describe two patterns you notice in your graph.

Step 4 What is the largest value that $\cos\theta$ can have? What is the smallest value that $\cos\theta$ can have?

θ	$\cos\theta$
0°	1.00
15°	0.97
30°	0.87
45°	0.71
60°	?
75°	?
90°	?
⋮	⋮
345°	?
360°	?

Background

This lesson introduces functions that map θ to $\cos\theta$ or $\sin\theta$. After Activity 1, this should be a relatively easy lesson to read.

Some texts introduce the graphs of the sine and cosine functions only after radians have been discussed. We believe such a presentation can cause difficulty for students because they are graphing an unfamiliar function in an unfamiliar unit. So we introduce these graphs with the familiar unit of degrees. In Lesson 10-9, the graphs are shown with the arguments of the functions in radians.

Lesson 10-6

GOAL

Discuss the graphs of the functions $y = \cos x$ and $y = \sin x$.

SPUR Objectives

J Identify properties of the sine and cosine functions using their graphs.

Materials/Resources

- Lesson Masters 10-6A and 10-6B
- Resource Masters 194–196
- Quiz 2
- Calculator

HOMEWORK

Suggestions for Assignment

- Questions 1–28
- Question 29 (extra credit)
- Reading Lesson 10-7
- Covering the Ideas 10-7

Local Standards

1 Warm-Up

Do Activity 1 to graph the cosine function.

2 Teaching

Notes on the Lesson

The class discussion of this lesson can be particularly illuminating.

Additional Answers can be found in the back of the book.

A graph of the cosine function The key here is that because the image of (1, 0) under a rotation of magnitude θ is ($\cos\theta$, $\sin\theta$), the value of θ determines two functions: the cosine and the sine. You may wish to do both graphs simultaneously in Activity 1.

Properties of the sine and cosine functions Because graphing utilities can so easily display these graphs, there is time to focus on the individual points that constitute the graphs and on their general properties: periodicity, *x*-intercepts, *y*-intercepts, domain, and range.

Note-Taking Tips

When students record their own graphs of the cosine and sine functions, encourage them to label the quadrants on the horizontal axis and to confirm that the sign of the function in each quadrant agrees with what they know about the sign of $\cos\theta$ or $\sin\theta$ for angles in Quadrants I, II, III, and IV.

Recall that as θ takes on values greater than 360°, $\cos\theta$ repeats its values. So the graph of $y = \cos\theta$ repeats every 360°. Below is a graph of this function when $-360° \le \theta \le 720°$.

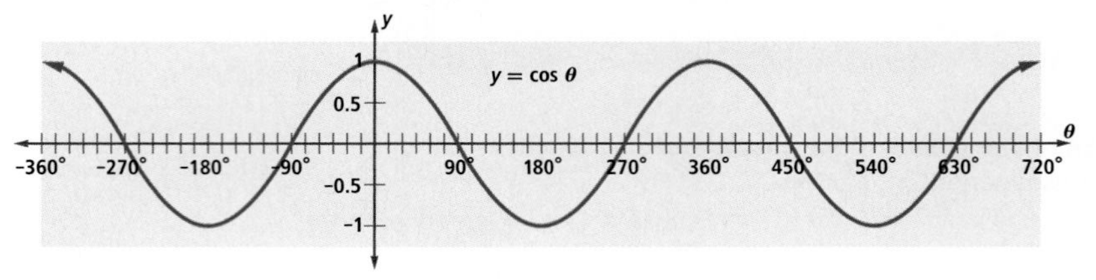

The Graph of the Sine Function

The graph of the sine function is constructed by a similar process, using the second coordinate of the rotation image of (1, 0) as the dependent variable. For instance, $R_{60}(1, 0) = \left(\frac{1}{2}, \frac{\sqrt{3}}{2}\right)$, so $\sin 60° = \frac{\sqrt{3}}{2}$ and the point $\left(60°, \frac{\sqrt{3}}{2}\right)$ is on the graph of the sine function. Below is a graph of $y = \sin\theta$. Notice that the graph of the sine function looks congruent to the graph of the cosine function.

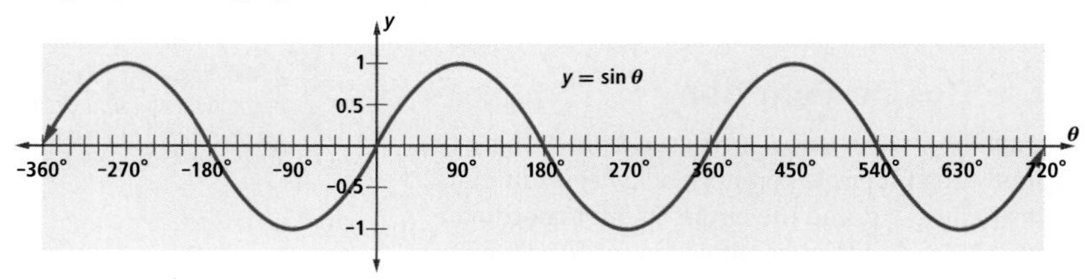

Properties of the Sine and Cosine Functions

A function is a **periodic function** if its graph can be mapped onto itself by a horizontal translation. Algebraically, this means that a function f is periodic if there is a positive number p such that $f(x + p) = f(x)$ for all values of x. The smallest positive number p with this property is called the **period** of the function. Both the sine and cosine functions are periodic because their values repeat every 360°. That is, for all θ, $\sin(\theta + 360°) = \sin\theta$ and $\cos(\theta + 360°) = \cos\theta$. This means that under a horizontal translation of magnitude 360°, the graph of $y = \sin\theta$ coincides with itself. Similarly, under this translation, the graph of $y = \cos\theta$ coincides with itself.

Notice that each of these functions has range $\{y \mid -1 \le y \le 1\}$. Also, each function has infinitely many x-intercepts, but still only one y-intercept. These and other properties of sine and cosine functions are summarized in the table on the next page.

Accommodating the Learner

a. Ask students if $\sin(\theta + 45°) - \sin\theta$ is the same for all values of θ. No; Sample: If $\theta = 0°$, then $\sin 45° - \sin 0° \approx 0.7071$; if $\theta = 1°$, then $\sin 46° - \sin 1° \approx 0.7019$.

b. Ask students to find two values of θ that are 45° apart so that the difference of their sine ratios is *maximized* and justify their answer. Answers vary. Sample: -22.5° and 22.5°. In general, for each *x*-intercept x_i of the domain, the two values $\sin(x_i - 22.5)$ and $\sin(x_i + 22.5)$ are a maximum distance apart for two angles that differ by 45°. An explanation is that these sections of the graph of $y = \sin\theta$ are the sections that are closest to straight lines.

c. Ask students to find two values of θ that are 45° apart so that the difference of the sine ratios is *minimized*. Answers vary. Sample: $\sin(90 - 22.5) = \sin(90 + 22.5)$, so the difference between $\sin 67.5°$ and $\sin 112.5°$ is 0.

	Cosine Function	Sine Function
Domain	set of all real numbers	set of all real numbers
Range	$\{y \mid -1 \le y \le 1\}$	$\{y \mid -1 \le y \le 1\}$
***x*-intercepts**	odd multiples of 90° $\{..., -90°, 90°, 270°, 450°, ...\}$	even multiples of 90° $\{..., -180°, 0°, 180°, 360°, ...\}$
Period	360°	360°
***y*-intercept**	1	0

The graph of the cosine function can be mapped onto the graph of the sine function by a horizontal translation of 90°. So the graphs of $y = \cos \theta$ and $y = \sin \theta$ are congruent. Both graphs are called *sine waves.*

Definition of Sine Wave

A **sine wave** is a graph that can be mapped onto the graph of the sine function s: $\theta \rightarrow \sin \theta$ by any composite of translations, scale changes, or reflections.

Because the graph of the cosine function $c: \theta \rightarrow \cos \theta$ is a translation image of the graph of $s: \theta \rightarrow \sin \theta$, its graph is a sine wave. Situations that lead to sine waves are said to be **sinusoidal**.

Example

The Great Ferris Wheel built in 1893 for the Columbian Exposition in Chicago had a 125-foot radius and a center that stood 140 feet off the ground. A ride on the wheel took about 20 minutes and allowed the rider to reach the top of the wheel twice. Assume that a ride began at the bottom of the wheel and did not stop. Which sine wave below models the rider's height *h* off the ground *t* minutes after the ride began? Explain your choice.

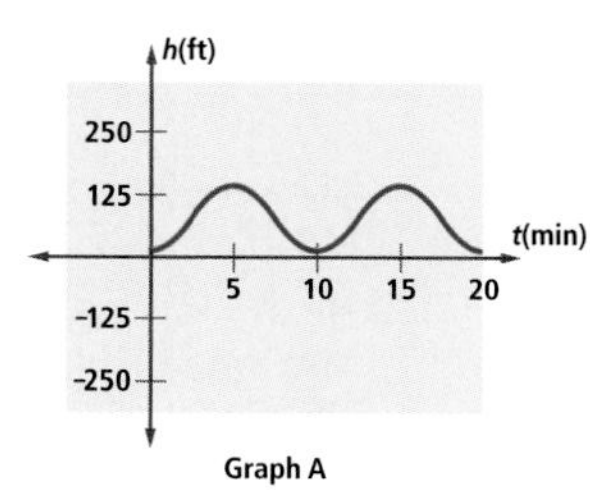

Graph A

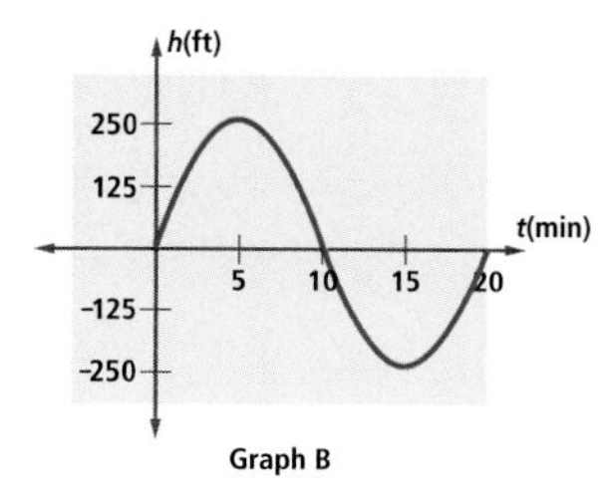

Graph B

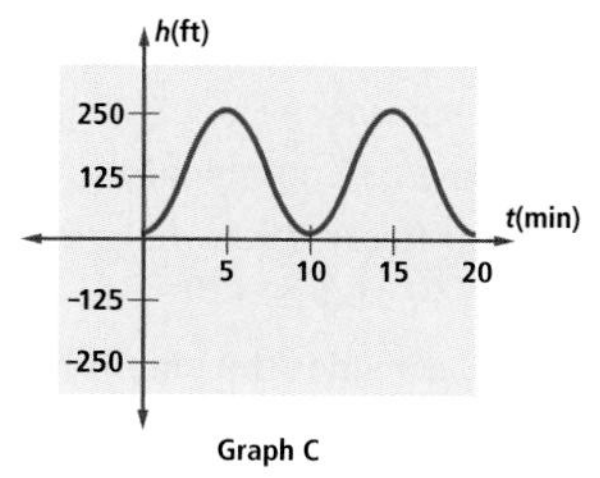

Graph C

(continued on next page)

Accommodating the Learner

Ask students to use the graphs of $y = \cos \theta$ and $y = \sin \theta$ to answer these questions.

a. What are two values of θ such that $270° \le \theta \le 450°$ and $\cos \theta = \cos 15°$? 345°, 375°

b. What are two values of θ such that $180° \le \theta \le 360°$ and $\sin \theta = -\sin 25°$? 205°, 335°

c. What are four values of θ such that $90° \le \theta \le 450°$ and $\cos \theta = |\cos 50°|$? 130°, 230°, 310°, 410°

ENGLISH LEARNERS

Vocabulary Development

In the section "Properties of the Sine and Cosine Functions," one row of the table uses the phrases "odd multiples" and "even multiples." Be sure students understand that the odd multiples of 90° are ..., -3(90°), -1(90°), 1(90°), 3(90°), ..., where 90° is multiplied by a positive or negative odd integer, while the even multiples of 90° are ..., -4(90°), -2(90°), 0(90°), 2(90°), ..., where 90° is multiplied by a negative even integer, zero, or a positive even integer.

10-6

Notes on the Lesson

Example The height of a person riding a Ferris wheel is the *y*-coordinate of a point moving around the unit circle, so we should expect a sine wave. However, a person riding a Ferris wheel does not typically get on at the middle height of the wheel, but gets on at its lowest position. That is why the sine wave looks more like graph C than a "typical" graph of the sine function. See Question 12.

Additional Example

Example Suppose a bird lands on a Ferris wheel basket at the basket's highest position and rides for one complete revolution. If the Ferris wheel has a diameter of 180 feet, the center of rotation is 110 feet above the ground, and the wheel takes 10 minutes to make one revolution, which sine wave below models the height of the bird *t* minutes after it lands on the Ferris wheel?

Graph A:

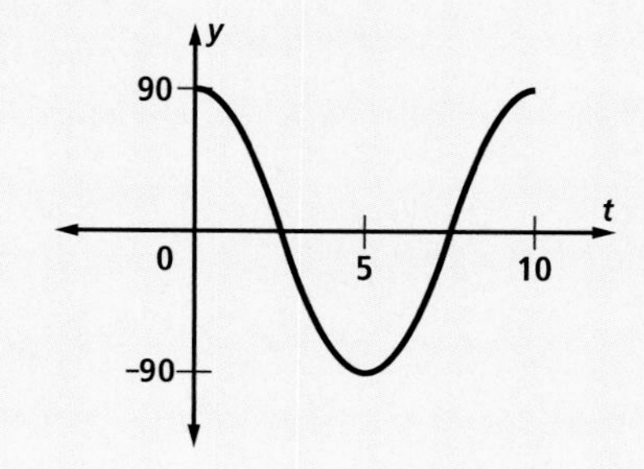

Graph B:

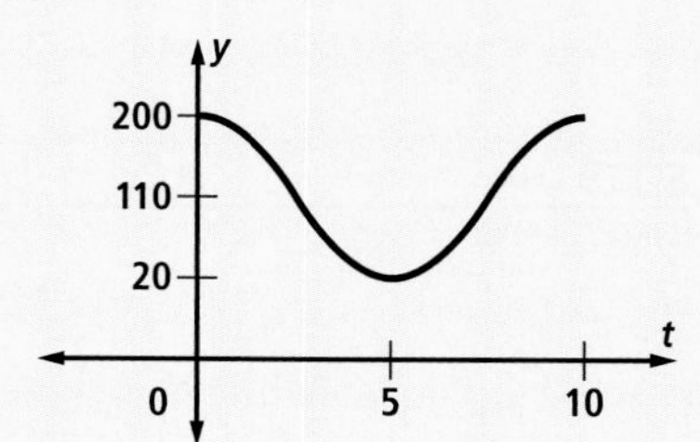

Graph C:

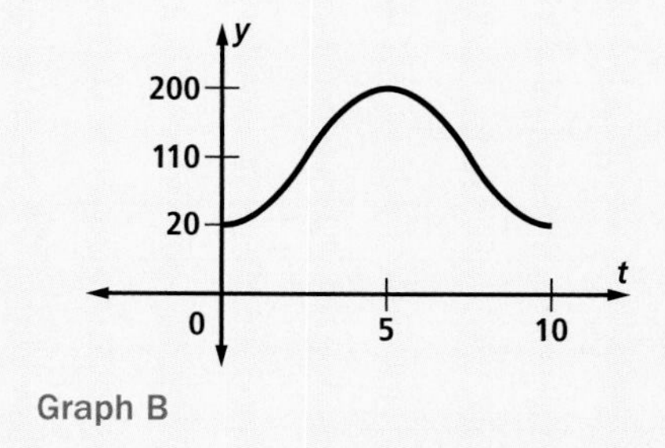

Graph B

3 Assignment

Recommended Assignment

- Questions 1–28
- Question 29 (extra credit)
- Reading Lesson 10-7
- Covering the Ideas 10-7

Solution Find the minimum and maximum height of a ride on the Ferris wheel.

The minimum height is the difference between the height of the center of the wheel and its radius, or 140 ft − 125 ft = 15 ft. The maximum height is then 250 ft + 15 ft = 265 ft, the diameter of the wheel plus the wheel's height off the ground.

Find when the minimum and maximum height of a ride occurred.

The maximum height occurred twice in 20 minutes. A complete revolution took 10 minutes, so, the rider is 15 feet high at $t = 0$, 10, and 20 minutes. Without stops, the rider reached the top at $t = 5$ and 15 minutes. So, graph C is the correct graph.

140 ft

125 ft

Sine waves occur frequently in nature: in ocean waves, sound waves, and light waves. Also, the graph of average daily temperatures for a specific location over the year often approximates a sine wave. The voltages associated with alternating current (AC), the type used in electrical transmission lines, have sinusoidal graphs. Sine waves can be converted to electrical signals and then viewed on an oscilloscope.

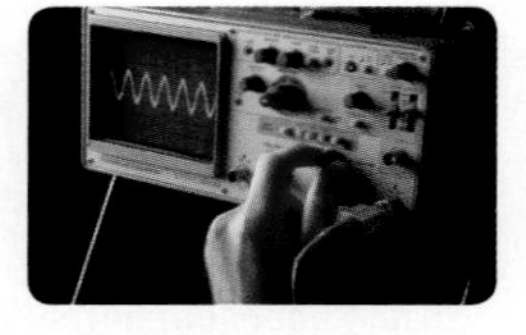

An oscilloscope can be used to test electronic equipment.

Questions

COVERING THE IDEAS

1. What function maps θ onto the first coordinate of the image of (1, 0) under R_θ? the cosine function
2. What function maps θ onto the second coordinate of the image of (1, 0) under R_θ? the sine function

In 3–5, consider the cosine function.

3. a. **Fill in the Blanks** As θ increases from 0° to 90°, cos θ decreases from __?__ to __?__. 1; 0
   b. **Fill in the Blanks** As θ increases from 90° to 180°, cos θ decreases from __?__ to __?__. 0; -1
   c. As θ increases from 180° to 270°, does the value of cos θ increase or decrease? increase
4. Name two points on the graph of the function when $\theta > 360°$.
5. How many solutions are there to the equation cos $\theta = 0.5$ if $-720° \le \theta \le 720°$? 8

In 6–8, consider the sine function.

6. Explain why its period is 360°.
7. Name all θ-intercepts between -360° and 360°.
8. How many solutions are there to the equation sin $\theta = 2$ if $-720° \le \theta \le 720°$? 0

4. Answers vary. Sample: (450°, 0) and (540°, -1)
6. sin x = sin($x + p$) for all x when p = 360°. This is the smallest value of p for which this is true.
7. -180°, 0°, 180°

Extension

Ask students to extend Activity 1 by replacing cos θ with tan θ. Ask students to use their values to graph $y = \tan \theta$ for $0 \le \theta \le 360$.

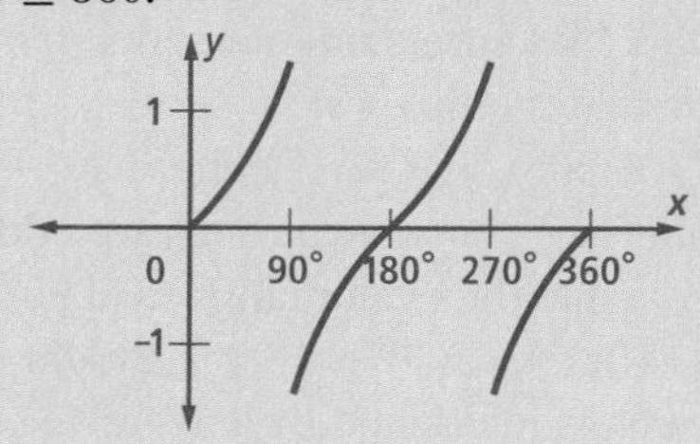

Ask: Is the tangent function periodic? If so, what is the period? 180° What are the domain and range? domain: all x except odd multiples of 90; range: all real numbers What are the x-intercepts? n(180°), where n is any integer

(*Note:* This activity can be a good introduction to Project 3, which asks students to explore the tangent function using radians.)

10-6A Lesson Master

Questions on SPUR Objectives
See Student Edition pages 724–727 for objectives.

SKILLS Objective J

1. On the same axes below, graph $f(\theta) = \sin \theta$ and $g(\theta) = \cos \theta$ over the domain $-360 \le \theta \le 360$. cosine in magenta; sine in light magenta

Use your graph from Question 1 to help answer Questions 2-5.

2. Give the domain and range of the cosine function. domain: set of all real numbers; range: $-1 \le \cos \theta \le 1$
3. Find all θ-intercepts of the sine function shown on the graph. -360°, -180°, 0°, 180°, 360°
4. Find a θ-intercept of the sine function that is *not* shown on the graph. Answers vary. Sample: 540°.
5. **Fill in the Blanks** As θ increases from 180° to 270°, sin θ decreases from 0 to -1.
6. The table below shows the time of sunset on the 1st day of each month in a given year for Seattle, WA. Answers vary. Samples are given.

Month	Jan	Feb	Mar	Apr	May	June	July	Aug	Sep	Oct	Nov	Dec
Sunset	4:28	5:10	5:55	7:40	8:22	9:00	9:11	8:43	7:49	6:48	5:51	4:20

   a. Explain why these data can be modeled by a periodic function.
   The time of sunset in a given month repeats year after year.
   b. Estimate the domain and range of a sinusoidal function that models these data.
   domain: set of integers (months), range: hours and minutes from 4:20 to 9:11

7. The height of a bouncing ball over time is graphed at the right. Explain why this graph is *not* periodic.
   Answers vary. Sample: The peak height of the ball's bounce does not repeat; it decreases with each bounce.

Advanced Algebra 531

In 9–11, true or false.

9. The graph of the cosine function is called a cosine wave. false
10. The graph of the sine function is the image of the graph of the cosine function under a horizontal translation of 180°. false
11. The ranges of the sine and cosine function are identical. true
12. Refer to the Example.
    a. Describe the Ferris Wheel ride shown by graph A.
    b. Why does graph B not describe a Ferris Wheel ride?

APPLYING THE MATHEMATICS

13. Use the graphs of the sine and cosine functions.
    a. Find two values of θ, one positive and one negative, such that $\cos \theta > \sin \theta$. Answers vary. Sample: –90°, 270°
    b. Name two values of θ for which $\cos \theta = \sin \theta$. Answers vary. Sample: 45°, 225°
14. Consider these situations leading to periodic functions. What is the period?
    a. days of the week 7 days
    b. the ones digit in the successive integers in base 10 10

In 15–18, part of a function is graphed. Does the function appear to be periodic? If so, what is the period? If not, why not?

15.

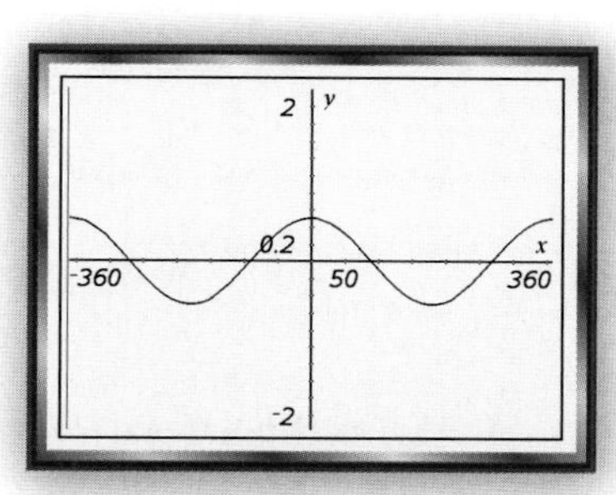

16.
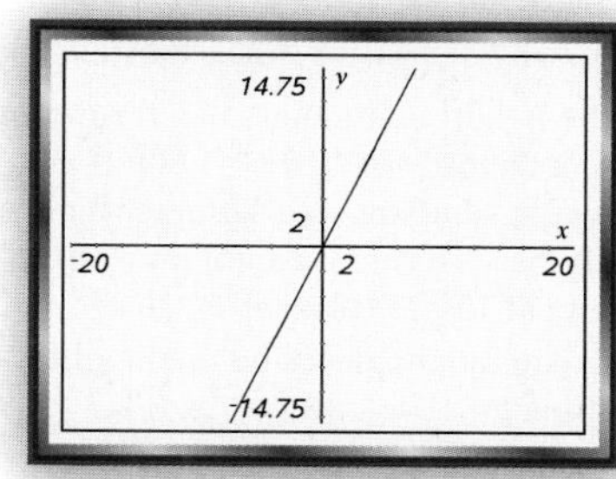

17.
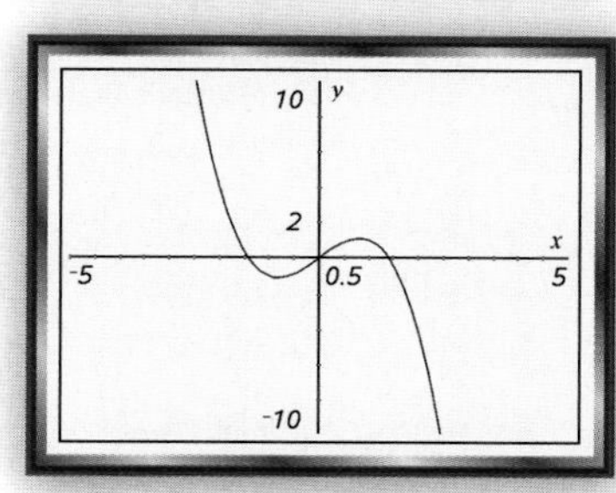

18.
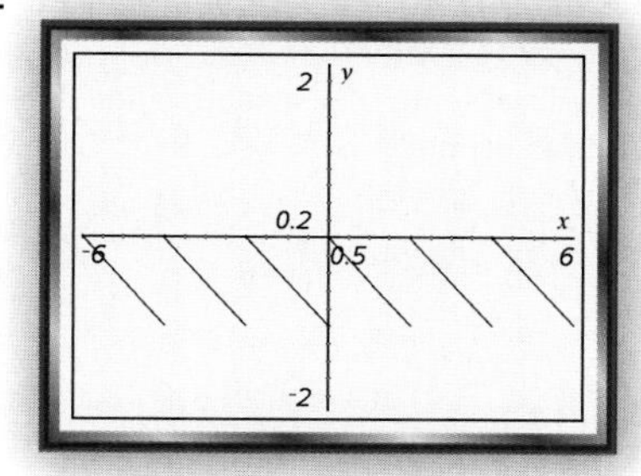

12a. Answers vary. Sample: This graph shows a Ferris wheel with a 62.5-ft radius and a center that stands 77.5 ft off the ground. The wheel rotates such that a rider reaches the top twice in 20 min.

12b. This graph takes negative values, which would describe a Ferris wheel that goes underground.

15. yes; 360°

16. No; the function is linear.

17. No; this is a polynomial function.

18. yes; 2

Notes on the Questions

Question 16 The graph is translation-symmetric but not periodic because the translation is not horizontal.

Question 17 The graph is rotation-symmetric.

Notes on the Questions

Question 19 Average temperatures in a given location are periodic with a period of a year. Less obvious is that they can usually be modeled closely by a sine wave. This is related to the fact that the lengths of days can be modeled by a sine wave.

Additional Answers

20a.

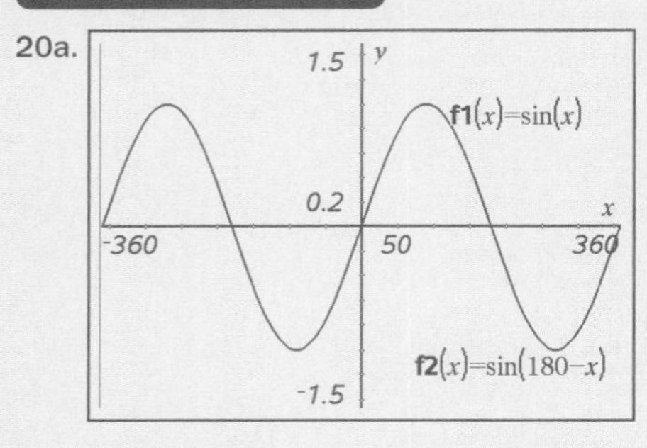

21a. Yes; period: 360°

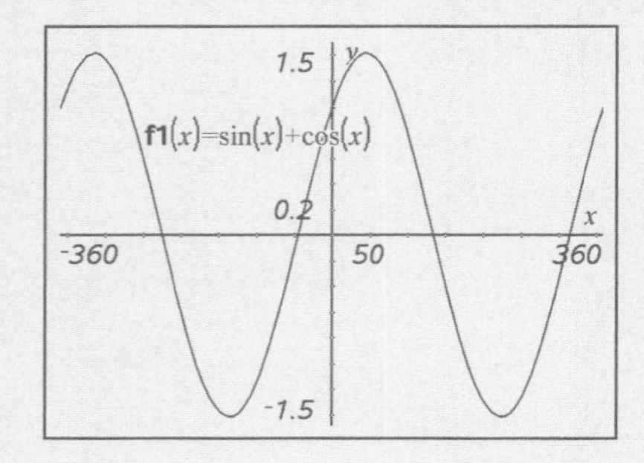

25b.

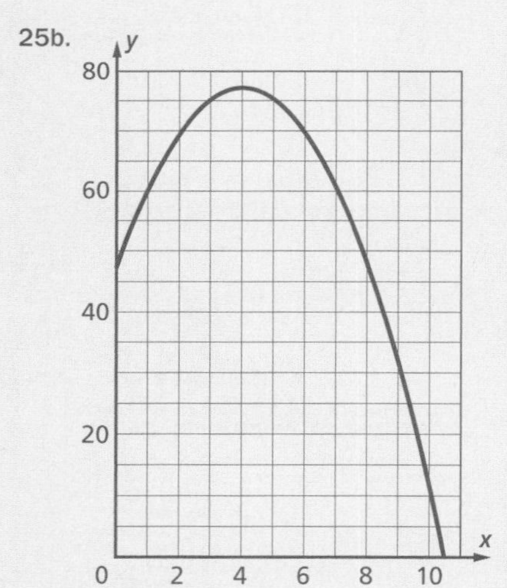

19. Below is a table of average monthly high temperatures T (all in degrees Fahrenheit) for Phoenix, Arizona.

Jan.	Feb.	Mar.	Apr.	May	June	July	Aug.	Sept.	Oct.	Nov.	Dec.
66	70	75	84	93	103	105	103	99	88	75	66

   a. Explain why these data could be modeled by a sine wave.
   b. Estimate the domain and range of a sinusoidal function that models these data. domain: all real numbers; range: $66 \le T \le 105$

20. a. Graph $y = \sin x$ and $y = \sin(180° - x)$. See margin.
   b. What identity is suggested by the graphs?

21. a. Graph the function with equation $y = \sin x + \cos x$. Does this appear to be a periodic function? If so, what is its period?
   b. What are the domain and range of this function? See margin.

19a. Answers vary. Sample: Temperatures are annually affected by the seasons; therefore, the data are periodic with period 1 yr.

20b. $\sin x = \sin(180° - x)$

21b. domain: all real numbers; range: $-\sqrt{2} \le y \le \sqrt{2}$

REVIEW

22. **Multiple Choice** Which of the following is equal to sin (-45°)? (Lesson 10-5) D
   A sin 45°
   B sin 135°
   C sin 405°
   D sin 675°

In 23 and 24, give the exact value without using a calculator. (Lesson 10-4)

23. cos 270° 0

24. tan 180° 0

25. On Mars, the height h in meters of a thrown object at time t seconds is given by $h = -1.86t^2 + v_0t + h_0$. A space traveler standing on a 47-meter high Martian cliff tosses a rock straight up with an initial velocity of $15\frac{\text{m}}{\text{sec}}$. (Lessons 6-7, 6-4)
   a. Write an equation to describe the height of the rock at time t. $h = -1.86t^2 + 15t + 47$
   b. Graph your equation in Part a. See margin.
   c. What is the maximum height of the rock to the nearest meter? 77 m
   d. To the nearest tenth of a second, when does the rock hit the Martian ground? 10.5 sec

Cape Verde juts out from the walls of Victoria Crater on Mars.

In 26 and 27, $A = \begin{bmatrix} -72 & -27 \\ 8 & 3 \end{bmatrix}$.

26. a. Find det A. 0
    b. Does A^{-1} exist? If so, find it. If not, explain why it does not exist. **(Lesson 5-5)**

26b. The inverse does not exist because det $A = 0$.

27. a. Find an equation for the line through the two points represented by matrix A. $y = -\frac{1}{9}x$
    b. What kind of variation is described by the answer to Part a? **(Lessons 4-1, 3-4, 2-1)** direct

28. Approximate QW to the nearest hundredth. **(Lesson 4-4)** 64.03

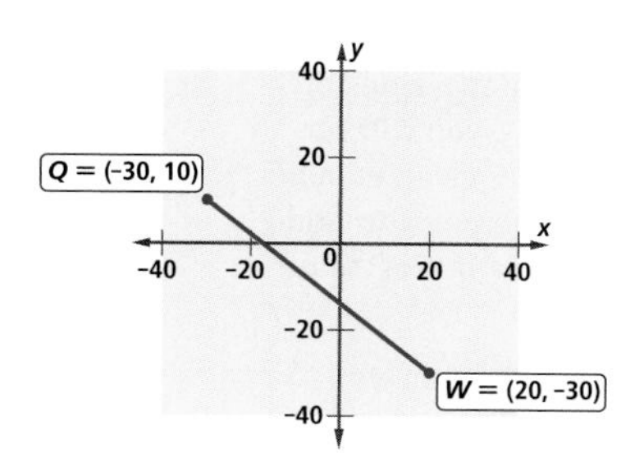

EXPLORATION

29. Oscilloscopes can be used to display sound waves. Search the Internet to find some sites that simulate oscilloscope output for different sounds. Do additional research about sound waves and report on the following.
    a. the oscilloscope patterns for at least two sound waves (for example, whistling a tune, middle C on the piano)
    b. the meaning of frequency and amplitude of a sound wave
    c. the effect on sound tone as a result of changes in amplitude and frequency a–c. See margin.

Notes on the Questions

Question 28 The Pythagorean Distance Formula is used in Lesson 10-8.

Question 29 Ask a physics teacher to bring an oscilloscope to your class to show how amplitude and frequency change as the intensity (volume) and pitch of a sound changes.

4 Wrap-Up

Ongoing Assessment

Give students an angle A whose measure is between 90° and 360°. Then ask them to describe how to use the graphs of $y = \cos\theta$ and $y = \sin\theta$ to relate $\cos A$ and $\sin A$ to the cosine and sine ratios of an angle between 0° and 90°.

Administer Quiz 2 (or a quiz of your own) after students complete this lesson.

Project Update

Project 1, *Area Under a Sine Curve*, on page 718 and Project 4, *The Pendulum Swings*, on page 719 relate to the content of this lesson.

Additional Answers

29a.

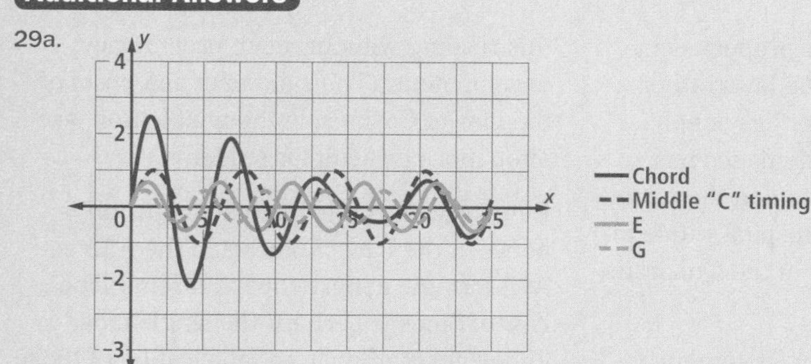

29b. Amplitude is the magnitude (loudness) of a sound wave and frequency is the number of oscillations per second (and is related to pitch).

29c. Increasing the amplitude increases the loudness and increasing the frequency increases the pitch of a sound wave.

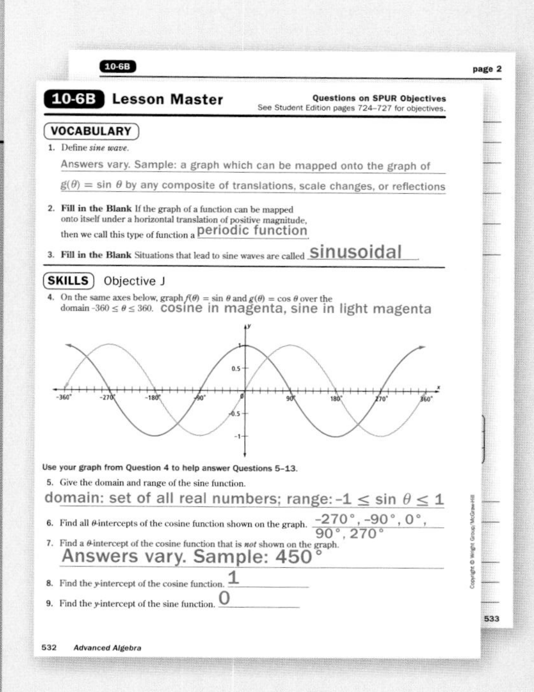

10-6B page 2

10-6B Lesson Master

Questions on SPUR Objectives
See Student Edition pages 724–727 for objectives.

VOCABULARY

1. Define *sine wave*.
   Answers vary. Sample: a graph which can be mapped onto the graph of $g(\theta) = \sin\theta$ by any composite of translations, scale changes, or reflections

2. **Fill in the Blank** If the graph of a function can be mapped onto itself under a horizontal translation of positive magnitude, then we call this type of function a periodic function.

3. **Fill in the Blank** Situations that lead to sine waves are called sinusoidal.

SKILLS Objective J

4. On the same axes below, graph $f(\theta) = \sin\theta$ and $g(\theta) = \cos\theta$ over the domain $-360 \le \theta \le 360$. cosine in magenta, sine in light magenta

Use your graph from Question 4 to help answer Questions 5–13.

5. Give the domain and range of the sine function.
   domain: set of all real numbers; range: $-1 \le \sin\theta \le 1$

6. Find all θ-intercepts of the cosine function shown on the graph. -270°, -90°, 0°, 90°, 270°

7. Find a θ-intercept of the cosine function that is *not* shown on the graph.
   Answers vary. Sample: 450°

8. Find the y-intercept of the cosine function. 1

9. Find the y-intercept of the sine function. 0

Copyright © Wright Group/McGraw-Hill

532 Advanced Algebra 533

Lesson

10-7

GOAL

Deduce the Law of Sines; use the Law of Sines to find lengths of sides in a triangle when an ASA or AAS congruence condition is given.

SPUR Objectives

B Determine the measure of an angle given its sine, cosine, or tangent.

C Find missing side lengths and angle measures of a triangle using the Law of Sines.

F Identify and use theorems relating sines and cosines.

H Solve real-world problems using the Law of Sines.

Materials/Resources

- Lesson Masters 10-7A and 10-7B
- Resource Masters 197 and 198
- Ruler, protractor

HOMEWORK

Suggestions for Assignment

- Questions 1–18
- Questions 19 and 20 (extra credit)
- Reading Lesson 10-8
- Covering the Ideas 10-8

Local Standards

1 Warm-Up

Do the Activity as a Warm-Up.

Lesson 10-7 The Law of Sines

Vocabulary

solving a triangle

▶ **BIG IDEA** Given AAS or ASA in a triangle, the Law of Sines enables you to find the lengths of the remaining sides.

One of the most important applications of trigonometry is to find unknown or inaccessible lengths or distances. In previous lessons, you learned to use trigonometric ratios to find unknown sides or angles of *right* triangles. In this lesson and the next, you will see how to find unknown sides or angles in *any* triangle, given enough information to determine the triangle. Using trigonometry to find all the missing measures of sides and angles of a triangle is called **solving the triangle**.

Mental Math

How many lines of symmetry does the graph of each equation have?

a. $y = -x^2$ 1

b. $y = -x^3$ 0

c. $y = -x$ infinitely many (any line parallel to $y = x$)

Solutions to cos $\theta = k$ When $0° < \theta < 180°$

Although the sine and cosine functions are periodic over the domain of real numbers, it is important to remember that if θ is an angle in a triangle, then $0° < \theta < 180°$.

When $0° < \theta < 180°$, the equation $\cos \theta = k$ has a unique solution. To see why, consider the graph of $y = \cos \theta$ on this interval. For any value of k between -1 and 1, the graph of $y = k$ intersects $y = \cos \theta$ at a single point. The θ-coordinate of this point is the solution to $\cos \theta = k$.

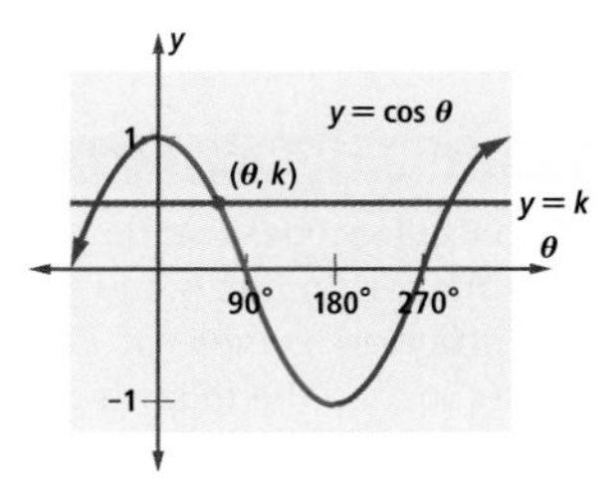

STOP QY1

▶ **QY1**

Solve $\cos \theta = -\frac{1}{2}$ when $0° < \theta < 180°$ using the inverse cosine function.

Solutions to sin $\theta = k$ When $0° < \theta < 180°$

The situation is different for the equation $\sin \theta = k$. On the interval $0° < \theta < 180°$, for any value of k between 0 and 1, the graph of $y = k$ intersects $y = \sin \theta$ in two points. In the graph at the right, we call these points (θ_1, k) and (θ_2, k). The numbers θ_1 and θ_2 are the solutions to $\sin \theta = k$.

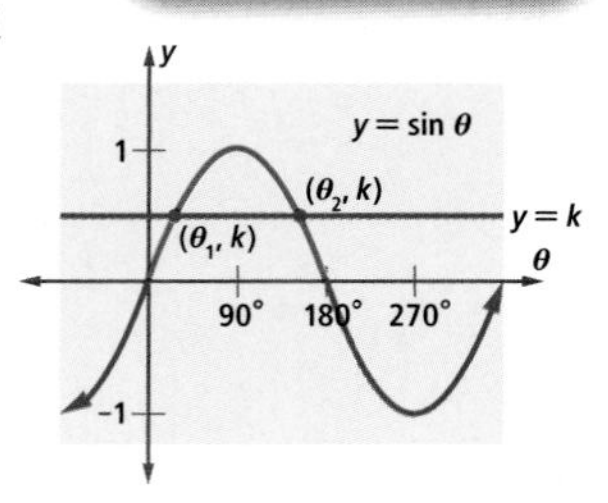

Background

Why are the trigonometric properties in Lessons 10-6 and 10-7 called laws rather than theorems? The answer lies simply in historical practice. Mathematics has many words for *theorem*, among them *law*, *proposition*, *rule* (as in L'Hospital's Rule in calculus), and *formula* (as in the Quadratic Formula).

For most students, both the statement of the Law of Sines and its proof are fairly easy. Consequently, you can assign this reading without much preliminary development. (The statement and proof of the Law of Cosines, in the next lesson, are often more difficult for students.)

Emphasize to students the connection between the Law of Sines and the AAS and ASA triangle congruence theorems. The Law of Sines is perhaps the single most important mathematical application of those congruence theorems.

The points (θ_1, k) and (θ_2, k) are reflection images of each other over the vertical line with equation $\theta = 90°$. This is because when $0 < k < 1$, the two solutions to $\sin \theta = k$ between 0° and 180° are supplementary angles.

Supplements Theorem

For all θ in degrees, $\sin \theta = \sin(180° - \theta)$.

The Supplements Theorem allows you to solve equations of the form $\sin \theta = k$ without graphing.

Example 1

Find all solutions to $\sin \theta = 0.842$ in the interval $0° < \theta < 180°$.

Solution Use the inverse sine function to find a solution between 0° and 90°. $\theta_1 = \sin^{-1} 0.842 \approx 57.4°$

The second solution is the supplement of the first.

$\theta_2 = 180° - \theta_1 \approx 180° - 57.4° = 122.6°$

So, when $\sin \theta = 0.842$, $\theta \approx 57.4°$ or $122.6°$.

Check $\sin 57.4° \approx 0.842$ and $\sin 122.6° \approx 0.842$. They check.

QY2

▶ QY2

a. Solve $\sin \theta = -\frac{1}{2}$ when $0° < \theta < 180°$ using the inverse sine function or the graph of $y = \sin x$.

b. Solve $\sin \theta = \frac{1}{2}$ when $0° < \theta < 180°$ using the inverse sine function or the graph of $y = \sin x$.

The Law of Sines

Activity

MATERIALS ruler, protractor

Work with a partner. Steps 1–3. See margin.

Step 1 Each partner should draw a different triangle *ABC* on a sheet of notebook paper. Measure the side lengths to the nearest tenth of a centimeter and the angles as accurately as you can.

Step 2 Let *a*, *b*, and *c* be the lengths of the sides opposite angles *A*, *B*, and *C*, respectively. Use a calculator to compute $\frac{\sin A}{a}$, $\frac{\sin B}{b}$, and $\frac{\sin C}{c}$ to the nearest hundredth.

Step 3 Compare your results to those of your partner. What do you notice?

The results of the Activity are instances of a theorem that enables a triangle to be solved when the measures of two angles and one side are known.

Accommodating the Learner

In an isosceles triangle, one angle is 50° and one side is 4 units. Sketch the *four* possible triangles that can be formed. Then use the Law of Sines for each triangle to find the unknown length in the triangle.

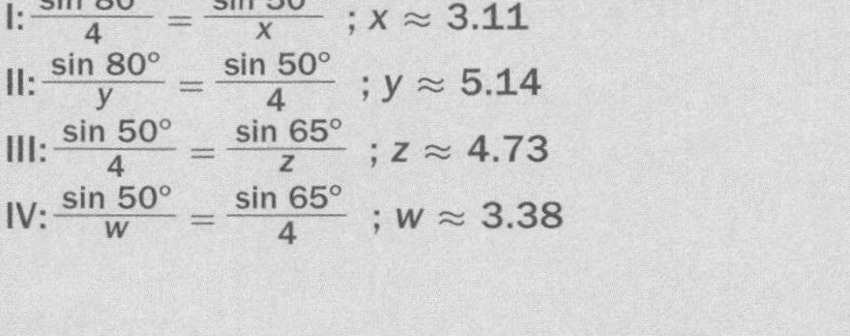

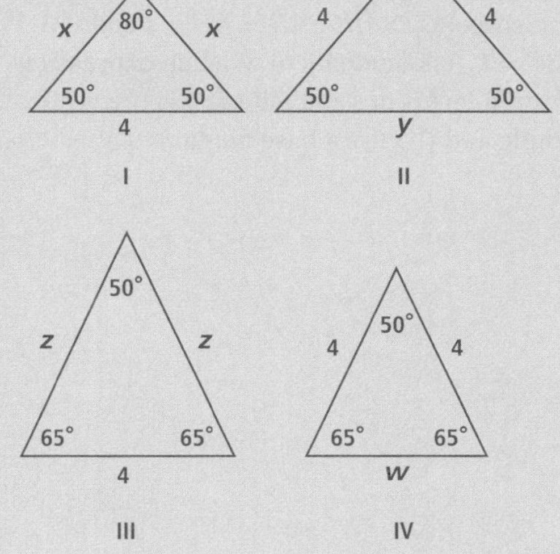

2 Teaching

Notes on the Lesson

The Law of Sines is amazing and is one of the most beautiful theorems in all of mathematics. Who would think that if we form three ratios, each comparing a side of a triangle and the sine of the opposite angle, that the three ratios are equal? Many teachers use this result as an opportunity to express their own enthusiasm for mathematics.

Additional Example

Example 1 Find all solutions to $\sin \theta = 0.528$ in the interval $0° < \theta < 180°$. 31.9°, 148.1°

Note-Taking Tips

During the Activity, encourage students to write in their notes that capital letters are commonly used to represent angles of a triangle and that the side opposite each angle is represented by the lowercase version of the same letter.

Additional Answers

Activity

Step 1.

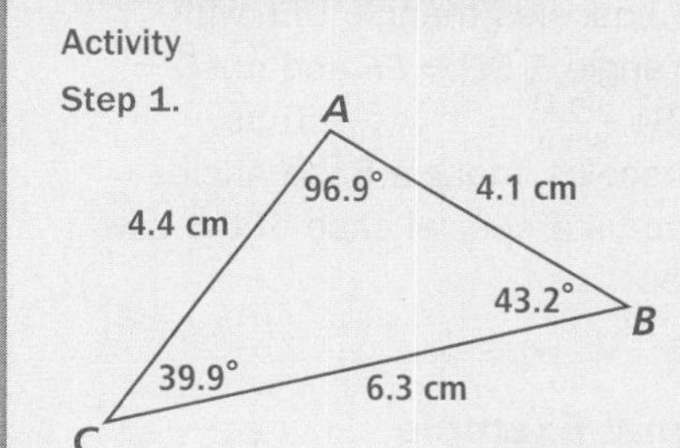

Step 2. $\frac{\sin A}{a} = \frac{\sin B}{b} = \frac{\sin C}{c} \approx 0.158$

Step 3. The ratios of the sines of $\triangle ABC$'s angles to the lengths of its sides opposite them are equal, but these ratios are not equal to the corresponding ratios of my partner's triangle.

Notes on the Lesson

In the proof of the Law of Sines, some students have trouble seeing why the area of $\triangle ABC$ can be represented by the expression $\frac{1}{2}bc \sin A$ and also by $\frac{1}{2}ac \sin B$. For such students, it may help to draw the altitudes to $\overline{AB}$ and $\overline{BC}$, as shown below.

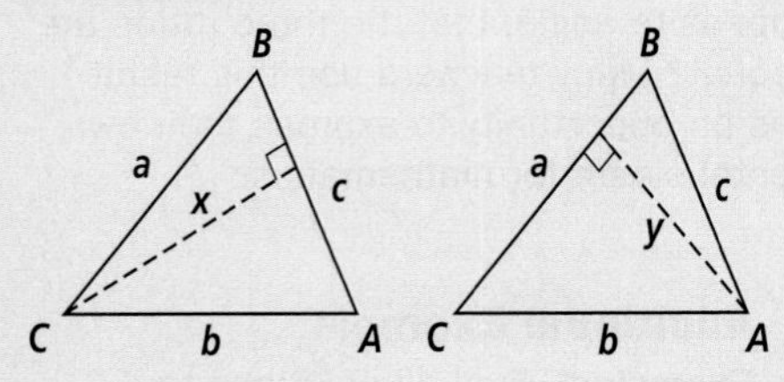

You may also want students to explore the Law of Sines in special triangles.

- In any right triangle ABC with right angle C, $\frac{\sin A}{\sin B} = \frac{\frac{a}{c}}{\frac{b}{c}}$ (using the right-triangle definitions). Simplifying the right side of the equation, $\frac{\sin A}{\sin B} = \frac{a}{b}$. In words, the ratio of the sines of the acute angles of a right triangle equals the ratio of the legs opposite those angles.
- In any isosceles triangle DEF with vertex angle F, $DF = EF$ and $m\angle D = m\angle E$. So $\frac{\sin D}{\sin E} = 1 = \frac{EF}{DF}$. Thus, the Isosceles Triangle Base Angles Theorem is a special case of the Law of Sines.

Additional Example

Example 2 In Example 2, suppose stations S and T are 18 miles apart, the ranger at S sees a fire at an angle of 42° with $\overrightarrow{ST}$, and the ranger at T sees a fire at an angle of 74° with $\overrightarrow{TS}$. Find the distance from station T to the fire.

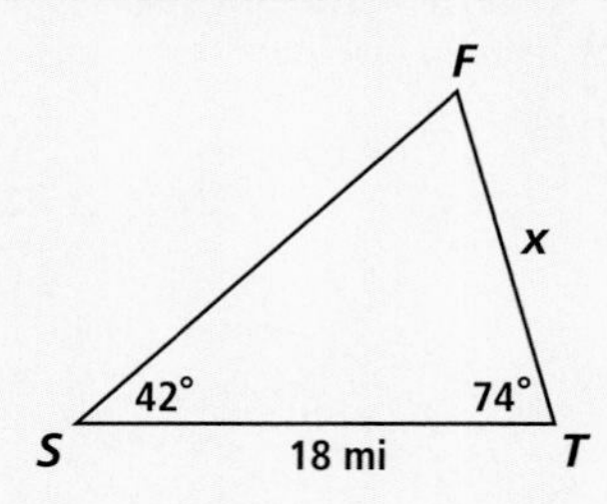

$\frac{\sin 64°}{18} = \frac{\sin 42°}{x}$; $x = \frac{18(\sin 42°)}{\sin 64°} \approx \frac{18(0.6691)}{0.8988} \approx 13.4$; about 13.4 mi

Law of Sines Theorem

In any triangle ABC, $\frac{\sin A}{a} = \frac{\sin B}{b} = \frac{\sin C}{c}$.

The Law of Sines states that in any triangle, the ratios of the sines of its angles to the lengths of the sides opposite them are equal. A proof of the theorem is given below. You are asked in Question 13 to fill in the missing information.

Proof Recall from Question 15 of Lesson 10-1 that the area of a triangle is $\frac{1}{2}$ the product of two sides and the sine of the included angle. Consequently, area($\triangle ABC$) $= \frac{1}{2}ab \sin C$, area($\triangle ABC$) $= \frac{1}{2}ac \sin B$, and area($\triangle ABC$) $= \frac{1}{2}bc \sin A$. So, by the __?__, $\frac{1}{2}ab \sin C = \frac{1}{2}ac \sin B = \frac{1}{2}bc \sin A$. Multiply all three parts of this equation by 2. The result is __?__. Divide all three parts by abc. You get __?__. Simplify the fractions to get $\frac{\sin C}{c} = \frac{\sin B}{b} = \frac{\sin A}{a}$.

Transitive Property of Equality; $ab \sin C = ac \sin B = bc \sin A$; $\frac{ab \sin C}{abc} = \frac{ac \sin B}{abc} = \frac{bc \sin A}{abc}$

Example 2

Two forest rangers are in their stations, S and T, 30 miles apart. On a certain day, the ranger at S sees a fire at F, at an angle of 38° with segment $\overline{ST}$. The ranger at T sees the same fire at an angle of 64° with $\overline{ST}$. Find the distance from station T to the fire.

Solution Let s be the desired distance. The angle opposite s is $\angle S$, with measure 38°. To use the Law of Sines, you need the measures of another angle and its opposite side. Because the sum of the measures of the angles in a triangle is 180°, $\angle F$ has measure 78°. Now there is enough information to use the Law of Sines.

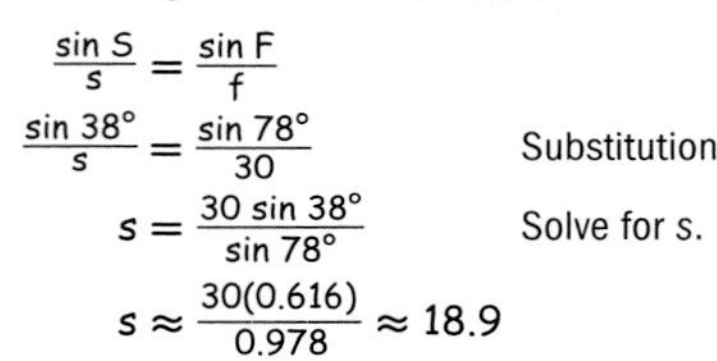

$$\frac{\sin S}{s} = \frac{\sin F}{f}$$

$$\frac{\sin 38°}{s} = \frac{\sin 78°}{30} \quad \text{Substitution}$$

$$s = \frac{30 \sin 38°}{\sin 78°} \quad \text{Solve for } s.$$

$$s \approx \frac{30(0.616)}{0.978} \approx 18.9$$

The fire is about 19 miles from station T.

The Law of Sines also can be used to find lengths in triangles when you know two angles and an adjacent side, the AAS (Angle-Angle-Side) condition from geometry.

Accommodating the Learner

In isosceles $\triangle ABC$, $AB = AC = s$ and $BC = t$. Ask students to write an expression for t in terms of s and θ if **(a)** θ is the vertex angle and **(b)** θ is a base angle.

a. If θ is the vertex angle, then each base angle has measure $\frac{180 - \theta}{2}$. Because $\frac{\sin A}{t} = \frac{\sin B}{s}$, then $\frac{\sin \theta}{t} = \frac{\sin\left(\frac{180-\theta}{2}\right)}{s}$ and $t = \frac{s(\sin \theta)}{\sin\left(\frac{180-\theta}{2}\right)}$.

b. If θ is a base angle, then the vertex angle has measure $180 - 2\theta$. Using $\frac{\sin B}{s} = \frac{\sin A}{t}$, then $\frac{\sin \theta}{s} = \frac{\sin(180 - 2\theta)}{t}$ and $t = \frac{s \cdot \sin(180 - 2\theta)}{\sin \theta}$.

GUIDED

Example 3

In $\triangle ALG$ at the right, $m\angle A = 55°$, $m\angle G = 17°$, and $a = 7$. Find g.

Solution

$\frac{\sin A}{a} = \frac{\sin G}{g}$ Law of Sines

$\underline{?} = \underline{?}$ Substitution $\frac{\sin 55°}{7}$; $\frac{\sin 17°}{g}$

$g \approx \underline{?}$ Solve for g. 2.5

Ptolemy knew of the Law of Sines in the 2nd century CE. This led eventually to *triangulation*, the process of dividing a region into triangular pieces, making a few accurate measurements, and using trigonometry to determine most of the unknown distances. This made it possible for reasonably accurate maps of parts of Earth to be drawn well before the days of artificial satellites. Now, Global Positioning Systems (GPS) use triangulation along with accurate data about the contours of Earth to produce highly accurate maps and to calculate the precise latitude and longitude of GPS devices.

Questions

COVERING THE IDEAS

1. Explain why the equation $\sin\theta = k$ for $0° < \theta < 180°$ and $0 < k < 1$ has two solutions.
2. Solve $\sin\theta = 0.954$ for $0° < \theta < 180°$ by graphing.
3. Since $\sin 45° = \frac{\sqrt{2}}{2}$, for what other value of θ with $0° < \theta < 180°$ does $\sin\theta = \frac{\sqrt{2}}{2}$? 135°
4. Explain how the Activity illustrates the Law of Sines.
5. Write a description of the Law of Sines as if you were explaining it to a friend.
6. Refer to Example 2. Find the distance from the fire to station S.

In 7 and 8, find r.

7.

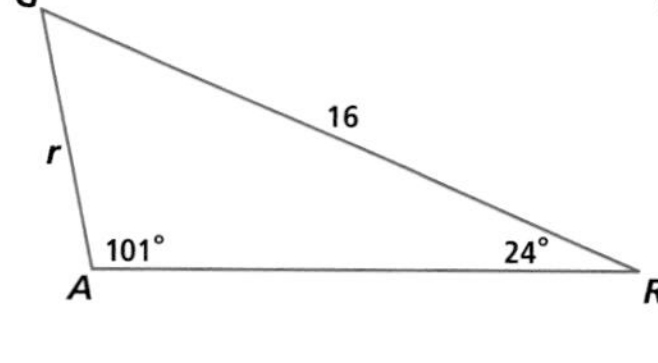

8.

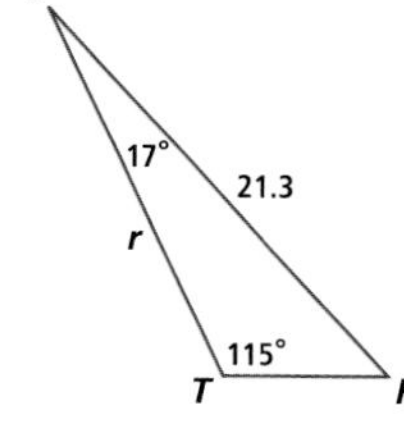

1. For any value of k between 0 and 1 and for $0° < \theta < 180°$, the graph of $y = k$ intersects the graph of $y = \sin\theta$ in two points.
2. $\theta = 72.55°$ or $\theta = 107.45°$
4. The Activity shows that for any drawn triangle, the ratios of the sines of its angles to the lengths of its opposite sides are equal.
5. In any triangle, the ratios of the sines of its angles to the lengths of the sides opposite them are equal.
6. about 27.6 mi
7. $r \approx 6.63$
8. $r \approx 17.47$

Additional Example

Example 3 In $\triangle TRI$, $m\angle R = 25°$, $m\angle I = 72°$, and $r = 13$. Find t.

Solution Sketch the figure.

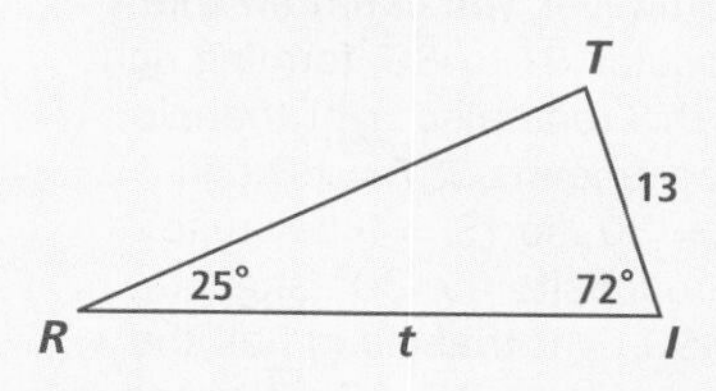

Use the Law of Sines: $\frac{\sin R}{r} = \frac{\sin T}{t}$.

$\frac{\sin \underline{?}}{\underline{?}} = \frac{\sin \underline{?}}{\underline{?}}$ 25°; 13; 83°; t

$t = \underline{?}$

$\frac{13(\sin 83°)}{\sin 25°} \approx \frac{13(0.9925)}{0.4226} = 30.53$

3 Assignment

Recommended Assignment

- Questions 1–18
- Questions 19 and 20 (extra credit)
- Reading Lesson 10-8
- Covering the Ideas 10-8

ENGLISH LEARNERS

Vocabulary Development

Help students understand how the phrases *solve an equation* and *solve a triangle* are alike and how they are different. One way they are alike is that both phrases refer to finding unknown values. One way they are different is that solving an equation refers to writing a string of equivalent equations, ending with a variable isolated on one side, while solving a triangle refers to using properties of trigonometry and geometry to find values for all the angles and side lengths of the triangle.

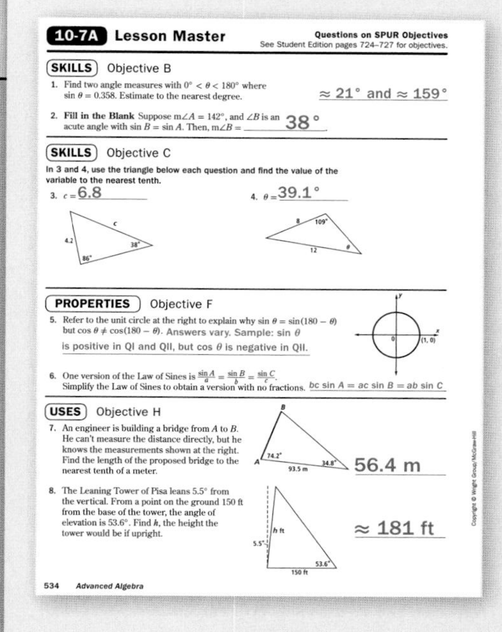

10-7A Lesson Master Questions on SPUR Objectives
See Student Edition pages 724–727 for objectives.

SKILLS Objective B

1. Find two angle measures with $0° < \theta < 180°$ where $\sin\theta = 0.358$. Estimate to the nearest degree. $\approx 21°$ and $\approx 159°$
2. **Fill in the Blank** Suppose $m\angle A = 142°$, and $\angle B$ is an acute angle with $\sin B = \sin A$. Then, $m\angle B =$ 38°.

SKILLS Objective C

In 3 and 4, use the triangle below each question and find the value of the variable to the nearest tenth.

3. $c =$ 6.8
4. $\theta =$ 39.1°

PROPERTIES Objective F

5. Refer to the unit circle at the right to explain why $\sin\theta = \sin(180 - \theta)$ but $\cos\theta \neq \cos(180 - \theta)$. Answers vary. Sample: $\sin\theta$ is positive in QI and QII, but $\cos\theta$ is negative in QII.
6. One version of the Law of Sines is $\frac{\sin A}{a} = \frac{\sin B}{b} = \frac{\sin C}{c}$. Simplify the Law of Sines to obtain a version with no fractions. $bc \sin A = ac \sin B = ab \sin C$

USES Objective H

7. An engineer is building a bridge from A to B. He can't measure the distance directly, but he knows the measurements shown at the right. Find the length of the proposed bridge to the nearest tenth of a meter. 56.4 m
8. The Leaning Tower of Pisa leans 5.5° from the vertical. From a point on the ground 150 ft from the base of the tower, the angle of elevation is 53.6°. Find h, the height the tower would be if upright. ≈ 181 ft

534 *Advanced Algebra*

Notes on the Questions

Question 9 You cannot use the Law of Sines to find BG because the measure of a second angle is not known. However, you can draw the perpendicular $\overline{BT}$ to $\overline{SG}$, forming right triangle BTS (and also right triangle BTG). Because $m\angle BST = 60$ and $m\angle SBT = 30$, so $TS = 9$ because the side opposite the 30° angle in a 30-60-90 right triangle is half the hypotenuse. Then $BT = 9\sqrt{3}$ by the Pythagorean Theorem applied to $\triangle BTS$. So the legs of right $\triangle BTG$ have lengths $9\sqrt{3}$ and 30, and by the Pythagorean Theorem,

$BG = \sqrt{(9\sqrt{3})^2 + 30^2} = \sqrt{1143}$.

Questions 10 and 12 These are classic uses of trigonometry to find inaccessible distances.

Additional Answer

19a. $\frac{\sin A}{a} = \frac{\sin B}{b} = \frac{\sin C}{c} \approx 0.6$, using inches as the unit of distance measure.

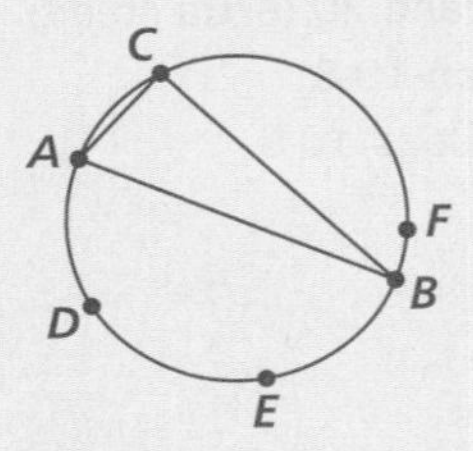

19b. $\frac{\sin D}{d} = \frac{\sin E}{e} = \frac{\sin F}{f} \approx 0.6$

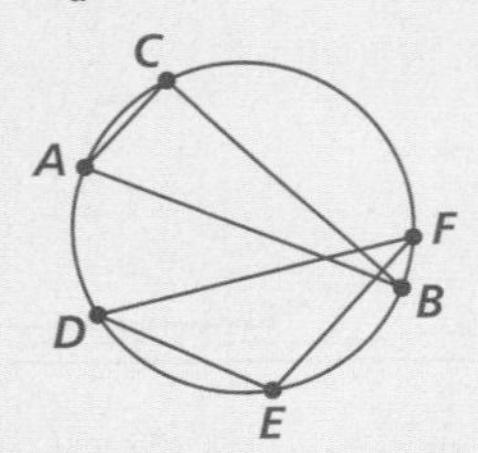

19c. The ratios from Parts a and b are equal. The ratios are equal to the reciprocal of the length of the diameter.

APPLYING THE MATHEMATICS

9. Refer to $\triangle BSG$ at the right.
   a. Why is the statement $\sin 120° = \frac{21}{BG}$ incorrect?
   b. Can you use the Law of Sines to find BG? Explain your answer.

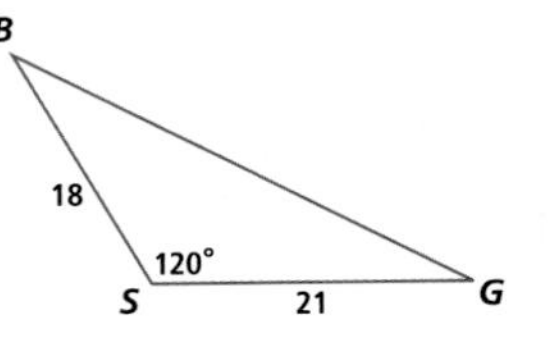

9a. The statement is incorrect because $\triangle BSG$ is not a right triangle.

9b. No, the Law of Sines can be used only when either the AAS condition or the ASA condition is satisfied.

10. Refer to the picture below. A rock at C and a house at D are 100 feet apart. A tree is across the river at B. $m\angle BCD = 47°$ and $m\angle BDC = 80°$. Find the distance across the river from the house to the tree. about 91.6 ft

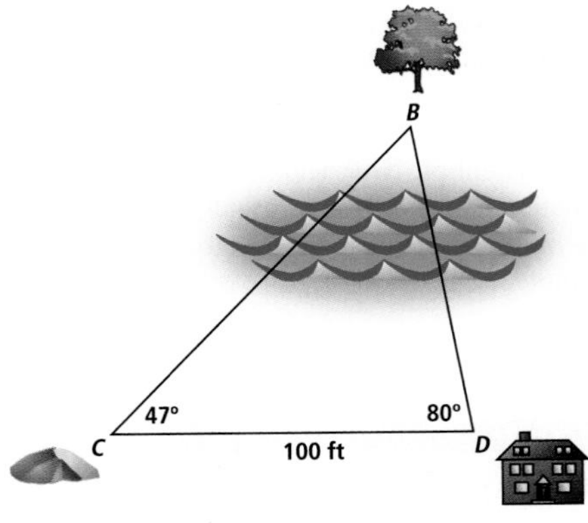

11. When a beam of light traveling through air strikes the surface of a diamond, it is *refracted*, or bent, as shown at the right. The relationship between α and θ is known as Snell's Law,

$$\frac{\sin \alpha}{\text{speed of light in air}} = \frac{\sin \theta}{\text{speed of light in diamond}}.$$

The speed of light in air is about $3 \cdot 10^8$ meters per second.
   a. If $\alpha = 45°$ and $\theta = 17°$, estimate the speed of light in diamond. about $1.24 \cdot 10^8 \frac{\text{m}}{\text{sec}}$
   b. Diamonds are identified as authentic by their *refractive index*. The refractive index of an object is the ratio of the speed of light in air to the speed of light in that object. Find the refractive index for a diamond. about 2.42
   c. Cubic zirconia, a lab-created alternative to diamond, has a refractive index of 2.2. Estimate the speed of light through cubic zirconia. about $1.36 \cdot 10^8 \frac{\text{m}}{\text{sec}}$

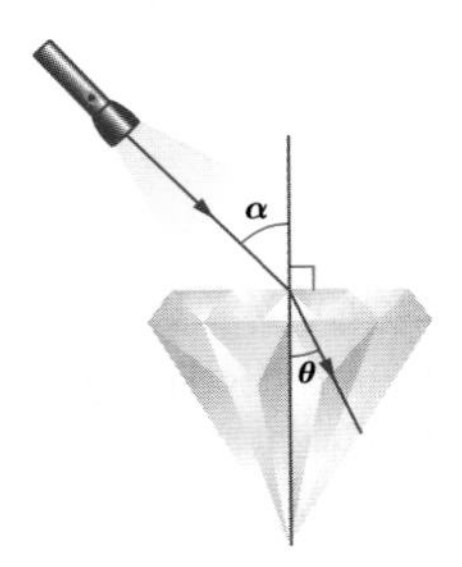

Extension

Ask students to describe the relationship between θ_1 and θ_2 in this diagram. Then ask them to solve $\triangle ABC$, $\triangle ACD$, and $\triangle ABD$.

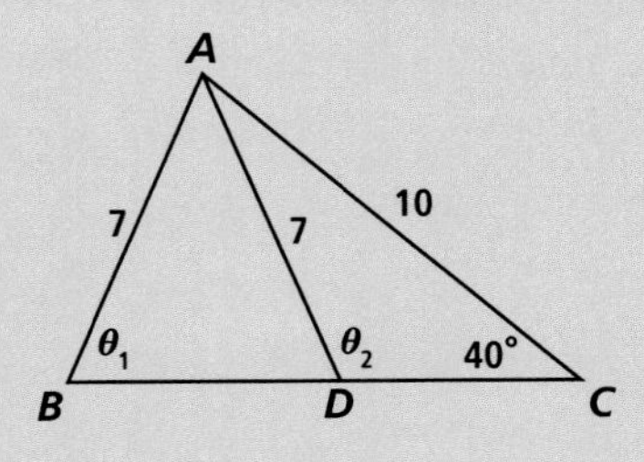

$\triangle ABD$ is isosceles, so $m\angle ADB = \theta_1$. Then $\theta_2 = 180 - \theta_1$. In $\triangle ABC$, $\frac{\sin 40°}{7} = \frac{\sin \theta_1}{10}$, $\sin \theta_1 = \frac{10(\sin 40°)}{7} \approx 0.9183$ and $\theta_1 = 66.67°$. $m\angle BAC = 180 - (66.67 + 40) = 73.33°$, so $\frac{\sin 73.33°}{BC} = \frac{\sin 40°}{7}$, $BC = \frac{7(\sin 73.33°)}{\sin 40°} = 10.43$. The sides are 7, 10, and 10.43; the angles are 66.67°, 73.33°, and 40°. In $\triangle ACD$, $\theta_2 = 180 - \theta_1 = 180 - 66.67 = 113.33°$, $m\angle CAD = 180 - (113.33 + 40) = 26.67°$;

12. Because surveyors cannot get inside a mountain, every mountain's height must be measured indirectly. Refer to the diagram at the right. Assume all labeled points lie in a single plane.

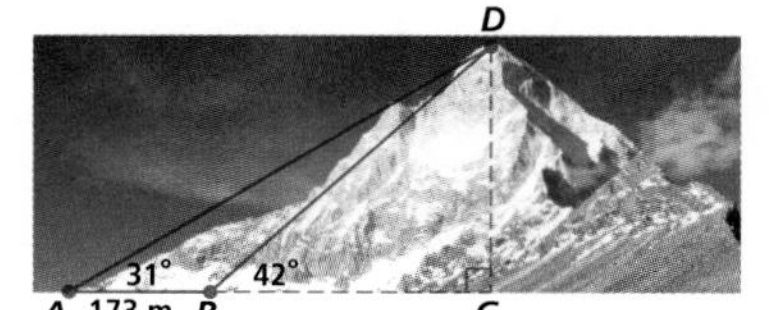

   a. Find the measures of $\angle ABD$ and $\angle ADB$ without trigonometry.
   b. Find BD. about 467 m
   c. Find DC, the height of the mountain. 312.5 m

12a. $m\angle ABD = 138°$; $m\angle ADB = 11°$

13. Fill in the blanks in the proof of the Law of Sines on page 702.

13. Transitive Property of Equality; $\triangle ABC$; $ab \sin C = ac \sin B = bc \sin A$; $\frac{ab \sin C}{abc} = \frac{ac \sin B}{abc} = \frac{bc \sin A}{abc}$

REVIEW

14. **Fill in the Blank** A function is periodic if its graph can be mapped onto itself under a __?__. (Lesson 10-6) horizontal translation

15. Name three x-intercepts of the graph of $y = \cos x$. (Lesson 10-6)

15. Answers vary. Sample: 90°, 270°, 450°

Fill in the Blank In 16 and 17, complete each statement with a trigonometric expression to make the equation true for all θ. (Lesson 10-5)

16. $\cos^2 \theta +$ __?__ $= 1$ $\sin^2 \theta$

17. $\cos \theta =$ __?__ $\pm\sqrt{1 - \sin^2 \theta}$

18. Estimate to the nearest thousandth. (Lessons 9-8, 9-7, 9-5)
   a. $\log 49$ 1.690
   b. $\ln 49$ 3.892
   c. $\log_2 49$ 5.615

EXPLORATION

19. Use a DGS to draw a circle with diameter $\overline{AB}$ and mark points C, D, E, and F not equally spaced on the circle. See margin.
   a. Draw $\triangle ABC$ and measure to find $\frac{\sin A}{a}$, $\frac{\sin B}{b}$, and $\frac{\sin C}{c}$.
   b. Draw $\triangle DEF$ and measure to find $\frac{\sin D}{d}$, $\frac{\sin E}{e}$, and $\frac{\sin F}{f}$.
   c. What do you notice about your results in Parts a and b? What is the connection between the ratios and the length of the diameter?

20. In QY 2, you were asked to solve $\sin \theta = 0.5$ using its inverse function or the graph of $y = \sin x$. See margin.
   a. Solve $\sin \theta = 0.5$ on a CAS.
   b. One CAS gives the results at the right.
      θ = 360 · (n1 + .416667) or
      θ = 360 · (n1 + .083333)
      Interpret what the CAS display means.

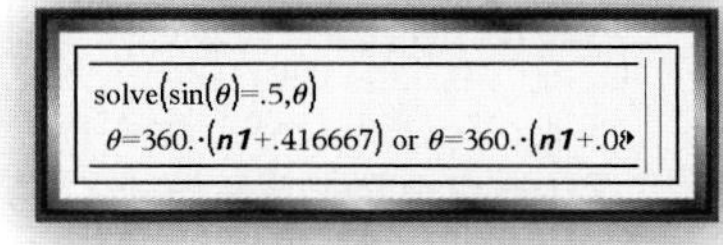

QY ANSWERS

1. $\theta = 120°$
2. a. There are no solutions.
   b. $\theta = 30°$ or $150°$

$\frac{\sin 26.67°}{CD} = \frac{\sin 40°}{7}$, $CD = \frac{7(\sin 26.67°)}{\sin 40°} \approx$ 4.89. The sides are 4.89, 7, and 10; the angles are 40°, 113.33°, and 26.67°. In $\triangle ABD$, the angles are 66.67°, 66.67°, and 180 − 2(66.67) = 46.66°; the sides are 7, 7, and 10.43 − 4.89 = 5.54.

Notes on the Questions

Question 18 You might ask for the ratio of the answer to Part a to the answer to Part b. $\log_e 10 = \ln 10$

Question 19c One way to describe the connection is that in any triangle, the ratio of a side of a triangle to the sine of the opposite angle is equal to the diameter of the circumcircle of the triangle.

4 Wrap-Up

Ongoing Assessment

Show students an acute triangle with two known angle measurements and one known side length. Ask students to use the Law of Sines to write two proportions that can be solved to find the other two side lengths of the triangle. Answers vary. Check students' work.

Additional Answers

20a. Answers vary. Sample: $\theta = 360 \cdot (n + 0.41\overline{6})$ or $\theta = 360 \cdot (n + 0.08\overline{3})$.

20b. The display means that for $\theta = 360 \cdot (n + 0.41\overline{6})$ or $\theta = 360 \cdot (n + 0.08\overline{3})$, for integer values of n, $\sin \theta = 0.5$.

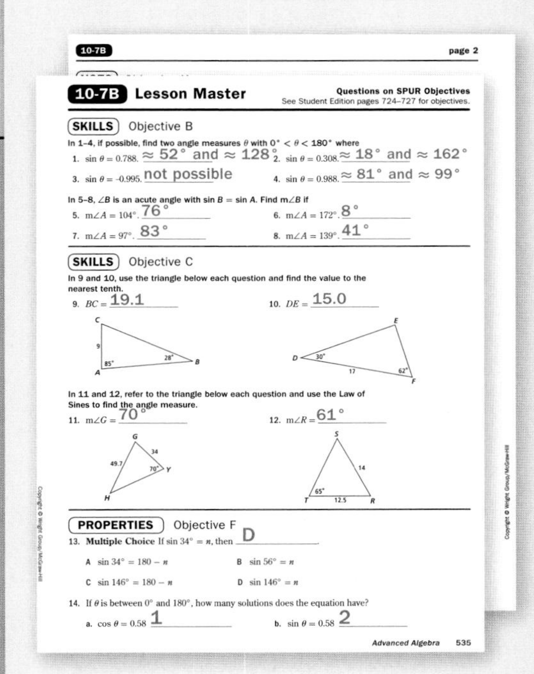

10-7B page 2

10-7B Lesson Master

Questions on SPUR Objectives
See Student Edition pages 724–727 for objectives.

SKILLS Objective B

In 1–4, if possible, find two angle measures θ with $0° < \theta < 180°$ where

1. $\sin \theta = 0.788$. ≈ 52° and ≈ 128°
2. $\sin \theta = 0.308$. ≈ 18° and ≈ 162°
3. $\sin \theta = -0.995$. not possible
4. $\sin \theta = 0.988$. ≈ 81° and ≈ 99°

In 5–8, $\angle B$ is an acute angle with $\sin B = \sin A$. Find $m\angle B$ if

5. $m\angle A = 104°$. 76°
6. $m\angle A = 172°$. 8°
7. $m\angle A = 97°$. 83°
8. $m\angle A = 139°$. 41°

SKILLS Objective C

In 9 and 10, use the triangle below each question and find the value to the nearest tenth.

9. $BC =$ 19.1
10. $DE =$ 15.0

In 11 and 12, refer to the triangle below each question and use the Law of Sines to find the angle measure.

11. $m\angle G =$ 70°
12. $m\angle R =$ 61°

PROPERTIES Objective F

13. **Multiple Choice** If $\sin 34° = n$, then D
   A $\sin 34° = 180 - n$
   B $\sin 56° = n$
   C $\sin 146° = 180 - n$
   D $\sin 146° = n$

14. If θ is between 0° and 180°, how many solutions does the equation have?
   a. $\cos \theta = 0.58$ 1
   b. $\sin \theta = 0.58$ 2

Advanced Algebra 535

Lesson

10-8

GOAL

Derive and apply the Law of Cosines.

SPUR Objectives

C Find missing side lengths and angle measures of a triangle using the Law of Cosines.

H Solve real-world problems using the Law of Cosines.

Materials/Resources

- Lesson Masters 10-8A and 10-8B
- Resource Masters 199 and 200

HOMEWORK

Suggestions for Assignment

- Questions 1–24
- Question 25 (extra credit)
- Reading Lesson 10-9
- Covering the Ideas 10-9

Local Standards

1 Warm-Up

Evaluate the expression $\sqrt{a^2 + b^2 - 2ab(\cos\theta)}$ when $a = 3$, $b = 4$, and θ has the given value.

1. 45° $\sqrt{25 - 12\sqrt{2}}$
2. 90° 5
3. 120° $\sqrt{37}$

Lesson

10-8 The Law of Cosines

BIG IDEA Given SAS or SSS in a triangle, the Law of Cosines enables you to find the lengths of the remaining sides or measures of angles of the triangle.

The Law of Sines enables you to solve a triangle if you know two angles and a side of the triangle (the ASA or AAS conditions). However, if you know the measures of two sides and the included angle (the SAS condition) or the measures of three sides of a triangle (the SSS condition), the Law of Sines cannot be used to solve the triangle. Fortunately, you can find other measures in the triangle using the *Law of Cosines*.

Mental Math

True or False

a. The length of your hair varies directly with the amount of time since your last haircut. true

b. The length of your hair varies directly with the number of haircuts you've had this year. false

c. The amount of money you spend on haircuts each year varies jointly with the price of each haircut and the number of haircuts you have. true

Law of Cosines Theorem

In any triangle ABC,
$c^2 = a^2 + b^2 - 2ab \cdot \cos C$.

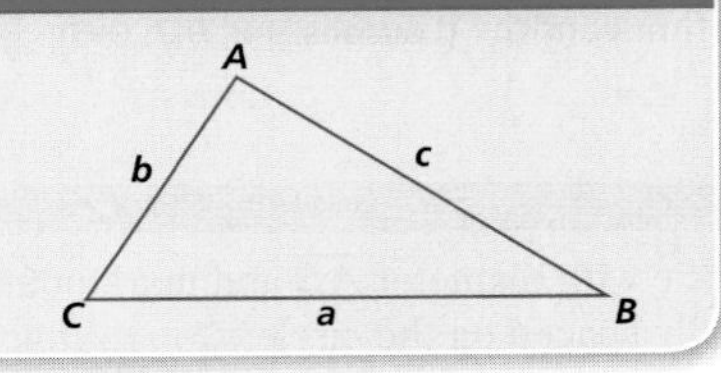

Proof Set up $\triangle ABC$ on a coordinate plane so that $C = (0, 0)$ and $A = (b, 0)$. To find the coordinates of point B, notice that B is the image of $(\cos C, \sin C)$ under a size change of magnitude a. Thus, $B = (a \cos C, a \sin C)$. Recall the Pythagorean Distance Formula for the distance d between (x_1, y_1) and (x_2, y_2), $d = \sqrt{|x_2 - x_1|^2 + |y_2 - y_1|^2}$. Use it to find c and square the result.

$c = \sqrt{\lvert a\cos C - b\rvert^2 + \lvert a\sin C - 0\rvert^2}$	Pythagorean Distance Formula
$c^2 = \lvert a\cos C - b\rvert^2 + \lvert a\sin C - 0\rvert^2$	Square both sides.
$c^2 = a^2\cos^2 C - 2ab \cdot \cos C + b^2 + a^2\sin^2 C$	Expand the binomials.
$c^2 = a^2\cos^2 C + a^2\sin^2 C + b^2 - 2ab \cdot \cos C$	Commutative Property of Addition
$c^2 = a^2(\cos^2 C + \sin^2 C) + b^2 - 2ab \cdot \cos C$	Distributive Property
$c^2 = a^2 + b^2 - 2ab \cdot \cos C$	Pythagorean Identity

Background

SAS triangle congruence suggests that there is a formula for the length of the third side of a triangle when two sides and the included angle are known. The Law of Cosines lets us find the third side; then another application of the Law of Cosines (or an application of the Law of Sines) lets us find the other angles.

Although a property equivalent to the Law of Cosines was known to Euclid, the form of that property was quite different from today's form. The cosine of the angle is not used (because cosines had not been identified); instead, the equivalent right-triangle ratio is found using projections of one side on another.

The historical importance of the Law of Cosines and the Law of Sines, and the entire realm of triangle trigonometry, should not be minimized. In past centuries, explorers mapped new regions of Earth using the method of triangulation, which requires only a knowledge of these laws. Not until the artificial satellites of the

The Law of Cosines applies to any two sides of a triangle and their included angle. So it is also true that in $\triangle ABC$,

$$a^2 = b^2 + c^2 - 2bc \cos A \text{ and } b^2 = a^2 + c^2 - 2ac \cos B.$$

In words the Law of Cosines says that in any triangle, the sum of the squares of two sides minus twice the product of these sides and the cosine of the included angle equals the square of the third side.

Using the Law of Cosines to Find a Length

With the Law of Cosines, finding the length of the third side of a triangle when two sides and the included angle are known requires only substitution.

Example 1

Two straight roads meet in Canton at a 27° angle. Anton is 7 miles down one road, and Banton is 8 miles down the other. How far apart are Anton and Banton?

Solution 1 Because this is an SAS situation, use the Law of Cosines. Let c be the distance between Anton and Banton.

$c^2 = a^2 + b^2 - 2ab \cos C$

Substitute. $c^2 = 8^2 + 7^2 - 2 \cdot 8 \cdot 7 \cdot \cos 27°$

$c^2 \approx 13.207$

$c \approx \pm 3.63$

Because lengths of sides of triangles must be positive numbers, only the positive solution makes sense in this situation. So $c \approx 3.63$. Anton and Banton are about 3.6 miles apart.

Solution 2 Enter the equation into a CAS and then take the square root of the result.

This display shows both exact and approximate solutions. They agree with Solution 1.

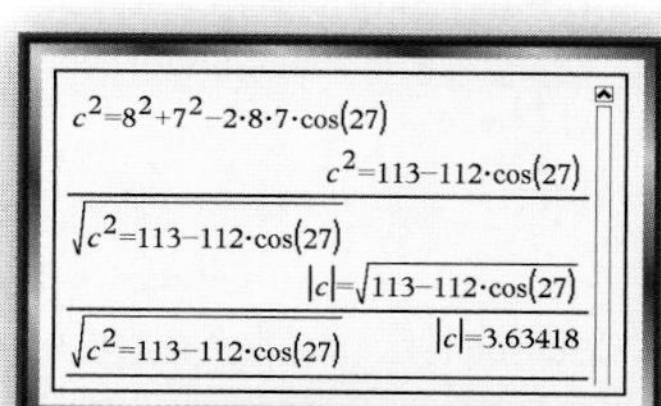

You can also use the Law of Cosines to find a length in triangles that meet the SsA condition, where the lengths of two sides are known, along with the measure of the angle opposite the longer side.

1960s were significantly better methods available for mapping. Using triangulation and other mathematics, a global positioning system (GPS) device can display its current location (latitude and longitude), speed, and direction. Many Web sites provide more information about GPSs, including many by "geocachers" who play treasure hunting games with GPS devices.

ENGLISH LEARNERS

Vocabulary Development

This lesson can provide a natural opportunity to review the term *included,* as in "if you know two sides and the included angle of a triangle ..." or "if you know two angles and the included side of a triangle ...." Encourage students to use the terms *included* and *nonincluded* when they describe what measurements are known in a triangle.

2 Teaching

Notes on the Lesson

Although the concepts in this lesson are not difficult for most *Advanced Algebra* students, the equation in the Law of Cosines is potentially intimidating. We recommend that you read through this lesson with students. Alternatively, you may want to preview it using the Warm-Up or using a problem such as Example 1. It is also helpful to prove the theorem in class.

Stress to students that it is important to memorize the Law of Cosines. For students having difficulty remembering the formula, you might want to point out that they can start with the Pythagorean Theorem $c^2 = a^2 + b^2$, then subtract the "correction term" $2ab(\cos C)$, helping students see that the correction term subtracts a positive value if angle C is acute and adds a positive value if C is obtuse. (The correction term is 0 if angle C is a right angle.)

To reinforce algebraic skills, have students solve for $\cos C$, $\cos B$, and $\cos A$ in the three forms of the Law of Cosines.

When finding an unknown side length, emphasize that the side length is the square root of the right-hand side. Also, once the solution is found, have students determine if the answer is feasible. Students may discover a calculation or substitution error.

You might need to remind students that when two sides and a nonincluded angle of a triangle are known, the triangle is only determined if the shorter of the two sides is adjacent to the known angle. Otherwise, two triangles are possible. This is why the congruence condition is written as SsA, not SSA.

Additional Example

Example 1 In Example 1, suppose that the two straight roads meet in Canton at an angle of 38°, Anton is 11 miles down one road, and Banton is 5 miles down the other. How far apart are Anton and Banton?

$c^2 = a^2 + b^2 - 2ab(\cos C)$;
$c^2 = 11^2 + 5^2 - 2(11)(5)\cos 38°$;
$c^2 \approx 121 + 25 - 86.6812 \approx 59.3188$;
$c \approx 7.7$ mi

Notes on the Lesson

Some books present this alternate proof of the Law of Cosines, which uses right-triangle definitions only.

Given: ABC

Prove: $c^2 = a^2 + b^2 - 2ab(\cos C)$

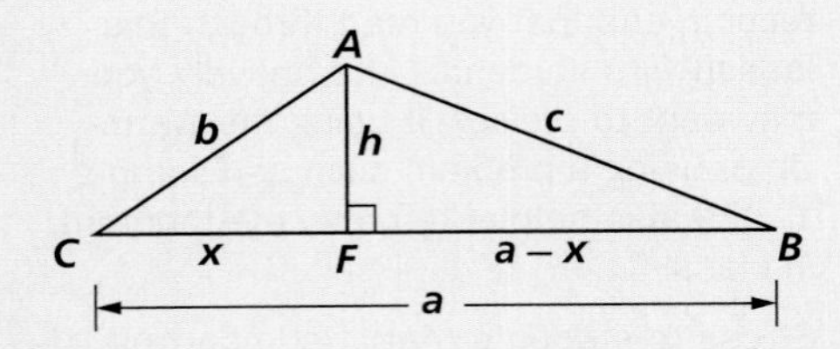

Let h be the length of the altitude $\overline{AF}$ from A to $\overline{BC}$; suppose the altitude divides $\overline{BC}$ into lengths x and $a - x$ as shown. By the Pythagorean Theorem in $\triangle AFB$, $c^2 = h^2 + (a - x)^2 = h^2 + a^2 - 2ax + x^2$ (1). Now consider $\triangle ACF$ and note that both h and x can be expressed in terms of the known quantities b and C.

$$\cos C = \frac{x}{b} \Rightarrow x = b \cos C$$

$$\sin C = \frac{h}{b} \Rightarrow h = b \sin C$$

Substituting for h and x in equation (1):

$$\begin{aligned} c^2 &= (b \sin C)^2 + a^2 - 2a(b \cos C) + (b \cos C)^2 \\ &= a^2 + b^2(\sin C)^2 + b^2(\cos C)^2 - 2ab(\cos C) \\ &= a^2 + b^2[(\sin C)^2 + (\cos C)^2] - 2ab(\cos C) \end{aligned}$$

But $(\sin C)^2 + (\cos C)^2 = 1$ by the Pythagorean Identity. So $c^2 = a^2 + b^2 - 2ab(\cos C)$.

This proof is valid only if $\overline{AF}$ is in the interior of $\triangle ABC$, that is, if angle C is acute. It is no shorter than the proof on page 706. In contrast, the proof given in the text applies to all triangles ABC, regardless of the measure of angle C.

Note-Taking Tips

Encourage students to record the following conditions under which they can use the Law of Sines or the Law of Cosines:

- Law of Sines: one side and any two angles; two sides and any two angles; two sides and the angle opposite one of the sides
- Law of Cosines: all three sides; two sides and the angle included between them

Example 2

In $\triangle ABC$, $c = 6$ cm, $a = 8$ cm, and $m\angle A = 30°$. Find b.

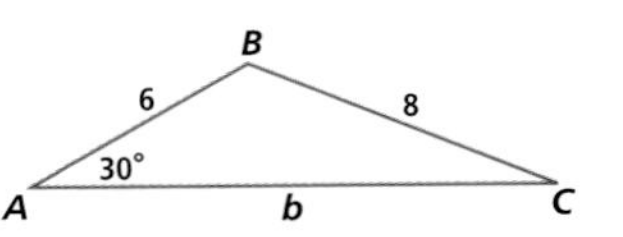

Solution This SsA situation indicates that you can use the Law of Cosines.

$$a^2 = b^2 + c^2 - 2bc \cos A$$

$$8^2 = b^2 + 6^2 - 2 \cdot 6 \cdot b \cdot \cos 30°$$

Solve on a CAS.

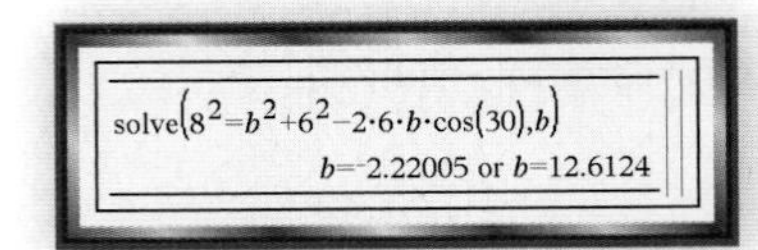

Because side lengths must be positive numbers, $b \approx 12.6$ cm.

Using the Law of Cosines to Find an Angle

You can also use the Law of Cosines to find the measure of any angle in a triangle when you know the lengths of all three sides (the SSS condition).

GUIDED

Example 3

A city wants to build a grass-covered playground on a small triangle-shaped lot with boundaries of length 12 m, 14 m, and 20 m. Through what angle measure should an automatic sprinkler be set to water the grass if it is placed at the corner C?

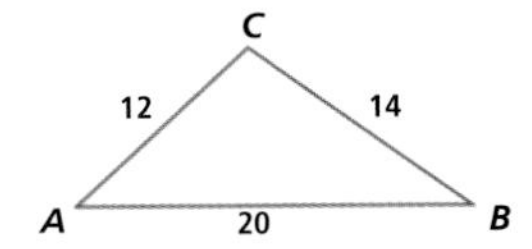

Solution In this SSS situation, you want to find $m\angle C$. Use the Law of Cosines.

Let a = __?__, b = __?__, and c = __?__. 14; 12; 20

$$c^2 = a^2 + b^2 - 2ab \cos C$$

Substitute. __?__^{2} = __?__^{2} + __?__^{2} − 2 • __?__ • __?__ cos C 20; 14; 12; 14; 12

__?__ = __?__ − __?__ cos C 400; 340; 336

Solve for cos C. __?__ = __?__ cos C 60; -336

cos $C \approx$ __?__ -0.1786

Apply $\cos^{-1}$ to both sides. $m\angle C \approx$ __?__ 100.29°

The sprinkler should be set to cover an angle of about __?__. 100°

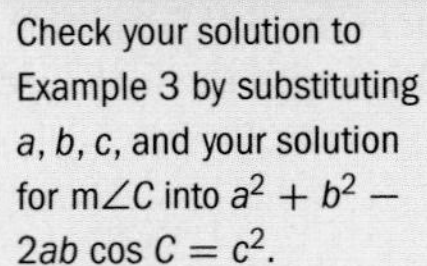

STOP QY

Accommodating the Learner

Ask students to use the Law of Cosines to find an expression for the length of a median to a triangle in terms of the lengths of the sides of the triangle.

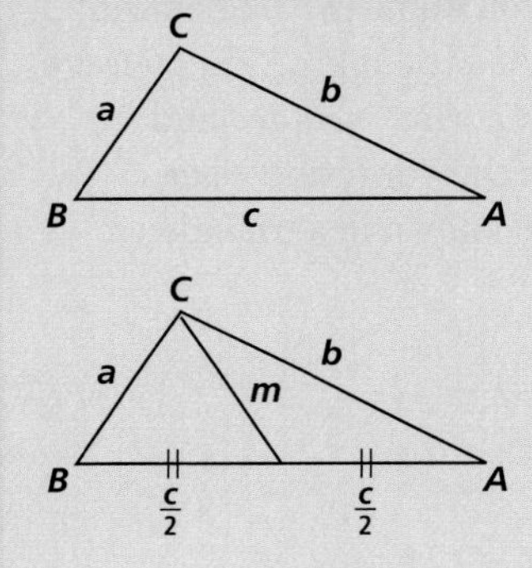

To find the median from C to $\overline{AB}$, start by finding an expression for cos B: $b^2 = a^2 + c^2 - 2ac(\cos B)$, $\cos B = \frac{b^2 - a^2 - c^2}{-2ac} = \frac{a^2 - b^2 + c^2}{2ac}$. Then $m^2 = a^2 + \left(\frac{c}{2}\right)^2 - 2(a)\left(\frac{c}{2}\right)\cos B$ or $m^2 = a^2 + \frac{c^2}{4} - \frac{2ac}{2} \cdot \frac{a^2 - b^2 + c^2}{2ac} = \frac{4a^2}{4} + \frac{c^2}{4} - \frac{2(a^2 - b^2 + c^2)}{4} = \frac{4a^2 + c^2 - 2a^2 + 2b^2 - 2c^2}{4} = \frac{2a^2 + 2b^2 - c^2}{4}$, and $m = \frac{1}{2} \cdot \sqrt{2a^2 + 2b^2 - c^2}$.

The Law of Cosines ($a^2 + b^2 - 2ab\cos C = c^2$) is the Pythagorean Theorem ($a^2 + b^2 = c^2$) with an extra term, $-2ab \cos C$. Consider three different triangles:

- If $\angle C$ is acute, as in Example 1, then $\cos C$ is positive and the extra term, $-2ab \cos C$, is negative. So $c^2 < a^2 + b^2$.
- If $\angle C$ is obtuse, as in Example 3, then $\cos C$ is negative and the extra term, $-2ab \cos C$, is positive. So $c^2 > a^2 + b^2$.
- If $\angle C$ is a right angle, then the extra term, $-2ab \cos 90°$, is equal to 0, and $c^2 = a^2 + b^2$.

This shows that the Law of Cosines is a generalization of the Pythagorean Theorem.

The last two lessons can be summarized as follows. If you need to find a side or an angle of a triangle, use the simplest methods possible before using trigonometry. If you still have sides or angles to find:

- Use right-angle trigonometric ratios when the missing side or angle is part of a right triangle.
- Use the Law of Sines for triangles meeting the ASA or AAS conditions.
- Use the Law of Cosines for triangles meeting the SAS, SSS, or SsA conditions.

Questions

COVERING THE IDEAS

In 1–3, according to the Law of Cosines, what expression is equal to the following in $\triangle PQR$?

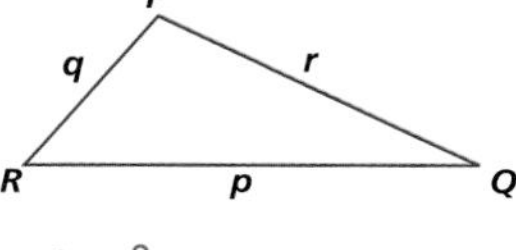

1. $p^2 + r^2 - 2pr \cos Q$ 2. $r^2 + q^2 - 2rq \cos P$ 3. r^2

4. **Multiple Choice** Which of the following describes the Law of Cosines? C
   - **A** The third side of a triangle equals the sum of the squares of the other two sides minus the product of the two sides and the included angle.
   - **B** The square of the third side of a triangle equals the sum of the squares of the other two sides minus the product of the two sides and the cosine of the included angle.
   - **C** The square of the third side of a triangle equals the sum of the squares of the other two sides minus twice the product of the two sides and the cosine of the included angle.
   - **D** none of the above

1. q^2
2. p^2
3. $p^2 + q^2 - 2pq \cos R$

Accommodating the Learner

Ask students to find the lengths of the two diagonals of a parallelogram if the sides are 6 units and 10 units, and one angle of the parallelogram measures 50°. The two diagonals are the third sides of two triangles. Each triangle has side lengths 6 and 10, meeting to form a 50° or a 130° angle. Diagonal d_1: $(d_1)^2 = 6^2 + 10^2 - 2(6)(10)\cos 50° \approx 136 - 77.1345 \approx 58.865$, so $d_1 \approx 7.67$ units. Diagonal d_2: $(d_2)^2 = 6^2 + 10^2 - 2(6)(10)\cos 130° \approx 136 + 77.1345 \approx 213.1345$, so $d_2 \approx 14.599$.

Additional Examples

Example 2 In $\triangle PQR$, $r = 10$, $p = 18$, and $m\angle P = 45°$. Find q.

Q, 10, 18, 45°, P, q, R

$18^2 = 10^2 + q^2 = 2(10)(q)\cos 45°$; $q \approx 23.62$

Example 3 In the diagram for Example 3, suppose $AC = 15$, $CB = 18$, and $AB = 23$. What is $m\angle C$?

Solution Using the Law of Cosines, $a =$ __?__, $b =$ __?__, and $c =$ __?__. 18; 15; 23

$c^2 = a^2 + b^2 - 2ab(\cos C)$

__?__ = __?__ + __?__ − 2 • __?__ • __?__ • cos C 23^2; 18^2; 15^2; 18; 15

__?__ = __?__ − __?__ (cos C) 529; 549; 540

__?__ ≈ cos C 0.037

$m\angle C \approx$ __?__ 87.8°

3 Assignment

Recommended Assignment

- Questions 1–24
- Question 25 (extra credit)
- Reading Lesson 10-9
- Covering the Ideas 10-9

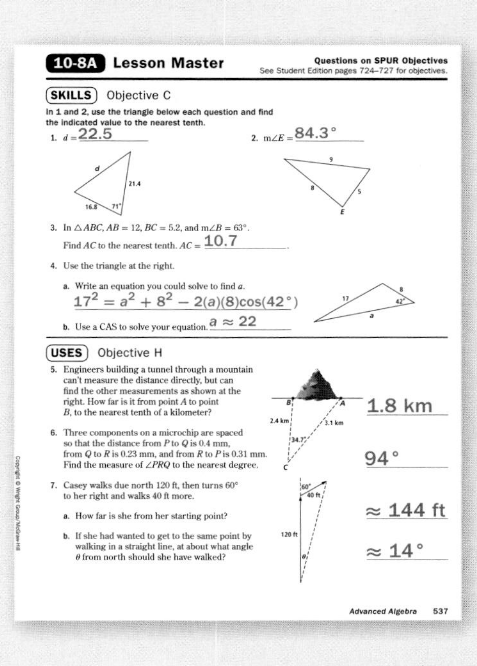

10-8A Lesson Master

Questions on SPUR Objectives
See Student Edition pages 724–727 for objectives.

SKILLS Objective C

In 1 and 2, use the triangle below each question and find the indicated value to the nearest tenth.

1. $d =$ 22.5
2. $m\angle E =$ 84.3°

3. In $\triangle ABC$, $AB = 12$, $BC = 5.2$, and $m\angle B = 63°$. Find AC to the nearest tenth. $AC =$ 10.7.

4. Use the triangle at the right.
   a. Write an equation you could solve to find a. $17^2 = a^2 + 8^2 - 2(a)(8)\cos(42°)$
   b. Use a CAS to solve your equation. $a \approx 22$

USES Objective H

5. Engineers building a tunnel through a mountain can't measure the distance directly, but can find the other measurements as shown at the right. How far is it from point A to point B, to the nearest tenth of a kilometer? 1.8 km

6. Three components on a microchip are spaced so that the distance from P to Q is 0.4 mm, from Q to R is 0.23 mm, and from R to P is 0.31 mm. Find the measure of $\angle PRQ$ to the nearest degree. 94°

7. Casey walks due north 120 ft, then turns 60° to her right and walks 40 ft more.
   a. How far is she from her starting point? ≈ 144 ft
   b. If she had wanted to get to the same point by walking in a straight line, at about what angle θ from north should she have walked? ≈ 14°

Advanced Algebra 537

10-8

Notes on the Questions

Question 12 Be sure students understand that the answer provided by the Law of Cosines is an estimate because the surface of Earth (and the cruising path of an airplane) is curved.

Additional Answers

16b. If the defendant was at D, the victim was at V, and the witness was at W, the Law of Cosines would say that $d^2 = w^2 + v^2 - 2wv \cos D$, or $100^2 = 25^2 + 65^2 - 2(25)(65) \cos D$. But then $\cos D = -1.58$, which is impossible.

5. In $\triangle ABC$, $m\angle A = 27.5°$, $AB = 10$, and $AC = x$. Write an expression for the length of BC. $\sqrt{x^2 + 100 - 20x \cos 27.5°}$

6. Refer to Example 1. Danton is a town on the road between Canton to Banton, 5 miles from Canton, with a straight road connecting Danton and Anton. What is the direct distance from Danton to Anton?

7. Check the answer to Example 2 by following these steps.
   Step 1 Solve $\frac{\sin A}{a} = \frac{\sin C}{c}$ for $m\angle C$. $m\angle C = \sin^{-1}\left(\frac{c}{a} \sin A\right) \approx 22.02°$
   Step 2 Find $m\angle B$. $m\angle B \approx 180° - 30° - 22.02° = 127.98°$
   Step 3 Solve $\frac{\sin A}{a} = \frac{\sin B}{b}$ for b. $b = \frac{\sin B}{\sin A} \cdot a \approx 12.6$ cm

8. Refer to Guided Example 3. Find $m\angle B$. 36.18°

9. For $\triangle ABC$, use the Law of Cosines to prove that, if $\angle C$ is acute, then $a^2 + b^2 > c^2$.

APPLYING THE MATHEMATICS

10. In $\triangle ABC$, $m\angle A = 53°$, $m\angle B = 102°$, and $m\angle C = 25°$. Explain why this triangle cannot be solved.

11. In $\triangle ABC$, use the Law of Cosines to get a formula for $\cos A$ in terms of a, b, and c. $\cos A = \frac{a^2 - b^2 - c^2}{-2bc}$

12. An airplane flies the 261 miles from Albany, New York, to Buffalo, New York. It then changes its direction by turning 26° left and flies a distance of 454 miles to Chicago, Illinois. What is the direct distance from Albany to Chicago? about 698 mi

13. Refer to the triangle at the right.
    a. Find a. ≈ 54.35 m
    b. Find θ. $\approx 12.51°$

12.7 m 112° 48.3 m θ a

14. The diagonals of a rectangle are 40 centimeters long and intersect at an angle of 28.5°. How long are the sides of the rectangle? 9.846 cm and 38.769 cm

15. The sides of a rectangle are 4 inches and 7 inches. Find the measure of the acute angle formed by the diagonals. 59.49°

16. At a criminal trial, a witness gave the following testimony: "The defendant was 25 feet from the victim. I was 65 feet from the defendant and about 100 feet from the victim when the robbery occurred. I saw the whole thing."
    a. Draw a triangle to represent the situation.
    b. Use the Law of Cosines to show that the testimony has errors. See margin.
    c. How else could you know that the testimony has errors? By the Triangle Inequality, this is impossible. The sum of the two shorter sides is less than the longer side.

6. 3.41 mi

9. Consider $\triangle ABC$ with $\angle C$ acute. By the Law of Cosines, $c^2 - a^2 - b^2 = -2ab \cos C$. Since C is acute, $\cos C > 0$, so $-2ab \cos C < 0$. Thus, $c^2 - a^2 - b^2 < 0$, and $c^2 < a^2 + b^2$.

10. AAA is not a triangle congruence condition. Two triangles that are similar, but not congruent, can both satisfy these conditions.

16a. No such triangle can be drawn.

Extension

Ask students to show that the Law of Cosines can be used to prove the Triangle Inequality, which states that each side of a triangle must be shorter than the sum of the other two sides and must be longer than the absolute value of the difference of the other two sides. Answers vary. Sample: Suppose θ is the angle formed by sides a and b of a triangle, and the length of the third side is c. Then $0° < \theta < 180°$. When θ is close to 180°, then $\cos \theta$ is just greater than -1. Thus $c^2 = a^2 + b^2 - 2ab(\cos C) < a^2 + b^2 + 2ab = (a + b)^2$, so $c < a + b$. When θ is close to 0°, then $\cos \theta$ is just less than 1. Then $c^2 = a^2 + b^2 - 2ab(\cos \theta) > a^2 + b^2 - 2ab = (a - b)^2$, so $c > a - b$.

17. At a track meet, an electronic device measures the distance a discus travels to the nearest centimeter. The device is placed as shown in the diagram at the right. It first measures the distance p to the discus circle. After the athlete throws the discus, the device measures angle α and distance d and calculates the length w of the throw to the nearest centimeter. Suppose $p = 3.2$ m, $\alpha = 147.207°$ and $d = 47.40$ meters. How long was the throw? 50.12 m

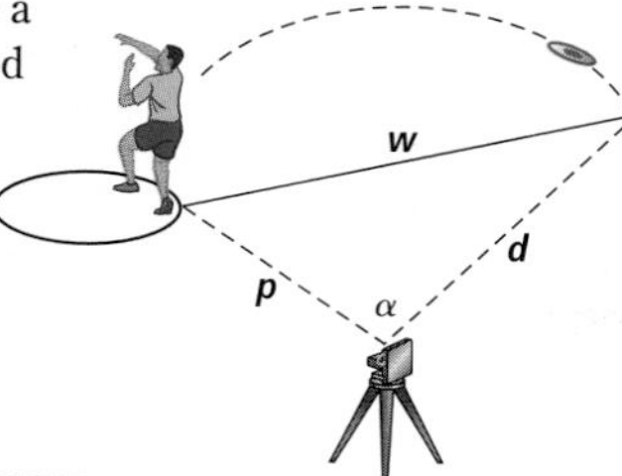

REVIEW

18. In $\triangle DOG$, $OG = 42$, $m\angle D = 118°$, and $m\angle G = 27°$. Find DO and DG. **(Lesson 10-7)** $DO = 21.6$, $DG = 27.3$

19. Does the graph of the function $f(x) = \sin x$ have any lines of symmetry? If so, give an equation for one such line. **(Lesson 10-6)** Yes; Equations vary. Sample: $x = 90°$.

20. a. Is the relationship graphed at the right a function? Why or why not? **(Lessons 10-6, 8-2, 1-2)**
    b. Is the relation periodic? If so, what is the period?
    c. Is the inverse of the relation a function? Why or why not? 20a–c. See margin.

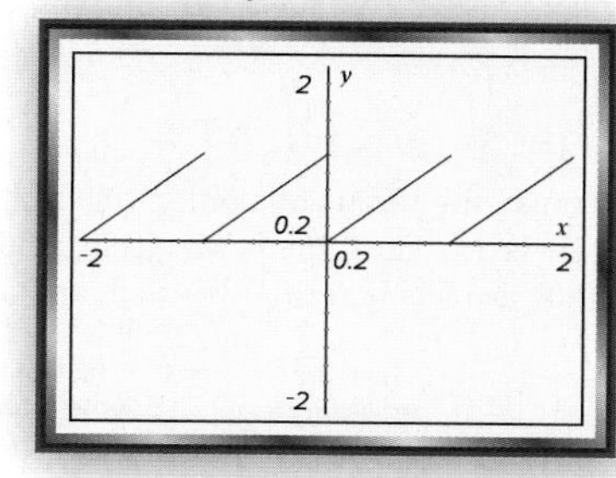

21. Use the Pythagorean Identity to prove that the point with coordinates $(r \cos \theta, r \sin \theta)$ has distance $|r|$ from the origin. **(Lesson 10-5, Previous Course)** See margin.

22. Find the area of the triangle at the right. **(Lesson 10-1)** ≈ 18.19

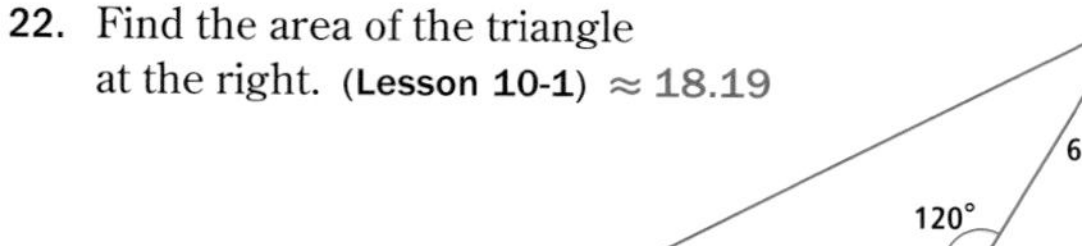

In 23 and 24, refer to circle *O* at the right. (Previous Course)

23. If $\theta = 85°$, what fraction of the circle's area is the area of the shaded sector? $\frac{85}{360} = \frac{17}{72}$

24. If the length of $\widehat{AB}$ is $\frac{9}{24}$ of the circumference of the circle, find θ. 135°

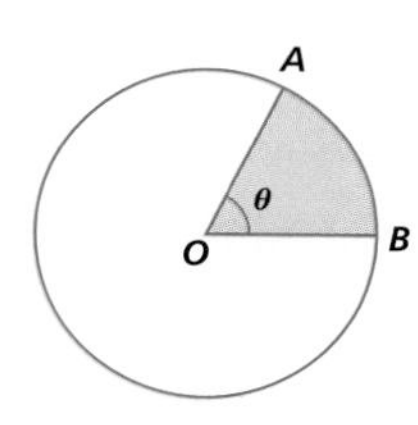

EXPLORATION

25. "You, who wish to study great and wonderful things, who wonder about the movement of the stars, must read these theorems about triangles. Knowing these ideas will open the door to all of astronomy and to certain geometric problems." This quotation is from *De Triangulis Omnimodis* by Regiomontanus. Find out more about this 15th-century mathematician and his work in trigonometry. See margin.

QY ANSWERS

$14^2 + 12^2 - 2 \cdot 14 \cdot 12 \cos 100° \approx 398 \approx 400 = 20^2$. It checks.

10-8

4 Wrap-Up

Ongoing Assessment

Show students a triangle with angles M, N, and P that are opposite sides m, n, and p. Ask them to write three versions of the Law of Cosines, one each that begins $m^2 = \ldots$, $n^2 = \ldots$, and $p^2 = \ldots$.

Project Update

Project 2, *Spherical Trigonometry*, on page 718 relates to the content of this lesson.

Additional Answers

20a. Yes; there is only one y-value for every x-value.

20b. Yes; 1

20c. No; the inverse of a periodic function is not a function.

21. By the Pythagorean Identity, we have $D = \sqrt{r^2 \cos^2 \theta + r^2 \sin^2 \theta} = \sqrt{r^2 (\cos^2 \theta + \sin \theta)} = \sqrt{r^2} = |r|$.

25a. Regiomontanus was an important German mathematician, astronomer, and astrologer. He wrote one of the first textbooks presenting the current state of trigonometry.

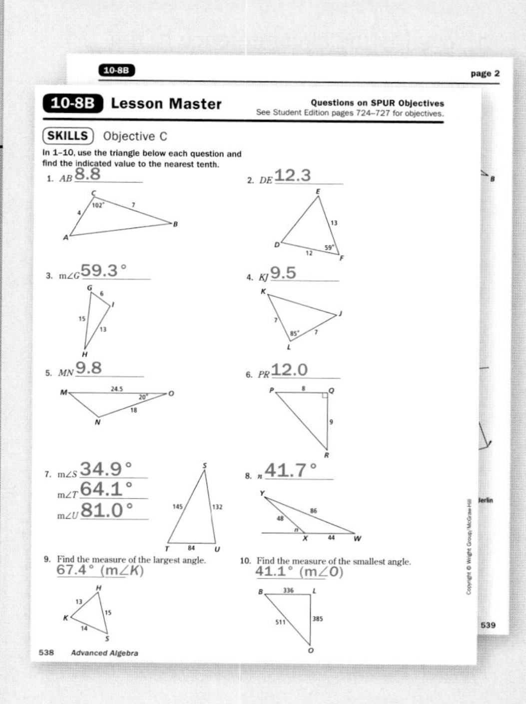

10-8B page 2

10-8B Lesson Master — Questions on SPUR Objectives. See Student Edition pages 724–727 for objectives.

SKILLS Objective C

In 1–10, use the triangle below each question and find the indicated value to the nearest tenth.

1. AB 8.8
2. DE 12.3
3. $m\angle G$ 59.3°
4. KJ 9.5
5. MN 9.8
6. PR 12.0
7. $m\angle S$ 34.9°; $m\angle T$ 64.1°; $m\angle U$ 81.0°
8. n 41.7°
9. Find the measure of the largest angle. 67.4° ($m\angle K$)
10. Find the measure of the smallest angle. 41.1° ($m\angle O$)

538 Advanced Algebra

Copyright © Wright Group/McGraw-Hill

539

Lesson

10-9

GOAL

Introduce radian measure for rotations, angles, and arcs; compare radian measure and degree measure.

SPUR Objectives

A Approximate values of trigonometric functions using a calculator.

D Convert angle measures from radians to degrees or from degrees to radians.

Materials/Resources

- Lesson Masters 10-9A and 10-9B
- Resource Masters 201–203

HOMEWORK

Suggestions for Assignment

- Questions 1–30
- Question 31 (extra credit)
- Self-Test

Local Standards

1 Warm-Up

1. What is the circumference of the unit circle? 2π
2. What is the length of a 20° arc on the unit circle? $\frac{\pi}{9}$
3. What is the length of an $x°$ arc on the unit circle? $\frac{\pi x}{180}$

Lesson

10-9 Radian Measure

Vocabulary

radian

▶ **BIG IDEA** The *radian* is an alternate unit of angle measure defined so the length of an arc in a unit circle is equal to the radian measure of that arc.

So far in this chapter you have learned to evaluate $\sin x$, $\cos x$, and $\tan x$ when x is given in degrees. Angles and magnitudes of rotations may also be measured in *radians*. In calculus and some other areas of mathematics, radians are used more often than degrees.

Mental Math

Ronin just returned from a trip and has several kinds of currency in his wallet. Assume there are 1.5 U.S. dollars in 1 euro, 100 Japanese yen in 1 U.S. dollar, and 0.75 South African rand in 10 Japanese yen.

a. How many euros can Ronin get for his $36? 24

b. About how many euros can he get for his 1700 yen? 11.33

c. How many U.S. dollars can he get for his 120 rand? 16

What Is a Radian?

Because the radius of a unit circle is 1, the circumference of a unit circle is 2π. Thus, on a unit circle, a 360° arc has length 2π. Similarly, a 180° arc has length $\frac{1}{2}(2\pi) = \pi$, and a 90° arc has length $\frac{1}{4}(2\pi) = \frac{\pi}{2}$.

360° arc
arc length 2π

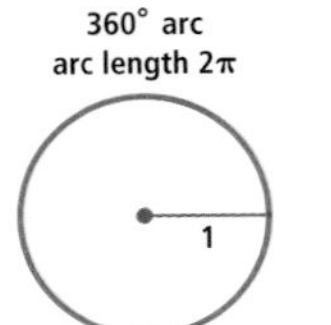

180° arc
arc length π

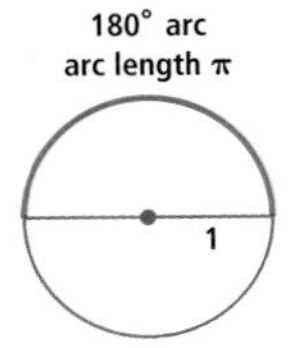

90° arc
arc length $\frac{\pi}{2}$

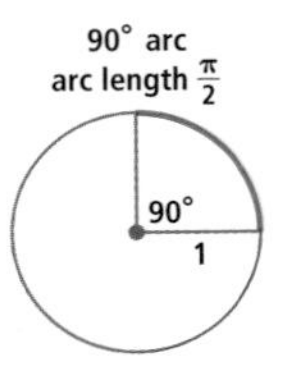

The radian is a measure created so that the arc *measure* and the arc *length* are the same number.

Definition of Radian

The **radian** is a measure of an angle, arc, or rotation such that π radians = 180 degrees.

Notice that a 180° arc on the unit circle has measure π radians, and this arc has length π. A 90° angle has measure $\frac{\pi}{2}$ radians, and its arc has length $\frac{\pi}{2}$. In general, *the measure of an angle, arc, or rotation in radians equals the length of its arc on the unit circle.*

QY

▶ **QY**

What is the length of a 60° arc on the unit circle?

Background

Although it is helpful for beginners to consider radians as a unit of measure, students will find in later courses that radians are not considered a unit but merely a signal that the argument of a function is a "unit-free" real number. Also, students should consider the idea that because a unit of volume has dimension 3, a unit of area has dimension 2, and a unit of length has dimension 1, then radians, like degrees, are a unit that has dimension 0.

Two reasons that radians are important are that the trigonometric functions in terms of radians have "nice" properties, and radians naturally connect arc *length* with arc *measure*. (An arc with measure x radians in a circle of radius r has length rx, while an arc with measure x degrees in a circle of radius r has length $\frac{\pi r x}{180}$.) Also, the formulas for calculating the values of the trigonometric functions (the formulas used in calculators) are based on radians.

Conversion Factors for Degrees and Radians

The definition of radian can be used to create conversion factors for changing degrees into radians, and vice versa. Begin with the equation

$$\pi \text{ radians} = 180°.$$

Dividing each side by π radians gives $\frac{\pi \text{ radians}}{\pi \text{ radians}} = \frac{180°}{\pi \text{ radians}}$.

So, $1 = \frac{180°}{\pi \text{ radians}}$.

Similarly, dividing each side by 180° gives $\frac{\pi \text{ radians}}{180°} = \frac{180°}{180°}$,

so, $\frac{\pi \text{ radians}}{180°} = 1$.

Conversion Factors for Degrees and Radians

To convert radians to degrees, multiply by $\frac{180°}{\pi \text{ radians}}$.

To convert degrees to radians, multiply by $\frac{\pi \text{ radians}}{180°}$.

You may be wondering how big a radian is. Example 1 gives an answer.

Example 1

Convert 1 radian to degrees.

Solution Because radians are given, multiply by the conversion factor with radians in the denominator.

$1 \text{ radian} = 1 \text{ radian} \cdot \frac{180°}{\pi \text{ radians}}$

$= \frac{180°}{\pi}$

$\approx 57.3°$

Notice that one radian is much larger than one degree.

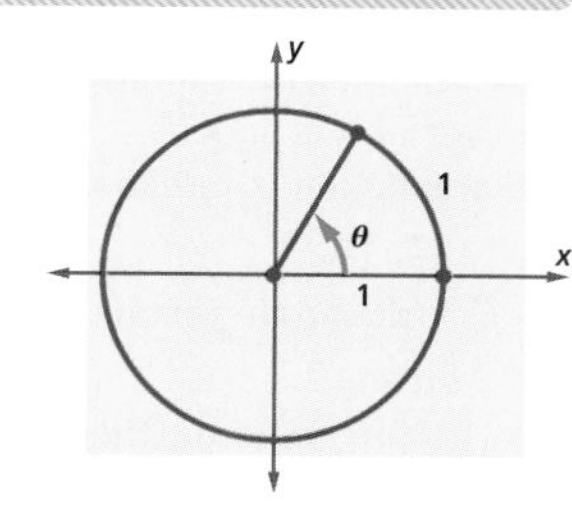

Because the measure of an angle in radians equals the length of its arc on the unit circle, the angle of 1 radian in Example 1 determines an arc of length 1. A unit circle has circumference $2\pi \approx 6.28$, so an arc length of 1 is a little less than $\frac{1}{6}$ of the circle's circumference. So the angle $\theta = 1$ radian measures a little less than $\frac{1}{6}$ of 360°, or a little less than 60°.

2 Teaching

Notes on the Lesson

Most students have seen "radian" (or "rad") on their calculators, and many are curious about what a radian is. We suggest you use the Warm-Up to introduce this lesson and ask students to find the lengths of the arcs determined by rotations of various amounts $\left(90° \longrightarrow \frac{\pi}{2}; 180° \longrightarrow \pi; 45° \longrightarrow \frac{\pi}{4}; 270° \longrightarrow \frac{3\pi}{2}\right)$. Then state the definition of radian given in the text. Develop the conversion factors as on page 713, or, if you prefer, have students use the proportion $\frac{180°}{\pi \text{ radians}} = \frac{D°}{R \text{ radians}}$ (where either D or R is given).

Have students practice converting in both directions, from degrees to radians and from radians to degrees. We suggest you use examples that are multiples of 30° or 45°, that is, $\frac{\pi}{6}$ or $\frac{\pi}{4}$ radians. For the benefit of students whose fraction skills are weak, you may want to point out that $\frac{a\pi}{b}$ can be rewritten as $\frac{a}{b}\pi$. Record your result on a circle with equivalent measures, similar to the one on page 714.

Virtually every student wants to know "how big" 1 radian is. As a class, have students convert 1 radian to degrees, as is done in Example 1. Finally, emphasize to students that this π is the same π they have seen for years; that is, 180° ≈ 3.141592 radians.

Additional Example

Example 1 Convert 1 degree to radians. ≈0.017 radian

Accommodating the Learner

Ask students to look at the diagram for Example 1. Point out that a region of a circle bound by two radii and the part of the circumference between the radii is called a sector. Ask students to find the area of a sector represented by 1 radian. The area of the entire unit circle is $\pi r^2 = \pi(1)^2 = \pi$. The entire unit circle represents 2π radians, so the needed area is $\frac{1}{2\pi} \cdot \pi = \frac{1}{2}$.

ENGLISH LEARNERS

Vocabulary Development

Some students confuse *arc length* and *arc measure*. You may want to point out that *arc length*, like other types of length, refers to a distance measured in inches, centimeters, or some other linear unit. *Arc measure* refers to angles and rotations.

Additional Example

Example 2

a. Convert 60° to its exact radian equivalent.

b. Convert $\frac{5}{6}\pi$ to its exact degree equivalent.

Solution

a. $60° \cdot$ __?__ $=$ __?__ radians $\frac{\pi}{180°}$; $\frac{\pi}{3}$

$60° =$ __?__ radians, exactly. $\frac{\pi}{3}$

b. $\frac{5}{6}\pi \cdot$ __?__ $=$ __?__ $\frac{180°}{\pi}$; $\frac{5\pi(180°)}{6\pi}$

$\frac{5}{6}\pi =$ __?__, exactly 150°

Note-Taking Tips

Encourage students to make copies of their graphs of $y = \cos\theta$ and $y = \sin\theta$ from Lesson 10-6 and use fractions of the form $\pm\frac{n\pi}{6}$ (when n is 1, 2, 3, 4, 5, or 6) to label points on the horizontal axis.

GUIDED

Example 2

a. Convert 45° to its exact radian equivalent.

b. Convert $\frac{2}{3}\pi$ radians to its exact degree equivalent.

Solution

a. Multiply 45° by one of the conversion factors. Because you want radians, choose the ratio with radians in the numerator.

$45° \cdot$ __?__ $=$ __?__ radians $\frac{\pi \text{ radians}}{180 \text{ degrees}}$; $\frac{45\pi}{180}$

$=$ __?__ radian $\frac{\pi}{4}$

$45° =$ __?__ radian, exactly. $\frac{\pi}{4}$

b. Multiply $\frac{2}{3}\pi$ radians by one of the conversion factors. Because you want degrees, choose the ratio with degrees in the numerator.

$\frac{2}{3}\pi \cdot$ __?__ $=$ __?__ $\frac{180 \text{ degrees}}{\pi \text{ radians}}$; $\frac{360}{3}$ degrees

$=$ __?__ 120°

$\frac{2}{3}\pi =$ __?__, exactly. 120°

Radian expressions are often left as multiples of π because this form gives an exact value. Usually in mathematics, the word *radian* or the abbreviation *rad* is omitted. In trigonometry, when no degree symbol or other unit is specified, we assume that the measure of the angle, arc, or rotation is radians.

$\theta = 2°$ means
"the angle (or the arc or rotation) θ has measure 2 degrees."

$\theta = 2$ means
"the angle (or the arc or rotation) θ has measure 2 radians."

Refer to Guided Example 2. Because $\frac{\pi}{4} = 45°$, you can conclude that $\frac{3\pi}{4} = 3 \cdot \frac{\pi}{4} = 3 \cdot 45° = 135°$.

Similarly, $\frac{5\pi}{4} = 5 \cdot 45° = 225°$.

The diagram at right shows some common equivalences of degrees and radians.

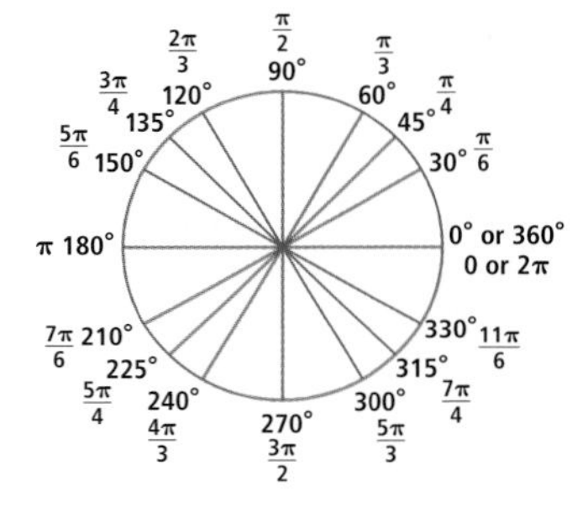

In general, the multiples of π and the simplest fractional parts of π ($\frac{\pi}{2}, \frac{\pi}{3}, \frac{\pi}{4}, \frac{\pi}{6}$, and their multiples) correspond to those angle measures that give exact values of sines, cosines, and tangents.

Trigonometric Values in Radians

Every scientific calculator can evaluate $\sin\theta$, $\cos\theta$, and $\tan\theta$, where θ is in radians.

Accommodating the Learner

Show students the vertical line $x = 1$ drawn on the same axes as a unit circle. Ask them to find the radian measure of the angle through $(1, n)$ for $n = \frac{1}{2}$, 1, 2, 3, 10, and n (where $n \geq 0$). In general, the ordered pair $(1, n)$ determines an angle θ such that $\tan\theta = n$.

n	θ
$\frac{1}{2}$	0.464
1	0.785
2	1.107
3	1.249
10	1.471
n	tan n

GUIDED

Example 3

Set your calculator to radian mode. Evaluate

a. cos 2. b. tan $\frac{3\pi}{4}$.

Solution

a. Enter cos _?_. You should find cos _?_ ≈ _?_. 2; 2; -0.416

b. Enter tan _?_. You should find tan _?_ = _?_. $\frac{3\pi}{4}$; $\frac{3\pi}{4}$; -1

Check

a. 1 radian ≈ _?_°, so 2 radians ≈ _?_°. 57.3; 114.6

cos _?_° ≈ _?_. It checks. 114.6°; -0.416

b. $\frac{3\pi}{4}$ radians = _?_°, and tan _?_° = _?_. It checks. 135°; 135°; -1

Graphs of the Sine and Cosine Functions Using Radians

The cosine and sine functions are graphed below with x measured in radians rather than degrees. Notice that each function is (still) periodic, but that each period is 2π rather than 360°.

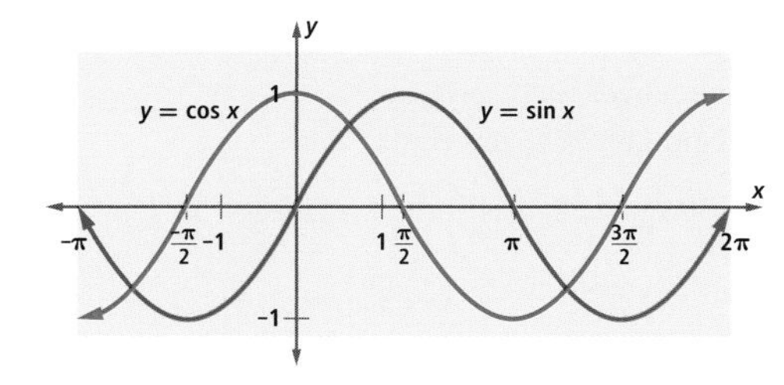

Questions

COVERING THE IDEAS

1. A circle has a radius of 1 unit. Give the length of an arc with the given measure.
   a. 360° 2π b. 180° π c. 90° $\frac{\pi}{2}$ d. 110° $\frac{11\pi}{18}$

2. **Fill in the Blanks**
   a. π radians = _?_° 180
   b. 1 radian = _?_° $\frac{180}{\pi}$
   c. _?_ radian(s) = 1° $\frac{\pi}{180}$

In 3–6, convert the radian measure to degrees.

3. 8π 1440° 4. $\frac{11\pi}{2}$ 990° 5. $\frac{14\pi}{45}$ 56° 6. $-\frac{5\pi}{4}$ -225°

Additional Example

Example 3 Set your calculator in radian mode.

a. Evaluate cos 6.

b. Evaluate tan $\frac{7\pi}{6}$.

Solution

a. Enter [COS] _?_. You should find cos _?_ ≈ _?_.
[6]; 6; 0.9602

b. Enter [TAN] _?_. You should find tan _?_ ≈ _?_.
[7] [×] [π] [÷] [6] [=]; $\frac{7\pi}{6}$; 0.5774

3 Assignment

Recommended Assignment

- Questions 1–30
- Question 31 (extra credit)
- Self-Test

Extension

Ask students to select several radian values between 0 and 0.6 and compare that value and the sine of that value. Ask students to use a unit circle to explain their results.

For small radian values of θ, $\theta \approx \sin\theta$. Sample explanation: For a point (x, y) on the unit circle, $\sin\theta = y$. If θ is small, then the value of y, the vertical distance from (x, y) to the x-axis, is very close to the distance, *along the unit circle,* between (x, y) and $(1, 0)$. That curved distance is equivalent to the radian value of θ, so $\theta \approx \sin\theta$.

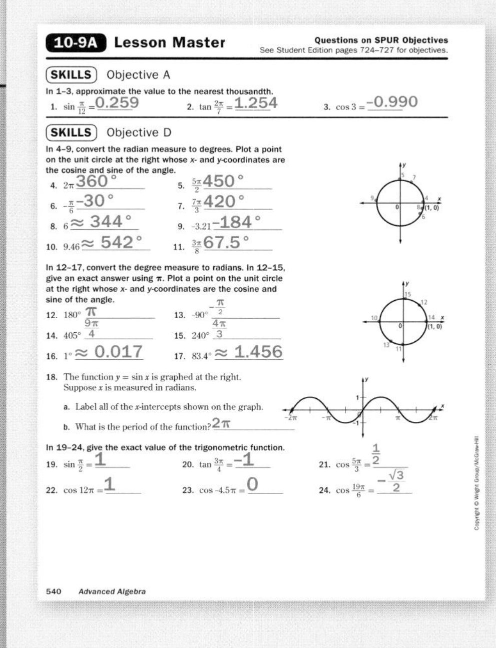
10-9A Lesson Master

Questions on SPUR Objectives
See Student Edition pages 724–727 for objectives.

SKILLS Objective A

In 1–3, approximate the value to the nearest thousandth.

1. $\sin\frac{\pi}{12}$ = 0.259 2. $\tan\frac{2\pi}{7}$ = 1.254 3. cos 3 = −0.990

SKILLS Objective D

In 4–9, convert the radian measure to degrees. Plot a point on the unit circle at the right whose x- and y-coordinates are the cosine and sine of the angle.

4. 2π 360° 5. $\frac{5\pi}{2}$ 450°
6. $-\frac{\pi}{6}$ −30° 7. $\frac{7\pi}{3}$ 420°
8. 6 ≈ 344° 9. -3.21 −184°
10. 9.46 ≈ 542° 11. $\frac{3\pi}{8}$ 67.5°

In 12–17, convert the degree measure to radians. In 12–15, give an exact answer using π. Plot a point on the unit circle at the right whose x- and y-coordinates are the cosine and sine of the angle.

12. 180° π 13. -90° $-\frac{\pi}{2}$
14. 405° $\frac{9\pi}{4}$ 15. 240° $\frac{4\pi}{3}$
16. 1° ≈ 0.017 17. 83.4° ≈ 1.456

18. The function $y = \sin x$ is graphed at the right. Suppose x is measured in radians.
   a. Label all of the x-intercepts shown on the graph.
   b. What is the period of the function? 2π

In 19–24, give the exact value of the trigonometric function.

19. $\sin\frac{\pi}{2}$ = 1 20. $\tan\frac{3\pi}{4}$ = −1 21. $\cos\frac{5\pi}{3}$ = $\frac{1}{2}$
22. $\cos 12\pi$ = 1 23. cos -4.5π = 0 24. $\cos\frac{19\pi}{6}$ = $-\frac{\sqrt{3}}{2}$

540 *Advanced Algebra*

Notes on the Questions

Question 12 This question will help students see the patterns in the common equivalents between degrees and radians.

Questions 15 and 16 You might have students graph the sine and cosine functions using a graphing utility in radian mode. Most calculators will exhibit decimal approximations to multiples of π for the period and the intercepts.

Questions 21–23 These questions relate arc length in a circle to the radius of the circle and the measure in radians of the angle that intercepts the arc. Discuss the formula for the area of a wedge of a circle in terms of radius and arc length, $A = \frac{1}{2}rs$, and point out its similarity to the Triangle Area Formula.

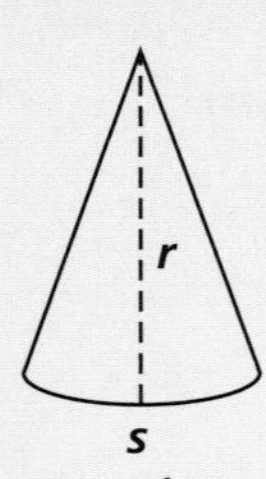

$A = \frac{1}{2}rs$

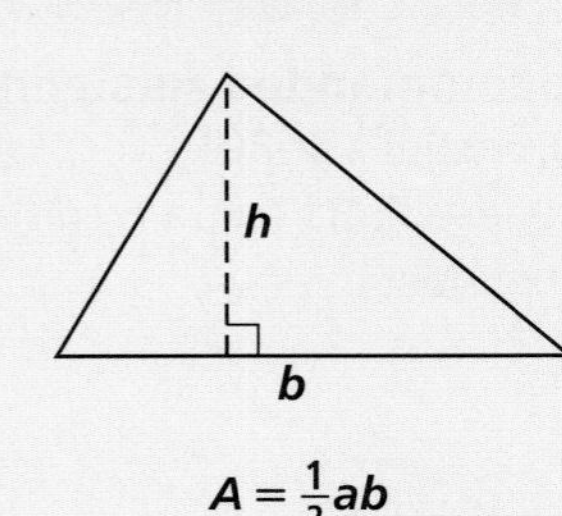

$A = \frac{1}{2}ab$

10-9B page 2

10-9B Lesson Master

Questions on SPUR Objectives
See Student Edition pages 724–727 for objectives.

VOCABULARY

1. Define *radian*.
Answers vary. Sample: the measure of an angle, an arc, or a rotation such that π radians = 180°

True or False In 2–4, if the statement is false, rewrite the statement to make it true.

2. The range of the sine function is the set of all real numbers.
False; the range of the sine function is the set of all numbers from –1 to 1.
3. The graph of the sine function has x-intercepts at the even-numbered multiples of 90°.
true
4. The graphs of $f(\theta) = \cos\theta$ and $g(\theta) = \sin\theta$ are congruent.
true

SKILLS Objective A

In 5–13, approximate the value to the nearest thousandth.

5. $\sin\frac{5\pi}{9}$ 0.985
6. $\tan\frac{\pi}{8}$ 0.414
7. $\cos\frac{\pi}{12}$ 0.966
8. $\sin -\frac{4\pi}{15}$ –0.743
9. $\tan -2.3\pi$ –1.376
10. $\cos 4.6\pi$ –0.309
11. $\sin 3$ 0.141
12. $\tan -5$ 3.381
13. $\sin 16\pi$ 0

SKILLS Objective D

In 14–23, convert the radian measure to degrees. Plot a point on the unit circle at the right whose x- and y-coordinates are the cosine and sine of the angle.

14. $\frac{\pi}{8}$ 22.5°
15. 3π 540°
16. $\frac{\pi}{2}$ 90°
17. $\frac{5\pi}{6}$ 150°
18. $\frac{11\pi}{12}$ 165°
19. $-\frac{\pi}{4}$ –45°
20. -4π –720°
21. 1.5π 270°
22. $\frac{8\pi}{3}$ 480°
23. $\frac{9\pi}{8}$ 202.5°

542 Advanced Algebra 541

In 7–10, convert to radians. Give your answer as a rational number times π.

7. 90° $\frac{\pi}{2}$
8. 15° $\frac{\pi}{12}$
9. 225° $\frac{5\pi}{4}$
10. 330° $\frac{11\pi}{6}$

11. a. Explain the different meanings of sin 6 and sin 6°.
 b. Evaluate sin 6 and sin 6°. -0.279, 0.105

12. Six equally-spaced diameters are drawn on a unit circle, as shown at the right. Copy and complete the diagram, giving equivalent measures in degrees and radians at the end of each radius.

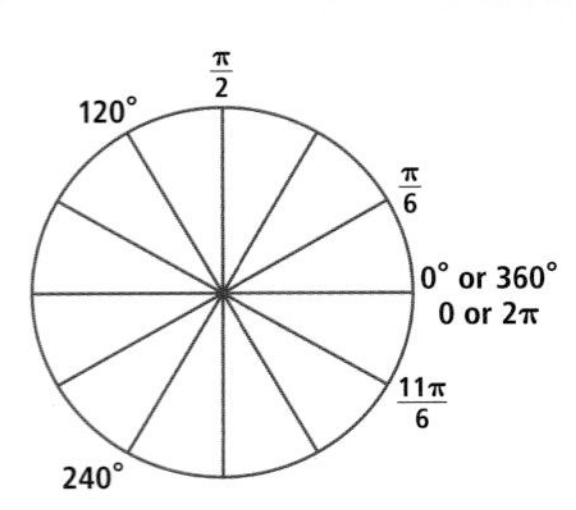

In 13 and 14,
 a. evaluate on a calculator in radian mode.
 b. check your answer using degrees.

13. $\cos\frac{3\pi}{2}$
14. $\tan\frac{\pi}{6}$

In 15 and 16, suppose x is in radians.

15. What is the period of the function $y = \sin x$? 2π
16. Name three x-intercepts of the function $y = \cos x$ on the interval $-2\pi < x < 2\pi$.

11a. sin 6 is the sine of 6 radians; sin 6° is the sine of 6 degrees.
12. See margin.
13a. 0
13b. cos 270° = 0
14a. $\frac{\sqrt{3}}{3}$
14b. tan 30° = $\frac{\sqrt{3}}{3}$
16. Answers vary. Sample: $-\frac{3\pi}{2}, -\frac{\pi}{2}, \frac{\pi}{2}$

APPLYING THE MATHEMATICS

17. **Multiple Choice** Suppose x is in radians. Which transformations map the graph of $y = \cos x$ onto itself? B and D
 A reflection over the x-axis
 B reflection over the y-axis
 C translation of π to the right
 D translation of 2π to the right

18. What is the measure of the obtuse angle made by the hands of a clock at 1:30
 a. in degrees? 135°
 b. in radians? $\frac{3\pi}{4}$

In 19 and 20, find the exact values.

19. $\sin\left(\frac{9\pi}{2}\right)$ 1
20. $\cos\left(\frac{11\pi}{4}\right)$ $-\frac{\sqrt{2}}{2}$

In 21–23, use the following relationship between radian measure and arc length: In a circle of radius r, a central angle of x radians has an arc of length rx.

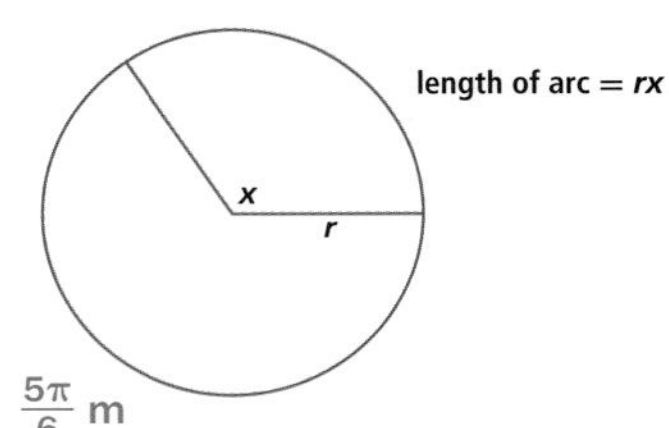

21. a. How long is the arc of a $\frac{\pi}{4}$-radian angle in a circle of radius 10? $\frac{5\pi}{2}$
 b. How long is a 45° arc in a circle of radius 20? 5π
22. On a circle of radius 2 meters, find the length of a 75° arc. $\frac{5\pi}{6}$ m
23. How long is the arc of a $\frac{2\pi}{3}$-radian angle in a circle of radius 8 feet? $\frac{16\pi}{3}$ ft

Additional Answers

12.

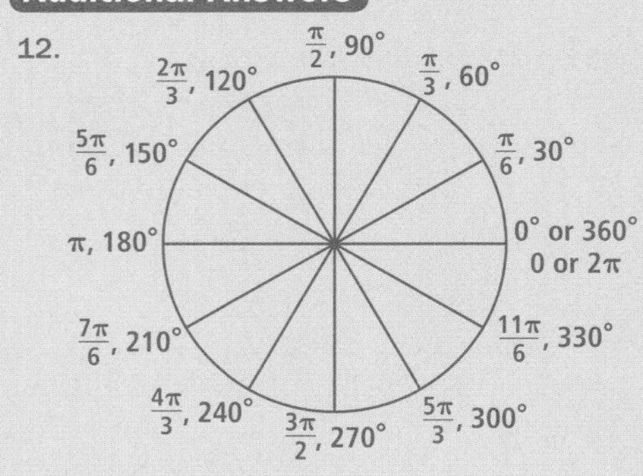

REVIEW

24. In $\triangle ABC$, $m\angle B = 16°$, $b = 10$, and $c = 24$. Explain why there are two possible measures of $\angle C$, and find both of them. (Lesson 10-8)

25. Suppose $0° < \theta < 180°$. Solve $\sin \theta = 0.76$. (Lesson 10-7) See margin.

26. In $\triangle MAP$, $m = 22$, $m\angle M = 149°$, and $m\angle P = 23°$. Find the lengths of p and a. (Lesson 10-7) $p = 16.69$, $a = 5.94$

24. By the Law of Sines, $\frac{\sin 16°}{10} = \frac{\sin C}{24}$, or $\sin C = 2.4 \sin 16° \approx 0.66$. When $0° < \theta < 180°$; $\sin \theta = k$ has two solutions. So, $m\angle C = 41.4°$ or $m\angle C = 138.6°$.

In 27 and 28, evaluate the expression without using a calculator. (Lesson 10-5)

27. $(\sin 450°)^2 + (\cos 450°)^2$ 1

28. $\tan 135°$ -1

29. The newspaper article at the right is from the *Detroit Free Press*, January 29, 1985. Using the drawing below, explain why the construction technique leads to an angle of 26.5°. (Lesson 10-2) See margin.

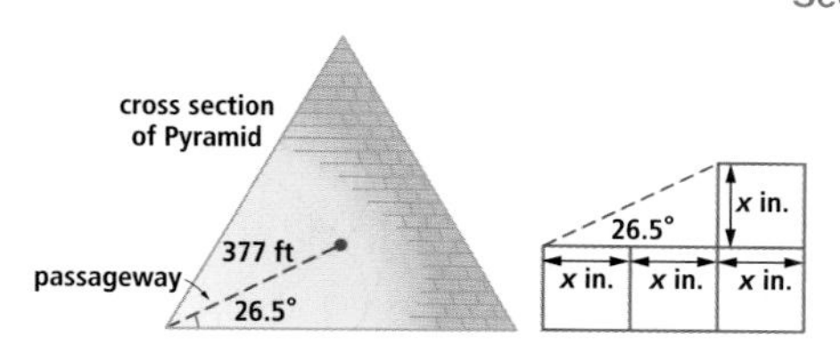

Astronomer Solves Riddle of Pyramid

United Press International

A Navy astronomer has devised a surprisingly simple explanation for the angle of a descending passageway in the Great Pyramid of Cheops in Egypt.

In the early 19th century, English astronomer John Herschel suggested the 377-foot-long passageway was built at its angle of 26.5230 degrees to point at the North Star, making the pyramid an astronomical observatory as well as a tomb for Cheops.

Richard Walker, a U.S. Naval Observatory astronomer based at Flagstaff, Ariz., checked Herschel's idea and found that, because of the wobble of the Earth's axis in its orbit around the sun, no prominent star could have been seen from the base of the passageway built in 2800 BC when the pyramid was built.

Then why was the passageway inclined at an angle of 26.5 degrees?

According to Walker's report, the angle merely was the result of the construction technique.

By placing three stones of equal length horizontally and then placing a fourth stone of equal size on the top of the third horizontal stone, Walker determined that the angle from the top stone to the bottom stone at the other end is 26.5 degrees.

30. One of Murphy's Laws says that the relative frequency r of rain is inversely proportional to the diameter d of the umbrella you are carrying. (Lesson 2-2)
    a. Write an equation relating r and d. $r = \frac{k}{d}$
    b. If the probability of rain is $\frac{1}{4}$ when you are carrying a 46″-diameter umbrella, what is the probability when you are carrying a 36″-diameter umbrella? $\frac{23}{72}$

EXPLORATION

31. When x is in radians, $\sin x$ can be estimated by the formula $\sin x = x - \frac{x^3}{6} + \frac{x^5}{120} - \frac{x^7}{5040}$. 31a–c. See margin.
    a. How close is the value of this expression to $\sin x$ when $x = \frac{\pi}{4}$?
    b. To get greater accuracy, you can add $\frac{x^9}{362,880}$ to the value you got in Part a. Where does the 362,880 come from?
    c. Add $\frac{\left(\frac{x}{4}\right)^9}{362,000}$ to your answer to Part a. How close is this value to $\sin \frac{\pi}{4}$?

QY ANSWER

$\frac{\pi}{3}$

Additional Answers

25. $\theta \approx 49.46°$ or $\theta \approx 130.54°$

29. The stones form a right triangle, with legs of 2 and 1, and $\tan^{-1}\left(\frac{1}{2}\right) = 26.57°$. Thus using this technique will always give about a 26.5° angle.

31a. The estimate gives $\sin\left(\frac{\pi}{4}\right) \approx 0.7071064696$; the exact answer is $\sin\left(\frac{\pi}{4}\right) = \frac{\sqrt{2}}{2}$, which is approximately 0.7071067812, so the estimate is within one millionth of the exact answer.

31b. $362,880 = 9!$

31c. The estimate gives $\sin\left(\frac{\pi}{4}\right) \approx 0.7071067829$, which is one billionth of the exact answer.

Notes on the Questions

Question 30 Do not expect your students to be familiar with the phrase *Murphy's Law.* Some students may even think that Murphy was an ancient mathematician or physicist. In the book *Murphy's Law and Other Reasons Why Things Go Wrong* (Los Angeles: Price/Stern/Sloan Publishers, Inc., 1978), Arthur Bloch states that the original Murphy was Captain Ed Murphy, a development engineer for Northrup Aircraft, who was quoted in 1949 at Wright Field as saying, "If there is any way to do it wrong, he will," referring to a technician who had wired something incorrectly. The name Murphy's Law was given by George E. Nichols of the same company at a press conference, when he announced that Northrup's fine safety record was due to its constant vigilance because of its belief in Murphy's Law.

Question 31 This question gives the first few terms of an infinite series for sin *x*. You might ask students to find the series for cos *x* and tan *x*.

4 Wrap-Up

Ongoing Assessment

Ask students to work in groups. Taking turns, one student should write an expression such as tan 5 or $\cos \frac{7\pi}{4}$, where the angle is measured in radians. Half the group should evaluate that trigonometric ratio. The other half should convert the radian measure to degrees and calculate the same trigonometric ratio for the equivalent degree measure. Answers vary. Using the expressions here, tan(5 radians) ≈ -3.3805, 5 radians ≈ 286.479°, and tan 286.479° ≈ -3.3805; $\cos\left(\frac{7\pi}{4}\text{ radians}\right) \approx \cos(5.497787\text{ radians}) \approx 0.7071$, $\frac{7\pi}{4}$ radians = 315°, and cos 315° ≈ 0.7071.

Project Update

Project 3, *Amplitudes, Periods, and the Tangent Function,* on page 718 relates to the content of this lesson.

Chapter 10

The projects relate to the content of the lessons of this chapter as follows:

Project	Lesson(s)
1	10-6
2	10-8
3	10-9
4	10-6
5	10-3
6	10-3

1 Area Under a Sine Curve

If students can use a graphing utility to find the area bounded by particular lines and curves, encourage them to use the graphing utility to check (not replace!) their answers to Parts a–e of this project.

2 Spherical Trigonometry

As an extension to this project, ask students to explore the question of how many points of intersection are formed if the number of great circles is 2, 3, 4, ..., n. Answers vary. Sample: Each additional great circle intersects each of the previous great circles in two points, so the total number of intersections is $2(0 + 1 + 2 + 3 + ... + (n - 1)) = 2 \cdot \frac{(n-1)n}{2} = n(n - 1)$.

3 Amplitudes, Periods, and the Tangent Function

As an introduction to this project, ask students to graph $y = \sin^2 x + \cos^2 x$ for $0 \le x \le 2\pi$ on a graphing utility. Then ask them to relate their graph to the Pythagorean Identity in Lesson 10-5.

Chapter 10 Projects

The roof of the Kresge Auditorium on the Massachusetts Institute of Technology campus is a spherical triangle.

1 Area Under a Sine Curve

a. Draw a graph of the equation $y = \sin x$ from $x = 0$ to $x = \pi$ radians on graph paper. Let one gridline equal 0.1 unit on each axis.

b. Using the scale of your graph, what is the area of each square?

c. How many whole squares are between the sine curve and the x-axis? Estimate the number of whole squares you can make from the remaining partial squares. Add these to estimate the total number of squares between the sine curve and the x-axis.

d. Calculate $\frac{\text{area}}{\text{square}} \cdot$ (number of squares) to estimate the total area under the graph of $y = \sin x$ from $x = 0$ to $x = \pi$. The final answer should be surprisingly simple.

e. Predict the area under the curve $y = \cos x$ from $x = 0$ to $x = \frac{\pi}{2}$. Devise a method to test your prediction and carry it out.

f. Summarize what you found.

2 Spherical Trigonometry

When three great circles on a sphere intersect at 3 different points, they determine regions called *spherical triangles*. Research the Law of Sines and Law of Cosines for spherical triangles.

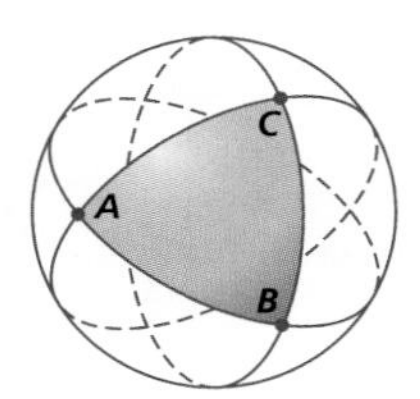

3 Amplitudes, Periods, and the Tangent Function

Set a graphing utility to radian mode.

a. Graph $y = A\sin(x)$ and $y = A\cos(x)$ for several values of A. How does the value of A appear to affect the graphs of these functions?

b. Choose a value of A and graph $y = A\sin(Bx)$ and $y = A\cos(Bx)$ for $B = \{-2\pi, -\pi, 0, \pi, 2\pi\}$. How does the value of B appear to affect the graphs of these functions?

c. Graph $y = \tan(x)$. Determine the period. Describe all asymptotes.

d. Do your conjectures in Parts a and b apply to the graph of $y = A\tan(Bx)$? Explain your answer.

Project Rubric

Advanced	Student correctly provides all of the details asked for in the project as well as additional correct independent conclusions.
Proficient	Student correctly provides all of the details asked for in the project.
Partially proficient	Student correctly provides some of the details asked for in the project or provides all details with some inaccuracies.
Not proficient	Student correctly provides few of the details asked for in the project or provides all details with many inaccuracies.
No attempt	Student makes little or no attempt to complete the project.

4 The Pendulum Swings

a. Using a motion detecting device, record the distance between a pendulum and the device at different times.

b. From this data, determine a curve to model the situation. What is the period of the pendulum swing?

c. Repeat the process for pendulums of different lengths. How does the period depend on the pendulum length?

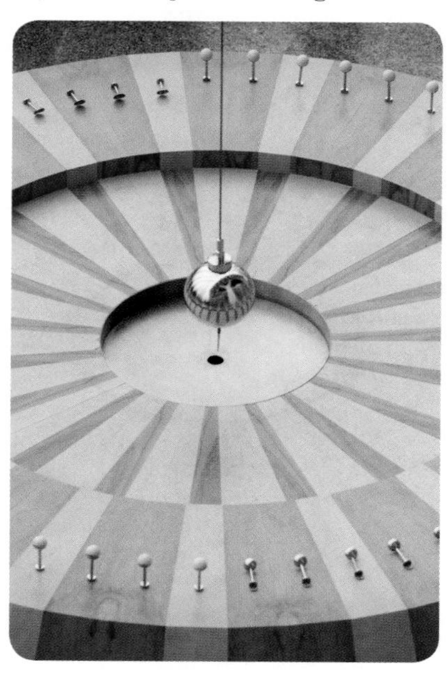

5 Benjamin Banneker

Benjamin Banneker was one of the first African-American mathematicians. Among other things, he was responsible for surveying Washington, D.C., when it was first being developed. Find out more about Banneker and how he used mathematics, particularly trigonometry, in his work.

6 The Great Trigonometric Survey

In the 19th century a trigonometric survey was commissioned in India. Initially, William Lambton and George Everest participated in the work. Research this significant mapping project and find out how the Himalayan Mountains were measured. Summarize your findings in a report.

Notes

4 The Pendulum Swings

Students may be interested to know that Galileo used his own pulse to confirm that, for a given length of a pendulum, the time for each swing of the pendulum remains constant even though the distance traveled during each swing slowly diminishes.

5 Benjamin Banneker

One of Banneker's skills was as a watchmaker. You may want to encourage students to explore the importance of timekeeping for ship's captains, who needed precise clocks to accurately identify the position of their ships based on the locations of stars.

6 The Great Trigonometric Survey

As preparation for this project, ask students to find the coordinates (in Quadrant I) of the other three vertices of a regular pentagon if two consecutive vertices have coordinates (10, 0) and (20, 0). Counterclockwise from (20, 0): (23.09017, 9.51057), (15, 15.38842), (6.90983, 9.51057)

Sample answers for projects are in the Solution Manual in the Electronic Teacher's Edition.

Chapter

10

Summary and Vocabulary

The Summary gives an overview of the entire chapter and provides an opportunity for students to consider the material as a whole. Thus, the Summary can be used to help students relate and unify the concepts presented in the chapter.

Vocabulary words and symbols are listed by lesson to provide a checklist of concepts that students must know. Emphasize to students that they should read the vocabulary list carefully before starting the Self-Test on pages 722–723. If students do not understand the meaning of a vocabulary word, they should refer back to the indicated lesson.

Theorems and Properties covered in the chapter are listed below the Summary with page references included to lead students back to the location in the chapter where the theorem or property is stated.

Chapter 10 Summary and Vocabulary

- Trigonometry is the study of relationships between sides and angles in triangles. In a right triangle, three important trigonometric ratios are the **sine**, **cosine**, and **tangent** of an acute angle θ, defined as follows for $0° < \theta < 90°$:

$$\sin\theta = \frac{\text{leg opposite } \theta}{\text{hypotenuse}};$$

$$\cos\theta = \frac{\text{leg adjacent to } \theta}{\text{hypotenuse}};$$

$$\tan\theta = \frac{\text{leg opposite } \theta}{\text{leg adjacent to } \theta}.$$

hypotenuse
leg opposite θ
θ
leg adjacent to θ

- The sine, cosine, and tangent ratios are frequently used to find lengths in situations involving right triangles. Angle measures are found using inverses of the trigonometric functions: $\mathbf{sin^{-1}}$, $\mathbf{cos^{-1}}$, and $\mathbf{tan^{-1}}$. Applications include finding **angles of elevation**, **depression**, and **parallax**.

- The trigonometric ratios can be generalized to find sines, cosines, and tangents for any real number θ. Every point on a **unit circle** is a rotation image of the point (1, 0) about the origin with magnitude θ. $\cos\theta$ is the x-coordinate of $R_\theta(1, 0)$, and $\sin\theta$ is the y-coordinate of $R_\theta(1, 0)$.

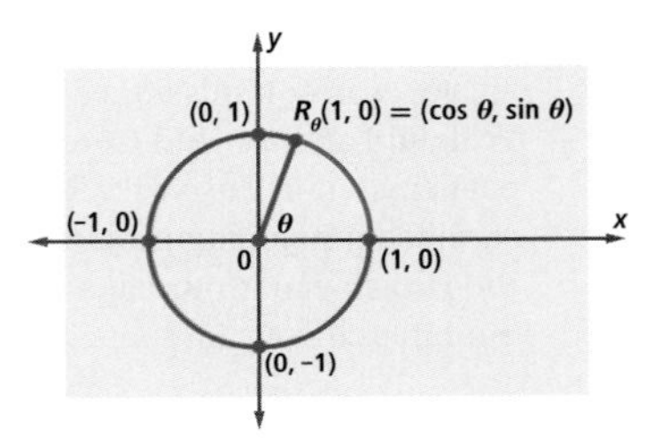

Vocabulary

10-1
right-triangle definitions of sine (sin), cosine (cos) and tangent (tan)
*sine function
*cosine function
*tangent function
*angle of elevation

10-2
*inverse sine function, $\sin^{-1}$
*inverse cosine function, $\cos^{-1}$
*inverse tangent function, $\tan^{-1}$
*angle of depression

10-3
*parallax angle

10-4
*unit circle
unit-circle definition of cosine and sine

10-5
identity
tangent of θ (for all values of θ)

10-6
*periodic function, period
*sine wave
sinusoidal

10-7
*solving a triangle

10-9
*radian

- The mappings $\theta \rightarrow \cos\theta$ and $\theta \rightarrow \sin\theta$ are functions whose domains are the set of real numbers and whose ranges are $\{y \mid -1 \le y \le 1\}$. When θ is in degrees, the graphs of these functions are **sine waves** with **period** 360°. When θ is in **radians**, the period is 2π, because radians are defined such that π radians = 180°.

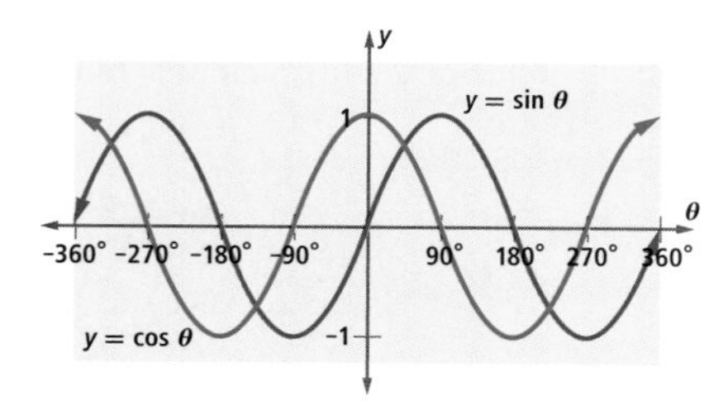

- The Law of Cosines and the Law of Sines relate sides and measures of angles in triangles. In any triangle ABC,

$\frac{\sin A}{a} = \frac{\sin B}{b} = \frac{\sin C}{c}$ (Law of Sines)

$c^2 = a^2 + b^2 - 2ab\cos C$ (Law of Cosines).

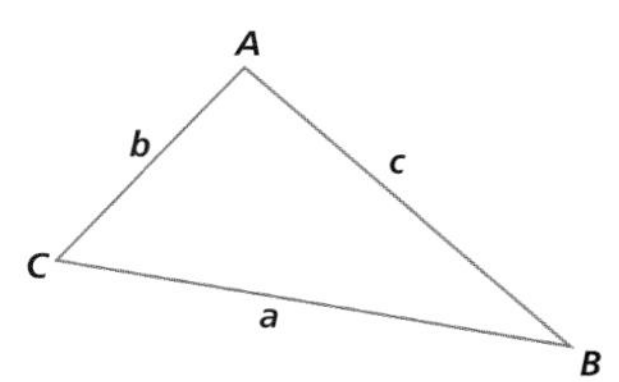

These theorems can be used to **solve a triangle**, that is, to find unknown sides and angle measures in triangles. The Law of Cosines is most useful when an SAS, SSS, or SsA condition is given; the Law of Sines can be used in all other situations that determine triangles.

Theorems and Properties

Pythagorean Identity Theorem (p. 688)
Supplements Theorem (p. 701)
Law of Sines Theorem (p. 702)
Law of Cosines Theorem (p. 706)

Summary and Vocabulary 721

Self-Test

For the development of mathematical competence, feedback and correction, along with the opportunity for practice, are necessary. The Self-Test provides the opportunity for feedback and correction; the Chapter Review provides additional opportunities for practice. We cannot overemphasize the importance of these end-of-chapter materials. It is at this point that the material gels for many students, allowing them to solidify skills and understanding. In general, student performance should improve after these pages.

Assign the Self-Test as a one-night assignment. Worked-out solutions for all questions are in the Selected Answers section of the student book. Encourage students to take the Self-Test honestly, grade themselves, and then be prepared to discuss the test in class.

Advise students to pay special attention to those Chapter Review questions (pages 724–727) that correspond to the questions they missed on the Self-Test.

Chapter 10 Self-Test

Take this test as you would take a test in class. You will need a calculator. Then use the Selected Answers section in the back of the book to check your work.

1. Let $\theta = 17.4°$. Approximate to the nearest thousandth.
   a. $\cos\theta$ b. $\sin\theta$

2. Suppose $0 < \theta < 90°$ and $\tan\theta = 0.64$. Approximate θ to the nearest thousandth of a degree.

3. Use the triangle below. Evaluate.

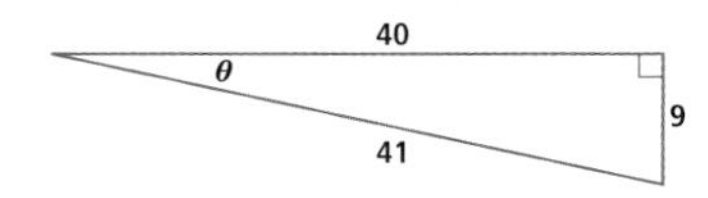

   a. $\cos\theta$ b. $\tan\theta$

4. If $\sin\theta = 0.280$ and $90° < \theta < 180°$, what is $\cos\theta$? See margin.

5. a. What are the exact coordinates of $R_{-423}(1, 0)$? $(\cos(-423°), \sin(-423°))$
   b. Justify your answer to Part a. See margin.

6. For what value of x such that $0° < x \le 180°$ and $x \ne 17°$ does $\sin 17° = \sin x$? See margin.

1a. $\cos 17.4° \approx 0.954$
1b. $\sin 17.4° \approx 0.299$
2. $\tan^{-1}(\tan\theta) = \tan^{-1}(0.64)$; $\theta \approx 32.619°$
3a. $\cos\theta = \frac{\text{adj.}}{\text{hyp.}} = \frac{40}{41}$
3b. $\tan\theta = \frac{\text{opp.}}{\text{adj.}} = \frac{9}{40}$
7. *a*, because the angle that the radius through (a, b) makes with the *x*-axis measures about 70°, and cosine is the *x*-coordinate of points on the unit circle.

In 7 and 8, refer to the unit circle below. Name the letter that could be equal to the value of the trigonometric function.

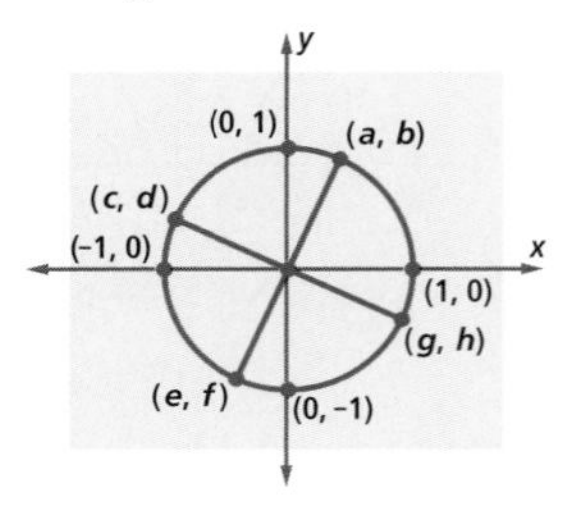

7. $\cos 70°$
8. $\sin 250°$ See margin.

9. Ten minutes ago, Robin Hood spied the Sheriff of Nottingham 250 meters down the road. In order to sneak around, Robin left the road at a 35° angle and traveled 175 meters into the forest as shown below. If the Sheriff has not moved, how far is Robin Hood from the Sheriff now, to the nearest meter? See margin.

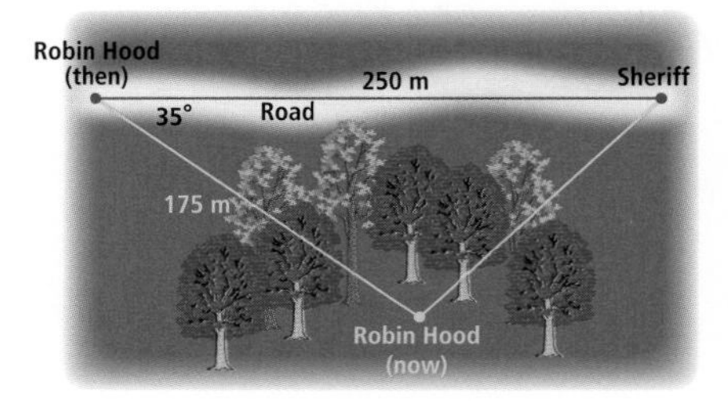

10. In $\triangle SLR$, $m\angle L = 12°$, $s = 425$, and $\ell = 321$. Approximate $m\angle S$ to the nearest 0.1 degree.
    According to the Law of Sines, $\frac{\sin S}{s} = \frac{\sin L}{\ell}$.
    Therefore, $\frac{\sin S}{425} = \frac{\sin 12°}{321}$;
    $m\angle S \approx \sin^{-1}\left(425 \cdot \left(\frac{\sin 12°}{321}\right)\right) \approx 16.0°$

Additional Answers

4. $1 - \sin^2\theta = \cos^2\theta$; $1 - (0.280)^2 = \cos^2\theta$; $\cos\theta = 0.9216$; $\cos\theta = \pm 0.96$. Since $90° < \theta < 180°$, $\cos\theta = -0.96$.

5b. According to the unit-circle definitions of cosine and sine, for any θ, the point $(\cos\theta, \sin\theta)$ is the image of $(1, 0)$ under R_θ.

6. $x = 163°$; since $\sin\theta = \sin(180° - \theta)$, $\sin(180° - 17°) = \sin 163° = \sin 17°$.

8. *f*, because (e, f) is in the third quadrant, and sine is the *y*-coordinate of points on the unit circle.

9. According to the Law of Cosines, $c^2 = a^2 + b^2 - 2ab\cos C$. Therefore, $c^2 = 250^2 + 175^2 - 2(250)(175)\cos 35°$; $c^2 \approx 21{,}449.2$; $c \approx 146.455$; he is about 146 m away.

In 11 and 12, consider the function graphed below.

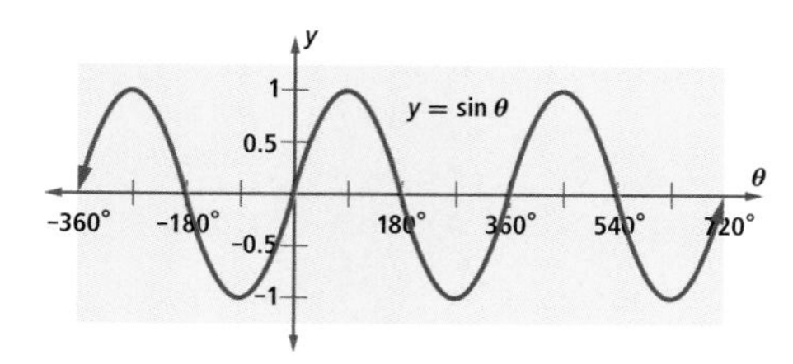

11. What is the period of this function?

12. Name 2 intervals on which the function increases as θ increases.

13. A parallelogram has sides of length 20 and 30. If the shorter diagonal has length 15, find the measures of the angles of the parallelogram. See margin.

14. The star Betelgeuse has a parallax angle of about 0.008 arc-second when viewed from the endpoints of Earth's orbit. How many light-years away is it? Use the facts that 1 arc-second is $\frac{1}{3600}$ degree, 1 light-year is $5.88 \cdot 10^{12}$ miles, and Earth's orbit has a radius of about 93,000,000 miles.

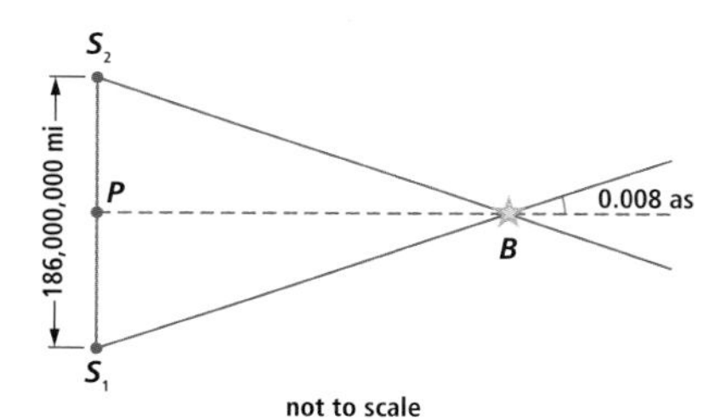

Convert 0.008 arc-second to degrees:

0.008 arc-second $\cdot \frac{1 \text{ degree}}{3600 \text{ arc-seconds}} \approx 0.000002°$.

Let d be the distance from Earth to Betelgeuse.

$\tan(0.000002°) = \frac{93{,}000{,}000}{d}$;

$d \approx 2.66 \cdot 10^{15}$ miles.

Convert miles to light-years.

$d \approx 2.66 \cdot 10^{15}$ miles $\cdot \frac{1 \text{ light-year}}{5.88 \cdot 10^{12} \text{ mi}} \approx 452.4$ light-years

15. Convert to radians. Give your answer as a rational number times π.

a. 60°   b. 25°

16. Convert to degrees. Round your answer to the nearest tenth.

a. 4π radians   b. $\frac{\pi}{7}$ radian

17. A photographer is in a hot air balloon 1500 feet above the ground. She tilts her camera down 36° from horizontal to aim it at an African elephant.

a. How far away from the elephant is the photographer?

b. How far away from the elephant is her assistant, who is standing directly beneath the balloon?

11. $\sin(\theta + 360°) = \sin \theta$ for all values of θ; therefore, the period is 360°.

12. Answers vary. Sample: $-360° < \theta < -270°$ and $-90° < \theta < 90°$

15a. $60° \cdot \frac{\pi}{180°} = \frac{\pi}{3}$

15b. $25° \cdot \frac{\pi}{180°} = \frac{5\pi}{36}$

16a. $4\pi \cdot \frac{180°}{\pi} = 720°$

16b. $\frac{\pi}{7} \cdot \frac{180°}{\pi} \approx 25.7°$

17a. $\sin 36° = \frac{1500}{d}$; $d = \frac{1500}{\sin 36°} \approx 2552$ ft

17b. $\tan 36° = \frac{1500}{a}$; $a = \frac{1500}{\tan 36°} \approx 2065$ ft

Additional Answers

13. $15^2 = 20^2 + 30^2 - 2(20)(30)\cos\theta$; $\cos\theta = \frac{43}{48}$; $\theta = \cos^{-1}\left(\frac{43}{48}\right) = 26.38°$; The sum of the measures of the angles of a parallelogram is 360°, and opposite angles are equal. Therefore, $360 - 2(26.38) = 2\theta$; $\theta = 153.62$. The angles of the parallelogram have measures 153.62°, 26.38°, 153.62°, and 26.38°.

Chapter Review

The main objectives for the chapter are organized in the Chapter Review under the four types of understanding this book promotes: Skills, Properties, Uses, and Representations.

Whereas end-of-chapter material may be considered optional in some texts, in UCSMP *Advanced Algebra* we have selected these objectives and questions with the expectation that they will be covered. Students should be able to answer these questions with about 85% accuracy after studying the chapter.

You may assign these questions over a single night to help students prepare for a test the next day or you may assign the questions over a two-day period. If you work the questions over two days, we recommend assigning the evens for homework the first night so that students get feedback in class the next day, and then assigning the odds the night before the test because the answers are provided to the odd-numbered questions in the Selected Answers section at the back of the book.

It is effective to ask students which questions they still do not understand and use the day as a total class discussion of the material that the class finds most difficult.

Resources

- Assessment Resources: Chapter 10 Test Forms A–D; Chapter 10 Test, Cumulative Form

Technology Resources

Teacher's Assessment Assistant, Ch. 10
Electronic Teacher's Edition, Ch. 10

Chapter 10 Chapter Review

SKILLS
PROPERTIES
USES
REPRESENTATIONS

SKILLS Procedures used to get answers

OBJECTIVE A **Approximate values of trigonometric functions using a calculator.** (Lessons 10-1, 10-9)

In 1–6, evaluate to the nearest thousandth.

1. $\sin 34°$ 0.559
2. $\cos^2 125°$ 0.329
3. $\sin\left(-\frac{\pi}{8}\right)$ -0.383
4. $\cos 3$ -0.990
5. $\sin\left(\frac{8\pi}{5}\right)$ -0.951
6. $\tan 167°$ -0.231

OBJECTIVE B **Determine the measure of an angle given its sine, cosine, or tangent.** (Lessons 10-2, 10-7)

In 7–10, find all θ between 0° and 180° satisfying the given equation. 7. $\theta = 30°$ or $150°$

7. $\sin \theta = 0.5$
8. $\cos \theta = \frac{\sqrt{2}}{2}$ $\theta = 45°$
9. $\cos \theta = 0$ $\theta = 90°$
10. $\tan \theta = 1$ $\theta = 45°$

OBJECTIVE C **Find missing side lengths and angle measures of a triangle using the Law of Sines or the Law of Cosines.** (Lessons 10-7, 10-8)

In 11–15, use the Law of Sines or the Law of Cosines to solve for the variable. Round your answers to the nearest tenth.

11.

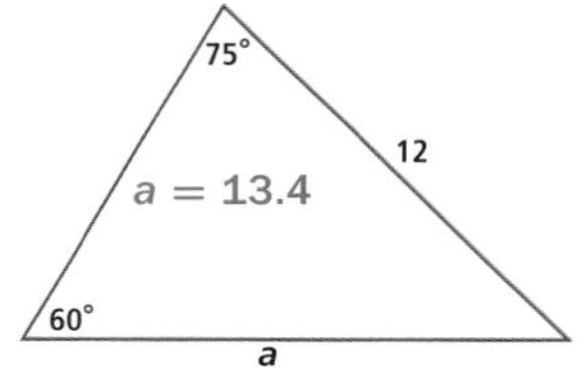

12.

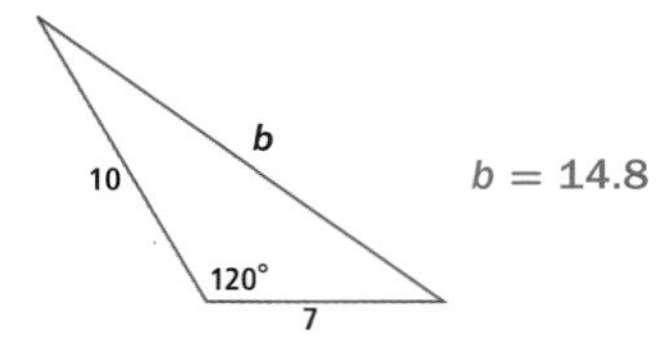

$b = 14.8$

13.

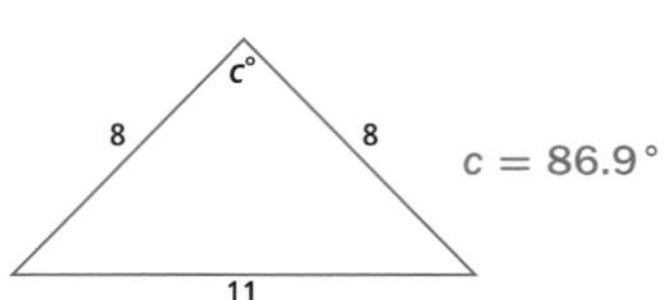

$c = 86.9°$

14.

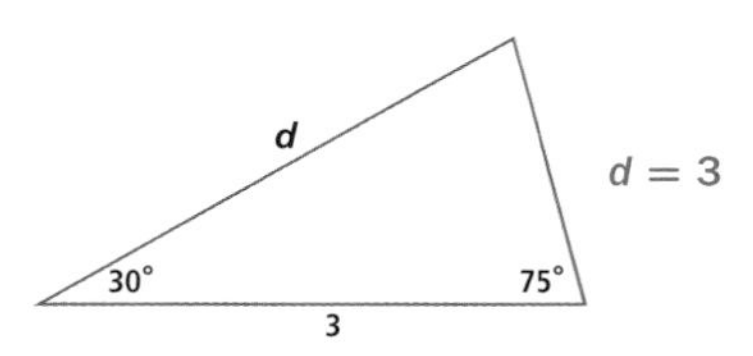

$d = 3$

15.

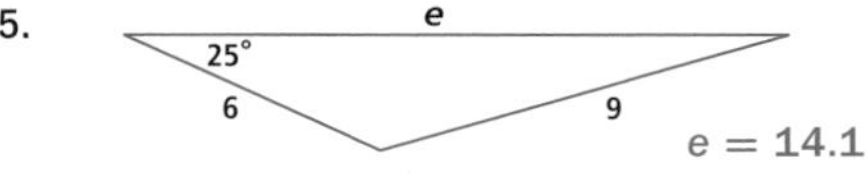

$e = 14.1$

OBJECTIVE D **Convert angle measures from radians to degrees or from degrees to radians.** (Lesson 10-9)

In 16–19, convert to radians. Express your answers in terms of π.

16. $30°$ $\frac{\pi}{6}$
17. $-105°$ $-\frac{7\pi}{12}$
18. $360°$ 2π
19. $405°$ $\frac{9\pi}{4}$

In 20–23, convert the radian measure to degrees. Round your answers to the nearest tenth.

20. π 180°
21. $\frac{3\pi}{2}$ 270°
22. $-\frac{\pi}{8}$ -22.5°
23. $\frac{7\pi}{6}$ 210°

PROPERTIES Principles behind the mathematics

OBJECTIVE E Identify and use the definitions of sine, cosine, and tangent. (Lessons 10-1, 10-4, 10-5)

Multiple Choice In 24–27, use the diagram below. Identify the given trigonometric function as one of the following ratios.

A $\frac{AB}{BC}$ B $\frac{AC}{BC}$

C $\frac{AB}{AC}$ D $\frac{AC}{AB}$

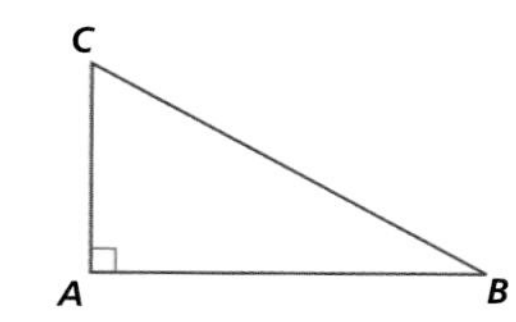

24. $\sin B$ B
25. $\tan B$ D
26. $\cos C$ B
27. $\tan C$ C

In 28–30, use the triangle below. Evaluate each trigonometric function.

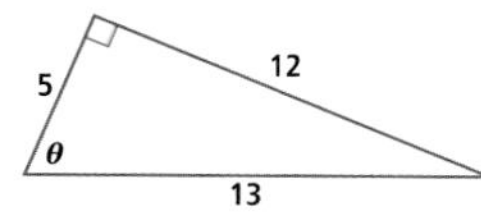

28. $\sin \theta$ $\frac{12}{13}$
29. $\cos \theta$ $\frac{5}{13}$
30. $\tan \theta$ $\frac{12}{5}$

31. **True or False** $\sin \frac{4\pi}{7} = \tan \frac{4\pi}{7} \cdot \cos \frac{4\pi}{7}$. Justify your answer without a calculator.

32. **Multiple Choice** What is the image of (1, 0) under R_{-600}? D
   - A $(-\sin 600°, -\cos 600°)$
   - B $(-\cos 600°, -\sin 600°)$
   - C $(\sin -600°, \cos -600°)$
   - D $(\cos -600°, \sin -600°)$

31. true; $\tan x \cdot \cos x = \frac{\sin x}{\cos x} \cdot \cos x = \sin x$ as long as x is not an odd multiple of $\frac{\pi}{2}$.

33. **Fill in the Blanks** Because $R_{253}(1, 0) \approx (-0.292, -0.956)$, $\cos 253° \approx$ _?_ and $\sin 253° \approx$ _?_. −0.292; −0.956

OBJECTIVE F Identify and use theorems relating sines and cosines. (Lessons 10-5, 10-7). 34–36. See margin.

34. **True or False** For all real numbers θ, $\sin \theta - \sin(180° - \theta) = 0$. Justify your answer.

35. **True or False** For all real numbers θ, $\cos \theta - \cos(180° - \theta) = 0$. Justify your answer.

36. Suppose $0° \le \theta < 90°$. If $\sin \theta = \frac{3}{5}$, use the Pythagorean Identity to determine $\cos \theta$.

37. Suppose $\sin x = 0.25$. What are all possible values of $\cos x$? $\cos x \approx \pm 0.968$

USES Applications of mathematics in real-world situations

OBJECTIVE G Solve real-world problems using the trigonometry of right triangles. (Lessons 10-1, 10-2, 10-3)

38. A tower is anchored by a 250-foot guy wire attached to the tower at a point 150 feet above the ground. What is the angle of elevation of the wire, to the nearest degree? 37°

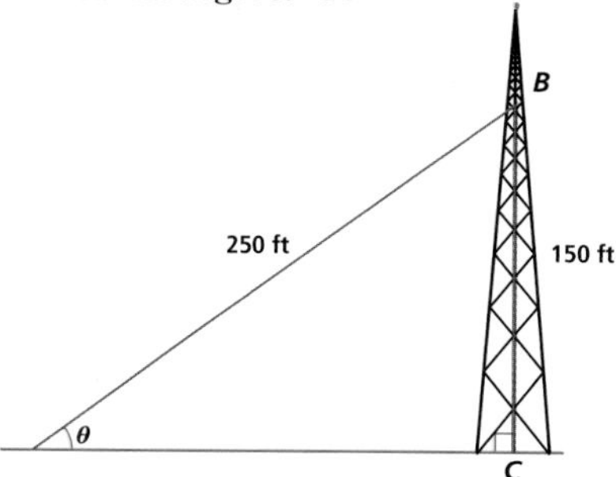

Additional Answers

34. True; $\sin \theta - \sin(180° - \sin(180° - \theta)) = \sin \theta - \sin \theta = 0$
35. False; $\cos \theta - \cos(180° - \theta) = \cos \theta + \cos \theta \neq 0$
36. $x = 4$, $\cos \theta = \frac{4}{5}$

Additional Answers

42. *B* is closer; the fire is about 10.8 miles away from it.

44. *A* is 16.3 mi and *B* is 11.2 mi from the ship.

46. $\frac{\sqrt{2}-\sqrt{6}}{4}$

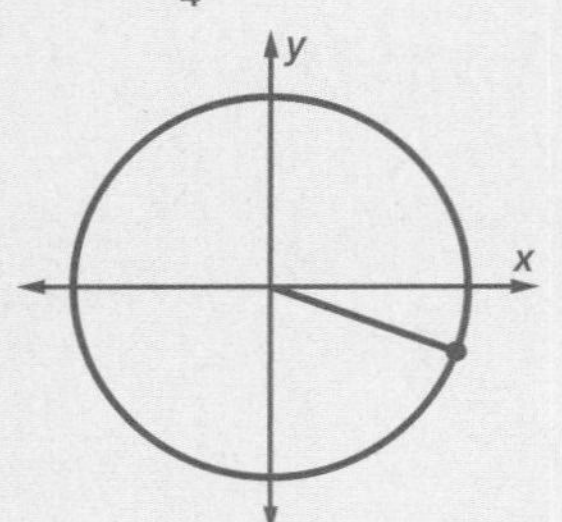

47. $\frac{\sqrt{2}-\sqrt{6}}{4}$

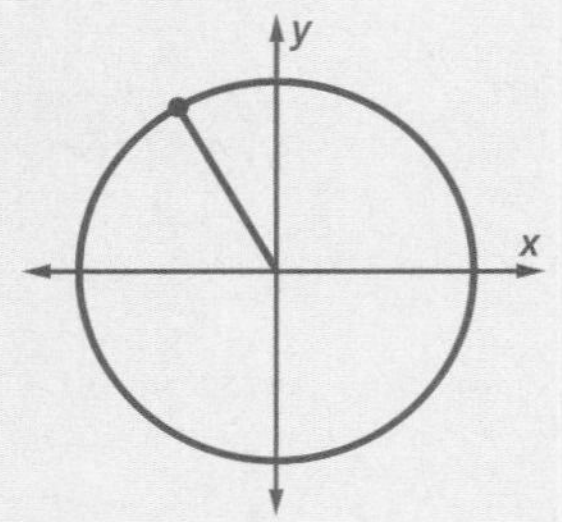

48. $\frac{-\sqrt{2}-\sqrt{6}}{4}$

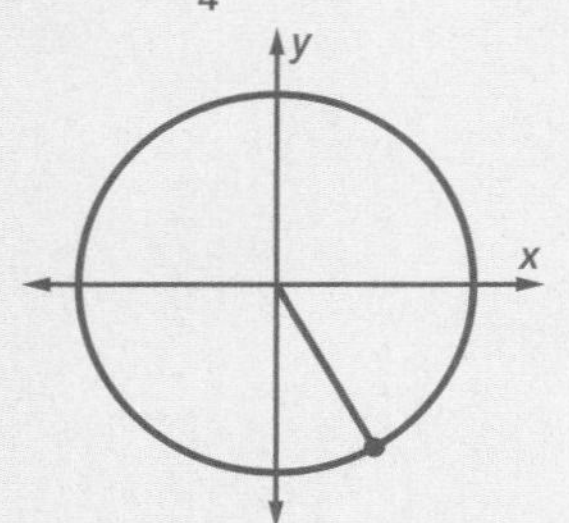

49. $\frac{-\sqrt{2}-\sqrt{6}}{4}$

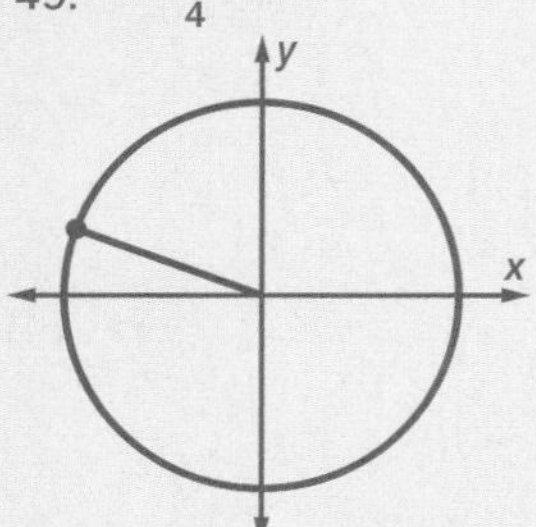

39. A wheelchair ramp is built with slope $\frac{1}{12}$. To the nearest tenth of a degree, what angle does the ramp make with the horizontal? 4.8°

40. A ship sails 560 kilometers at an angle 35° clockwise from north. How far east of its original position is the ship? about 321.2 km

41. Neil and Buzz are exploring the Moon. At one moment, the Sun is shining directly over Neil. Meanwhile, Buzz has just set up a 10-meter tall flagpole 150 kilometers away from Neil. The flagpole casts a shadow that is 86 centimeters long. Using this information, compute the circumference of the Moon to the nearest 100 kilometers. 11,000 km

OBJECTIVE H Solve real-world problems using the Law of Sines or Law of Cosines. (Lessons 10-7, 10-8)

42. Observers in two ranger stations 8 miles apart spot a fire. The observer in station *A* spots the fire at an angle of 44° with the line between the two stations, while the observer in station *B* spots the fire at a 105° angle with the same line. Which station is closer to the fire, and how far away is the fire from this station? See margin.

43. Pictured below is the top view of a chandelier with 10 spokes equally spaced around a central point in the same plane. If each spoke is 50 cm long, what is the perimeter of the chandelier? about 309 cm

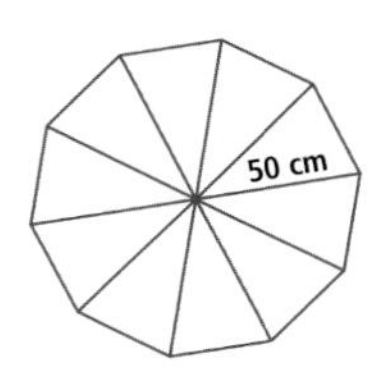

44. Two observers are in lighthouses 25 miles apart, as shown below. The observer in lighthouse *A* spots a ship in distress at an angle of 20° with the line between the lighthouses. The observer in lighthouse *B* spots the ship at an angle of 30° with that line. How far is the ship from each lighthouse? See margin.

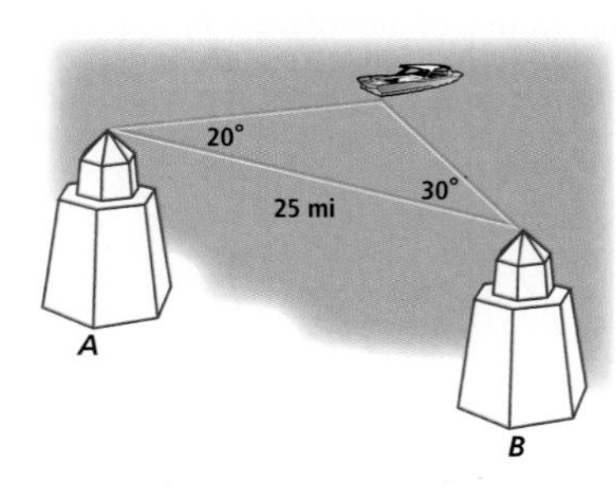

45. The White House, the Washington Monument, and the Lincoln Memorial form the triangle shown below. To the nearest degree, find the angle θ between the Lincoln Memorial and the White House at the Washington Monument. 84°

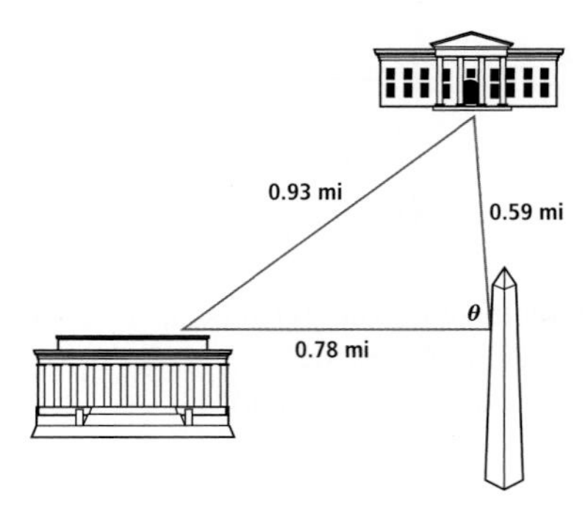

Additional Answers

50. $\frac{\sqrt{2}-\sqrt{6}}{4}$

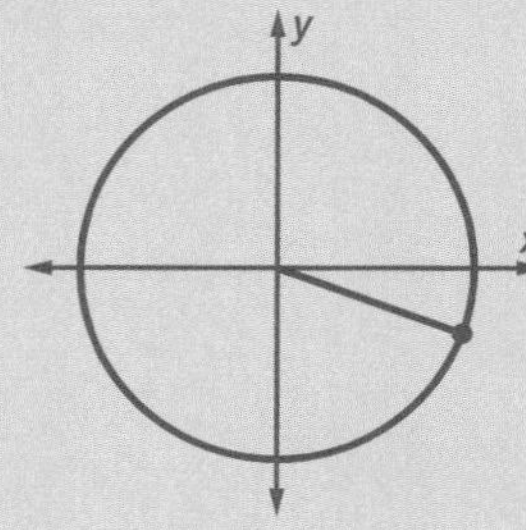

51. $\frac{\sqrt{6}-\sqrt{2}}{4}$

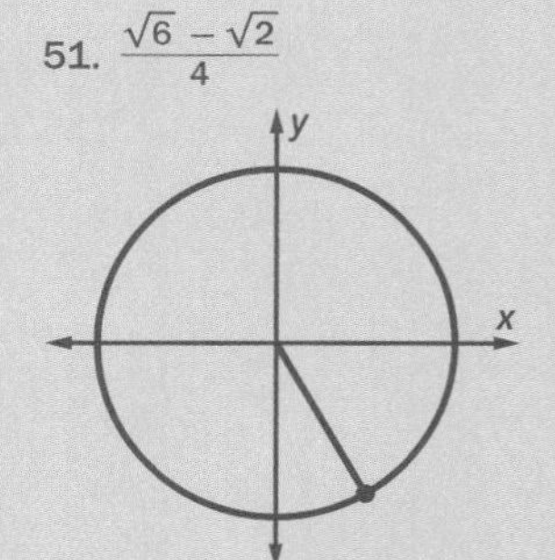

REPRESENTATIONS Pictures, graphs, or objects that illustrate concepts

OBJECTIVE I Use the properties of a unit circle to find values of trigonometric functions. (Lessons 10-4, 10-5)

In 46–51, use the fact that

$\sin 15° = \cos 75° = \frac{\sqrt{6} - \sqrt{2}}{4}$,

and $\sin 75° = \cos 15° = \frac{\sqrt{6} + \sqrt{2}}{4}$.

Evaluate without a calculator. Draw a picture to explain your result. 46–51. See margin.

46. $\sin 345°$
47. $\cos 105°$
48. $\sin 285°$
49. $\cos 165°$
50. $\sin(-15°)$
51. $\cos(-435°)$

In 52 and 53, use the diagram below.

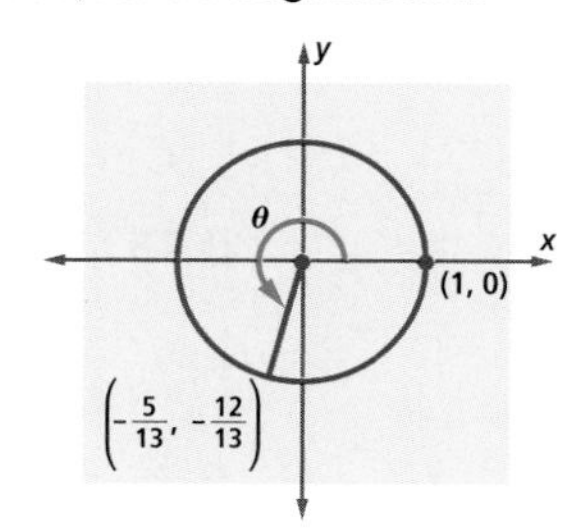

52. What is the value of $\sin \theta$? $-\frac{12}{13}$
53. Find θ to the nearest radian. 4 radians

In 54–56, use the unit circle below. Which letter could stand for the given number?

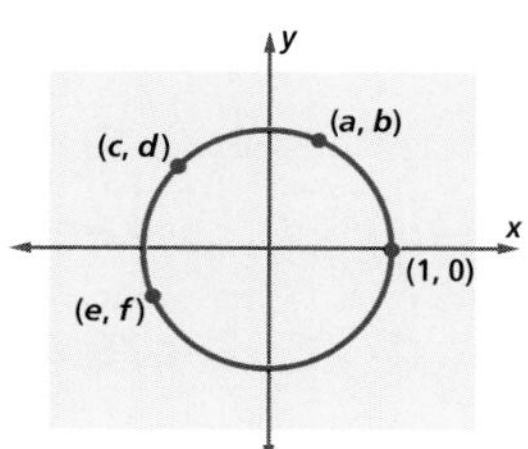

54. $\sin 67°$ *b*
55. $\cos 560°$ *e*
56. $\sin(-222°)$ *d*

OBJECTIVE J Identify properties of the sine and cosine functions using their graphs. (Lesson 10-6)

57. a. Graph the sine function on the interval $0° \le \theta \le 360°$. See margin.
    b. State the domain and range of the sine function.
    domain: all real numbers; range: $-1 \le y \le 1$
58. a. Graph the cosine function on the interval $-2\pi \le \theta \le 2\pi$. 58a–b. See margin.
    b. At what points does the graph of the cosine function intersect the *x*-axis?
    c. What is the period of the cosine function? 2π
59. The graph of $y = \cos x$ is the image of the graph of $y = \sin x$ under what translation?
    Answers vary. Sample: $T: (x, y) \rightarrow (x - 90°, y)$

In 60 and 61, use the graph below.

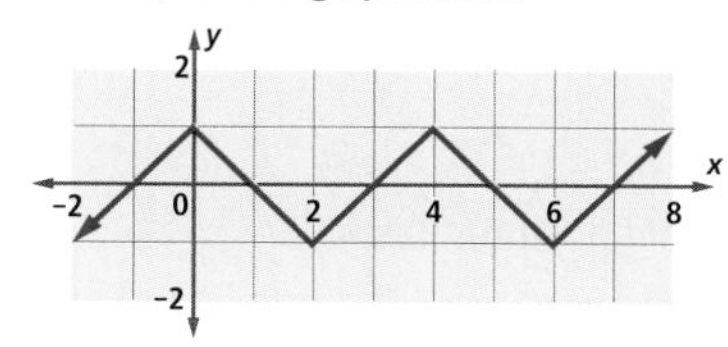

60. What is the period of this graph? 4
61. Is this graph a sine wave? Why or why not?
    No; this graph cannot be mapped onto the graph of the sine function $s: \theta \rightarrow \sin \theta$ by any composite of translations, scale changes, or reflections.

Assessment

Evaluation The *Assessment Resources* provide four forms of the Chapter 10 Test. Forms A and B present parallel versions of a short-answer format. Form C consists of four to six short-response questions that cover the SPUR objectives from Chapter 10. Form D offers performance assessment that covers a subset (or even just one) of the SPUR objectives for the chapter. The fifth type of test is a Chapter 10 Test, Cumulative Form. About 50% of this test covers Chapter 10, and the remaining 50% covers the previous chapters evenly.

Feedback After students have taken the test for Chapter 10 and you have scored the results, return the tests to students for discussion. Class discussion on the questions that caused trouble for most students can be very effective in identifying and clarifying misunderstandings. You might want to have them note the items they missed and work either in groups or at home to correct them. It is important for students to receive feedback on every chapter test, and we recommend that students see and correct their mistakes before proceeding too far into the next chapter.

Suggestions for Assignment Assign Lesson 11-1 for homework the evening of the test. It gives students work to do after they have completed the test and keeps the class moving. If you do not do this, you may cover one less chapter over the course of the year.

Additional Answers

57a.

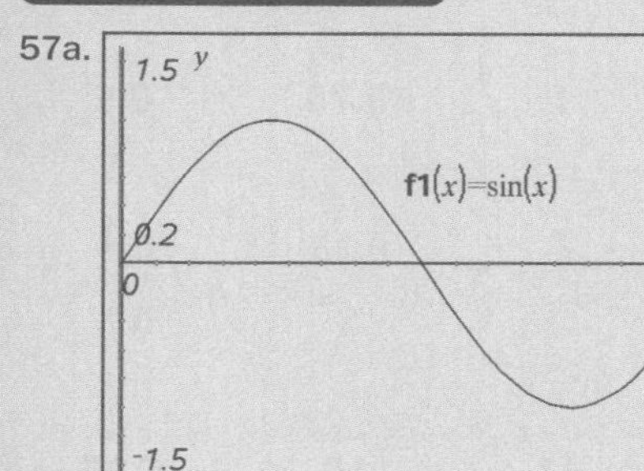

58a.

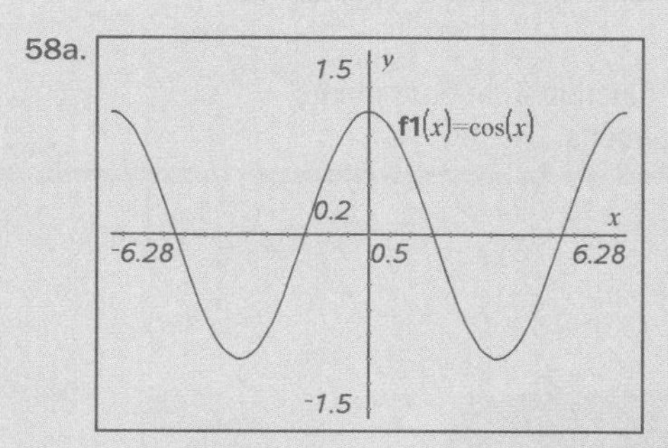

58b. $\theta = -\frac{3\pi}{2}, -\frac{\pi}{2}, \frac{\pi}{2}, \frac{3\pi}{2}$

Chapter

11 Polynomials

Chapter Overview

Lesson	Local Standards	Pacing (in days) Average	Advanced	Block
11-1 Introduction to Polynomials **E** Describe attributes of polynomials. **H** Use polynomials to model real-world situations. **J** Graph polynomial functions.		1	0.75	0.5
11-2 Multiplying Polynomials **A** Use the Extended Distributive Property to multiply polynomials. **E** Describe attributes of polynomials. **I** Use polynomials to describe geometric situations.		1	0.75	0.5
11-3 Quick-and-Easy Factoring **B** Factor polynomials. **E** Describe attributes of polynomials.		1	0.75	0.5
QUIZ 1		0.5	0.5	0.25
11-4 The Factor Theorem **C** Find zeros of polynomial functions by factoring. **F** Apply the Zero-Product Theorem, Factor Theorem, and Fundamental Theorem of Algebra. **J** Graph polynomial functions. **K** Estimate zeros of polynomial functions using graphs.		2	1	0.75
11-5 The Rational-Root Theorem **G** Apply the Rational-Root Theorem. **J** Graph polynomial functions. **K** Estimate zeros of polynomial functions using graphs.		1	0.75	0.5
11-6 Solving All Polynomial Equations **C** Find zeros of polynomial functions by factoring. **F** Apply the Zero-Product Theorem, Factor Theorem, and Fundamental Theorem of Algebra.		1	0.75	0.5
QUIZ 2		0.5	0.5	0.25
11-7 Finite Differences **D** Determine an equation for a polynomial function from data points.		1	0.75	0.5
11-8 Modeling Data with Polynomials **D** Determine an equation for a polynomial function from data points. **H** Use polynomials to model real-world situations.		1	0.75	0.5
	Self-Test	1	0.75	0.5
	Chapter Review	2	1	0.5
	Test	1	1	0.5
	TOTAL	14	10	6.25

Technology Resources

Teacher's Assessment Assistant, Ch. 11

Electronic Teacher's Edition, Ch. 11

Differentiated Options  Universal Access

	Accommodating the Learner	Vocabulary Development	Ongoing Assessment	Materials
11-1	pp. 732, 733	p. 731	oral, p. 737	CAS
11-2	pp. 740, 741	p. 739	written, p. 744	
11-3	pp. 748, 749	p. 747	written, p. 751	CAS
11-4	pp. 754–755, 756	p. 753	group, p. 759	CAS
11-5	pp. 762, 763		written, p. 765	
11-6	pp. 768, 769	p. 768	group, p. 771	CAS
11-7	pp. 773, 775	p. 774	group, p. 777	
11-8	pp. 779, 782–783		group, p. 785	

Objectives

Skills	Lessons	Self-Test Questions	Chapter Review Questions
A Use the Extended Distributive Property to multiply polynomials.	11-2	2, 3	1–4
B Factor polynomials.	11-3	15, 17	5–14
C Find zeros of polynomial functions by factoring.	11-4, 11-6	11, 12, 16	15–19
D Determine an equation for a polynomial function from data points.	11-7, 11-8	19, 20	20–24
Properties			
E Describe attributes of polynomials.	11-1, 11-2, 11-3	4, 7a	25-31
F Apply the Zero-Product Theorem, Factor Theorem, and Fundamental Theorem of Algebra.	11-4, 11-6	7b, 13	32-37
G Apply the Rational-Root Theorem.	11-5	8, 10a, 14	38–42
Uses			
H Use polynomials to model real-world situations.	11-1, 11-8	5, 6	43–46
I Use polynomials to describe geometric situations.	11-2	1	47–50
Representations			
J Graph polynomial functions.	11-1, 11-4, 11-5	18	51–54
K Estimate zeros of polynomial functions using graphs.	11-4, 11-5	9, 10b	55–57

Resource Masters Chapter 11

None of the generic Resource Masters apply to this chapter.

Resource Master 204 Lesson 11-1

Warm-Up

Fill in the Blanks In 1 and 2, fill in the blanks.

1. For all x, $-2x^5 + x^{10} - 11 =$ ____x^{10} + ____x^5 + ____x^2 + -11x____.
2. For all y, $(5 - 4y)(3y + 2) =$ ____y^2 + ____y + ____.

Additional Example

1. a. List all the coefficients of $3x^2 + 6x^5 - 47 - 8x^2$.
   b. What are the degree and leading coefficient of $3x^2 + 6x^5 - 47 - 8x^2$?
   c. Rewrite the polynomial in standard form.

   Solution

   a. First, combine like terms: $3x^2 + 6x^5 - 47 - 8x^2 =$ (____ − ____)x^2 + ____x^5 − ____ = ____.
   So, using the definition of a polynomial,
   $a_5 =$ ____, $a_4 =$ ____, $a_3 =$ ____,
   $a_2 =$ ____, $a_1 =$ ____, and $a_0 =$ ____.
   b. The largest exponent is ____. The degree of the polynomial is ____. The coefficient of the x^5 term is ____. The leading coefficient is ____.
   c. In standard form, the terms are in descending order. So, the standard form of this polynomial is ____x^5 − ____x^2 − ____.

Resource Master for Lesson 11-1

Resource Master 205 Lesson 11-1

Additional Examples

2. Consider the polynomial function P with equation $P(x) = 6x^5 - 3x^4 + 4x^2 - 2x - 70$.
   a. What is $P(2)$?
   b. Graph this function in the window $-3 \leq x \leq 3$, $-120 \leq y \leq 10$.
3. Let $f(x) = 5x^3 - 3x^2 + 4$ and $g(x) = 2x + 6$. Predict
   a. the degree of $f(x) \cdot g(x)$.
   b. the leading coefficient of $f(x) \cdot g(x)$.
   c. the degree of $f(g(x))$.
   d. the leading coefficient of $f(g(x))$.

   Solution

   a. Because the degree of f is 3 and the degree of g is 1, the degree of $f(x) \cdot g(x)$ is ____ + ____ = ____.
   b. Because the leading coefficient of f is 5 and the leading coefficient of g is 2, the leading coefficient of $f(x) \cdot g(x)$ is ____ · ____ = ____.
   c. Because the degree of f is 3 and the degree of g is 1, the degree of $f(g(x))$ is ____ · ____ = ____.
   d. Because the leading coefficient of f is 5, the leading coefficient of g is 2, and the degree of f is 3, the leading coefficient of $f(g(x))$ is ____ · (____)^3 = ____.

Resource Master for Lesson 11-1

Resource Master 206 Lesson 11-1

Additional Example

4. Getta D. Gree and her family will start saving for college when she graduates from eighth grade. At the end of each summer, they will deposit money into a savings plan with an annual percentage yield (APY) of 4.2%. Getta is planning to begin college in the fall following her graduation from high school. How much money will be in the account when she leaves for college, if no other money is added or withdrawn?

End of Summer After	Amount Deposited ($)
8th grade	2000
9th grade	2500
10th grade	2200
11th grade	2050
12th grade	2100

Polynomial Degrees

Degree	Polynomial Name	Example
1	Linear	$mx + b$
2	Quadratic	$ax^2 + bx + c$
3	Cubic	$ax^3 + bx^2 + cx + d$
4	Quartic	$ax^4 + bx^3 + cx^2 + dx + e$
5	Quintic	$ax^5 + bx^4 + cx^3 + dx^2 + ex + f$

Resource Master for Lesson 11-1

Resource Master 207 Lesson 11-2

Warm-Up

A given rectangle has length L and width W.

1. The length of the rectangle is multiplied by a, and the width is multiplied by b. What is the effect on the area of the rectangle? Explain.
2. **Multiple Choice** The length of the rectangle is increased by a, and the width is increased by b. What is the effect on the area of the rectangle? Explain.
   A The area is increased by ab.
   B The area is increased by $a + b$.
   C The area is increased by $2a + 2b$.
   D The amount the area is increased depends on the original length and width.

Additional Examples

1. Expand $(5x^2 - 4x + 3) \cdot (x - 7)$ and write your answer in standard form.
2. a. Find the volume V of the large box by multiplying its dimensions.
   b. Find the volume V of the large box by adding the volumes of the small boxes.
   c. Show that the answers to Parts a and b are equal.

Resource Master for Lesson 11-2

Resource Master 208 Lesson 11-2

Additional Examples

3. Without expanding, find the leading term, the last term, and the coefficient of the x^3 term of $(3x^2 + 4)(2x^2 - 7)(8x + 1)$ when written in standard form.
   Solution The leading term is the product of the leading terms of the factors. The leading term of the product is (____)(____)·(____) = ____.
   The last term is the product of the last terms of the factors: (____)(____)·(____) = ____.
   A term with x^3 will arise from multiplying $3x^2$ from the first factor, -7 from the second factor, and $8x$ from the third factor. The only other term with x^3 will arise from multiplying 4 from the first factor, ____ from the second factor, and ____ from the third factor.
   The first product is ____x^3; the second is ____x^3. After combining like terms, the x^3 term in the product is ____x^3.
4. A square piece of tin measuring 24 inches by 24 inches is to be folded into an open container after cutting squares of side length x from each corner. Let $V(x)$ be the volume of the box.
   a. Write a polynomial formula for $V(x)$ in standard form.
   b. What is the maximum possible volume?

Resource Master for Lesson 11-2

Resource Master 209 Lesson 11-2

Example 4

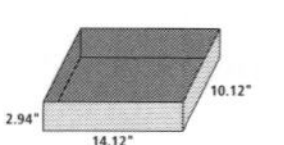

Question 11

x	$V(x)$
1	252
2	
3	420
4	
5	
6	192
7	
8	
9	-36
10	

Resource Master for Lesson 11-2

Resource Master 210 Lesson 11-3

Warm-Up

For 1–5, factor without using a CAS.

1. $64x^2 - 49x$
2. $64x^2 - 49$
3. $64x^2 + 49$
4. $64x^2 - 112x + 49$
5. $64x^2 - 441x - 49$

Additional Examples

1. Factor $6x^4 + 24x^2$.
2. Factor each polynomial.
   a. $49x^4y^2 - 81y^4$
   b. $m^2 + 16m + 64$

   Solution

   a. $49x^4y^2 = (7x^2y)^2$ and $81y^4 = (9y^2)^2$, so this polynomial is a difference of squares. Use difference of squares factoring: $49x^4y^2 - 81y^4 = (\_\_\_\_)^2 - (\_\_\_\_)^2 = (\_\_\_\_ + \_\_\_\_)(\_\_\_\_ - \_\_\_\_)$.

   b. This polynomial is in binomial square form with $a = m$ and $b = \pm 8$. For the signs to agree with the first pattern in the Binomial Square Factoring Theorem, you need $b = 8$. So, $m^2 + 16m + 64 = m^2 + 2 \cdot \_\_\_ \cdot \_\_\_ + (\_\_\_)^2 = (\_\_\_\_)^2$.
3. Factor $x^2 + 4x - 21$.
4. a. Is $x^2 - 6$ prime over the integers?
   b. Is $x^2 - 6$ prime over the real numbers?

Resource Master for Lesson 11-3

Resource Master 211 Lesson 11-4

Warm-Up

For 1–3, find an x-intercept of the graph of the function P by graphing. Then, check by using a CAS.

1. $P(x) = 7x^{17} + 12x^9 - 1.6x$
2. $P(x) = 7(x + 2)^{17} + 12(x + 2)^9 - 1.6(x + 2)$
3. $P(x) = 7(x - 4.5)^{17} + 12(x - 4.5)^9 - 1.6(x - 4.5)$

Additional Examples

1. In Additional Example 4 of Lesson 11-2, the volume $V(x)$ of the box shown below is given by $V(x) = x(24 - 2x)(24 - 2x) = 4x^3 - 96x^2 + 576x$. Find the zeros of V.

   24 − 2x
   x
   24 − 2x

2. Find the roots of $P(x) = x^4 - x^3 - 20x^2$ by factoring.

Resource Master for Lesson 11-4

Resource Master 212 Lesson 11-4

Additional Examples

3. A polynomial function p with degree 4 and leading coefficient 1 is graphed below. Find the factors of $p(x)$ and use them to write a formula for $p(x)$.

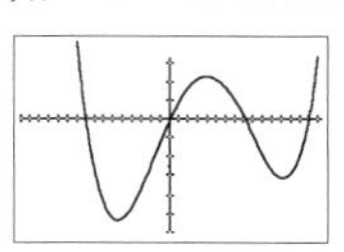

Solution From the graph, the zeros appear to be -9, 0, 8, and 15. By the Factor Theorem, the factors are $x - (-9)$, ____, ____, and $x - 15$.
Therefore, $p(x) = (x + 9)(\_\_\_\_)(\_\_\_\_)(x - 15)$. After expanding, the standard form is $p(x) = x^4 - 14x^3 - 87x^2 + 1080x$.

4. Find the general form of a polynomial function P whose only zeros are -4, $\frac{7}{2}$, and $\frac{5}{3}$.

Resource Master for Lesson 11-4

Resource Master 213 Lesson 11-5

Warm-Up

Multiple Choice In 1–12, identify the type of number.

A Rational
B Irrational
C Neither rational nor irrational

1. $\sqrt{441}$
2. $\sqrt{440}$
3. $-\sqrt{439}$
4. $\sqrt{-438}$
5. $\sqrt{-400}$
6. $-6\frac{2}{3}$
7. 2π
8. $\frac{7\pi}{2\pi}$
9. $\sqrt{2} \cdot \sqrt{8}$
10. $\sqrt[3]{2}$
11. $\sqrt{-2} \cdot \sqrt{-8}$
12. 3.14159…

Additional Examples

1. Apply the Rational-Root Theorem to *identify* possible rational roots of $f(x) = 3x^4 - 10x^2 - 8x + 15$.
2. Use the Rational-Root Theorem to *find* all the rational roots of $f(x)$ from Additional Example 1.
3. Use the Rational-Root Theorem to show that $\sqrt{3}$ is an irrational number.

Resource Master for Lesson 11-5

Resource Master 214 Lesson 11-6

Warm-Up

For 1–4, consider the function f with $f(x) = 0.01(3x + 2)^2(4x - 5)(x - 6) + d$. By graphing f for various values of d, find a value of d so that f has

1. three real zeros.
2. two real zeros.
3. one real zero.
4. no real zeros.

Additional Example

Consider the polynomial function P defined by $P(x) = x^5 - 7x^3 + 15x^2 - 7$.
a. How many real zeros does P have?
b. How many nonreal complex zeros does P have?

Resource Master for Lesson 11-6

Resource Master 215 Lesson 11-7

Warm-Up

In 1–3, the first two terms of a linear sequence are given. What are the next two terms? (This isn't as easy as it appears. Be careful!)

1. $\frac{1}{3}, \frac{1}{5}, \ldots$
2. $\frac{6}{5}, \frac{7}{6}, \ldots$
3. $x, y, \ldots$

Additional Example

1. Use the method of finite differences to determine the degree of the polynomial function mapping a onto b.

a	1	2	3	4	5	6
b	1	8	27	64	125	216

Resource Master for Lesson 11-7

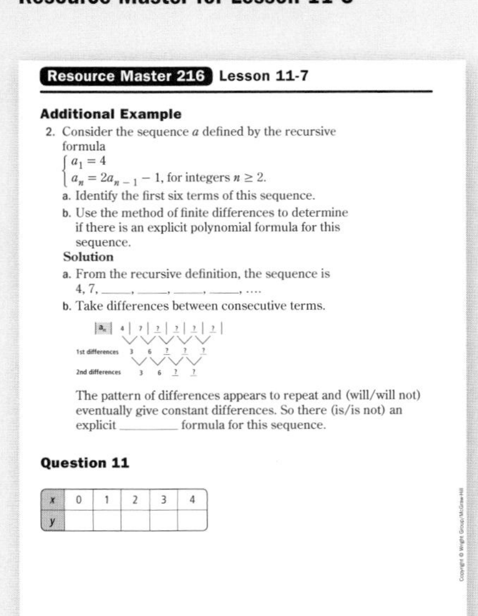

Resource Master 216 Lesson 11-7

Additional Example

2. Consider the sequence a defined by the recursive formula
$\begin{cases} a_1 = 4 \\ a_n = 2a_{n-1} - 1, \text{ for integers } n \geq 2. \end{cases}$
   a. Identify the first six terms of this sequence.
   b. Use the method of finite differences to determine if there is an explicit polynomial formula for this sequence.

   Solution

   a. From the recursive definition, the sequence is 4, 7, ____, ____, ____, ____, ….
   b. Take differences between consecutive terms.

   a_n: 4, 7, ?, ?, ?, ?
   1st differences: 3, 6, ?, ?, ?
   2nd differences: 3, 6, ?, ?

   The pattern of differences appears to repeat and (will/will not) eventually give constant differences. So there (is/is not) an explicit ________ formula for this sequence.

Question 11

x	0	1	2	3	4
y					

Resource Master for Lesson 11-7

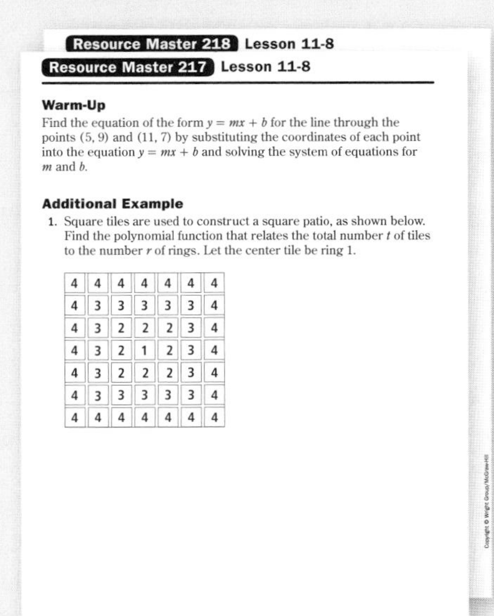

Resource Master 218 Lesson 11-8

Resource Master 217 Lesson 11-8

Warm-Up

Find the equation of the form $y = mx + b$ for the line through the points (5, 9) and (11, 7) by substituting the coordinates of each point into the equation $y = mx + b$ and solving the system of equations for m and b.

Additional Example

1. Square tiles are used to construct a square patio, as shown below. Find the polynomial function that relates the total number t of tiles to the number r of rings. Let the center tile be ring 1.

4	4	4	4	4	4	4
4	3	3	3	3	3	4
4	3	2	2	2	3	4
4	3	2	1	2	3	4
4	3	2	2	2	3	4
4	3	3	3	3	3	4
4	4	4	4	4	4	4

Resource Masters for Lesson 11-8

Resource Master 220 Lesson 11-8

Resource Master 219 Lesson 11-8

Additional Example 2 (cont.)

The third differences are equal, so the data can be represented by a polynomial function of degree ____.
Now use a system of equations to find a polynomial model of the form $V = an^3 + bn^2 + cn + d$. Substitute $n = 4, 3, 2$, and 1 and the corresponding values of V into the equation and solve the resulting system.

$$\begin{cases} 60 = a(4)^3 + b(4)^2 + c(4) + d \\ 28 = a(3)^3 + b(3)^2 + c(3) + d \\ 10 = a(2)^3 + b(2)^2 + c(2) + d \\ 2 = a(1)^3 + b(1)^2 + c(1) + d \end{cases}$$

So $a = \_\_\_\_$, $b = \_\_\_\_$, $c = \_\_\_\_$, and $d = \_\_\_\_$.
A formula for V in terms of n is $V = \_\_\_\_\_\_\_\_$.
Check by using cubic regression.

Guided Example 2

n	1		2		3		4		5		6
S	1		5		14		30		55		91
1st differences		4									
2nd differences											
3rd differences											

Resource Masters for Lesson 11-8

Chapter 11

Pacing

Each lesson in this chapter is designed to be covered in 1 day. Lesson 11-4 may take 2 days. At the end of the chapter, you should plan to spend 1 day to review the Self-Test, 1 to 2 days for the Chapter Review, and 1 day for a test. You may wish to spend a day on projects and possibly a day is needed for quizzes. This chapter should therefore take 13–15 days. We strongly advise you not to spend more than 16 days on this chapter.

Overview

Students have already studied special cases of polynomial expressions and functions: linear expressions and functions in Chapters 2 and 3, quadratic functions in Chapters 2 and 6, and power functions in Chapter 7. In this chapter, we extend students' previous experiences to *general* polynomial expressions and functions. Although the definitions and theorems apply to any polynomial of degree *n,* the examples and questions usually involve polynomials of degree 5 or less.

You can use the example on these pages to introduce students to the idea of a polynomial. To fit a polynomial to n points, a polynomial of at least degree $n - 1$ is usually required. The coefficients of a polynomial model of higher degree would typically be messy, as are the ones in this polynomial.

The graph in this opener is based on a set of points made to look like the roller coaster. In particular, these points are (0, 0), (1, -0.6), (2, -0.8), (3, -0.9), (4, -0.7), (5, -0.4), (6, 0), (7, 1), (8, 2), (9, 3.3), (10, 4.6), (11, 6.0), (12, 7.8), (13, 9), (14, 10.2), (15, 11), (16, 11.4), (17, 11.3), (18, 10.7), (19, 8.8), and (20, 6.5). Quartic regression was then used on these 21 points, resulting in the function H. Notice that the units on the x- and y-axes are not normal units, like feet, because the graph is of the roller coaster as seen from an angle.

Chapter 11 Polynomials

Contents

The shape of the roller coaster track in the picture below cannot be modeled by any of the types of functions you have studied so far. However, using techniques similar to those you used to fit quadratic models to data, an equation can be found for a curve that approximates the track.

Chapter 11 Overview

The first six lessons of the chapter develop the concepts, notation, and properties associated with polynomials; the work with graphs assumes the use of graphing technology and knowing the general properties of functions. These lessons, however, depart from traditional materials in two significant ways: (1) Polynomials are presented in many realistic contexts, and (2) the power of a CAS to factor and expand polynomials and to solve polynomial equations is employed to help students see properties of polynomials and deal with complicated manipulations.

The first three lessons review ideas students should have seen before. Lesson 11-1 introduces polynomials, motivating them by annuity-type situations arising from compound interest. Lesson 11-2 reviews how polynomials arise from area and volume situations, while Lesson 11-3 reviews the factoring of perfect squares and the difference of two squares.

Let the origin be the left most point of the roller coaster in the photo, and let $H(x)$ be the height of the track in the picture at a horizontal distance x from the origin. Then the track as seen in this picture can be modeled by
$H(x) = 0.001x^4 + 0.010x^3 + 0.060x^2 - 0.564x - 0.011$.

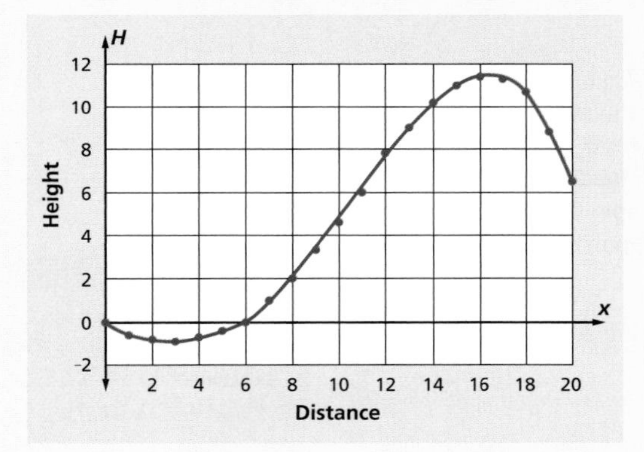

The expression on the right side of this equation is a *polynomial* and the equation is a *polynomial equation*. The function H described by this equation is a *polynomial function*. For any finite set of points, no two of which are on the same vertical line, there is a polynomial function whose graph contains those points. In this chapter, you will study situations that lead to polynomial functions. You will learn how to graph and analyze them, and how to describe data with a polynomial model.

729

Lessons 11-4 through 11-6 relate the graphs of polynomial functions, the zeros of those functions, the solutions of corresponding polynomial equations, and the factors of the polynomial. This is done at a higher level than students have previously seen, as irrational and nonreal zeros are also considered. This part of the chapter culminates with some history and the statement of the Fundamental Theorem of Algebra. However, the theorem is not proved here.

Lessons 11-7 and 11-8 cover material that is only occasionally found in algebra texts at this level. We include the method of finite differences and modeling data with polynomials because (1) these concepts involve a technique that is useful for generating formulas for certain common sequences; (2) the ability to obtain formulas for patterns is highly motivating to students; and (3) they are important in mathematical modeling, which continues a theme that was introduced in Chapter 2.

Using Pages 728–729

Some calculators are programmed for quartic regression. They can find the fourth degree polynomial that best fits (using the least squares criterion) a set of five points, no two of which lie on the same vertical line. You might have students pick five points on the graph, estimate their coordinates, and then use quartic regression to see if a polynomial similar to $H(x)$ arises.

In general, polynomial models are reasonably good for estimating coordinates of points between two given points but are very poor tools for extrapolating outside the points.

Ask students for the meanings of the terms *polynomial equation* and *polynomial function*. Ask: When finding a graph of a polynomial function through a finite set of points, why can no two points lie on the same vertical line? It would not be a function.

Chapter 11 Projects

At the end of each chapter, you will find projects related to the chapter. At this time, you might want to have students look over the projects on pages 786 and 787. You might want to have students tentatively select a project on which to work. Then, as students read and progress through the chapter, they can finalize their project choices.

Sometimes students might work alone. At other times, you might let them collaborate with classmates for a presentation and discussion. We recommend that you allow for diversity and encourage students to use their imaginations when presenting their projects. As students work on projects throughout the year, they should see many uses of mathematics in the real world.

Lesson

11-1

GOAL

Review some language dealing with polynomials in one variable and work with polynomials that arise from compound-interest situations.

SPUR Objectives

The SPUR Objectives for all of Chapter 11 are found in the Chapter Review on pages 792–795.

E Describe attributes of polynomials.

H Use polynomials to model real-world situations.

J Graph polynomial functions.

Materials/Resources

- Lesson Masters 11-1A and 11-1B
- Resource Masters 204–206
- CAS

HOMEWORK

Suggestions for Assignment

- Questions 1–23
- Question 24 (extra credit)
- Reading Lesson 11-2
- Covering the Ideas 11-2

Local Standards

1 Warm-Up

In 1 and 2, fill in the blanks.

1. For all x, $-2x^5 + x^{10} - 11 =$ $\underline{\ ?\ }x^{10} + \underline{\ ?\ }x^5 + \underline{\ ?\ }x^2 + -11x^{\underline{?}}$. 1, -2, 0, 0
2. For all y, $(5 - 4y)(3y + 2) =$ $\underline{\ ?\ }y^2 + \underline{\ ?\ }y + \underline{\ ?\ }$. -12, 7, 10

Lesson

11-1 Introduction to Polynomials

BIG IDEA *Polynomials* are a common type of algebraic expression that arise from many kinds of situations, including those of multiple investments compounded over different lengths of time.

Vocabulary

degree of a polynomial
term of a polynomial
polynomial in x of degree n
standard form of a polynomial
coefficients of a polynomial
leading coefficient
constant term, constant
polynomial function

You are likely to have studied polynomials in a previous course. This lesson reviews some of the terminology that is used to describe them.

Mental Math

Give an example of the following or say that it does not exist.

a. a number without a multiplicative inverse 0

b. a matrix without an inverse

c. a relation without an inverse does not exist

d. a function whose inverse is not a function

b. Answers vary. Sample: $\begin{bmatrix} 2 & 1 \\ 6 & 3 \end{bmatrix}$

d. Answers vary. Sample: $f: x \rightarrow 1$

Vocabulary Used with Polynomials

The expression

$$-0.001x^4 + 0.010x^3 + 0.060x^2 - 0.564x - 0.011$$

from the previous page is a *polynomial in the variable x*. When the polynomial is in only one variable, the largest exponent of the variable is the **degree of the polynomial**. The polynomial above has degree 4. The expressions $-0.001x^4$, $0.010x^3$, $0.060x^2$, $-0.564x$, and -0.011 are the **terms of the polynomial**. A polynomial is the sum of its terms.

Definition of Polynomial in x of Degree n

A **polynomial in x of degree n** is an expression of the form $a_nx^n + a_{n-1}x^{n-1} + a_{n-2}x^{n-2} + \ldots + a_1x^1 + a_0$, where n is a nonnegative integer and $a_n \neq 0$.

The **standard form** of the general nth-degree polynomial is the one displayed in the definition. Notice that the terms are written in descending order of exponents. The numbers $a_n, a_{n-1}, a_{n-2}, \ldots, a_0$ are the **coefficients of the polynomial**, with **leading coefficient** a_n. The number a_0 is the **constant term**, or simply the **constant**. For instance, the standard form of a 4th-degree polynomial is

$$a_4x^4 + a_3x^3 + a_2x^2 + a_1x^1 + a_0.$$

It has coefficients a_4, a_3, a_2, a_1, and a_0, with leading coefficient a_4.

 QY1

QY1

What is the constant term of the 4th-degree polynomial $a_4x^4 + a_3x^3 + a_2x^2 + a_1x^1 + a_0$?

Background

This lesson introduces technical vocabulary and shows how polynomial functions arise from annuity situations.

Example 4 In this mathematical application, the formula provides the basis from which the amounts are calculated. An analogy can be made to lines. Some situations are inherently linear and a formula can be derived for them. A common example is the Fahrenheit–Celsius conversion formula. Here, we are deriving the data from the values of a polynomial function, just as we derive temperatures from outputs of the Fahrenheit–Celsius conversion formula. In other situations, points seem to lie close to a line and we describe the points with a line of best fit. We will discuss fitting a polynomial function to data in Lessons 11-7 and 11-8.

GUIDED

Example 1

a. List all the coefficients of $x^2 - 16x^4 + 3x^2 + 96$.

b. What are the degree and leading coefficient of $x^2 - 16x^4 + 3x^2 + 96$?

c. Rewrite the polynomial in standard form.

Solution

a. First, combine like terms.

$x^2 - 16x^4 + 3x^2 + 96 = (\underline{?} + \underline{?})x^2 - \underline{?}\,x^4 + \underline{?}$ 1; 3; 16; 96

$= \underline{?}\,x^2 - \underline{?}\,x^4 + \underline{?}$ 4; 16; 96

So, by the definition on the previous page, $a_4 = \underline{?}$, $a_3 = \underline{?}$, -16; 0
$a_2 = \underline{?}$, $a_1 = \underline{?}$, and $a_0 = \underline{?}$. 4; 0; 96

b. The largest exponent is ___?___. So, the degree of the polynomial 4 is ___?___. The coefficient of the x^4 term is ___?___. Thus, the leading 4; -16 coefficient is ___?___. -16

c. In standard form, the terms are in descending order. So, the standard form of this polynomial is
$\underline{?}\,x^4 + \underline{?}\,x^2 + \underline{?}$. -16; 4; 96

Check Enter $x^2 - 16x^4 + 3x^2 + 96$ into a CAS. It automatically puts the polynomial in standard form.

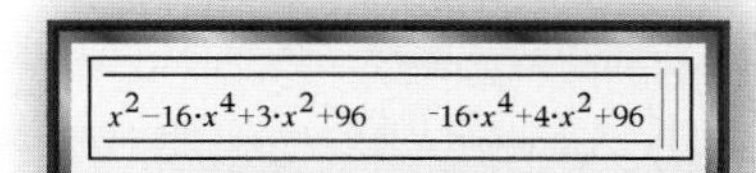

Polynomials can be classified by their degree. Those of degree 1 through 5 have special names.

Degree	Polynomial Name	Example
1	Linear	$mx + b$
2	Quadratic	$ax^2 + bx + c$
3	Cubic	$ax^3 + bx^2 + cx + d$
4	Quartic	$ax^4 + bx^3 + cx^2 + dx + e$
5	Quintic	$ax^5 + bx^4 + cx^3 + dx^2 + ex + f$

You can think of nonzero constants such as 5, $\pi + 2$, or a_0 as polynomials of degree 0. This is because a constant k can be written $k \cdot x^0$, which is a polynomial of degree 0. However, the constant 0 is not assigned a degree because its leading coefficient is zero.

Polynomial Functions and Graphs

A **polynomial function** is a function of the form $P: x \to P(x)$, where $P(x)$ is a polynomial. Polynomial functions of degree 1 are the linear functions and have graphs that are lines.

2 Teaching

Notes on the Lesson

In discussing the vocabulary and Example 1, it may not be clear to students that standard form means that the terms are in *descending order* of the exponents. There are applications, however, in which the reverse, or ascending order, is more appropriate. This is particularly true when the absolute value of the variable x is less than 1; in that case, ascending order leads to the terms with the greatest values being calculated first.

Additional Example

Example 1

a. List all the coefficients of $3x^2 + 6x^5 - 47 - 8x^2$.

b. What are the degree and leading coefficient of $3x^2 + 6x^5 - 47 - 8x^2$?

c. Rewrite the polynomial in standard form.

Solution

a. First, combine like terms: $3x^2 + 6x^5 - 47 - 8x^2 = (\underline{?} - \underline{?})x^2 + \underline{?}\,x^5 - \underline{?} = \underline{?}$. 3; 8; 6; 47; $-5x^2 + 6x^5 - 47$ So, using the definition of a polynomial, $a_5 = \underline{?}$, $a_4 = \underline{?}$, $a_3 = \underline{?}$, $a_2 = \underline{?}$, $a_1 = \underline{?}$, and $a_0 = \underline{?}$. 6; 0; 0; -5; 0; -47

b. The largest exponent is ___?___. 5 The degree of the polynomial is ___?___. 5 The coefficient of the x^5 term is ___?___. 6 The leading coefficient is ___?___. 6

c. In standard form, the terms are in descending order. So the standard form of this polynomial is $\underline{?}\,x^5 - \underline{?}\,x^2 - \underline{?}$. 6; 5; 47

ENGLISH LEARNERS

Vocabulary Development

Remind students that a *polynomial* (*poly-*, many terms) is either a *monomial* (*mono-*, one term) or a sum of monomials. You might also review the terms *binomial* and *trinomial,* which are polynomials with two and three terms, respectively.

Write $4y - 6y^3 + 3y^2 + 8y^3 + 16 - 2y$ on the board. Have volunteers identify the variable of the polynomial and its degree. *y*; 3 Be sure that students realize that the degree of the polynomial is the *greatest* exponent in the expression. Then have someone write the polynomial in *standard form,* being sure to combine like terms, with terms written in descending order by degree. $2y^3 + 3y^2 + 2y + 16$ Then have volunteers identify the leading coefficient and the constant term. 2; 16 Finally, have students evaluate the polynomial for $y = 3$. 103

Notes on the Lesson

Example 2 Example 2 is a straightforward example designed to show students that they can easily graph even complicated polynomial functions if they use a graphing utility. You might point out that before the existence of such technology, it took a great deal of work to determine the shape of this graph. Warn students that if they use the default window, they will see very little of the graph of this function, so some analysis of a function is still needed before graphing.

Additional Example

Example 2 Consider the polynomial function *P* with equation $P(x) = 6x^5 - 3x^4 + 4x^2 - 2x - 70$.

a. What is *P*(2)? 86

b. Graph this function in the window $-3 \le x \le 3$, $-120 \le y \le 10$.

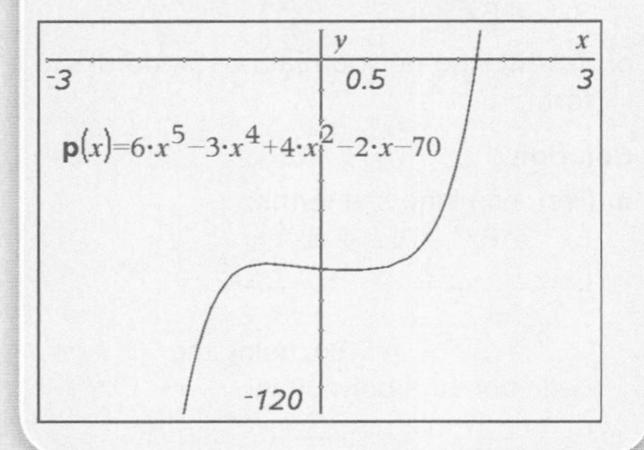

Additional Answers

Activity 1

Step 1

a. $f(x) + g(x) = 5x^3 + 2x^2 + 3x + 5$; degree 3

b. $f(x) - g(x) = -5x^3 + 2x^2 + 3x + 3$; degree 3

Step 3

a.

Define $f(x)=2\cdot x^2+3\cdot x+4$	*Done*
Define $g(x)=5\cdot x^3+1$	*Done*
expand$(f(x)\cdot g(x))$	
	$10\cdot x^5+15\cdot x^4+20\cdot x^3+2\cdot x^2+3\cdot x+4$

Polynomial functions of degree 2 are the quadratic functions and have graphs that are parabolas. For linear and quadratic functions, the coefficients of the polynomial help identify key points or properties of the graph such as slope, vertices, or intercepts. For polynomials of higher degree, the connection between the polynomial's coefficients and its graph is not as simple.

Example 2

Consider the polynomial function *P* with equation $P(x) = x^4 + 8x^3 + 20x^2 + 16x$.

a. What is *P*(-1)?

b. Graph this function in the window $-5 \le x \le 2$, $-5 \le y \le 4$.

Solution

a. Substitute −1 for *x*.

$$P(-1) = (-1)^4 + 8(-1)^3 + 20(-1)^2 + 16(-1)$$
$$= 1 - 8 + 20 - 16$$
$$= -3$$

b. A graph of *P* is shown at the right. The curve is related to the graph of $y = x^4$. The extra terms are responsible for the waves and translation off of the origin.

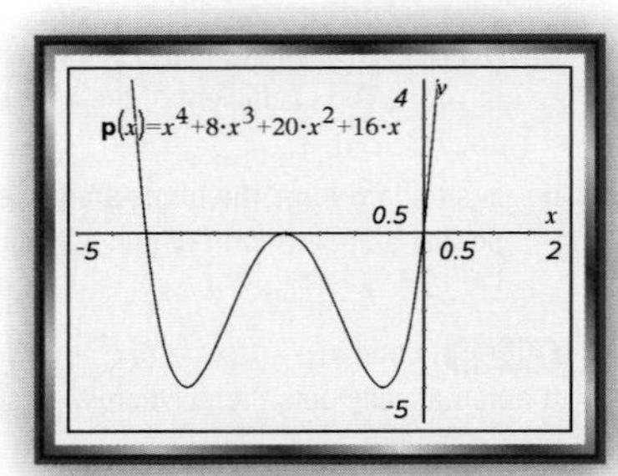

You will further explore relationships between coefficients and graphs in Lesson 11-5.

Operations on Polynomials and Polynomial Functions

Sums, differences, products, and powers of polynomials are themselves polynomials. The degree of the result of operations with polynomials depends on the degrees of the polynomials.

Activity 1

MATERIALS CAS

Let $f(x) = 2x^2 + 3x + 4$ and $g(x) = 5x^3 + 1$.

Step 1 Evaluate each expression. Write your answer in standard form and give the degree. Step 1a–b. See margin.

a. $f(x) + g(x)$ **b.** $f(x) - g(x)$

Step 2 Without multiplying the polynomials, predict

a. the degree of $f(x) \cdot g(x)$. Answers vary. Sample: 5

b. the leading coefficient of $f(x) \cdot g(x)$. Answers vary. Sample: 10

Accommodating the Learner

Be sure that students understand that when we are dealing with polynomial functions, *P*(*x*) represents a polynomial in *x*. It does *not* mean *P times x*. Also be sure that students understand notation such as *P*(2), which stands for the value of the function when $x = 2$.

Step 3 a. Define the functions f and g on a CAS. Expand $f(x) \cdot g(x)$ and write the result in standard form.
b. Check your answers to Parts a and b of Step 2.

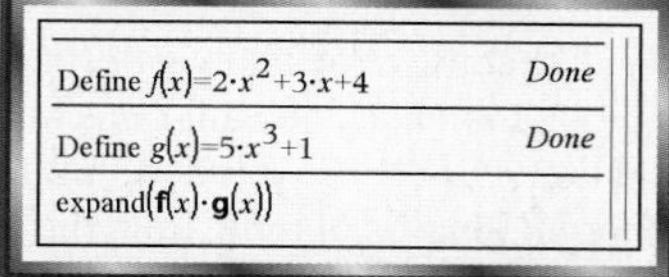

Step 4 Generalize the results of Steps 2 and 3:
The degree of the product of two polynomials is the __?__ of the degrees of the polynomials. The leading coefficient of the product of two polynomials is the __?__ of the leading coefficients of the polynomials. sum; product

Step 3
a. See margin.
b. Answers vary. Sample: They are the same.

The composite of two polynomial functions is a polynomial function.

Activity 2

MATERIALS CAS
Use the polynomials $f(x)$ and $g(x)$ from Activity 1.

Step 1 Write an unsimplified expression for $f(g(x))$ and use it to predict
a. the degree of $f(g(x))$. Answers vary. Sample: 6
b. the leading coefficient of $f(g(x))$. Answers vary. Sample: 50

Step 2 a. Expand $f(g(x))$ on a CAS and write the result in standard form. $50x^6 + 35x^3 + 9$
b. Check your answers to Parts a and b of Step 1.

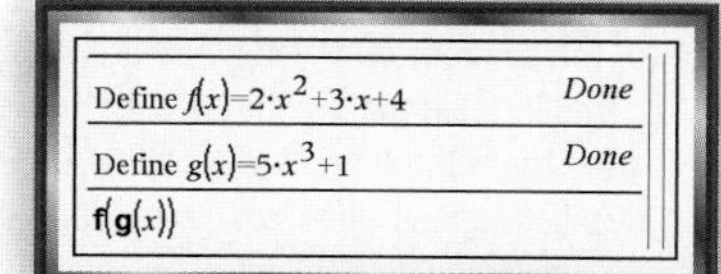

Step 3 Generalize the results of Steps 1 and 2.

Step 1
$f(g(x)) = 2(5x^3 + 1)^2 + 3(5x^3 + 1) + 4$

Step 2
b. Answers vary. Sample: They are the same.

Step 3
Answers vary. Sample: The degree of the composite of two polynomial functions is the product of the degrees of the polynomial functions. The leading coefficient of $f(g(x))$ is the leading coefficient of $g(x)$ to the power of the degree of $f(x)$ multiplied by the leading coefficient of $f(x)$.

GUIDED

Example 3

Let $f(x) = 3x^2 + 2x + 1$ and $g(x) = 4x - 5$. Predict
a. the degree of $f(x) \cdot g(x)$.
b. the leading coefficient of $f(x) \cdot g(x)$.
c. the degree of $f(g(x))$.
d. the leading coefficient of $f(g(x))$.

Solution

a. Because the degree of f is 2 and the degree of g is 1, the degree of $f(x) \cdot g(x)$ is __?__ + __?__ = __?__. 2; 1; 3
b. Because the leading coefficient of f is 3 and the leading coefficient of g is 4, the leading coefficient of $f(x) \cdot g(x)$ is __?__ · __?__ = __?__. 3; 4; 12
c. Because the degree of f is 2 and the degree of g is 1, the degree of $f(g(x))$ is __?__ · __?__ = __?__. 2; 1; 2
d. Because the leading coefficient of f is 3, the leading coefficient of g is 4, and the degree of f is 2, the leading coefficient of $f(g(x))$ is __?__ · __?__ ^{2} = __?__. 3; 4; 48

Additional Example

Example 3 Let $f(x) = 5x^3 - 3x^2 + 4$ and $g(x) = 2x + 6$. Predict
a. the degree of $f(x) \cdot g(x)$.
b. the leading coefficient of $f(x) \cdot g(x)$.
c. the degree of $f(g(x))$.
d. the leading coefficient of $f(g(x))$.

Solution

a. Because the degree of f is 3 and the degree of g is 1, the degree of $f(x) \cdot g(x)$ is __?__ + __?__ = __?__. 3; 1; 4
b. Because the leading coefficient of f is 5 and the leading coefficient of g is 2, the leading coefficient of $f(x) \cdot g(x)$ is __?__ · __?__ = __?__. 5; 2; 10
c. Because the degree of f is 3 and the degree of g is 1, the degree of $f(g(x))$ is __?__ · __?__ = __?__. 3; 1; 3
d. Because the leading coefficient of f is 5, the leading coefficient of g is 2, and the degree of f is 3, the leading coefficient of $f(g(x))$ is __?__ · (__?__)^3 = __?__. 5; 2; 40

Note-Taking Tips

Have students add to their journals a polynomial function in x, in standard form, with degree n. For this function, have them identify the degree of the polynomial, the leading coefficient, and the constant term (or constant).

Accommodating the Learner

After discussing Activity 2 and Example 3, give students the functions below and ask them to predict the degree and the leading coefficient of $p(x) \cdot q(x) \cdot r(x)$ and $p(q(r(x)))$. Then have them check the results with a CAS.

$p(x) = 4x^2 - 2x$

$q(x) = 3x - 7$

$r(x) = x^4 - x + 1$

$p(x) \cdot q(x) \cdot r(x)$: degree 7, leading coefficient 12; $p(q(r(x)))$: degree 8, leading coefficient 36

Notes on the Lesson

Savings and polynomials In Example 4, each coefficient and each exponent has a meaning that comes directly from the data in the situation. The general situation is known as an *annuity,* or an investment in which money is deposited periodically rather than all at one time. The largest money concerns we deal with in our lifetimes can be considered as annuities: retirement accounts, home or car loans, insurance, and even salaries.

Additional Example

Example 4 Getta D. Gree and her family will start saving for college when she graduates from eighth grade. At the end of each summer, they will deposit money into a savings plan with an annual percentage yield (APY) of 4.2%. Getta is planning to begin college in the fall following her graduation from high school. How much money will be in the account when she leaves for college, if no other money is added or withdrawn?

End of Summer After	Amount Deposited ($)
8th grade	2000
9th grade	2500
10th grade	2200
11th grade	2050
12th grade	2100

$2000(1.042)^4 + 2500(1.042)^3 + 2200(1.042)^2 + 2050(1.042) + 2100 = \$11{,}810.96$

Savings and Polynomials

Recall that the total value over time of a single investment compounded at a constant rate can be described by an exponential function. If, instead, you have multiple investments compounded over different lengths of time, then the total value can be described by a polynomial function. Example 4 illustrates such a situation.

Example 4

Anita Loan and her family start saving for college when she graduates from eighth grade. At the end of each summer, they deposit money into a savings plan with an annual percentage yield (APY) of 5.8%. Anita is planning to go to college in the fall following her graduation from high school. How much money will be in the account when she leaves for college, if no other money is added or withdrawn?

End of Summer after:	Amount Deposited ($)
8th grade	1200
9th grade	850
10th grade	975
11th grade	1175
12th grade	1300

Solution The money deposited at the end of the summer after 8th grade earns interest for 4 years, so it is worth $\$1200(1.058)^4$ when Anita goes to college. Similarly, the amount deposited at the end of the summer after 9th grade is worth $\$850(1.058)^3$ because it only earns interest for 3 years. Adding the values at the end of each summer gives the total amount that will be in Anita's account. Notice that, because the last deposit does not earn any interest, the last term is not multiplied by a power of 1.058.

$$\underbrace{1200(1.058)^4}_{\text{End of summer after 8th grade}} + \underbrace{850(1.058)^3}_{\text{End of summer after 9th grade}} + \underbrace{975(1.058)^2}_{\text{End of summer after 10th grade}} + \underbrace{1175(1.058)^1}_{\text{End of summer after 11th grade}} + \underbrace{1300}_{\text{End of summer after 12th grade}}$$

Evaluating this expression shows that Anita will have about $6144.74 in her account when she leaves for college.

In Example 4, you could replace 1.058 with x. Then when Anita goes to college she will have (in dollars)

$$1200x^4 + 850x^3 + 975x^2 + 1175x + 1300.$$

If you let $x = 1 + r$, where r is the APY, evaluating this expression gives the amount in the account for any APY. You could use the expression to compare the total savings for different rates, or to compute the rate required to obtain a certain total. Since the first deposit earns interest for 4 years, the polynomial has degree 4.

 QY2

QY2
How much would Anita have if the APY in the account is 4.95%?

Questions

COVERING THE IDEAS

In 1–3, tell whether the expression is a polynomial. If it is, state its degree and its leading coefficient. If it is not a polynomial, explain why not.

1. $17 + 8y$
2. $14x^3 + 5x^{-1}$
3. $14x^3 + 12x^2 + 6x^5 + 3$

4. Refer to the definition of a polynomial of degree n. State each value for the polynomial $-x^6 + 16x^4 + 3x^3 + \frac{4x}{7} - 17$.
   a. n 6
   b. a_n -1
   c. a_{n-1} 0
   d. a_0 -17
   e. a_1 $\frac{4}{7}$
   f. a_2 0
   g. a_4 16

5. Write the standard form of a quartic polynomial in the variable t.

6. **True or False** The number π is a polynomial. true

7. Consider the polynomial function P with equation $P(x) = x^3 - 6x^2 + 3x + 10$.
   a. Evaluate $P(4)$. -10
   b. Graph P in the window $-2 \le x \le 6$, $-30 \le y \le 30$. See margin.

In 8 and 9, let $f(x) = 2x^4 - 1$ and $g(x) = \frac{3}{2}x^2 + 4x$. An expression is given.
   a. Predict its degree.
   b. Predict its leading coefficient.
   c. Expand the expression and write the result in standard form.

8. $g(x) \cdot f(x)$
9. $g(f(x))$

10. Refer to Example 4. Suppose that in successive summers beginning after high school graduation, Javier put \$1250, \$750, \$2250, \$3500, and \$3300 into a bank account.
   a. Assume Javier goes to graduate school in the fall immediately after finishing 4 years of college and that the annual percentage yield is r. If no other money is added or withdrawn, how much is in his account when he goes to graduate school? Express your answer in terms of x, where $x = 1 + r$.
   b. Evaluate your answer to Part a when $r = 4.5\%$. \$11,761.08
   c. What is the degree of the polynomial you found in Part a? 4

11. Suppose $f(x)$ is a polynomial of degree 3, and $g(x)$ is a polynomial of degree 5.
   a. What is the degree of $f(x) + g(x)$? 5
   b. What is the degree of $f(x) \cdot g(x)$? 8
   c. What is the degree of $f(g(x))$? 15

1. Yes; its degree is 1 and its leading coefficient is 8.
2. No; the exponents in a polynomial must be positive.
3. Yes; its degree is 5 and its leading coefficient is 6.
5. $a_4t^4 + a_3t^3 + a_2t^2 + a_1t + a_0$

8a. 6
8b. 3
8c. $3x^6 + 8x^5 - \frac{3}{2}x^2 - 4x$
9a. 8
9b. 6
9c. $6x^8 + 2x^4 - \frac{5}{2}$
10a. $1250x^4 + 750x^3 + 2250x^2 + 3500x + 3300$

11-1

Notes on the Lesson

When discussing this Example 4, you might ask:

- How much would Anita have at the end of her fourth year in college if the summer after her senior year in high school she saved \$1500, and if each summer thereafter she saved \$150 more than she did the previous summer? $1500(1.058)^4 + 1650(1.058)^3 + 1800(1.058)^2 + 1950(1.058) + 2100 = \$10,011.49$ In general, the formula is $1500x^4 + 1650x^3 + 1800x^2 + 1950x + 2100$, where $x = 1 + r$, and r is the annual percentage yield.
- In this problem, how much would Anita have saved if she had been able to earn only 4% interest on her money? \$9685.69 How much of this amount is interest? \$685.69

3 Assignment

Recommended Assignment

- Questions 1–23
- Question 24 (extra credit)
- Reading Lesson 11-2
- Covering the Ideas 11-2

Notes on the Questions

Question 4f *Error Analysis* Some students may think that there is no coefficient a_2. Stress that a_n is the coefficient of the term of degree n, and any coefficient except the leading coefficient may be zero.

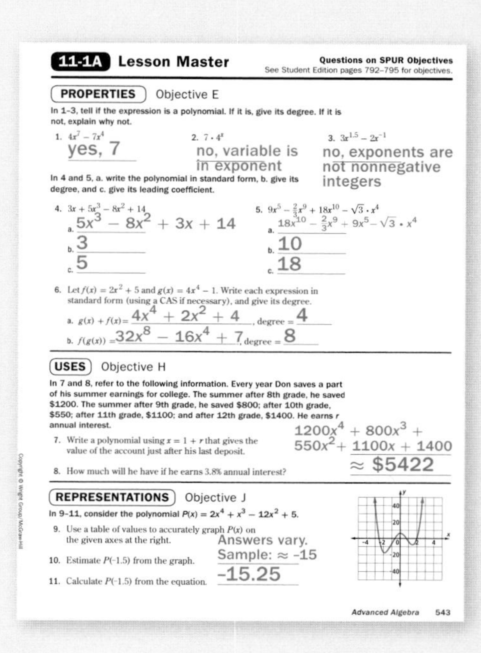

11-1A Lesson Master

Questions on SPUR Objectives
See Student Edition pages 792–795 for objectives.

PROPERTIES Objective E

In 1-3, tell if the expression is a polynomial. If it is, give its degree. If it is not, explain why not.

1. $4x^7 - 7x^4$ yes, 7
2. $7 \cdot 4^x$ no, variable is in exponent
3. $3x^{1.5} - 2x^{-1}$ no, exponents are not nonnegative integers

In 4 and 5, a. write the polynomial in standard form, b. give its degree, and c. give its leading coefficient.

4. $3x + 5x^3 - 8x^2 + 14$
   a. $5x^3 - 8x^2 + 3x + 14$
   b. 3
   c. 5
5. $9x^5 - \frac{2}{3}x^9 + 18x^{10} - \sqrt{3} \cdot x^4$
   a. $18x^{10} - \frac{2}{3}x^9 + 9x^5 - \sqrt{3} \cdot x^4$
   b. 10
   c. 18

6. Let $f(x) = 2x^2 + 5$ and $g(x) = 4x^4 - 1$. Write each expression in standard form (using a CAS if necessary), and give its degree.
   a. $g(x) + f(x) = 4x^4 + 2x^2 + 4$, degree = 4
   b. $f(g(x)) = 32x^8 - 16x^4 + 7$, degree = 8

USES Objective H

In 7 and 8, refer to the following information. Every year Don saves a part of his summer earnings for college. The summer after 8th grade, he saved \$1200. The summer after 9th grade, he saved \$800; after 10th grade, \$550; after 11th grade, \$1100; and after 12th grade, \$1400. He earns r annual interest.

7. Write a polynomial using $x = 1 + r$ that gives the value of the account just after his last deposit. $1200x^4 + 800x^3 + 550x^2 + 1100x + 1400$
8. How much will he have if he earns 3.8% annual interest? $\approx$ \$5422

REPRESENTATIONS Objective J

In 9-11, consider the polynomial $P(x) = 2x^4 + x^3 - 12x^2 + 5$.

9. Use a table of values to accurately graph $P(x)$ on the given axes at the right.
10. Estimate $P(-1.5)$ from the graph. Answers vary. Sample: $\approx$ -15
11. Calculate $P(-1.5)$ from the equation. -15.25

Advanced Algebra 543

Additional Answers

7b.

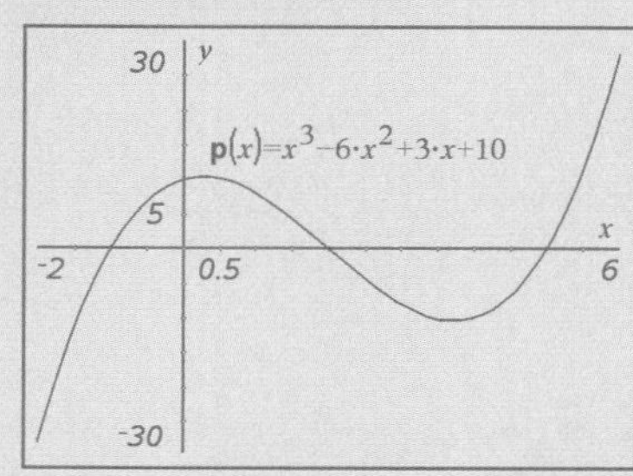

Notes on the Questions

Question 15 In Part b, point out that in base 8, no digit can be greater than 7, just as in base 10 no digit can be greater than 9.

Question 16 Because the amount given is the same on each birthday, the terms of the polynomial form a finite geometric sequence, and a formula for the sum is discussed in Lesson 13-2. The Hebrew word for life is *chai* (with a guttural "ch"), from which the toast *l'chaim,* meaning "to life," originates. The letter for "ch" stands for the number 8, and the letter for "ai" stands for the number 10.

APPLYING THE MATHEMATICS

12. Let $q(x) = 4x^2 - 3$.
    a. If $p(x) + q(x)$ has degree 3, what do you know about the degree of $p(x)$? It has degree 3.
    b. If $r(x) \cdot q(x)$ has degree 8, what do you know about the degree of $r(x)$? It has degree 6.
    c. If $s(x) \cdot q(x)$ has a leading coefficient of -28, what do you know about the leading coefficient of $s(x)$? It is -7.

13. Recall the formula for the height h in feet of an object thrown upward: $h = -\frac{1}{2}gt^2 + v_0t + h_0$, where t is the number of seconds after being thrown, h_0 is the initial height in feet, v_0 is the initial velocity in $\frac{\text{ft}}{\text{sec}}$, and g is the acceleration due to gravity ($32\frac{\text{ft}}{\text{sec}^2}$ on Earth). This formula describes a polynomial function in t.
    a. What is the degree of this polynomial? 2
    b. What is the leading coefficient? $-\frac{1}{2}g$ or -16
    c. Suppose a ball is thrown upward from the ground with initial velocity $55\frac{\text{ft}}{\text{sec}}$. Find its height after 1.6 seconds. 47.04 ft

14. Consider $f(x) = 4^x$ and $g(x) = x^4$.
    a. Which of f or g is a polynomial function? g
    b. Which of f or g is an exponential function? f
    c. Explain how to tell the difference between an exponential function and a polynomial function.

14c. A polynomial function has its variable in the base of the expression, whereas an exponential function has its variable in the exponent.

15. The whole number 45,702 can be written as the polynomial function $P(x) = 4x^4 + 5x^3 + 7x^2 + 0x^1 + 2$, with $x = 10$.
    a. Verify that $P(10) = 45{,}702$. $40{,}000 + 5000 + 700 + 2 = 45{,}702$
    b. What is the base-10 value of the base-8 number 45,702? 19,394

16. In Hebrew, the number 18 stands for life and, for this reason, one custom is to give a child \$18 each year to save until his or her 18th birthday.

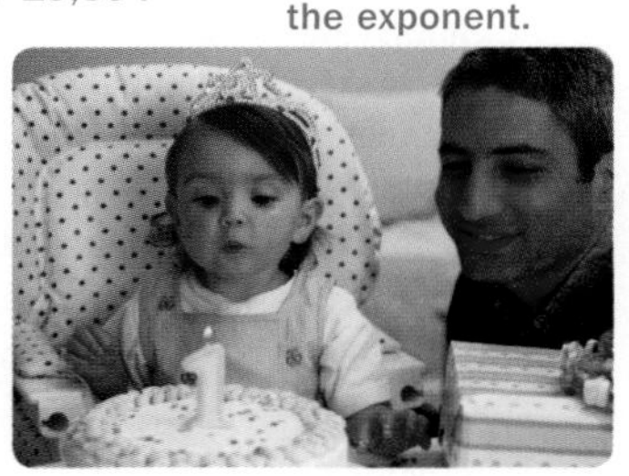

    a. Suppose a child is given \$18 on each birthday (including the day he or she is born) until his or her 18th birthday, and that these gifts are put into an account with an annual yield of r. (No money is given on the 18th birthday itself.) Write a polynomial expression to give the total amount in the account on the child's 18th birthday. Let $x = 1 + r$.

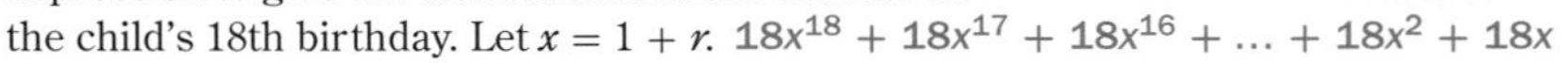

$18x^{18} + 18x^{17} + 18x^{16} + \ldots + 18x^2 + 18x$
    b. Evaluate your answer to Part a for an APY of 4.2%. \$489.93

REVIEW

17. Of the sequences A and B below, one is arithmetic, the other geometric. **(Lessons 7-5, 3-8, 3-6)**

A: 49, 7, 1, $\frac{1}{7}$, ... B: 47, 36, 25, 14, ...

a. Write the next two terms of each sequence. $\frac{1}{49}, \frac{1}{343}$; 3, -8

b. Write an explicit formula for the geometric sequence. $A_n = 49 \cdot \left(\frac{1}{7}\right)^{n-1}$

c. Write an explicit formula for the arithmetic sequence. $B_n = 47 - 11(n - 1)$

d. Which sequence might model the successive maximum heights of a bouncing ball? A

18. Solve this system of equations: $\begin{cases} r = 5t \\ s = r - 7 \\ t = r + 2s \end{cases}$. **(Lesson 5-3)** $r = 5, s = -2, t = 1$

19. A cat stalking a mouse creeps forward for 2 seconds at 0.5 $\frac{\text{ft}}{\text{sec}}$ then stops for 2 seconds. The cat springs forward at a rate of 10 $\frac{\text{ft}}{\text{sec}}$, but is stopped after 1 second by the refrigerator that the mouse ran under. Graph the situation, plotting time on the horizontal axis and distance on the vertical axis. **(Lesson 3-4)** See margin.

In 20 and 21, refer to the four equations below. (Lessons 2-6, 2-5, 2-4)

A $y = kx$ B $y = kx^2$ C $y = \frac{k}{x}$ D $y = \frac{k}{x^2}$

20. Which equations have graphs that are symmetric to the y-axis? B, D

21. The graph of which equation is a parabola? B

22. The weight of a body varies inversely with the square of the distance from the center of Earth. If Deja weighs 110 pounds on the surface of Earth, how much will she weigh in space, 6000 miles from the surface? (The radius of Earth is approximately 4000 miles.) **(Lesson 2-2)** about 17.6 lb

23. Refer to kite $FLYR$ at the right. **(Previous Course)**

a. Find LY. 3 b. Find m$\angle R$. 128°

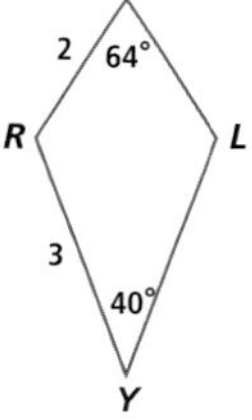

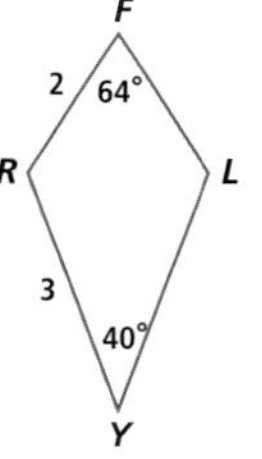

EXPLORATION

24. Suppose $f(x)$ and $g(x)$ are polynomials of degree 4. Justify your answers with examples or proofs. 24a–c. See margin.

a. What are the possible degrees of $f(x) + g(x)$?

b. What are the possible degrees of $f(x) \cdot g(x)$?

c. What are the possible degrees of $f(g(x))$?

QY ANSWERS

1. a_0

2. $6045.48

Notes on the Questions

Question 24 Our experience is that students do not have much intuition about the answers to these questions before they try them.

4 Wrap-Up

Ongoing Assessment

Write a polynomial $P(x)$ on the board. Have students volunteer to identify the degree and the leading coefficient of $P(x)$ and to evaluate $P(3)$. Repeat with different polynomials until all students have responded. Students should correctly identify the leading coefficient and the degree and correctly evaluate $P(3)$ for the given polynomial.

Additional Answers

19.

Distance (feet)

Time (seconds)

Additional Answers

24a. 0–4; Suppose a coefficient of f is k. If the coefficient for the same degree term in g is $-k$, then a term of that degree will not appear in the sum.

24b. 8; Since a_4 and b_4, the leading coefficients of f and g respectively, are nonzero by definition, then the term of highest degree in $f(x) \cdot g(x)$ will be $a_4x^4 \cdot b_4x^4 = a_4b_4x^8$.

24c. 16; By definition, f and g must have an x^4 term. So the leading term of $f(g(x))$ will be $a_n(b_nx^4)^4 = a_nb_n^4x^{16}$.

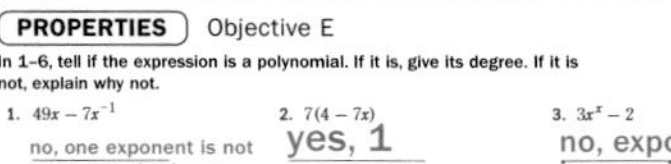

11-1B page 2

11-1B Lesson Master Questions on SPUR Objectives
See Student Edition pages 792–795 for objectives.

PROPERTIES Objective E

In 1–6, tell if the expression is a polynomial. If it is, give its degree. If it is not, explain why not.

1. $49x - 7x^{-1}$ no, one exponent is not a nonnegative integer
2. $7(4 - 7x)$ yes, 1
3. $3x^x - 2$ no, exponent is a variable
4. $19x^7 - 7x$ yes, 7
5. $1.8x^{10} - \sqrt{15} \cdot x^{17}$ yes, 17
6. 0 no, leading coefficient is 0

In 7–14, a. write the polynomial in standard form, b. give its degree, c. give its leading coefficient, and d. give the number of terms it has.

7. $9x^2 + 7x^3$ a. $7x^3 + 9x^2$ b. 3 c. 7 d. 2
8. $8x^2 + 4 - 6x$ a. $8x^2 - 6x + 4$ b. 2 c. 8 d. 3
9. $x^5 - 2x^3 - x^2 - 5$ a. $x^5 - 2x^3 - x^2 - 5$ b. 5 c. 1 d. 4
10. $12 - 6x$ a. $-6x + 12$ b. 1 c. -6 d. 2
11. $-14x^7 + 6x^{19} - x^3 - x + 4x^{10}$ a. $6x^{19} + 4x^{10} - 14x^7 - x^3 - x$ b. 19 c. 6 d. 5
12. $12x^4$ a. $12x^4$ b. 4 c. 12 d. 1

In 13 and 14, write each expression in standard form (using a CAS if necessary), and give its degree.

13. Let $f(x) = x^2 + x$ and $g(x) = x - 1$.
a. $g(x) + f(x) = x^2 + 2x - 1$, degree = 2
b. $f(g(x)) = x^2 - x$, degree = 2

14. Let $f(x) = x^2 - 5$ and $g(x) = 2x^3 + 3$.
a. $g(x) + f(x) = 2x^3 + x^2 - 2$, degree = 3
b. $f(g(x)) = 4x^6 + 12x^3 + 4$, degree = 6

545

544 Advanced Algebra

Lesson 11-2

GOAL

Use the Extended Distributive Property to multiply polynomials with more than two terms; illustrate the Extended Distributive Property by calculating volume in two different ways.

SPUR Objectives

A Use the Extended Distributive Property to multiply polynomials.

E Describe attributes of polynomials.

I Use polynomials to describe geometric situations.

Materials/Resources

- Lesson Masters 11-2A and 11-2B
- Resource Masters 207–209

HOMEWORK

Suggestions for Assignment

- Questions 1–25
- Question 26 (extra credit)
- Reading Lesson 11-3
- Covering the Ideas 11-3

Local Standards

1 Warm-Up

A given rectangle has length L and width W.

1. The length of the rectangle is multiplied by a, and the width is multiplied by b. What is the effect on the area of the rectangle? Explain. The area is multiplied by ab because $(aL) \cdot (bW) = abLW$.

Lesson 11-2 Multiplying Polynomials

Vocabulary

monomial, binomial, trinomial

degree of a polynomial in several variables

▶ **BIG IDEA** The product of two or more polynomials is a polynomial whose degree is the sum of the degrees of the factors.

Classifying Polynomials by the Number of Terms

In Lesson 11-1, you saw that polynomials can be classified by their degree. They can also be classified according to the number of terms they have after combining like terms. A **monomial** is a polynomial with one term, a **binomial** is a polynomial with two terms, and a **trinomial** is a polynomial with three terms. Below are some examples.

monomials: $-7, x^2, 3y^4$

binomials: $x^2 - 11, 3y^4 + y, 12a^5 + 4a^3$

trinomials: $x^2 - 5x + 6, 10y^6 - 9y^5 + 17y^2$

Notice that monomials, binomials, and trinomials can be of any degree. No special name is given to polynomials with more than three terms.

When a polynomial in one variable is added to or multiplied by a polynomial in another variable, the result is a polynomial in several variables. The **degree of a polynomial in several variables** is the largest sum of the exponents of the variables in any term. For instance, $x^3 + 8x^2y^3 + xy^2$ is a trinomial in x and y of degree 5. Notice that the sum of the exponents in the middle term is 5, while in both the first and last terms the sum of the exponents is 3.

Mental Math

A square park is 1 block on a side. A person walks from the midpoint of one side to the midpoint of the next, and so on, until he returns to his starting point. How far has he walked?

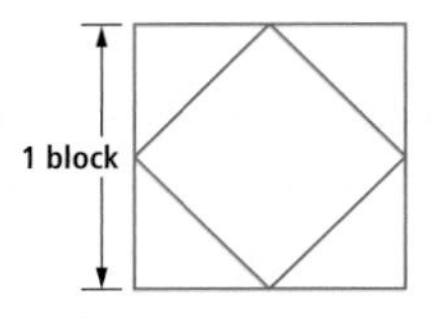

$2\sqrt{2} \approx 2.8$ blocks

The Extended Distributive Property

The product of a monomial and a binomial can be found using the Distributive Property, which says that for all numbers a, b, and c, $a(b + c) = ab + ac$. So, to multiply a monomial by a binomial, multiply the monomial by each term of the binomial and then add the products.

Repeated application of the Distributive Property allows you to find the product of any two polynomial factors. In general, if one polynomial has m terms and the second n terms, there will be mn terms in their product before combining like terms.

▶ **READING MATH**

The prefixes *mono-*, *bi-*, *tri-*, and *poly-* mean "one," "two," "three," and "many," respectively. These prefixes are used in many common English words, such as monopoly, bicycle, and tricycle, and in geometric terms such as triangle and polyhedron.

Background

Most of the concepts in this lesson are extensions of those previously learned, and the examples are clearly presented. Therefore, you might assign the reading for this lesson without further discussion. If done in order, the questions outline the major ideas of the lesson.

Most students are familiar with the prefixes *mono-* (one), *bi-* (two), and *tri-* (three) from previous mathematics courses and know how to multiply two binomials. The Extended Distributive Property, an extension of the Distributive Property $a(b + c) = ab + ac$, is presented in UCSMP *Algebra*, and the multiplication of binomials is considered a special case. In general, if one factor has m terms and the other has n terms, then the product is the sum of mn terms, some of which may be combined because they are like terms.

Students should be encouraged to use a CAS to check their answers.

Example 1

Expand $(2x^3 + 3x^2 - 2)(5x^2 + 4)$ and write your answer in standard form.

Solution 1 Expand on a CAS.

```
expand((2·x^3+3·x^2−2)·(5·x^2+4))
                10·x^5+15·x^4+8·x^3+2·x^2−8
```

Solution 2 Use the Distributive Property by treating $(2x^3 + 3x^2 - 2)$ as a single unit.

$$(2x^3 + 3x^2 - 2)(5x^2 + 4)$$
$$= (2x^3 + 3x^2 - 2)(5x^2) + (2x^3 + 3x^2 - 2)(4)$$

Now use the Distributive Property to expand each product on the right side.

$$= 2x^3 \cdot 5x^2 + 3x^2 \cdot 5x^2 + -2 \cdot 5x^2 + 2x^3 \cdot 4 + 3x^2 \cdot 4 + -2 \cdot 4$$
$$= 10x^5 + 15x^4 - 10x^2 + 8x^3 + 12x^2 - 8$$

There are six terms. Combine like terms and write in standard form.

$$= 10x^5 + 15x^4 + 8x^3 + 2x^2 - 8$$

 QY

Notice that in Example 1 each of the terms of the trinomial $2x^3 + 3x^2 - 2$ is multiplied by each of the terms of the binomial $5x^2 + 4$. We call this generalization of the Distributive Property the *Extended Distributive Property.*

▶ QY

Check Example 1 by letting $x = 2$ in both the given expression and the answer.

Extended Distributive Property

To multiply two polynomials, multiply each term in the first polynomial by each term in the second and add the products.

The Extended Distributive Property is applied several times when multiplying more than two polynomials. Because multiplication is associative and commutative, one way to multiply three polynomials is to start by multiplying any two of the polynomials and then multiplying their product by the remaining polynomial.

Used together, the Extended Distributive Property and the Associative Property of Multiplication let you multiply any number of polynomials in any order.

2. **Multiple Choice** The length of the rectangle is increased by *a*, and the width is increased by *b*. What is the effect on the area of the rectangle? Explain.
   A The area is increased by *ab*.
   B The area is increased by $a + b$.
   C The area is increased by $2a + 2b$.
   D The amount the area is increased depends on the original length and width.

D; $(L + a) \cdot (W + b) = LW + aW + bL + ab$, so the increase is $aW + bL + ab$, which depends on *L* and *W*.

2 Teaching

Notes on the Lesson

Example 1 Example 1 illustrates the Extended Distributive Property. Notice in Solution 1 that the CAS automatically collects like terms. Solution 2 shows how to do the expansion with paper and pencil. Emphasize the ability to check by substitution, as done in the QY.

Additional Example

Example 1 Expand $(5x^2 - 4x + 3) \cdot (x - 7)$ and write your answer in standard form.

Solution 1 Expand on a CAS.

```
expand((5x^2−4x+3)(x−7))
                5·x^3−39·x^2+31·x−21
```

Solution 2 Use the Distributive Property by treating $(5x^2 - 4x + 3)$ as a single unit: $(5x^2 - 4x + 3)(x - 7) = (5x^2 - 4x + 3)(x) + (5x^2 - 4x + 3)(-7)$. Use the Distributive Property to expand each product on the right side and then combine like terms: $(5x^2 \cdot x) + (-4x \cdot x) + (3 \cdot x) + (5x^2 \cdot (-7)) + (-4x \cdot (-7)) + (3 \cdot (-7)) = 5x^3 - 4x^2 + 3x - 35x^2 + 28x - 21 = 5x^3 - 39x^2 + 31x - 21$.

ENGLISH LEARNERS

Vocabulary Development

To help students remember the meanings of the terms *monomial, binomial,* and *trinomial,* stress that the prefix *mono-* means one, *bi-* means two, and *tri-* means three. Explain that there are no special terms for a polynomial with more than three terms. You might review that the prefix *poly-* means many. Have students think of words that begin with these prefixes and how the prefixes relate to the words named. Some samples are monologue and monotone; bicycle and bisect; tricycle and triplet; and polygon and polyhedron.

Then review the idea of the *degree of a polynomial.* Stress that when a polynomial has *several variables,* the degree of the polynomial is the greatest sum of the exponents of the variables in any term. For example, $5x^3 + 3x^2y^3 - x^2y^4$ is a trinomial in *x* and *y* of degree 6, the sum of 2 + 4.

Notes on the Lesson

Example 2 Example 2 shows that when the Extended Distributive Property involves three factors that are sums, it can be pictured using volume. Plan on discussing this example in detail. In Part c, show that you get the same result if you multiply $Q + W$ by $R + S + T$ first. That is, $(Q + W)(R + S + T)D = (QR + QS + QT + WR + WS + WT)D = QRD + QSD + QTD + WRD + WSD + WTD$. This is a consequence of the fact that multiplication is associative.

Additional Example

Example 2

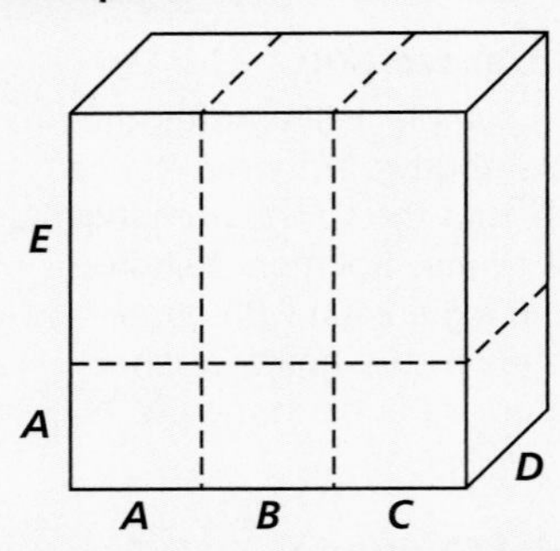

a. Find the volume V of the large box by multiplying its dimensions. $V = (A + B + C)(A + E)D$

b. Find the volume V of the large box by adding the volumes of the small boxes. $V = AED + BED + CED + A^2D + BAD + CAD$

c. Show that the answers to Parts a and b are equal. Expanding the result of Part a $V = A^2D + AED + BAD + BED + CAD + CED$; using the Commutative Property will give the result of Part b.

Note-Taking Tips

Have students add to their journals a statement of the Extended Distributive Property and include an example to illustrate its use.

Example 2

a. Find the volume of the large box by multiplying its dimensions.

b. Find the volume of the large box by adding the volumes of each of the small boxes.

c. Show that the answers to Parts a and b are equal.

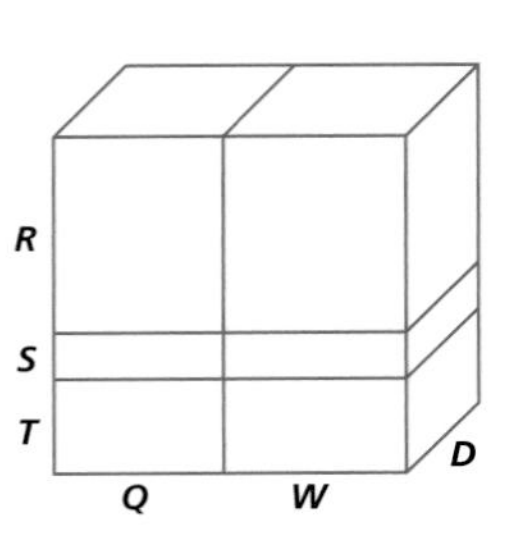

Solution

a. The box has width $Q + W$, height $R + S + T$, and depth D. Its volume is the product of its dimensions.

$$\text{Volume} = (Q + W)(R + S + T)D$$

b. There are six small boxes, each with depth D. The volume of the big box is the sum of the volumes of the 6 smaller boxes (2 smaller boxes in each of 3 layers), from the top, left to right:

$$\text{Volume} = QRD + WRD + QSD + WSD + QTD + WTD$$

c. The two expressions in Parts a and b must be equivalent because they represent the same volume. To show this, you can expand the product from Part a. Because of the Associative Property of Multiplication, either $Q + W$ can be multiplied by $R + S + T$ first, or $R + S + T$ can be multiplied by D first. We begin by multiplying by D first.

$$\text{Volume} = (Q + W)(RD + SD + TD)$$

Now apply the Distributive Property, distributing $(Q + W)$ over the trinomial $RD + SD + TD$.

$$\text{Volume} = (Q + W)RD + (Q + W)SD + (Q + W)TD$$

Apply the Distributive Property again.

$$\text{Volume} = QRD + WRD + QSD + WSD + QTD + WTD$$

Notice how each term of the expanded form is the product of a term from $Q + W$, a term from $R + S + T$, and the term D.

Finding Terms of Products without Finding the Entire Product

In Example 1, you found that the product $(2x^3 + 3x^2 - 2)(5x^2 + 4)$ of two polynomials is equal to the polynomial $10x^5 + 15x^4 + 8x^3 + 2x^2 - 8$. All three polynomials were written in standard form. Notice the leading term $10x^5$ of the product is the product of the leading terms of the polynomial factors. Also, the last term -8 of the product is the product of the last terms of the factors.

Accommodating the Learner

Have students solve the following problem: A farmer installs two fence posts along a line parallel to the side of a chicken coop and then forms a rectangular pen using 120 meters of fencing from the side of the coop and perpendicular to it, around the posts, and back to the coop. The posts are s meters from the coop. The farmer then adds a ceiling to the pen that is 2 feet above his head when he stands up straight. The farmer is h meters tall. Draw a diagram that represents the situation and write a polynomial in s and h that expresses the volume of the enclosed space.

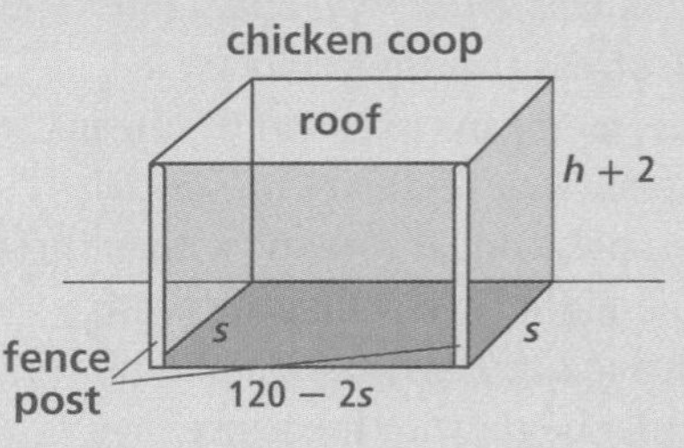

$V = (120 - 2s)(s)(h + 2) = -2hs^2 - 4s^2 + 120hs + 240s$

In general, the leading term of the product of n polynomials written in standard form is the product of the leading terms of the polynomial factors, and the last term is the product of the last terms of the factors.

GUIDED

Example 3

Without expanding, find the leading term, the last term, and the coefficient of the term with x^3 of the product $(5x^2 + 2)(4x^2 + 8)(11x - 3)$ when written in standard form.

Solution The leading term is the product of the leading terms of the factors.

The leading term of the product is
$\underline{?} \cdot \underline{?} \cdot \underline{?} = \underline{?}$. $5x^2$; $4x^2$; $11x$; $220x^5$

The last term is the product of the last terms of the factors.

The last term of the product is
$\underline{?} \cdot \underline{?} \cdot \underline{?} = \underline{?}$. 2; 8; -3; -48

A term with x^3 will arise from multiplying $5x^2$ from the first factor, 8 from the second factor, and $11x$ from the third factor. The only other term with x^3 will arise from multiplying 2 from the first factor, _?_ from the second factor, and _?_ from the third factor. The first product is _?_ x^3; the second is _?_ x^3. So, after combining like terms, the term with x^3 in the product is $528x^3$.
$4x^2$; $11x$; 440; 88

Check Expand on a CAS and check the leading and last terms and the coefficient of x^3 in the product.

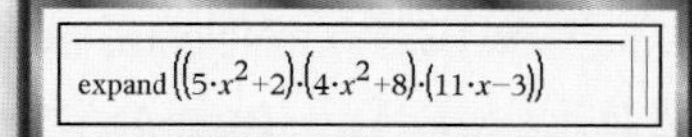

Applications of Polynomials

A classic problem in mathematics is to find the maximum volume of an open box like the one in Example 4.

Example 4

A rectangular piece of cardboard measuring 16 inches by 20 inches is to be folded into an open box after cutting squares of side length x from each corner. Let $V(x)$ be the volume of the box.

a. **Write a polynomial formula for $V(x)$ in standard form.**

b. **Use the graph of the function V to find the maximum possible volume.**

(continued on next page)

Notes on the Lesson

Example 3 This example reinforces the Extended Distributive Property. Be certain that students realize how the coefficient of the x^3 term is found. You might ask for the coefficient of the x^4 term ($5 \cdot 4 \cdot (-3)$, or -60, as the only way to obtain a term of the fourth power is by the product of $5x^2$, $4x^2$, and -3).

Additional Example

Example 3 Without expanding, find the leading term, the last term, and the coefficient of the x^3 term of $(3x^2 + 4)(2x^2 - 7)(8x + 1)$ when written in standard form.

Solution The leading term is the product of the leading terms of the factors. The leading term of the product is (_?_)(_?_) · (_?_) = _?_. $3x^2$; $2x^2$; $8x$; $48x^5$ The last term is the product of the last terms of the factors: (_?_)(_?_) · (_?_) = _?_. 4; -7; 1; -28 A term with x^3 will arise from multiplying $3x^2$ from the first factor, -7 from the second factor, and $8x$ from the third factor. The only other term with x^3 will arise from multiplying 4 from the first factor, _?_ from the second factor, and _?_ from the third factor. $2x^2$; $8x$ The first product is _?_ x^3; the second is _?_ x^3. -168; 64 After combining like terms, the x^3 term in the product is _?_ x^3. -104

Example 4 Here is a construction of a box from a rectangular piece of cardboard—a classic maximization situation treated in calculus. The solution is estimated by examining the graph and substituting values. Some calculators have a function maximum command called fmax that may be used to find the maximum value of a function over a specified interval. Other calculators have a graphical function maximum feature that requires the user to specify an interval on the graph where the maximum will be found. Be certain to review the graph on page 742 so that students understand what the graph represents. Question 11 will help with this.

Accommodating the Learner

In Additional Example 4, some students may try to multiply both $(24 - 2x)$ terms by x. Remind them that when three factors are multiplied, the Associative Property of Multiplication allows them to find the product of two neighboring factors and then multiply this product by the third factor. This may be more obvious with a case involving integers such as $3 \cdot 4 \cdot 5$, for which the product is $12 \cdot 5$ or $3 \cdot 20$.

Extension

Ask students to find a pair of binomials whose product, when written in standard form, has two terms. Then have them find pairs of binomials whose products in standard form have three terms and four terms. Ask if it is possible for the product of two binomials to have five terms. Answers vary. Sample: two terms: $2x + 6$ and $x - 3$; three terms: $3x + 1$ and $2x + 4$; four terms: $x^2 + x$ and $x^3 + 3$; not possible.

Additional Example

Example 4 A square piece of tin measuring 24 inches by 24 inches is to be folded into an open container after cutting squares of side length x from each corner. Let $V(x)$ be the volume of the box.

a. Write a polynomial formula for $V(x)$ in standard form. Draw a diagram and write the formula for the box's volume.

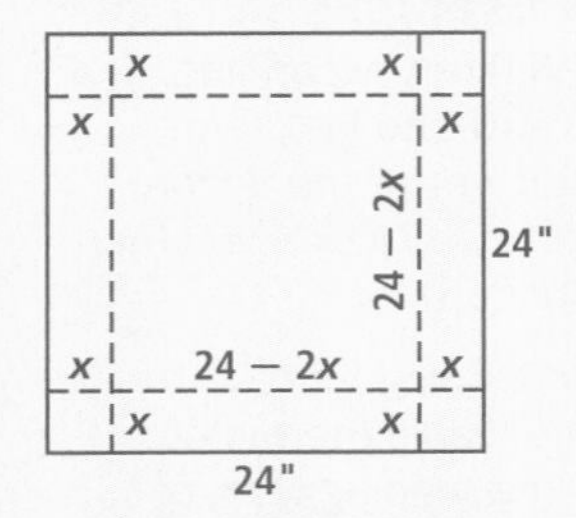

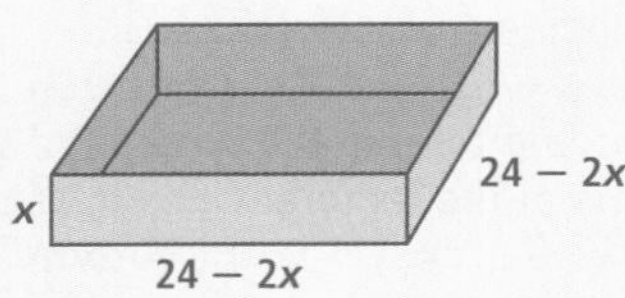

$V(x) = (24 - 2x)(24 - 2x)(x)$

Use a CAS to expand this product.

expand((24–2·x)·(24–2·x)·x)

4·x^3–96·x^2+576·x

So $V(x) = 4x^3 - 96x^2 + 576x$.

b. What is the maximum possible volume? Because the dimensions must be positive, $x > 0$ and $24 - 2x > 0$, so $0 < x < 12$ is the largest domain for V. Graphing V over this domain shows that the maximum volume is 1024 in^3, which occurs when $x = 4$ in. Substitute this value for x to find that the box dimensions for this volume are 16 in. long by 16 in. wide by 4 in. high.

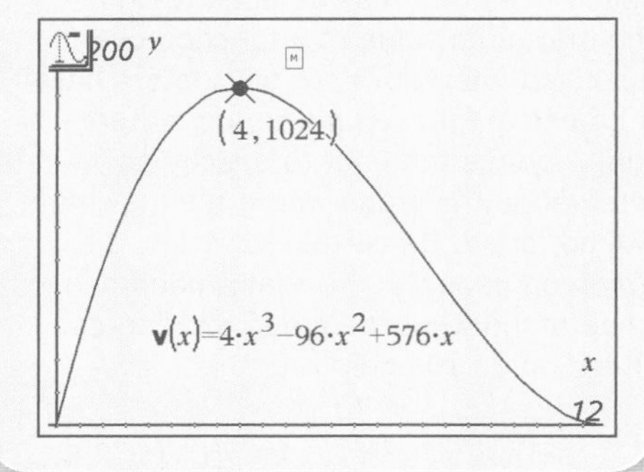

Solution

a. Draw a diagram.

When the cardboard is folded up, the dimensions of the box are $(20 - 2x)$ inches long by $(16 - 2x)$ inches wide by x inches high. The volume is the product of these dimensions.

$$V(x) = (20 - 2x)(16 - 2x)(x)$$

Use a CAS to expand this product. The CAS will automatically write the product in standard form.

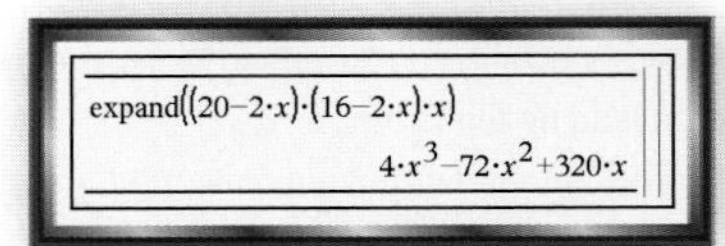

So $V(x) = 4x^3 - 72x^2 + 320x$.

b. Because dimensions of a box are positive, $x > 0$, $20 - 2x > 0$ and $16 - 2x > 0$. Solving these inequalities for x, we have $x > 0$, $x < 10$, and $x < 8$, which means that $0 < x < 8$ is the largest domain for V in this situation. Graphing V over this domain shows that the largest possible volume is approximately 420.1 in^3, which occurs when $x \approx 2.94$ in. You can substitute this value for x to find that the box dimensions for this volume are 14.12 inches long by 10.12 inches wide by 2.94 inches high.

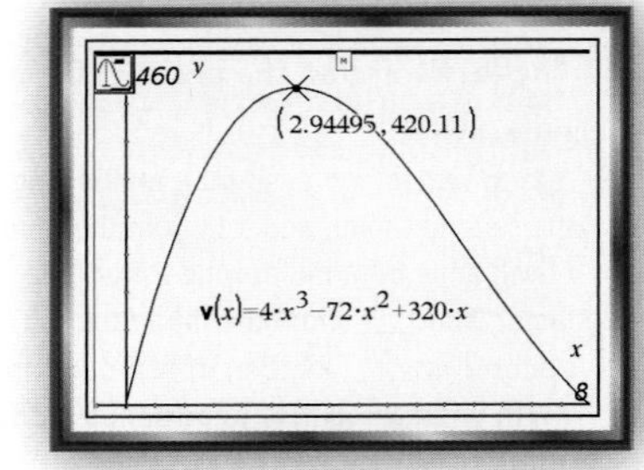

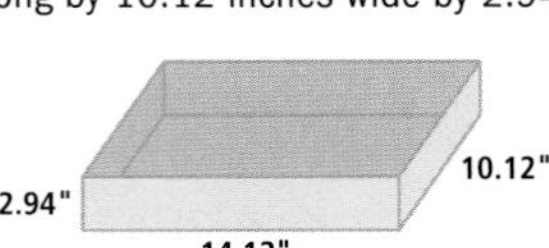

Questions

COVERING THE IDEAS

In 1–6, a polynomial is given.

a. State whether the polynomial is a monomial, a binomial, a trinomial, or none of these.

b. Give its degree.

1. $w^7 - w^5z^3 + \left(\frac{3}{2}\right)z^5$
2. $6a \cdot 2a \cdot \left(\frac{1}{3}\right)a$ b. 3
3. $x^3 - x$ b. 3
4. $4x^3 - 6x^2 - 5$ b. 3
5. 3^2 b. 0
6. $182x^4wt^2$ b. 7
7. Give an example of a 5th-degree binomial in two variables. Answers vary. Sample: $2xy^4 + y$

1a. trinomial
1b. 8
2a. monomial
3a. binomial
4a. trinomial
5a. monomial
6a. monomial

In 8 and 9, multiply by hand and write in standard form.

8. $\left(5x^2 + \frac{1}{2}x - 2\right)\left(x + \frac{1}{5}\right)$ 9. $(b^2 + 1)(2b - 3)(5b)$

10. Polynomial P is the product in standard form of $(12x^3 + 7)\left(3x^2 + \frac{3}{8}x - 1\right)(7x^2 - x)$. $252x^7$, $7x$
Without expanding, write the first and last terms of P.

In 11 and 12, refer to Example 4.

11. a. Use $V(x) = 4x^3 - 72x^2 + 320x$ to complete the table below for $x = 0$ to 10.

x	1	2	3	4	5	6	7	8	9	10
V(x)	252	?	420	?	?	192	?	?	-36	?
		384		384	300		84	0		0

b. For what integer value of x from 0 to 10 is $V(x)$ largest? $x = 3$

12. Give a reasonable domain for V if a new box has volume $V(x) = (15 - 2x)(18 - 2x)x$. $0 < x < 7.5$

APPLYING THE MATHEMATICS

13. Expand and write in standard form.
a. $(x^2 - 3x + 3)(x^2 + 3x + 3)$ b. $(x^2 - 4x + 4)(x^2 + 4x + 4)$
c. $(x^2 - 5x + 5)(x^2 + 5x + 5)$ d. $(x^2 - 6x + 6)(x^2 + 6x + 6)$
e. Based on your answers to Parts a–d, what do you predict the expanded form of $(x^2 - nx + n)(x^2 + nx + n)$ will be for any positive integer n?

14. A box measures 12 inches by 18 inches by 10 inches. A y-foot long roll of wrapping paper is x feet wide. Assuming no overlap, how much wrapping paper will be left after wrapping the box?

15. A piece of material is in the shape of an equilateral triangle. Each side measures 15 inches. Kites with sides x and $x\sqrt{3}$ are cut from each corner. Then the flaps are folded up to form an open box.
a. Write a formula for the volume $V(x)$ of the box as a product of polynomials. 15a–c. See margin.
b. Write $V(x)$ in standard form.
c. Find $V(4)$.
d. Find the maximum possible value of $V(x)$. 62.5 in^3

16. Melissa knows that $347 = 3 \cdot 10^2 + 4 \cdot 10 + 7$. Explain how Melissa can use what she knows together with the Extended Distributive Property to multiply any 3-digit number $a \cdot 10^2 + b \cdot 10 + c$ in base 10, where a, b, and c are single digits, by any 4-digit number in base 10. See margin.

8. $5x^3 + \frac{3}{2}x^2 - \frac{19}{10}x - \frac{2}{5}$

9. $10b^4 - 15b^3 + 10b^2 - 15b$

13a. $x^4 - 3x^2 + 9$

13b. $x^4 - 8x^2 + 16$

13c. $x^4 - 15x^2 + 25$

13d. $x^4 - 24x^2 + 36$

13e. $x^4 - (n^2 - 2n)x^2 + n^2$

14. $(144xy - 1032) \text{ in}^2$

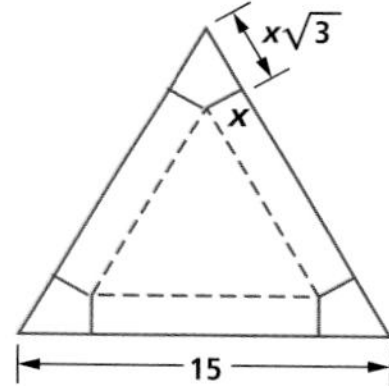

Additional Answers

15a. $V(x) = \frac{1}{2}x(15 - 2x\sqrt{3})\left(\frac{15}{2}\sqrt{3} - 3x\right)$

15b. $V(x) = 3\sqrt{3}x^3 - 45x^2 + \frac{225\sqrt{3}x}{4}$

15c. $V(4) = 417\sqrt{3} - 720 \approx 2.27$

16. If we know this property of 3-digit numbers, then we know 4-digit numbers can be represented as $w \cdot 10^3 + x \cdot 10^2 + y \cdot 10 + z$ in base 10, where w, x, y, and z are single digits. Therefore, the product of a 3-digit number and a 4-digit number is: $(a \cdot 10^2 + b \cdot 10 + c) \cdot (w \cdot 10^3 + x \cdot 10^2 + y \cdot 10 + z) = 10^5aw + 10^4ax + 10^3ay + 10^2az + 10^4bw + 10^3bx + 10^2by + 10bz + 10^3cw + 10^2cx + 10cy + cz = aw10^5 + (ax + bw)10^4 + (ay + bx + cw)10^3 + (az + by + cx)10^2 + (bz + cy)10 + cz$

3 Assignment

Recommended Assignment

- Questions 1–25
- Question 26 (extra credit)
- Reading Lesson 11-3
- Covering the Ideas 11-3

Notes on the Questions

Question 13 We expect students to use a CAS only on Parts a–d of this question. Students should try to answer Part e by hand, using a CAS to check their work.

Question 15 This question is an analogue to Example 4.

Question 16 One algorithm that uses Melissa's idea to multiply multidigit numbers is called *Napier's bones.*

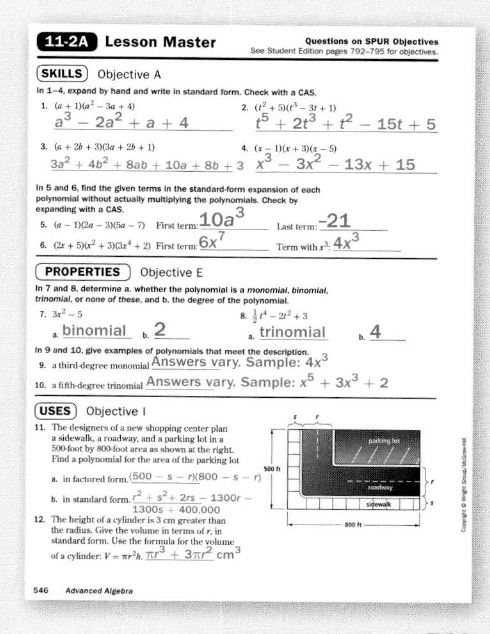

11-2A Lesson Master

Questions on SPUR Objectives
See Student Edition pages 792–795 for objectives.

SKILLS Objective A

In 1–4, expand by hand and write in standard form. Check with a CAS.

1. $(a + 1)(a^2 - 3a + 4)$ $a^3 - 2a^2 + a + 4$
2. $(t^2 + 5)(t^3 - 3t + 1)$ $t^5 + 2t^3 + t^2 - 15t + 5$
3. $(a + 2b + 3)(3a + 2b + 1)$ $3a^2 + 4b^2 + 8ab + 10a + 8b + 3$
4. $(x - 1)(x + 3)(x - 5)$ $x^3 - 3x^2 - 13x + 15$

In 5 and 6, find the given terms in the standard-form expansion of each polynomial without actually multiplying the polynomials. Check by expanding with a CAS.

5. $(a - 1)(2a - 3)(5a - 7)$ First term: $10a^3$ Last term: -21
6. $(2x + 5)(x^2 + 3)(3x^4 + 2)$ First term: $6x^7$ Term with x^3: $4x^3$

PROPERTIES Objective E

In 7 and 8, determine a. whether the polynomial is a *monomial, binomial, trinomial,* or *none of these,* and b. the degree of the polynomial.

7. $3x^2 - 5$ a. binomial b. 2
8. $\frac{1}{2}t^4 - 2t^2 + 3$ a. trinomial b. 4

In 9 and 10, give examples of polynomials that meet the description.

9. a third-degree monomial Answers vary. Sample: $4x^3$
10. a fifth-degree trinomial Answers vary. Sample: $x^5 + 3x^3 + 2$

USES Objective I

11. The designers of a new shopping center plan a sidewalk, a roadway, and a parking lot in a 500-foot by 800-foot area as shown at the right. Find a polynomial for the area of the parking lot
a. in factored form. $(500 - s - r)(800 - s - r)$
b. in standard form. $r^2 + s^2 + 2rs - 1300r - 1300s + 400{,}000$

12. The height of a cylinder is 3 cm greater than the radius. Give the volume in terms of r, in standard form. Use the formula for the volume of a cylinder: $V = \pi r^2h$. $\pi r^3 + 3\pi r^2 \text{ cm}^3$

546 Advanced Algebra

Notes on the Questions

Question 22 This model is based on actual data.

Question 26 This question can be done without a CAS, but a CAS provides a nice check.

4 Wrap-Up

Ongoing Assessment

Have students refer to Example 4 on pages 741–742 and write a similar example. Then have them find a polynomial formula in standard form for $V(x)$, assign a particular value for x, and calculate the volume using the formula. Students should demonstrate an ability to use polynomials to describe a geometric situation.

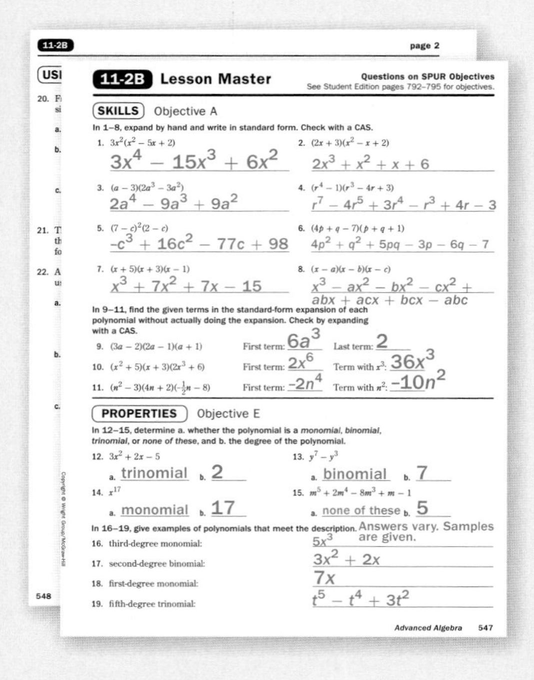

11-2B page 2

11-2B Lesson Master

Questions on SPUR Objectives
See Student Edition pages 792–795 for objectives.

SKILLS Objective A

In 1–8, expand by hand and write in standard form. Check with a CAS.

1. $3x^2(x^2 - 5x + 2)$ $3x^4 - 15x^3 + 6x^2$
2. $(2x + 3)(x^2 - x + 2)$ $2x^3 + x^2 + x + 6$
3. $(a - 3)(2a^3 - 3a^2)$ $2a^4 - 9a^3 + 9a^2$
4. $(r^4 - 1)(r^3 - 4r + 3)$ $r^7 - 4r^5 + 3r^4 - r^3 + 4r - 3$
5. $(7 - c)^2(2 - c)$ $-c^3 + 16c^2 - 77c + 98$
6. $(4p + q - 7)(p + q + 1)$ $4p^2 + q^2 + 5pq - 3p - 6q - 7$
7. $(x + 5)(x + 3)(x - 1)$ $x^3 + 7x^2 + 7x - 15$
8. $(x - a)(x - b)(x - c)$ $x^3 - ax^2 - bx^2 - cx^2 + abx + acx + bcx - abc$

In 9–11, find the given terms in the standard-form expansion of each polynomial without actually doing the expansion. Check by expanding with a CAS.

9. $(3a - 2)(2a - 1)(a + 1)$ First term: $6a^3$ Last term: 2
10. $(x^2 + 5)(x + 3)(2x^3 + 6)$ First term: $2x^6$ Term with x^3: $36x^3$
11. $(n^2 - 3)(4n + 2)(-\frac{1}{2}n - 8)$ First term: $-2n^4$ Term with n^2: $-10n^2$

PROPERTIES Objective E

In 12–15, determine a. whether the polynomial is a *monomial, binomial, trinomial,* or *none of these,* and b. the degree of the polynomial.

12. $3x^2 + 2x - 5$ a. trinomial b. 2
13. $y^7 - y^3$ a. binomial b. 7
14. x^{17} a. monomial b. 17
15. $m^5 + 2m^4 - 8m^3 + m - 1$ a. none of these b. 5

In 16–19, give examples of polynomials that meet the description. Answers vary. Samples are given.

16. third-degree monomial: $5x^3$
17. second-degree binomial: $3x^2 + 2x$
18. first-degree monomial: $7x$
19. fifth-degree trinomial: $t^5 - t^4 + 3t^2$

548 Advanced Algebra 547

17. A town's zoning ordinance shows an aerial view of a lot like the one at the right. Distances a, b, and c are the minimum setbacks allowed to the street, the side lot lines, and the rear lot line, respectively. If a rectangular lot has 75 feet of frontage and is 150 feet deep, what is the maximum ground area possible for a one-story house in terms of a, b, and c? See margin.

18. Find a monomial and a binomial whose product is $2p^2q + 4p$.

19. Find two binomials whose product is $2y^2 + 15y + 7$.

20. Find a binomial and a trinomial whose product is $3a^2 + 7ab + 2b^2 + 3a + b$. $(3a + b)(a + 2b + 1)$

REVIEW

21. Nancy invested different amounts at an APY of r. On the fifth anniversary of her initial investment her savings were $872x^5 + 690x^4 + 737x^3 + 398x^2 + 1152x + 650$ dollars, where $x = 1 + r$. (Lesson 11-1)
    a. What is the degree of the polynomial? 5
    b. If Nancy invested at an APY of 5.125%, how much did Nancy have in the account on the fifth anniversary? \$5119.36

22. During the early part of the twentieth century, the deer population of the Kaibab Plateau in Arizona grew rapidly. Later, the increase in population depleted the food supply and the deer population declined quickly. The number $N(t)$ of deer from 1905 to 1930 is approximated by $N(t) = -0.125t^5 + 3.125t^4 + 4000$, where t is the time in years after 1905. This function is graphed at the right. (Lessons 11-1, 1-4)

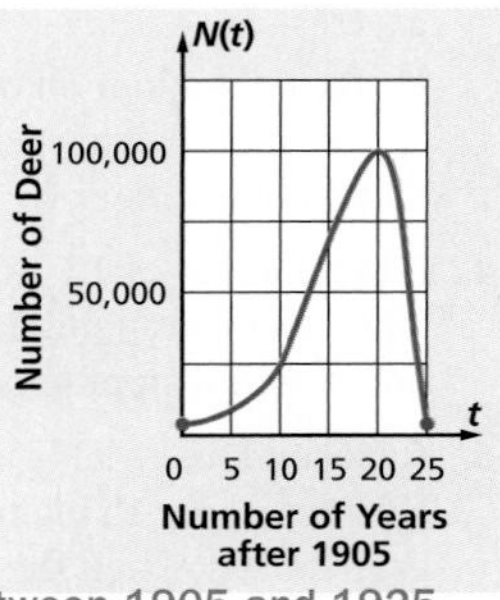

    a. What is the degree of this polynomial function? 5
    b. Estimate the deer population in 1905. 4000 deer
    c. Estimate the deer population in 1930. 4000 deer
    d. Over what time period was the deer population increasing? between 1905 and 1925

23. a. Graph $c(x) = \cos x$ when $0° \le x \le 360°$. (Lesson 10-6) a–b. See margin.
    b. For what values of x in this domain does $c(x) = 0$?

24. Solve $3x^2 - 16x - 64 = 0$. (Lesson 6-7) $x = -\frac{8}{3}$ or $x = 8$

25. Expand $(x + 7)^2$. (Lesson 6-1) $x^2 + 14x + 49$

EXPLORATION

26. a. Find the products below. 26a. $x^2 - 1$; $x^3 - 1$; $x^4 - 1$
    $(x - 1)(x + 1)$ $\quad (x - 1)(x^2 + x + 1)$ $\quad (x - 1)(x^3 + x^2 + x + 1)$
    b. State a general rule about polynomials whose product is $x^n - 1$, where $n = 2, 3, 4, 5....$

18. Answers vary. Sample: p and $2pq + 4$

19. $2y + 1$ and $y + 7$

26b. The factors of $x^n - 1$ are $(x - 1)$ and $(x^{n-1} + x^{n-2} + ... + x + 1)$.

QY ANSWER

When $x = 2$, $(2x^3 + 3x^2 - 2) \cdot (5x^2 + 4) = (16 + 12 - 2) \cdot (20 + 4) = 624$.

When $x = 2$, $10x^5 + 15x^4 + 8x^3 + 2x^2 - 8 = 320 + 240 + 64 + 8 - 8 = 624$. It checks.

Additional Answers

17. $(75 - 2b)(150 - a - c) = 11{,}250 + 2ab + 2bc - 75a - 300b - 75c$

23a.

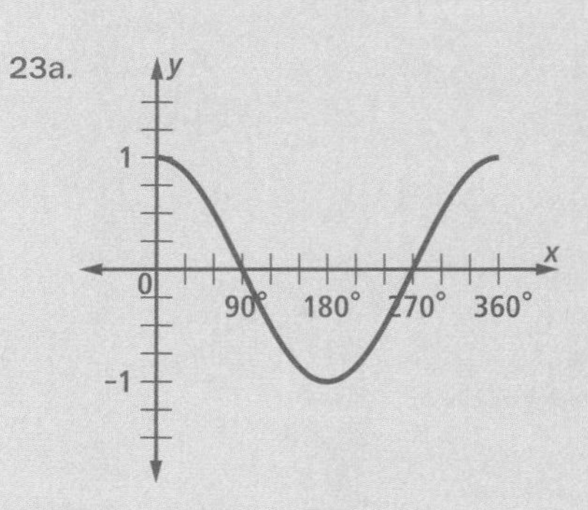

23b. $x = 90°$, $x = 270°$

Lesson 11-3 Quick-and-Easy Factoring

Vocabulary

factoring a polynomial
factored form of a polynomial
greatest common monomial factor
prime polynomial, irreducible polynomial

BIG IDEA Some polynomials can be factored into polynomials of lower degree; several processes are available to find factors.

Mental Math

Let $\sin x = 0.15$. Find each of the following.

a. $\sin(-x)$ −0.15

b. $\sin(180° - x)$ 0.15

c. $\sin(180° + x)$ −0.15

d. $\sin(360° + x)$ 0.15

A polynomial is, by definition, a sum.

$$P(x) = a_nx^n + a_{n-1}x^{n-1} + a_{n-2}x^{n-2} + \ldots + a_2x^2 + a_1x^1 + a_0,\ a_n \neq 0$$

However, polynomials are sometimes written as a product. For instance, recall the polynomial $4x^3 - 72x^2 + 320x$ from Lesson 11-2 that represents the volume of a box with sides of length x, $20 - 2x$, and $16 - 2x$. A *factored form* of this polynomial is $x(20 - 2x)(16 - 2x)$. By factoring out a 2 from each binomial in the factored form you can obtain another factored form. The expressions below are all equivalent.

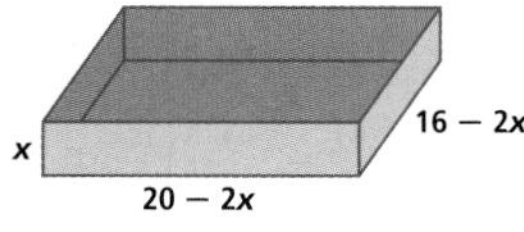

$4x^3 - 72x^2 + 320x \qquad (16 - 2x)(20 - 2x)x \qquad 4x(8 - x)(10 - x)$

The process of rewriting a polynomial as a product of two or more factors is called **factoring the polynomial**, or writing the polynomial in **factored form**. Factoring undoes multiplication. Most factoring is based on three properties:

- Distributive Property (common monomial factoring)
- Special Factoring Patterns (difference of squares, etc.)
- Factor Theorem (for polynomials)

You may have used some of these properties to factor polynomials in earlier courses. The Factor Theorem is introduced in the next lesson. This lesson discusses how to apply the other two properties when factoring polynomials.

Background

This is entirely a skills and review lesson. The material in this and the following lesson will be applied in Lessons 11-5 and 11-6 to find zeros of polynomial functions. Although there is a lot here, you do not need to spend much time because there is quite a bit more work with factoring before the chapter ends.

How much factoring should students be able to do with paper and pencil, and what algorithm(s) should they use? This always been up to debate. The existence of CAS that automatically factor virtually any polynomial has made the arguments for spending a great deal of time on factoring less potent. We encourage its use to factor polynomial that cannot be factored by inspection. However, that makes it more important that students: (1) learn the Factor Theorem in the next lesson; (2) learn the special cases in this lesson; and (3) continually remember that the process of factoring is the reverse of multiplication, so answers can be checked by either multiplication or by substituting numbers for the variables.

(continued on next page)

Lesson 11-3

GOAL

Review common monomial factoring, factoring the differences of two squares, factoring perfect-square trinomials, and factoring quadratic trinomials.

SPUR Objectives

B Factor polynomials.

E Describe attributes of polynomials.

Materials/Resources

- Lesson Masters 11-3A and 11-3B
- Resource Master 210
- Quiz 1
- CAS

HOMEWORK

Suggestions for Assignment

- Questions 1–35
- Question 36 (extra credit)
- Reading Lesson 11-4
- Covering the Ideas 11-4

Local Standards

1 Warm-Up

For 1–5, factor without using a CAS.

1. $64x^2 - 49x$ $x(64x - 49)$
2. $64x^2 - 49$ $(8x + 7)(8x - 7)$
3. $64x^2 + 49$ prime over the integers; $(8x + 7i)(8x - 7i)$ over the complex numbers
4. $64x^2 - 112x + 49$ $(8x - 7)^2$
5. $64x^2 - 441x - 49$ $(64x + 7)(x - 7)$

(*Note:* These questions serve to diagnose how much students remember from earlier work with factoring.)

2 Teaching

Notes on the Lesson

Most students will need only a brief review of the factoring techniques for a common monomial, perfect square trinomial, difference of two squares, and general trinomial factoring. Emphasize that each of the *quadratic* expressions $a^2 + 2ab + b^2$, $a^2 - 2ab + b^2$, and $a^2 - b^2$ can be written as the product of two *linear* factors.

Additional Answers

Activity

Step 1.

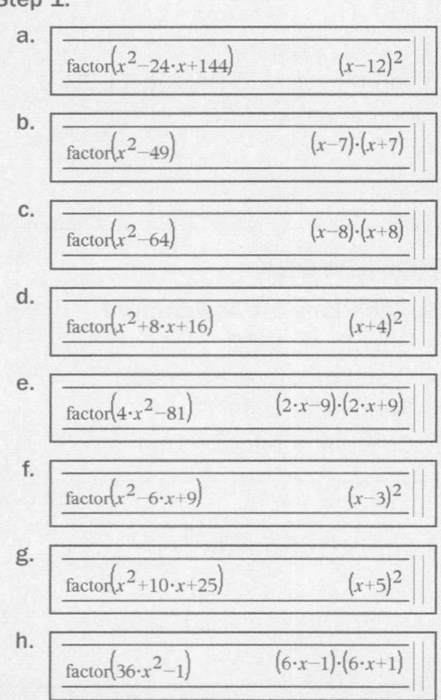

Step 2. (d) and (g) have the form $(a + b)^2$, (a) and (f) have the form $(a - b)^2$, and (b), (c), (e), and (h) have the form $(a - b)(a + b)$.

Common Monomial Factoring

Similar to the greatest common factor of a set of numbers, the **greatest common monomial factor** of the terms of a polynomial is the monomial with the greatest coefficient and highest degree that evenly divides all the terms of the polynomial. Common monomial factoring applies the Distributive Property.

Example 1

Factor $5x^3 - 15x^2$.

Solution Look for the greatest common monomial factor of the terms. The greatest common factor of 5 and 15 is 5. x^2 is the highest power of x that divides each term. So, $5x^2$ is the greatest common monomial factor of $5x^3$ and $-15x^2$. Now apply the Distributive Property.

$$5x^3 - 15x^2 = 5x^2(x - 3)$$

$5x^2(x - 3)$ is completely factored; it cannot be factored further.

Check Expand $5x^2(x - 3)$. $5x^2(x - 3) = 5x^2 \cdot x - 5x^2 \cdot 3 = 5x^3 - 15x^2$. It checks.

Special Factoring Patterns

CAS machines have built-in operations for factoring polynomials. In this Activity, you will use a CAS to discover some special factoring patterns.

Activity

MATERIALS CAS

Work with a partner. Steps 1–2. See margin.

Step 1 Factor the following expressions on a CAS.

a. $x^2 - 24x + 144$ b. $x^2 - 49$
c. $x^2 - 64$ d. $x^2 + 8x + 16$
e. $4x^2 - 81$ f. $x^2 - 6x + 9$
g. $x^2 + 10x + 25$ h. $36x^2 - 1$

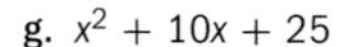

factor(x^2-24x+144)

Step 2 Based on the results of Step 1, sort the polynomials into groups. Describe how you factor the polynomials in each group.

Step 3 Use your descriptions in Step 2 to factor the following.

a. $x^2 - y^2$ $(x + y)(x - y)$
b. $x^2 - 2xy + y^2$ $(x - y)^2$
c. $x^2 + 2xy + y^2$ $(x + y)^2$

The three factoring relationships in the Activity are common enough to be worth knowing, and are summarized on the next page.

Each CAS has different commands for factoring over the rational numbers, factoring over the real numbers, and giving approximate answers. At the right are displays from the TI-NSpire and the Casio Classpad that indicate how these particular models display factorizations. In the last display on the Casio screen, the difference in commands is due to the CAS being in approximate rather than exact mode, which cannot be seen on the screen.

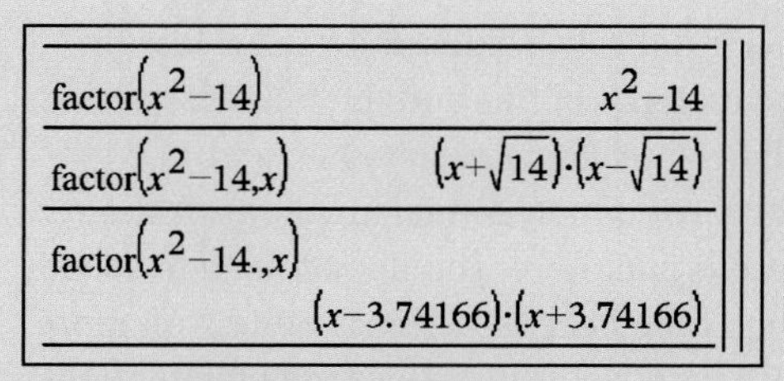

factor(x^2-14)
x^2-14
rfactor(x^2-14)
(x+√14)·(x-√14)
rfactor(x^2-14)
(x+3.741657387)·(x-3.741▸

Difference of Squares Factoring Theorem

For all a and b,

$$a^2 - b^2 = (a + b)(a - b).$$

Binomial Square Factoring Theorem

For all a and b,

$$a^2 + 2ab + b^2 = (a + b)^2;$$
$$a^2 - 2ab + b^2 = (a - b)^2.$$

Be aware that many polynomials do not factor into binomials involving integers, or do not factor at all. For example, the sum of two squares, $a^2 + b^2$, cannot be factored over the set of polynomials with real coefficients.

GUIDED

Example 2

Factor each polynomial.

a. $9x^6 - 100y^2$

b. $p^2 - 18p + 81$

Solution

a. $9x^6 = (3x^3)^2$ and $100y^2 = (10y)^2$, so this polynomial is a difference of squares. Use difference of squares factoring.

$9x^6 - 100y^2 = (\underline{\ ?\ })^2 - (\underline{\ ?\ })^2$ $3x^3$; $10y$

$= (\underline{\ ?\ } + \underline{\ ?\ })(\underline{\ ?\ } - \underline{\ ?\ })$ $3x^3$; $10y$; $3x^3$; $10y$

b. This polynomial is in binomial square form with $a = p$ and $b = \pm 9$. In order for the signs to agree with the second Binomial Square Factoring pattern, you need $b = 9$. So,

$p^2 - 18p + 81 = p^2 - 2 \cdot \underline{\ ?\ } \cdot \underline{\ ?\ } + \underline{\ ?\ }^2$ p; 9; 9

$= (\underline{\ ?\ })^2$ $p - 9$

Trial and Error

When there is no common monomial factor and the polynomial does not fit any of the special factoring patterns discussed above, a CAS can be used to factor. Additionally, some polynomials are simple enough that you can guess their factors and check by multiplying. Before CAS, some algebra students spent many hours learning strategies to guess more efficiently.

ENGLISH LEARNERS

Vocabulary Development

Review with students the concept of *factoring* a number, that is, to express the number as a product of numbers. Give them a variety of prime and composite numbers to factor. Be sure that students find all factorizations, not just the products of two factors. Then review the idea of *greatest common factor* of two or more numbers, with appropriate examples. Relate this idea to the idea of *greatest monomial factor* when factoring a polynomial. Again, provide a variety of examples and try to engage every student in the discussion. Explain that the *factored form of a polynomial* is the expression of the polynomial as a product of factors. Give several examples to illustrate that there may be more than one way to factor a polynomial. Stress that a polynomial is not completely factored until all the factors are prime, just as a number is not completely factored until all factors are prime.

Notes on the Lesson

You might wish to point out that the Difference of Squares Factoring and Binomial Square Factoring patterns are theorems because they are deduced from the Distributive Property.

Example 2 The key here is to realize that, in Difference of Squares Factoring, a and b can each be expressions. You might want to begin with something simple, such as the expressions in this example, which are $a = 3x^3$ and $b = 10y$. Then, make things more complicated, such as $a = \frac{1}{9}$, $b = x^2$; $a = 6.25m^{10}$, $b = \frac{x^4}{y^6}$; $a = x$, $b = y + z$; and so on.

Additional Examples

Example 1 Factor $6x^4 + 24x^2$.
$6x^2(x^2 + 4)$

Example 2 Factor each polynomial.

a. $49x^4y^2 - 81y^4$

b. $m^2 + 16m + 64$

Solution

a. $49x^4y^2 = (7x^2y)^2$ and $81y^4 = (9y^2)^2$, so this polynomial is a difference of squares. Use difference of squares factoring: $49x^4y^2 - 81y^4 = (\underline{\ ?\ })^2 - (\underline{\ ?\ })^2 = (\underline{\ ?\ } + \underline{\ ?\ }) \cdot (\underline{\ ?\ } - \underline{\ ?\ })$. $7x^2y$; $9y^2$; $7x^2y$; $9y^2$; $7x^2y$; $9y^2$

b. This polynomial is in binomial square form with $a = m$ and $b = \pm 8$. For the signs to agree with the first pattern in the Binomial Square Factoring Theorem, you need $b = 8$. So, $m^2 + 16m + 64 = m^2 + 2 \cdot \underline{\ ?\ } \cdot \underline{\ ?\ } + (\underline{\ ?\ })^2 = (\underline{\ ?\ })^2$. m; 8; 8; $m + 8$

Note-Taking Tips

Have students add to their journals the theorems in this lesson, along with appropriate examples.

Notes on the Lesson

Some teachers like to spend time factoring the sum and difference of two cubes: $x^3 + y^3 = (x + y)(x^2 - xy + y^2)$ and $x^3 - y^3 = (x - y)(x^2 + xy + y^2)$. These patterns are found in both UCSMP *Functions, Statistics, and Trigonometry* and *Precalculus and Discrete Mathematics*, so we do not discuss them here.

Additional Examples

Example 3 Factor $x^2 + 4x - 21$.
$(x - 3)(x + 7)$

Example 4

a. Is $x^2 - 6$ prime over the integers? If $x^2 - 6$ factors over the integers, then you can find integers a and b so that $x^2 - 6 = (x + a)(x + b)$. Use trial and error to test values of a and b when $ab = -6$. The integer factors of -6 are 1 and -6, -1 and 6, 2 and -3, or -2 and 3. Expand each combination: $(x + 1)(x - 6) = x^2 - 5x - 6$; $(x - 1)(x + 6) = x^2 + 5x - 6$; $(x + 2)(x - 3) = x^2 - x - 6$; $(x - 2)(x + 3) = x^2 + x - 6$. None of these products expand to equal $x^2 - 6$. So $x^2 - 6$ is prime over the set of integers.

b. Is $x^2 - 6$ prime over the real numbers? If $x^2 - 6$ factors over the real numbers, then you can find real numbers a and b so that $x^2 - 6 = (x + a)(x + b)$. Because a and b do not need to be integers, you can use difference of squares factoring: $x^2 - 6 = x^2 - (\sqrt{6})^2 = (x + \sqrt{6})(x - \sqrt{6})$. So $x^2 - 6$ is not prime over the set of real numbers.

Example 3

Factor $x^2 - 2x - 15$.

Solution You want solutions to $x^2 - 2x - 15 = (x + \underline{\ ?\ })(x + \underline{\ ?\ })$.

Because -15 is the product of the two missing numbers on the right side, begin by considering the factors of -15. The factors are either -15 and 1, 15 and -1, 5 and -3, or -5 and 3. Try each combination by expanding until you find one that checks:

$(x - 15)(x + 1) = x^2 - 14x - 15$ Not correct

$(x + 15)(x - 1) = x^2 + 14x - 15$ Not correct

$(x + 5)(x - 3) = x^2 + 2x - 15$ Not correct

$(x - 5)(x + 3) = x^2 - 2x - 15$ Correct!

So, $x^2 - 2x - 15 = (x - 5)(x + 3)$.

Prime Polynomials

How do you know when a polynomial is factored completely? When you factor a number such as $12 = 2 \cdot 2 \cdot 3$, the number is factored completely when all the factors are prime. Similarly, a polynomial is factored completely when all the factors are *prime polynomials*. A polynomial is **prime**, or **irreducible**, over a set of numbers if it cannot be factored into polynomials of lower degree whose coefficients are in the set. Writing a polynomial as a product of factors with coefficients in a set is called *factoring over* that set.

Example 4

a. **Is $x^2 - 14$ prime over the integers?**

b. **Is $x^2 - 14$ prime over the real numbers?**

Solution

a. If $x^2 - 14$ factors over the integers, then you can find integers a and b so that $x^2 - 14 = (x + a)(x + b)$. Use trial and error to test values of a and b when $ab = -14$.

The integer factors of -14 are 1 and -14, -1 and 14, 2 and -7, or -2 and 7. Expand each combination.

$(x + 1)(x - 14) = x^2 - 13x - 14$

$(x - 1)(x + 14) = x^2 + 13x - 14$

$(x + 2)(x - 7) = x^2 - 5x - 14$

$(x - 2)(x + 7) = x^2 + 5x - 14$

Accommodating the Learner

Have students work in pairs to factor polynomials of the form $x^2 + bx + c$ when b and c are not integers. Have them factor each of these expressions.

1. $x^2 + \frac{2}{9}x + \frac{1}{81}$ $\left(x + \frac{1}{9}\right)^2$
2. $x^2 - x + \frac{1}{4}$ $\left(x - \frac{1}{2}\right)^2$
3. $x^2 - \frac{25}{36}$ $\left(x + \frac{5}{6}\right)\left(x - \frac{5}{6}\right)$
4. $x^2 + \frac{7}{3}x + \frac{2}{3}$ $(x + 2)\left(x + \frac{1}{3}\right)$
5. $x^2 - \frac{3}{4}x - \frac{1}{4}$ $(x - 1)\left(x + \frac{1}{4}\right)$

None of these products expand to equal $x^2 - 14$.

So, $x^2 - 14$ is prime over the set of integers.

b. If $x^2 - 14$ factors over the real numbers, then you can find real numbers a and b so that $x^2 - 14 = (x + a)(x + b)$. Because a and b do not need to be integers, you can use Difference of Squares factoring.

$$x^2 - 14 = x^2 - \left(\sqrt{14}\right)^2 = \left(x + \sqrt{14}\right)\left(x - \sqrt{14}\right)$$

This factorization shows that $x^2 - 14$ is not prime over the set of real numbers.

By default, most CAS machines factor over the rationals. However, a CAS will also factor over the real numbers, as shown below. Different machines may have different commands for factoring over the reals. Some machines factor over the reals when ",x" is entered after a polynomial in x. The machine output pictured at the left below uses an `rfactor` command to factor over the reals.

Note that when a polynomial is prime over a set, a CAS command to factor over that set will produce an output identical to the original polynomial. For example, the screen at the right below shows that $x^2 - 14$ is prime over the rationals.

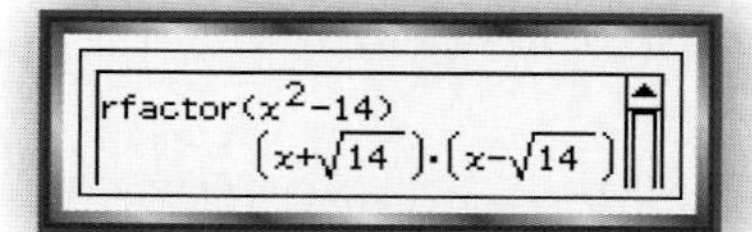

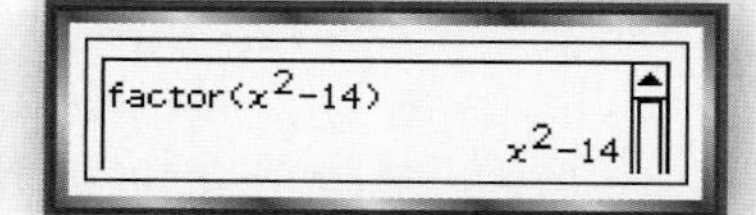

Questions

COVERING THE IDEAS

1. **Fill in the Blanks** Copy and complete: $3m^2$; $5m$; $-2n$
$21m^3n + 35m^2n - 14mn^2 = 7mn(\underline{\ ?\ } + \underline{\ ?\ } + \underline{\ ?\ })$

In 2 and 3, factor out the greatest common monomial. Check with a CAS.

2. $25y^4 - 50y$ $25y(y^3 - 2)$
3. $90x^3y^2 + 270xy^2 + 180x^2y^2$

In 4–9, a polynomial is given.

a. Tell whether the polynomial is a binomial square, a difference of squares, or neither.

b. Factor over the real numbers, if possible.

4. $a^2 - b^2$
5. $x^2 - 2xy + y^2$
6. $r^2 - 121$
7. $49x^2 - 144b^2$
8. $25b^2 - 70bc + 49c^2$
9. $y^2 + 25$

3. $90xy^2(x^2 + 3 + 2x)$

4a. difference of squares

4b. $(a - b)(a + b)$

5a. binomial square

5b. $(x - y)^2$

6a. difference of squares

6b. $(r + 11)(r - 11)$

7a. difference of squares

7b. $(7x - 12b)(7x + 12b)$

8a. binomial square

8b. $(5b - 7c)^2$

9a. neither

9b. not possible

Notes on the Lesson

Example 4 It is important to discuss this example. In the set of real numbers, $x^2 - 14$ can be considered as the difference of two squares because 14 is the square of $\sqrt{14}$.

Emphasize that a polynomial is not completely factored unless each polynomial in the factored form is prime.

To emphasize the difference in domains of factorization, factor the polynomial $x^4 + x^2 - 12$ in different domains, as follows:

- over the rationals: $(x^2 + 4)(x^2 - 3)$
- over the reals: $(x^2 + 4)(x - \sqrt{3}) \cdot (x + \sqrt{3})$
- over the complex numbers: $(x + 2i)(x - 2i))(x - \sqrt{3})(x + \sqrt{3})$

3 Assignment

Recommended Assignment

- Questions 1–35
- Question 36 (extra credit)
- Reading Lesson 11-4
- Covering the Ideas 11-4

Notes on the Questions

Questions 4–9 In each question, encourage students to identify a factoring pattern before they begin to factor each expression. Advise students to write that pattern on their paper until they are comfortable finding the pattern without it.

Accommodating the Learner

A common mistake that students make when factoring polynomials is that they neglect to first look for a common monomial factor, which may be a constant or a variable term. Even when they do find a common monomial factor, they sometimes forget to check the remaining polynomial factor to determine if it can be factored further. Remind students that a polynomial is not *completely* factored until each polynomial in the factored form is prime.

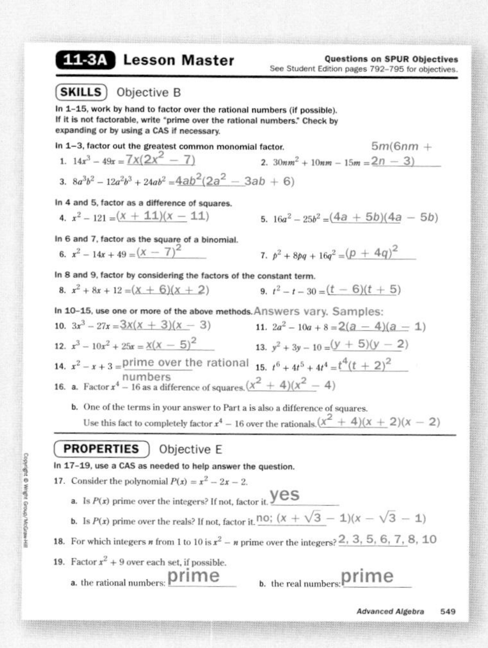

11-3A Lesson Master

Questions on SPUR Objectives
See Student Edition pages 792–795 for objectives.

SKILLS Objective B

In 1–15, work by hand to factor over the rational numbers (if possible). If it is not factorable, write "prime over the rational numbers." Check by expanding or by using a CAS if necessary.

In 1–3, factor out the greatest common monomial factor.

1. $14x^3 - 49x = 7x(2x^2 - 7)$
2. $30nm^2 + 10nm - 15m = 5m(6nm + 2n - 3)$
3. $8a^3b^2 - 12a^2b^3 + 24ab^2 = 4ab^2(2a^2 - 3ab + 6)$

In 4 and 5, factor as a difference of squares.

4. $x^2 - 121 = (x + 11)(x - 11)$
5. $16a^2 - 25b^2 = (4a + 5b)(4a - 5b)$

In 6 and 7, factor as the square of a binomial.

6. $x^2 - 14x + 49 = (x - 7)^2$
7. $p^2 + 8pq + 16q^2 = (p + 4q)^2$

In 8 and 9, factor by considering the factors of the constant term.

8. $x^2 + 8x + 12 = (x + 6)(x + 2)$
9. $t^2 - t - 30 = (t - 6)(t + 5)$

In 10–15, use one or more of the above methods. Answers vary. Samples:

10. $3x^3 - 27x = 3x(x + 3)(x - 3)$
11. $2a^2 - 10a + 8 = 2(a - 4)(a - 1)$
12. $x^3 - 10x^2 + 25x = x(x - 5)^2$
13. $y^2 + 3y - 10 = (y + 5)(y - 2)$
14. $x^2 - x + 3 =$ prime over the rational numbers
15. $t^6 + 4t^5 + 4t^4 = t^4(t + 2)^2$
16. a. Factor $x^4 - 16$ as a difference of squares. $(x^2 + 4)(x^2 - 4)$
b. One of the terms in your answer to Part a is also a difference of squares. Use this fact to completely factor $x^4 - 16$ over the rationals. $(x^2 + 4)(x + 2)(x - 2)$

PROPERTIES Objective E

In 17–19, use a CAS as needed to help answer the question.

17. Consider the polynomial $P(x) = x^2 - 2x - 2$.
a. Is $P(x)$ prime over the integers? If not, factor it. yes
b. Is $P(x)$ prime over the reals? If not, factor it. no; $(x + \sqrt{3} - 1)(x - \sqrt{3} - 1)$
18. For which integers n from 1 to 10 is $x^2 - n$ prime over the integers? 2, 3, 5, 6, 7, 8, 10
19. Factor $x^2 + 9$ over each set, if possible.
a. the rational numbers: prime
b. the real numbers: prime

Advanced Algebra 549

Notes on the Questions

Questions 26 and 27 Stress that looking for a common monomial factor should almost *always* be the first step in a factoring problem.

Additional Answers

10. a: $(3x^3 + 10y)(3x^3 - 10y) = 9x^6 - 30x^3y + 30x^3y - 100y^2 = 9x^6 - 100y^2$; b: $(p - 9)^2 = (p - 9)(p - 9) = p^2 - 9p - 9p + 81 = p^2 - 18p + 81$

11b. $(12t^2 + 12t)(t - 1) = 12t^3 - 12t^2 + 12t^2 - 12t = 12t^3 - 12t$

26a. $a^2b^2(242a^2 - b^2)$; this is the complete factorization over the rationals

26b. $a^2b^2(242a^2 - b^2) = 242a^4b^2 - a^2b^4$

27a. $5x(x^2 - 2x - 35) = 5x(x - 7)(x + 5)$

27b. $(5x^2 - 35x)(x + 5) = 5x^3 + 25x^2 - 35x^2 - 175x = 5x^3 - 10x^2 - 175x$

10. Check your solutions to Example 2 by expanding your answers. See margin.

11. a. Factor $12t^3 - 12t$ into linear factors.
    b. Check by multiplying. See margin.

In 12 and 13, factor completely over the rational numbers and check your answer.

12. $64s^2 - 49$
13. $x^4 - 10x^2 + 9$

In 14–18, factor the polynomial completely over the rational numbers and state which factoring method(s) you used. If it is not factorable, write "prime over the rational numbers."

14. $3x^2 + 24x + 36$
15. $-1 - 10y - 25y^2$
16. $b^2 - 3b + 8$
17. $12x^3 - 75x$
18. a. $y^2 + 5y - 6$
    b. $y^2 - 5y - 6$
    c. $y^2 + 5y + 6$
    d. $y^2 - 5y + 6$

19. a. Is $x^2 - 30$ prime over the integers? If not, factor it. yes
    b. Is $x^2 - 30$ prime over the reals? If not, factor it.

APPLYING THE MATHEMATICS

20. $48^2 = 2304$. Use this information to factor $2303 = 48^2 - 1$.

21. **Multiple Choice** Which of the following is a perfect square trinomial? A
    A $16x^2 + 24x + 9$
    B $q^4 - 16q^3 + 64$
    C $t^2 - 64$
    D $4x^2 + 16x + 25$

22. a. Write $x^4 - 16$ as the product of two binomials.
    b. Write $x^4 - 64$ as the product of three binomials.

23. One factor of $12x^2 + x - 35$ is $(3x - 5)$. Find the other factor. $4x + 7$

In 24 and 25, factor the polynomial by trial and error and check with a CAS.

24. $8z^2 + 6z + 1$ $(4z + 1)(2z + 1)$
25. $6q^2 + 2q - 4$ $2(q + 1)(3q - 2)$

In 26 and 27, a polynomial is given. 26–27. See margin.
 a. **First factor out the greatest common monomial factor. Then complete the factorization.**
 b. **Check by multiplying.**

26. $242a^4b^2 - a^2b^4$
27. $5x^3 - 10x^2 - 175x$

28. **Multiple Choice** Which is a factorization of $a^2 + 100$ over the complex numbers? C
    A $(a + 10)(a + 10)$
    B $(a + 10i)(a + 10i)$
    C $(a + 10i)(a - 10i)$
    D $(a + 10i)^2$

11a. $12t(t + 1)(t - 1)$

12. $(8s-7)(8s+7)$; For $s = 2$, $64(2^2) - 49 = 207$ and $(8(2) - 7)(8(2) + 7) = 9(23) = 207$.

13. $(x + 3)(x - 3) \cdot (x + 1)(x - 1)$; For $x = -3$, $(-3)^4 - 10(-3)^2 + 9 = 0$ and $(-3 + 3)(-3 - 3) \cdot (-3 + 1)(-3 - 1) = 0(-6)(-2)(-4) = 0$.

14. $3(x + 6)(x + 2)$; common monomial factoring, trial and error

15. $-1(1 + 5y)^2$; common monomial factoring, binomial square factoring

16. prime over the rational numbers

17. $3x(2x + 5)(2x - 5)$; common monomial factoring, difference of squares

18a. $(y + 6)(y - 1)$; trial and error

18b. $(y - 6)(y + 1)$; trial and error

18c. $(y + 3)(y + 2)$; trial and error

18d. $(y - 2)(y - 3)$; trial and error

19b. no; $(x - \sqrt{30}) \cdot (x + \sqrt{30})$

20. $48^2 - 1 = (48 + 1) \cdot (48 - 1) = (49) \cdot (47) = 7 \cdot 7 \cdot 47$

22a. $(x^2 - 4)(x^2 + 4)$

22b. $(x + \sqrt{8})(x - \sqrt{8}) \cdot (x^2 + 8)$

Extension

Introduce to students the following method for finding the square of a number. Because $a^2 - b^2 = (a + b)(a - b)$, then $a^2 = (a + b)(a - b) + b^2$. To find 96^2, let $a = 96$ and choose a value of b such that $a + b$ or $a - b$ is a number that is easy to multiply mentally. In this case, we choose $b = 4$. By the Difference of Squares Factoring Theorem, $96^2 = (96 + 4)(96 - 4) + 4^2 = (100)(92) + 16 = 9216$. Have students work in groups or pairs to find 97^2, 53^2, and 48^2 using this method.

Answers vary. Sample: $97^2 = (97 + 3)(97 - 3) + 3^2 = (100)(94) + 9 = 9409$; $53^2 = (53 + 3)(53 - 3) + 3^2 = (56)(50) + 9 = 2809$; $48^2 = (48 + 2)(48 - 2) + 2^2 = (50)(46) + 4 = 2304$

29. Consider the expression $\frac{4x^2 - 9}{2x^2 + x - 3}$.
   a. Factor the numerator and denominator.
   b. Because binomials are numbers, they may be multiplied and divided in the same way numbers are. Simplify your answer to Part a.
   c. Using your factored expression in Part a, determine the domain of the function $f(x) = \frac{4x^2 - 9}{2x^2 + x - 3}$. Explain your reasoning.

29a. $\frac{(2x + 3)(2x - 3)}{(2x + 3)(x - 1)}$

29b. $\frac{(2x - 3)}{(x - 1)}$

29c. The domain includes all real numbers x such that $x \neq -1.5$ and $x \neq 1$. If x took these values, the denominator of the expression would equal zero.

REVIEW

In 30 and 31, consider a closed rectangular box with dimensions $2h$, $h + 2$, and $2h + 3$. Write a polynomial in standard form for each measure.

30. $S(h)$, the surface area of the box **(Lesson 11-2)** $16h^2 + 34h + 12$

31. $V(h)$, the volume of the box **(Lesson 11-2)** $4h^3 + 14h^2 + 12h$

32. Give an example of a cubic binomial. **(Lesson 11-1)** Answers vary. Sample: $16x^3 - 31$

33. The lateral height of a cone is 9 centimeters and its height is h. **(Lessons 11-1, 1-7)** 33a–c. See margin.
   a. Write a formula for the volume of the cone in terms of r and h.
   b. Write a formula for the radius r of the cone in terms of h.
   c. Substitute your expression for r in Part b into your formula in Part a.
   d. **True or False** The volume of this cone is a polynomial function of h. true

34. Write $\log_7 99 - \log_7 33$ as a logarithm of a single number. **(Lesson 9-9)** $\log_7 3$

35. Evaluate $\log_{13}\left(\frac{1}{13}\right)$. **(Lesson 9-7)** -1

EXPLORATION

36. Consider the polynomial $P(x) = \left(x - \frac{2}{3}\right)\left(x + \frac{3}{4}\right)$.
   a. Write $P(x)$ in expanded form. $x^2 + \frac{1}{12}x - \frac{1}{2}$
   b. Use a CAS to factor the expanded form. See margin.
   c. The answer to Part b does not look like the form you started with. What did the CAS do to the expanded form before it factored it? The CAS factored out $\frac{1}{12}$.
   d. Use the ideas in Parts a–c to factor $x^2 - \frac{5}{6}x + \frac{1}{6}$. $\frac{(2x - 1)(3x - 1)}{6}$ or $\frac{1}{6}(2x - 1)(3x - 1)$

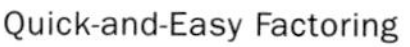

4 Wrap-Up

Ongoing Assessment

Have students write a brief paragraph describing the three factoring patterns discussed in this lesson. Then have them write examples of polynomials that can be factored using each of these factoring patterns and factor the polynomials. Students should demonstrate an understanding of factoring patterns and an ability to factor polynomial functions.

Administer Quiz 1 (or a quiz of your own) after students complete this lesson.

Additional Answers

33a. $V = \frac{1}{3}\pi r^2 h$

33b. $r = \sqrt{81 - h^2}$

33c. $V = \frac{1}{3}\pi h\left(\sqrt{81 - h^2}\right)^2 = \frac{1}{3}\pi(81h - h^3)$

36b.

$\text{factor}\left(x^2 + \frac{x}{12} - \frac{1}{2}\right)$	$\frac{(3\cdot x-2)\cdot(4\cdot x+3)}{12}$

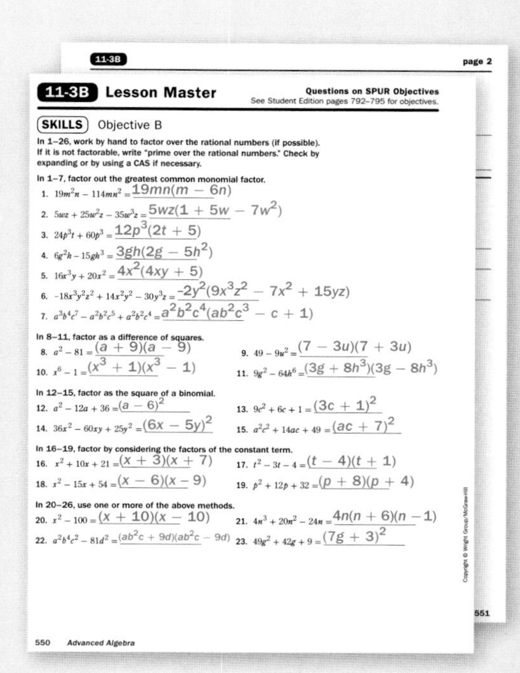

11-3B page 2

11-3B Lesson Master Questions on SPUR Objectives See Student Edition pages 792–795 for objectives.

SKILLS Objective B

In 1–26, work by hand to factor over the rational numbers (if possible). If it is not factorable, write "prime over the rational numbers." Check by expanding or by using a CAS if necessary.

In 1–7, factor out the greatest common monomial factor.

1. $19m^2n - 114mn^2 =$ $19mn(m - 6n)$
2. $5wz + 25w^2z - 35w^3z =$ $5wz(1 + 5w - 7w^2)$
3. $24p^3t + 60p^3 =$ $12p^3(2t + 5)$
4. $6g^2h - 15gh^3 =$ $3gh(2g - 5h^2)$
5. $16x^3y + 20x^2 =$ $4x^2(4xy + 5)$
6. $-18x^3y^2z^2 + 14x^2y^2 - 30y^3z =$ $-2y^2(9x^3z^2 - 7x^2 + 15yz)$
7. $a^3b^4c^7 - a^2b^2c^5 + a^2b^2c^4 =$ $a^2b^2c^4(abc^3 - c + 1)$

In 8–11, factor as a difference of squares.

8. $a^2 - 81 =$ $(a + 9)(a - 9)$
9. $49 - 9u^2 =$ $(7 - 3u)(7 + 3u)$
10. $x^6 - 1 =$ $(x^3 + 1)(x^3 - 1)$
11. $9g^2 - 64h^6 =$ $(3g + 8h^3)(3g - 8h^3)$

In 12–15, factor as the square of a binomial.

12. $a^2 - 12a + 36 =$ $(a - 6)^2$
13. $9c^2 + 6c + 1 =$ $(3c + 1)^2$
14. $36x^2 - 60xy + 25y^2 =$ $(6x - 5y)^2$
15. $a^2c^2 + 14ac + 49 =$ $(ac + 7)^2$

In 16–19, factor by considering the factors of the constant term.

16. $x^2 + 10x + 21 =$ $(x + 3)(x + 7)$
17. $t^2 - 3t - 4 =$ $(t - 4)(t + 1)$
18. $x^2 - 15x + 54 =$ $(x - 6)(x - 9)$
19. $p^2 + 12p + 32 =$ $(p + 8)(p + 4)$

In 20–26, use one or more of the above methods.

20. $x^2 - 100 =$ $(x + 10)(x - 10)$
21. $4n^3 + 20n^2 - 24n =$ $4n(n + 6)(n - 1)$
22. $a^2b^4c^2 - 81d^2 =$ $(ab^2c + 9d)(ab^2c - 9d)$
23. $49g^2 + 42g + 9 =$ $(7g + 3)^2$

550 Advanced Algebra

551

Lesson

11-4

GOAL

Use graphing and the factoring from Lesson 11-3 to develop and deduce the Factor Theorem.

SPUR Objectives

C Find zeros of polynomial functions by factoring.

F Apply the Zero-Product Theorem and the Factor Theorem.

J Graph polynomial functions.

K Estimate zeros of polynomial functions using graphs.

Materials/Resources

- Lesson Masters 11-4A and 11-4B
- Resource Masters 211 and 212
- CAS

HOMEWORK

Suggestions for Assignment

- Questions 1–28
- Question 29 (extra credit)
- Reading Lesson 11-5
- Covering the Ideas 11-5

Local Standards

1 Warm-Up

For 1–3, find an *x*-intercept of the graph of the function *P* by graphing. Then check by using a CAS.

1. $P(x) = 7x^{17} + 12x^9 - 1.6x$ 0
2. $P(x) = 7(x + 2)^{17} + 12(x + 2)^9 - 1.6(x + 2)$ -2
3. $P(x) = 7(x - 4.5)^{17} + 12(x - 4.5)^9 - 1.6(x - 4.5)$ 4.5

(*Note:* This exercise is a good lead-in for the proof of the Factor Theorem.)

Lesson

11-4 The Factor Theorem

Vocabulary

zero of a polynomial, root of a polynomial

BIG IDEA If $P(x)$ is a polynomial, then a is a solution to the equation $P(x) = 0$ if and only if $x - a$ is a factor of $P(x)$.

Zeros of a Polynomial

Consider an equation in which there is a polynomial on each side, such as

$$14x^3 + 3x - 10 = 5x - 9x^2 + 5.$$

Add the opposite of $5x - 9x^2 + 5$ to each side. Then

$$14x^3 + 9x^2 - 2x - 15 = 0.$$

In this way, every equality of two polynomials in x can be converted into an equivalent equation of the form $P(x) = 0$. More generally, any equation involving two expressions in x can be converted into an equation of the form $f(x) = 0$.

As you know, when f is a function, then a solution to the equation $f(x) = 0$ is called a *zero* of f. When P is a polynomial function, then a zero of P is also called a **zero** or **root of the polynomial** $P(x)$. For example, when $P(x) = 3x - 18$, then 6 is a zero, or root, of $P(x)$ because $3 \cdot 6 - 18 = 0$. A zero of $P(x)$ is an x-intercept of the graph of P, as shown at the right.

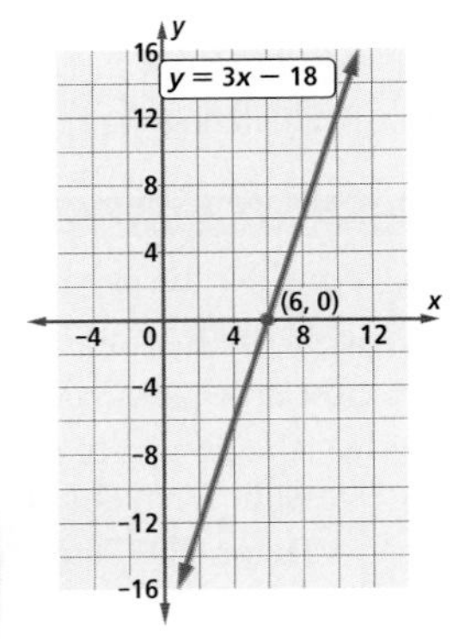

The factors of a polynomial $P(x)$ are connected to its zeros, or x-intercepts. Understanding this connection can help you to solve equations with polynomials and to understand their algebraic structure.

Recall that a product of numbers equals 0 if and only if one of the factors equals 0. We call this result the *Zero-Product Theorem*.

Zero-Product Theorem

For all a and b, $ab = 0$ if and only if $a = 0$ or $b = 0$.

For instance, if $f(x) = 0$ and $f(x) = g(x) \cdot h(x)$, then $g(x) = 0$ or $h(x) = 0$. This is one reason for manipulating an equation so that 0 is on one side.

Mental Math

Let h be a sequence with explicit formula $h_n = h_0 \cdot r^n$ that models the maximum height of a ball after n bounces. Are the following *always*, *sometimes but not always*, or *never* true?

a. r is greater than 1. never

b. r is less than zero. never

c. h_0 is greater than h_3. always

d. h_4 is greater than h_3. never

Background

The method of solving a quadratic by factoring and applying the Zero-Product Theorem dates back to, at least, the Englishman Thomas Harriott (1560–1621), who, in 1587, had been a member of Sir Walter Raleigh's expedition to Virginia. (He traveled with Raleigh before modern algebraic notation had been introduced and did his work with factoring later.) Later, Harriott's method was applied to polynomials of higher degree, so, that by Gauss's time (1777–1855), the ideas of this lesson were well known to mathematicians.

Harriott did his work before the invention of coordinate graphs. Immediately after coordinate graphing was developed, the connection between factoring and graphs was seen. Today, the existence of CAS and graphing technology has changed the way the idea can be developed. Polynomial functions are now easy to graph and rational zeros are easy to find. Thus, we can present a graphical representation of zeros to go along with the factoring view.

Example 1

In Example 4 of Lesson 11-2, the volume $V(x)$ of the box shown at the right is given by $V(x) = x(20 - 2x)(16 - 2x) = 4x^3 - 72x^2 + 320x$. Find the zeros of V.

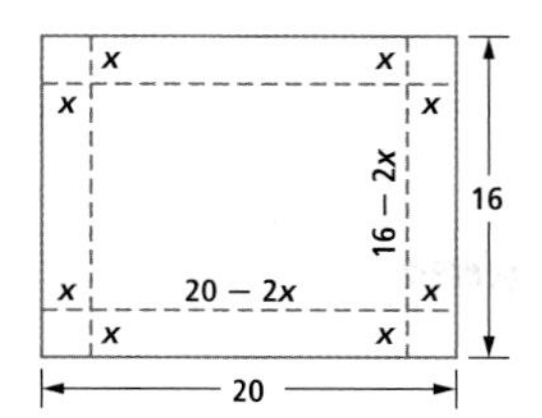

Solution To find the zeros, solve $x(20 - 2x)(16 - 2x) = 0$. By the Zero-Product Theorem, at least one of these factors must equal zero.

Either $x = 0$ or $20 - 2x = 0$ or $16 - 2x = 0$.

So, $x = 0$ or $x = 10$ or $x = 8$.

The zeros are 0, 8, and 10.

Check Notice that the zeros are the three values of x for which one of the dimensions of the box is 0, so there would be no volume.

Activity 1

MATERIALS CAS Steps 1–5. See the Additional Answers section at the back of the book.

Work with a partner and use a graphing utility. One partner should work with $p(x) = x^3 - 3x^2 - 13x + 15$, the other with $q(x) = x^4 - x^3 - 24x^2 + 4x + 80$.

Step 1 Graph your polynomial equation in the window $-10 \le x \le 10$; $-100 \le y \le 100$.

Step 2 Find the x-intercepts of your graph.

Step 3 Factor your polynomial on a CAS.

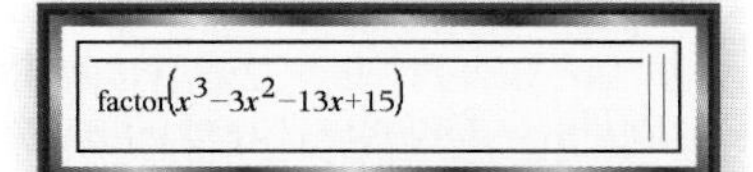

Step 4 Compare your results with your partner's. How are the x-intercepts of each graph related to the factors of each polynomial?

Step 5 Use your answer to Step 4 to write a polynomial whose graph has x-intercepts 4, 5, and –1.

The results of Activity 1 show that the zeros of a polynomial function correspond to the polynomial's linear factors. For example, the zeros of p are –3, 1, and 5, and the factors of $p(x)$ are $x + 3$, $x - 1$, and $x - 5$. The following theorem generalizes this relationship.

Factor Theorem

$x - r$ is a factor of $P(x)$ if and only if $P(r) = 0$, that is, r is a zero of P.

Factor Theorem The proof we give of the Factor Theorem is a nontrivial application of the Graph-Translation Theorem. The idea is simple: A polynomial $P(x)$ is divisible by x if and only if 0 is a solution to $P(x) = 0$. Example 1 provides an example of such a polynomial. So, translating horizontally r units, $P(x)$ is divisible by $x - r$ if and only if r is a solution to $P(x) = 0$.

ENGLISH LEARNERS

Vocabulary Development

Review with students the idea that the solution to $f(x) = 0$ is called a *zero* of f. So a *zero of a polynomial function* P is a solution to $P(x) = 0$. The term *root of a polynomial* $P(x)$ has the same meaning; it is a value of x for which $P(x) = 0$. Point out that the zeros of a polynomial function are the x-intercepts of its graph, that is, the points where $y = 0$.

2 Teaching

Notes on the Lesson

Many classes will need 2 days to cover this lesson. One way to approach this lesson is to have students do the two activities on the first day. Then, each student should list the main points of the lesson. The first assignment could be the Questions Covering the Ideas and the Review Questions. The second assignment could be the Applying the Mathematics Questions and the Exploration.

Additional Example

Example 1 In Additional Example 4 of Lesson 11-2, the volume $V(x)$ of the box shown below is given by $V(x) = x(24 - 2x)(24 - 2x) = 4x^3 - 96x^2 + 576x$. Find the zeros of V.

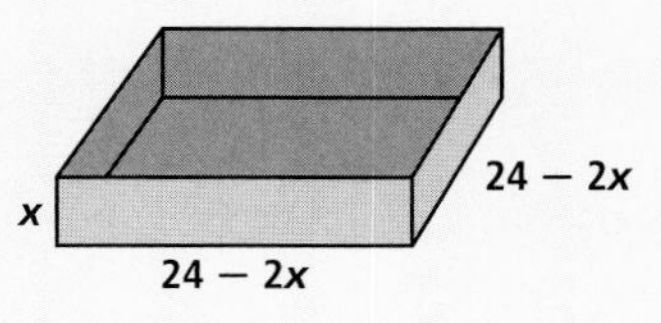

0 and 12

Activity 1 With graphing and CAS technology, students can generate many instances of the Factor Theorem quickly and easily. The Factor Theorem should be reasonably obvious after completing this activity.

Additional Answers can be found in the back of the book.

Note-Taking Tips

Have students add to their journals the theorems in this lesson, along with appropriate examples.

Notes on the Lesson

Example 2 You might graph the function in this example. Use the zoom or rescale features of a graphing utility to illustrate that P has zeros at 3, -3, $\sqrt{5}$, and $-\sqrt{5}$.

Additional Example

Example 2 Find the roots of $P(x) = x^4 - x^3 - 20x^2$ by factoring.

Solution Use a CAS command to factor $P(x)$ over the rationals.

factor$(x^4-x^3-20x^2)$
$x^2(x-5)\cdot(x+4)$

The roots are the solutions to $x^2(x-5)(x+4) = 0$. Using the Zero-Product Theorem, $x^2 = 0$, $x - 5 = 0$, or $x + 4 = 0$. Thus $x = 0$, $x = 5$, or $x = -4$. So the roots of $P(x)$ are 0, 5, and -4.

Proof If $x - r$ is a factor of $P(x)$, then for all x, $P(x) = (x - r) \cdot Q(x)$, where $Q(x)$ is some polynomial. Substitute r for x in this formula.

$$P(r) = (r - r) \cdot Q(r) = 0 \cdot Q(r) = 0.$$

Proving the other direction of the theorem, that $P(r) = 0$ implies that $x - r$ is a factor of $P(x)$, requires more work. Consider the special case where $r = 0$. Write $P(x)$ in general form:

$$P(x) = a_nx^n + a_{n-1}x^{n-1} + ... + a_1x + a_0.$$

Then $P(r) = P(0) = a_n0^n + a_{n-1}0^{n-1} + ... + a_10 + a_0$.

So $P(0) = a_0$, the constant term.

Thus, when $r = 0$ and $P(0) = 0$, $a_0 = 0$.

So, x is a factor of every term of $P(x)$, and we can write

$$P(x) = x(a_nx^{n-1} + a_{n-1}x^{n-2} + ... + a_1).$$

So $x = x - 0$ is a factor of $P(x)$.

If $r \neq 0$ and $P(r) = 0$, then the graph of $y = P(x)$ contains the point $(r, 0)$. Think of the graph of $y = P(x)$ as a translation image r units to the right of the graph of a polynomial function G that contains (0, 0). Because $G(0) = 0$, the case above applies to $G(x)$, so $G(x) = x \cdot H(x)$ for some polynomial $H(x)$. By the Graph-Translation Theorem, $P(x)$ can be formed by replacing x in $G(x)$ by $x - r$. Therefore, $P(x) = (x - r) \cdot H(x - r)$, and so $x - r$ is a factor of $P(x)$.

QY1

▸ QY1

5 is a zero of q in Activity 1. What factor of $q(x)$ is associated with this zero?

Finding Zeros by Factoring

Both the Zero-Product Theorem and the Factor Theorem provide methods for finding zeros of polynomials by factoring.

Example 2

Find the roots of $P(x) = x^4 - 14x^2 + 45$ by factoring.

Solution 1 Use a CAS command to factor $P(x)$ over the rationals, as shown at the right.

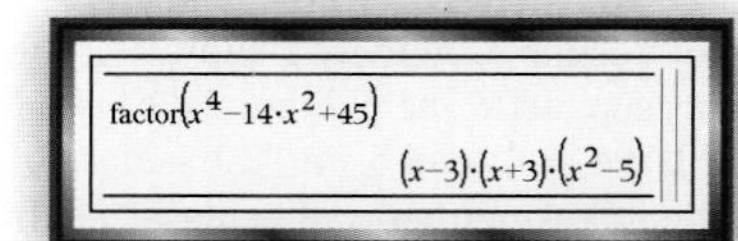

The roots are the solutions to $(x - 3)(x + 3)(x^2 - 5) = 0$.

Use the Zero-Product Theorem.

$x - 3 = 0$ or $x + 3 = 0$ or $x^2 - 5 = 0$

$x = 3$ or $x = -3$ or $x = \sqrt{5}$ or $-\sqrt{5}$

So, the roots of $P(x)$ are 3, -3, $\sqrt{5}$ and $-\sqrt{5}$.

Accommodating the Learner

Have students work in groups to graph $P(x) = k(x + 4)(x - 4)(x - 0.5)$, using three or four nonzero integer values of k. Then ask them to discuss how the shapes of the graphs are related.

Each graph has x-intercepts at -4, 0.5, and 4. The graphs are stretch images of each other.

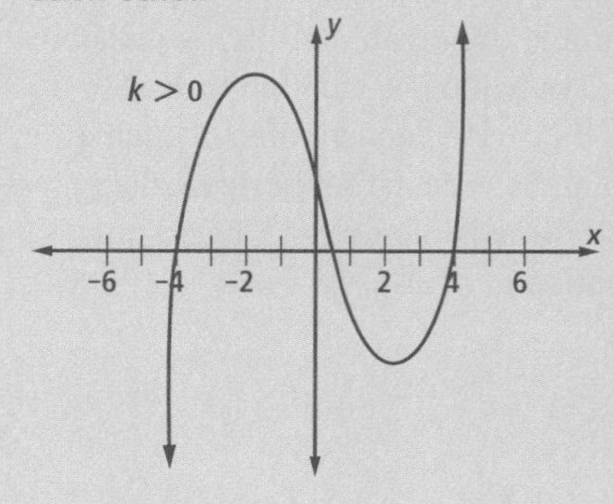

Solution 2 Use a CAS command to factor $P(x)$ over the reals. Notice the difference in the command in the screenshot at the right. This shows

$$P(x) = (x - 3)(x + 3)(x + \sqrt{5})(x - \sqrt{5}).$$

factor($x^4-14\cdot x^2+45,x$)
$(x-3)\cdot(x+3)\cdot(x+\sqrt{5})\cdot(x-\sqrt{5})$

Now use the Factor Theorem.

The factor $x - 3$ means that 3 is a root of P.
The factor $x + 3 = x - (-3)$ means that -3 is a root of P.
The factor $x - \sqrt{5}$ means that $\sqrt{5}$ is a root of P.
The factor $x + \sqrt{5} = x - (-\sqrt{5})$ means that $-\sqrt{5}$ is a root of P.
So, the roots of P(x) are 3, -3, $\sqrt{5}$ and $-\sqrt{5}$.

QY2

▸ QY2
Use the factorization of $x^2 - 225$ to find the roots of $f(x) = x^2 - 225$.

Finding Equations from Zeros

The Factor Theorem also says that if you know the zeros of a polynomial function, then you can determine the polynomial's factors.

GUIDED

Example 3

A polynomial function p with degree 4 and a leading coefficient of 1 is graphed at the right. Find the factors of $p(x)$ and use them to write a formula for $p(x)$.

Solution From the graph, the zeros appear to be -6, -2, -1, and 2.
By the Factor Theorem, the factors are $x - (-6)$, ___?___, ___?___, and $x - 2$. Therefore, $p(x) = (x + 6)($___?___$)($___?___$)(x - 2)$.
In standard form, $p(x) = x^4 + 7x^3 + 2x^2 - 28x - 24$.

$x - (-2)$; $x - (-1)$
$x + 2$; $x + 1$

Check Graph $y = p(x) = x^4 + 7x^3 + 2x^2 - 28x - 24$ in the window $-8 \le x \le 4$; $-100 \le y \le 50$. Does it match the given graph?

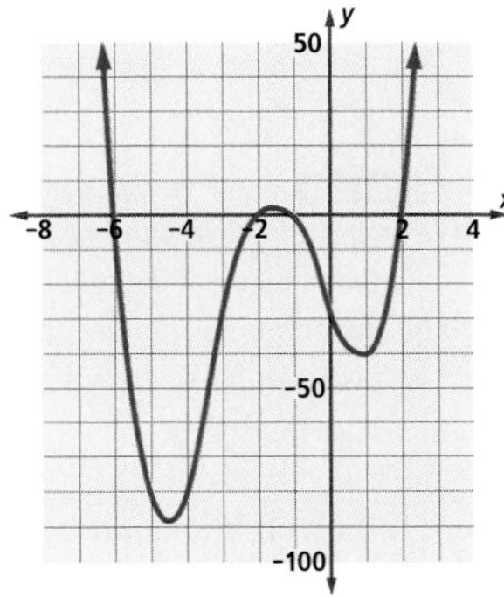

Check: Graph should match the one in Guided Example 3.

As you saw in Example 3, given a set of zeros, you can create a polynomial function with those zeros by multiplying the associated factors. However, if you do not restrict the degree or leading coefficient, different polynomial functions can have the same zeros.

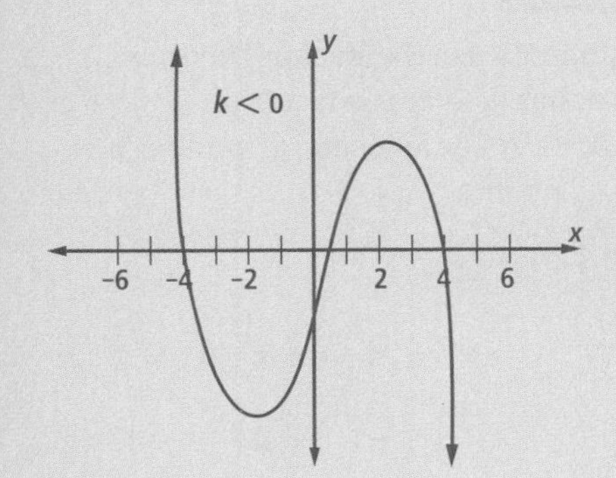

Additional Example

Example 3 A polynomial function p with degree 4 and leading coefficient 1 is graphed below. Find the factors of $p(x)$ and use them to write a formula for $p(x)$.

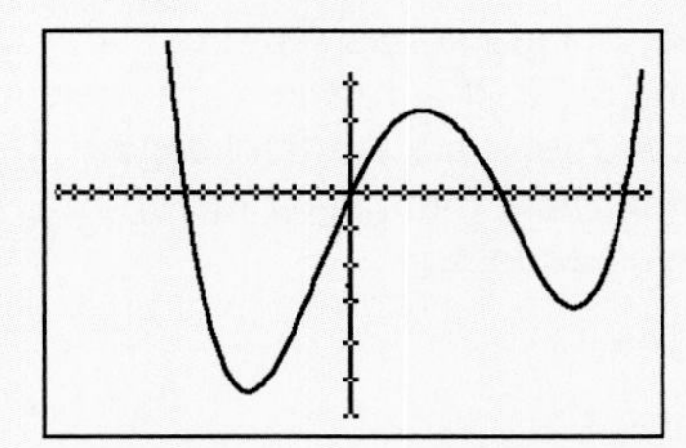

Solution From the graph, the zeros appear to be -9, 0, 8, and 15. By the Factor Theorem, the factors are $x - (-9)$, ___?___, ___?___, and $x - 15$. $x - 0$; $x - 8$ Therefore, $p(x) = (x + 9)($___?___$)$ • $($___?___$)(x - 15)$. x; $x - 8$
After expanding, the standard form is $p(x) = x^4 - 14x^3 - 87x^2 + 1080x$.

Notes on the Lesson

Activity 2 This is not a difficult activity, but its result may surprise many students.

11-4

Notes on the Lesson

Example 4 Even after doing Activity 2, students may not realize the generality of this example without picking their own functions. Have students pick values of a, b, c, and k and graph each polynomial function P. Have them observe that, in every case, the graph has x-intercepts at -3.5, 2, and 0.25. If a, b, and c are fixed, then all the graphs are stretch images of each other, with the magnitude of the stretch being equal to k.

Additional Example

Example 4 Find the general form of a polynomial function P whose only zeros are -4, $\frac{7}{2}$, and $\frac{5}{3}$. By the Factor Theorem, $(x - (-4))$, $\left(x - \frac{7}{2}\right)$, and $\left(x - \frac{5}{3}\right)$ are factors of $P(x)$. Because P has no other zeros, these factors are the only factors. Any of these factors can be raised to any positive integer power, and the entire polynomial could be multiplied by any nonzero constant. So $P(x) = k(x + 4)^a\left(x - \frac{7}{2}\right)^b\left(x - \frac{5}{3}\right)^c$ where $k \neq 0$ and a, b, and c are positive integers.

3 Assignment

Recommended Assignment

- Questions 1–28
- Question 29 (extra credit)
- Reading Lesson 11-5
- Covering the Ideas 11-5

Notes on the Questions

Students should be encouraged to use a graphing calculator and CAS to check their work.

Activity 2

Step 1 Find the zeros of each polynomial function below without graphing.

a. $f(x) = x(x + 4)(x - 3)$ **b.** $g(x) = 4x(x + 4)(x - 3)$

c. $h(x) = x^2(x + 4)(x - 3)$ **d.** $k(x) = -\frac{1}{4}x^2(x + 4)(x - 3)^3$

Step 1.
a. -4, 0, 3
b. -4, 0, 3
c. -4, 0, 3
d. -4, 0, 3

Step 2 Graph the four functions from Step 1 in the window $-5 \le x \le 5$; $-100 \le y \le 100$. How are their graphs similar? Describe any differences. See margin.

Step 3 Find an equation for a polynomial function whose zeros are 0, -4, and 3, but whose graph is different from the graphs in Step 2.

Step 3. Answers vary. Sample: $m(x) = x(x + 4)^2(x - 3)$

Activity 2 illustrates that a polynomial can be transformed in at least two ways to produce another polynomial with the same zeros:

- The original polynomial can be multiplied by a constant factor k.
- One or more factors of the original polynomial can be raised to a different positive integer power.

For example, every polynomial of the form $kx^a(x + 4)^b(x - 3)^c$ has the same zeros as the polynomial $x(x + 4)(x - 3)$.

Example 4

Find the general form of a polynomial function P whose only zeros are $-\frac{7}{2}$, $\frac{1}{4}$, and 2.

Solution By the Factor Theorem, $x - \left(-\frac{7}{2}\right)$, $x - \frac{1}{4}$, and $x - 2$ are factors of $P(x)$, and because P has no other zeros, these factors are the only factors. Any of these factors can be raised to any positive integer power, and the entire polynomial could be multiplied by any nonzero constant.

So, $P(x) = k\left(x + \frac{7}{2}\right)^a\left(x - \frac{1}{4}\right)^b(x - 2)^c$ where $k \neq 0$ and a, b, c are positive integers.

From the given information in Example 4, you know the degree of $P(x)$ is at least three. However, you have no information about the exponents a, b, and c except that they are positive integers. Therefore, you cannot be sure of the degree of $P(x)$.

Questions

COVERING THE IDEAS

1. State the Zero-Product Theorem. For all a and b, $ab = 0$ if and only if $a = 0$ or $b = 0$.

In 2 and 3, find the roots of the equation.

2. $(x - 5)(6x + 33) = 0$ $-\frac{11}{2}$, 5
3. $\left(-\frac{3}{5}k + 12\right)(k^2 - 2)(k + 1) = 0$ $-\sqrt{2}$, -1, $\sqrt{2}$, 20

Accommodating the Learner

When students apply the Factor Theorem, some of them may be confused by the case when r is negative. Remind them that if $r = -5$, then $(x - r) = x - (-5) = x + 5$. If $(x + 5)$ is a factor, then -5 is a root.

Extension

Have students use the Factor Theorem to prove that $(x - r)$ is a factor of $P(x) = x^n - r^n$ for any natural number n. If $P(x) = x^n - r^n$, then $P(r) = r^n - r^n = 0$. By the Factor Theorem, since $P(r) = 0$, $(x - r)$ is a factor of $P(x)$.

4. If $f(x) = 4x(x - 2)(x + 16)$, find the zeros of f. -16, 0, 2

5. **Multiple Choice** If the graph of a polynomial function intersects the x-axis at (5, 0) and (-2, 0), then which of the following must be two of the polynomial's linear factors? C

   A $x - 5$ and $x - 2$ B $x + 5$ and $x - 2$
   C $x - 5$ and $x + 2$ D $x + 5$ and $x + 2$

6. Suppose that P is a polynomial function and $P(1.7) = 0$. According to the Factor Theorem, what can you conclude?

In 7 and 8, an equation for a polynomial function is given.
a. Factor the polynomial.
b. Find the zeros of the function.

7. $r(t) = 2t^3 - t^2 - 21t$
8. $w(b) = -b^4 + 4b^3 + 11b^2 - 30b$

9. a. Write the general form of an equation for a polynomial function whose only zeros are 5.6 and -2.9.
   b. Graph two different third-degree polynomial functions satisfying the condition in Part a. See margin.

10. **Multiple Choice** A polynomial has real zeros 4, -2, and 6. What must the degree of the polynomial be? E

    A 2 B 3 C 8
    D 12 E an integer ≥ 3

APPLYING THE MATHEMATICS

11. The graph of a polynomial function is shown at the right. There are no other x-intercepts and the degree of the function is 4. Give an equation for the function.

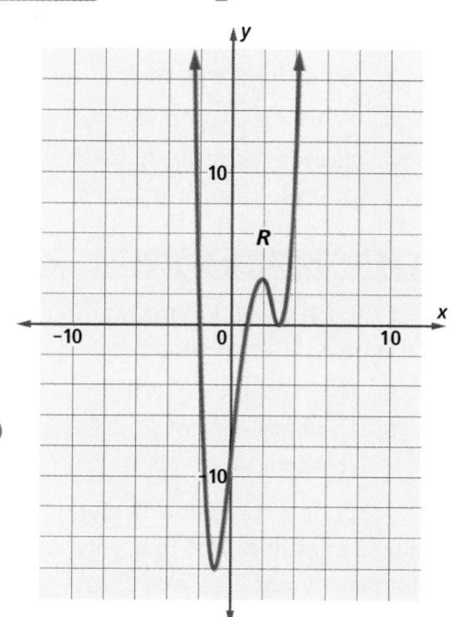

12. a. Is it possible to have a polynomial with integer coefficients that has 3 and $\frac{3}{5}$ as zeros, and no other zeros? Justify your answer. yes; $5x^2 - 18x + 9$
    b. Is it possible to have a polynomial with integer coefficients that has 3 and $\sqrt{5}$ as zeros, and no other real zeros? Justify your answer.

13. Consider the polynomial function $P(x) = x^3 + 5x^2 + 3x$.
    a. Factor $P(x)$ over the rationals. $P(x) = x(x^2 + 5x + 3)$
    b. Use the factors you found in Part a to find the zeros of the function. 13b–c. See margin.
    c. Your answer to Part b should suggest that there are other factors. Use a CAS to factor over the reals and compare your result to your factorization in Part a. 12b. No; at least one coefficient would be an integer multiple of $\sqrt{5}$, which is not an integer.

6. $(x - 1.7)$ is a factor of $P(x)$.

7a. $r(t) = t(t + 3)(2t - 7)$
7b. $-3, 0, \frac{7}{2}$
8a. $w(b) = -b(b - 5)(b - 2)(b + 3)$
8b. -3, 0, 2, 5
9a. $p(x) = k(x - 5.6)^a \bullet (x + 2.9)^b$, where $k \neq 0$ and a and b are positive integers.
11. $y = \frac{1}{2}(x + 2)(x - 1)(x - 3)^2$

Notes on the Questions

Questions 7 and 8 Point out that these questions can be checked by graphing the function written in standard form and in factored form on the same set of axes. Note that the graphs coincide, reinforcing that these are equivalent forms. Point out that the zeros of each function are the x-intercepts of the graph.

Additional Answers

9b. Answers vary. Sample:

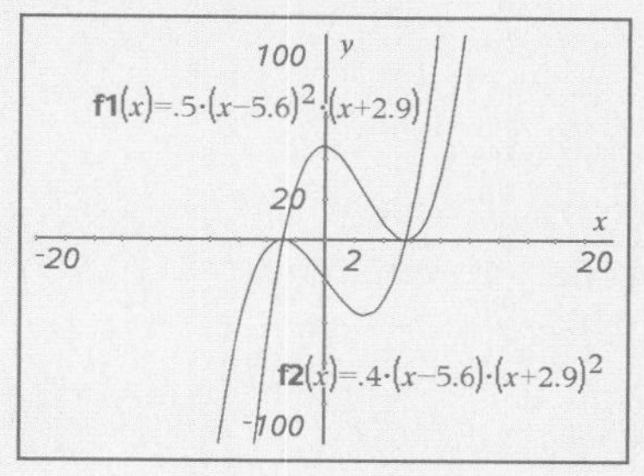

13b. $x = 0, x = \frac{-5 \pm \sqrt{13}}{2}$

13c. $P(x) = x\left(x + \frac{5 - \sqrt{13}}{2}\right)\left(x + \frac{5 + \sqrt{13}}{2}\right)$; the second factor in Part a has been factored.

Additional Answers

Activity 2

Step 2.

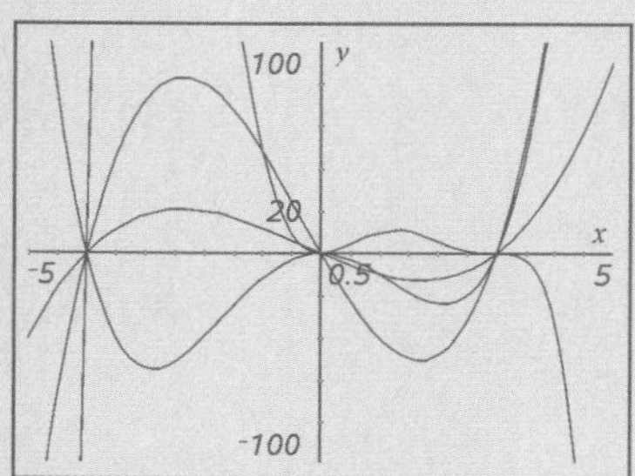

The four graphs have the same x-intercepts. The function paths between the x-intercepts are different.

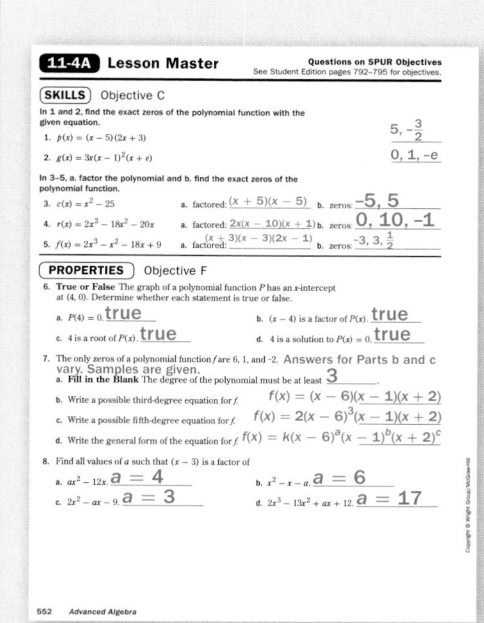

11-4A Lesson Master

Questions on SPUR Objectives
See Student Edition pages 792–795 for objectives.

SKILLS Objective C

In 1 and 2, find the exact zeros of the polynomial function with the given equation.

1. $p(x) = (x - 5)(2x + 3)$ $5, -\frac{3}{2}$
2. $g(x) = 3x(x - 1)^2(x + e)$ 0, 1, -e

In 3–5, a. factor the polynomial and b. find the exact zeros of the polynomial function.

3. $c(x) = x^2 - 25$ a. factored: $(x + 5)(x - 5)$ b. zeros: -5, 5
4. $r(x) = 2x^3 - 18x^2 - 20x$ a. factored: $2x(x - 10)(x + 1)$ b. zeros: 0, 10, -1
5. $f(x) = 2x^3 - x^2 - 18x + 9$ a. factored: $(x + 3)(x - 3)(2x - 1)$ b. zeros: $-3, 3, \frac{1}{2}$

PROPERTIES Objective F

6. **True or False** The graph of a polynomial function P has an x-intercept at (4, 0). Determine whether each statement is true or false.
   a. $P(4) = 0$. true
   b. $(x - 4)$ is a factor of $P(x)$. true
   c. 4 is a root of $P(x)$. true
   d. 4 is a solution to $P(x) = 0$. true

7. The only zeros of a polynomial function f are 6, 1, and -2. Answers for Parts b and c vary. Samples are given.
   a. **Fill in the Blank** The degree of the polynomial must be at least 3.
   b. Write a possible third-degree equation for f. $f(x) = (x - 6)(x - 1)(x + 2)$
   c. Write a possible fifth-degree equation for f. $f(x) = 2(x - 6)^3(x - 1)(x + 2)$
   d. Write the general form of the equation for f. $f(x) = k(x - 6)^a(x - 1)^b(x + 2)^c$

8. Find all values of a such that $(x - 3)$ is a factor of
   a. $ax^2 - 12x$. $a = 4$
   b. $x^2 - x - a$. $a = 6$
   c. $2x^2 - ax - 9$. $a = 3$
   d. $2x^3 - 13x^2 + ax + 12$. $a = 17$

552 *Advanced Algebra*

11-4

Notes on the Questions

Question 15 This important question shows the limitations of using graphs to find zeros. This function has two nonreal zeros: i and $-i$.

Additional Answers

16a.

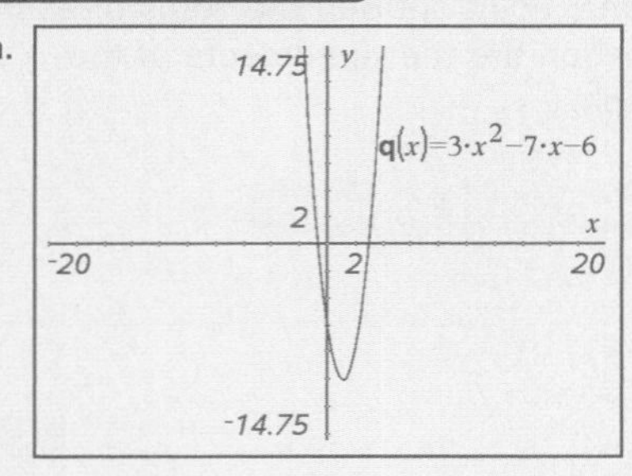

The roots are $-\frac{2}{3}$ and 3.

18c. Answers vary. Sample:

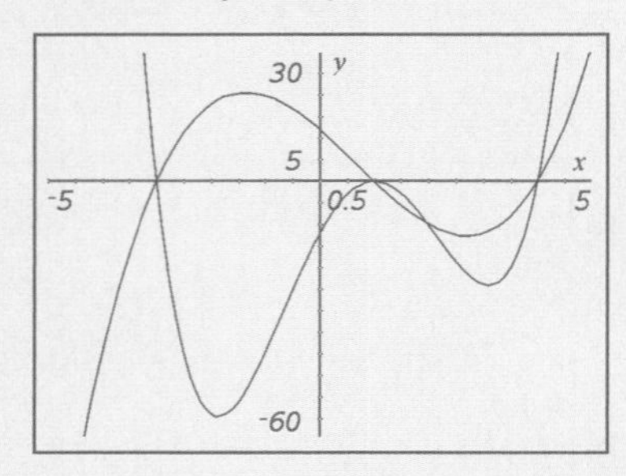

The graphs have the same x-intercepts but behave differently at the ends and in between x-intercepts.

19d.

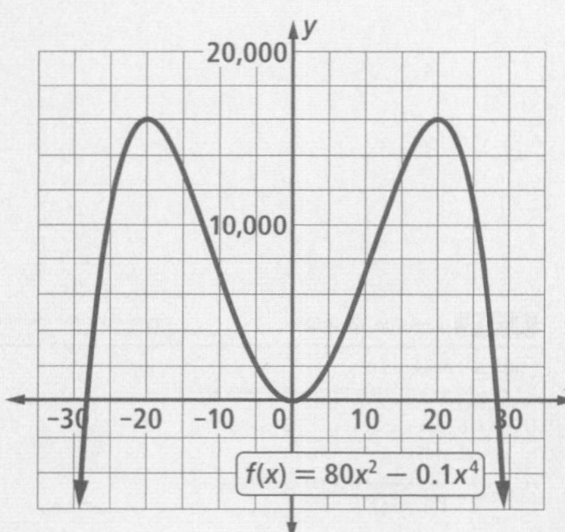

A reasonable domain for this situation is $0 \le n \le \sqrt{800}$.

23. yes; 2

14. Find all possible values of a such that $x - 2$ is a factor of $x^3 + x^2 + ax + 4$. $a = -8$

15. The graph of the polynomial function with equation $y = \frac{1}{2}(x^2 + 1) \cdot (x + 2)^2(x - 3)$ has only two x-intercepts: -2 and 3. Why does the factor $x^2 + 1$ not change the number or location of the x-intercepts? $x^2 + 1 \neq 0$ for all real numbers x.

16. Let $q(x) = 3x^2 - 7x - 6$.
   a. Graph q. Where do the roots of $q(x)$ appear to be located? See margin.
   b. Use the quadratic formula to solve $3x^2 - 7x - 6 = 0$. $x = -\frac{2}{3}$ or $x = 3$
   c. Use your result from Part b to factor $q(x)$. $q(x) = (3x + 2)(x - 3)$

17. Let $p(x) = k(x - 2)^2(x + 3)$, where $k \neq 0$.
   a. What are the roots of $p(x)$? -3, 2
   b. If $p(-2) = 4$, find the value of k. $k = \frac{1}{4}$

18. Let $q(m)$ be a polynomial, and let $q(m) = 0$ when $m = -3$, $m = 1$, and $m = 4$.
   a. Write a possible 3rd-degree equation for q.
   b. Write a possible equation for q that has degree 4.
   c. Graph your equations from Parts a and b. Describe any similarities and differences you see. See margin.

19. A manufacturer determines that n employees on a production line will produce $f(n)$ units per month where $f(n) = 80n^2 - 0.1n^4$.
   a. Factor the polynomial over the reals.
   b. Find the zeros of f.
   c. What do the zeros represent in this situation?
   d. Sketch a graph of f. Give a reasonable domain for this model. See margin.

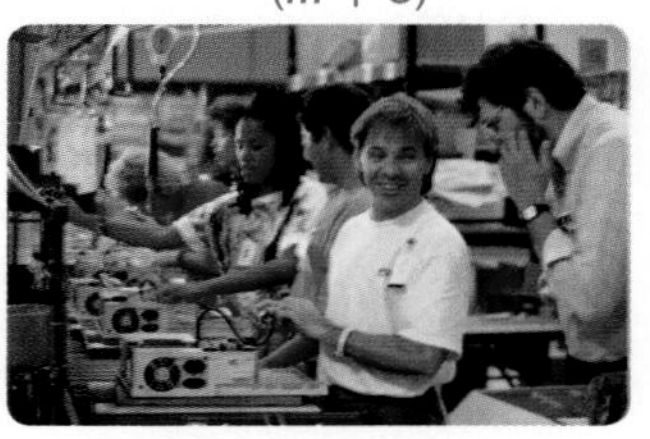

REVIEW

20. Consider the polynomial $p(x) = (2x - 3)(x^2 + 4)(10 - x)$. Without expanding the polynomial, find
   a. the leading term of $p(x)$ when written in standard form. $-2x^4$
   b. the last term of $p(x)$ when written in standard form. (Lesson 11-2) -120

In 21–23, an expression is given. Tell whether the expression is a polynomial in x. If it is a polynomial in x, give its degree. If not, indicate why not. (Lesson 11-1)

21. $x^2y + xy^2 - \frac{1}{x}y^3$
22. $\log(x^2y + xy^2)$
23. $\sqrt{3}x^2y + \frac{\pi}{2}z$ See margin.

18a. Answers vary. Sample: $q(m) = (m - 1)(m - 4) \cdot (m + 3)$

18b. Answers vary. Sample: $q(m) = (m - 1)^2(m - 4) \cdot (m + 3)$

19a. $f(n) = -0.1n^2 \cdot (n - \sqrt{800}) \cdot (n + \sqrt{800})$

19b. $-\sqrt{800} \approx -28.2843$, 0, $\sqrt{800} \approx 28.2843$

19c. The zeros represent the number of employees that results in 0 units produced per month.

21. No; this expression contains a negative integer power of x.

22. No; this is a logarithmic expression.

In 24 and 25, use the graph below of the sine function.

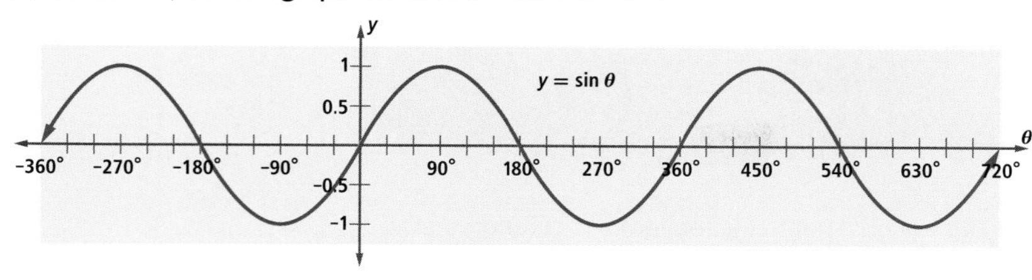

24. What is the period of this function? **(Lesson 10-6)** 360°

25. **Fill in the Blanks** As θ increases from 90° to 180°, the value of $\sin\theta$ decreases from __?__ to __?__. **(Lesson 10-6)** 1; 0

26. In the general compound interest formula $A = P\left(1 + \frac{r}{n}\right)^{nt}$, as the value of n increases while r and t are kept constant, the value of A gets closer and closer to what number? **(Lesson 9-3)** Pe^{rt}

27. a. **True or False** $\sqrt{12} \cdot \sqrt{3} = \sqrt{2} \cdot \sqrt{18}$. Justify your answer.
    b. **True or False** $\sqrt{-12} \cdot \sqrt{-3} = \sqrt{2} \cdot \sqrt{18}$. Justify your answer. **(Lessons 8-7, 8-5)** 27a–b. See margin.

28. A student, removing the bolts from the back of a large cabinet in a science lab, knew that it was easier to turn a bolt with a long wrench than with a short one. The student decided to investigate the force required with wrenches of various lengths, and obtained the data at the right. **(Lessons 2-7, 2-6, 2-2)**
    a. Graph these data points. See margin.
    b. Which variation equation is a better model for this situation, $F = \frac{k}{L}$ or $F = \frac{k}{L^2}$? Justify your answer.
    c. How much force would be required to turn one of these bolts with a 12-inch wrench? 30 lb

Length of Wrench (in.) L	Force (lb) F
3	120
5	72
6	60
8	45
9	40

28b. $F = \frac{k}{L}$; as L doubles, F is divided by 2, not 4.

EXPLORATION

29. If $P(x) = (x - 5)(x - 3)^2(x + 1)^3$, 3 is called a *zero of multiplicity 2* and -1 is called a *zero of multiplicity 3*. Give equations for several different polynomial functions whose only real zeros are 5, 3, and -1, and graph them. How does the multiplicity of a zero affect the way the graph looks at the zero?
    See the Additional Answers section at the back of the book.

QY ANSWERS

1. $x - 5$
2. The factorization is $(x + 15)(x - 15)$. The roots are 15 and -15.

Notes on the Questions

Question 27 This question is tricky for many students. Following the rules for the order of operations, work inside the radical sign should be done before any multiplications. Students become confused because the property $\sqrt{a} \cdot \sqrt{b} = \sqrt{ab}$ for positive real numbers a and b means that, for those numbers, you can multiply before taking the radical.

Question 29 "... the way the graph looks at the zero" is an informal way of saying "the behavior of the graph near the x-axis."

4 Wrap-Up

Ongoing Assessment

Have students work in small groups. Have each group choose as roots three different integers, at least one of which is negative. Have each group work together to write the general form of an equation for a polynomial function with the three chosen roots. Finally, have each member of the group write a specific equation for which the three integers are roots and graph the function. Have students compare their graphs. Students should demonstrate an understanding of writing equations from zeros and graphing polynomial functions.

Project Update

Project 4, *Synthetic Division*, Project 5, *Effect of Coefficients on* $y = ax^4 + bx^3 + cx^2 + e$, and Project 6, *Factoring and Solving Cubic Polynomial Functions*, on page 787 relate to the content of this lesson.

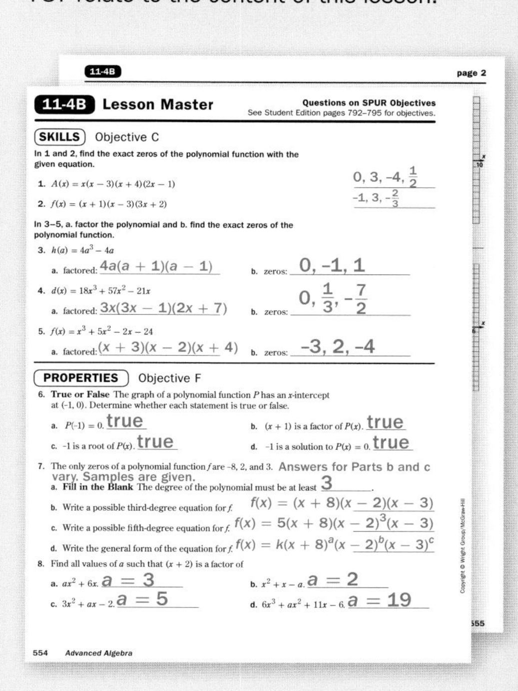

11-4B page 2

11-4B Lesson Master — Questions on SPUR Objectives. See Student Edition pages 792–795 for objectives.

SKILLS Objective C

In 1 and 2, find the exact zeros of the polynomial function with the given equation.

1. $A(x) = x(x - 3)(x + 4)(2x - 1)$ $0, 3, -4, \frac{1}{2}$
2. $f(x) = (x + 1)(x - 3)(3x + 2)$ $-1, 3, -\frac{2}{3}$

In 3–5, a. factor the polynomial and b. find the exact zeros of the polynomial function.

3. $h(a) = 4a^3 - 4a$
   a. factored: $4a(a + 1)(a - 1)$ b. zeros: $0, -1, 1$
4. $d(x) = 18x^3 + 57x^2 - 21x$
   a. factored: $3x(3x - 1)(2x + 7)$ b. zeros: $0, \frac{1}{3}, -\frac{7}{2}$
5. $f(x) = x^3 + 5x^2 - 2x - 24$
   a. factored: $(x + 3)(x - 2)(x + 4)$ b. zeros: $-3, 2, -4$

PROPERTIES Objective F

6. **True or False** The graph of a polynomial function P has an x-intercept at (-1, 0). Determine whether each statement is true or false.
   a. $P(-1) = 0$. true
   b. $(x + 1)$ is a factor of $P(x)$. true
   c. -1 is a root of $P(x)$. true
   d. -1 is a solution to $P(x) = 0$. true
7. The only zeros of a polynomial function f are -8, 2, and 3. Answers for Parts b and c vary. Samples are given.
   a. **Fill in the Blank** The degree of the polynomial must be at least 3.
   b. Write a possible third-degree equation for f. $f(x) = (x + 8)(x - 2)(x - 3)$
   c. Write a possible fifth-degree equation for f. $f(x) = 5(x + 8)(x - 2)^3(x - 3)$
   d. Write the general form of the equation for f. $f(x) = k(x + 8)^a(x - 2)^b(x - 3)^c$
8. Find all values of a such that $(x + 2)$ is a factor of
   a. $ax^2 + 6x$. $a = 3$
   b. $x^2 + x - a$. $a = 2$
   c. $3x^2 + ax - 2$. $a = 5$
   d. $6x^3 + ax^2 + 11x - 6$. $a = 19$

554 Advanced Algebra

555

Additional Answers

27a. true; $\sqrt{12} \cdot \sqrt{3} = \sqrt{36} = \sqrt{2} \cdot \sqrt{18}$ by the Root of a Product Theorem

27b. false; $\sqrt{-12} \cdot \sqrt{-3} = i\sqrt{12} \cdot i\sqrt{3} = i^2\sqrt{36} = -\sqrt{36} \neq \sqrt{36} = \sqrt{2} \cdot \sqrt{18}$

Lesson

11-5

GOAL

Obtain the rational roots of any polynomial equation with integer coefficients by using the Rational-Root Theorem.

SPUR Objectives

G Apply the Rational-Root Theorem.

J Graph polynomial functions.

K Estimate zeros of polynomial functions using graphs.

Materials/Resources

- Lesson Masters 11-5A and 11-5B
- Resource Master 213

HOMEWORK

Suggestions for Assignment

- Questions 1–15
- Question 16 (extra credit)
- Reading Lesson 11-6
- Covering the Ideas 11-6

Local Standards

1 Warm-Up

Multiple Choice In 1–12, identify the type of number.

A Rational
B Irrational
C Neither rational nor irrational

1. $\sqrt{441}$ A	2. $\sqrt{440}$ B
3. $-\sqrt{439}$ B	4. $\sqrt{-438}$ C
5. $\sqrt{-400}$ C	6. $-6\frac{2}{3}$ A
7. 2π B	8. $\frac{7\pi}{2\pi}$ A
9. $\sqrt{2} \cdot \sqrt{8}$ A	10. $\sqrt[3]{2}$ B
11. $\sqrt{-2} \cdot \sqrt{-8}$ A	12. 3.14159... B

Lesson

11-5 The Rational-Root Theorem

BIG IDEA The Rational-Root Theorem gives a criterion that any rational root of a polynomial equation must satisfy, and typically limits the number of rational numbers that need to be tested to a small number.

Remember that a ***rational number*** is a number that can be written as a quotient of two integers, that is, as a simple fraction. Any integer n is a rational number, because n can be written as $\frac{n}{1}$. Zero is a rational number because, for example, $0 = \frac{0}{26}$. The number 10.32 is rational because $10.32 = 10 + \frac{3}{10} + \frac{2}{100} = \frac{1032}{100}$. An ***irrational number*** is a real number that is not rational. The irrational numbers are infinite nonrepeating decimals, including $\sqrt{60}$, $\pi + 5$, and e. Nonreal complex numbers such as $3i$ and $i - 4$ are neither rational nor irrational.

Every *real* zero of a function f corresponds to an x-intercept of the graph of $y = f(x)$. But it can be difficult to tell from a graph which zeros are rational. However, there is a theorem that details the possible rational zeros that a polynomial function can have. The following Activity is about this theorem.

Activity

Let $Q(x) = (2x - 3)(9x + 4)$ and $P(x) = (2x - 3)(9x + 4)(5x + 7)$.

Step 1 Solve $Q(x) = 0$ and $P(x) = 0$ for x. Steps 1–4. See Margin.

Step 2 Without expanding the polynomials, find the first and last terms of $Q(x)$ and $P(x)$ when they are written in standard form.

Step 3 Describe the connection between the denominators of the roots of the polynomial equation $Q(x) = 0$ and the coefficient of the first term of the expanded polynomial $Q(x)$. Repeat for $P(x)$.

Step 4 Describe the connection between the numerators of the roots of the polynomial equation $Q(x) = 0$ and the constant term of the expanded polynomial $Q(x)$. Repeat for $P(x)$.

Mental Math

a. Which is the better value, an 8-oz box of pasta for $2.50 or a 12-oz box of pasta for $3.50? 12-oz box

b. Should you buy a $30 sweater using a 30%-off coupon or using a $10-off coupon? $10-off coupon

c. Do you save more when a $25 instant rebate on contact lenses is taken before tax is calculated or after tax is calculated? before tax

d. Which will pay more interest, an account with 3.5% interest compounded annually, or an account with continuously compounded interest with an APY of 3.5%? They pay the same amount.

Background

The Rational-Root Theorem was called the Rational-Zero Theorem in previous editions of UCSMP *Advanced Algebra*. An Internet search indicates that both names are common, but the name we use in this edition is more common.

The Rational-Root Theorem is one of a family of theorems that formerly constituted the content of a course called *Theory of Equations* that many mathematics majors took before the existence of calculator and computer technology. In this course, students would learn a variety of techniques for approximating roots to polynomial equations, including Descartes' Rule of Signs (for providing an upper bound on the number of positive and the number of negative roots, see Question 16) and methods for finding an upper limit of positive real roots and an upper limit of the absolute value of nonreal roots. Today, there is little need for such methods because roots can be easily estimated by examining the graph of a function.

A generalization of the results of the Activity is called the *Rational-Root Theorem,* or *Rational-Zero Theorem.*

Rational-Root (or Rational-Zero) Theorem

Suppose that all the coefficients of the polynomial function described by

$$f(x) = a_n x^n + a_{n-1}x^{n-1} + \ldots + a_2x^2 + a_1x + a_0$$

are integers with $a_n \neq 0$ and $a_0 \neq 0$. If $\frac{p}{q}$ is a root of $f(x)$ in lowest terms, then p is a factor of a_0 and q is a factor of a_n.

Stated another way, the Rational-Root Theorem says that if a simple fraction in lowest terms (a rational number) is a root of a polynomial function with integer coefficients, then the numerator of the rational root is a factor of the constant term of the polynomial, and the denominator of the rational root is a factor of the leading coefficient of the polynomial. A proof of this theorem is left to a later course.

Identifying Possible and Actual Rational Roots

Notice that the Rational-Root Theorem gives a way to decide the *possible* rational roots of a polynomial. It does not determine which of these possible roots are actual roots of the polynomial.

Example 1

Apply the Rational-Root Theorem to *identify* possible rational roots of $f(x)$ when $f(x) = 4x^4 + 3x^3 + 4x^2 + 11x + 6$.

Solution Let $\frac{p}{q}$ in lowest terms be a rational root of $f(x)$. Then p is a factor of 6 and q is a factor of 4.

So, p equals $\pm1, \pm2, \pm3$, or ±6, and q equals $\pm1, \pm2$, or ±4. Now take all possible quotients $\frac{p}{q}$. It looks like there are as many as $8 \cdot 6 = 48$ possible quotients, but actually there are fewer because many of them, such as $\frac{6}{2}$ and $\frac{-3}{-1}$, are equal. So, the possible rational roots are $\pm1, \pm2, \pm3, \pm6, \pm\frac{1}{2}, \pm\frac{3}{2}, \pm\frac{1}{4}$, and $\pm\frac{3}{4}$.

QY1

Example 1 shows that there can be several possible rational roots for a polynomial. You can test each possible root by hand, but with a graphing utility, a CAS, the Rational-Root Theorem, and the Factor Theorem, you can greatly reduce the time it takes to identify roots.

QY1

$\frac{2}{4}$ and $\frac{6}{2}$ are both possible rational roots of $f(x)$ in Example 1. Why do they not appear in this form on the list in the solution to Example 1?

In many applications, it makes no difference whether zeros are rational or not. So it is natural for some students to wonder why they need to know this theorem. Here are some reasons for learning this theorem. (1) Whenever possible, we aim to obtain exact roots because only then can we calculate exactly how far off any approximation to that root is. (2) The Rational-Root Theorem can quickly be used to show that certain numbers are irrational (see Example 3 and Question 6). (3) The Rational-Root Theorem enables us to factor certain polynomials that otherwise would very difficult to factor, which, in turn, enables us to simplify some fractions and other expressions.

2 Teaching

Notes on the Lesson

We do not give a proof of the Rational-Root Theorem in the text because it is quite difficult for most students at this level to follow. It requires that students know that if a is a factor of bc, and a and b have no common factors (that is, they are relatively prime), then a is a factor of c. Here is a proof.

Let $f(x) = a_nx^n + a_{n-1}x^{n-1} + \ldots + a_2x^2 + a_1x + a_0$, with $a_n \neq 0$ and $a_0 \neq 0$. We want to show that if a rational number $\frac{p}{q}$ in lowest terms is a zero of f, then p is a factor of a_0 and q is a factor of a_n.

Proof:

1. Suppose that $\frac{p}{q}$ is a rational number in lowest terms and is a zero of f. Then, by definition of a zero, $a_n\left(\frac{p}{q}\right)^n + a_{n-1}\left(\frac{p}{q}\right)^{n-1} + \ldots + a_2\left(\frac{p}{q}\right)^2 + a_1\left(\frac{p}{q}\right) + a_0 = 0$.
2. To clear the fractions, multiply both sides of the equation by q^n: $a_np^n + a_{n-1}p^{n-1}q + \ldots + a_2p^2q^{n-2} + a_1pq^{n-1} + a_0q^n = 0$.
3. Solve for a_np^n and factor out q: $a_np^n = -a_{n-1}p^{n-1}q - \ldots - a_2p^2q^{n-2} - a_1pq^{n-1} - a_0q^n = q(-a_{n-1}p^{n-1} - \ldots - a_2p^2q^{n-3} - a_1pq^{n-2} - a_0q^{n-1})$
4. This equation shows that q is a factor of a_np^n. But q and p have no common factors because $\frac{p}{q}$ is in lowest terms. So q must be a factor of a_n.
5. To complete the proof, solve the equation in Step 2 for a_0q^n and factor out p: $a_0q^n = p(-a_np^{n-1} - a_{n-1}p^{n-2}q - \ldots - a_2pq^{n-2} - a_1q^{n-1})$.
6. So, p is a factor of a_0q^n. As before, p and q cannot have any common factors. So p must be a factor of a_0.

Notice that the Rational-Root Theorem does not tell what the rational zeros are. It only limits the rational zeros to certain values. Examining the graph of the function can significantly reduce the number of zeros that need to be tested.

Additional Examples

Example 1 Apply the Rational-Root Theorem to *identify* possible rational roots of $f(x) = 3x^4 - 10x^2 - 8x + 15$.

Let $\frac{p}{q}$ in lowest terms be a rational root of $f(x)$. Then p is a factor of 15, and q is a factor of 3. So p equals $\pm 1, \pm 3, \pm 5$, or ± 15, and q equals ± 1 or ± 3. So, the possible rational roots are $\pm 1, \pm\frac{1}{3}, \pm 3, \pm 5, \pm\frac{5}{3}$, and ± 15.

Example 2 Use the Rational-Root Theorem to *find* all the rational roots of $f(x)$ from Additional Example 1.

The possible rational roots of $f(x)$ are $\pm 1, \pm\frac{1}{3}, \pm 3, \pm 5, \pm\frac{5}{3}$ and ± 15. The least possible rational root is -15, and the greatest is 15, so graph f on the interval $-15 \leq x \leq 15$ to see where the rational roots might be. The graph below shows that there are two real roots on the interval $0 \leq x \leq 2$.

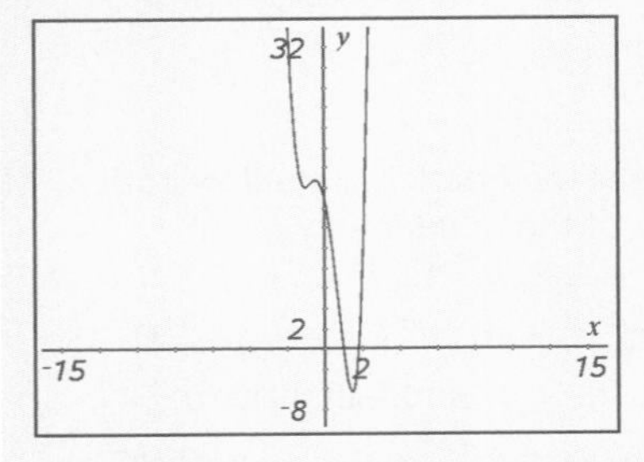

The possible rational roots for $f(x)$ in that interval are 1, $\frac{1}{3}$, and $\frac{5}{3}$. $f(1) = 0$, $f\left(\frac{1}{3}\right) \approx 11.26$, and $f\left(\frac{5}{3}\right) \approx -2.963$. So, 1 is the only rational root of $f(x)$.

Additional Answers

Activity

Step 1. $x = \frac{3}{2}$ or $x = -\frac{4}{9}$; $x = \frac{3}{2}, x = -\frac{4}{9}$, or $x = -\frac{7}{5}$

Step 2. $18x^2$, -12; $90x^3$, -84

Step 3. For both $Q(x)$ and $P(x)$, the denominators of the roots of the equation are factors of the coefficient of the leading term.

Step 4. For both $Q(x)$ and $P(x)$, the numerators of the roots of the equation are factors of the constant term.

Example 2

Use the Rational-Root Theorem to *find* all rational roots of $f(x) = 4x^4 + 3x^3 + 4x^2 + 11x + 6$ from Example 1.

Solution The possible rational roots of $f(x)$ are $\pm 1, \pm 2, \pm 3, \pm 6, \pm\frac{1}{2}, \pm\frac{3}{2}, \pm\frac{1}{4}$, and $\pm\frac{3}{4}$.

The smallest possible rational root is -6 and the largest is 6, so graph f on the interval $-6 \leq x \leq 6$ to see where rational roots might be.

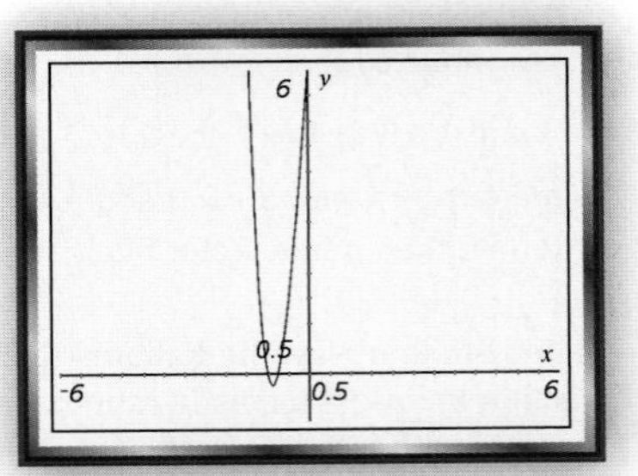

The graph at the right shows that there are two real roots on the interval $-1 \leq x \leq 0$.

The possible rational roots for $f(x)$ in that interval are $-\frac{1}{4}, -\frac{1}{2}, -\frac{3}{4}$, and -1. Test these values in the equation for f.

$f\left(-\frac{1}{4}\right) \approx 3.47$ $\quad f\left(-\frac{1}{2}\right) \approx 1.38$

$f\left(-\frac{3}{4}\right) = 0$ $\quad f(-1) = 0$

So, -1 and $-\frac{3}{4}$ are the only rational roots of $f(x)$.

Check Use a graphing utility to find the x-intercepts of the graph of f. The answers check.

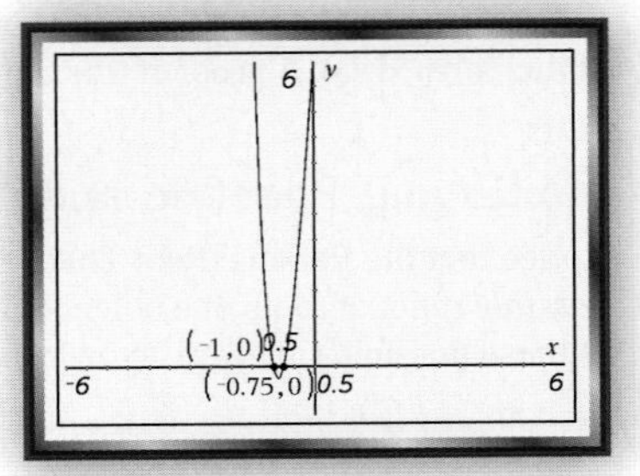

Irrational Roots

The Rational-Root Theorem identifies all possible rational roots of a polynomial with integer coefficients. So, any real roots that are not identified must be irrational.

Example 3

In a Hans Magnus Enzensberger book, a boy named Robert argues with a sprite about $\sqrt{2}$. The sprite tries to convince Robert that $\sqrt{2}$ is irrational by showing him that its decimal expansion is infinite. How could the sprite show that $\sqrt{2}$ is irrational using the Rational-Root Theorem?

Solution $\sqrt{2}$ is a solution to the equation $x^2 = 2$ and a root of $x^2 - 2 = 0$. By the Rational-Root Theorem, if $\frac{a}{b}$ is a rational root of $x^2 - 2 = 0$, then a is a factor of 2 and b is a factor of 1.

Accommodating the Learner

Some students may correctly determine the factors of the leading coefficient and the constant term of a polynomial function. However, when they write the possible rational roots, they may interchange the numerators and denominators. Explain that the *first* number we usually write for a fraction is the numerator, but the numerator is a factor of the *last* term. Likewise, the *last* number written, the denominator, is a factor of the *first* coefficient. "First is last and last is first" may help students remember which number is used to find the numerator and the denominator of a possible root.

Thus, the only possible rational roots of $x^2 - 2 = 0$ are $\pm\frac{2}{1}$ and $\pm\frac{1}{1}$, that is, 2, -2, 1, and -1.

Substitute to see if any of these numbers is a root of the equation $x^2 - 2 = 0$.

$1^2 - 2 = -1 \neq 0 \quad (-1)^2 - 2 = -1 \neq 0$

$2^2 - 2 = 2 \neq 0 \quad (-2)^2 - 2 = 2 \neq 0$

None of the possible rational roots is a root of the equation. Thus, $x^2 - 2 = 0$ has no rational roots, so $\sqrt{2}$ must be irrational.

 QY2

▶ **QY2**

What equation can you consider in order to prove that $\sqrt[3]{9}$ is irrational?

Questions

COVERING THE IDEAS

1. Suppose that $\frac{7}{5}$ is a root of a polynomial equation with integer coefficients. What can you say about the leading coefficient and the constant term of the polynomial?
2. Does the Rational-Root Theorem apply to finding roots of $Q(x) = 10x^4 - 4\sqrt{2}x + 9$? Explain your response.

In 3 and 4, a polynomial equation is given.

a. **Use the Rational-Root Theorem to list the possible rational roots.**

b. **Find all of the rational roots.**

3–7. See the Additional Answers section at the back of the book.

3. $8x^3 - 4x^2 + 44x + 24 = 0$
4. $f(n) = -n^2 + 3n^3 + 5n^5 - 8n + 12 - 11n^4$
5. The graph of a polynomial function with equation $R(x) = 7x^4 - 2x^3 - 42x^2 - 61x - 14$ is shown at the right.
   a. Using the Rational-Zero Theorem, list all possible rational zeros of R.
   b. Which possible rational zeros of R are actual zeros? How did you decide which roots to test?
6. Prove that $\sqrt[3]{9}$ is irrational.

APPLYING THE MATHEMATICS

7. Consider the function f, where $f(n) = 2n^4 + 5n^3 + 12$.
   a. List all possible rational zeros of this function.
   b. Graph f and explain why it has no rational zeros.

1. 5 is a factor of the leading coefficient, and 7 is a factor of the constant term.
2. No; a condition for the Rational-Root Theorem is that the coefficients of the polynomial function are integers.

Additional Example

Example 3 Use the Rational-Root Theorem to show that $\sqrt{3}$ is an irrational number. $\sqrt{3}$ is a solution to the equation $x^2 = 3$ and a root of $x^2 - 3 = 0$. By the Rational-Root Theorem, if $\frac{a}{b}$ is a rational root of $x^2 - 3 = 0$, then a is a factor of 3, and b is a factor of 1. Thus, the only possible rational roots of $x^2 - 3 = 0$ are $\pm\frac{3}{1}$ and $\pm\frac{1}{1}$, that is, 3, -3, 1, and -1. Substitute to see if any of these numbers are roots of the equation $x^2 - 3 = 0$: $3^2 - 3 = 6 \neq 0$; $(-3)^2 - 3 = 6 \neq 0$; $1^2 - 3 = -2 \neq 0$; $(-1)^2 - 3 = -2 \neq 0$. None of the possible rational roots are roots of the equation. Thus, $x^2 - 3 = 0$ has no rational roots, so $\sqrt{3}$ must be irrational.

Note-Taking Tips

Have students add to their journals the Rational-Root Theorem, along with an appropriate example.

3 Assignment

Recommended Assignment

- Questions 1–15
- Question 16 (extra credit)
- Reading Lesson 11-6
- Covering the Ideas 11-6

Notes on the Questions

Question 6 In general, if the nth root of an integer is not an integer, then it is irrational.

Additional Answers can be found in the back of the book.

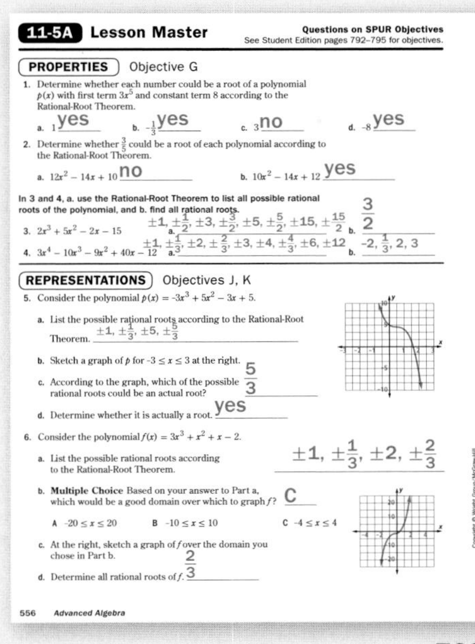

11-5A Lesson Master

Questions on SPUR Objectives See Student Edition pages 792–795 for objectives.

PROPERTIES Objective G

1. Determine whether each number could be a root of a polynomial $p(x)$ with first term $3x^5$ and constant term 8 according to the Rational-Root Theorem.
   a. 1 yes b. $-\frac{1}{3}$ yes c. 3 no d. -8 yes
2. Determine whether $\frac{3}{5}$ could be a root of each polynomial according to the Rational-Root Theorem.
   a. $12x^2 - 14x + 10$ no b. $10x^2 - 14x + 12$ yes

In 3 and 4, a. use the Rational-Root Theorem to list all possible rational roots of the polynomial, and b. find all rational roots.

3. $2x^3 + 5x^2 - 2x - 15$ a. $\pm1, \pm\frac{1}{2}, \pm3, \pm\frac{3}{2}, \pm5, \pm\frac{5}{2}, \pm15, \pm\frac{15}{2}$ b. $\frac{3}{2}$
4. $3x^4 - 10x^3 - 9x^2 + 40x - 12$ a. $\pm1, \pm\frac{1}{3}, \pm2, \pm\frac{2}{3}, \pm3, \pm4, \pm\frac{4}{3}, \pm6, \pm12$ b. $-2, \frac{1}{3}, 2, 3$

REPRESENTATIONS Objectives J, K

5. Consider the polynomial $p(x) = -3x^3 + 5x^2 - 3x + 5$.
   a. List the possible rational roots according to the Rational-Root Theorem. $\pm1, \pm\frac{1}{3}, \pm5, \pm\frac{5}{3}$
   b. Sketch a graph of p for $-3 \le x \le 3$ at the right.
   c. According to the graph, which of the possible rational roots could be an actual root? $\frac{5}{3}$
   d. Determine whether it is actually a root. yes
6. Consider the polynomial $f(x) = 3x^3 + x^2 + x - 2$.
   a. List the possible rational roots according to the Rational-Root Theorem. $\pm1, \pm\frac{1}{3}, \pm2, \pm\frac{2}{3}$
   b. **Multiple Choice** Based on your answer to Part a, which would be a good domain over which to graph f? C
   A $-20 \le x \le 20$ B $-10 \le x \le 10$ C $-4 \le x \le 4$
   c. At the right, sketch a graph of f over the domain you chose in Part b.
   d. Determine all rational roots of f. $\frac{2}{3}$

556 *Advanced Algebra*

Accommodating the Learner

Have students work in groups to write pairs of polynomials such that one polynomial's coefficients are the second polynomial's coefficients in reverse order. For example, students could use $10x^3 - 4x^2 + 5x - 20$ and $-20y^3 + 5y^2 - 4y + 10$. Have group members compare how the zeros of the two polynomials are related and describe any patterns they notice. The zeros are reciprocals. If one polynomial has a zero r, then the other has a zero $\frac{1}{r}$.

Extension

Have students use the Rational-Root Theorem to show that if f is a polynomial function, then any integer zeros of $f(x)$ must be factors of the constant term. Any integer zero p could be written as the rational number $\frac{p}{1}$. According to the Rational-Root Theorem, because $\frac{p}{1}$ is in lowest terms, p must be a factor of the constant term.

11-5

Notes on the Questions

Question 9 Suppose that it is known that $\sqrt{p}$ is irrational when p is not a perfect square. Then when a is an integer, another way to deduce that $a + \sqrt{p}$ is irrational is to use an indirect proof. Suppose that $a + \sqrt{p}$ is a rational number, say r. Then $a + \sqrt{p} = r$, so $\sqrt{p} = r - a$. But the difference of two rational numbers is a rational number. Thus, we have an irrational number ($\sqrt{p}$) equaling a rational number ($r - a$). This contradiction indicates that our supposition cannot be true. So $a + \sqrt{p}$ is irrational.

If a is positive, still another way to deduce that $a + \sqrt{p}$ is irrational is to examine its decimal expansion. The decimal for $\sqrt{p}$ is infinite and nonrepeating; the decimal for $a + \sqrt{p}$ is also infinite and nonrepeating because all that is changed is the integer part of the decimal when a is positive. Thus, $a + \sqrt{p}$ is irrational. This proof is somewhat different if a is negative.

Question 10 This questions looks harder than it is.

Additional Answers

8. Using the Rational-Root Theorem, we can find possible roots of the polynomial equation. By plugging these values into the original equation, we can determine which ones are roots of the equation. We can then find the factors using the Factor Theorem.

9b. Assume that $a + \sqrt{p}$ is rational. Therefore, it should be able to be expressed as $\frac{m}{n}$ and with $n \neq 1$ since $a + \sqrt{p}$ is not an integer. However, according to the Rational-Root Theorem, n is a factor of the leading coefficient, which is 1. Thus, $a + \sqrt{p}$ cannot be rational.

8. Explain how the Rational-Root Theorem and the Factor Theorem can be used to factor a polynomial equation with only rational roots. See margin.

9. When a polynomial equation with integer coefficients has a root of the form $a + \sqrt{p}$, where p is not a perfect square, then $a - \sqrt{p}$ must also be a root of the equation.
   a. Use this fact to find a polynomial equation with integer coefficients in which $a + \sqrt{p}$ is a root.
   b. If p is a prime number and a is an integer, show that $a + \sqrt{p}$ is irrational. See margin.

10. Let $f(x) = a_3x^3 + a_2x^2 + a_1x + a_0$ and $g(x) = 7a_3x^3 + 7a_2x^2 + 7a_1x + 7a_0$, where a_3, a_2, a_1, and a_0 are integers with $a_3 \neq 0$ and $a_0 \neq 0$.
    a. How are the possible rational zeros of these functions related? Explain your reasoning.
    b. Let $f(x)$ be defined as in Part a and $h(x) = k \cdot f(x)$, where k is a nonzero constant. How are the possible rational zeros of f and h related?

9a. Answers vary. Sample: $y = x^2 - 2ax + (a^2 - p)$

10a. The sets of possible rational zeros for the two functions are equal because $\frac{7a_0}{7a_3} = \frac{a_0}{a_3}$ in lowest terms.

10b. The possible rational zeros of f and h are the same.

REVIEW

11. A horizontal beam has its left end built into a wall, and its right end resting on a support, as shown at the right. The beam is loaded with weight uniformly distributed along its length. As a result, the beam sags downward according to the equation $y = -x^4 + 24x^3 - 135x^2$, where x is the distance (in meters) from the wall to a point on the beam, and y is the distance (in hundredths of a millimeter) of the sag from the x-axis to the beam. **(Lesson 11-3)**
    a. What is the appropriate domain for x if the beam is 9 meters long? $0 \leq x \leq 9$
    b. Find the zeros of this function. 0, 9, 15
    c. Tell what the roots represent in this situation. See margin.

y
wall
uniform load
x
beam
support

12. Insulation tubing for hot water pipes is shaped like a cylindrical solid of outer radius R from which another cylindrical solid of inner radius r has been removed. The figure at the right shows a piece of insulation tubing. **(Lessons 11-1, 1-7, Previous Course)**
    a. Suppose the piece of tubing has length L. Find a formula for the volume V of the tube in terms of r, R, and L.
    b. Suppose $R = 1$ inch and $L = 6$ feet. Write a formula for V as a function of r. $V = 72\pi(1 - r^2)$
    c. What is the degree of the polynomial in Part b? 2

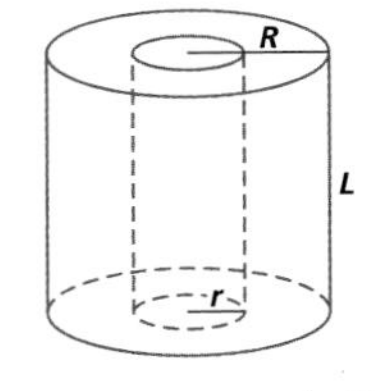

12a. $V = L\pi(R^2 - r^2)$

Additional Answers

11c. The beam has no sag when $x = 0$ (the point is on the wall) or $x = 9$ (the point is on the support). $x = 15$ is a zero for the function, but this value is not in the domain in this problem.

13. The building code in one state specifies that accessibility ramps into public swimming pools must not drop more than one inch for every horizontal foot. What is the maximum angle of depression a ramp can make with the surface of the water? **(Lesson 10-2)** about 4.8°

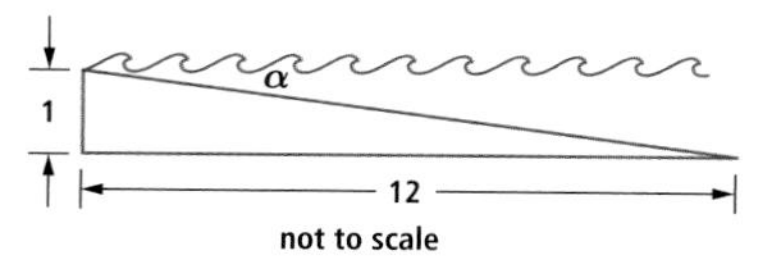

14. Find the roots of $z^2 + 2z + 6 = 0$. **(Lesson 6-10)** $-1 \pm \sqrt{5}i$

15. Triangle MAP is shown below. **(Lessons 4-7, 4-6)**

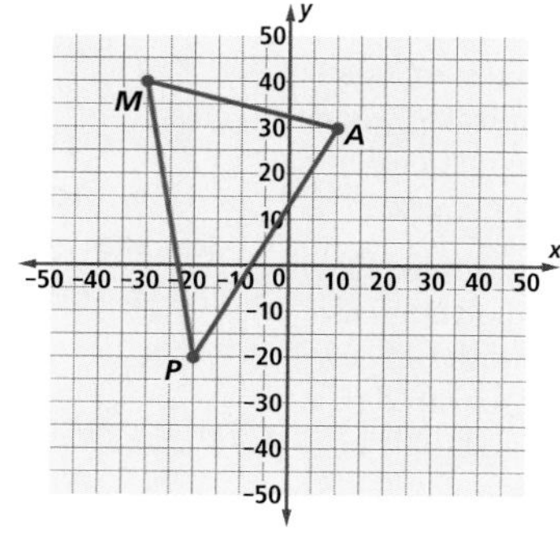

a. Graph the reflection image of $\triangle MAP$ over the x-axis. Label the vertices M', A', and P', respectively. See margin.

b. Graph the reflection image of $\triangle M'A'P'$ over the y-axis. Label the vertices M'', A'', and P'', respectively. See margin.

c. What single transformation maps $\triangle MAP$ onto $\triangle M''A''P''$?

15c. a rotation of 180° about the origin

EXPLORATION

16. Find information about *Descartes' Rule of Signs* for polynomials, and then explain what it tells you about $P(x)$ from the Activity in this lesson.

Answers vary. Sample: Descartes' Rule of Signs allows you to determine the possible numbers of positive and negative roots of a polynomial $P(x)$ by counting the sign changes of $P(x)$ and $P(-x)$. Because $P(x) = 90x^3 + 31x^2 - 193x - 84$ in the Activity, there is one sign change and $P(x)$ has one positive root. $P(-x) = -90x^3 + 31x^2 + 193x - 84$ has two sign changes, so there are either 2 or 0 negative roots. So, the rule shows that there are 2 negative roots and 1 positive root, or 0 negative roots, 1 positive root, and 2 complex nonreal roots.

QY ANSWERS

1. $\frac{2}{4}$ and $\frac{6}{2}$ are not in lowest terms, which the theorem requires.
2. $x^3 - 9 = 0$

4 Wrap-Up

Ongoing Assessment

Refer students to Example 2 on page 762. Have them write a paragraph explaining why it is helpful to use both graphing and the Rational-Root Theorem when determining the rational roots of a function. Students should recognize that the Rational-Root Theorem tells all the possible rational roots, but the graph helps to eliminate some of the possible roots.

Project Update

Project 1, *Proving That Certain nth Roots Are Irrational,* on page 786 relates to the content of this lesson.

Additional Answers

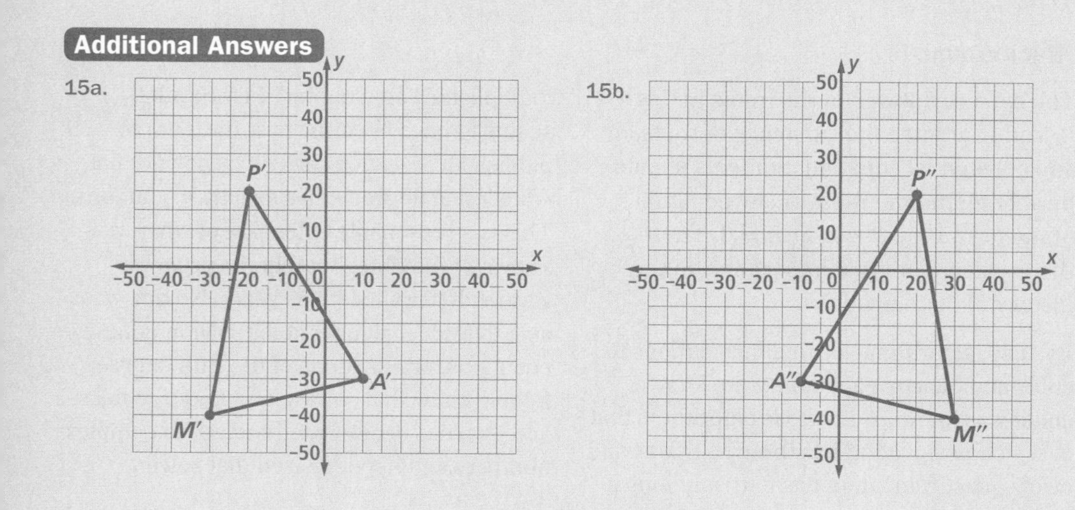

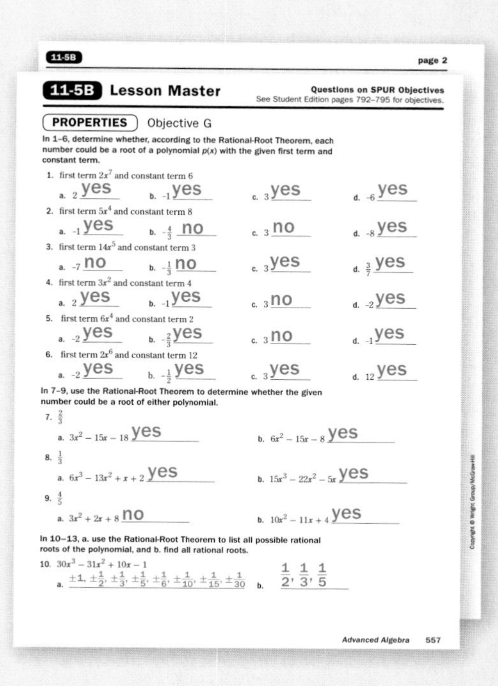

11-5B page 2

11-5B Lesson Master

Questions on SPUR Objectives
See Student Edition pages 792–795 for objectives.

PROPERTIES Objective G

In 1–6, determine whether, according to the Rational-Root Theorem, each number could be a root of a polynomial $p(x)$ with the given first term and constant term.

1. first term $2x^7$ and constant term 6
   a. 2 yes b. -1 yes c. 3 yes d. -6 yes
2. first term $5x^4$ and constant term 8
   a. -1 yes b. $-\frac{4}{3}$ no c. 3 no d. -8 yes
3. first term $14x^5$ and constant term 3
   a. -7 no b. $-\frac{1}{3}$ no c. 3 yes d. $\frac{3}{7}$ yes
4. first term $3x^2$ and constant term 4
   a. 2 yes b. -1 yes c. 3 no d. -2 yes
5. first term $6x^4$ and constant term 2
   a. -2 yes b. $-\frac{2}{3}$ yes c. 3 no d. -1 yes
6. first term $2x^6$ and constant term 12
   a. -2 yes b. $-\frac{1}{2}$ yes c. 3 yes d. 12 yes

In 7–9, use the Rational-Root Theorem to determine whether the given number could be a root of either polynomial.

7. $\frac{2}{3}$
   a. $3x^2 - 15x - 18$ yes b. $6x^2 - 15x - 8$ yes
8. $\frac{1}{3}$
   a. $6x^3 - 13x^2 + x + 2$ yes b. $15x^3 - 22x^2 - 5x$ yes
9. $\frac{4}{5}$
   a. $3x^2 + 2x + 8$ no b. $10x^2 - 11x + 4$ yes

In 10–13, a. use the Rational-Root Theorem to list all possible rational roots of the polynomial, and b. find all rational roots.

10. $30x^3 - 31x^2 + 10x - 1$
   a. $\pm 1, \pm\frac{1}{2}, \pm\frac{1}{3}, \pm\frac{1}{5}, \pm\frac{1}{6}, \pm\frac{1}{10}, \pm\frac{1}{15}, \pm\frac{1}{30}$ b. $\frac{1}{2}, \frac{1}{3}, \frac{1}{5}$

Advanced Algebra 557

Lesson

11-6

GOAL

Learn the history of the Fundamental Theorem of Algebra and its use in determining the number of real and nonreal solutions to polynomial equations.

SPUR Objectives

C Find zeros of polynomial functions by factoring.

F Apply the Fundamental Theorem of Algebra.

Materials/Resources

- Lesson Masters 11-6A and 11-6B
- Resource Master 214
- Quiz 2
- CAS

HOMEWORK

Suggestions for Assignment

- Questions 1–25
- Questions 26 (extra credit)
- Reading Lesson 11-7
- Covering the Ideas 11-7

Local Standards

1 Warm-Up

For 1–4, consider the function f with $f(x) = 0.01(3x + 2)^2(4x - 5)(x - 6) + d$. By graphing f for various values of d, find a value of d so that f has

1. three real zeros. Answers vary. Sample: 0
2. two real zeros. Answers vary. Sample: -10
3. one real zero. ≈ 46.88
4. no real zeros. Answers vary. Sample: 50

Lesson 11-6

Solving All Polynomial Equations

Vocabulary

double root, root of multiplicity 2

multiplicity

BIG IDEA Every polynomial equation of degree $n \geq 1$ has exactly n solutions, counting multiplicities.

What Types of Numbers Are Needed to Solve Polynomial Equations?

An exact solution to any linear equation with real coefficients is always a real number, but exact solutions to quadratic equations with real coefficients sometimes are not real. It is natural to wonder whether exact solutions to higher-order polynomial equations require new types of numbers beyond the complex numbers.

As early as 2000 BCE, the Babylonians developed algorithms to solve problems using quadratic polynomials. The study of polynomials progressed to cubics and quartics, with much early work done in Persia, China, and Italy. In 1535, Niccolo Tartaglia discovered a method for solving all cubic equations. Soon after that, Ludovico Ferrari discovered how to solve any quartic equation.

Surprisingly, no numbers beyond complex numbers are needed to solve linear, quadratic, cubic, and quartic polynomial equations. However, when over 250 years passed without finding a general solution to every *quintic* (5th-degree) polynomial equation, mathematicians began wondering whether new numbers might be needed. At last, in 1824, the Norwegian mathematician Niels Henrik Abel proved that there is no general formula for solving quintic polynomial equations. Shortly after that, Evariste Galois deduced that there is no general formula involving complex numbers for finding roots of all polynomials of degree five or higher.

But how do we know that new numbers beyond the complex numbers were not necessary? In 1797, at the age of 18, Carl Gauss offered a proof of the following theorem, the name of which indicates its significance.

Fundamental Theorem of Algebra

Every polynomial equation $P(x) = 0$ of any degree ≥ 1 with complex number coefficients has at least one complex number solution.

Mental Math

How many lines of symmetry does each of the following have at a minimum?

a. a rhombus 2

b. a rectangle 2

c. an isosceles triangle 1

d. a circle infinitely many

Carl Friedreich Gauss is often called "the prince of mathematicians."

Background

The two very powerful theorems in this lesson guarantee the existence of roots for any polynomial equation. Students should be able to find the roots of any equation of the form $x^n(ax^2 + bx + c) = 0$. These theorems are of great importance in the history of mathematics.

By 1550, algorithms for finding solutions to cubic and quartic equations were known, and it was known from those algorithms that every cubic equation has three solutions and every quartic equation has four solutions if multiplicities are counted. Peter Rothe seems to have been the first (in 1608) to publish an assertion that every polynomial equation of degree n has exactly n solutions. This is a reasonable extension of what was known at the time, but then no progress was made for almost 150 years. No one was able to find an algorithm for solving quintic equations, or equations of the fifth degree. People knew that solving quadratics, cubics, and quartics necessitated the use of complex numbers and hypothesized that solving

From the Fundamental Theorem of Algebra and the Factor Theorem it is possible to prove that *every solution to a polynomial equation with complex coefficients is a complex number.* (Remember that complex numbers include the real numbers.) Thus, no new type of number is needed to solve higher-degree polynomial equations. So, for instance, the solutions to $x^5 + 2x^4 - 3ix^2 + 3 + 7i = 0$ are complex numbers.

How Many Complex Solutions Does a Given Polynomial Equation Have?

It is easy to show that every solution to a polynomial equation is complex when the degree of the polynomial is small. For example, if $a \neq 0$, the linear equation $ax + b = 0$ has one root: $x = -\frac{b}{a}$. Therefore, every linear polynomial has exactly one complex root.

The quadratic equation $ax^2 + bx + c = 0$, $a \neq 0$, has two solutions, given by the quadratic formula: $x = \frac{-b \pm \sqrt{b^2 - 4ac}}{2a}$. When the discriminant $b^2 - 4ac > 0$, the roots are real numbers. When $b^2 - 4ac < 0$, the roots are nonreal complex numbers. When the discriminant $b^2 - 4ac = 0$, the two roots are equal, and the root is called a **double root**, or a **root of multiplicity 2**. For instance, consider $x^2 - 10x + 25 = 0$. Here $b^2 - 4ac = (-10)^2 - 4 \cdot 1 \cdot 25 = 0$, so there is a double root. Because $x^2 - 10x + 25 = (x - 5)^2$, that double root is 5. So every quadratic has two complex roots, although the two roots might not be distinct.

In general, the **multiplicity** of a root r in an equation $P(x) = 0$ is the highest power of the factor $x - r$. For example, in $17(x - 4)(x - 11)^3 = 0$, 11 is a root of multiplicity 3, and 4 is a root of multiplicity 1. So $P(x) = 0$ has four roots altogether.

STOP QY1

▶ **QY1**

State the multiplicity of each root of $4(x - 3)^2 \cdot (x + 5)^4(x - 17) = 0$. How many roots does the equation have altogether?

Activity

Consider the polynomial function P defined by $P(x) = x^3 + 2x^2 - 14x - 3$. Steps 1–4. See margin.

Step 1 Verify that 3 is a zero of P. What theorem justifies the conclusion that $x - 3$ is a factor of $P(x)$?

Step 2 If $P(x) = (x - 3)Q(x)$, what is the degree of $Q(x)$?

Step 3 Without finding $Q(x)$ explicitly, how many roots does the equation $Q(x) = 0$ have? Why are these roots also roots of $P(x) = 0$?

Step 4 Check your answer to Step 3 by solving $P(x) = 0$ on a CAS.

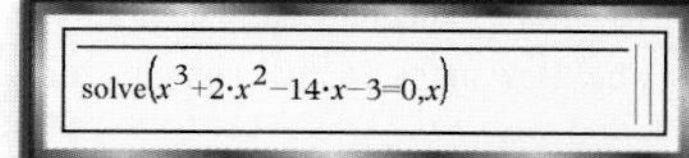

2 Teaching

Notes on the Lesson

Start the lesson by having students solve a linear equation $(9x - 6 = 17)$, a quadratic equation $(x^2 + x - 15 = 0)$, a cubic equation $(x^3 - 64 = 0)$, and, perhaps, a quartic equation $(x^4 - 1 = 0)$. Discussing the solutions to these equations can easily lead to the two theorems in this lesson, which are easy to conjecture but difficult to prove.

Point out that, although the Number of Roots of a Polynomial Equation Theorem tells us how many roots a polynomial equation has, it does not explain how to find them. It is what is known as an *existence* theorem. (It tells how many roots exist.)

The historical notes in the lesson are often quite interesting to students. They are usually fascinated by the fact that some of these mathematicians were rather young at the time that they made their most important discoveries.

How many complex solutions does a given polynomial equation have? The Fundamental Theorem of Algebra seems to have a rather weak result. It states that there is a solution to every polynomial equation with complex number coefficients. Yet, it does not tell you the solution or even the number of solutions. However, by the Factor Theorem, every zero r of a polynomial $P(x)$ gives rise to a factor $(x - r)$ of $P(x)$. This fact leads to the conclusion that, if we allow multiplicities of zeros, a polynomial of degree n has n zeros. This is a beautiful and powerful result.

higher-degree equations might require another entirely new set of numbers.

In 1746, the French mathematician Jean le Rond d'Alembert presented a proof that every polynomial equation of degree greater than or equal to 1 has a root. His proof would not be considered rigorous enough today. Still, it contained the germ of a valid proof.

The first rigorous proof was given in 1797 by Gauss using methods different from d'Alembert's. Gauss's proof was astonishing in three ways: He was only 18 years old, he solved a problem that had been around for 200 years, and the result was that no new numbers were needed regardless of the degree of the polynomial.

Additional Answers

Activity

Step 1. $P(3) = 3^3 + 2(3)^2 - 14(3) - 3 = 0$; the Factor Theorem

Step 2. 2

Step 3. 2 roots; If $Q(x) = 0$, then $P(x) = (x - r) \cdot 0 = 0$. Thus, the roots of a factor of a polynomial are also the roots of the polynomial itself.

Step 4.

solve$(x^3+2\cdot x^2-14\cdot x-3=0,x)$

$x=\frac{-(\sqrt{21}+5)}{2}$ or $x=\frac{\sqrt{21}-5}{2}$ or $x=3$

Notes on the Lesson

The Fundamental Theorem of Algebra is generally proved in college courses in complex variables, not before. We do not offer a proof here.

Finding real solutions to polynomial equations Students should realize that if a polynomial function with real coefficients has an odd degree (1, 3, 5, ...), then it must have a real zero. Why? First, notice that the leading term a_nx^n can dominate all other terms if $|x|$ is large enough. Suppose the leading coefficient a_n is positive. Then a_nx^n will be positive when x is very large and negative when x is very small (that is, quite negative). So the graph of the function will ultimately go up to the right and down to the left, as in the graph in the Example. So the graph of the function must cross the x-axis at some point. If the leading coefficient a_n is negative, then the graph of the function goes up to the left and down to the right. So, when the coefficients of a polynomial of odd degree are real numbers, the Fundamental Theorem of Algebra is obvious. However, it turns out that the Fundamental Theorem of Algebra holds even when the coefficients of a polynomial are nonreal.

When the coefficients of a polynomial function are real and the degree of the polynomial is even, then the graph of the polynomial does not have to intersect the x-axis. In fact, by suitably adding or subtracting a constant, the graph of every polynomial of even degree can be vertically translated into a graph that does not intersect the x-axis, as the Warm-Up suggests.

Note-Taking Tips

Have students add to their journals the two theorems in this lesson, along with appropriate examples.

The Fundamental Theorem of Algebra only guarantees the existence of a single complex (possibly real) root r_1 for any polynomial $P(x)$. However, using the Factor Theorem, you can rewrite $P(x) = (x - r_1) \cdot Q(x)$, where the degree of $Q(x)$ is one less than the degree of $P(x)$. By applying the Fundamental Theorem of Algebra to $Q(x)$, you get another root r_2, and therefore another factor. So you could write $P(x) = (x - r_1)(x - r_2)Q_2(x)$, where the degree of $Q_2(x)$ is *two* less than the degree of $P(x)$. This process can continue until you "run out of degrees," that is, until $Q(x)$ is linear.

For example, if you start with a 4th degree polynomial $P(x)$, you can factor it as

$$\begin{aligned} P(x) &= (x - r_1)Q_1(x) \\ &= (x - r_1)(x - r_2)Q_2(x) \\ &= (x - r_1)(x - r_2)(x - r_3)Q_3(x), \end{aligned}$$

and now $Q_3(x)$ is linear. So, $P(x) = 0$ has four roots: r_1, r_2, r_3, and the single root of $Q_3(x) = 0$. These four roots are *not* necessarily four different real numbers. In fact, some or all of them may be nonreal complex numbers. This conclusion is summarized in the following theorem.

Number of Roots of a Polynomial Equation Theorem

Every polynomial equation of degree n has exactly n roots, provided that multiple roots are counted according to their multiplicities.

QY2

QY2

How many roots does each equation have?

a. $5x^{12} - 64x^3 + 4x^2 + 1 = 0$

b. $4ex^5 + 3ix^2 - (2 + i)x + 4 = 0$

Finding Real Solutions to Polynomial Equations

The Number of Roots of a Polynomial Equation Theorem tells you how many roots a polynomial equation $P(x) = k$ has. It does not tell you how to find the roots, nor does it tell you how many of the roots are real. To answer these questions, you can apply the methods studied in this chapter for finding and analyzing zeros of polynomial functions.

Example

Consider the polynomial function P defined by $P(x) = x^5 - x^4 - 21x^3 - 37x^2 - 98x - 24$.

a. How many real zeros does P have?

b. How many nonreal complex zeros does P have?

Accommodating the Learner

When discussing the Example, stress that the graph indicates three real roots because the graph intersects the x-axis three times. Some students may need to be reminded that when the graph crosses the x-axis, the value of the function is zero, so the value of x is a root of the polynomial equation. Explain that we cannot tell whether the root is rational or irrational. By applying the Rational-Root Theorem, however, we can determine which rational roots are possible and then test them to see if $f(x) = 0$.

ENGLISH LEARNERS

Vocabulary Development

Have students read again the definition of multiplicity of a root as given on page 767: The multiplicity of a root r in an equation $P(x) = 0$ is the highest power of the factor $x - r$. Have them describe in their own words what this means. Then stress that double root and root of multiplicity 2 have the same meaning.

Solution 1

a. Solve $P(x) = 0$ on a CAS in real-number mode. The CAS shows that P has three real zeros. One zero, 6, is rational, but the other two real zeros, $-2 \pm \sqrt{3}$, are irrational.

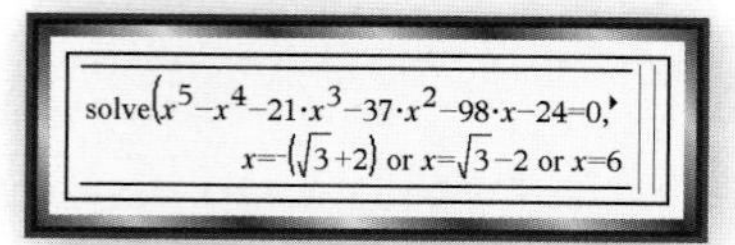

Confirm with a graph of $y = P(x)$ that the three x-intercepts correspond to the three real zeros.

b. Because the degree of $P(x)$ is five, there are five zeros altogether by the Number of Roots of a Polynomial Equation Theorem. Since there are three real zeros, there are two nonreal complex zeros. Solve in complex-number mode on a CAS to find all five real and nonreal zeros. There are two nonreal zeros, $-\frac{1}{2} \pm \frac{\sqrt{15}}{2}i$. So, of the five zeros of P(x), one is rational, two are irrational, and two are nonreal complex.

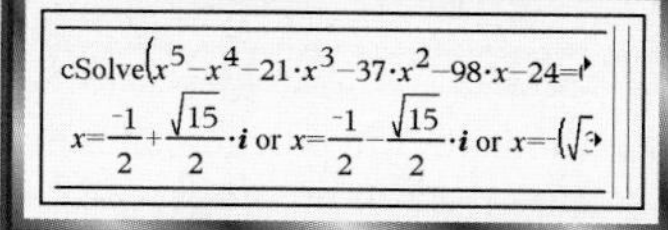

Check Factor $P(x)$ on a CAS in complex mode. Part of the solution line is shown at the right. The entire output is

$$\frac{(x-6)(x+\sqrt{3}+2)(x-\sqrt{3}+2)(2x-(-1+\sqrt{15}\,i))(2x+1+\sqrt{15}\,i)}{4}.$$

When the constant $\frac{1}{4}$ is factored out, there are five factors that can be set equal to zero and solved for x. Solving shows that one root of P(x) is rational, two are irrational, and two are nonreal. It checks.

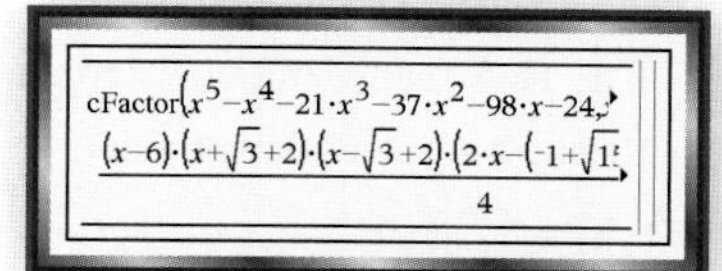

Questions

COVERING THE IDEAS

1. State the Fundamental Theorem of Algebra. *1. Every polynomial equation $P(x) = 0$ of any degree ≥ 1 with complex number coefficients has at least one complex number solution.*
2. Zelda is confused. The polynomial $x^3 - 25x$ is supposed to have three complex roots, but the roots 0, 5, and -5 are all real numbers. Resolve Zelda's confusion. *2. The set of complex numbers includes real numbers.*
3. **Multiple Choice** The equation $\pi w^3 - 3iw + \frac{1}{17} = 0$ has how many complex solutions? C

   A none B two C three D four
4. Who first proved the Fundamental Theorem of Algebra? Carl Gauss

Notes on the Lesson

Example Students may wonder how we know that the function does not intersect the x-axis in more than the three places indicated. The reason is that the term x^5 dominates the other terms. That is, when $|x|$ is sufficiently large, the other terms cannot add up to enough to change the sign of the value of the x^5 term. So the graph of this function gets closer and closer to the graph of $y = x^5$, whose behavior we know from Chapter 7. The Example uses a CAS solve command to find all complex roots and a CAS factor command to check the solutions. The commands to solve or factor in complex mode vary by CAS model. For example, on the TI-Nspire, the cSolve and cFactor commands are used to find all nonreal solutions and complex factors. On the Casio ClassPad, the solve and factor commands are used, but the calculator must be set to complex mode.

Additional Example

Example Consider the polynomial function P defined by $P(x) = x^5 - 7x^3 + 15x^2 - 7$.

a. How many real zeros does P have? three real zeros: -3.35875, 0.851365, and -0.606609

b. How many nonreal complex zeros does P have? two nonreal zeros: $1.557 - 1.2693i$ and $1.557 + 1.2693i$

3 Assignment

Recommended Assignment

- Questions 1–25
- Question 26 (extra credit)
- Reading Lesson 11-7
- Covering the Ideas 11-7

Accommodating the Learner

Have students work with a partner. Each partner should write a polynomial of degree no greater than 5. Have them exchange papers and write a different polynomial equation that has the same possible rational roots as their partner's equation. Then challenge them to write another polynomial equation that has the same *actual* rational roots as the original equation. Answers vary. Check students' work.

Extension

Ask students to write an equation of degree 4 that has real coefficients and the roots $2i$ and $-4i$. $x^4 + 20x^2 + 64 = 0$ Then have students suppose that $a + bi$ is a zero of a polynomial function with real coefficients and to find another zero of that polynomial. $a - bi$

11-6

Notes on the Questions

Question 7 Ask students for a simple explanation why this equation cannot have a positive root. The left side would be positive and not equal zero. Then ask if the equation can have a negative root.

Question 11 Ask students for a simple explanation why this equation cannot have a real root. The left side would be a nonreal complex number and could not equal 0.

Additional Answers

7. $x = -8$, rational; $x = -8$, multiplicity 2
8. $y = 0$, rational; $y = \pm 2\sqrt{2}$, irrational; no multiple roots
9. $z = 3$, rational; $z = \frac{22}{7}$, rational; $z = 3 \pm 4i$, nonreal; $z = 3$, multiplicity 4

10a. One of the solutions, $x = -2$, is a multiple root.

10b. $(x - 3)(x + 2)(x + 2)$

16b. $\sqrt{2} \pm \sqrt{2}i$, $-\sqrt{2} \pm \sqrt{2}i$

16c. 3; -2, $1 + \sqrt{3}i$, $1 - \sqrt{3}i$

17. $p(x) = 3(x + 4)\left(x - \frac{2}{3}\right)(x - 5) = 3x^3 - 5x^2 - 58x + 40$

11-6A Lesson Master

Questions on SPUR Objectives
See Student Edition pages 792–795 for objectives.

SKILLS Objective C

In 1 and 2, a polynomial is written factored over the rational numbers. a. Give the degree of the polynomial, and b. find all zeros and their multiplicities.

1. $(x - 1)(x + 9)^3(2x - 5)$ a. 5 b. 1 (mult. 1), -9 (mult. 3), $\frac{5}{2}$ (mult. 1)
2. $(3x + 1)^2(x^2 - 8x + 20)$ a. 4 b. $-\frac{1}{3}$ (mult. 2), $4 - 2i$ (mult. 1), $4 + 2i$ (mult. 1)

In 3 and 4, use a CAS to factor the polynomial a. over the real numbers, and b. over the complex numbers. c. List all zeros and their multiplicities.

3. $2x^3 - 7x^2 + 18x - 63$
   a. $(2x - 7)(x^2 + 9)$
   b. $(2x - 7)(x + 3i)(x - 3i)$
   c. $\frac{7}{2}$, $-3i$, $3i$ (all mult. 1)
4. $x^4 - 6x^3 + 10x^2 + 18x - 39$
   a. $(x + \sqrt{3})(x - \sqrt{3})(x^2 - 6x + 13)$
   b. $(x + \sqrt{3})(x - \sqrt{3})(x - 3 + 2i)(x - 3 - 2i)$
   c. $\sqrt{3}$, $-\sqrt{3}$, $3 - 2i$, $3 + 2i$ (all mult. 1)

PROPERTIES Objective F

5. How many complex roots does the equation $3x^4 - \pi x + i = 0$ have? four
6. P is a cubic polynomial whose only roots are 4 and -1. Write a possible equation for P in factored form. Answers vary. Sample: $P(x) = (x - 4)^2(x + 1)$
7. The function $f(x) = x^4 - 9x^3 + 14x^2 + 46x - 52$ is graphed at the right. The graph shows all intercepts.
   a. How many complex zeros does f have? four
   b. How many of the zeros are real numbers? two
   c. How many of the zeros are nonreal numbers? two
8. The function $f(x) = x^3 + 2x^2 - 5x + k$ is graphed at the right for $k = -6$.
   a. How many of the zeros of f are real numbers? three
   b. Find a value of k so that f has one real zero. Answers vary. Sample: $k = 4$.
   c. Explain why there is no real value of k where f has no real zeros.
   Answers vary. Sample: No matter how much you shift the graph vertically, it will always have at least one x-intercept.

Advanced Algebra 559

In 5 and 6, $a \neq 0$. Solve for x.

5. $ax + b = 0$ $x = -\frac{b}{a}$
6. $ax^2 + bx + c = 0$ $x = \frac{-b \pm \sqrt{b^2 - 4ac}}{2a}$

In 7–9, an equation is given. Find and classify all solutions as rational, irrational, or nonreal. Then, identify any multiple roots. 7–9. See margin.

7. $x^2 + 16x + 64 = 0$
8. $y^3 - 8y = 0$
9. $(z - 3)^4(7z - 22)(z^2 - 6z + 25) = 0$

10. a. The equation $x^3 + x^2 - 8x - 12 = 0$ has only two roots, as the CAS screen shows at the right. However, the Number of Roots of a Polynomial Equation Theorem says that a cubic equation has three roots. How is this possible? a–b. See margin.

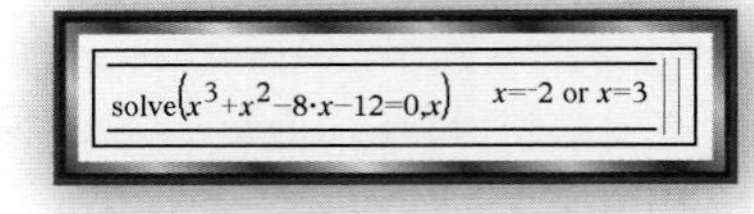

   b. Without using a CAS, give a factorization of $x^3 + x^2 - 8x - 12$ that explains the result in Part a.

11. How many complex roots does the equation $x^5 + 14ix = 0$ have? 5

APPLYING THE MATHEMATICS

12. Consider the polynomial function P defined by $P(x) = 4x^5 + x^3 - 5x^2 - 18x + 10$ graphed at the right.

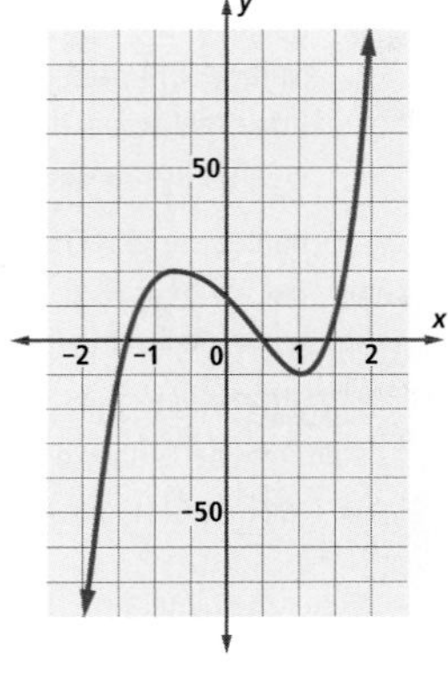

   a. How many real zeros does P have? 3
   b. How many nonreal zeros does it have? 2
   c. The graph shows that the real zeros are approximately -1.4, $\frac{1}{2}$, and 1.4. Which of these is an exact zero? $\frac{1}{2}$
   d. How many irrational zeros does this function have? 2

In 13 and 14, solve the equation.

13. $-4ix + 8 + 16i = 0$
14. $ix^2 + 10x + 11i = 0$

15. Consider $f(x) = x^5 - 6x^4 - 5x^3 + 42x^2 + 40x + k$, where k is a real number. The case where $k = 0$ is graphed at the right.

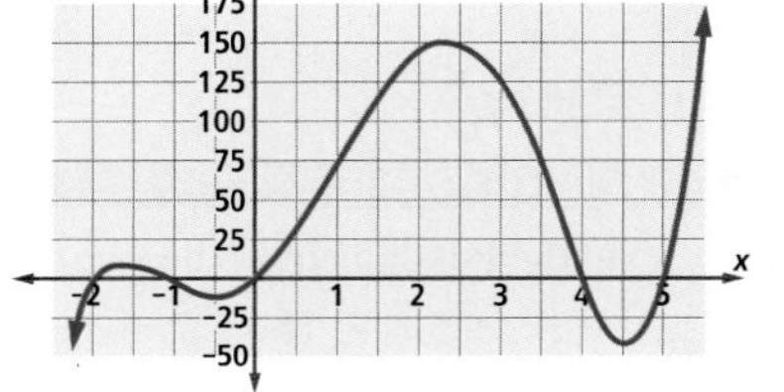

   a. What effect does changing the value of k have on the graph of $y = f(x)$?

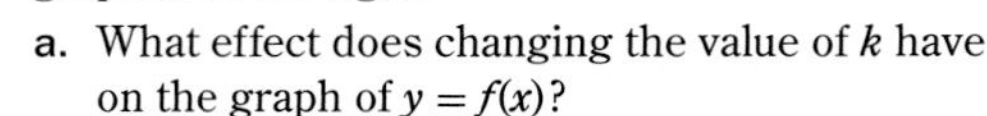

   b. Find a value of k for which f has exactly two nonreal zeros. $k = 40$
   c. For what values of k (approximately) does f have exactly four nonreal zeros? $k > 40$

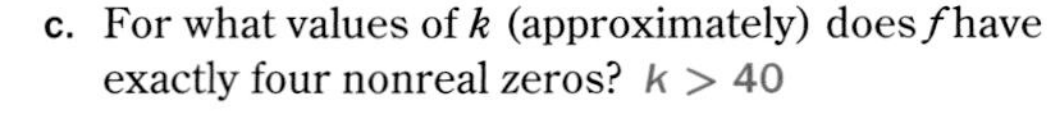

16. The 4th roots of -16 are nonreal complex numbers. If z is a 4th root of -16, then $z^4 = -16$ and $z^4 + 16 = 0$. 16b–c. See margin.

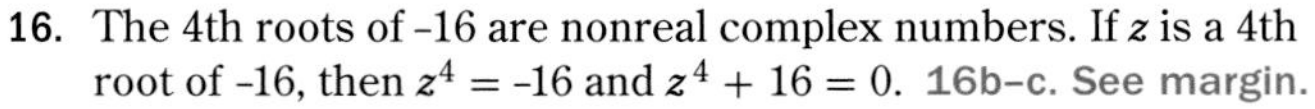

   a. How many complex solutions does $z^4 + 16 = 0$ have? 4
   b. Use a CAS to find all of the complex fourth roots of -16.
   c. By similar logic as in Parts a and b, -8 has ___?___ complex cube roots. Find them.

13. $x = 4 - 2i$

14. $x = 11i$ or $x = -i$

15a. The graph will be translated vertically when k is changed.

REVIEW

17. A 3rd-degree polynomial with leading coefficient 3 has roots -4, $\frac{2}{3}$, and 5. Find an equation for the polynomial. **(Lesson 11-4)** See margin.

18. The sum of the cube and the square of a number is 3. To the nearest thousandth, what is the number? **(Lessons 11-3, 11-1)** 1.175

19. Myron makes a bread pan by cutting squares of side length w from each corner of a 5-inch by 10-inch sheet of aluminum and folding up the sides. Let $V(w)$ represent the volume of the pan. **(Lesson 11-2)**
    a. Find a polynomial formula for $V(w)$. $V(w) = 4w^3 - 30w^2 + 50w$
    b. Can Myron's process yield a pan with volume of 25 in^3? no
    c. What value of w produces the pan with the greatest volume? $w \approx 1.06$

20. a. Which is more help in finding the distance c in the diagram at the right, the Law of Sines or the Law of Cosines? Law of Cosines
    b. Find c. **(Lesson 10-8)** about 1.78 mi

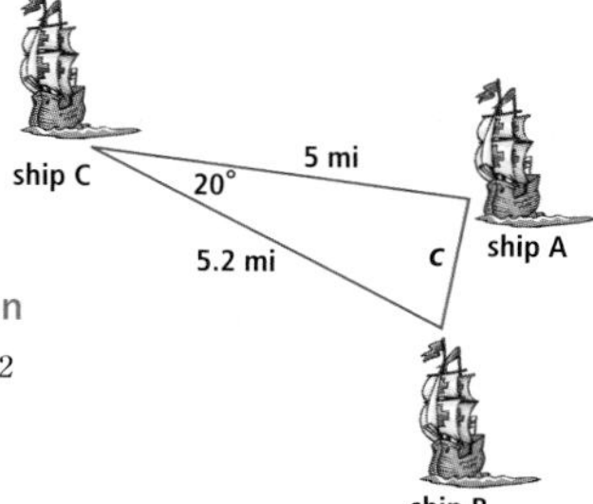

In 21 and 22, solve. (Lessons 10-6, 9-5)

21. $2 \log x = 4$ 100

22. $2 \sin x = 4$ no solution

23. a. State an equation for the image of the graph of $y = 3x^2$ under $T_{-3,4}$.
    b. Graph the image in Part a. **(Lesson 6-3)** See margin.

23a. $y = 3(x + 3)^2 + 4$

24. The wind force on a vertical surface varies jointly as the area A of the surface and the square of the wind speed S. The force is 340 newtons on a vertical surface of 1 m^2 when the wind blows at $18\frac{\text{m}}{\text{sec}}$. Find the force exerted by a $35\frac{\text{m}}{\text{sec}}$ wind on a vertical surface of area 2 m^2. (*Note:* One newton equals one $\frac{\text{kilogram-meter}}{\text{sec}^2}$.) **(Lesson 2-9)** about 2571 newtons

25. Make a spreadsheet to create the table of values for $y = 4x^2 - 13x$ as shown at the right. Use the table to find y when $x = 3.7$. **(Lesson 1-6)** See margin.

	A	B	C	D	E
◆		=4*a[]^2–13*a[]			
1	-6	222			
2	-5.9	215.94			
3	-5.8	209.96			
4	-5.7	204.06			
5	-5.6	198.24			
6	-5.5	192.5			

A

EXPLORATION

26. **Fill in the Blanks** Because $1^n = 1$ for all n, $x^n = 1$ has the solution 1 for all n. Thus, for all n, by the Factor Theorem, $x^n - 1$ has the factor $x - 1$.
    a. $x^2 - 1$ is the product of $x - 1$ and __?__. $x + 1$
    b. $x^3 - 1$ is the product of $x - 1$ and __?__. $x^2 + x + 1$
    c. $x^4 - 1$ is the product of $x - 1$ and __?__. $x^3 + x^2 + x + 1$
    d. Generalize Parts a–c. See margin.

QY ANSWERS

1. 3 is a root of multiplicity 2; –5 is a root of multiplicity 4; 17 is a root of multiplicity 1. It has 7 roots altogether.

2. a. 12
   b. 5

Additional Answers

23b.

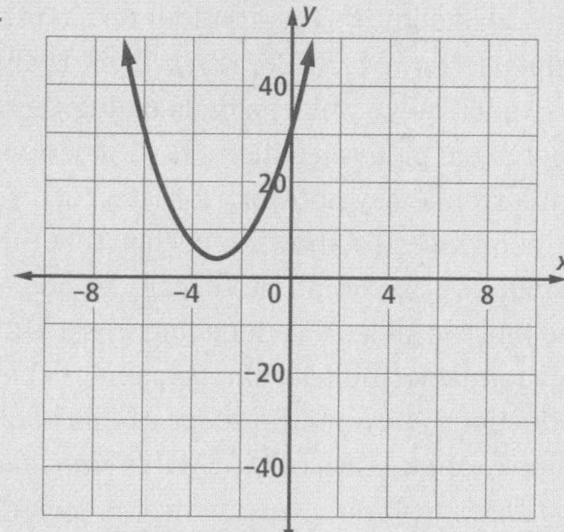

25.

	A	B	C	D	E
◆		=4*a[]^2–13*a[]			
1	3.3	.66			
2	3.4	2.04			
3	3.5	3.5			
4	3.6	5.04			
5	3.7	6.66			
6	3.8	8.36			

B5 =6.66

26d. $x^n - 1$ is the product of $x - 1$ and $x^{n-1} + x^{n-2} + \ldots + x + 1$.

Notes on the Questions

Question 17 Students may check their work arithmetically by substitution or with a graph.

Question 26 Sometimes the factor of $x^n - 1$ other than $x - 1$ can be factored over the rationals. For example, $x^4 - 1 = (x - 1)(x + 1)(x^2 + 1)$. A very interesting question is to ask whether any factor in the factored form has a coefficient other than 1, -1, or 0. The answer is "Yes," but the least value of n for which this occurs is over 100.

4 Wrap-Up

Ongoing Assessment

Ask students to explain the concept of multiplicity and why it is significant in solving equations. Then have them work in groups to give examples of equations that involve multiplicity. Students should recognize that the zeros of a function corresponding to identical factors are said to have multiplicity equal to the greatest number of times the identical factors occur. Students should supply appropriate examples.

Administer Quiz 2 (or a quiz of your own) after students complete this lesson.

Project Update

Project 2, *Polynomial Inequalities*, on page 786 and Project 6, *Factoring and Solving Cubic Polynomial Functions*, on page 787 relate to the content of this lesson.

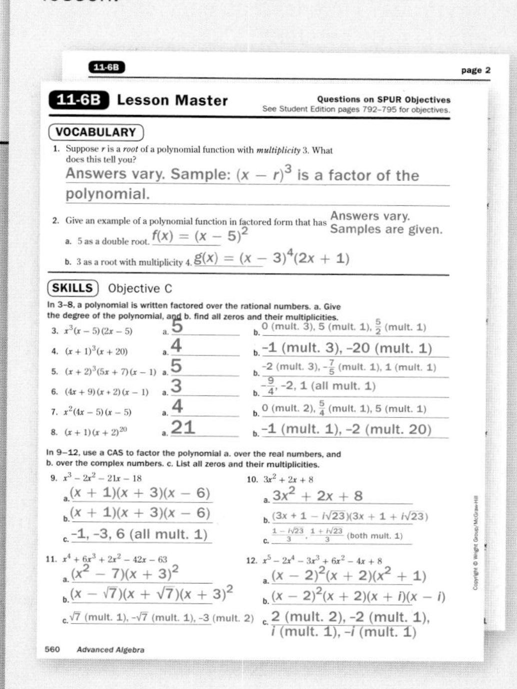

11-6B page 2

11-6B Lesson Master

Questions on SPUR Objectives
See Student Edition pages 792–795 for objectives.

VOCABULARY

1. Suppose r is a *root* of a polynomial function with *multiplicity* 3. What does this tell you?
   Answers vary. Sample: $(x - r)^3$ is a factor of the polynomial.

2. Give an example of a polynomial function in factored form that has
   Answers vary. Samples are given.
   a. 5 as a double root. $f(x) = (x - 5)^2$
   b. 3 as a root with multiplicity 4. $g(x) = (x - 3)^4(2x + 1)$

SKILLS Objective C

In 3–8, a polynomial is written factored over the rational numbers. a. Give the degree of the polynomial, and b. find all zeros and their multiplicities.

3. $x^3(x - 5)(2x - 5)$ a. 5 b. 0 (mult. 3), 5 (mult. 1), $\frac{5}{2}$ (mult. 1)
4. $(x + 1)^3(x + 20)$ a. 4 b. –1 (mult. 3), –20 (mult. 1)
5. $(x + 2)^3(5x + 7)(x - 1)$ a. 5 b. –2 (mult. 3), $-\frac{7}{5}$ (mult. 1), 1 (mult. 1)
6. $(4x + 9)(x + 2)(x - 1)$ a. 3 b. $-\frac{9}{4}$, –2, 1 (all mult. 1)
7. $x^2(4x - 5)(x - 5)$ a. 4 b. 0 (mult. 2), $\frac{5}{4}$ (mult. 1), 5 (mult. 1)
8. $(x + 1)(x + 2)^{20}$ a. 21 b. –1 (mult. 1), –2 (mult. 20)

In 9–12, use a CAS to factor the polynomial a. over the real numbers, and b. over the complex numbers. c. List all zeros and their multiplicities.

9. $x^3 - 2x^2 - 21x - 18$
   a. $(x + 1)(x + 3)(x - 6)$
   b. $(x + 1)(x + 3)(x - 6)$
   c. –1, –3, 6 (all mult. 1)

10. $3x^2 + 2x + 8$
    a. $3x^2 + 2x + 8$
    b. $(3x + 1 - i\sqrt{23})(3x + 1 + i\sqrt{23})$
    c. $\frac{1 - i\sqrt{23}}{3}$, $\frac{1 + i\sqrt{23}}{3}$ (both mult. 1)

11. $x^4 + 6x^3 + 2x^2 - 42x - 63$
    a. $(x^2 - 7)(x + 3)^2$
    b. $(x - \sqrt{7})(x + \sqrt{7})(x + 3)^2$
    c. $\sqrt{7}$ (mult. 1), $-\sqrt{7}$ (mult. 1), –3 (mult. 2)

12. $x^5 - 2x^4 - 3x^3 + 6x^2 - 4x + 8$
    a. $(x - 2)^2(x + 2)(x^2 + 1)$
    b. $(x - 2)^2(x + 2)(x + i)(x - i)$
    c. 2 (mult. 2), –2 (mult. 1), i (mult. 1), $-i$ (mult. 1)

560 Advanced Algebra

Lesson

11-7

GOAL

Use finite differences to determine the degree of a polynomial that models a given set of data.

SPUR Objectives

D Determine an equation for a polynomial function from data points.

Materials/Resources

- Lesson Masters 11-7A and 11-7B
- Resource Masters 215 and 216

HOMEWORK

Suggestions for Assignment

- Questions 1–18
- Question 19 (extra credit)
- Reading Lesson 11-8
- Covering the Ideas 11-8

Local Standards

1 Warm-Up

In 1–3, the first two terms of a linear sequence are given. What are the next two terms? (This isn't as easy as it appears. Be careful!)

1. $\frac{1}{3}, \frac{1}{5}, \ldots$ $\frac{1}{15}, -\frac{1}{15}$
2. $\frac{6}{5}, \frac{7}{6}, \ldots$ $\frac{17}{15}, \frac{11}{10}$
3. $x, y, \ldots$ $2y - x, 3y - 2x$

Lesson

11-7 Finite Differences

Vocabulary

method of finite differences

BIG IDEA Given n points in the plane, no two of which have the same first coordinate, it is possible to determine whether there is a polynomial function of degree less than $n - 1$ that contains all the points.

Mental Math
a. $(c^7 + 10)(c^7 - 10)$
b. $(r - 5)^2$
c. $\pi x^3(x - 13)$
d. $(2p + 3q)^2$

Mental Math

Factor.

a. $c^{14} - 100$

b. $r^2 - 10r + 25$

c. $\pi x^4 - 13\pi x^3$

d. $4p^2 + 12pq + 9q^2$

When you find an equation of a line through two data points, you have an *exact model* for the data. When you find an equation for a regression line through a set of data points that are roughly linear, you have an *approximate model* for the data. Similarly, you can find exact and approximate quadratic and exponential models. This lesson is about finding exact polynomial models through data points.

Consider the data points and their scatterplot at the right. The graph looks like part of a parabola, perhaps with its vertex at the origin, so it is reasonable to think that a quadratic polynomial function models these data. But the graph also looks somewhat like an exponential function, translated down one unit.

s	0	10	20	30	40
d	0	8	33	75	134

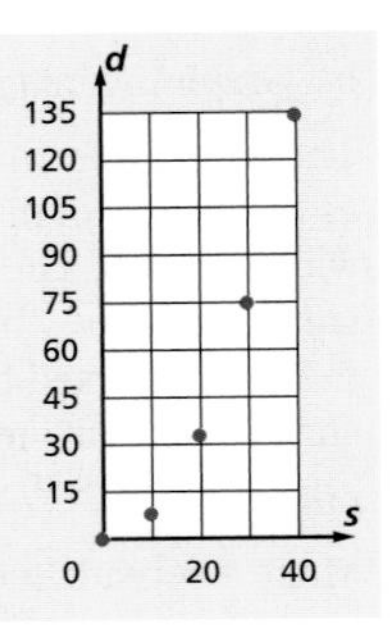

Differences between Values of Polynomial Functions

It is possible to determine that a quadratic function is an exact model for these data. The determination relies on finding differences between certain values of the function.

Consider the spreadsheet at the right. Columns A and B show values of x and y, respectively, for the linear function with equation $y = 2x + 7$ when $x = 1, 2, 3, 4, 5,$ and 6.

	A	B	C	D	E	F
◆		=2*a[]+7				
1	1	9				
2	2	11	2			
3	3	13	2			
4	4	15	2			
5	5	17	2			
6	6	19	2			

The values in the cells of column C are the differences between consecutive values in the cells of column B.

$$C2 = B2 - B1 = 11 - 9 = 2;$$
$$C3 = B3 - B2 = 13 - 11 = 2;$$
$$C4 = B4 - B3 = 15 - 13 = 2; \text{ and so on.}$$

Notice that all these differences are 2, which is the slope of the line with equation $y = 2x + 7$. So, the spreadsheet shows the constant increase of the linear polynomial $2x + 7$.

Background

If a function contains n points, no two of which are on the same vertical line, then there is *always* a polynomial function of degree at most $n - 1$ that contains them. Students have seen this when $n = 2$; there is a line through the two points. They may be surprised even by the case $n = 3$; there is a quadratic function containing any three points, no two of which are on the same vertical line. For $n = 4$, the pattern may even be more surprising; and so on.

Thus, if one knows the first four terms of a sequence, say 54, 50, 36, 18, ..., there is always an explicit polynomial formula of degree at most 3 that generates them. But, of course, that formula may not work for later terms of the sequence. To know for certain that the formula works for infinitely many values, one must be able to deduce that there is a polynomial formula for the sequence. That deduction is beyond the scope of this book. Some examples are in UCSMP *Precalculus and Discrete Mathematics,* which is meant to be studied two years after this course.

Activity 1

Step 1 a. Make a spreadsheet to show *x*- and *y*-values for the quadratic polynomial function with equation $y = 4x^2 - 5x - 3$, for $x = 1$ to 7. The first six rows of our spreadsheet are shown at the right.

b. Define a third column showing the difference between consecutive *y*-values.

c. Define a fourth column showing the difference between consecutive cells of the third column. a–c. See margin.

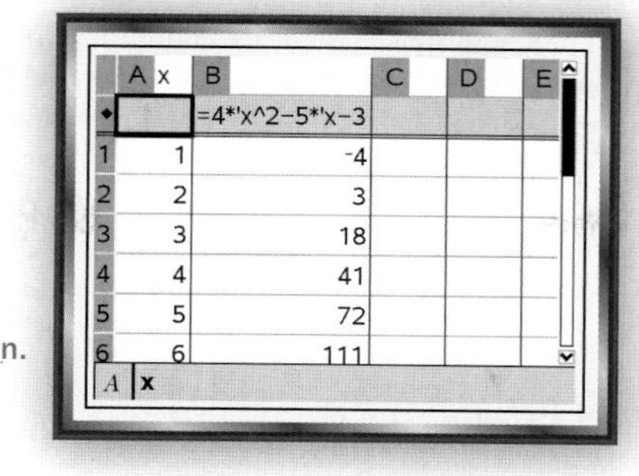

	A x	B	C	D	E
◆		=4*x^2-5*x-3			
1	1	-4			
2	2	3			
3	3	18			
4	4	41			
5	5	72			
6	6	111			

A | x

Step 2 a. Make another spreadsheet and repeat Step 1 for the cubic polynomial function with equation $y = x^3 - 3x^2 + 4x - 5$.

b. Define a fifth column that finds the difference between consecutive terms of the fourth column. a–b. See margin.

Step 3 Make a conjecture about what will happen if you calculate four consecutive sets of differences of *y*-values with $y = -2x^4 + 8x^3 + 11x^2 - 3x$ for $x = 1$ to 7.

Step 3. Answers vary. Sample: The fourth set of differences will all be the same.

The Polynomial-Difference Theorem

Activity 1 shows that if you evaluate a polynomial of degree *n* for consecutive integer values of *x* and take differences between consecutive *y*-values, then after *n* sets of differences you get a constant difference. You can see the results of the calculations for the polynomial of Step 3 at the right.

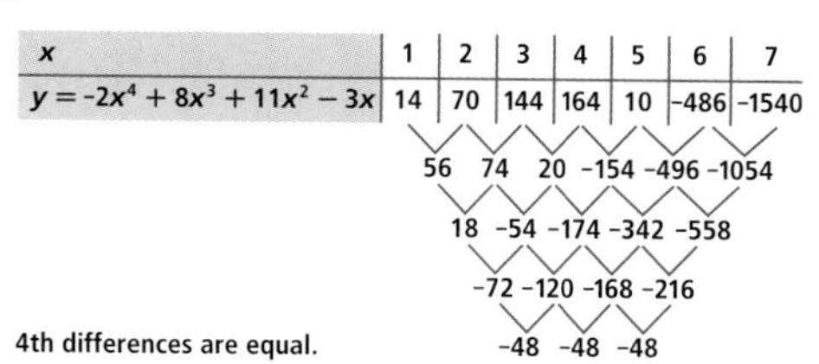

x	1	2	3	4	5	6	7
$y = -2x^4 + 8x^3 + 11x^2 - 3x$	14	70	144	164	10	-486	-1540

56 74 20 -154 -496 -1054

18 -54 -174 -342 -558

-72 -120 -168 -216

-48 -48 -48

4th differences are equal.

Consider again the linear function $y = 2x + 7$. Instead of using consecutive integers for *x*-values, use the arithmetic sequence -5, -1, 3, 7, 11, ...

x	-5	-1	3	7	11
$y = 2x + 7$	-3	5	13	21	29

1st differences 8 8 8 8

Again the 1st differences are equal. Each of these examples is an instance of the following theorem.

Polynomial-Difference Theorem

$y = f(x)$ is a polynomial function of degree *n* if and only if, for any set of *x*-values that form an arithmetic sequence, the *n*th differences of corresponding *y*-values are equal and the $(n - 1)$st differences are not equal.

2 Teaching

Notes on the Lesson

After completing Activity 1, students should be able to grasp the material in this lesson by reading it themselves. You may want to reserve some class time for them to do so before you discuss the material.

Point out that the Polynomial-Difference Theorem does not give a method for finding a specific formula, but it does let us know whether it is worth the time to look for such a formula.

Note-Taking Tips

Have students add to their journals the Polynomial-Difference Theorem.

Additional Answers

Activity 1

Step 1a–c.

	A x	B	C	D	E
◆		=4*x^2-5*x-3			
1	1	-4			
2	2	3	7		
3	3	18	15	8	
4	4	41	23	8	
5	5	72	31	8	
6	6	111	39	8	

D3 | =c3-c2

Step 2a–b.

	A x	B	C	D	E	F
◆		=x^3-				
1	1	-3				
2	2	-1	2			
3	3	7	8	6		
4	4	27	20	12	6	
5	5	65	38	18	6	
6	6	127	62	24	6	

E4 | =d4-d3

Finite differences are the discrete analogues to derivatives of continuous functions. Specifically, the Polynomial-Difference Theorem is the analogue of the fact that the *n*th derivative of a polynomial function of degree *n* is a constant. The property of $y = 3^x$ in Activity 2 is the analogue of the theorem that the derivative of an exponential function is also an exponential function.

Accommodating the Learner

Be sure that students realize that the process of finding finite differences is meaningful only if the *x*-values form an arithmetic, or linear, sequence. In other words, there must be a constant difference between successive *x*-values. Emphasize, however, that the values we test to find the differences are the *y*-values.

Additional Example

Example 1 Use the method of finite differences to determine the degree of the polynomial function mapping *a* onto *b*.

a	1	2	3	4	5	6
b	1	8	27	64	125	216

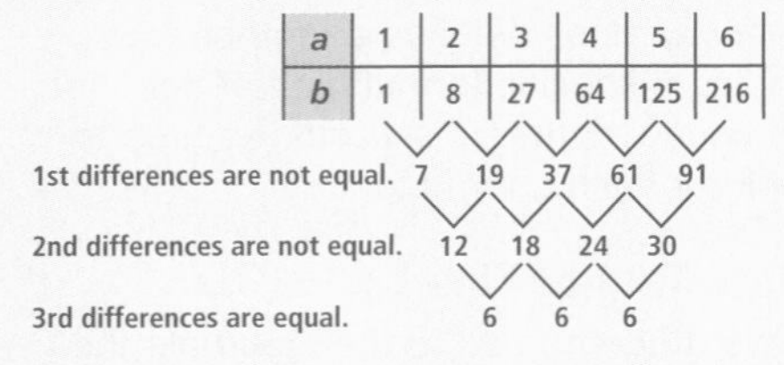

b is a 3rd-degree polynomial function of *a* because the third differences are equal.

Notes on the Lesson

The fact that a polynomial equation does not exist for certain data does not mean that no equation exists. The data could be described by a logarithmic, exponential, or trigonometric equation, a factorial function; or any number of other special functions or combinations thereof. In Activity 2, each sequence of differences is a multiple of the original sequence. This is a property of geometric sequences.

Example 2 There is no explicit polynomial formula for this sequence, but there is a simple exponential formula: For all *n*, $a_n = 2^{n+1} - 1$.

Additional Answers

Activity 2

Step 1

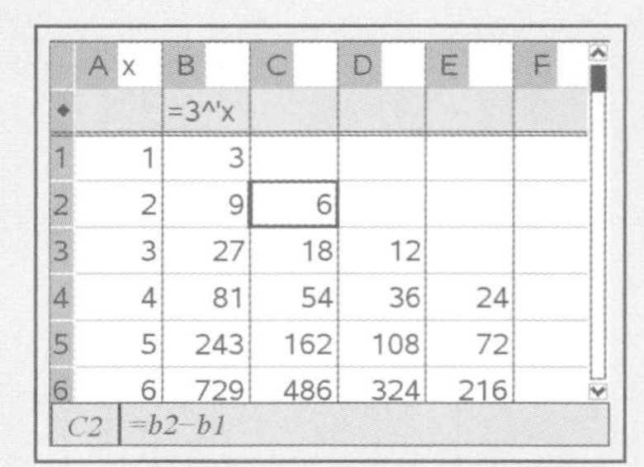

	A x	B	C	D	E	F
◆		=3^x				
1	1	3				
2	2	9	6			
3	3	27	18	12		
4	4	81	54	36	24	
5	5	243	162	108	72	
6	6	729	486	324	216	

C2 =b2–b1

The Polynomial-Difference Theorem provides a technique to determine whether a polynomial function of a particular degree can be an exact model for a set of points. The technique is called the **method of finite differences**. From a table of *y*-values corresponding to an arithmetic sequence of *x*-values, take differences of consecutive *y*-values and continue to take differences of the resulting *y*-value differences as needed. Only if those differences are eventually constant is the function a polynomial function, and the number of the differences indicates the polynomial function's degree.

Example 1

Consider the data from the beginning of the lesson. Use the method of finite differences to determine the degree of the polynomial function mapping *s* onto *d*.

Solution Notice that the values of the independent variable *s* form an arithmetic sequence, so the Polynomial-Difference Theorem applies. Calculate the differences.

s	0	10	20	30	40
d	0	8	33	75	134

1st differences are not equal. 8 25 42 59

2nd differences are equal. 17 17 17

d is a 2nd-degree polynomial function of s because the 2nd differences are equal.

The Polynomial-Difference Theorem does *not* generalize to nonpolynomial functions.

Activity 2

Step 1 Make a spreadsheet to show *x*- and *y*-values of $y = 3^x$ for $x = 1$ to 7. See margin.

Step 2 Analyze the data using the method of finite differences through at least 3rd differences. Describe what you observe.

Step 2. Answers vary. Sample: The method of finite differences does not produce a set of constant differences. Instead, the pattern of differences seems to repeat in each column.

Activity 2 shows that when the method of finite differences is used with functions other than polynomial functions, the differences do not become constant.

ENGLISH LEARNERS

Vocabulary Development

Stress that the Polynomial-Difference Theorem gives a technique to determine whether a polynomial function of a particular degree can be an exact model for a set of points. If the differences become constant after taking subsequent differences, there is a polynomial function that models the data whose degree is the number of the row of equal differences. The term *finite* in the phrase *method of finite differences* is descriptive of the method, as finite means "having a limit," and the limit in this case is the point at which the differences become constant. Contrast the term *finite* with the term *infinite,* or "limitless."

GUIDED

Example 2

Consider the sequence a defined by the recursive formula

$$\begin{cases} a_1 = 3 \\ a_n = 2a_{n-1} + 1, \text{ for integers } n \geq 2. \end{cases}$$

a. Identify the first seven terms of this sequence.

b. Use the method of finite difference to decide if there is an explicit polynomial formula for this sequence.

Solution

a. From the recursive definition, the sequence is 3, 7, __?__, __?__, __?__, __?__, ... 15; 31; 63; 127

b. Take differences between consecutive terms.

a_n	3	7	?	?	?	?
1st differences		4	8	?	?	?
2nd differences			4	8	?	?

The pattern of differences appears to repeat and (will/will not) eventually give constant differences. So, there (is/is not) an explicit __?__ formula for this sequence. will not; is not; polynomial

first row: 15; 31; 63; 127; second row: 16; 32; 64; third row: 16; 32

Questions

COVERING THE IDEAS

In 1 and 2, refer to Activity 1.

1. How many sets of differences did you need to take for the cubic function before the values were equal? 3
2. How many sets of differences would you need to take for the function with equation $y = 2x^2 + 3x^5 + x$? 5
3. If a set of x-values is an arithmetic sequence, the 11th differences of corresponding y-values are not all equal, but the 12th differences are equal, is y a polynomial function of x? If so, what is its degree? If not, why not? yes; 12
4. a. According to the Polynomial-Difference Theorem, how many sets of differences will it take to get equal differences when $y = 5x^7 - 4x^5 + 6x^2$? 7

   b. Check your answer to Part a by making a spreadsheet to calculate y and the finite differences for x = -2, -1, 0, 1, 2, 3, 4, and 5. See margin.
5. Tanner calculated three sets of finite differences for $y = x^2$ beginning with the table of values at the right. While Tanner knows this is a polynomial function, he did not get a constant set of differences. Explain why. See margin.

x	-3	0	1	4	5	7
y	9	0	1	16	25	49

Additional Example

Example 2 Consider the sequence a defined by the recursive formula

$$\begin{cases} a_1 = 4 \\ a_n = 2a_{n-1} - 1, \text{ for integers } n \geq 2 \end{cases}$$

a. Identify the first six terms of this sequence.

b. Use the method of finite differences to determine if there is an explicit polynomial formula for this sequence.

Solution

a. From the recursive definition, the sequence is 4, 7, __?__, __?__, __?__, __?__, ... 13; 25; 49; 97

b. Take differences between consecutive terms.

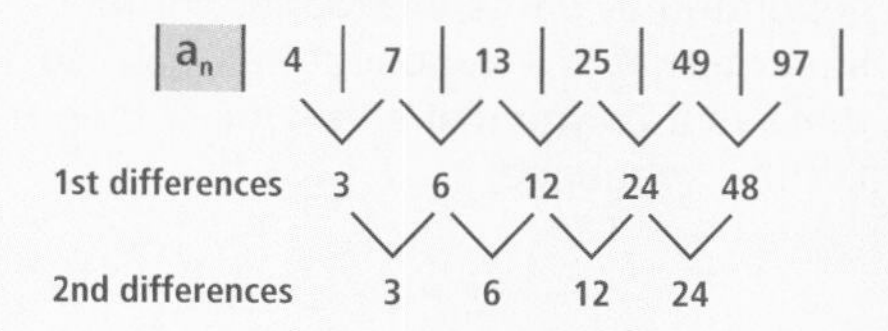

The pattern of differences appears to repeat and (will/will not) eventually give constant differences. So there (is/is not) an explicit __?__ formula for this sequence. will not; is not; polynomial

3 Assignment

Recommended Assignment

- Questions 1–18
- Question 19 (extra credit)
- Reading Lesson 11-8
- Covering the Ideas 11-8

Notes on the Questions

Question 5 Do not skip this basic question.

Accommodating the Learner

Give students the following pattern:

$f(1) = 1^3 = 1$

$f(2) = 1^3 + 2^3 = 9$

$f(3) = 1^3 + 2^3 + 3^3 = 36$

$f(4) = 1^3 + 2^3 + 3^3 + 4^3 = 100$

Have them find $f(5)$, $f(6)$, and $f(7)$. Then have them use the Polynomial-Difference Theorem to determine the degree of $f(n)$. $f(5) = 225$; $f(6) = 441$; $f(7) = 784$; the degree of $f(n)$ is 4.

Additional Answers

4b.

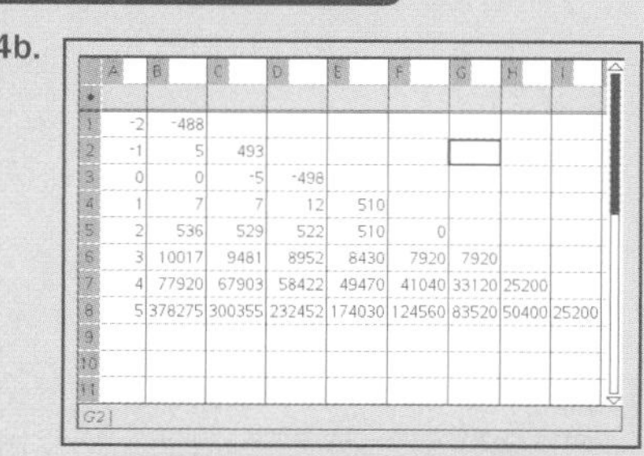

	A	B	C	D	E	F	G	H	I
1	-2	-488							
2	-1	5	493						
3	0	0	-5	-498					
4	1	7	7	12	510				
5	2	536	529	522	510	0			
6	3	10017	9481	8952	8430	7920	7920		
7	4	77920	67903	58422	49470	41040	33120	25200	
8	5	378275	300355	232452	174030	124560	83520	50400	25200
9									
10									
11									

G2

5. Tanner is not using x-values that form an arithmetic sequence.

Notes on the Questions

Questions 7 and 8 We have to limit the degree of the polynomial because if enough differences are taken from a finite set, then there will be a time when there is only one difference, and so all differences will be equal. Thus, there is a polynomial in *x* equal to *y* in both cases, but here we are not interested in polynomials of degree 9 or 10 fitting these data.

Question 9 In general, when a sequence is generated by sums of products of *n* linear terms, there is a polynomial of degree $n + 1$ that fits the sequence. The analogy is that the *n*th derivative of a polynomial function of degree $n + 1$ is constant.

Question 10 Here the sequence is generated by sums of products of four linear terms (the exponent being 4), so there is a polynomial of degree 5 that fits the sequence.

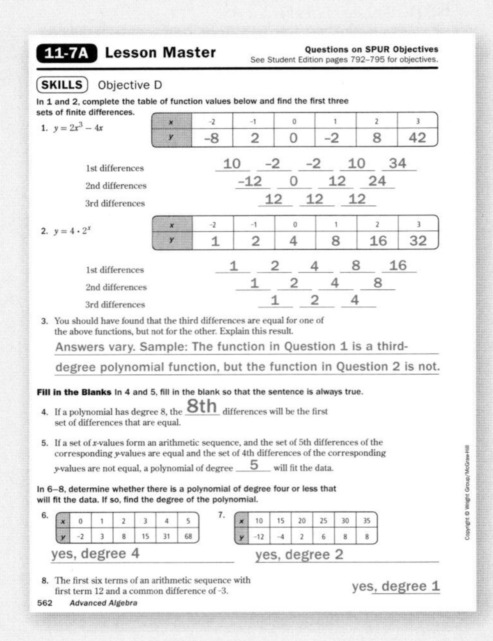

11-7A Lesson Master — Questions on SPUR Objectives. See Student Edition pages 792–795 for objectives.

SKILLS Objective D

In 1 and 2, complete the table of function values below and find the first three sets of finite differences.

1. $y = 2x^3 - 4x$

x	-2	-1	0	1	2	3
y	-8	2	0	-2	8	42

1st differences: 10, -2, -2, 10, 34
2nd differences: -12, 0, 12, 24
3rd differences: 12, 12, 12

2. $y = 4 \cdot 2^x$

x	-2	-1	0	1	2	3
y	1	2	4	8	16	32

1st differences: 1, 2, 4, 8, 16
2nd differences: 1, 2, 4, 8
3rd differences: 1, 2, 4

3. You should have found that the third differences are equal for one of the above functions, but not for the other. Explain this result. Answers vary. Sample: The function in Question 1 is a third-degree polynomial function, but the function in Question 2 is not.

Fill in the Blanks In 4 and 5, fill in the blank so that the sentence is always true.

4. If a polynomial has degree 8, the 8th differences will be the first set of differences that are equal.

5. If a set of *x*-values form an arithmetic sequence, and the set of 5th differences of the corresponding *y*-values are equal and the set of 4th differences of the corresponding *y*-values are not equal, a polynomial of degree 5 will fit the data.

In 6–8, determine whether there is a polynomial of degree four or less that will fit the data. If so, find the degree of the polynomial.

6.

x	0	1	2	3	4	5
y	-2	3	8	15	31	68

yes, degree 4

7.

x	10	15	20	25	30	35
y	-12	-4	2	6	8	8

yes, degree 2

8. The first six terms of an arithmetic sequence with first term 12 and a common difference of -3. yes, degree 1

562 *Advanced Algebra*

6. Consider the sequence $\begin{cases} a_1 = 0.3 \\ a_n = a_{n-1} - 1 \text{ for integers } n \geq 2 \end{cases}$.
   a. Generate the first seven terms of the given sequence.
   b. Tell whether the sequence can be described explicitly by a polynomial function of degree less than 4.

6a. 0.3, -0.7, -1.7, -2.7, -3.7, -4.7, -5.7

6b. Yes; the sequence can be described explicitly by a linear polynomial function.

In 7 and 8, use the data points listed in the table.
   a. Determine if *y* is a polynomial function of *x* of degree ≤ 5.
   b. If the function is a polynomial, state its degree.

7.

x	-3	-2	-1	0	1	2	3	4	5
y	67.5	16	1.5	0	-0.5	0	13.5	64	187.5

7a. yes

7b. 4

8.

x	0	1	2	3	4	5	6	7	8	9
y	1	1	0	-1	0	7	28	79	192	431

8a. no

8b. not a polynomial

APPLYING THE MATHEMATICS

9. Consider the following sequence of sums of products of three consecutive integers.
   $f(1) = 1 \cdot 2 \cdot 3 = 6$
   $f(2) = 1 \cdot 2 \cdot 3 + 2 \cdot 3 \cdot 4 = 30$
   $f(3) = 1 \cdot 2 \cdot 3 + 2 \cdot 3 \cdot 4 + 3 \cdot 4 \cdot 5 = 90$
   $f(4) = 1 \cdot 2 \cdot 3 + 2 \cdot 3 \cdot 4 + 3 \cdot 4 \cdot 5 + 4 \cdot 5 \cdot 6 = 210$
   $f(5) = 1 \cdot 2 \cdot 3 + 2 \cdot 3 \cdot 4 + 3 \cdot 4 \cdot 5 + 4 \cdot 5 \cdot 6 + 5 \cdot 6 \cdot 7 = 420$
   $f(6) = 1 \cdot 2 \cdot 3 + 2 \cdot 3 \cdot 4 + 3 \cdot 4 \cdot 5 + 4 \cdot 5 \cdot 6 + 5 \cdot 6 \cdot 7 + 6 \cdot 7 \cdot 8 = 756$
   $f(7) = 1 \cdot 2 \cdot 3 + 2 \cdot 3 \cdot 4 + 3 \cdot 4 \cdot 5 + 4 \cdot 5 \cdot 6 + 5 \cdot 6 \cdot 7 + 6 \cdot 7 \cdot 8 + 7 \cdot 8 \cdot 9 = 1260$
   Determine whether or not there is a polynomial function *f* of degree less than 5 that models these data exactly. yes (degree = 4)

10. Let $f(n)$ = the sum of the 4th powers of the integers from 1 to *n*.
   $f(1) = 1^4 = 1$
   $f(2) = 1^4 + 2^4 = 17$
   $f(3) = 1^4 + 2^4 + 3^4 = 98$
   $f(4) = 1^4 + 2^4 + 3^4 + 4^4 = 354$, and so on.
   a. Find $f(5), f(6), f(7)$, and $f(8)$. 979, 2275, 4676, 8772
   b. According to the Polynomial-Difference Theorem, what is the degree of the polynomial $f(n)$? 5

11a. *b*; $m + b$; $2m + b$; $3m + b$; $4m + b$

11b. *m*, *m*, *m*, *m*; this is a linear function, thus, it has degree 1 and its first differences are equal.

11. a. Fill in the table of values for the linear function with equation $y = mx + b$.
   b. Find the first differences for the table in Part a and explain your results.

x	0	1	2	3	4
y	?	?	?	?	?

12. If the second differences for $y = kx^2$ all equal $\frac{2}{9}$, what is the value of *k*? $k = \frac{1}{9}$

REVIEW

13. Consider the function f with equation $f(x) = 3x^4 - 10x^2 - 8x + 10$. **(Lessons 11-6, 11-5)**
   a. How many roots does $f(x)$ have? Justify your answer.
   b. According to the Rational-Root Theorem, what are the possible rational roots?
   c. Find all roots of $f(x)$. Write all rational roots as fractions. Approximate all irrational roots to the nearest hundredth.

14. Find all the roots of $z^4 - 1 = 0$ by factoring and using the Zero-Product Theorem. **(Lessons 11-6, 11-3)**

15. Let $P(x) = (x - 1)(-x^2 + 3x + 3)$.
   a. Rewrite $P(x)$ in standard form. $P(x) = -x^3 + 4x^2 - 3$
   b. How many x-intercepts does the graph of $y = P(x)$ have? Find the exact value of the largest of these. **(Lessons 11-4, 11-1, 6-7)**

13a. 4 by the Number of Roots of a Polynomial Equation theorem.

13b. $\pm1, \pm2, \pm5, \pm10, \pm\frac{1}{3}, \pm\frac{2}{3}, \pm\frac{5}{3}, \pm\frac{10}{3}$

13c. $x \approx -1.33 + 0.78i$, $x \approx -1.33 - 0.78i$, $x \approx 0.71$, $x \approx 1.96$

14. $z = -1$, $z = 1$, $z = i$, or $z = -i$

15b. 3; $\frac{\sqrt{21} + 3}{2}$

16. Refer to the figure at the right. A boat sails 20 miles from A to B, then turns 175° as indicated and sails 12 miles to point C. How far is A from C? **(Lesson 10-8, Previous Course)** about 8.1 mi

17. Solve the system $\begin{cases} 4x - 2y + 3z = 1 \\ 8x - 3y + 5z = 4 \\ 7x - 2y + 4z = 5 \end{cases}$ using matrices. **(Lesson 5-6)** See margin.

18. **Multiple Choice** Determine which equation describes the relationships graphed below, where k is a constant. **(Lesson 2-8)** C

z, w constant

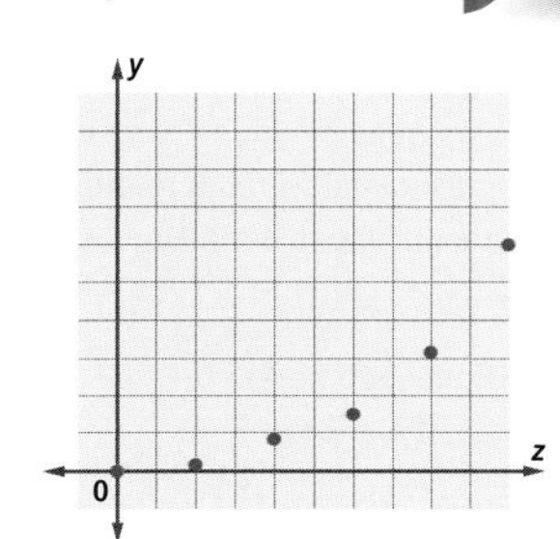

w, x constant

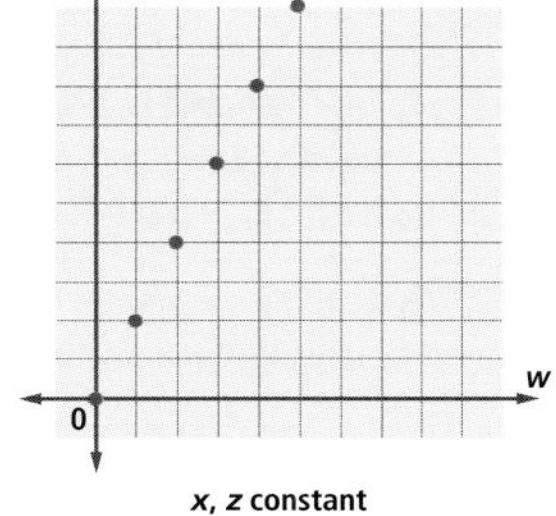

x, z constant

A $y = \frac{kwz}{x^2}$ B $y = kwxz$ C $y = \frac{kwz^2}{x}$ D $y = \frac{kwx^2}{z}$

EXPLORATION

19. Find a sequence for which the 3rd differences are all 30.
Answers vary. Sample: $a_n = 5n^3 + 30$

Additional Answers

17. $\text{solve}\left(\begin{bmatrix} 4 & -2 & 3 \\ 8 & -3 & 5 \\ 7 & -2 & 4 \end{bmatrix} \cdot \begin{bmatrix} x \\ y \\ z \end{bmatrix} = \begin{bmatrix} 1 \\ 4 \\ 5 \end{bmatrix}, x, y, z\right)$
$x=1$ and $y=3$ and $z=1$

Notes on the Questions

Question 17 This question reviews solving a simple 3 × 3 system in preparation for Lesson 11-8.

4 Wrap-Up

Ongoing Assessment

Have students work in pairs. Have each student write a second-, third-, or fourth-degree equation giving y in terms of x. On a separate sheet of paper, have them make a table and assign values to x from 1 through 5 and find the corresponding y-values for their equations. Finally, have students exchange tables and determine the degree of their partner's original equation. Students should determine the degree of an equation from data points.

Project Update

Project 3, *Sums of Products,* on page 786 relates to the content of this lesson.

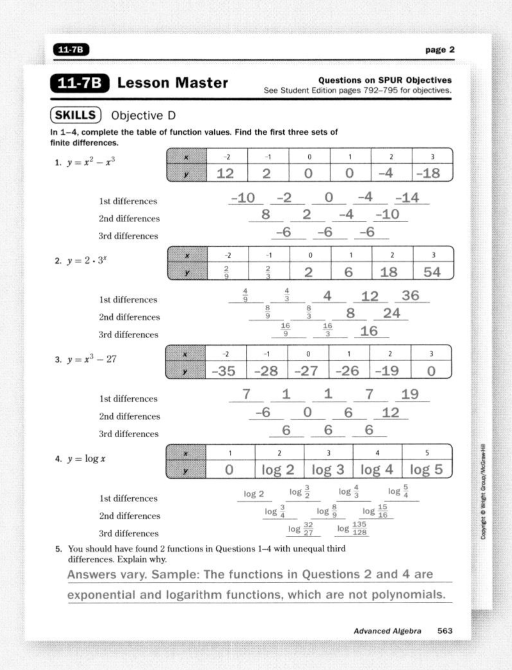

11-7B page 2

11-7B Lesson Master

Questions on SPUR Objectives
See Student Edition pages 792–795 for objectives.

SKILLS Objective D

In 1–4, complete the table of function values. Find the first three sets of finite differences.

1. $y = x^2 - x^3$

x	-2	-1	0	1	2	3
y	12	2	0	0	-4	-18

1st differences: -10, -2, 0, -4, -14
2nd differences: 8, 2, -4, -10
3rd differences: -6, -6, -6

2. $y = 2 \cdot 3^x$

x	-2	-1	0	1	2	3
y	$\frac{2}{9}$	$\frac{2}{3}$	2	6	18	54

1st differences: $\frac{4}{9}$, $\frac{4}{3}$, 4, 12, 36
2nd differences: $\frac{8}{9}$, $\frac{8}{3}$, 8, 24
3rd differences: $\frac{16}{9}$, $\frac{16}{3}$, 16

3. $y = x^3 - 27$

x	-2	-1	0	1	2	3
y	-35	-28	-27	-26	-19	0

1st differences: 7, 1, 1, 7, 19
2nd differences: -6, 0, 6, 12
3rd differences: 6, 6, 6

4. $y = \log x$

x	1	2	3	4	5
y	0	log 2	log 3	log 4	log 5

1st differences: $\log 2$, $\log \frac{3}{2}$, $\log \frac{4}{3}$, $\log \frac{5}{4}$
2nd differences: $\log \frac{3}{4}$, $\log \frac{8}{9}$, $\log \frac{15}{16}$
3rd differences: $\log \frac{32}{27}$, $\log \frac{135}{128}$

5. You should have found 2 functions in Questions 1–4 with unequal third differences. Explain why.
Answers vary. Sample: The functions in Questions 2 and 4 are exponential and logarithm functions, which are not polynomials.

Advanced Algebra 563

Lesson 11-8

GOAL

Determine the degree of the polynomial needed to model given data (if any); use algebraic techniques to find the coefficients of the polynomial and so find the formula itself.

SPUR Objectives

D Determine an equation for a polynomial function from data points.

H Use polynomials to model real-world situations.

Materials/Resources

- Lesson Masters 11-8A and 11-8B
- Resource Masters 217–220

HOMEWORK

Suggestions for Assignment

- Questions 1–20
- Question 21 (extra credit)
- Self-Test

Local Standards

1 Warm-Up

Find the equation of the form $y = mx + b$ for the line through the points (5, 9) and (11, 7) by substituting the coordinates of each point into the equation $y = mx + b$ and solving the system of equations for m and b. $y = -\frac{1}{3}x + \frac{32}{3}$

Lesson 11-8 Modeling Data with Polynomials

BIG IDEA Given n points in the plane, no two of which have the same first coordinate, it is generally possible to find an equation for a polynomial function that contains all the points.

In Lesson 11-7, you saw how to determine whether a polynomial formula exists for a given function. Now, if the formula exists, you will see how to find the coefficients of the polynomial.

Mental Math

Consider the equation $x^2 + bx + 4 = 0$. Give a value of b so that

a. the equation has no real roots.

b. the equation has two irrational roots.

c. the equation has two different rational roots.

d. the equation has a double root.

a. Answers vary. Sample: 2

b. Answers vary. Sample: −8

c. 5 or −5

d. 4 or −4

Example 1

In the land of Connectica, it was deemed that all cities built must be joined to every other city directly by a straight road. When the land was first developed, there were three cities and only three roads were needed. After a few years there were more cities and the government found itself having to build more and more roads.

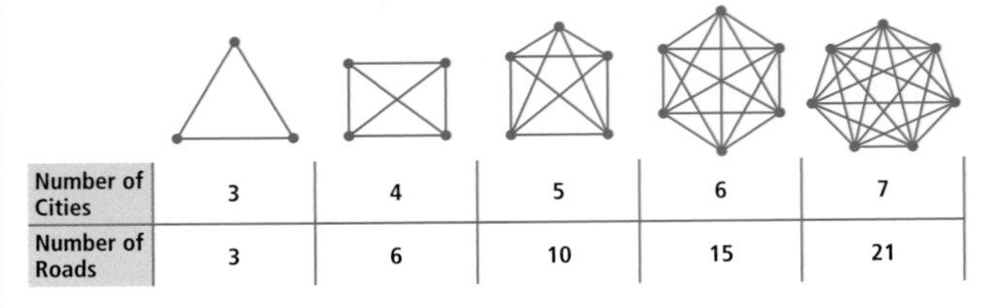

Number of Cities	3	4	5	6	7
Number of Roads	3	6	10	15	21

The city planners wondered if there is a polynomial formula relating r, the number of roads needed, with x, the number of cities built. Does such a formula exist? If so, find the formula.

Solution Use the method of finite differences to determine the degree of a polynomial that will fit the data, if it exists.

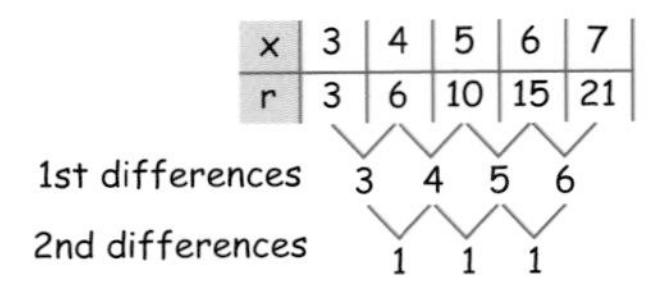

Because the 2nd differences are equal, there is a quadratic polynomial that is an exact model for these five data points. That is,

$$r = ax^2 + bx + c.$$

Background

This lesson is enjoyable for most students. They are able to use skills that they have learned in other lessons (finding finite differences, solving systems of equations, and writing formulas) to solve problems that involve interesting applications. Obtaining a formula that works is a good feeling.

Examples 1 and 2 Here students need to solve a 3×3 or 4×4 system of equations to find the coefficients. We use inverse matrices to solve the systems. There are at least three other ways: by hand, using the solve command with technology, and using polynomial regression. A by-hand solution for Example 1 is requested in Question 9.

Now you need to find values of the coefficients a, b, and c. As in Lesson 6-6, we find a, b, and c by solving a system of equations.

First, substitute three known ordered pairs (x, r) into the above equation. We choose (3, 3), (4, 6), and (5, 10).

Substitute the ordered pairs into the equation to get the following system.

$$\begin{cases} 3 = a \cdot 3^2 + b \cdot 3 + c \\ 6 = a \cdot 4^2 + b \cdot 4 + c \\ 10 = a \cdot 5^2 + b \cdot 5 + c \end{cases}$$

You may solve this system by using linear combinations or by using matrices. Our matrix solution is shown below. You see that $a = \frac{1}{2}$, $b = -\frac{1}{2}$, and $c = 0$. So, $r = \frac{1}{2}x^2 - \frac{1}{2}x$ models the data from the city planners.

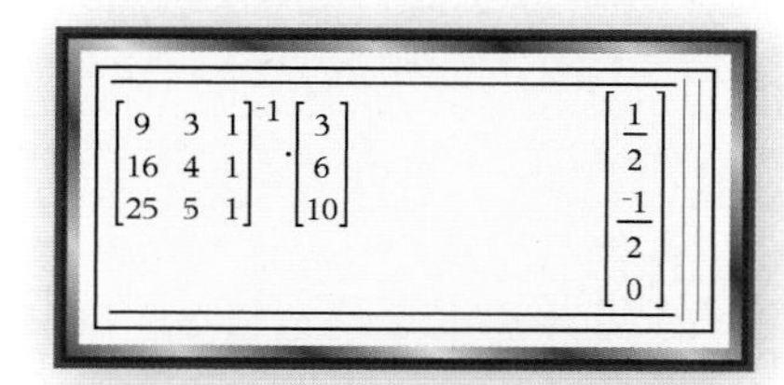

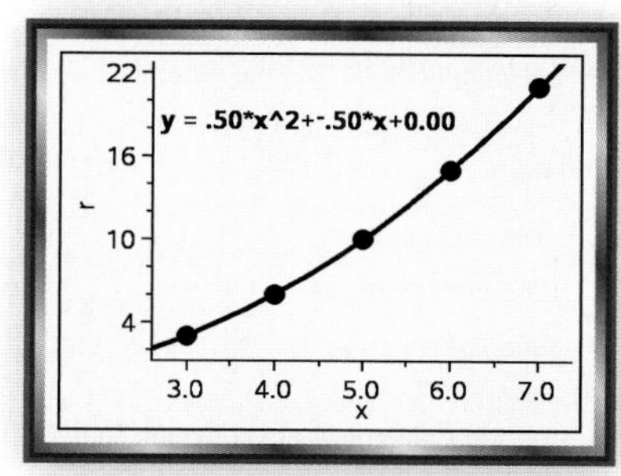

Check Enter the data into a CAS and run a quadratic regression. We obtain the results at the right. It checks.

STOP QY1

▸ **QY1**

How many roads would be needed for 10 cities in Connectica?

Finding Higher-Degree Polynomials

The idea of Example 1 can be used to find a polynomial function of degree greater than 2 that exactly fits some data. Consider the sequence of squares shown on the next page.

Let S be the total number of squares of any size that can be found on an n-by-n checkerboard.

For example, on the 3-by-3 checkerboard there are:

9 squares this size: □, 4 squares this size: ⊞, and 1 square this size: ▦.

So, when $n = 3$, $S = 9 + 4 + 1 = 14$. There are 14 squares on a 3×3 board. The numbers of squares for $n = 1$ through 6 are given on the next page.

Accommodating the Learner

Some students will not immediately see how we found the system of equations in Example 1. Remind them that the values in the table form a set of ordered pairs of the form (x, r), where x is the number of cities built, and r is the number of roads needed. In Example 2, the values in the table form a set of ordered pairs of the form (n, S), where n is the number of squares along one side, and S is the total number of squares. Review how to find differences and then write the corresponding equations using the variables a, b, c, and d.

2 Teaching

Notes on the Lesson

Example 1 Question 9 involves solving this system by hand. Solving a 3×3 system by hand can be tedious, but if the substituted domain values are consecutive terms of an arithmetic sequence, the system can be solved by repeatedly subtracting equations from each other. Here is a paper-and-pencil way to solve this system. The system itself is found as shown in the text. Each equation in the next system is found by subtracting an equation from the equation immediately above it. We recommend that students' work look something like this:

$$\begin{cases} 9a + 3b + c = 3 \\ 16a + 4b + c = 6 \\ 25a + 5b + c = 10 \end{cases} \Rightarrow \begin{cases} 7a + b = 3 \\ 9a + b = 4 \end{cases}$$
$$\Rightarrow 2a = 1 \Rightarrow a = 0.5.$$

Substitute $a = 0.5$ into $7a + b = 3$ to get $3.5 + b = 3$, so $b = -0.5$. Substitute for a and b in $9a + 3b + c = 3$ to get $4.5 - 1.5 + c = 3$, so $c = 0$. This is the same solution as given by matrices.

Additional Example

Example 1 Square tiles are used to construct a square patio, as shown below. Find the polynomial function that relates the total number t of tiles to the number r of rings. Let the center tile be ring 1.

4	4	4	4	4	4	4
4	3	3	3	3	3	4
4	3	2	2	2	3	4
4	3	2	1	2	3	4
4	3	2	2	2	3	4
4	3	3	3	3	3	4
4	4	4	4	4	4	4

Generate a table of values for the function and use the method of finite differences.

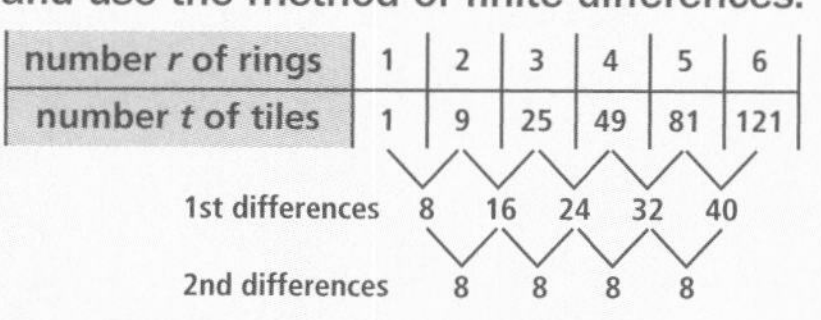

number r of rings	1	2	3	4	5	6
number t of tiles	1	9	25	49	81	121

1st differences: 8, 16, 24, 32, 40

2nd differences: 8, 8, 8, 8

Second differences are constant, so the quadratic polynomial $t = ar^2 + br + c$ models this situation. Substitute three known ordered pairs, (1, 1), (2, 9), and (3, 25) into the equation:

$$\begin{cases} 1 = a \cdot 1^2 + b \cdot 1 + c \\ 9 = a \cdot 2^2 + b \cdot 2 + c. \\ 25 = a \cdot 3^2 + b \cdot 3 + c \end{cases}$$

Use linear combinations to solve for a, b, and c: $a = 4$, $b = -4$, $c = 1$. So, $t = 4r^2 - 4r + 1$.

Additional Example

Example 2 A sculpture is to be placed on a concrete structure formed of square prisms as shown. Each prism is 0.5 foot high. The top prism is a square 2 feet on a side, the next larger prism is 4 feet on a side, the third prism is 6 feet on a side, and so on. Find the *total* volume V of concrete needed for n prisms.

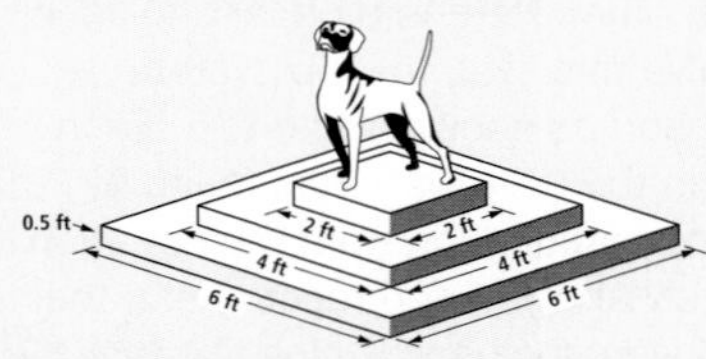

Solution Find the total volume for 1–6 prisms. Then use the method of finite differences to determine whether a polynomial model fits the data. (See below right for table.)

The third differences are equal, so the data can be represented by a polynomial function of degree __?__. 3 Now use a system of equations to find a polynomial model of the form $V = an^3 + bn^2 + cn + d$. Substitute $n = 4$, 3, 2, and 1 and the corresponding values of V into the equation and solve the resulting system.

$$\begin{cases} 60 = a(4)^3 + b(4)^2 + c(4) + d \\ 28 = a(3)^3 + b(3)^2 + c(3) + d \\ 10 = a(2)^3 + b(2)^2 + c(2) + d \\ 2 = a(1)^3 + b(1)^2 + c(1) + d \end{cases}$$

So $a =$ __?__, $b =$ __?__, $c =$ __?__, and $d =$ __?__. $\frac{2}{3}$; 1; $\frac{1}{3}$; 0 A formula for V in terms of n is $V =$ __?__. $\frac{2}{3}n^3 + n^2 + \frac{1}{3n}$ You can check by using cubic regression.

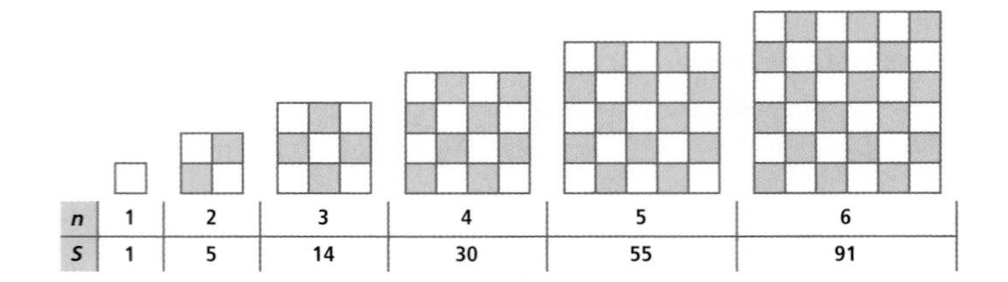

n	1	2	3	4	5	6
S	1	5	14	30	55	91

GUIDED

Example 2

How many squares are on an $n \times n$ checkerboard?

Solution First, use the method of finite differences to determine whether a polynomial model fits the data.

n	1		2		3		4		5		6
S	1		5		14		30		55		91
1st differences		4		?		?		?		?	
2nd differences			?		?		?		?		
3rd differences				?		?		?			

9; 16; 25; 36
5; 7; 9; 11
2; 2; 2

The 3rd differences are constant. Therefore, the data can be modeled by a polynomial function of degree __?__. 3

Now use a system of equations to find a polynomial model. You know that the polynomial is of the form $S = an^3 + bn^2 + cn + d$. Substitute $n = 4$, 3, 2, then 1 and the corresponding values of S into the equation and solve the resulting system.

$$\begin{cases} 30 = a(4)^3 + b(4)^2 + c(4) + d \\ 14 = a(3)^3 + b(3)^2 + c(3) + d \\ 5 = a(2)^3 + b(2)^2 + c(2) + d \\ 1 = a(1)^3 + b(1)^2 + c(1) + d \end{cases}$$

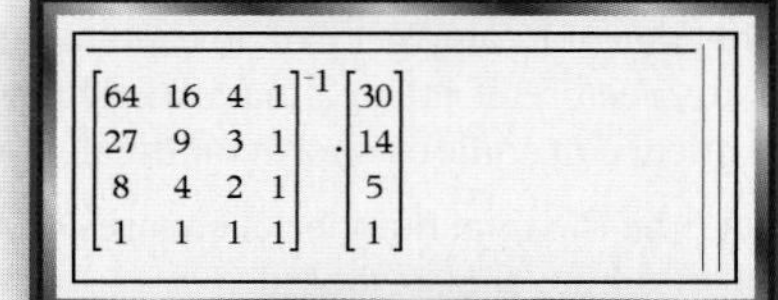

Thus, $a =$ __?__, $b =$ __?__, $c =$ __?__, and $d =$ __?__. $\frac{1}{3}$; $\frac{1}{2}$; $\frac{1}{6}$; 0

So, a formula for S in terms of n is $S =$ __?__. $\frac{1}{3}n^3 + \frac{1}{2}n^2 + \frac{1}{6}n$

Check Use *cubic regression* on a CAS to find the model.

n	1		2		3		4		5		6
V	2		10		28		60		110		182
1st differences		8		18		32		50		72	
2nd differences			10		14		18		22		
3rd differences				4		4		4			

Modeling a Finite Set of Points

In Examples 1 and 2, you were asked to find a polynomial function model that related two variables, and in each case the independent variable could take on an infinite number of values. Consequently, you need a way to prove that the polynomial function works for all values. Sometimes you can appeal to the definition of the function (see Question 10). At other times you may need to use methods beyond the scope of this course.

Year	Population
1900	1,850,000
1920	2,284,000
1940	1,890,000
1960	1,698,000
1980	1,428,000
2000	1,537,000

However, when you need a model only to fit a finite number of values in a function, you can always find a polynomial model. Such a model exists even when the data do not follow a simple pattern.

The population of Manhattan Island (part of New York City) has gone up and down over the past 100 years. At the right are a table and a graph showing the population every 20 years from 1900 to 2000.

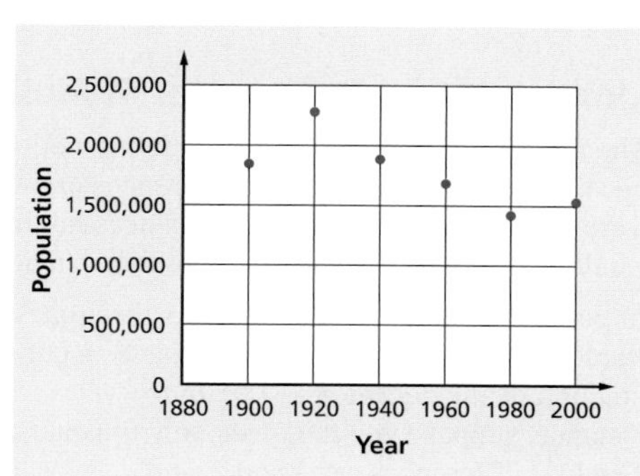

Let x = the number of 20-year periods since 1900. Let $P(x)$ be the population (in millions) of Manhattan at these times. Here is how to find a polynomial expression for $P(x)$ that contains the six points in the table.

Use the methods of Examples 1 and 2 and find 1st, 2nd, 3rd, 4th, and 5th differences. When you reach the 5th differences, there is only one value. So all the 5th differences are equal! Consequently, by the Polynomial-Difference Theorem, *for these six points* there is a polynomial of degree 5 that fits:

$$P(x) = ax^5 + bx^4 + cx^3 + dx^2 + ex + f.$$

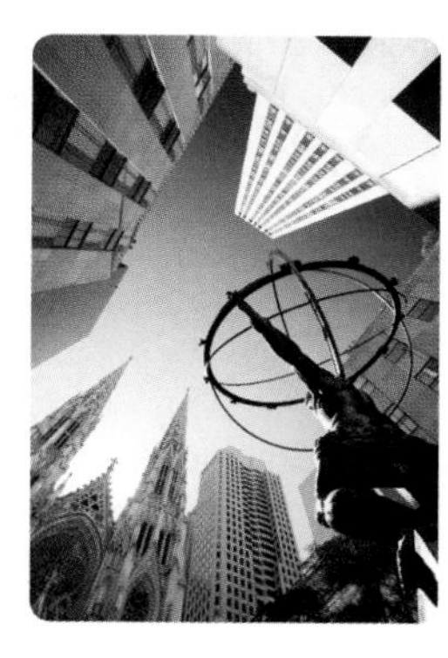

To find a, b, c, d, e, and f, you need to solve a system of six linear equations in six variables. These equations arise from the six given data points. For instance, for the year 1940, $x = 2$, the number of 20-year periods since 1900, and $P(x) = 1.890$, the population of Manhattan in millions. Substituting 2 for x in the general formula above,

$$P(2) = 1.89 = a \cdot 2^5 + b \cdot 2^4 + c \cdot 2^3 + d \cdot 2^2 + e \cdot 2 + f$$
$$= 32a + 16b + 8c + 4d + 2e + f.$$

Similarly, you can find the other five equations. When the system is solved, it turns out that, to four decimal places, $a = 0.0171$, $b = -0.2252$, $c = 1.0962$, $d = -2.3823$, $e = 1.9282$, and $f = 1.85$. So,

$P(x) = 0.0171x^5 - 0.2252x^4 + 1.0962x^3 - 2.3823x^2 + 1.9282x + 1.85.$

Notes on the Lesson

Example 2 Challenge students to solve a system of four equations with four variables by using the method shown in the Notes on the Lesson for Example 1. The computations are less difficult than they appear.

$$\begin{cases} 64a + 16b + 4c + d = 30 \\ 27a + 9b + 3c + d = 14 \\ 8a + 4b + 2c + d = 5 \\ a + b + c + d = 1 \end{cases}$$
$$\Rightarrow \begin{cases} 37a + 7b + c = 16 \\ 19a + 5b + c = 9 \\ 7a + 3b + c = 4 \end{cases}$$
$$\Rightarrow \begin{cases} 18a + 2b = 7 \\ 12a + 2b = 5 \end{cases}$$
$$\Rightarrow 6a = 2 \Rightarrow a = \frac{1}{3}$$

By substituting back, the other values can be found. This becomes the more difficult part of the solution. Point out that it is always advisable to check additional data points in the formula that is obtained to be certain that it is correct.

Extension

Have students look up the population of your city or state in each of the last five years. Tell them to use the earlier four data points to generate a polynomial model for the data and then use the model to predict the population for the latest year. Then have them find a model using the first two data points and the last two data points and use the model to predict the population for the middle year. Ask: How close is each prediction? Which prediction is more accurate? What does this tell you about polynomial models? Answers vary. Check students' work. The prediction for the middle year should be more accurate than the prediction for the final year because polynomial models are better tools for interpolating between points than for extrapolating outside points.

Notes on the Lesson

Limitations of polynomial modeling
Because a polynomial function can be fit through any set of n points with no two on the same vertical line, it is important to distinguish between a polynomial function that fits only the particular given data points given and a polynomial function that has predictive ability. It is important to have some reason that the type of function model is reasonable so that it can be used for predictions.

Unfortunately, polynomial regression on most calculators stops at a 4th-degree polynomial. But some computer spreadsheets and data-analysis applications allow you to find regression equations to 5th and higher degrees. We found the equation for $P(x)$ using a spreadsheet. Although this polynomial model fits the data, because the decimal coefficients are rounded, evaluating the polynomial $P(x)$ will not produce exact populations.

 QY2

In general, if you have n points of a function, there exists a polynomial formula of some degree less than n that models those n points exactly.

▶ **QY2**
Substitute 3 for x in the formula for the population of Manhattan.
What year's population of Manhattan should you obtain?
How close is your result to that year's population?

Limitations of Polynomial Modeling

The model for Manhattan's population is a 5th-degree polynomial because you could take finite differences only five times. If there were more data, then the 5th differences might not be equal and you would need a larger degree polynomial to fit all the points.

In general, if you have n data points through which you want to fit a polynomial function exactly, a polynomial function of any degree $n - 1$ *or more* will work. For instance, suppose you are given only the data at the right. The first differences are 1 and 2, and there is only one 2nd difference. So, there is a quadratic function that fits the data. That function has the formula $y = \frac{x^2 - x + 2}{2}$. If (4, 7) and (5, 11) are two more given data points, then the second differences are still equal and the same formula models all the data.

x	1		2		3
y	1		2		4
1st differences		1		2	
2nd difference			1		

x	1		2		3		4		5
y	1		2		4		7		11
1st differences		1		2		3		4	
2nd differences			1		1		1		

However, if (4, 8) and (5, 15) are the next data points, then the second differences are no longer equal. The 3rd differences are equal, so there is a 3rd-degree polynomial equation modeling the data: $y = \frac{x^3 - 3x^2 + 8x}{6}$.

x	1		2		3		4		5
y	1		2		4		8		15
1st differences		1		2		4		7	
2nd differences			1		2		3		
3rd differences				1		1			

In this way, you can see that $y = \frac{x^2 - x + 2}{2}$ and $y = \frac{x^3 - 3x^2 + 8x}{6}$ are only two of many polynomial formulas fitting the original three data points (1, 1), (2, 2), and (3, 4).

Accommodating the Learner

Give pairs of students these diagrams of the first three pentagonal numbers. Then have them complete steps a–c.

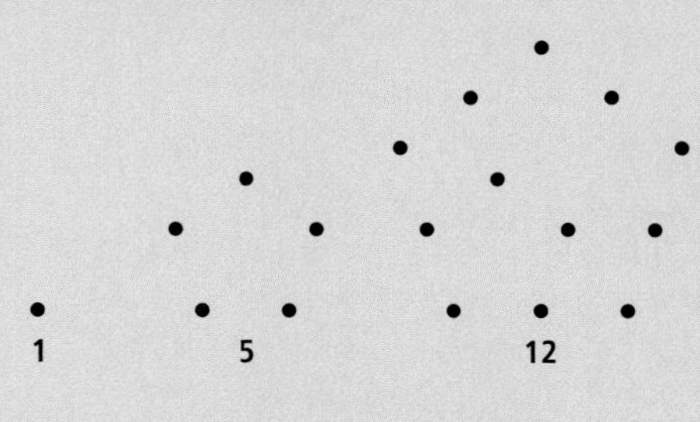

a. Draw the fourth pentagonal number.

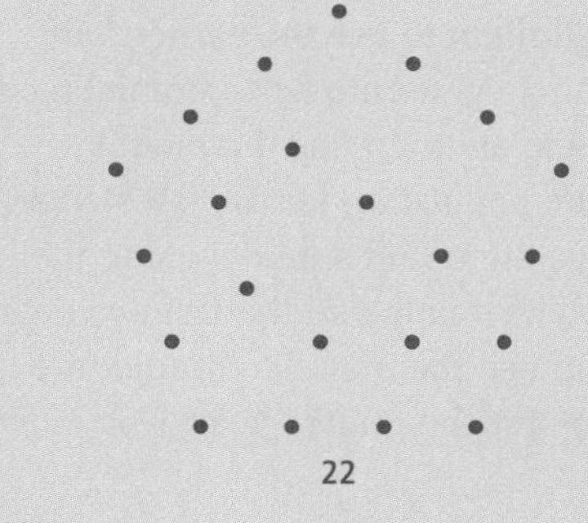

Since many different polynomial functions can fit a set of n data points, polynomial models based on only a few points are usually not good models for making predictions. However, polynomial models do provide an efficient way to store data because the model fits all the given points exactly.

Questions

COVERING THE IDEAS

In 1–3, refer to Example 1.

1. How did the planners know what degree polynomial model would fit the data? They used the method of finite differences.
2. Show that the model is correct for $x = 6$.
3. Use the model to calculate how many roads would be needed for 20 cities. 190

In 4 and 5, refer to Example 2.

4. How many squares of any size are on a standard 8-by-8 checkerboard? 204
5. How many more squares of any size are created when you turn an 8-by-8 checkerboard into a 9-by-9 checkerboard? 81
6. Consider the data at the right.
   a. Determine the lowest possible degree of a polynomial function that fits these data. 4
   b. Find a formula for the function. $y = x^4 - x^3 - 2x^2 + 3x + 1$

x	0	1	2	3	4	5
y	1	2	7	46	173	466

7. Suppose the data in the table at the right are modeled by a formula of the form $y = ax^2 + bx + c$. What three equations are satisfied by a, b, and c?

x	2	5	8
y	12	60	162

8. Refer to the formula modeling Manhattan's population. Verify that the model accurately stores the population for the given year.
   a. 1920 b. 2000

2. The corresponding data point is (6, 15). $\frac{1}{2}(6)^2 - \frac{1}{2}(6) = 15$; the model fits.

7. $12 = 4a + 2b + c$, $60 = 25a + 5b + c$, $162 = 64a + 8b + c$

8a. The corresponding data point is (1920, 2.284); $P(1) = 2.284$, the model is accurate.

8b. The corresponding data point is (2000, 1.537); $P(5) = 1.646$, the model is fairly accurate.

APPLYING THE MATHEMATICS

9. Ronin did not use matrices to solve the system of Example 1. Instead he reordered the equations so that the largest coefficients are on the top line as shown below, then repeatedly subtracted each equation from the one above it. Use this method to solve the system and check the solution to Example 1. $a = \frac{1}{2}, b = -\frac{1}{2}, c = 0$

$$\begin{cases} 25a + 5b + c = 10 \\ 16a + 4b + c = 6 \\ 9a + 3b + c = 3 \end{cases}$$

11-8

3 Assignment

Recommended Assignment

- Questions 1–20
- Question 21 (extra credit)
- Self-Test

b. What are the next two pentagonal numbers? Create a table to show how the number of the pattern is related to the number of dots in the pattern.

n	1	2	3	4	5	6
$p(n)$	1	5	12	22	35	51

c. Write a formula for $p(n)$, the nth pentagonal number. $p(n) = \frac{3}{2}n^2 - \frac{1}{2}n$

As an additional extension, ask students to investigate triangular, square, or hexagonal numbers in the same way.

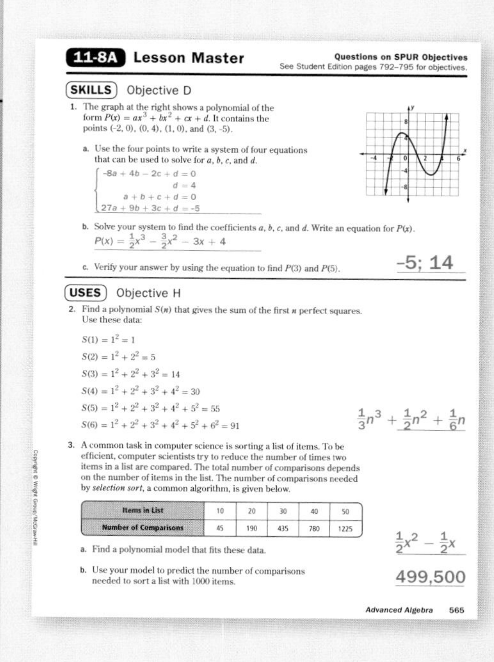

11-8A Lesson Master

Questions on SPUR Objectives
See Student Edition pages 792–795 for objectives.

SKILLS Objective D

1. The graph at the right shows a polynomial of the form $P(x) = ax^3 + bx^2 + cx + d$. It contains the points (-2, 0), (0, 4), (1, 0), and (3, -5).
   a. Use the four points to write a system of four equations that can be used to solve for a, b, c, and d.
   $$\begin{cases} -8a + 4b - 2c + d = 0 \\ d = 4 \\ a + b + c + d = 0 \\ 27a + 9b + 3c + d = -5 \end{cases}$$
   b. Solve your system to find the coefficients a, b, c, and d. Write an equation for $P(x)$. $P(x) = \frac{1}{2}x^3 - \frac{3}{2}x^2 - 3x + 4$
   c. Verify your answer by using the equation to find $P(3)$ and $P(5)$. –5; 14

USES Objective H

2. Find a polynomial $S(n)$ that gives the sum of the first n perfect squares. Use these data:
   $S(1) = 1^2 = 1$
   $S(2) = 1^2 + 2^2 = 5$
   $S(3) = 1^2 + 2^2 + 3^2 = 14$
   $S(4) = 1^2 + 2^2 + 3^2 + 4^2 = 30$
   $S(5) = 1^2 + 2^2 + 3^2 + 4^2 + 5^2 = 55$
   $S(6) = 1^2 + 2^2 + 3^2 + 4^2 + 5^2 + 6^2 = 91$
   $\frac{1}{3}n^3 + \frac{1}{2}n^2 + \frac{1}{6}n$

3. A common task in computer science is sorting a list of items. To be efficient, computer scientists try to reduce the number of times two items in a list are compared. The total number of comparisons depends on the number of items in the list. The number of comparisons needed by *selection sort*, a common algorithm, is given below.

Items in List	10	20	30	40	50
Number of Comparisons	45	190	435	780	1225

   a. Find a polynomial model that fits these data. $\frac{1}{2}x^2 - \frac{1}{2}x$
   b. Use your model to predict the number of comparisons needed to sort a list with 1000 items. 499,500

Advanced Algebra 565

Notes on the Questions

Questions 11 and 12 These questions ask students to use all the skills they have learned in this lesson and in Lesson 11-7. They must organize data, use patterns, and find formulas.

Additional Answers

10a. $f(n) = \frac{1}{2}n^2 - \frac{1}{2}n$; $f(n - 1) = \frac{1}{2}(n - 1)^2 - \frac{1}{2}(n - 1) = \frac{1}{2}n^2 - 1.5n + 1$

10b. $f(n) - f(n - 1) = n - 1$

10c. The fact that you must add $n - 1$ roads to go from $n - 1$ to n cities makes sense according to the data given in Example 1. Roads must be built from the nth city to each of the $n - 1$ previous cities.

13b.

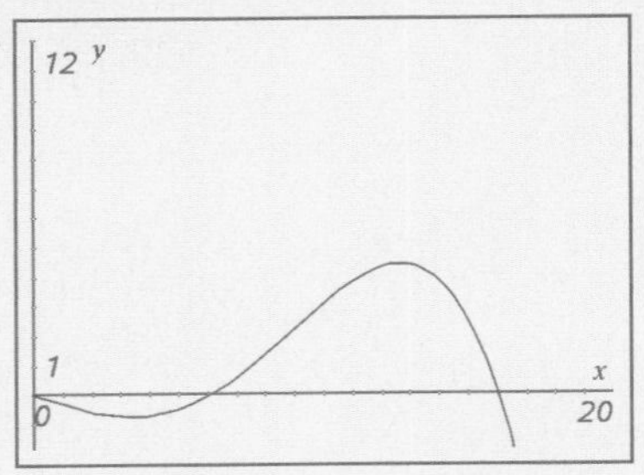

The graph does not have the same shape as the picture due to rounding error and using a limited number of points.

10. Example 1 shows that $r = \frac{1}{2}x^2 - \frac{1}{2}x$ fits the values of the function for integers x with $1 \le x \le 6$. Check that this formula works for any integer x by going through the following steps. See margin.
    a. Let $r = f(x)$ and calculate $f(n)$ and $f(n - 1)$.
    b. The expression $f(n) - f(n - 1)$ is the difference between connecting n cities and connecting $n - 1$ cities. Find an expression for $f(n) - f(n - 1)$ in terms of n.
    c. Interpret your answer to Part b by referring back to the meaning of $f(n)$.

11. The employees at Primo's Pizzeria like to cut pizza into oddly-shaped pieces. In so doing, they noticed that there is a maximum number of pieces that can be formed from a given number of cuts. Write a polynomial model for finding the maximum number of pieces from the number of cuts. $y = \frac{1}{2}x^2 + \frac{1}{2}x + 1$

Number of Cuts	0	1	2	3	4
Maximum Number of Pieces	1	2	4	7	11

12. Recall that a *tessellation* is a pattern of shapes that covers a surface completely without overlaps or gaps. One cross section of a honeycomb is a tessellation of regular hexagons, with three hexagons meeting at each vertex. One way to construct the tessellation is to start with 1 hexagon then surround it with 6 more hexagons and then surround these with another "circle" of 12 hexagons, and so on. If this pattern were to continue, find
    a. the number of hexagons in the fourth circle. 18
    b. the total number of hexagons in the first four circles. 37
    c. a polynomial equation which expresses the *total* number of hexagons h as a function of the number of circles n. $h = 3n^2 - 3n + 1$
    d. the total number of hexagons in a honeycomb with 10 circles. 271

13. Refer to the roller coaster on the first page of the chapter. The table below gives the roller coaster's height $H(x)$ in the picture for different values of horizontal distance x along the picture.

x	0	4	8	12	16
$H(x)$	0	-0.7	2	7.8	11.4

    a. Use the method of Examples 1 and 2 to fit a polynomial function to these data points. $H(x) \approx -0.001x^4 + 0.019x^3 - 0.028x^2 - 0.313x$
    b. Graph the polynomial you find to see how close its graph is to the picture. See margin.

14. The drawings given in Example 1 look similar to the drawings you saw in geometry when you learned that the number d of diagonals in a polygon with n sides is given by $d = \frac{n(n-3)}{2}$.
    a. Show that the formula for the number of diagonals and the formula for the number of roads are not equivalent.
    b. Subtract the polynomial for the number of diagonals from the polynomial for the number of connections. What is the difference? What does the difference mean?

14a. $\frac{n^2 - 3n}{2} = \frac{1}{2}n^2 - \frac{3}{2}n \neq \frac{1}{2}n^2 - \frac{1}{2}n$ for $n \neq 0$.

14b. n; n is the number of sides of the polygon, which are included in the number of roads built in Example 1.

REVIEW

15. Consider the data at the right. **(Lesson 11-7)**
    a. Can the data be modeled by a polynomial function? yes
    b. If so, what degree is the polynomial? 3

r	1	2	3	4	5	6	7	8	9
t	3	11	31	69	131	223	351	521	739

16. How much larger is the volume of a cube with side $x + 1$ than the volume of a cube with side $x - 1$? **(Lesson 11-2)** $6x^2 + 2$

17. May Vary invested different amounts each year for the past 6 years as summarized in the table at the right. Each amount is invested at 4.6% APY. What is the total current value of her investments? **(Lesson 11-1)** $40,784.87

Years Ago	Amount ($)
5	7100
4	6600
3	5800
2	5100
1	6000
0	5500

18. Describe three properties of the graph of $f(x) = \sin x$. **(Lesson 10-6)** See margin.

19. Express as a logarithm of a single number. **(Lesson 9-9)**
    a. $\log_7 36 - \log_7 6$ $\log_7 6$
    b. $4 \log 3$ $\log 81$
    c. $\frac{1}{6} \log 64$ $\log 2$

20. Ivan Speeding was driving 25% faster than the speed limit. By what percent must he reduce his speed to be driving at the speed limit? **(Previous Course)** He should reduce his speed by 20%.

EXPLORATION

21. In the last part of this lesson, the functions with equations $y = \frac{x^2 - x + 2}{2}$ and $y = \frac{x^3 - 3x^2 + 8x}{6}$ are shown to fit the points $(1, 1)$, $(2, 2)$, and $(3, 4)$. 21a–c. See margin.
    a. Explain why $y = \frac{x^3 - 3x^2 + 8x}{6} + (x - 1)(x - 2)(x - 3)$ describes another 3rd degree polynomial function that contains these points.
    b. Find an equation for a polynomial function of 4th degree that contains these points.
    c. Explain how you could find as many different polynomials as desired that contain these three points.

QY ANSWERS

1. 45 roads
2. 1960; $P(3) = 1.7054$, or 1,705,400 people. This is 7400 more than the actual population.

Notes on the Questions

Question 17 For this question, students may need to be reminded that ax^n represents the total amount of deposit and interest on the a dollars that has been in account for n years at an interest rate r where $x = 1 + r$.

4 Wrap-Up

Ongoing Assessment

Have students work in pairs. Have each student write a quadratic equation of the form $y = ax^2 + bx + c$. On a separate sheet of paper, have them make a table of y-values for $x = 2$, 4, and 6. Next have students exchange tables, write a system of three equations in three unknowns, and solve the system for a, b, and c. Have students check their partner's solutions and make any necessary corrections. Students should demonstrate the ability to write, solve, and check quadratic models.

Additional Answers

18. Answers vary. Sample: The domain is all real numbers; the range is $\{y : -1 \leq y \leq 1\}$, and the period is 2π.

21a. If we plug in 1, 2, or 3 for x, the second part of the equation equals 0, and thus the value of the equation is equivalent to $\frac{x^3 - 3x^2 + 8x}{6}$.

21b. Answers vary. Sample: Multiply the second term of the equation in Part a by a linear factor, for example $y = \frac{x^3 - 3x^2 + 8x}{6} + (x - 1)(x - 2)(x - 3)x$.

21c. Answers vary. Sample: Start with the polynomial in Part a. The second term of the polynomial can be multiplied by any other polynomial, and the resulting polynomial will contain the three points because the second term will always equal 0 when $x = 1$, $x = 2$, or $x = 3$.

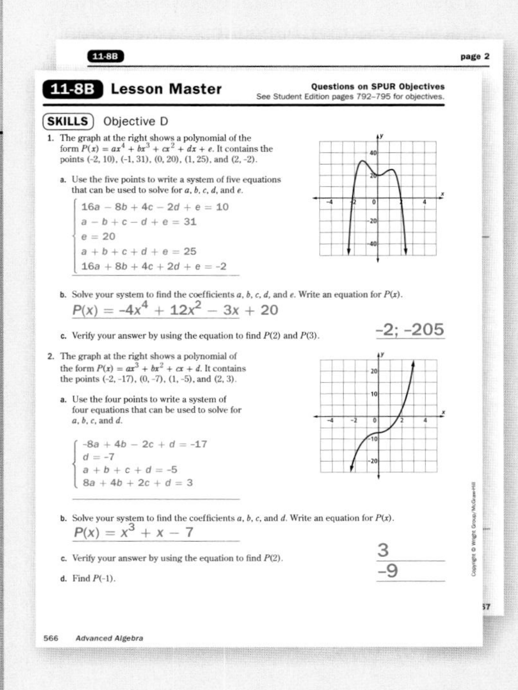

11-8B page 2

11-8B Lesson Master Questions on SPUR Objectives
See Student Edition pages 792–795 for objectives.

SKILLS Objective D

1. The graph at the right shows a polynomial of the form $P(x) = ax^4 + bx^3 + cx^2 + dx + e$. It contains the points (-2, 10), (-1, 31), (0, 20), (1, 25), and (2, -2).
   a. Use the five points to write a system of five equations that can be used to solve for a, b, c, d, and e.
   $16a - 8b + 4c - 2d + e = 10$
   $a - b + c - d + e = 31$
   $e = 20$
   $a + b + c + d + e = 25$
   $16a + 8b + 4c + 2d + e = -2$
   b. Solve your system to find the coefficients a, b, c, d, and e. Write an equation for $P(x)$. $P(x) = -4x^4 + 12x^2 - 3x + 20$
   c. Verify your answer by using the equation to find $P(2)$ and $P(3)$. -2; -205

2. The graph at the right shows a polynomial of the form $P(x) = ax^3 + bx^2 + cx + d$. It contains the points (-2, -17), (0, -7), (1, -5), and (2, 3).
   a. Use the four points to write a system of four equations that can be used to solve for a, b, c, and d.
   $-8a + 4b - 2c + d = -17$
   $d = -7$
   $a + b + c + d = -5$
   $8a + 4b + 2c + d = 3$
   b. Solve your system to find the coefficients a, b, c, and d. Write an equation for $P(x)$. $P(x) = x^3 + x - 7$
   c. Verify your answer by using the equation to find $P(2)$. 3
   d. Find $P(-1)$. -9

Copyright © Wright Group/McGraw-Hill

566 Advanced Algebra

Chapter 11

The projects relate to the content of the lessons of this chapter as follows:

Project	Lesson(s)
1	11-5
2	11-6
3	11-7
4	11-4
5	11-4
6	11-4, 11-6

1 Proving That Certain *n*th Roots Are Irrational

Part ai is answered by showing that $f(x) = x^2 - 37$ has no rational roots. Part aii is answered in the same manner as ai but with $g(x) = x^3 - 7$. Part aiii is answered in the same manner as aii but with $h(x) = x^5 - 2$. In Part c, when students test the possible solutions 49, -49, 7, and -7 in the equation $x^2 - 49 = 0$, they find that two of these numbers satisfy the equation.

2 Polynomial Inequalities

Students can use graphs, factoring, or the Quadratic Formula to solve the equations. Three online resources for this project are http://www.purplemath.com/modules/ineqpoly.htm, http://www.sosmath.com/algebra/inequalities/ineq04/ineq04.html, and http://www.analyzemath.com/Inequalities_Polynomial/Inequalities_Polynomial_T.html.

3 Sums of Products

Students should use the methods in Lesson 11-8 to find the polynomial formulas. They might be interested in testing sums of other products as well.

Chapter 11 Projects

1 Proving That Certain *n*th Roots Are Irrational

In Lesson 11-5, you proved that $\sqrt{2}$ and $\sqrt[3]{9}$ are irrational.

a. Use the same idea to prove that the following numbers are irrational.

i. $\sqrt{37}$ ii. $\sqrt[3]{7}$ iii. $\sqrt[5]{2}$

b. Prove that some other number of your choosing is irrational.

c. Explain why this process does not work to prove that $\sqrt{49}$ is irrational.

2 Polynomial Inequalities

a. Consider $P(x) = 3x^2 - 20$. Solve $P(x) = 0$. Using a graph, solve $P(x) < 0$ and $P(x) > 0$.

b. Describe how to solve the inequalities in Part a algebraically. Check your method for other polynomials of the form $ax^2 + b$.

c. Suppose $Q(x) = 2x^2 + x - 6$. Solve $Q(x) = 0$. Using a graph, solve $Q(x) < 0$ and $Q(x) > 0$.

d. Describe how to solve the inequalities in Part c algebraically. Check your method for other polynomials of the form $ax^2 + bx + c$.

e. Extend your strategy in Part d to describe how to solve $0 < ax^3 + bx^2 + cx + d$.

3 Sums of Products

a. Use the method of finite differences to find an explicit formula for the sequence a of sums of squares shown below.

$a_1 = 1^2 = 1$
$a_2 = 1^2 + 2^2 = 5$
$a_3 = 1^2 + 2^2 + 3^2 = 14$
$a_4 = 1^2 + 2^2 + 3^2 + 4^2 = 30$, and so on.

b. Use the method of finite differences to find an explicit formula for the sequence b of sums of products of consecutive integers shown below.

$b_1 = 3 \cdot 4 = 12$
$b_2 = 3 \cdot 4 + 4 \cdot 5 = 32$
$b_3 = 3 \cdot 4 + 4 \cdot 5 + 5 \cdot 6 = 62$
$b_4 = 3 \cdot 4 + 4 \cdot 5 + 5 \cdot 6 + 6 \cdot 7 = 104$, and so on.

c. Use the method of finite differences to find an explicit formula for the sequence c of sums of products of integers that differ by 3 shown below.

$c_1 = 2 \cdot 5 = 10$
$c_2 = 2 \cdot 5 + 3 \cdot 6 = 28$
$c_3 = 2 \cdot 5 + 3 \cdot 6 + 4 \cdot 7 = 56$
$c_4 = 2 \cdot 5 + 3 \cdot 6 + 4 \cdot 7 + 5 \cdot 8 = 96$, and so on.

d. What do all the polynomial formulas in Parts a–c have in common?

e. Write another sequence of sums of products that you think has an explicit formula that shares the characteristic you gave in Part d. Use the method of finite differences to check your prediction.

Project Rubric

Advanced	Student correctly provides all of the details asked for in the project as well as additional correct independent conclusions.
Proficient	Student correctly provides all of the details asked for in the project.
Partially proficient	Student correctly provides some of the details asked for in the project or provides all details with some inaccuracies.
Not proficient	Student correctly provides few of the details asked for in the project or provides all details with many inaccuracies.
No attempt	Student makes little or no attempt to complete the project.

4 Synthetic Division

A polynomial can be divided by a linear binomial $x - r$ using a process called *synthetic division.* To perform synthetic division, start by writing the coefficients of the polynomial to be divided in a line across the page. Multiply the first coefficient by r and add the second coefficient. Multiply the resulting sum by r and add the next coefficient. Repeat this process until the final coefficient has been added. The sums you find in each step are the coefficients of the quotient, and the final sum is the remainder. For example, to divide $P(x) = 2x^4 - 9x^3 + 4x - 7$ by $x - 5$, you would write the coefficients 2, -9, 0, 4, and -7. Then follow the arrows to perform the calculation. The quotient $Q(x)$ is $2x^3 + x^2 + 5x + 29$ with a remainder R of 138.

	2	-9	0	4	-7
+	↓	10	5	25	145
	2	1	5	29	138

(multiply by 5)

a. Verify that the division was done correctly by using a CAS to show that $P(x) = Q(x) \cdot (x - 5) + R$.

b. Find the value of $P(5)$ by substituting $x = 5$ into the expression for $P(x)$ in Part a.

c. When a polynomial is divided by $x - r$, what does the remainder tell you about the value of the polynomial at r?

d. Use synthetic division to divide $G(x) = 3x^4 + 2x^3 - 20x^2 - 3x + 12$ by $x - 7$ and evaluate $G(7)$.

5 Effect of Coefficients on $y = ax^4 + bx^3 + cx^2 + dx + e$

Use a DGS or CAS to create a dynamic graph of $y = ax^4 + bx^3 + cx^2 + dx + e$, where a, b, c, d, and e are real numbers and can be varied. Explore several possible values of each coefficient to decide how each affects the graph of the function. Summarize your findings in a report.

6 Factoring and Solving Cubic Polynomial Functions

Factoring the general cubic polynomial function has a rich history. While a general formula for factoring any cubic polynomial in one variable exists, there are a few special forms that do not require the general formula.

a. Find out how to factor $x^3 - a^3$ and $x^3 + a^3$, where a is any real number.

b. Find out how to solve $x^3 + mx = n$, where m and n are any real numbers.

c. Research the history of solving the general cubic polynomial equation

$$a_3x^3 + a_2x^2 + a_1x + a_0 = 0.$$

Summarize your research into a brief report that includes information about the person who first created the general formula.

Mathematicians have developed a method for solving cubic equations with origami.

4 Synthetic Division

Synthetic division makes use of the fact that when a polynomial in a single variable is arranged in descending powers with each power included, so that an nth degree polynomial has $n + 1$ terms, the polynomial is completely characterized by its coefficients. When using synthetic division, only the coefficients of the polynomial, including 0 for any missing terms, need to be written.

5 Effect of Coefficients on $y = ax^4 + bx^3 + cx^2 + dx + e$

Ask students what happens to the graph when the coefficients are doubled, tripled, quadrupled, and halved.

6 Factoring and Solving Cubic Polynomial Functions

Students will find that they can factor $x^3 - a^3$ and $x^3 + a^3$ by first dividing by $(x - a)$ and $(x + a)$, respectively. The remaining polynomials are not factorable over the real numbers. The cubic formula has its beginnings in 15th- and 16th-century Italy. Good sources for information on the cubic formula can be found online at http://mathworld.wolfram.com/CubicFormula.html, http://www.sosmath.com/algebra/factor/fac11/fac11.html, and http://www.sosmath.com/algebra/factor/fac111/fac111.html.

Sample answers for projects are in the Solution Manual in the Electronic Teacher's Edition.

Notes

Chapter 11

Summary and Vocabulary

The Summary gives an overview of the entire chapter and provides an opportunity for students to consider the material as a whole. Thus, the Summary can be used to help students relate and unify the concepts presented in the chapter.

Vocabulary words and symbols are listed by lesson to provide a checklist of concepts that students must know. Emphasize to students that they should read the vocabulary list carefully before starting the Self-Test on pages 790–791. If students do not understand the meaning of a vocabulary word, they should refer back to the indicated lesson.

Theorems and Properties covered in the chapter are listed below the Summary with page references included to lead students back to the location in the chapter where the theorem or property is stated.

Chapter 11 Summary and Vocabulary

- A **polynomial in *x* of degree *n*** is an expression that can be written in the standard form

$$a_nx^n + a_{n-1}x^{n-1} + \ldots + a_2x^2 + a_1x + a_0,$$

where $a_n \neq 0$. a_n is called the **leading coefficient**, and a_0 is the **constant term**. Polynomials written in factored form can be rewritten in standard form using the Extended Distributive Property. **Polynomial functions** include linear, quadratic, and functions of higher degree such as the ones graphed below.

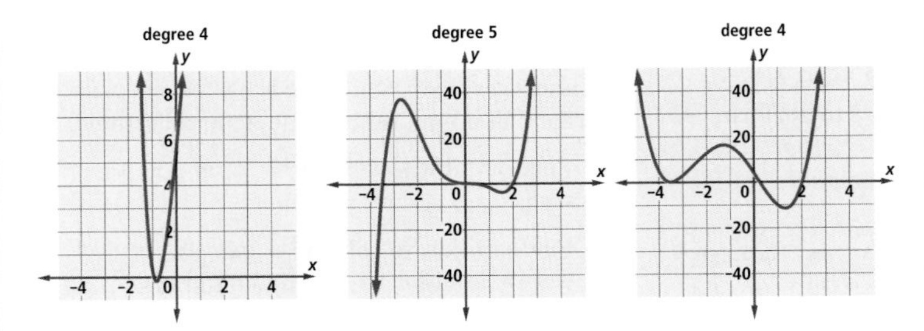

- When a polynomial $P(x)$ of degree n is set equal to zero, the resulting equation has n **roots**, or **zeros**. The Fundamental Theorem of Algebra guarantees that $P(x) = 0$ has at least one complex root. The Factor Theorem states that if r is a root of $P(x) = 0$, then $P(x)$ can be factored as $P(x) = (x - r) \cdot Q(x)$. From this we can deduce that a polynomial function of degree n has exactly n complex roots, although some may be **multiple roots**.

- If the degree of a polynomial function is less then 5, formulas such as the Quadratic Formula can be used to find exact zeros. For polynomials of degree 5 or higher, such formulas do not exist. The Rational-Root Theorem provides a way to identify all the possible rational roots of a polynomial with integer coefficients. A CAS can be used to find exact or approximate roots, or to factor or expand polynomials.

Vocabulary

Lesson 11-1
degree of a polynomial
term of a polynomial
*polynomial in *x* of degree *n*
standard form of a polynomial
coefficients of a polynomial
leading coefficient
constant term, constant
polynomial function

Lesson 11-2
monomial, binomial, trinomial
degree of a polynomial in several variables

Lesson 11-3
factoring a polynomial
factored form of a polynomial
greatest common monomial factor
*prime polynomial, irreducible polynomial

Lesson 11-4
zero of a polynomial, root of a polynomial

Lesson 11-6
double root, root of multiplicity 2
multiplicity

Lesson 11-7
method of finite differences

- Polynomials arise directly from compound-interest situations, orbits, and questions about volume. They describe many numerical patterns. They can model many other real-world situations based on finite sets of data points. The degree of the model's polynomial can be found by the **method of finite differences**, and the coefficients of the polynomial can be found by solving a system of linear equations or polynomial regression.

Theorems and Properties

Extended Distributive Property (p. 739)
Difference of Squares Factoring Theorem (p. 747)
Binomial Square Factoring Theorem (p. 747)
Zero-Product Theorem (p. 752)
Factor Theorem (p. 753)
Rational-Root (or Rational-Zero) Theorem (p. 761)
Fundamental Theorem of Algebra (p. 766)
Number of Roots of a Polynomial Equation Theorem (p. 768)
Polynomial-Difference Theorem (p. 773)

Self-Test

For the development of mathematical competence, feedback and correction, along with the opportunity for practice, are necessary. The Self-Test provides the opportunity for feedback and correction; the Chapter Review provides additional opportunities for practice. We cannot overemphasize the importance of these end-of-chapter materials. It is at this point that the material gels for many students, allowing them to solidify skills and understanding. In general, student performance should improve after these pages.

Assign the Self-Test as a one-night assignment. Worked-out solutions for all questions are in the Selected Answers section of the student book. Encourage students to take the Self-Test honestly, grade themselves, and then be prepared to discuss the test in class.

Advise students to pay special attention to those Chapter Review questions (pages 792–795) that correspond to the questions they missed on the Self-Test.

Additional Answers

1. To calculate the volume, we take the width of the box as $40 - 2x$, the length of the box as $30 - 2x$, and the height of the box as x. Since $V = lwh$, $V(x) = (30 - 2x)(40 - 2x)x = 4x^3 - 140x^2 + 1200x$.
2. A; this is the only term that contains a single term from all three factors.
3. Use the Extended Distributive Property $(z + 5)(z^2 - 3z + 1) = (z + 5)(z^2) + (z + 5)(-3z) + (z + 5)(1) = z^3 + 5z^2 - 3z^2 - 15z + z + 5$. Now combine like terms and write the resulting terms in descending order, $z^3 + 2z^2 - 14z + 5$.
4. The degree is the largest sum of the exponents of the variables in any term. A binomial is a polynomial with two terms. Answers vary. Sample: $3xy + z^4$.
5. $680x^4 + 850x^3 + 1020x^2 + 1105x + 935$; the degree of x in each term is the number of years Francesca has held that summer's savings.

Chapter 11 Self-Test

Take this test as you would take a test in class. Use the Selected Answers section in the back of the book to check your work.

1. Khalil has a 30-inch by 40-inch rectangular piece of cardboard. He forms a box by cutting out squares with sides of length x from each corner and folding up the sides. Write a polynomial formula for the volume $V(x)$ of the box. 1–10. See margin.
2. **Multiple Choice** Which term appears in the expansion of $(a + b)(c + d + e)(f + g)$?
   A acf B bde
   C af^2 D ad^2g
3. Write $(z + 5)(z^2 - 3z + 1)$ in the standard form of a polynomial.
4. Give an example of a binomial with degree 4.

In 5 and 6, use these facts: When Francesca turned 16, she began saving money from her summer jobs. After the first summer, she saved \$680. After the second summer, she saved \$850. After the third, she saved \$1020, and after the following two summers she saved \$1105 and \$935, respectively. Francesca invested all this money at an annual percentage yield r and did not deposit or withdraw any other money.

5. If $x = (1 + r)$, write a polynomial in terms of x that gives the final amount of money in Francesca's account the summer after her 20th birthday.
6. How much money would she have the summer after her 20th birthday if she were able to invest all the money at an APY of 5.1%?

In 7 and 8, consider the polynomial function P where $P(x) = x^5 - 17x^2 + 4x^6 + 11$.

7. a. What is the degree of the polynomial?
   b. How many complex roots does the polynomial have?
8. State all rational roots of $P(x) = 0$ that are possible according to the Rational-Root Theorem.

In 9 and 10, consider the polynomial function with equation $y = x^5 - 11x^3 + 12x^2 - 35x - 12$. A graph of the function is given below.

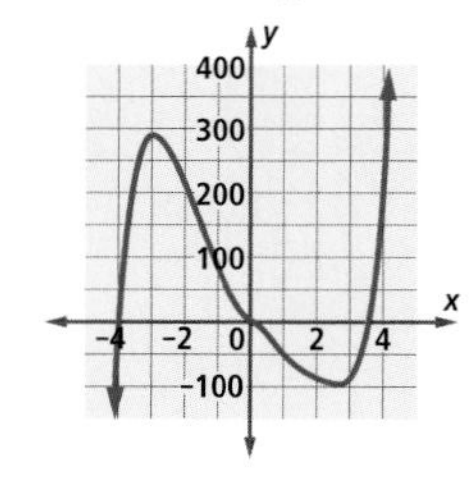

9. a. How many real zeros does the function have? Assume no multiplicities are greater than 1.
   b. How many nonreal zeros does the function have?
10. a. List all possible rational zeros of the function according to the Rational-Root Theorem.
    b. Using the results of Part a and the graph, between what pairs of consecutive integers must irrational zeros be located?

Additional Answers

6. Substitute 0.051 for r, so $x = 1.051$; $680(1.051)^4 + 850(1.051)^3 + 1020(1.051)^2 + 1105(1.051) + 935 \approx$ \$5,039.54

7a. The degree is the largest sum of the exponents of the variables in any term. The degree of $P(x)$ is 6.

7b. A polynomial of degree n has n complex roots. Thus $P(x)$ has 6 complex roots.

8. According to the Rational-Root Theorem, if $\frac{a}{b}$ is a rational root of a polynomial function, then a is a factor of the polynomial's constant term and b is a factor of the coefficient of the leading term. Here, a is a factor of 11 and b is a factor of 4. Therefore, the possible rational roots are $\pm 11, \pm\frac{11}{2}, \pm\frac{11}{4}, \pm 1, \pm\frac{1}{2}$, and $\pm\frac{1}{4}$.

In 11 and 12, consider the polynomial function g where $g(x) = (x - 2)^3(11x + 37)(x^2 - 7)$.

11. Find the zeros of g.

12. What is the multiplicity of each zero you found in Question 11?

13. Multiple Choice Suppose $x - r$ and $x - s$ are factors of a quadratic polynomial $P(x)$. Which of the following is *not* true for all x?

A $P(r) = 0$ B $k(x - r)(x - s) = P(x)$

C $P(s) = 0$ D $(x - r)(x - s) = 0$

14. Use the Rational-Root Theorem to prove that $\sqrt{21}$ is an irrational number.

In 15 and 16, consider the polynomial function r with $r(y) = y^5 - 5y^3 - 27y^2 + 135$.

15. a. Factor $r(y)$ over the rationals.

b. Factor $r(y)$ over the complex numbers.

16. Find all complex zeros of r.

11. Set each factor equal to 0 and solve for x: $(x - 2)^3 = 0, x - 2 = 0, x = 2$; $(11x + 37) = 0, 11x = -37, x = -\frac{37}{11}$; $x^2 - 7 = 0, x^2 = 7, x = \pm\sqrt{7}$. So the zeros of g are $2, -\frac{37}{11}, \sqrt{7}$, and $-\sqrt{7}$.

12. The multiplicity of a zero r is the highest power of $x - r$ that appears as a factor of the polynomial. The multiplicity of 2 is 3, and the multiplicity of each other zero is 1.

13. D; D is only true when $x = r$ or $x = s$. The rest are true for all x by the Factor Theorem and the Number of Roots of a Polynomial Equation Theorem.

14. $\sqrt{21}$ is a solution to $x^2 = 21$ and a root of $x^2 - 21 = 0$. According to the Rational-Root Theorem, if $\frac{a}{b}$ is a rational root of a polynomial, then a is a factor of the polynomial's constant term and b is a factor of the coefficient of the leading term. Here, a is a factor of -21, and b is a factor of 1. Therefore, the possible rational roots are $\pm21, \pm7, \pm3$, and ±1. If we test these values, none are solutions for the equation $x^2 - 21 = 0$. Thus, $\sqrt{21}$ is irrational.

17. Factor completely: $10uv^2w + 24vw$.

18. A polynomial function p has a root at $x = -2$ and a double root at $x = 6$. Write a possible equation for p and graph it. See margin.

19. A function f produces the table of values below.

n	1	2	3	4	5	6
$f(n)$	0	6	24	60	120	210

a. Can f be modeled by a polynomial?

b. If so, what is the smallest possible degree of the polynomial? If not, why not?

20. Find an equation for a polynomial function that describes the data points below.

t	-2	-1	0	4	2	3	4
r	12	4	0	0	4	12	24

See margin.

15a. Use a CAS: $(y - 3)(y^2 - 5)(y^2 + 3y + 9)$

15b. Use a CAS or use difference of squares factoring and the quadratic formula on the quadratic factors you found in Part a: $(y - 3)(y + \sqrt{5})(y - \sqrt{5}) \cdot \left(y + \frac{3}{2} + \frac{3}{2}i\sqrt{3}\right)\left(y + \frac{3}{2} - \frac{3}{2}i\sqrt{3}\right)$

16. By the Factor Theorem, a is a zero of r if $y - a$ is a factor of $r(y)$. So by your answer to 15b, the zeros are $3, \sqrt{5}, -\sqrt{5}, -\frac{3}{2} + \frac{3\sqrt{3}}{2}i$, and $-\frac{3}{2} - \frac{3\sqrt{3}}{2}i$.

17. Factor out the greatest common monomial factor: $2vw(5uv + 12)$; these two factors are prime, so the polynomial is factored completely.

19a. Yes, the 3rd differences are equal; therefore, f can be modeled by a polynomial.

19b. 3; the 3rd differences are equal, and the 2nd differences are not.

Additional Answers

9a. The graph intersects the x-axis 3 times, so there are 3 real zeros.

9b. The function has a total of 5 complex zeros and 3 real zeros, so there are 2 nonreal zeros.

10a. According to the Rational-Root Theorem, if $\frac{a}{b}$ is a rational root of a polynomial function, then a is a factor of the polynomial's constant term and b is a factor of the coefficient of the leading term. Here, a is a factor of 12, and b is a factor of 1. Therefore, the possible rational roots are $\pm12, \pm6, \pm4, \pm3, \pm2$, and ±1.

10b. Looking at the graph, there are two real zeros between consecutive integers that must be irrational because the rational roots are all integer values. The irrational zeros must lie between -1 and 0 and 3 and 4.

18. For a polynomial to have a single root at $x = -2$ and a double root at $x = 6$, $x + 2$ must appear at as a factor once and $x - 6$ must appear as a factor twice. Answers vary. Sample: $p(x) = (x + 2)(x - 6)^2 = x^3 - 10x^2 + 12x + 72$. *(continued below left)*

Additional Answers

18. *(continued)*

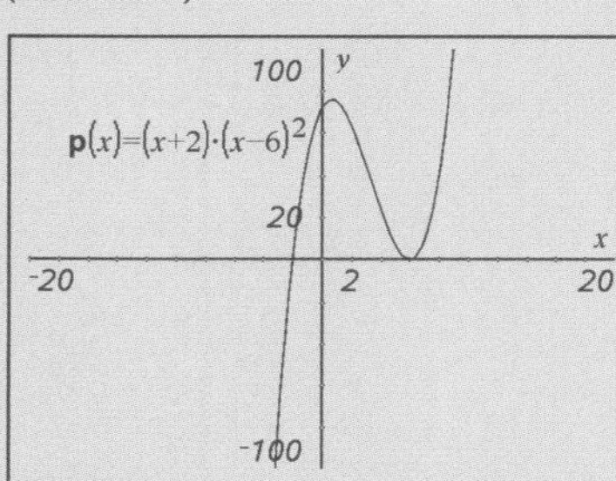

20. Using the method of finite differences, we find that the 2nd set of differences are constant; therefore, these data can be modeled by a quadratic function. The function has the form $r = at^2 + bt + c$. To solve for the coefficients and constant term, we pick three data points, substitute, and solve the resulting system. For example, substitute (-2, 12), (0, 0) and (3, 12).

Solving $\begin{cases} 12 = 4a - 2b + c \\ 0 = c \\ 12 = 9a + 3b + c \end{cases}$

gives $a = 2, b = -2, c = 0$. So, the equation is $r = 2t^2 - 2t$.

Chapter Review

The main objectives for the chapter are organized in the Chapter Review under the four types of understanding this book promotes: Skills, Properties, Uses, and Representations.

Whereas end-of-chapter material may be considered optional in some texts, in UCSMP *Advanced Algebra* we have selected these objectives and questions with the expectation that they will be covered. Students should be able to answer these questions with about 85% accuracy after studying the chapter.

You may assign these questions over a single night to help students prepare for a test the next day or you may assign the questions over a two-day period. If you work the questions over two days, we recommend assigning the evens for homework the first night so that students get feedback in class the next day, and then assigning the odds the night before the test because the answers are provided to the odd-numbered questions in the Selected Answers section at the back of the book.

It is effective to ask students which questions they still do not understand and use the day as a total class discussion of the material that the class finds most difficult.

Resources

- Assessment Resources: Chapter 11 Test Forms A–D; Chapter 11 Test, Cumulative Form

Technology Resources

Teacher's Assessment Assistant, Ch. 11
Electronic Teacher's Edition, Ch. 11

Chapter 11 Chapter Review

SKILLS
PROPERTIES
USES
REPRESENTATIONS

SKILLS Procedures used to get answers

OBJECTIVE A Use the Extended Distributive Property to multiply polynomials. (Lesson 11-2)

In 1 and 2, write the polynomial in standard form.

1. $(x + 1)(x^2 - 2x + 3)$ $x^3 - x^2 + x + 3$
2. $(a + 2)(a + 3)(a + 4)$ $a^3 + 9a^2 + 26a + 24$

In 3 and 4, expand and combine like terms.

3. $(x - y)^2(x + y)$
4. $(r + s + t)(r - s + t)$

OBJECTIVE B Factor polynomials. (Lesson 11-3) 5–6. See margin

Fill in the Blanks In 5 and 6, complete the factoring.

5. $15a^7b^{11} - 40a^{13}b^6 =$ __?__ $(3b^5 -$ __?__ $)$
6. $z^2 +$ __?__ $+ 81 = (z +$ __?__ $)^2$

In 7–10, factor over the set of integers by hand and check with a CAS. 7–14. See margin.

7. $x^2 - 6x + 9$
8. $9m^2 - 48m + 64$
9. $p^4q^4 - 16$
10. $x^2 + 5x + 6$

In 11–14, factor over the reals, if possible.

11. $a^2 + b^2$
12. $y^2 + 7y + 10$
13. $37 + 3t - t^2$
14. $z^2 - 17$

OBJECTIVE C Find zeros of polynomial functions by factoring. (Lessons 11-4, 11-6)

In 15–17, solve the equation and identify any multiple roots. 15–17. See margin.

15. $0 = 6n(n + 3)(8n - 7)$
16. $0 = (t + 13)^3(2t - 3)^2$
17. $x^3 + 12x^2 + 36x = 0$

3. $x^3 - x^2y - xy^2 + y^3$
4. $r^2 - s^2 + 2rt + t^2$

In 18 and 19, find the exact zeros of the polynomial function.

18. $f(x) = x(x - \pi)(2x + 1)$ $0, \pi, -\frac{1}{2}$
19. $P(a) = a^4 - 25a^2$ $0, 5, -5$

OBJECTIVE D Determine an equation for a polynomial function from data points. (Lessons 11-7, 11-8)

20. Consider the polynomial function of smallest degree that models the data points below.

x	1	2	3	4	5	6
y	1	5	14	30	55	91

a. What is the degree? 3

b. **Multiple Choice** Which system of equations could be solved to find the coefficients of the polynomial? i

i. $\begin{cases} 64a + 16b + 4c + d = 30 \\ 27a + 9b + 3c + d = 14 \\ 8a + 4b + 2c + d = 5 \\ a + b + c + d = 1 \end{cases}$

ii. $\begin{cases} 4x^3 + 4x^2 + 4x + 4 = 0 \\ 3x^3 + 3x^2 + 3x + 3 = 0 \\ 2x^3 + 2x^2 + 2x + 2 = 0 \\ x^3 + x^2 + x + 1 = 0 \end{cases}$

iii. $\begin{cases} a + b + c + d = 5 \\ a + 2b + c + d = 19 \\ a + 2b + 3c + d = 43 \\ a + 2b + 3c + 4d = 77 \end{cases}$

iv. none of these

c. Determine an equation for the polynomial function. $y = \frac{1}{3}x^3 + \frac{1}{2}x^2 + \frac{1}{6}x$

Additional Answers

5. $5a^7b^6$; $8a^6$
6. $18z$; 9
7. $(x - 3)^2$
8. $(3m - 8)^2$
9. $(pq + 2)(pq - 2)(p^2q^2 + 4)$
10. $(x + 3)(x + 2)$
11. not possible
12. $(y + 5)(y + 2)$
13. not possible
14. $(z + \sqrt{17})(z - \sqrt{17})$
15. $n = 0, n = -3, n = \frac{7}{8}$; no multiple roots
16. $t = -13, t = \frac{3}{2}$; $t = -13$ is a triple root; $t = \frac{3}{2}$ is a double root
17. $x = 0, x = -6$; $x = -6$ is a double root

In 21–23, can the given relation be described by a polynomial function of degree ≤ 3? If so, find an equation for the function. If not, explain why not. Assume the first variable is the independent variable. 21–23. See margin.

21.

x	1	2	3	4	5	6
y	1	1	3	7	15	31

22.

x	1	2	3	4	5	6
y	56	58	62	74	100	146

23. the sequence defined by
$$\begin{cases} a_1 = 4 \\ a_n = 2a_{n-1} - 1, \text{ for integers } n \geq 2 \end{cases}$$

24. The graph of a function G below contains (-2, 0), (0, 6), (1, 0), and (3, 0). Suppose $G(x) = a_3x^3 + a_2x^2 + a_1x + a_0$. b. See margin.

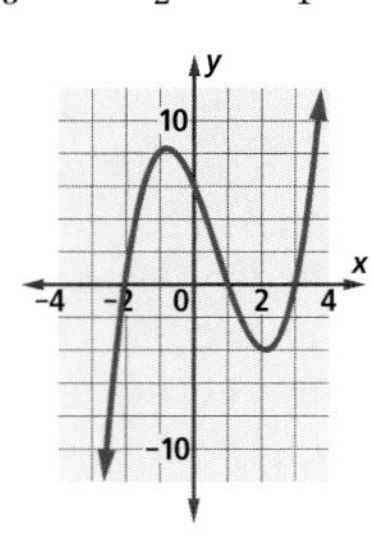

a. What is the value of a_0? 6

b. Find the values of a_1, a_2, and a_3.

c. Give the value of $G(5)$. 56

PROPERTIES Principles behind the mathematics

OBJECTIVE E Describe attributes of polynomials. (Lessons 11-1, 11-2, 11-3)

In 25 and 26, state: a. the degree and b. the leading coefficient of the polynomial.

25. $18c^6 + 9c^4 + 2c + 15$ a. 6; b. 18

26. $3 + 2d - 2d^5 - 35d^9$ a. 9; b. -35

Multiple Choice In 27–29, choose the term that applies to the polynomial.

A monomial B binomial

C trinomial D none of these

27. $p^7 - 8$ B 28. $17r^4t^5$ A 29. $\frac{\pi}{h^2}$ D

30. Give an example of a trinomial with degree 7. 30–31. See margin.

31. a. Is $x^2 - 42$ prime over the rationals? If not, factor it.

b. Is $x^2 - 42$ prime over the reals? If not, factor it.

OBJECTIVE F Apply the Zero-Product Theorem, Factor Theorem, and Fundamental Theorem of Algebra. (Lessons 11-4, 11-6)

In 32 and 33, explain why the Zero-Product Theorem cannot be used directly on the given equation. 32–33. See margin.

32. $(x + 11)(x + 6) = 4$

33. $3(m + 2) - (2m - 6) = 0$

34. Suppose $g(t) = (t + 4)^3(t - 5)^a$. If g has degree 8, what is the value of a? 5

35. **True or False** If $(r - \pi)$ is a factor of a polynomial function V, then $V(\pi) = 0$. true

36. **Multiple Choice** Suppose $p(x)$ is a polynomial, $p(r) = 0$, $p(s) = 0$, and $p(t) = 5$. Which of the following is *not* true? B

A $p(s) \cdot p(r) = 0$

B $k(x - r)(x - s)(x - t) = p(x)$

C r and s are intercepts of the graph of $p(x)$.

D r and s are roots of the equation $p(x) = 0$.

37. Suppose a 7th-degree polynomial equation has 5 real roots and 2 irrational roots.

a. How many rational roots does the equation have? 3

b. How many nonreal complex roots does it have? 2

Additional Answers

21. No; there are no constant differences in the 1st through 3rd differences.
22. Yes; $y = x^3 - 5x^2 + 10x + 50$
23. No; there are no constant differences in the 1st through 3rd differences.

24b. $a_3 = 1$, $a_2 = -2$, $a_1 = -5$

30. Answers vary. Sample: $31x^7 + 14x^4 - 3x$

31a. yes

31b. no; $(x + \sqrt{42})(x - \sqrt{42})$

32. The product is not equal to 0.
33. The left side of the equation is not a product.

Additional Answers

39a. $\pm 3, \pm \frac{3}{2}, \pm 1, \pm \frac{1}{2}$

39b. $x = 3$ and $x = \frac{1}{2}$

40. Possible rational roots:

$\pm 30, \pm 15, \pm 10, \pm 6, \pm 5, \pm 3, \pm 2, \pm 1$;

$(z - 5)(z - 1)(z + 2)(z + 3)$

41a. $\pm 6, \pm 3, \pm 2, \pm 1, \pm \frac{3}{2}, \pm \frac{6}{5}, \pm \frac{3}{5}, \pm \frac{1}{2}, \pm \frac{2}{5}, \pm \frac{3}{10}, \pm \frac{1}{5}, \pm \frac{1}{10}$

41b.

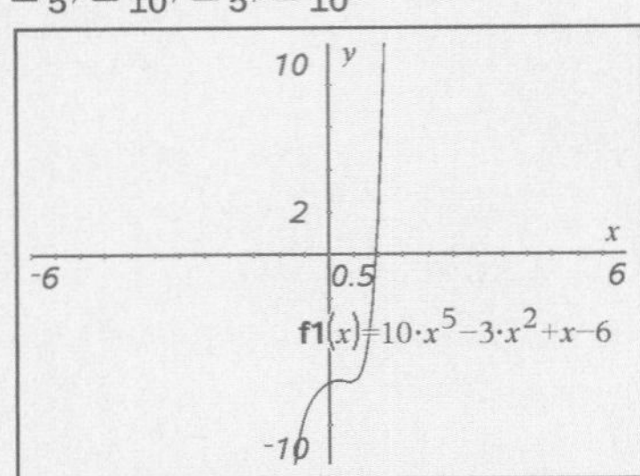

The range of possible rational roots is from $x = -6$ to $x = 6$. By restricting the graph to this range, we see that the graph of f only intersects the x-axis once in this interval, and not at any of the possible values that we found in Part a. Therefore, f has exactly one irrational zero.

42. $25^{\frac{1}{3}}$ is a solution to the equation $x^3 - 25 = 0$. By the Rational-Root Theorem, the possible rational roots of this equation are $\pm 25, \pm 5$, and ± 1. Plugging in each of these values for x shows that none of the possible rational roots is an actual root. Therefore, $25^{\frac{1}{3}}$ is irrational.

44a. Answers vary. Sample: Suppose interest is compounded annually in Anna's savings account, and $x = 1 + r$, where r is the interest rate. The first year, she deposits \$75. The second year she deposits \$100. The third year she deposits \$150. This year (the fourth year), she deposits \$250. If the annual interest rate is 4.7%, how much money is in the account now?

50a. $r = \sqrt{529 - h^2}$

50b. $V = \frac{1}{3}\pi h(529 - h^2)$

OBJECTIVE G Apply the Rational-Root Theorem. (Lesson 11-5) 39–42. See margin.

38. **True or False** By the Rational-Root Theorem, $P(x) = 11x^2 - 5x + 3$ could have a rational root at $x = -\frac{11}{3}$. false

39. a. List all possible rational roots of $R(x) = 2x^4 - 7x^3 + 5x^2 - 7x + 3$, according to the Rational-Root Theorem.
    b. Find the rational zeros of R.

40. Use the Rational-Root Theorem to factor $z^4 - z^3 - 19z^2 - 11z + 30$ over the integers.

41. Consider $f(n) = 10n^5 - 3n^2 + n - 6$.
    a. List all possible rational zeros of f, according to the Rational-Root Theorem.
    b. Use a graph to explain why f has exactly one irrational zero.

42. Prove that $25^{\frac{1}{3}}$ is an irrational number.

USES Applications of mathematics in real-world situations

OBJECTIVE H Use polynomials to model real-world situations. (Lessons 11-1, 11-8)

43. The number G of games needed for n tic-tac-toe players to play every other player twice is given in the following table.

n	2	3	4	5	6
G	2	6	12	20	30

    a. Find a polynomial function relating n and G. $G = n^2 - n$
    b. Assume there are 24 students in your class. How many games will your class play if each student plays every other student twice? 552

44. Consider $75x^3 + 100x^2 + 150x + 250$.
    a. Write a question involving money that could be answered by evaluating this expression. See margin.
    b. Answer your question in Part a. \$602.73

45. Gary's grandmother put \$250 in a savings account each year starting on Gary's tenth birthday. The account compounds at an APY of r. a. $250x^5 + 250x^4 + 250x^3 + 250x^2 + 250x + 250$
    a. Write a polynomial in x, where $x = 1 + r$, that represents the value of the account on Gary's fifteenth birthday.
    b. If the account pays 6% interest annually, calculate how much money Gary would have on his fifteenth birthday. \$1743.83
    c. If Gary had \$1700 on his fifteenth birthday, what rate of interest did he earn on his account? about 4.99%

46. Recall that when a beam of light in the air strikes the surface of water, it is refracted. Below are the earliest known data on the relation between i, the angle of incidence in degrees, and r, the angle of refraction in degrees, recorded by Ptolemy in the 2nd century CE.

i	10	20	30	40	50	60	70	80
r	8	15.5	22.5	29	35	40.5	45.5	50

    a. Can these data be modeled by a polynomial function? yes
    b. If so, what is the degree of the function? If not, explain why not. 2

OBJECTIVE I Use polynomials to describe geometric situations. (Lesson 11-2)

47. A student forms a small open box out of a 3-inch by 5-inch index card by cutting squares of side length s out of the corners and folding up the sides. Write a polynomial for the volume $V(s)$ of the box. $V(s) = 4s^3 - 16s^2 + 15s$

Additional Answers

51.

$f(x) = (x - 3)(x + 2)(3x + 2)$

52.

$g(x) = x(x + 4)(x - 5)$

In 48 and 49, an open box is formed out of a 50-cm by 80-cm sheet of cardboard by removing squares of side length x cm from each corner and folding up the four sides.

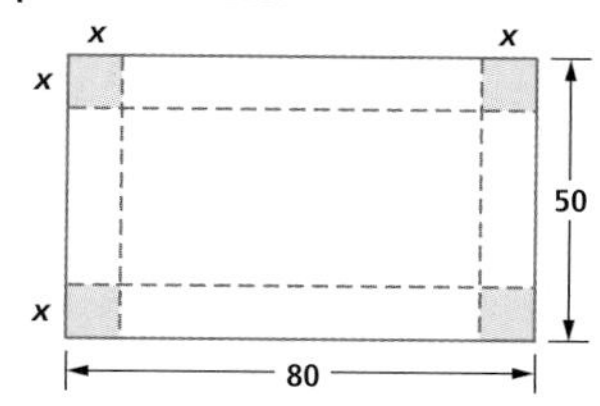

48. Write an expression for the area of the bottom of the box. $4x^2 - 260x + 4000$

49. Write a formula for the volume $V(x)$ of the box. $4x^3 - 260x^2 + 4000x$

50. A right circular cone has a slant height $s = 23$. See margin.
    a. Express its radius r in terms of its altitude h.
    b. Use the results of Part a to express the volume V of this cone as a polynomial function in h.

REPRESENTATIONS Pictures, graphs, or objects that illustrate concepts

OBJECTIVE J Graph polynomial functions. (Lessons 11-1, 11-4, 11-5)

In 51 and 52, an equation for a function is given. Graph the function. Then, use the graph to factor the polynomial. 51–53. See margin.

51. $f(x) = 3x^3 - x^2 - 20x - 12$

52. $g(x) = x^3 - x^2 - 20x$

53. A polynomial function h with degree 4 has zeros at -1, 0, 1, and 3.
    a. Write a possible equation for h in factored form.
    b. Suppose that the leading coefficient of $h(x)$ is 3. Find an equation for h.
    c. Graph your equation in Part b.

54. A polynomial function f of degree 3 has zeros at -4, -1, and 5. a–d. See margin.
    a. Write an equation for one function satisfying these conditions.
    b. Graph the function in Part a.
    c. Write the general form of an equation for f.
    d. What do the graphs of all functions with equations of the form in Part c have in common with the graph in Part b?

OBJECTIVE K Estimate zeros of polynomial functions using graphs. (Lessons 11-4, 11-5) 55–57. See margin.

55. A 4th-degree polynomial function with equation $y = g(x)$ and integer zeros is graphed at the right. List the four zeros.

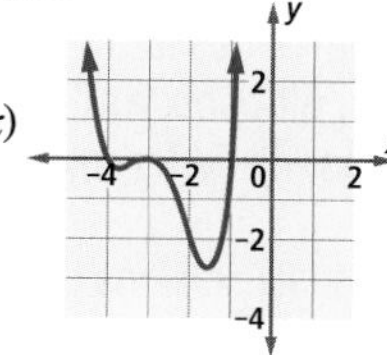

56. Refer to the graph of a function at the right. Name two pairs of consecutive integers between which a zero of f must occur.

57. Let $p(x) = 2x^4 + 3x^2 + 2x - 6$.
    a. List all the possible rational roots of $p(x)$, according to the Rational-Root Theorem.
    b. A graph of p is shown at the right. Based on the graph, which possible rational roots from Part a should you test? Explain.
    c. Find all rational roots of $p(x)$.

Assessment

Evaluation The *Assessment Resources* provide four forms of the Chapter 11 Test. Forms A and B present parallel versions of a short-answer format. Form C consists of four to six short-response questions that cover the SPUR objectives from Chapter 11. Form D offers performance assessment that covers a subset (or even just one) of the SPUR objectives for the chapter. The fifth type of test is a Chapter 11 Test, Cumulative Form. About 50% of this test covers Chapter 11, and the remaining 50% covers the previous chapters evenly.

Feedback After students have taken the test for Chapter 11 and you have scored the results, return the tests to students for discussion. Class discussion on the questions that caused trouble for most students can be very effective in identifying and clarifying misunderstandings. You might want to have them note the items they missed and work either in groups or at home to correct them. It is important for students to receive feedback on every chapter test, and we recommend that students see and correct their mistakes before proceeding too far into the next chapter.

Suggestions for Assignment Assign Lesson 12-1 for homework the evening of the test. It gives students work to do after they have completed the test and keeps the class moving. If you do not do this, you may cover one less chapter over the course of the year.

Additional Answers

53a. Answers vary. Sample: $h(x) = x(x + 1)(x - 1)(x - 3)$

53b. $h(x) = 3x^4 - 9x^3 - 3x^2 + 9x$

53c.

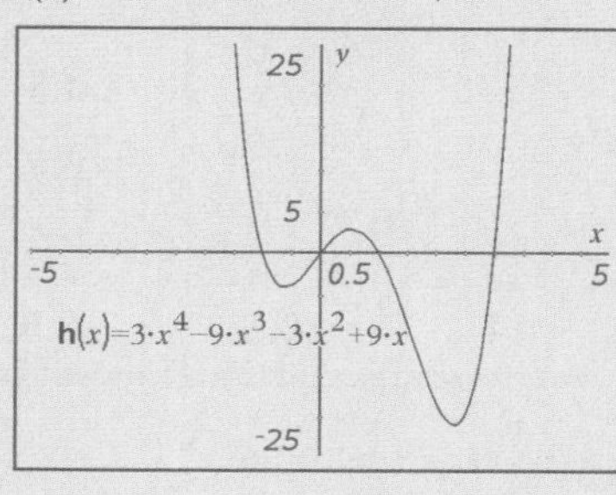

54a. Answers vary. Sample: $f(x) = x^3 - 21x - 20$

54b.

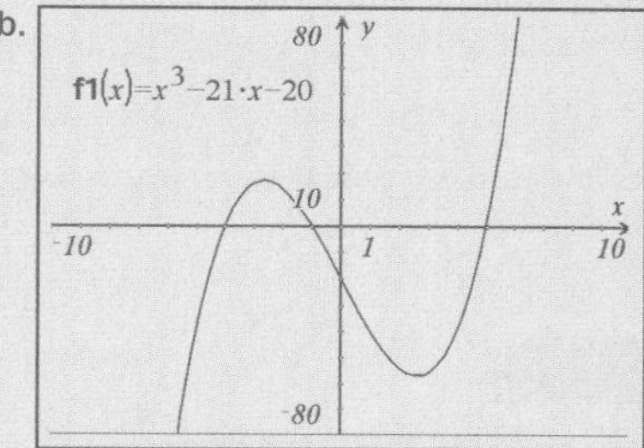

54c. $f(x) = k(x + 4)(x + 1)(x - 5)$

54d. They have the same x-intercepts.

Additional Answers

55. $x = -4$, $x = -3$, $x = -3$, or $x = -1$

56. 4 and 5; 9 and 10

57a. $\pm6, \pm3, \pm2, \pm\frac{3}{2}, \pm1, \pm\frac{1}{2}$

57b. You should test ±1 and $-\frac{3}{2}$ because the graph indicates that the function does not cross the x-axis around the other values.

57c. There are no rational roots.

Chapter

12 Quadratic Relations

Chapter Overview

	Local Standards	Pacing (in days) Average	Advanced	Block
12-1 Parabolas **B** Write equations for quadratic relations and inequalities for their interiors and exteriors. **E** Identify characteristics of parabolas, circles, ellipses, and hyperbolas. **F** Classify curves as circles, ellipses, parabolas, or hyperbolas using algebraic or geometric properties. **L** Draw a graph or interpret drawings or graphs of conic sections based on their definitions.		1	0.75	0.5
12-2 Circles **B, E, F, L** See 12-1. **G** Use circles and ellipses to solve real-world problems. **I** Graph quadratic relations when given equations for them in standard form, and vice versa.		1	0.75	0.5
12-3 Semicircles, Interiors, and Exteriors of Circles **B** See 12-1. **G** See 12-2. **J** Graph interiors and exteriors of ellipses when given inequalities for them, and vice versa.		1	0.75	0.5
QUIZ 1		0.5	0.5	0.25
12-4 Ellipses **B, E, F** See 12-1. **G, I, L** See 12-2.		1	0.75	0.5
12-5 Relationships between Ellipses and Circles **C** Find the area of an ellipse. **F, G** See 12-2.		1	0.75	0.5
12-6 Equations for Some Hyperbolas **B, E, F, L** See 12-1. **I** See 12-2.		1	0.75	0.5
12-7 A General Equation for Quadratic Relations **A** Rewrite an equation for a conic section in the standard form of a quadratic equation in two variables. **B, E, I** See 12-2.		1	0.75	0.5
QUIZ 2		0.5	0.5	0.25
12-8 Quadratic-Linear Systems **D** Solve systems of one linear and one quadratic equation or two quadratic equations with and without technology. **H** Use systems of quadratic equations to solve real-world problems. **K** Interpret representations of quadratic-linear and quadratic-quadratic systems.		1	0.75	0.5
12-9 Quadratic-Quadratic Systems **D, H, K** See 12-8.		1	0.75	0.5
	Self-Test	1	0.75	0.5
	Chapter Review	2	1	0.5
	Test	1	1	0.5
	TOTAL	14	10.5	6.5

Technology Resources

Teacher's Assessment Assistant, Ch. 12

Electronic Teacher's Edition, Ch. 12

Differentiated Options  Universal Access

	Accommodating the Learner	Vocabulary Development	Ongoing Assessment	Materials
12-1	pp. 801, 803	p. 800	group, p. 803	compass, straightedge
12-2	pp. 805, 808–809	p. 809	group, p. 809	
12-3	pp. 811, 814	p. 814	written, p. 815	
12-4	pp. 817, 818–819	p. 817	written, p. 823	conic graph paper with 8 units between the centers of the circles
12-5	pp. 826, 827	p. 826	written, p. 830	
12-6	pp. 833, 834	p. 835	oral, p. 837	conic graph paper with 6 units between the centers of the circles
12-7	pp. 841, 842	p. 839	written, p. 843	
12-8	pp. 846–847	p. 845	group, p. 849	
12-9	pp. 852, 854	p. 851	written, p. 855	DGS (optional)

Objectives

Skills	Lessons	Self-Test Questions	Chapter Review Questions
A Rewrite an equation for a conic section in the standard form of a quadratic equation in two variables.	12-7	1a, 1b	1–6
B Write equations for quadratic relations and inequalities for their interiors and exteriors.	12-1, 12-2, 12-3, 12-4, 12-6, 12-7	2, 3, 18	7–16
C Find the area of an ellipse.	12-5	8	17–20
D Solve systems of one linear and one quadratic equation or two quadratic equations with and without technology.	12-8, 12-9	12	21–27
Properties			
E Identify characteristics of parabolas, circles, ellipses, and hyperbolas.	12-1, 12-2, 12-4, 12-6, 12-7	4, 10, 13b, 13c	28–34
F Classify curves as circles, ellipses, parabolas, or hyperbolas using algebraic or geometric properties.	12-1, 12-2, 12-4, 12-5, 12-6	1c , 5, 9, 13a	35–41
Uses			
G Use circles and ellipses to solve real-world problems.	12-2, 12-3, 12-4, 12-5	14, 16, 19	42–45
H Use systems of quadratic equations to solve real-world problems.	12-8, 12-9	6, 15	46–49
Representations			
I Graph quadratic relations when given equations for them in standard form, and vice versa.	12-2, 12-4, 12-6, 12-7	7, 10	50–57
J Graph interiors and exteriors of ellipses when given inequalities for them, and vice versa.	12-3	20	58–60
K Interpret representations of quadratic-linear and quadratic-quadratic systems.	12-8, 12-9	11, 17	61–64
L Draw a graph or interpret drawings or graphs of conic sections based on their definitions.	12-1, 12-2, 12-4, 12-6	18	65–71

Resource Masters Chapter 12

Resource Master 12, Graph Paper (page 2), can be used with Lesson 12-2, 12-4, 12-6, and 12-8.

Resource Master 222 Lesson 12-1

Resource Master 221 Lesson 12-1

Warm-up

You are given line ℓ with equation $y = 10$ and the point $P = (0, 0)$. The distance from a point to a line is the length of a perpendicular segment from that point to the line. Find three points, each of whose distance from ℓ is equal to its distance from P.

Additional Example

What is an equation for a parabola with focus (0, 1) and directrix $y = -1$?

Resource Masters for Lesson 12-1

Resource Master 224 Lesson 12-2

Resource Master 223 Lesson 12-2

Warm-Up

1. What is the distance between (a, b) and (c, d)?
2. What is the *square* of the distance between (a, b) and (c, d)?
3. What is the distance between (x, y) and $(5, -8)$?
4. If the distance between (x, y) and (h, k) is r, what is an equation relating all five variables?

Additional Examples

1. Suppose a pebble dropped in still water starts a series of ripples that radiate outward at a speed of 2 meters/second. Find an equation for the location of points on the first ripple in 5 seconds.
2. What is an equation for the circle with radius $\frac{15}{4}$ and center $\left(5, \frac{7}{4}\right)$?

   Solution Let (x, y) be any point on the circle. Using the Distance Formula,
   $\sqrt{(x - \_\_\_)^2 + (y - \_\_\_)^2} = \_\_\_$. Squaring both sides,
   $(x - \_\_\_)^2 + (y - \_\_\_)^2 = \_\_\_$.
3. a. Find the center and radius of a circle with equation $(x - 7)^2 + (y + 8)^2 = 121$.

   b. Graph this circle.

   c. What transformation maps the circle with equation $x^2 + y^2 = 121$ onto the circle you graphed in Part b?

Resource Masters for Lesson 12-2

Resource Master 225 Lesson 12-2

Extension

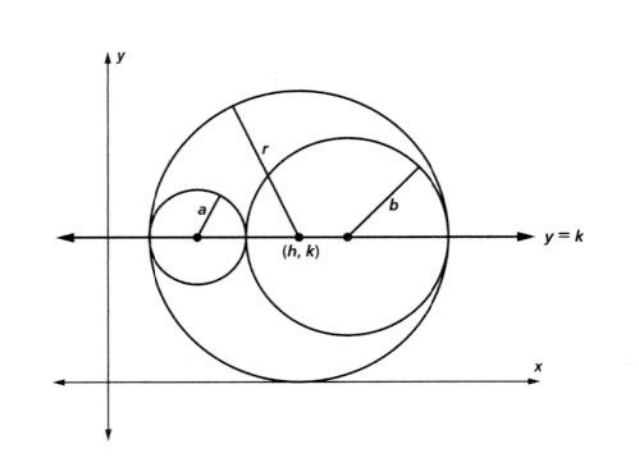

Resource Master for Lesson 12-2

Resource Master 227 Lesson 12-3

Resource Master 226 Lesson 12-3

Warm-Up

In 1–7, tell whether the point is on, inside, or outside a circle with center (0, 0) and radius 65.

1. (1, 8)
2. (65, 65)
3. (-25, 60)
4. (-56, -33)
5. $(\sqrt{65}, 0)$
6. $(4\sqrt{66}, -4\sqrt{66})$
7. (23, 61)

Additional Examples

1. For the situation in Example 1, suppose the passageway is 10 feet wide and 12 feet tall with a semicircular arch at its top. Also suppose the x-axis represents the floor, with the origin at the center of the passageway.
   a. What is an equation for the semicircle representing the arch?
   b. How high is the arch at a point on the ground 4 feet from the center of the passageway?
2. Graph the points satisfying $(x - 3)^2 + (y + 2)^2 > 5$.

Resource Masters for Lesson 12-3

Resource Master 228 Lesson 12-3

Accommodating the Learner

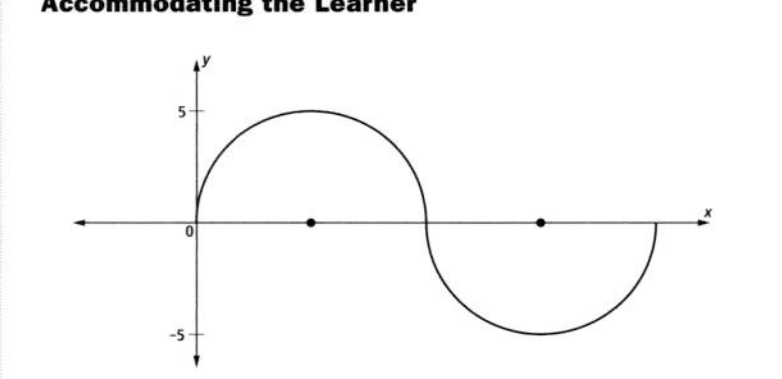

Extension

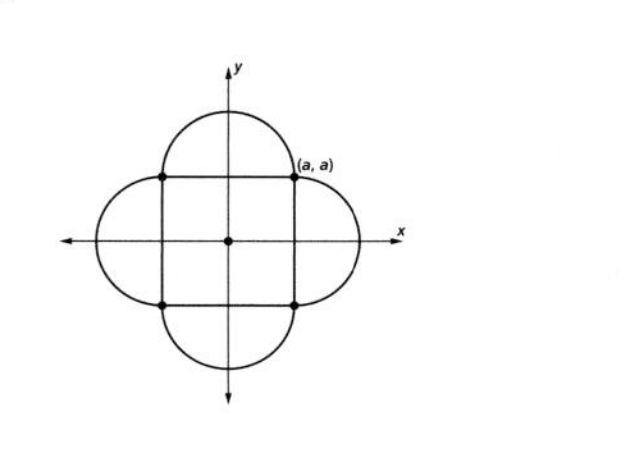

Resource Master for Lesson 12-3

Resource Master 230 Lesson 12-4

Resource Master 229 Lesson 12-4

Warm-Up

In 1–3, consider the equation $\frac{x^2}{25} + \frac{y^2}{16} = 1$.

1. The point (5, 0) satisfies this equation. What are three other points on the axes that satisfy the equation? Graph the four points.
2. Use substitution to show that the point (4, 2.4) satisfies this equation. Use the symmetry of the graph to find three other points on the graph. Graph the four points.
3. When $x = 3$, find the two values of y that satisfy the equation. Repeat with $x = -3$. Graph the four points.

Activity

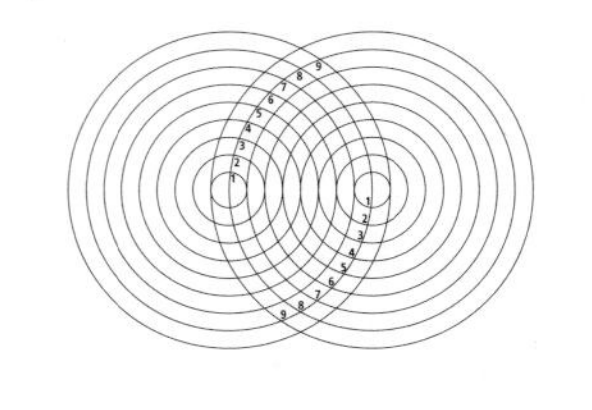

Resource Masters for Lesson 12-4

Resource Master 232 Lesson 12-4

Resource Master 231 Lesson 12-4

Additional Examples

2. Find the endpoints of the major and minor axes, the foci, and an equation for an ellipse formed when there are 4 units between the centers of the circles. The focal constant is 5. How does this equation relate to the figure constructed in the Activity on page 816?

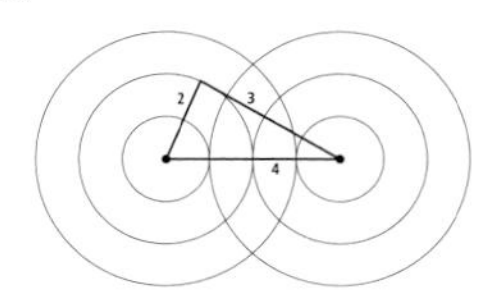

Solution Position a coordinate system on the ellipse with origin at the center of the ellipse and the foci on the x-axis. The radius of the smallest circle is 1 unit. The major axis has length _____, so $a =$ _____. The minor axis has length _____, so $b =$ _____. Therefore, in standard position, the endpoints of the major axis of the ellipse are _________ and _________, and the endpoints of the minor axis are _________ and _________. The foci for the ellipse are _________ and _________. An equation for this ellipse is _________.

3. Consider the ellipse with equation $\frac{x^2}{8} + \frac{y^2}{16} = 1$.
   a. Identify the endpoints and the lengths of the major and minor axes.
   b. Graph the ellipse.

Resource Masters for Lesson 12-4

Resource Master 234 Lesson 12-5

Resource Master 233 Lesson 12-5

Warm-Up

1. Find the area of a triangle with vertices $A = (-2, 5)$, $B = (8, 5)$, and $C = (8, 9)$.
2. What is the image $\triangle A'B'C'$, of the above triangle under $S_{4,6}$?
3. What is the area of $\triangle A'B'C'$?

Additional Example

What is an equation for the image of the unit circle $x^2 + y^2 = 1$ under $S_{9,5}$?

Solution Let (x', y') be the image of (x, y) on the circle. Then $(x', y') = (9x, 5y)$. So $x' = 9x$ and $y' = 5y$. Solve these equations for x and y: $x =$ _________ and $y =$ _________. Because $x^2 + y^2 = 1$, substitute the expressions for x and y involving x' and y' into $x^2 + y^2 = 1$ to get an equation for the image: _________ + _________ = 1. Using x and y for x' and y', the equation is _________ + _________ = 1. That equation represents an ellipse with a minor axis of length _____ and a major axis of length _____.

Resource Masters for Lesson 12-5

Resource Master 236 Lesson 12-6

Resource Master 235 Lesson 12-6

Warm-Up

In 1–3, complete the table of values for each equation.

1. $\frac{x^2}{9} - \frac{y^2}{9} = 1$

x	3	4	5	6
y				

2. $\frac{x^2}{25} - y^2 = 1$

x	-5	-10	-15	-20
y				

3. $x^2 - \frac{y^2}{4} = 1$

x	-4	-2	2	4
y				

Additional Examples

1. Find an equation for the hyperbola with foci F_1 and F_2, where $F_1F_2 = 26$ and $|PF_1 - PF_2| = 10$, on a rectangular system in standard position.
2. Graph the hyperbola with equation $\frac{x^2}{25} - \frac{y^2}{4} = 1$.

Resource Masters for Lesson 12-6

Resource Master 238 Lesson 12-7

Resource Master 237 Lesson 12-7

Warm-Up

According to the theorem on page 841, the graph of $xy = 50$ is a hyperbola with foci (10, 10) and (-10, -10) and focal constant 20.

1. Show that the difference between the distances from the point (2, 25) to the two foci is 20.
2. Show that the difference between the distances from the point (-1, -50) to the two foci is also 20.

Additional Examples

1. Show that the circle with equation $(x + 3)^2 + (y - 5)^2 = 8$ is a quadratic relation.
2. Find an equation of the form $y = \frac{k}{x}$ for the hyperbola with foci (4, 4) and (-4, -4) and focal constant 8.
3. Find an equation of the form $y = \frac{k}{x}$ for the hyperbola with foci (3, 3) and (-3, -3) and focal constant 6.

   Solution The hyperbola has foci $(\sqrt{2k}, \sqrt{2k})$ and _________. So (_____, _____) = $(\sqrt{2k}, \sqrt{2k})$. Solve for k: _____ $= \sqrt{2k}$, _____ $= 2k$, so _____ $= k$. Substitute _____ for k in $y = \frac{k}{x}$. An equation for the hyperbola is $y =$ _________.

Resource Masters for Lesson 12-7

Resource Master 239 Lesson 12-8

Warm-Up

What are at least two ways to answer the following question? A room in a dance hall is to be a square with area 2500 square feet. A stage needs to be added at one end for musicians, which lengthens the room into a rectangle. If the stage is 15 feet deep and the total area of the room cannot be greater than 2500 square feet, how large (rounded to the nearest inch) can the original square be?

Additional Examples

1. Find exact solutions to the system $\begin{cases} xy = 6 \\ 2x + y = 8 \end{cases}$.
2. In this graph below of the equations $x^2 + y^2 = 25$ and $y = \frac{4}{3}x + \frac{25}{3}$, it appears that there is only one point of intersection, (-4, 3). Is this so? Justify your answer.

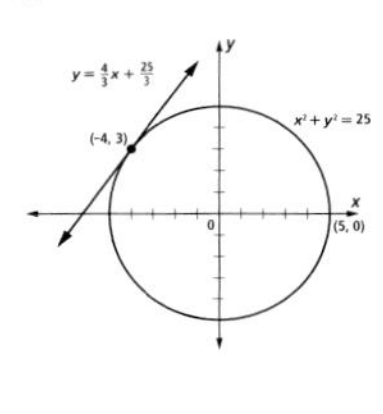

Resource Master for Lesson 12-8

Resource Master 240 Lesson 12-8

Additional Example

3. Find the points of intersection of the line $y = \frac{x}{2} + 1$ and the parabola $y = -x^2$.

   Solution Solve the system $\begin{cases} y = \frac{x}{2} + 1 \\ y = -x^2 \end{cases}$. Substitute _________ for y in the second equation: _________ $= -x^2$. Put this equation in standard form: _________ = 0. From the Quadratic Formula, $x =$ _________ or _________. Both solutions are nonreal complex numbers, so there are _____ points of intersection.

Solutions to Quadratic-Linear Systems, Geometrically

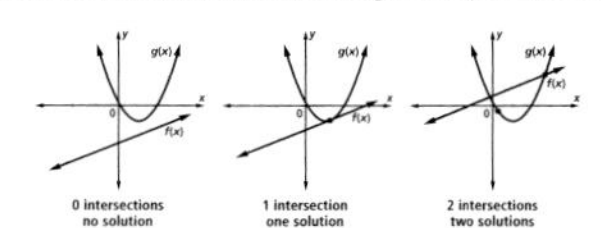

Accommodating the Learner

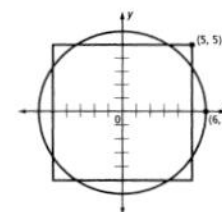

Resource Master for Lesson 12-8

Resource Master 241 Lesson 12-8

Activity

Quadratic Relation	Number of Intersections within Line
Parabola	0, 1, or 2
Circle	
Ellipse	
Hyperbola	

Extension

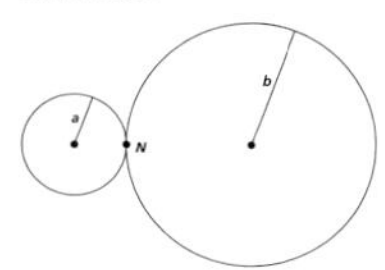

Resource Master for Lesson 12-8

Resource Master 242 Lesson 12-9

Warm-Up

1. Solve $4a + 3b = 37$ and $3a - b = 5$.
2. How many pairs of numbers are there so that the sum of the numbers is 11 and the sum of the squares of the numbers is 100?

Additional Examples

1. On a coordinate system, P is 4 units from the origin and 3 units from the point (-2, -1). Find the possible locations for point P.
2. Find all solutions (x, y) to $\begin{cases} 2x^2 + y^2 = 41 \\ 4x^2 - 3y^2 = 7 \end{cases}$.

   Solution This system represents the intersection of a(n) _________ and a(n) _________. There are 0, 1, 2, 3, or 4 possible solutions. Use the linear combination method to find them. Multiply the first equation by 3 and add the equations to eliminate y:

   $6x^2 + 3y^2 = 123$
   _____ x^2 − _____ y^2 = _____
   _____ x^2 = _____
   x^2 = _____
   x = _____

   Substitute each value of x into one of the given equations. If $x =$ _____, then $2($_____$)^2 + y^2 = 41$, so $y = \pm$ _________. If $x =$ _____, then $2($_____$)^2 + y^2 = 7$, so $y = \pm$ _________. So, this system has four solutions: _________, _________, _________, and _________.

Resource Master for Lesson 12-9

Resource Master 243 Lesson 12-9

Additional Example

3. Yesterday, a music store took in \$845 from CD sales. Today, they lowered the price of CDs by \$4 each and took in \$855 in CD sales by selling 30 more CDs than yesterday. Find the cost of a CD yesterday and today.

Activity

	Parabola	Circle	Ellipse	Hyperbola
Parabola				
Circle				
Ellipse		0, 1, 2, 3, 4 or infinitely many		
Hyperbola				

Resource Master for Lesson 12-9

Chapter 12

Pacing

Each lesson in this chapter is designed to be covered in 1 day. At the end of the chapter, you should plan to spend 1 day to review the Self-Test, 1 to 2 days for the Chapter Review, and 1 day for a test. You may wish to spend a day on projects and possibly a day is needed for quizzes. This chapter should therefore take 13 to 17 days. We strongly advise you not to spend more than 18 days on this chapter.

Overview

The graphs of quadratic relations are *conic sections.* The systematic study of conic sections dates back to Apollonius in about 225 BCE. In the 17th century, Fermat and Descartes studied them analytically. Traditionally, they are covered either in a second-year course in algebra or in a precalculus course. This chapter contains the only in-depth discussion of quadratic relations in the UCSMP secondary school curriculum.

There are many interesting applications of conic sections. Applications to the orbits of planets, satellites, and comets are of great scientific and historical importance and should be part of every person's education. The reflection properties of the conics, as used in headlights, satellite dishes, and radio antennas, are common, everyday applications.

Quadratic relations complete an area of study, including inequalities and nonfunctions, and provide a picture of all quadratic sentences in two variables, that is, sentences of the form $Ax^2 + Bxy + Cy^2 + Dx + Ey + F$ __?__ 0 (where the blank is either $=, <, >, \leq$, or $\geq$). This role is also played by linear relations of the form $Ax + By$ __?__ C.

Quadratic relations also provide a second look at quadratic equations and systems of equations. Asymptotes and limits with hyperbolas and transformations with circles and ellipses are also reviewed. Thus, quadratic relations provide skill

Chapter 12 Quadratic Relations

Contents

The general quadratic equation in two variables x and y is the equation

$$Ax^2 + Bxy + Cy^2 + Dx + Ey + F = 0,$$

where A, B, C, D, E, and F are real numbers, and at least one of A, B, or C is not zero. The set of ordered pairs that satisfy a sentence equivalent to one in the above form is called a *quadratic relation* in two variables.

Chapter 12 Overview

This chapter continues and deepens the study of quadratic equations started in Chapter 2 (with a discussion of $y = kx^2$) and continued in Chapter 6 (with a discussion of $y = ax^2 + bx + c$). By the end of this chapter, students will have studied all the quadratic relations. We attempt to balance the traditional skills of manipulating expressions and solving equations with an analysis of the relationship between the coefficients of equations and the properties of graphs.

Quadratic relations may be defined in three ways: (1) geometrically in three dimensions, such as intersections of a plane with a double cone; (2) geometrically in one dimension, such as the locus of points in a plane satisfying certain conditions; and (3) algebraically, by equations. This chapter uses the first type of definition to show the broad geometric relationships among the curves and then makes connections between the three definitions.

Quadratic relations have connections with a wide variety of ideas you have already studied. Those ideas include the parabolas you studied in Chapters 2 and 6 and the hyperbolas you saw in Chapter 2. Quadratic relations also describe the orbits of comets, satellites, and planets, and the shapes of communication receivers and mirrors used in car headlights.

Quadratic relations may also be defined geometrically as the intersection of a plane and a *double cone*. Such cross sections of a double cone are called *conic sections*, or simply *conics*. They include hyperbolas, parabolas, and ellipses. In this description, circles are special cases of ellipses.

In this chapter, you will study quadratic relations both algebraically, as equations and inequalities, and geometrically, as figures with certain properties. You will also see some of the many situations these relations model.

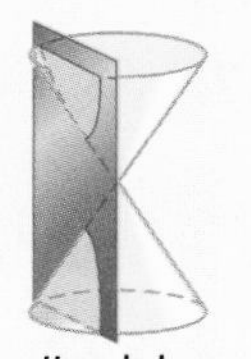

Hyperbola: A plane intersects both cones.

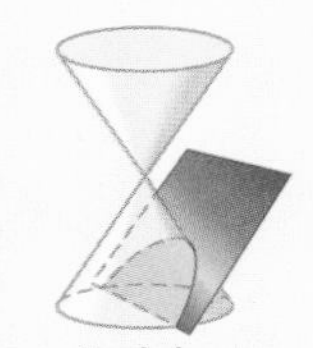

Parabola: A plane intersects one cone and is parallel to the cone's edge.

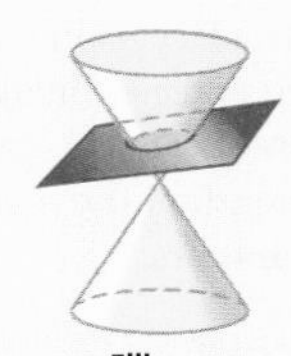

Ellipse: A plane intersects one cone but is not parallel to the cone's edge.

Lesson 12-1 introduces the parabola geometrically as the set of points equidistant from a given point and a given line. This approach enables us to prove that $y = x^2$ is indeed a parabola. The chapter continues with two lessons on circles (Lessons 12-2 and 12-3), followed by three (Lessons 12-4 through 12-6). The chapter puts all the quadratic relations together in Lesson 12-7 and closes with two lessons (Lessons 12-8 and 12-9) on quadratic systems.

review and enhancement by practicing and extending previous knowledge without introducing new concepts.

Using Pages 796–797

Suggest that students examine the chapter objectives on pages 862–865. Point out that many ideas from earlier chapters are extended in this chapter.

We use the term *double cone* in place of a two-napped cone, as it is sometimes called, because the latter is seldom used outside of an algebra classroom. A double cone is formed by rotating a line (in space) about a line it intersects (its axis). Any of the possible images of the line is an *edge* of the cone.

As an introduction to the chapter, you may want to use a cone, if available, to illustrate how the conic sections can be viewed geometrically in three dimensions. Discuss the connection between conic sections and quadratic relations (circles, "sideways" parabolas, ellipses, and hyperbolas) that students will study in this chapter. Ask students to give a few examples of quadratic equations that describe parabolas and hyperbolas. Show how these equations are special cases of $Ax^2 + By^2 + Cxy + Dx + Ey + F = 0$—the general quadratic equation.

Chapter 12 Projects

At the end of each chapter, you will find projects related to the chapter. At this time you might want to have students look over the projects on pages 856 and 857. You might want to have students tentatively select a project on which to work. Then, as students read and progress through the chapter, they can finalize their project choices.

Sometimes students might work alone. At other times, you might let them collaborate with classmates for a presentation and discussion. We recommend that you allow for diversity and encourage students to use their imaginations when presenting their projects. As students work on projects throughout the year, they should see many uses of mathematics in the real world.

Lesson

12-1

GOAL

Introduce a locus-type definition for the parabola; derive an equation of the form $y = ax^2$, where $a = \frac{1}{4k}$, for a parabola with focus $(0, k)$ and horizontal directrix $y = -k$.

SPUR Objectives

The SPUR Objectives for all of Chapter 12 are found in the Chapter Review on pages 862–865.

B Write equations for parabolas.

E Identify characteristics of parabolas.

F Classify curves as parabolas using algebraic or geometric properties.

L Draw a graph or interpret drawings or graphs of parabolas based on their definitions.

Materials/Resources

- Lesson Masters 12-1A and 12-1B
- Resource Masters 221 and 222
- Compass, straightedge

HOMEWORK

Suggestions for Assignment

- Questions 1–21
- Question 22 (extra credit)
- Reading Lesson 12-2
- Covering the Ideas 12-2

Local Standards

1 Warm-Up

You are given line ℓ with equation $y = 10$ and the point $P = (0, 0)$. The distance from a point to a line is the length of a perpendicular segment from that point to the line. Find three points, each of whose distance from ℓ is equal to its distance from P. Answers vary. Sample: Three points that are on the parabola with focus (0, 0) and directrix $y = 10$ are (0, 5), (10, 0), and (–10, 0).

Lesson

12-1 Parabolas

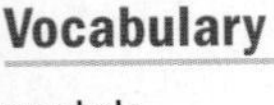

Vocabulary

parabola
focus, directrix
axis of symmetry
vertex of a parabola
paraboloid

BIG IDEA From the geometric definition of a parabola, it can be proved that the graph of the equation $y = ax^2$ is a *parabola*.

Mental Math

Which expression or equation is not equivalent to the others?

a. $\log_{10} 1742$, $\log_{16} 1742$, $\log 1742$ $\log_{16} 1742$

b. $\log_3 100$, $2 \log_3 10$, $\log_3 20$ $\log_3 20$

c. $r = e^{3t}$, $r = 3e^t$, $\ln r = 3t$ $r = 3e^t$

d. $\frac{\ln 2}{\ln p}$, $\frac{\log 2}{\log p}$, $\frac{\log_6 2}{\log_6 p}$ All are equivalent.

What Is a Parabola?

In Chapter 6 you were told that the path of a shot or tossed object, such as a fly ball in baseball, is part of a *parabola*.

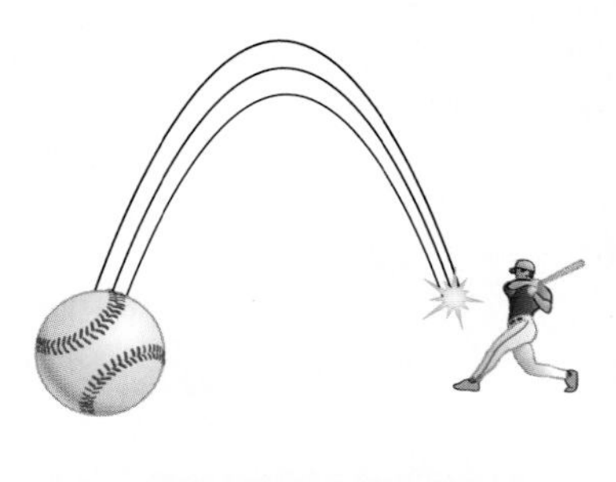

But how do we know this? In order to determine whether a curve is a parabola, a definition of *parabola* is necessary. Here is a geometric definition.

Definition of Parabola

Let ℓ be a line and F be a point not on ℓ. A **parabola** is the set of all points in the plane of ℓ and F equidistant from F and ℓ.

To understand the definition of parabola, recall that the distance from a point P to a line ℓ is the length of the perpendicular from P to ℓ. In the diagram at the right below, four points on a parabola, V, P_1, P_2, and P_3, are identified. Note that each is equidistant from F and the line ℓ. For example, $\overline{P_1Q_1} \perp \ell$ and $P_1Q_1 = P_1F$. Also, $\overline{P_2Q_2} \perp \ell$ and $P_2Q_2 = P_2F$, and so on.

F is the **focus** and ℓ is the **directrix** of the parabola. Thus, a parabola is the set of points in a plane equidistant from its focus and its directrix. Neither the focus nor directrix is on the parabola. The line through the focus perpendicular to the directrix is the **axis of symmetry** of the parabola. The point V on the parabola and on the axis of symmetry is the **vertex of the parabola**.

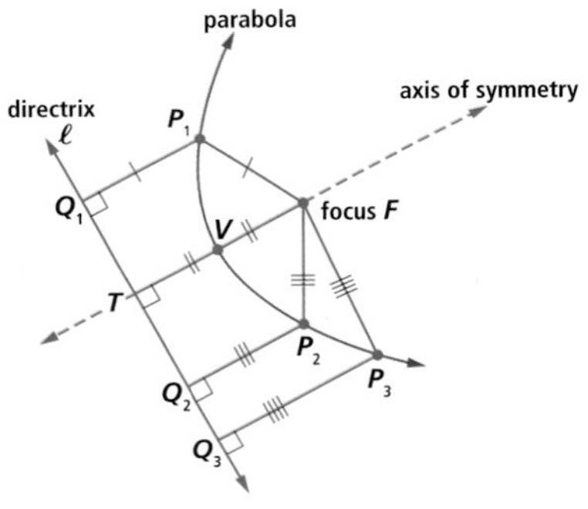

Background

This lesson extends concepts that students previously studied. Chapters 2 and 6 *asserted* that the graph of $y = x^2$ was a parabola. But how do we confirm that assertion if we do not have a definition of a *parabola*? Some possibilities are defining a parabola algebraically as the set of points that satisfy some general equation (see Lesson 2-5) or geometrically as a particular conic section (as on page 796). However, at this level, it is most common to define a parabola as a *locus*—a set of points that satisfies some condition(s). Students know the definition of a *circle* as a locus (it is the set of points in a plane at a particular distance from a fixed point), so they are familiar with the idea. We do not use *locus* or *locus of points* in the lesson; the phrase *set of points* works well without introducing a new term.

Example The parabola with focus $(0, k)$ and directrix $y = -k$ has equation $y = \frac{1}{4k}x^2$. The Example is a specific case of this general property, with $k = 2$. The theorem that

 QY1

Drawing a Parabola

You can draw as many points on a parabola as you wish using only a compass and a straightedge.

▶ QY1

FV is equal to what other distance shown in the diagram on the previous page?

Activity Steps 1–3a, 4, 5a, 6–7. See the Additional Answers section at the back of the book.

MATERIALS compass, straightedge

Step 1 Begin with a blank sheet of paper. Draw a directrix ℓ and a focus F not on ℓ. With H on ℓ, construct $\overleftrightarrow{FH}$ perpendicular to ℓ. Then construct the midpoint of $\overline{FH}$ and label it V for vertex. Your drawing should resemble the one at the right.

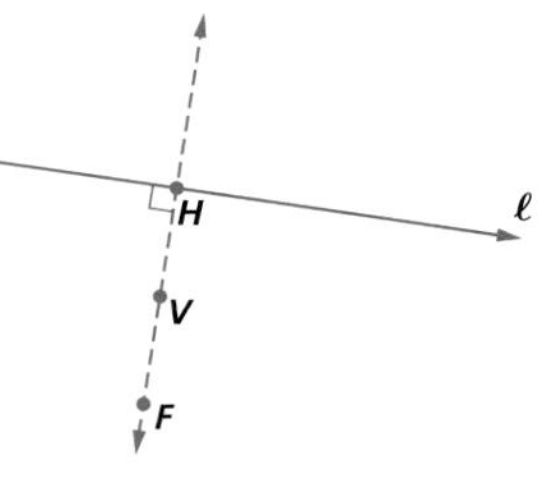

Step 2 Let $FH = d$. Construct a line segment parallel to ℓ of length $2d$ through F, where F is the midpoint. Label the endpoints of this segment P_1 and P_2.

Step 3 a. Construct perpendicular line segments from P_1 to ℓ and P_2 to ℓ. Note that P_1 and P_2 are vertices of squares with $\overline{FH}$ as the common side.

b. How does FP_1 compare to the perpendicular distance from P_1 to ℓ? What does this tell you about P_1?

c. How does FP_2 compare to the perpendicular distance from P_2 to ℓ? What does this tell you about P_2?

Step 4 Construct a circle with center F and any radius $r > \frac{d}{2}$.

Step 5 a. Construct a line n parallel to ℓ that is distance r from ℓ. (*Hint:* Use your compass to measure r.) Label the two intersections of this line and the circle P_3 and P_4.

b. Are P_3 and P_4 on the parabola? Justify your answer.

Step 6 Find two more points by repeating Steps 4 and 5 for a different $r > \frac{d}{2}$.

Step 7 You have found seven points on the parabola. Connect them with a smooth curve to sketch part of a parabola.

Step 3b. FP_1 = perpendicular distance from P_1 to ℓ. P_1 is on the parabola with focus F and directrix ℓ.

Step 3c. FP_2 = perpendicular distance from P_2 to ℓ. P_2 is also on the parabola.

Step 5b. Yes; they are equidistant from F and ℓ. (Each distance is r.)

Equations for Parabolas

Suppose that you know the coordinates of the focus and an equation for the directrix of a parabola. You can find an equation for the parabola by using the definition of parabola and the Pythagorean Distance Formula.

2 Teaching

Notes on the Lesson

You might begin the lesson by asking students to describe the set of points (in a plane) that are equidistant from two given points. the perpendicular bisector of the segment whose endpoints are the given points Next ask for the set of points equidistant from two parallel lines. the line parallel to the given lines and halfway between them Then ask for the set of points equidistant from two intersecting lines. the bisectors of the angles formed by the given lines Finally, ask for the set of points that are equidistant from a point and a line and show that they lie on a parabola. Alternatively, you may wish to begin the lesson by working through Question 22 with the class.

Activity The Activity on page 799 gives an algorithm for finding points on a parabola with focus F and directrix ℓ.

1. Draw the line at a distance r from ℓ on the same side as F.
2. Draw a circle with center F and radius r. If r is large enough, the line and circle will intersect in two points that are on the parabola. By picking other values of r, other points on the parabola can be found.

If students pick their own focus and directrix, eventually they will see the shape of a parabola emerging. The words *vertex, focus, directrix,* and *axis of symmetry* are easily discussed at this time.

This Activity is quite difficult for some students, so you may want to demonstrate it first or complete it together as a class.

Additional Answers can be found in the back of the book.

follows on page 801 replaces k by $\frac{1}{4a}$. Using the Graph-Translation Theorem, you can derive an equation for any parabola with a vertical line of symmetry. This is suggested in Question 11.

Focus and Directrix of a Parabola Theorem The theorem covers cases when a is positive and when a is negative. However, the examples in this lesson have $a > 0$. When $a < 0$, the parabola with equation $y = ax^2$ opens down because its directrix is above the x-axis ($-\frac{1}{4a}$ is positive) and the focus is below the x-axis. In general, a parabola opens up when its directrix is below its focus and opens down when its directrix is above its focus.

Notes on the Lesson

Example The definition of a parabola is used to find an equation for a parabola. Work through this process with students because it is a difficult derivation, although it is a type found throughout the chapter.

The Graph-Translation Theorem implies the following generalization of the Focus and Directrix of a Parabola Theorem on page 801: The graph of $y - k = a(x - h)^2$ is a parabola with focus at $\left(h, k + \frac{1}{4a}\right)$ and directrix at $y = k - \frac{1}{4a}$. Because any quadratic equation of the form $y = ax^2 + bx + c$ can be put into the vertex form $y - k = a(x - h)^2$, which is always a parabola with a vertical axis of symmetry, it immediately follows that the graph of any quadratic function in one variable is a parabola with a vertical axis of symmetry.

Additional Example

Example What is an equation for a parabola with focus (0, 1) and directrix $y = -1$? $(x, -1)$ is on the directrix, and (x, y) is on the parabola, so $\sqrt{(x - 0)^2 + (y - 1)^2} = \sqrt{(x - x)^2 + (y - (-1))^2}$. So $x^2 + (y - 1)^2 = (y + 1)^2$; $x^2 + y^2 - 2y + 1 = y^2 + 2y + 1$; $x^2 = 4y$; $y = \frac{1}{4}x^2$.

Example

Find an equation for the parabola with focus $F = (0, 2)$ and directrix $y = -2$.

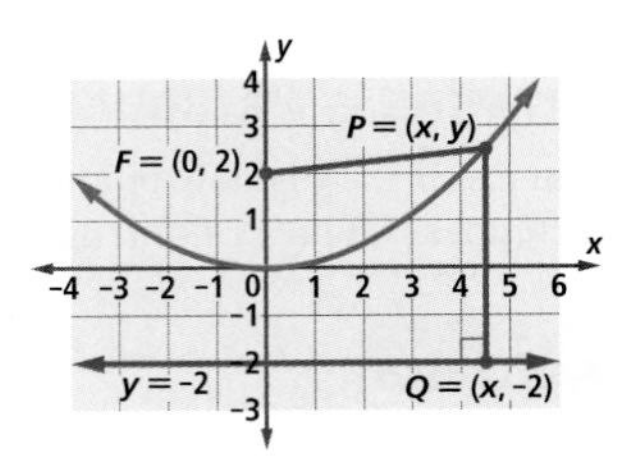

Solution Sketch the given information. Let $P = (x, y)$ be any point on the parabola. Because the directrix is a horizontal line, the distance from a point on the parabola to the directrix is measured along a vertical line. Let Q be the point on the directrix and on the vertical line through P. If $P = (x, y)$, then $Q = (x, -2)$.

$PF = PQ$	definition of parabola
$\sqrt{(x - 0)^2 + (y - 2)^2} = \sqrt{(x - x)^2 + (y - (-2))^2}$	Pythagorean Distance Formula
$x^2 + (y - 2)^2 = (y + 2)^2$	Square both sides.
$x^2 + y^2 - 4y + 4 = y^2 + 4y + 4$	Expand.
$x^2 - 4y = 4y$	Add $-y^2 - 4$ to both sides.
$x^2 = 8y$	Add $4y$ to both sides.
$y = \frac{1}{8}x^2$	Solve for y.

An equation for the parabola is $y = \frac{1}{8}x^2$.

Check Pick any point on $y = \frac{1}{8}x^2$. We use $A = (12, 18)$. Now show that A is equidistant from $F = (0, 2)$ and $y = -2$.

$$AF = \sqrt{(12 - 0)^2 + (18 - 2)^2} = \sqrt{12^2 + 16^2} = \sqrt{400} = 20$$

The distance from A to $y = -2$ is the distance from (12, 18) to (12, -2), which is 20, also. So, A is on the parabola with focus (0, 2) and directrix $y = -2$.

In the Example, if you replace the focus by $\left(0, \frac{1}{4}\right)$ and replace the directrix by $y = -\frac{1}{4}$, the equation for the parabola is $y = x^2$. If a is nonzero, (0, 2) is replaced by $\left(0, \frac{1}{4a}\right)$, and the directrix is replaced by $y = -\frac{1}{4a}$, then the parabola has equation $y = ax^2$. The derivation of both of these equations uses the same steps as the Example, and demonstrates the following theorem.

ENGLISH LEARNERS

Vocabulary Development

Although most students understand that *equidistant* refers to equal distances, some students are confused about how a point can be equidistant from both a point and a line. For the Example, guide students in understanding how $PF = \sqrt{(x - 0)^2 + (y - 2)^2}$ represents the distance between the two points (x, y) and (0, 2) and how $PQ = \sqrt{(x - x)^2 + (y - (-2))^2}$ represents the distance between the point (x, y) and the line $y = -2$.

Focus and Directrix of a Parabola Theorem

For any nonzero real number a, the graph of $y = ax^2$ is the parabola with focus at $\left(0, \frac{1}{4a}\right)$ and directrix at $y = -\frac{1}{4a}$.

QY2

Recall that because the image of the graph of $y = ax^2$ under the translation $T_{h,k}: (x, y) \rightarrow (x + h, y + k)$ is the graph with equation $y - k = a(x - h)^2$, the graph of any quadratic equation of the form $y = a(x - h)^2 + k$ or $y = ax^2 + bx + c$ is also a parabola. You can find the focus and directrix of a parabola with equation $y = a(x - h)^2 + k$ by applying the appropriate translation to the focus and directrix of $y = ax^2$.

When $a < 0$, you have learned that the parabola opens down. In this case, when the vertex is (0, 0), the directrix is above the x-axis, and the focus is below.

If a parabola is rotated in space around its axis of symmetry it creates a 3-dimensional **paraboloid**. The focus of a paraboloid is the focus of the rotated parabola. Paraboloids are common in modern technology. The shape of a satellite receiving dish is based on a paraboloid. Residents of a wheat-growing commune in southern China use a tiled solar reflector in the shape of a paraboloid. A teapot is placed at the focus of the paraboloid. Sunlight is reflected toward the teapot, boiling the water in 20 minutes without burning any wood, which is a precious resource. Cooking with a Dutch oven, as shown at the right, follows the same principle.

▶ QY2

Find the focus and directrix of the parabola with equation $y = -\frac{1}{6}x^2$.

Questions

COVERING THE IDEAS

1. a. Can the focus of a parabola be a point on the directrix? Why or why not? No; the focus is defined as a point not on the directrix.
   b. Can the vertex be on the directrix? Why or why not?

1b. No; the vertex must be equidistant from the focus and directrix, and a point on the directrix has distance zero from the directrix.

True or False In 2–4, refer to the parabola at the right with focus F and directrix ℓ. P_1, P_2, P_3, and P_4 are points on the parabola.

2. $P_3F = FG_3$ false
3. $FG_1 = FG_2$ false
4. The focus of this parabola is its vertex. false

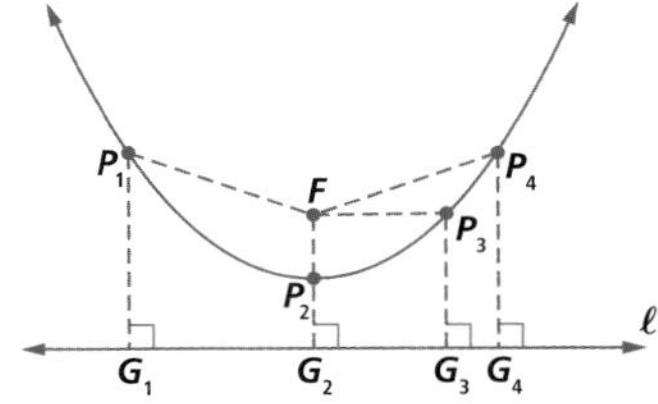

Note-Taking Tips

Encourage students to use two general headings for their notes in this lesson: "Description as a set of points" and "Algebraic description." General notes and comments about the focus and directrix would go under the first heading, while specific information about the focus $\left(0, \frac{1}{4a}\right)$ and the directrix $y = -\frac{1}{4a}$ for the graph of $y = ax^2$ would go under the second heading. Students will find these two headings useful in other lessons of the chapter.

3 Assignment

Recommended Assignment

- Questions 1–21
- Question 22 (extra credit)
- Reading Lesson 12-2
- Covering the Ideas 12-2

Accommodating the Learner ⬆

Give students a fixed point (a, b) and a horizontal line $y = c$. Tell them that (x, y) is any point equidistant from the point and the line and ask them to express y in terms of a, b, c, and x. The distance between (x, y) and (a, b) equals the distance between (x, y) and (x, c): $\sqrt{(x - a)^2 + (y - b)^2} = \sqrt{(x - x)^2 + (y - c)^2}$, so $x^2 - 2ax + a^2 + y^2 - 2by + b^2 = y^2 - 2cy + c^2$; $-2by + 2cy = c^2 - x^2 + 2ax - a^2 - b^2$. Therefore, $y(2c - 2b) = c^2 - x^2 + 2ax - a^2 - b^2$, so $y = \frac{c^2 + 2ax - x^2 - a^2 - b^2}{2c - 2b}$.

12-1A Lesson Master

Questions on SPUR Objectives
See Student Edition pages 862–865 for objectives.

SKILLS Objective B

In 1 and 2, write an equation for the parabola with the given focus and directrix.

1. focus (0, 6); directrix $y = -6$ $\quad y = \frac{1}{24}x^2$
2. focus $(0, -\frac{1}{2})$; directrix $y = \frac{1}{2}$ $\quad y = -\frac{1}{2}x^2$

PROPERTIES Objective E

In 3 and 4, the equation of a parabola is given. Find the coordinates of the focus and vertex and an equation for the directrix.

3. $y = \frac{1}{20}x^2$
   focus: (0, 5) vertex: (0, 0) directrix: $y = -5$
4. $y - 3 = 2(x + 5)^2$
   focus: $(-5, 3\frac{1}{8})$ vertex: (−5, 3) directrix: $y = 2\frac{7}{8}$
5. The point $(2, \frac{1}{3})$ is on the parabola $y = \frac{1}{12}x^2$. Find the distance from $(2, \frac{1}{3})$ to
   a. the point (0, 3). $\frac{10}{3}$
   b. the line $y = -3$. $\frac{10}{3}$

PROPERTIES Objective F

In 6–8, determine whether the figure described is a parabola.

6. The set of all points equidistant from $y = 5$ and (4, 4). yes
7. The set of all points equidistant from (0, 0) and (2, −3). no
8. The set of all points equidistant from $y = \frac{1}{2}x + 3$ and (2, 7). yes

REPRESENTATIONS Objective L

In 9 and 10, sketch the parabola with the given focus and directrix.

9.

10. focus (−1, 2), directrix $y = 4$

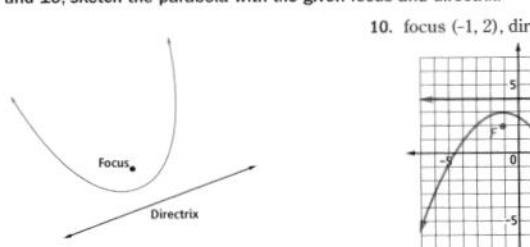

568 *Advanced Algebra*

Notes on the Questions

Question 6 When discussing this question, emphasize that because the focus is at $\left(0, -\frac{1}{4}\right)$ and the directrix is $y = \frac{1}{4}$, and because the vertex is a point of the parabola, the distance from the vertex to both the focus and the directrix is $\frac{1}{4}$.

Question 11 When the graph of a parabola is translated, its focus and its directrix are also translated.

Additional Answers

5a.

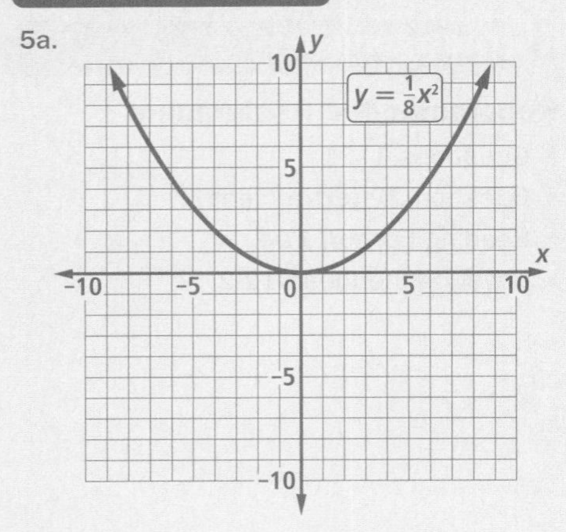

8a. Answers vary. Sample:

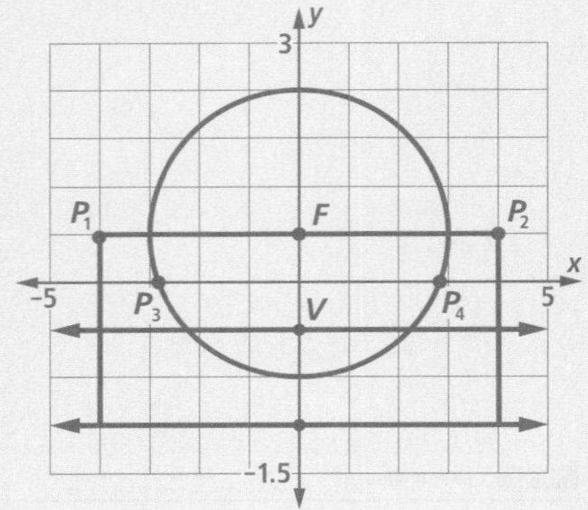

8c. The points are $V = (0, 0)$, $P_1 = (-2, 1)$, $P_2 = (2, 1)$, $P_3 \approx (-1.4, 0.5)$, and $P_4 \approx (1.4, 0.5)$. V is 1 unit from (0, 1) and $y = -1$. $P_1F = \sqrt{(-2-0)^2 + (1-1)^2} = 2$, and P_1 is $1 - (-1) = 2$ units from $y = -1$. Similarly, P_2, P_3, and P_4 are all equidistant from F and $y = -1$. So, all the points are on the parabola.

5. Refer to the Example.
   a. Graph the parabola with equation $y = \frac{1}{8}x^2$. See margin.
   b. Name its focus, vertex, and directrix.
   c. Verify that the point (5, 3.125) is equidistant from the focus and directrix, and therefore is a point on the parabola $y = \frac{1}{8}x^2$.
   d. Find another point on the graph of $y = \frac{1}{8}x^2$. Show that it is equidistant from the focus and directrix.
6. Verify that the graph of $y = -x^2$ is a parabola with focus $\left(0, -\frac{1}{4}\right)$ and directrix $y = \frac{1}{4}$ by choosing a point on the graph and showing that two appropriate distances are equal.
7. Let $F = (0, -3)$ and ℓ be the line with equation $y = 3$. Write an equation for the set of points equidistant from F and ℓ. $y = -\frac{1}{12}x^2$
8. a. Using graph paper, follow the steps of the Activity to draw five points that are on the parabola with focus $F = (0, 1)$ and directrix defined by $y = -1$. You do not need to construct with a ruler and compass. See margin.
   b. Refer to the Example. Find an equation for the parabola you drew in Part a. $y = \frac{1}{4}x^2$
   c. Verify that the points you drew in Part a are on the graph of the function defined in Part b. See margin.
9. Give the focus and directrix of the parabola with equation $y = -2xz^2$. $\left(0, -\frac{1}{8}\right)$; $y = \frac{1}{8}$
10. What is a paraboloid?

5b. focus: (0, 2); vertex: (0, 0); directrix: $y = -2$

5c. The distance from (5, 3.125) to (0, 2) is $\sqrt{(5-0)^2+(3.125-2)^2} = 5.125$, and the distance from (5, 3.125) to $y = -2$ is $3.125 - (-2) = 5.125$.

5d. Answers vary. Sample: (8, 8); $\sqrt{(8-0)^2+(8-2)^2} = 10 = 8 - (-2)$

6. Answers vary. Sample: (2, -4); $\sqrt{(2-0)^2+\left(-4-\left(-\frac{1}{4}\right)\right)^2} = 4.25 = \frac{1}{4} - (-4)$

10. A paraboloid is a 3-dimensional shape created by the rotation of a parabola in space about its axis of symmetry.

11. $\left(-5, \frac{25}{4}\right)$; $y = \frac{23}{4}$

APPLYING THE MATHEMATICS

11. What are the focus and directrix of $y - 6 = (x + 5)^2$?
12. Prove the Focus and Directrix of a Parabola Theorem. See margin.

In 13 and 14, an equation for a parabola is given.
a. Tell whether the parabola opens up or down.
b. Give the focus of the parabola.

13. $y = -5x^2$ a. down b. $\left(0, -\frac{1}{20}\right)$
14. $y = \frac{1}{4}x^2$ a. up b. (0, 1)
15. a. Find an equation for the parabola with focus (5, 0) and directrix $x = -5$. $x = \frac{1}{20}y^2$
    b. Give the coordinates of three points on this parabola, including the vertex.
    Answers vary. Sample: (0, 0), (20, 20), (20, -20)

The Municipal Asphalt Plant in New York City has a parabolic shape. This landmark facility is used for community sports, fitness, and recreation.

Extension

Have students do the following:

1. Consider the equation $x = \frac{1}{8}y^2$ and plot enough points to conclude that the graph of the equation is a parabola. Some of the points on $x = \frac{1}{8}y^2$ are (0, 0), (2, ±4), and (8, ±8); the graph is a "sideways" parabola with vertex (0, 0), axis $y = 0$, and opening to the right.
2. Adapt the Focus and Directrix of a Parabola Theorem to find the focus and directrix of the parabola. For any nonzero real number a, the graph of $x = ay^2$ is the parabola with focus at $\left(\frac{1}{4a}, 0\right)$ and directrix at $x = -\frac{1}{4a}$. So, for $x = \frac{1}{8}y^2$, $a = \frac{1}{8}$; the focus is at (2, 0), and the directrix is $x = -2$.
3. Identify any specific point on the parabola and show that it is equidistant from the focus and directrix. Answers vary. Sample: For the point (2, 4) on the parabola, the distance between (2, 4) and the focus (2, 0) is 4, while the distance between (2, 4) and (-2, 4)—the point (-2, 4) is on the directrix—is also 4.

REVIEW

16. An isotope has a half-life of 135 seconds. How long will it take 75 mg of this isotope to decay to 20 mg? **(Lesson 9-2)**

17. Solve for y. **(Lessons 8-8, 6-2)**
   a. $y^2 = 13$ $y = \pm\sqrt{13}$
   b. $(y + 3)^2 = 13$ $y = -3 \pm\sqrt{13}$
   c. $\sqrt{y} = 13$ $y = 169$
   d. $\sqrt{y + 3} = 13$ $y = 166$

18. Determine whether the set of points (x, y) satisfying the given equation describes y as a function of x. Explain your answer. **(Lessons 8-2, 2-5)**
   a. $y = (x + 1)^2$
   b. $x = (y + 1)^2$

19. Simplify. **(Lessons 7-8, 7-7)**
   a. $\left(\frac{16}{49}\right)^{\frac{1}{2}}$ $\frac{4}{7}$
   b. $(0.0001)^{-\frac{3}{4}}$ 1000

20. Suppose the transformation $T_{-3,2}$ is applied to the parabola with equation $y = \frac{5}{9}x^2$. Find an equation for its image. **(Lesson 6-3)**

21. **Fill in the Blank** If x is a real number, then $\sqrt{x^2} =$ __?__. **(Lesson 6-2)** C
   A x B $-x$ C $|x|$ D none of these

EXPLORATION

22. Parabolas can be formed without equations or graphs. Follow these steps to see how to make a parabola by folding paper.
   a. Start with a sheet of unlined paper. Fold it in half as shown at the right. Cut or tear along the fold to make two congruent pieces. On one piece mark a point P about one inch above the center of the lower edge. Fold the paper so that the lower edge touches P, and crease well as shown at the right. Then unfold the paper. Repeat 10 to 15 times, each time folding so that a different point on the bottom edge of the paper aligns with P. The creases represent the ***tangents*** to a parabola. (A ***tangent*** to a parabola is a line not parallel to its line of symmetry that intersects the parabola in exactly one point.) Where are the focus and directrix of this parabola?
   b. On the other piece of paper mark a point Q approximately in the center. Repeat the procedure used in Part a. Where are the focus and directrix for this parabola?
   c. **Fill in the Blank** The two parabolas formed in Parts a and b illustrate the property that as the distance between the focus and directrix increases, the parabola __?__. widens

P

P

16. about 257.4 sec, or about 4 min 17 sec

18a. Yes; each x-value is paired with exactly one y-value.

18b. No; Explanations vary. Sample: both of the points (4, 1) and (4, –3) are in the set.

20. $y - 2 = \frac{5}{9}(x + 3)^2$

22a. P is the focus; the lower edge of the paper is the directrix.

22b. Q is the focus; the lower edge of the paper is the directrix.

QY ANSWERS

1. VT
2. focus: (0, –24); directrix: $y = 24$

Notes on the Questions

Question 20 With the information in this lesson, students can determine the focus and directrix of the preimage parabola; then the focus and directrix of the image can be found.

Question 21 This question anticipates the use of the Distance Formula in Lesson 12-2.

Question 22 The creases are said to form the *envelope* of the parabola. (This question is a starting point for Project 5.)

4 Wrap-Up

Ongoing Assessment

Ask students to work in groups. Taking turns, one student should identify a point and an external line and label them "focus" and "directrix," respectively. The other students should identify several points that are equidistant from the focus and directrix, and the original student should draw a smooth curve through those points. Answers vary. Check students' work.

Accommodating the Learner

Ask students to verify that the points (0, 0), (2, 1), and (4, 4) are on the parabola $y = \frac{1}{4}x^2$. Then tell them that the parabola $y = \frac{1}{4}x^2$ has focus (0, 1) and directrix $y = -1$ (or have students use the Focus and Directrix of a Parabola Theorem to find the focus and directrix) and ask them to confirm that (0, 0), (2, 1), and (4, 4) are equidistant from (0, 1) and $y = -1$.

(0, 0): distance to (0, 1) is 1; distance to (0, –1), which is on $y = -1$, is 1. (2, 1): distance to (0, 1) is 2; distance to (2, –1), which is on $y = -1$, is 2. (4, 4): distance to (0, 1) is $\sqrt{16 + 9} = 5$; distance to (4, –1), which is on $y = -1$, is 5.

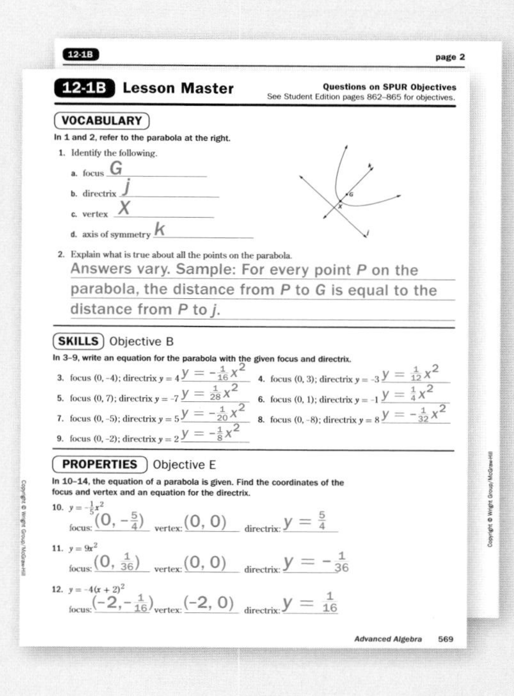
12-1B page 2

12-1B Lesson Master

Questions on SPUR Objectives
See Student Edition pages 862–865 for objectives.

VOCABULARY

In 1 and 2, refer to the parabola at the right.

1. Identify the following.
   a. focus G
   b. directrix j
   c. vertex X
   d. axis of symmetry k

2. Explain what is true about all the points on the parabola.
   Answers vary. Sample: For every point P on the parabola, the distance from P to G is equal to the distance from P to j.

SKILLS Objective B

In 3–9, write an equation for the parabola with the given focus and directrix.

3. focus (0, –4); directrix $y = 4$ $y = -\frac{1}{16}x^2$
4. focus (0, 3); directrix $y = -3$ $y = \frac{1}{12}x^2$
5. focus (0, 7); directrix $y = -7$ $y = \frac{1}{28}x^2$
6. focus (0, 1); directrix $y = -1$ $y = \frac{1}{4}x^2$
7. focus (0, –5); directrix $y = 5$ $y = -\frac{1}{20}x^2$
8. focus (0, –8); directrix $y = 8$ $y = -\frac{1}{32}x^2$
9. focus (0, –2); directrix $y = 2$ $y = -\frac{1}{8}x^2$

PROPERTIES Objective E

In 10–14, the equation of a parabola is given. Find the coordinates of the focus and vertex and an equation for the directrix.

10. $y = -\frac{1}{5}x^2$
   focus: $(0, -\frac{5}{4})$ vertex: (0, 0) directrix: $y = \frac{5}{4}$

11. $y = 9x^2$
   focus: $(0, \frac{1}{36})$ vertex: (0, 0) directrix: $y = -\frac{1}{36}$

12. $y = -4(x + 2)^2$
   focus: $(-2, -\frac{1}{16})$ vertex: (–2, 0) directrix: $y = \frac{1}{16}$

Advanced Algebra 569

Lesson

12-2

GOAL

Derive and apply a general equation (the center-radius form) for any circle.

SPUR Objectives

B Write equations for circles.

E Identify characteristics of circles.

F Classify curves as circles using algebraic or geometric properties.

G Use circles to solve real-world problems.

I Graph circles when given equations for them in standard form, and vice versa.

L Draw a graph or interpret drawings or graphs of circles based on their definitions.

Materials/Resources

- Lesson Masters 12-2A and 12-2B
- Resource Masters 1 and 223–225

HOMEWORK

Suggestions for Assignment

- Questions 1–19
- Question 20 (extra credit)
- Reading Lesson 12-3
- Covering the Ideas 12-3

Local Standards

1 Warm-Up

1. What is the distance between (a, b) and (c, d)? $\sqrt{(a-c)^2+(b-d)^2}$
2. What is the *square* of the distance between (a, b) and (c, d)? $(a-c)^2+(b-d)^2$
3. What is the distance between (x, y) and $(5, -8)$? $\sqrt{(x-5)^2+(y+8)^2}$
4. If the distance between (x, y) and (h, k) is r, what is an equation relating all five variables? $\sqrt{(x-h)^2+(y-k)^2}=r$

Lesson

12-2 Circles

Vocabulary

circle, radius, center
concentric circles
semicircle

▸ **BIG IDEA** From the geometric definition of a circle, an equation for any circle in the plane can be found.

As you know, a **circle** is the set of all points in a plane at a given distance (its **radius**) from a fixed point (its **center**). When a person throws a pebble into a calm body of water, *concentric circles* soon form around the point where the pebble hit the water. **Concentric circles** have the same center, but different radii. When an earthquake or mass movement of land (such as a volcanic eruption) occurs, various kinds of *seismic waves* radiate in roughly concentric circles from the *focus*, the point below Earth's surface where the earthquake began.

Mental Math

Suppose Aaron throws a rock off a cliff and its height h in meters t seconds after he throws it is given by $h = -4.9t^2 + 4.5t + 25$.

a. Did Aaron throw the rock upward or downward? upward

b. What was the rock's initial velocity? $4.5\ \frac{\text{m}}{\text{sec}}$

c. How high is the cliff? 25 m

d. Will the rock have hit the ground after 10 seconds? yes

After reaching the surface, seismic waves travel along the ground in concentric circles around the *epicenter*, or the point on Earth's surface above the focus. Warning systems for tsunamis and other natural disasters are triggered by measuring seismic waves with an instrument called a *seismograph*.

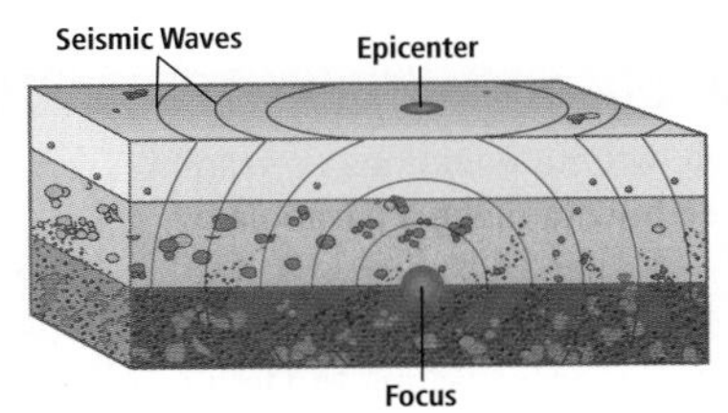

Seismic waves travel at the same speed in all directions. For earthquakes on land, the fastest seismic waves, called *P-waves* or *compression waves*, can travel at speeds of up to $8\frac{\text{km}}{\text{sec}}$. So the points on Earth's surface that a compression wave reaches at a given time make an approximate circle whose center is the epicenter of a quake.

Equations for Circles

You can find the equation for any circle using the definition of circle and the Pythagorean Distance Formula.

Background

Many students should have previously seen an equation for a circle. Be sure they understand that the equation is a simple application of the Distance Formula. Also, students should recall that the special case of the Circle Equation Theorem with center at the origin was seen in Lesson 10-4, along with a discussion of the unit circle.

The first three examples of this lesson illustrate specific cases of the Circle Equation Theorem.

Example 4 This example should be discussed so that students can graph circles. Because a circle is not the graph of a function in rectangular coordinates, graphing a circle usually means separating the equation into two equations, one for each of two semicircles. (But note that some technology *can* graph a circle given its center and radius.)

Example 1

Suppose the compression waves of an earthquake travel at a speed of $8\,\frac{\text{km}}{\text{sec}}$. Find an equation for the set of points that are reached by the compression waves in 7 seconds.

Solution Let the unit of a graph equal one kilometer, and the origin (0, 0) represent the epicenter of the quake. In 7 seconds, a compression wave travels about $8\,\frac{\text{km}}{\text{sec}}$ å• 7 sec = 56 km. So, the circle has radius 56.

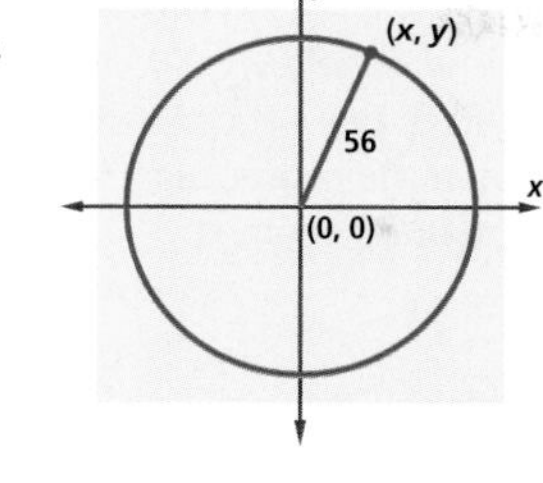

Let (x, y) be any point on the circle. By the definition of circle, the distance between (x, y) and (0, 0) is 56.

Use the Pythagorean Distance Formula.

$$\sqrt{(x-0)^2 + (y-0)^2} = 56$$

$$(x-0)^2 + (y-0)^2 = 56^2 \quad \text{Square both sides.}$$

$$x^2 + y^2 = 3136 \quad \text{Simplify.}$$

The equation you found in Example 1 is a quadratic equation in x and y. This is also true of equations for circles not centered at the origin.

GUIDED

Example 2

Find an equation for the circle with radius $\frac{27}{2}$ and center $\left(12, \frac{17}{2}\right)$.

Solution Let (x, y) be any point on the circle. $12; \frac{17}{2}; \frac{27}{2}$

Use the Distance Formula. $\sqrt{(x - \underline{\ ?\ })^2 + (y - \underline{\ ?\ })^2} = \underline{\ ?\ }$

Square both sides. $(x - \underline{\ ?\ })^2 + (y - \underline{\ ?\ })^2 = \underline{\ ?\ }$

$12; \frac{17}{2}; \frac{729}{4}$

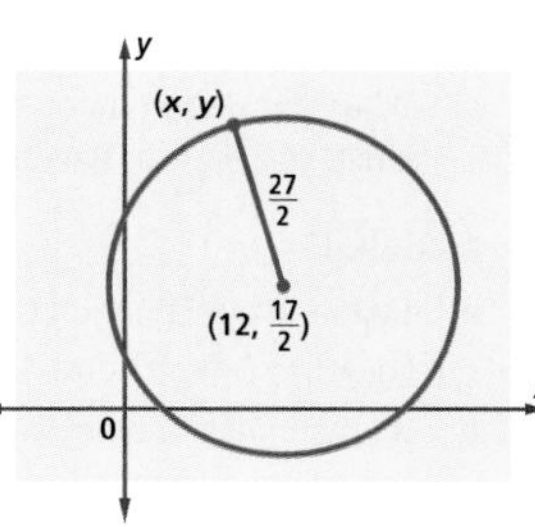

QY

Example 2 can be generalized to determine an equation for *any* circle. Let (h, k) be the center of a circle with radius r, and let (x, y) be any point on the circle. Then, by the definition of a circle, the distance between (x, y) and (h, k) equals r.

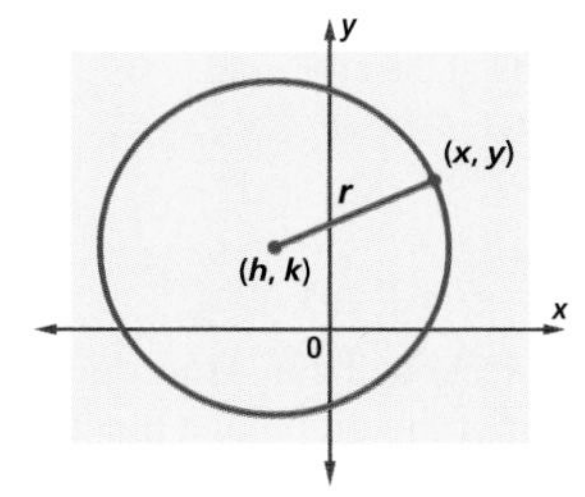

► **QY**

The point (25.5, 8.5) satisfies the equation in Example 2. Check your answer to Example 2 by showing that this point is $\frac{27}{2}$ units from the center of the circle.

Accommodating the Learner

Ask students to find the equations for three concentric circles, each with center (5, -1), if the area of the smallest circle is 16π units^2, the circumference of the largest circle is 14π units, and the area of the middle circle is one-half the area of the largest circle.

Smallest circle: $A = \pi r^2 = 16\pi$, so $r = 4$; the equation is $(x-5)^2 + (y+1)^2 = 16$. Largest circle: $C = 2\pi r = 14\pi$, so $r = 7$; the equation is $(x-5)^2 + (y+1)^2 = 49$. Middle circle: The area of the largest circle is 49π, so the area of the middle circle is 24.5π. Thus, $\pi r^2 = 24.5\pi$ and $r = \sqrt{24.5}$; the equation is $(x-5)^2 + (y+1)^2 = 24.5$.

2 Teaching

Notes on the Lesson

You might work from the Warm-Up. The answer to Warm-Up 4 is an equation for a circle. But to avoid square roots, we square both sides to obtain the standard form of an equation for a circle.

An alternate approach is to use the examples. Example 1 deals with a circle centered at the origin. Then you can use the Distance Formula with Example 2 to obtain a special case of the theorem.

Still another approach is to begin with $x^2 + y^2 = r^2$, in which the center of the circle is at (0, 0). Then apply the Graph-Translation Theorem, replacing x by $x - h$ and y by $y - k$, which yields the Circle Equation Theorem.

Additional Examples

Example 1 Suppose a pebble dropped in still water starts a series of ripples that radiate outward at a speed of 2 meters/second. Find an equation for the location of points on the first ripple in 5 seconds. If the center of the ripple is (0, 0), then $r = 5 \cdot 2 = 10$ m. The equation is $(x-0)^2 + (y-0)^2 = 10^2$ or $x^2 + y^2 = 100$.

Example 2 What is an equation for the circle with radius $\frac{15}{4}$ and center $\left(5, \frac{7}{4}\right)$?

Solution Let (x, y) be any point on the circle. Using the Distance Formula, $\sqrt{(x - \underline{\ ?\ })^2 + (y - \underline{\ ?\ })^2} = \underline{\ ?\ }$. $5; \frac{7}{4}; \frac{15}{4}$ Squaring both sides, $(x - \underline{\ ?\ })^2 + (y - \underline{\ ?\ })^2 = \underline{\ ?\ }$. $5; \frac{7}{4}; \frac{225}{16}$

Note-Taking Tips

Encourage students to label equations they write in their notes as "not a function" or "is a function." For example, they could label the equations $x^2 + y^2 = r^2$ and $(x-h)^2 + (y-k)^2 = r^2$ as "not a function," and the equations $y = \sqrt{(x+4)^2 - 49} + 5$ and $y = -\sqrt{(x+4)^2 - 49} + 5$ (from Example 4) as "is a function." Such labels can be especially useful when they want to graph circles (and other conics later in this chapter).

Notes on the Lesson

After discussing several instances of the Circle Equation Theorem, ask students to make generalizations about circles whose equations have

- equal values of r. They are congruent.
- different values of r but equal values of h and k. They are concentric.
- equal values of h but unequal values of k. Their centers are on the same vertical line.

Some students have difficulty distinguishing the variables x and y from the constants h and k. Stress that the point (h, k) represents a specific point (it is the center of the circle, not a point on the circle) while (x, y) represents a "movable" point on the circle. The set of all (x, y) that satisfy the equation $(x - h)^2 + (y - k)^2 = r^2$ is the set of all points on the circle.

Additional Example

Example 3

a. Find the center and radius of the circle with equation $(x - 7)^2 + (y + 8)^2 = 121$. $(h, k) = (7, -8)$; $r = \sqrt{121} = 11$

b. Graph this circle.

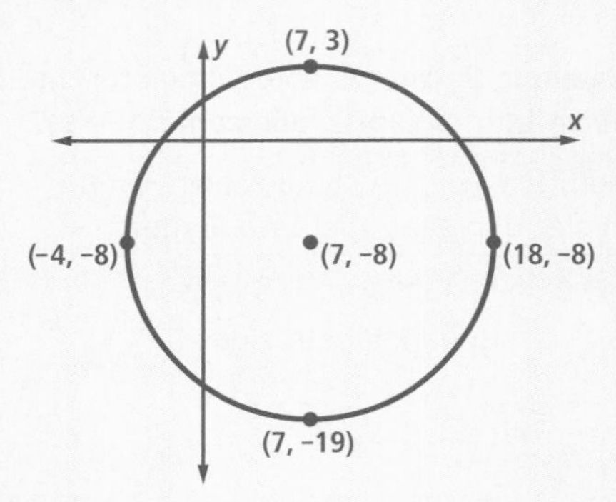

c. What transformation maps the circle with equation $x^2 + y^2 = 121$ onto the circle you graphed in Part b? $T_{7,-8}$

By the Distance Formula, $\sqrt{(x - h)^2 + (y - k)^2} = r$.

Squaring gives an equation without radicals: $(x - h)^2 + (y - k)^2 = r^2$.

This proves the following theorem.

Circle Equation Theorem

The circle with center (h, k) and radius r is the set of points (x, y) that satisfy $(x - h)^2 + (y - k)^2 = r^2$.

When the center of a circle is the origin, $(h, k) = (0, 0)$ and the equation becomes

$$x^2 + y^2 = r^2.$$

Graphing a Circle

By the Graph-Translation Theorem, the translation $T_{h,k}$ maps the circle with equation $x^2 + y^2 = r^2$ onto a circle with equation $(x - h)^2 + (y - k)^2 = r^2$.

Example 3

a. Find the center and radius of the circle with equation $(x + 4)^2 + (y - 5)^2 = 49$.

b. Graph this circle.

c. What translation maps the circle with equation $x^2 + y^2 = 49$ onto the circle you drew in Part b?

Solution

a. By the Circle Equation Theorem, the center $(h, k) = (-4, 5)$ and the radius $r = \sqrt{49} = 7$.

b. You can make a quick sketch of this circle by locating the center and then four points on the circle whose distance from the center is 7, as illustrated at the right.

c. The preimage circle is centered at the origin and the image circle is centered at $(-4, 5)$, so $T_{-4,5}$ translates $x^2 + y^2 = 49$ onto $(x + 4)^2 + (y - 5)^2 = 49$.

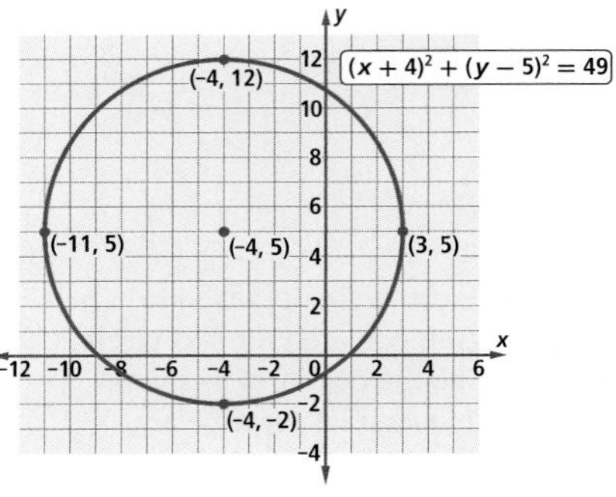

In Example 3, you graphed the circle by hand. How do you graph it on a graphing utility? A circle is not the graph of a function, and most graphing utilities will only graph functions. However, you can divide the circle in half with a horizontal line. Each half-circle, or **semicircle**, is the graph of a function, and both can be graphed in the same window to form a circle.

Extension

Show students the diagram at the right of two circles, tangent to each other and internally tangent to the circle whose equation is $(x - h)^2 + (y - k)^2 = r^2$. Ask students to find equations for the two smaller circles.

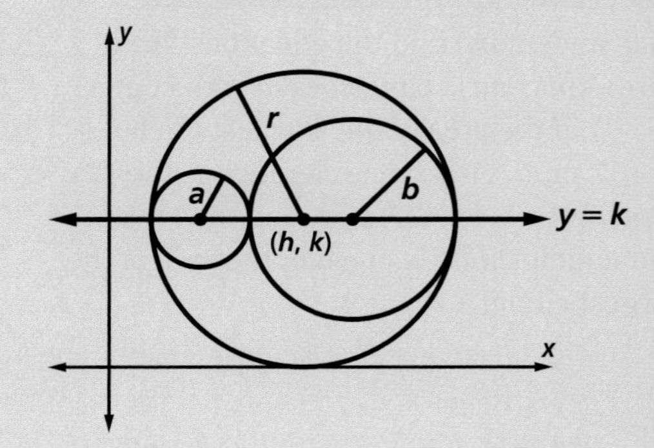

Example 4

a. Solve $(x + 4)^2 + (y - 5)^2 = 49$ for y.

b. Graph the circle with the equation in Part a on a graphing utility.

Solution

a. Solve for y on a CAS. One CAS solution is shown below.

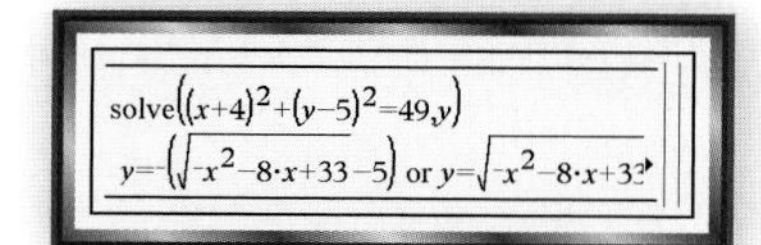

b. Copy the two equations into a graphing utility. Graph both on the same screen, using a square window. The graph of each equation is half of a circle, but due to the graphing utility's limitations, the circle's graph is not completely accurate.

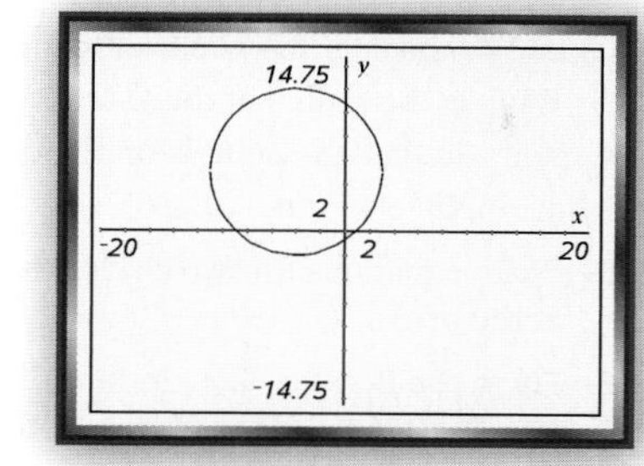

If you know an equation for a circle and one coordinate of a point on the circle, you can determine the other coordinate of that point.

GUIDED

Example 5

Refer to the circle in Examples 3 and 4. Find the y-coordinate of each point with x-coordinate 1.

Solution Substitute _?_ for x in the equation for the circle 1
$(x + 4)^2 + (y - 5)^2 = 49$ and solve for y.

$(\_?\_ + 4)^2 + (y - 5)^2 = 49$ — Substitute. 1

$(y - 5)^2 = \_?\_$ — Simplify. Then subtract _?_ from both sides. 24; 25

$|\_?\_| = \sqrt{\_?\_}$ — Take the square root of both sides and apply the Absolute Value-Square Root Theorem. $y - 5$; 24

$y - \_?\_ = \_?\_$ or $y - \_?\_ = \_?\_$ — Definition of absolute value 5; $2\sqrt{6}$; 5; $-2\sqrt{6}$

$y = \_?\_$ or $y = \_?\_$ — Add _?_ to both sides of each equation. $5 + 2\sqrt{6}$; $5 - 2\sqrt{6}$; 5

Check Solve the original equation for the circle on a CAS for y such that $x = 1$. One solution is shown at the right. If yours looks different, check to see that it is equivalent to this one.

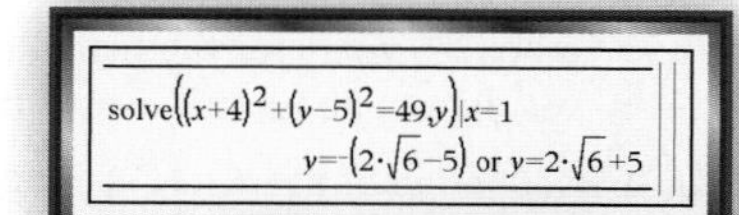

We know that the radii for the two small circles are a and b, so we need the coordinates for their centers. All three centers are on the line $y = k$.

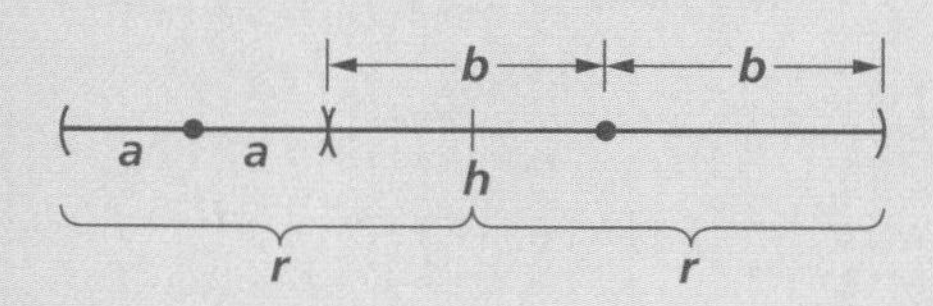

In the diagram on page 806, the center of the small circle on the left is $(h - r + a, k)$; the center of the small circle on the right is $(h + r - b, k)$. The equations are $((x - (h - r + a))^2 + (y - k)^2 = a^2$ and $((x - (h + r - b))^2 + (y - k)^2 = b^2$.

Notes on the Lesson

Example 4 You may want to demonstrate how to graph circles with the technology your students have. Even if your graphing utility can directly handle equations in the form $x^2 + y^2 = r^2$, it is useful to illustrate how the union of the two semicircles $y = \sqrt{r^2 - x^2}$ and $y = -\sqrt{r^2 - x^2}$ gives the same graph.

Note that some graphing utilities choose a default window with different scales on the x- and y-axes, thus distorting the graphs of the circles. You can usually adjust the window for each graph by choosing a square window. On other utilities, even when the x- and y-axes have the same scale, there is still some distortion. Generally, you can minimize the distortion on computer screens by adjusting the aspect ratio.

Additional Examples

Example 4 Solve $(x - 7)^2 + (y + 8)^2 = 121$ for y.
$y = \pm\sqrt{-x^2 + 14x + 72} - 8$

Example 5 Use the circle with equation $(x - 7)^2 + (y + 8)^2 = 121$ from Additional Examples 3 and 4. Find the y-coordinate of each point with x-coordinate 4.

Solution Substitute _?_ for x in the equation for the circle $(x - 7)^2 + (y + 8)^2 = 121$ and solve for y. 4

Substitute.

$(\_?\_ - 7)^2 + (y + 8)^2 = 121$ 4

Simplify; then subtract _?_ from both sides. 9

$(y + 8)^2 = \_?\_$ 112

Take the square root of both sides and apply the Absolute Value—Square Root Theorem.

$|\_?\_| = \_?\_$ $y + 8$; $4\sqrt{7}$

Apply the definition of absolute value.

$y + \_?\_ = \_?\_$ or $y + \_?\_ = \_?\_$ 8; $4\sqrt{7}$; 8; $-4\sqrt{7}$

Add _?_ to both sides of each equation. 8

$y = \_?\_$ or $y = \_?\_$
$4\sqrt{7} - 8$; $-4\sqrt{7} - 8$

3 Assignment

Recommended Assignment

- Questions 1–19
- Question 20 (extra credit)
- Reading Lesson 12-3
- Covering the Ideas 12-3

Notes on the Questions

Question 1 If students inquire, point out that a circle is not an exact model for the points reached by the compression wave in a given time. Because the speed of the compression depends on the makeup of Earth through which the waves pass, the speed is not constant.

Question 6 You might ask: Because $|x| = \sqrt{x^2}$, why can we not take the absolute value of both sides of the equation $\sqrt{(x-h)^2 + (y-k)^2} = r$ for a circle with center (h, k) and radius r and obtain $|x - h| + |y - k| = |r|$ as an equation for a circle? Answers vary. Sample: The radicand on the left side is not a square, so "the square root of each side" does not simplify.

12-2A page 2

12-2A Lesson Master Questions on SPUR Objectives
See Student Edition pages 862–865 for objectives.

SKILLS Objective B

In 1–3, give an equation for the circle with the given characteristics.

1. center (0, 0); radius 9 $x^2 + y^2 = 81$
2. center (3.2, 5.7); radius 1.3 $(x - 3.2)^2 + (y - 5.7)^2 = 1.69$
3. center (a, b); diameter d $(x - a)^2 + (y - b)^2 = \left(\frac{d}{2}\right)^2$

PROPERTIES Objective E

In 4 and 5, an equation for a circle is given. Find the center and radius.

4. $(x - 3)^2 + y^2 = 36$ center: (3, 0) radius: 6
5. $(x - t)^2 + (y - n)^2 = p$ center: (t, n) radius: $\sqrt{p}$
6. Find the coordinates of all points on the circle $(x - 2)^2 + (y - 3)^2 = 12$, where $y = 0$. $(2 + \sqrt{3}, 0), (2 - \sqrt{3}, 0)$

PROPERTIES Objective F

In 7–9, determine whether the figure described is a parabola, a circle, or neither.

7. The set of all points 2 units from (8.1, 12.3). circle
8. The set of all points equidistant from (8.1, 12.3) and (4.2, 1.9). neither
9. The set of all points equidistant from (8.1, 12.3) and $y = 1.9$. parabola

USES Objective G

10. Sol throws a rock into a pond. The ripples travel at 2 meters per second from the point where the rock hits the water. Using (0, 0) as the point where the rock hits, write an equation for the circle that represents a ripple three seconds after the rock hits the water. $x^2 + y^2 = 36$
11. Sally is making a scale drawing of Earth and its moon as shown at the right. She puts the center of Earth at the origin and uses a scale of 1 cm = 1000 km. (The picture at the right is NOT to scale.)
    a. The equatorial diameter of Earth is 12,756 km. Give an equation for the circle representing Earth. $x^2 + y^2 = 6.378^2$
    b. The diameter of Earth's moon is 3476 km, and its average distance from Earth (center to center) is 382,500 km. Give an equation for the circle representing Earth's moon. $(x - 382.5)^2 + y^2 = 1.738^2$

Advanced Algebra 571

Questions

COVERING THE IDEAS

1. Suppose the epicenter for an earthquake is at the origin. If 1 unit on the graph represents 1 km, find an equation describing the set of points (x, y) reached by compression waves in 1 minute if the waves travel at $8\frac{\text{km}}{\text{sec}}$. $x^2 + y^2 = 230{,}400$
2. Repeat Question 1 if the epicenter is at (40, 22). $(x - 40)^2 + (y - 22)^2 = 230{,}400$

In 3 and 4, consider the circle with equation $x^2 + y^2 = 34^2$.

3. What is the radius of this circle? 34
4. Tell whether the point is on the circle.
   a. (0, 0) no b. (-34, 0) yes c. (0, 34) yes d. $(\sqrt{34}, 0)$ no
5. Write equations for two circles that are concentric and centered at the origin. Answers vary. Sample: $x^2 + y^2 = 25$, $x^2 + y^2 = 16$
6. **Fill in the Blanks** The circle with equation $(x - h)^2 + (y - k)^2 = r^2$ has center _?_ and radius _?_. (h, k); r

In 7 and 8, an equation for a circle is given. State the center and radius of the circle, sketch the circle, and solve the equation for y.

7. $x^2 + y^2 = 121$
8. $(x + 7)^2 + (y + 3)^2 = 25$
9. Refer to the circle from Example 2. Find the y-coordinates of all points on the circle
   a. where $x = -6$.
   b. where $x = 800$.
10. Find an equation for the circle with center $\left(-\frac{1}{2}, \frac{5}{2}\right)$ and radius 8.

7. center: (0, 0); radius: 11

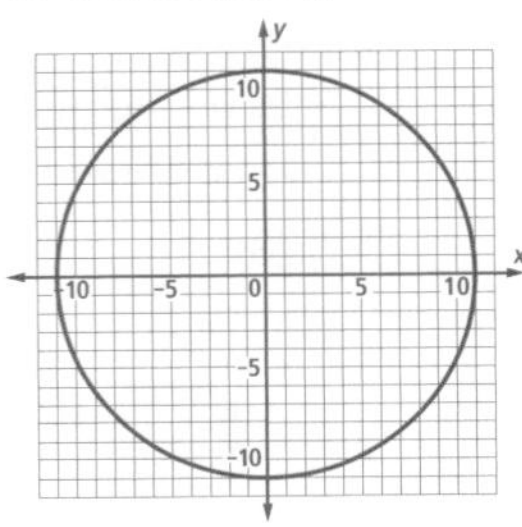

$y = \pm\sqrt{121 - x^2}$

8. center: (-7, -3); radius: 5

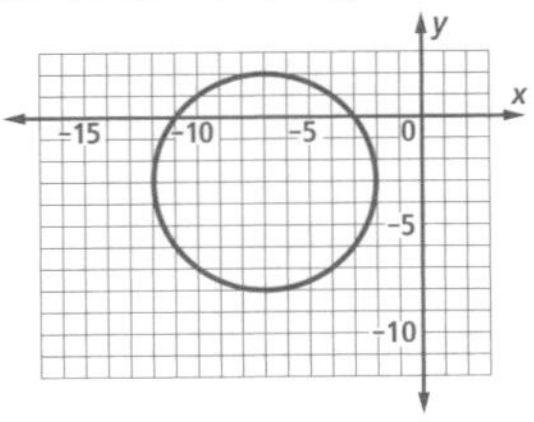

$y = \pm\sqrt{25 - (x + 7)^2} - 3$

9a. There are no points on the circle where $x = -6$.

9b. There are no points on the circle where $x = 800$.

APPLYING THE MATHEMATICS

11. Planets in our solar system travel in elliptical orbits about the Sun, but these orbits are nearly circular. In the late 1990s, as astronomers searched for solar systems similar to ours, they discovered other planets with almost circular orbits. One example, discovered in 2002, is a planet orbiting the star Tau Gruis. This planet is 2.5 astronomical units (AU) away from Tau Gruis. (1 AU is the average distance between Earth and the Sun.)
    a. Write an equation for the orbit of this planet about Tau Gruis.
    b. If Earth's orbit is assumed to be circular, it revolves about the Sun at a speed of approximately 67,062 miles per hour. If it takes 3.5 years for the planet orbiting Tau Gruis to make one revolution, about how fast is the planet moving? 47,901.4 mph

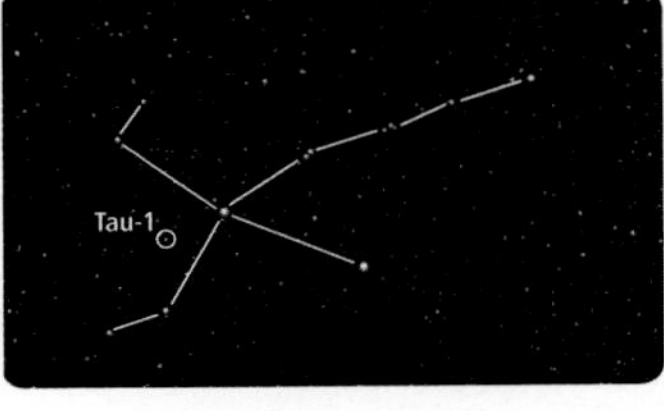

Tau Gruis, visible from the Southern Hemisphere, is located about 100 light-years from Earth.

12. The equation of the circle in Example 4 is equivalent to an equation of the form $Ax^2 + Bxy + Cy^2 + Dx + Ey + F = 0$. What are the values of A, B, C, D, E, and F? $A = 1, B = 0, C = 1, D = 8, E = -10, F = -8$

10. $\left(x + \frac{1}{2}\right)^2 + \left(y - \frac{5}{2}\right)^2 = 64$

11a. $x^2 + y^2 = 6.25$

Accommodating the Learner

Ask students to trace a quarter and let its center be the origin of a set of x, y-axes. Trace the quarter again, this time above the first, with its center on the y-axis. Then trace the quarter again, this time below the first, with its center on the y-axis. Finally trace the quarter four more times, arranged around the original circle and not overlapping. Have students note that all six circles around the original are tangent to the original and tangent to their two neighbors.

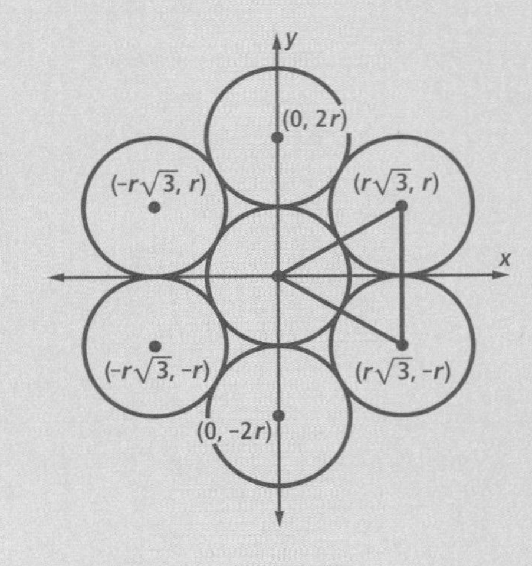

13. A circle centered at the origin has radius 5.
   a. Find the equation of its image under the translation $T_{4,-1}$. $(x - 4)^2 + (y + 1)^2 = 25$
   b. Identify one point on the circle. Verify that its image satisfies the image circle of Part a. Answers vary. Sample: (4, 3); image is (8, 2), $(8 - 4)^2 + (2 + 1)^2 = 25$

14. To locate the epicenter of an earthquake, data about waves originating from the epicenter are collected by earthquake research stations. Three circles, each centered at a research station with a radius equal to the distance from the epicenter to the particular station, allow one to determine the epicenter location. The location is given by a unique intersection shared by all three circles. Suppose that:

Earthquake data allow a research station to calculate its distance from an epicenter, but not its direction.

Station 1 is 7 miles from the epicenter and located at (6, 1).
Station 2 is 5 miles from the epicenter and located at (11, 8).
Station 3 is 4 miles from the epicenter and located at (2, 8).

   a. Graph the three circles defined above. See margin.
   b. Find the epicenter of the earthquake. (6, 8)

REVIEW

15. A parabola has focus (0, –1) and directrix $y = 1$. **(Lesson 12-1)**
   a. What is its vertex? Is it a minimum point or a maximum point? (0, 0); maximum
   b. Give an equation for the parabola. $y = -\frac{1}{4}x^2$
   c. Give an equation for its axis of symmetry. $x = 0$

16. Give the focus and directrix of the parabola $y = \frac{2}{3}x^2$. **(Lesson 12-1)**

17. What are the zeros of the 4th-degree polynomial function graphed at the right? **(Lesson 11-4)** –4, –1, 1, 4

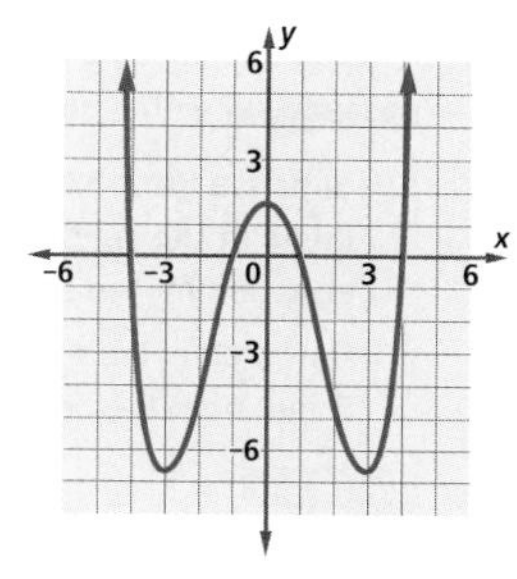

18. In 2007, Karla deposited \$5000 in a retirement account paying interest compounded continuously. If no additional deposits or withdrawals are made, when Karla retires in 2040 the account will be worth \$8172.40. What is the annual percentage yield of this account? **(Lessons 9-10, 9-1, 7-4)** about 1.5%

19. Find an equation for the line containing the origin and (–3, 7). **(Lesson 3-4)** $y = -\frac{7}{3}x$

EXPLORATION

20. A *lattice point* is a point with integer coordinates. If possible, find an equation for a circle that passes through
   a. no lattice points.
   b. exactly one lattice point.
   c. exactly two lattice points.
   d. exactly three lattice points.
   e. more than ten lattice points. not possible

16. focus: $\left(0, \frac{3}{8}\right)$; directrix: $y = -\frac{3}{8}$

20a. Answers vary. Sample: $x^2 + y^2 = 0.5$

20b. Answers vary. Sample: $(x - 3)^2 + (y - 0.2)^2 = 0.04$

20c. not possible

20d. not possible

QY ANSWER

$\left(12, \frac{17}{2}\right)$ and $\left(\frac{51}{2}, \frac{17}{2}\right)$ are on a horizontal line $\frac{51}{2} - 12 = \frac{27}{2}$ units apart.

4 Wrap-Up

Ongoing Assessment

Ask students to work in small groups. In each group, one student should select an ordered pair and another student should select a positive number. Then all students in the group should write the equation of the circle whose center is the given ordered pair and whose radius is the given positive number. Answers vary. Check students' work.

Project Update

Project 2, *Arches,* on page 856 relates to the content of this lesson.

Additional Answers

14a.

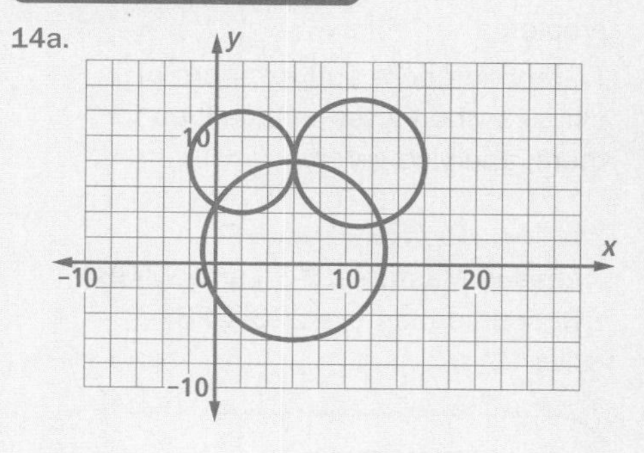

Assuming that the original quarter has center (0, 0) and radius r, ask students to find equations for the other six quarters. The two quarters above and below the original have centers $(0, 2r)$ and $(0, -2r)$; the other quarters have centers $(r\sqrt{3}, r)$, $(r\sqrt{3}, -r)$, $(-r\sqrt{3}, r)$ and $(-r\sqrt{3}, -r)$. So the six equations are $x^2 + (y \pm 2r)^2 = r^2$ and $(x \pm r\sqrt{3})^2 + (y \pm r)^2 = r^2$.

ENGLISH LEARNERS

Vocabulary Development

This lesson provides a natural opportunity to review translations and scale changes. This review will be especially useful for Lesson 12-5, which uses a scale change of a circle to calculate the area of an ellipse.

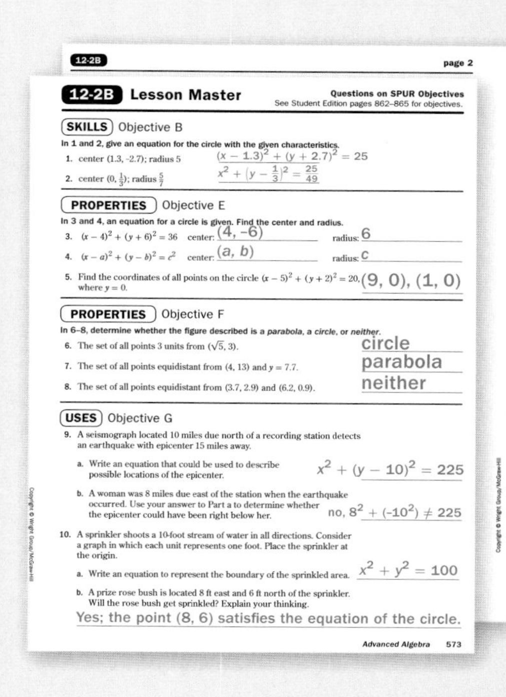

12-2B page 2

12-2B Lesson Master

Questions on SPUR Objectives
See Student Edition pages 862–865 for objectives.

SKILLS Objective B

In 1 and 2, give an equation for the circle with the given characteristics.

1. center (1.3, -2.7); radius 5 $(x - 1.3)^2 + (y + 2.7)^2 = 25$
2. center $(0, \frac{1}{3})$; radius $\frac{5}{7}$ $x^2 + \left(y - \frac{1}{3}\right)^2 = \frac{25}{49}$

PROPERTIES Objective E

In 3 and 4, an equation for a circle is given. Find the center and radius.

3. $(x - 4)^2 + (y + 6)^2 = 36$ center: (4, –6) radius: 6
4. $(x - a)^2 + (y - b)^2 = c^2$ center: (a, b) radius: c
5. Find the coordinates of all points on the circle $(x - 5)^2 + (y + 2)^2 = 20$, where $y = 0$. (9, 0), (1, 0)

PROPERTIES Objective F

In 6–8, determine whether the figure described is a *parabola*, a *circle*, or *neither*.

6. The set of all points 3 units from $(\sqrt{5}, 3)$. circle
7. The set of all points equidistant from (4, 13) and $y = 7.7$. parabola
8. The set of all points equidistant from (3.7, 2.9) and (6.2, 0.9). neither

USES Objective G

9. A seismograph located 10 miles due north of a recording station detects an earthquake with epicenter 15 miles away.
   a. Write an equation that could be used to describe possible locations of the epicenter. $x^2 + (y - 10)^2 = 225$
   b. A woman was 8 miles due east of the station when the earthquake occurred. Use your answer to Part a to determine whether the epicenter could have been right below her. no, $8^2 + (-10^2) \neq 225$
10. A sprinkler shoots a 10-foot stream of water in all directions. Consider a graph in which each unit represents one foot. Place the sprinkler at the origin.
   a. Write an equation to represent the boundary of the sprinkled area. $x^2 + y^2 = 100$
   b. A prize rose bush is located 8 ft east and 6 ft north of the sprinkler. Will the rose bush get sprinkled? Explain your thinking. Yes; the point (8, 6) satisfies the equation of the circle.

Advanced Algebra 573

Lesson 12-3

GOAL

Extend two ideas from Lesson 12-2: (1) derive an equation for a semicircle; (2) discuss and explore inequalities that describe the interior or exterior of a circle.

SPUR Objectives

B Write equations for quadratic relations and inequalities for their interiors and exteriors.

G Use circles to solve real-world problems.

J Graph interiors and exteriors of ellipses when given inequalities for them, and vice versa.

Materials/Resources

- Lesson Masters 12-3A and 12-3B
- Resource Masters 226–228
- Quiz 1

HOMEWORK

Suggestions for Assignment

- Questions 1–21
- Question 22 (extra credit)
- Reading Lesson 12-4
- Covering the Ideas 12-4

Local Standards

1 Warm-Up

In 1–7, tell whether the point is on, inside, or outside a circle with center (0, 0) and radius 65.

1. (1, 8) inside
2. (65, 65) outside
3. (-25, 60) on
4. (-56, -33) on
5. ($\sqrt{65}$, 0) inside
6. ($4\sqrt{66}$, $-4\sqrt{66}$) inside
7. (23, 61) outside

Lesson 12-3 Semicircles, Interiors, and Exteriors of Circles

Vocabulary

interior, exterior of a circle

BIG IDEA An inequality describing the points (x, y) in the *interior* or *exterior* of a circle can be found by replacing the equal sign in a circle's equation by $<$ or $>$.

Semicircles

In Lesson 12-2 you used two semicircles to create a graph of a circle on a graphing utility. In everyday life, semicircles often occur in design and architecture, as shown in the photo at the right of the Arc de Triomphe du Carrousel, located in Paris, France.

Mental Math

Suppose $P(x) = (x + 2)(x - 7)^2(2x + 3)$.

a. Give the degree of $P(x)$. 4

b. Determine all the roots of $P(x)$. $-2, 7, -\frac{3}{2}$

c. Determine all the roots with multiplicity greater than 1. 7

Example 1

An architect is designing a 6-foot wide and 8-foot tall passageway with a semicircular arch at its top.

a. Suppose the x-axis represents the floor with the origin at the center of the passageway. What is an equation for the semicircle representing the arch?

b. How high is the arch above a point on the ground 2 feet from the center of the passageway?

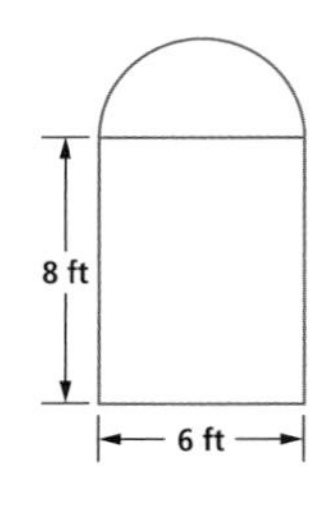

Solution

a. Let 1 unit in the coordinate system equal 1 foot. Then the circle whose top half is the arch has center (0, 8) and diameter 6, so its radius is 3. Therefore, its equation is $x^2 + (y - 8)^2 = 3^2$. Solve this equation for y.

$$x^2 + (y - 8)^2 = 9$$
$$(y - 8)^2 = 9 - x^2$$

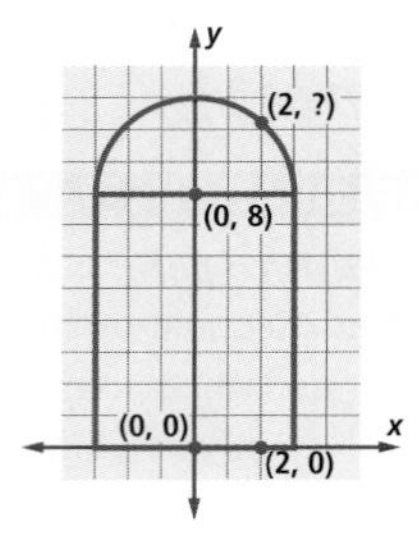

Background

The derivation of an equation for a semicircle characterizes a circle as the union of the graphs of two functions. Thus, it enables a circle to be drawn with any graphing utility that allows two graphs on the same screen. (Some graphing utilities make allowances and graph a circle without splitting it into two parts.)

Students have seen the idea of a set of points dividing a plane into regions in connection with lines. A line splits a plane into two half-planes. Sentences describing the half-planes can be found by replacing the = sign in the equation with $<$ or $>$. Similarly, a circle splits a plane into its interior and exterior, and sentences describing those two parts can be found in the same way.

Many applications involve interiors or exteriors of circles. For instance, it may be easier to think of a situation in which one cares about points *no more than* 2 miles from a given point rather than situations *exactly* 2 miles from a given point.

$$y - 8 = \pm\sqrt{9 - x^2}$$
$$y = \pm\sqrt{9 - x^2} + 8$$

Since we want the upper semicircle, $y = \sqrt{9 - x^2} + 8$ is the equation for the semicircle.

b. Since we have an equation for the semicircle, we can easily use it to find the height of the arch at any point. At a point 2 feet along the ground from the center of the passageway, $x = 2$ or $x = -2$. Substitute either x-value into the equation for the semicircle to find the corresponding y-value, which is the height of the arch above this point.

$$y = \sqrt{9 - 2^2} + 8$$
$$= \sqrt{5} + 8 \approx 10.24$$

The arch is about 10.24 feet high 2 feet from the center of the passageway.

Graph $y = \sqrt{9 - x^2} + 8$ using technology. Use the trace feature to estimate the y-value when $x = 2$. It checks.

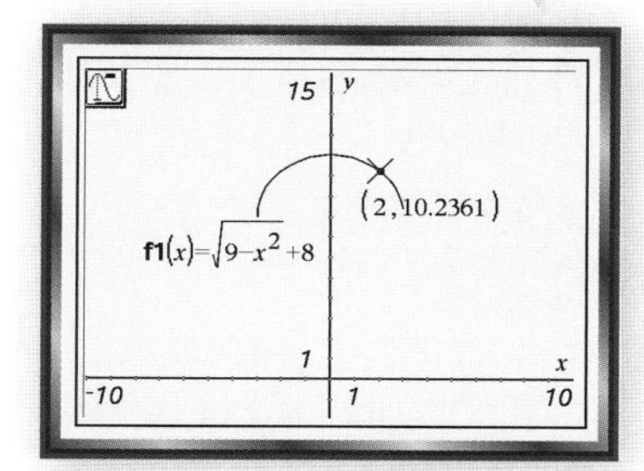

In general, when the equation $(x - h)^2 + (y - k)^2 = r^2$ is solved for y, the result is a pair of equations in the form $y = \pm\sqrt{r^2 - (x - h)^2} + k$. The equation with the positive square root describes the upper semicircle, and the equation with the negative square root describes the lower semicircle.

STOP QY

Interiors and Exteriors of Circles

Every circle separates the plane into two regions. The region inside the circle is called the **interior of the circle**. The region outside the circle is called the **exterior of the circle**. The circle itself is the boundary between these two regions and is not part of either region.

Regions bounded by concentric circles are often used in target practice. Consider the target shown at the right.

To describe the colored regions mathematically, you can place the target on a coordinate system with the origin at the target's center. Notice that the region worth 100 points is the interior of a circle with radius 2. All points in this region are less than 2 units from the origin. Thus if (x, y) is a point in the 100-point region, then $\sqrt{x^2 + y^2} < 2$.

QY

Write an equation for the lower semicircle of the circle in Example 1.

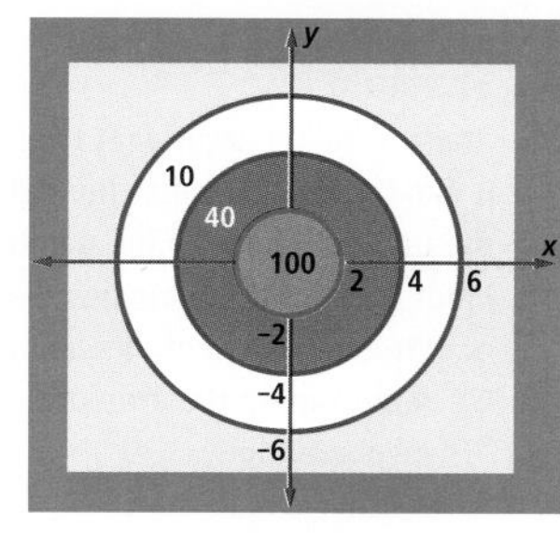

Accommodating the Learner

Ask students to write an equation to represent the curve at the right, which consists of two semicircles. (Some students may need the hint that the answer includes two equations joined by the word *or*.) The centers of the two semicircles are (5, 0) and (15, 0), with $r = 5$. So equations for the two circles would be $(x - 5)^2 + y^2 = 25$ and $(x - 15)^2 + y^2 = 25$. Using the top half of the first circle and the bottom half of the second circle, the solution is $y = \sqrt{25 - (x - 5)^2}$ or $y = -\sqrt{25 - (x - 15)^2}$.

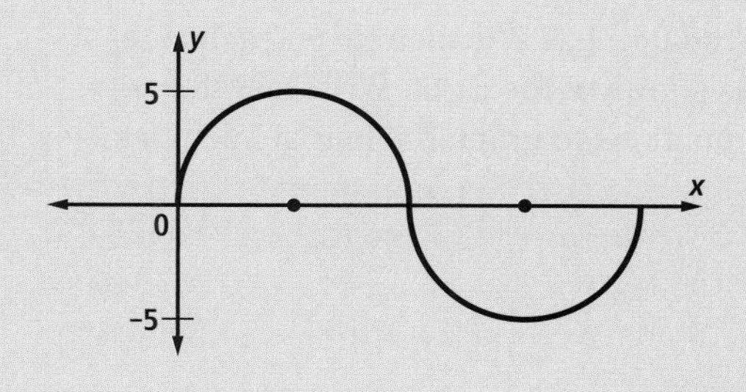

12-3

2 Teaching

Notes on the Lesson

Semicircles The inequalities in this lesson usually present few problems for students, so class discussion should center around the equations for semicircles. Use either Example 1 or Question 1 to initiate the discussion.

Additional Example

Example 1 For the situation in Example 1, suppose the passageway is 10 feet wide and 12 feet tall with a semicircular arch at its top. Also suppose the x-axis represents the floor, with the origin at the center of the passageway.

a. What is an equation for the semicircle representing the arch? The semicircle is part of a circle with center (0, 12) and radius 5; an equation for that circle is $x^2 + (y - 12)^2 = 25$. So $(y - 12)^2 = 25 - x^2$; $y - 12 = \pm\sqrt{25 - x^2}$; $y = \pm\sqrt{25 - x^2} + 12$; an equation for the upper semicircle is $y = \sqrt{25 - x^2} + 12$.

b. How high is the arch at a point on the ground 4 feet from the center of the passageway? At $x = 4$ ft, $y = \sqrt{25 - 16} + 12 = \sqrt{9} + 12 = 15$ ft.

Interiors and exteriors of circles Some graphing utilities enable you to indicate the exterior or interior of a circle by shading the appropriate region.

Additional Example

Example 2 Graph the points satisfying $(x - 3)^2 + (y + 2)^2 > 5$.
The graph is the exterior of a circle with center (3, –2) and radius $\sqrt{5} \approx 2.2$.

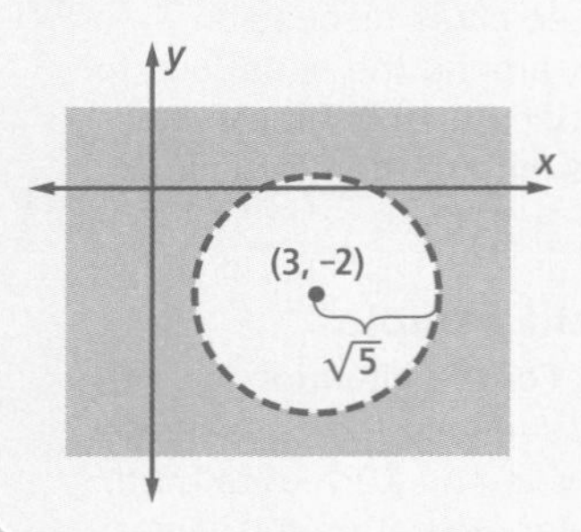

Notes on the Lesson

Example 3 We naturally think of a ring as the region between two circles, including the circles themselves. In finding the area of a ring, students have learned to subtract the area of the inner circle from the area of the outer circle, thus thinking of a ring as the interior of the outer circle with the interior of the inner circle removed. In Example 3, a third conception is used for describing a ring: A ring is the intersection of the exterior of the inner circle with the interior of the outer circle. As usual, if the ring is to include its boundaries, then each < sign should be replaced with ≤. A similar use of intersection is describing the segment $\overline{AB}$ as the intersection of the rays $\overrightarrow{AB}$ and $\overrightarrow{BA}$.

Note-Taking Tips

Encourage students to use a brace $\{$ to show the equations or inequalities of a system, as shown in the solution to Part a in Example 3. Using a brace to indicate a system will be especially useful in the last two lessons of this chapter.

The expressions on both sides of this inequality are positive. Recall that whenever a and b are positive and $a < b$, then $a^2 < b^2$. Thus, when both sides of the inequality are squared, the sentence becomes $x^2 + y^2 < 4$, which also describes the 100-point region.

Similarly, the points in the region worth less than 100 points constitute the exterior of the circle with radius 2. All (x, y) in this region satisfy the sentence $\sqrt{x^2 + y^2} > 2$, or $x^2 + y^2 > 4$.

The two instances above are generalized in the following theorem.

Interior and Exterior of a Circle Theorem

Let C be the circle with center (h, k) and radius r. Then the interior of C is described by

$$(x - h)^2 + (y - k)^2 < r^2$$

and the exterior of C is described by

$$(x - h)^2 + (y - k)^2 > r^2.$$

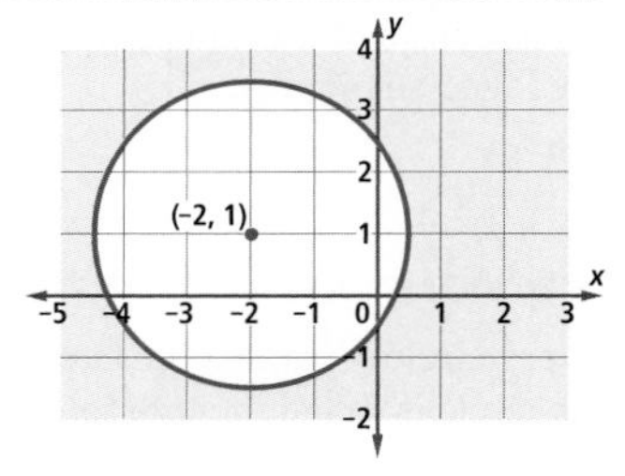

If ≥ or ≤ is used instead of > or < in the theorem above, the boundary (the circle itself) is included.

Example 2

Graph the points satisfying $(x + 2)^2 + (y - 1)^2 \geq 7$.

Solution The sentence represents the union of a circle, with center at (–2, 1) and radius $\sqrt{7}$, and its exterior. The shaded region and the circle at the right make up the graph.

Check Test a specific point. The point (0, 0) is not in the exterior, so it should not satisfy the inequality. This is the case, because $(0 + 2)^2 + (0 - 1)^2 = 5$ and $5 < 7$.

GUIDED

Example 3

Some scholars argue that King Arthur's round table had a hole in it like the one shown at the right. An estimate of the diameter of the table is 18 feet. (The painting is not to scale.) Suppose the inner circle of the table has diameter 5 feet.

a. Write a system of inequalities describing the tabletop.

b. Approximate the area of the tabletop to the nearest tenth of a square foot.

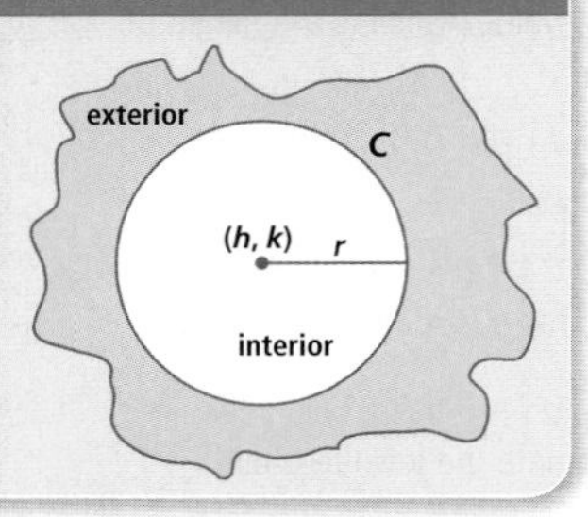

Extension

A square has a semicircle on each side, as shown at the right. Write a system of equations to graph the four semicircles. The centers of the four semicircles are (–a, 0), (0, a), (a, 0), and (0, –a); and the radius of each semicircle is a. So a system of equations, clockwise from the point (–2a, 0), is as follows (see page 813):

y =

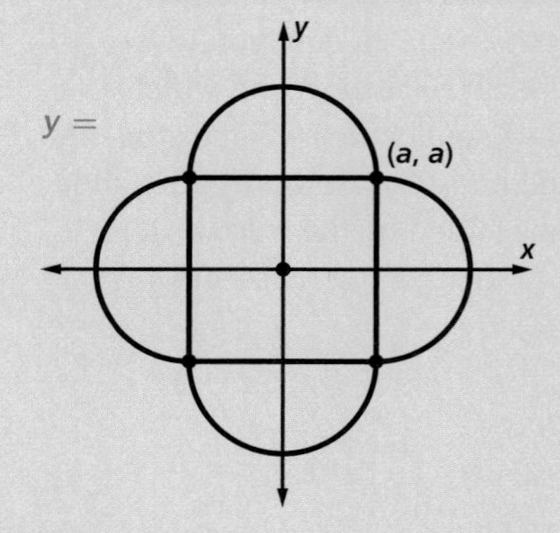

Solution

a. Sketch a top view of the table, and superimpose a coordinate system with the center of the table at the origin.

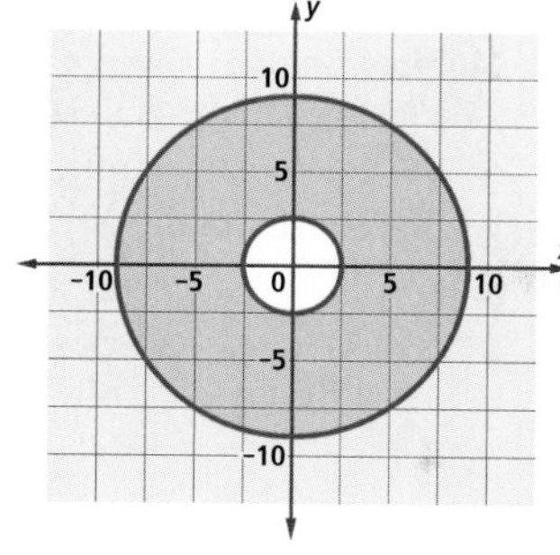

The inner circle has center __?__, radius __?__ ft, and equation __?__. The outer circle has center __?__, radius __?__ ft, and equation __?__.

The tabletop is the intersection of the interior of the outer circle and the exterior of the inner circle, also including the circles themselves. (0, 0); 2.5; $x^2 + y^2 = 6.25$; (0, 0); 9; $x^2 + y^2 = 81$

So, a system of inequalities describing the tabletop

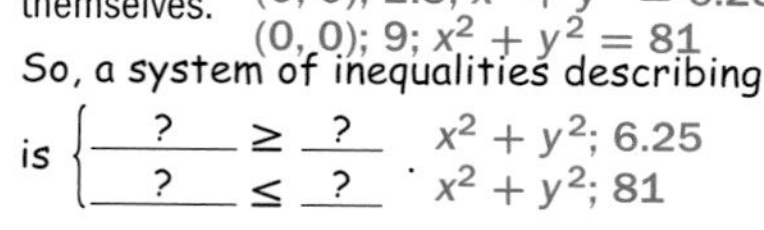

is $\begin{cases} \underline{\ ?\ } \geq \underline{\ ?\ } \\ \underline{\ ?\ } \leq \underline{\ ?\ } \end{cases}$. $x^2 + y^2$; 6.25 $x^2 + y^2$; 81

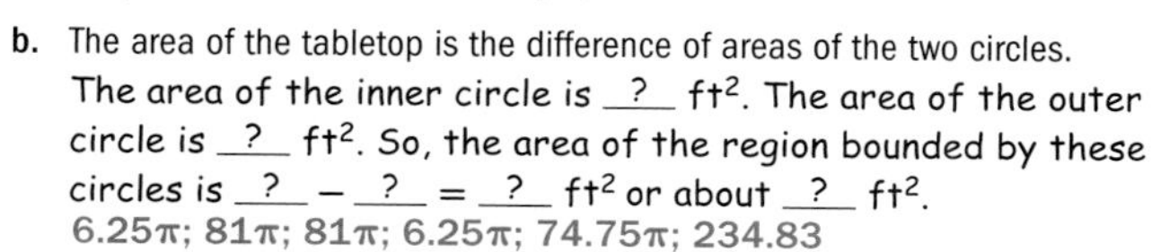

b. The area of the tabletop is the difference of areas of the two circles. The area of the inner circle is __?__ ft². The area of the outer circle is __?__ ft². So, the area of the region bounded by these circles is __?__ – __?__ = __?__ ft² or about __?__ ft².
6.25π; 81π; 81π; 6.25π; 74.75π; 234.83

Questions

COVERING THE IDEAS

1. Sketch the graph of each equation by hand on separate axes.
   a. $x^2 + y^2 = 25$
   b. $y = \sqrt{25 - x^2}$
   c. $y = -\sqrt{25 - x^2}$
2. Graph $x^2 + (y - 4)^2 \leq 25$. 1–2. See the Additional Answers section at the back of the book.
3. Use the equation for the arch found in Example 1. To the nearest inch, how high is the arch above a point on the ground 2 feet 6 inches from the center of the passage? 9 ft 8 in.
4. A bridge over water has a semicircular arch with radius 4 m set on pillars that extend 6 m above the water. How many meters above the water is the arch at a point 1.5 m from one of the pillars? about 9.12 m

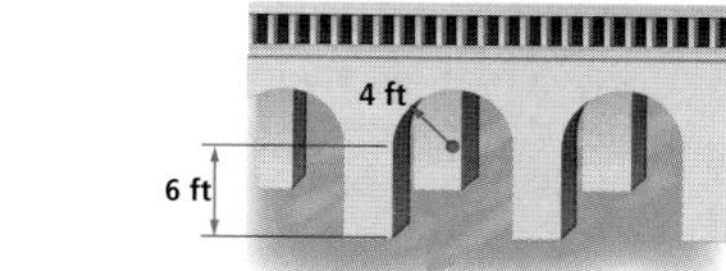

5. At the right, C is a circle. What is the shaded region called? the interior of the circle C

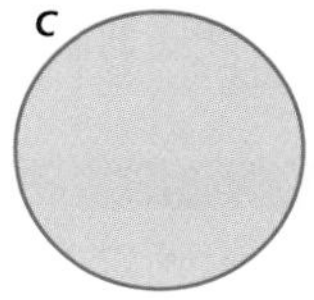

6. Refer to the target in this lesson. Write a system of inequalities to describe the set of points (x, y)
   a. in the 10-point region of the target.
   b. in the 40-point region of the target.

6a. $\begin{cases} x^2 + y^2 < 36 \\ x^2 + y^2 > 16 \end{cases}$

6b. $\begin{cases} x^2 + y^2 < 16 \\ x^2 + y^2 > 4 \end{cases}$

$$\begin{cases} \sqrt{a^2 - (x + a)^2} \text{ for } -2a \leq x \leq -a \\ \sqrt{a^2 - x^2} + a \text{ for } -a \leq x \leq a \\ \sqrt{a^2 - (x - a)^2} \text{ for } a \leq x \leq 2a \\ -\sqrt{a^2 - (x - a)^2} \text{ for } a \leq x \leq 2a \\ -\sqrt{a^2 - x^2} - a \text{ for } -a \leq x \leq a \\ -\sqrt{a^2 - (x + a)^2} \text{ for } -2a \leq x \leq a \end{cases}$$

$$-\sqrt{a^2 - (x + a)^2} \text{ for } -2a \leq x \leq a$$

Additional Example

Example 3 A washer has an outer diameter of 25 millimeters and an inner diameter of 8 millimeters.

a. Write a system of inequalities describing the area of a flat face of the washer.

b. Approximate the area of a flat face of the washer to the nearest tenth of a square millimeter.

Solution

a. Use the center of the washer as the origin for a coordinate system. The inner circle has center __?__, radius __?__ millimeters, and equation __?__. (0, 0); 4; $x^2 + y^2 = 16$ The outer circle has center __?__, radius __?__ millimeters, and equation __?__. (0, 0); 12.5; $x^2 + y^2 = 156.25$ A system of inequalities is __?__. $\begin{cases} x^2 + y^2 \geq 16 \\ x^2 + y^2 \leq 156.25 \end{cases}$

b. The area of a flat face of the washer is the difference of areas of the two circles. The area of the inner circle is __?__ square millimeters. 16π The area of the outer circle is __?__ square millimeters. 156.25π So the area of the region bounded by those circles is about __?__ – __?__ = __?__ square millimeters. 156.25π; 16π; 140.25π

3 Assignment

Recommended Assignment

- Questions 1–21
- Question 22 (extra credit)
- Reading Lesson 12-4
- Covering the Ideas 12-4

Notes on the Questions

Question 2 Unless the window of a graphing utility has the same scales on the two axes, the graph of a circle will appear to be an ellipse. In a drawing by hand, where the scales on axes tend to be the same, the graph should look like a circle.

Additional Answers can be found in the back of the book.

Notes on the Questions

Question 9 This question can initiate a discussion of what happens when the driver of a truck (or the driver of a car with a car-top carrier) misjudges the ability of the vehicle to fit under a bridge.

Additional Answers

10.

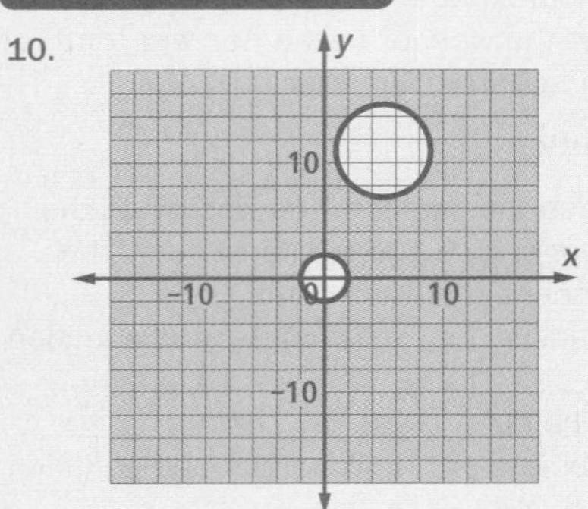

The graph includes all points exterior to two circles, one of radius 2 centered at the origin and one of radius 4 centered at (5, 11).

11. $\begin{cases} x < 3.35 \\ x > -3.35 \\ y < 3.35 \\ y > -3.35 \\ x^2 + y^2 > (2.275)^2 \end{cases}$

12. A circle is the set of all points in a plane that are at a given distance (its radius) from a fixed point (the center).

13. For a line ℓ and a point F not on ℓ a parabola is the set of all points in the plane of ℓ and F equidistant from F and ℓ.

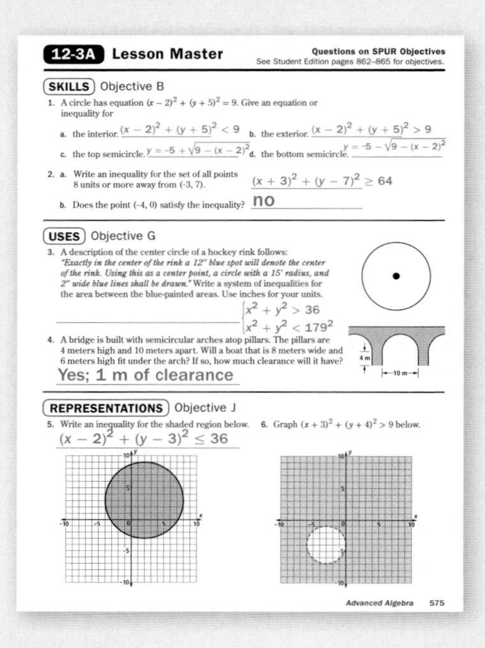

12-3A Lesson Master — Questions on SPUR Objectives. See Student Edition pages 862–865 for objectives.

SKILLS Objective B

1. A circle has equation $(x - 2)^2 + (y + 5)^2 = 9$. Give an equation or inequality for
   a. the interior. $(x - 2)^2 + (y + 5)^2 < 9$ b. the exterior. $(x - 2)^2 + (y + 5)^2 > 9$
   c. the top semicircle. $y = -5 + \sqrt{9 - (x - 2)^2}$ d. the bottom semicircle. $y = -5 - \sqrt{9 - (x - 2)^2}$
2. a. Write an inequality for the set of all points 8 units or more away from (-3, 7). $(x + 3)^2 + (y - 7)^2 \geq 64$
   b. Does the point (-4, 0) satisfy the inequality? no

USES Objective G

3. A description of the center circle of a hockey rink follows: *"Exactly in the center of the rink a 12" blue spot will denote the center of the rink. Using this as a center point, a circle with a 15' radius, and 2" wide blue lines shall be drawn."* Write a system of inequalities for the area between the blue-painted areas. Use inches for your units. $\begin{cases} x^2 + y^2 > 36 \\ x^2 + y^2 < 179^2 \end{cases}$
4. A bridge is built with semicircular arches atop pillars. The pillars are 4 meters high and 10 meters apart. Will a boat that is 8 meters wide and 6 meters high fit under the arch? If so, how much clearance will it have? Yes; 1 m of clearance

REPRESENTATIONS Objective J

5. Write an inequality for the shaded region below. $(x - 2)^2 + (y - 3)^2 \leq 36$
6. Graph $(x + 3)^2 + (y + 4)^2 > 9$ below.

Advanced Algebra 575

7. Write an inequality that describes all the points in the shaded region at the right. $(x - 2)^2 + (y - 3)^2 > 9$

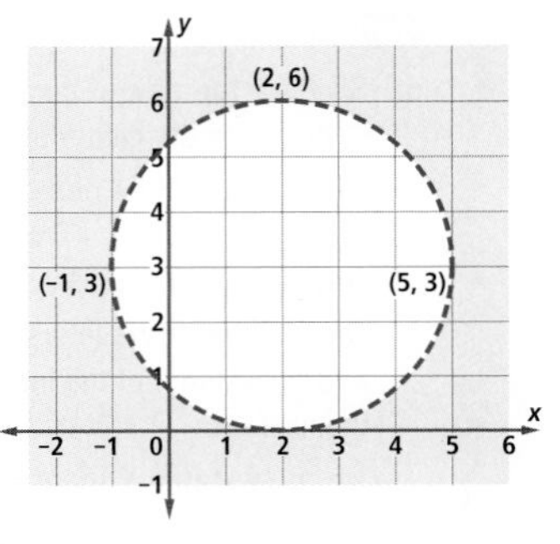

8. **Multiple Choice** Given a circle with center (h, k) and radius r, which of sentences A to D below describes
   a. the union of the circle with its interior? D
   b. the exterior of the circle? A

   A $(x - h)^2 + (y - k)^2 > r^2$ B $(x - h)^2 + (y - k)^2 < r^2$
   C $(x - h)^2 + (y - k)^2 \geq r^2$ D $(x - h)^2 + (y - k)^2 \leq r^2$

APPLYING THE MATHEMATICS

9. An architect designed a semicircular tunnel so that two trucks can pass each other with a 3-foot clearance between them and a 2-inch vertical clearance with the ceiling.
   a. If the trucks are 8 feet wide and 12 feet tall, what is the smallest possible radius of the semicircle?
   b. What is the tallest 8-foot wide vehicle that can drive down the center of the tunnel? about 14 ft 10 in.

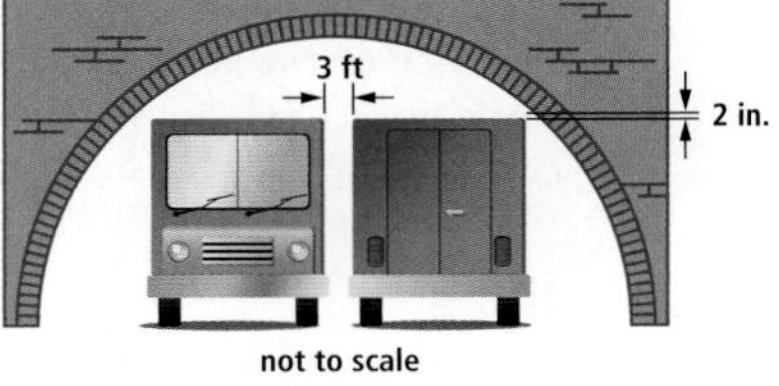

not to scale

9a. about 15 ft 5 in.

10. Graph the following system of inequalities and describe the graph. See margin.

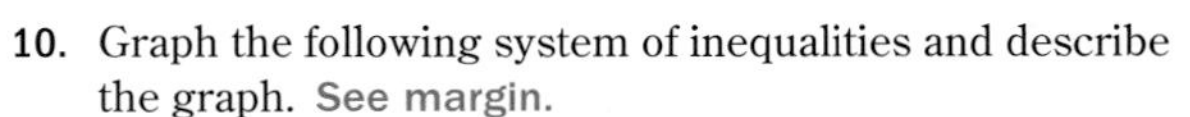

$$\begin{cases} x^2 + y^2 \geq 4 \\ (x - 5)^2 + (y - 11)^2 \geq 16 \end{cases}$$

11. In sumo wrestling, participants wrestle in a *dohyo*, a circular arena with a 4.55-meter diameter centered inside a square with side length 6.7 meters. Pushing your opponent out of the circle is one way to win the match. Sometimes the area between the circle and square is layered with fine sand to assist in determining when a wrestler falls outside of the circle. Put the origin at the center of the arena and describe the sandy region with a system of 5 inequalities. See margin.

REVIEW

In 12 and 13, define the term. (Lessons 12-2, 12-1) 12–13. See margin.

12. circle 13. parabola

14. Find an equation for the circle with center at (3, 6) and radius 2. (Lesson 12-2) $(x - 3)^2 + (y - 6)^2 = 4$

Accommodating the Learner

Ask students to write a system of equations to represent the right half of the circle whose equation is $(x - h)^2 + (y - k)^2 = r^2$. Answers vary. Sample: For the right half of the semicircle, $x \geq h$. So one description is $(x - h)^2 + (y - k)^2 = r^2$ for $x \geq h$. For graphing purposes, another solution is

$$y = \begin{cases} \sqrt{r^2 - (x - h)^2} + k \text{ for } x \geq h \\ -\sqrt{r^2 - (x - h)^2} + k \text{ for } x \geq h \end{cases}.$$

ENGLISH LEARNERS

Vocabulary Development

The paragraph following Example 1 (page 811) refers to an equation for the upper semicircle (which is $y = \sqrt{r^2 - (x - h)^2} + k$) and an equation for the lower semicircle (which is $y = -\sqrt{r^2 - (x - h)^2} + k$). Some students may benefit from treating the *upper semicircle* and the *lower semicircle* as vocabulary and associating the terms with specific versions of the general equations.

15. A circle with center at the origin passes through the point (5, 12). **(Lesson 12-2)**
    a. Find the radius of the circle. 13
    b. Find an equation for the circle. $x^2 + y^2 = 169$

16. Identify the focus and directrix of the parabola described by $y = \frac{1}{800}x^2$. **(Lesson 12-1)** focus: (0, 200); directrix: $y = -200$

17. Expand and simplify. **(Lessons 11-2, 6-1)**
    a. $(x + 8)^2 + y^2$
    b. $(x + y)^2 + 8^2$
    c. $(x + y + 8)^2$

18. A 3×5 drawing is enlarged to 6×10 by using a size change. **(Lesson 4-4)**
    a. What is a matrix for the size change?
    b. Suppose $A = (1, 2.3)$, $B = (0.3, 2)$, and $C = (2.7, 4.3)$ are three points on the smaller drawing. Write a matrix representing the locations of A', B', and C' on the image.
    c. Find the distance between A and B. $\frac{\sqrt{58}}{10} \approx 0.76$
    d. Find the distance between A' and B'. $\frac{\sqrt{58}}{5} \approx 1.52$

In 19 and 20, the graph of a function is given. State a. the function's domain, and b. its range. (Lesson 1-4)

19.

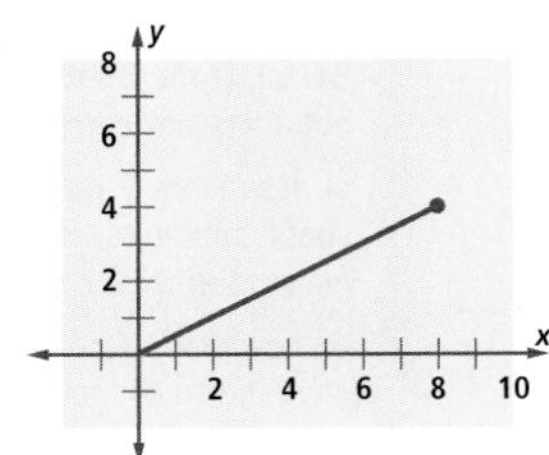

20.

21. Caleb has three scraps of wood with lengths 1.5 feet, 2.3 feet, and 4 feet. Without cutting them, can he use these scraps as the three sides of a triangular flower planter? Why or why not? **(Previous Course)**

EXPLORATION

22. a. A target with five circles all with center (0, 0) is shown at right. If the largest circle has radius 1 and the areas of the five nonoverlapping regions are all equal, find the radii and equations for the five circles.
    b. Generalize Part a. See margin.

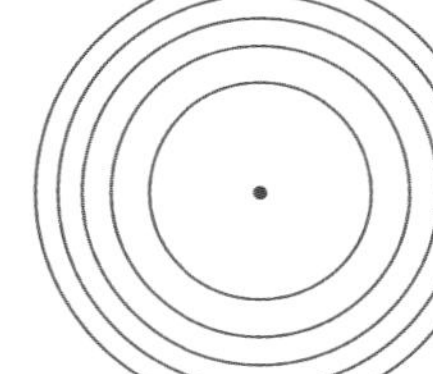

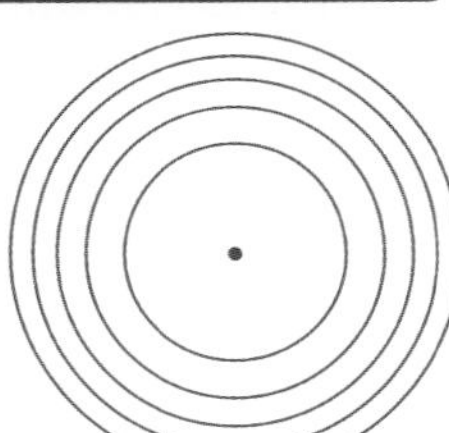

17a. $x^2 + 16x + y^2 + 64$

17b. $x^2 + 2xy + y^2 + 64$

17c. $x^2 + 2xy + 16x + y^2 + 16y + 64$

18a. $\begin{bmatrix} 2 & 0 \\ 0 & 2 \end{bmatrix}$

18b. $\begin{bmatrix} 2 & 0.6 & 5.4 \\ 4.6 & 4 & 8.6 \end{bmatrix}$

19a. $0 \le x \le 8$

19b. $0 \le y \le 4$

20a. $-5 \le x \le 5$

20b. $0 \le y \le 5$

21. No; the pieces do not satisfy the Triangle Inequality. To make a triangle, the sum of the measures of any two sides of the triangle should always be greater than the measure of the third side. Here, $1.5 + 2.3 < 4$.

22a. radii: 1, $\frac{2\sqrt{5}}{5}$, $\frac{\sqrt{15}}{5}$, $\frac{\sqrt{10}}{5}$, $\frac{\sqrt{5}}{5}$; equations: $x^2 + y^2 = 1$, $x^2 + y^2 = \frac{4}{5}$, $x^2 + y^2 = \frac{3}{5}$, $x^2 + y^2 = \frac{2}{5}$, $x^2 + y^2 = \frac{1}{5}$

QY ANSWER

$y = -\sqrt{9 - x^2} + 8$

Notes on the Questions

Question 22 The answer may surprise many students. You might want to ask for the inequality that describes each of the five regions.

4 Wrap-Up

Ongoing Assessment

Give students an ordered pair (a, b) and a length ℓ for the center and radius, respectively, of a circle. Ask students to write an equation for each region:

a. the interior of the circle, including the circle $(x - a)^2 + (y - b)^2 \le \ell^2$

b. the exterior of the circle, including the circle $(x - a)^2 + (y - b)^2 \le \ell^2$

c. the interior of the circle, not including the circle $(x - a)^2 + (y - b)^2 < \ell^2$

d. the exterior of the circle, not including the circle $(x - a)^2 + (y - b)^2 > \ell^2$

Administer Quiz 1 (or a quiz of your own) after students complete this lesson.

Additional Answers

22b. If you have a target with n circles of equal area, all with center (0, 0), and the largest circle has radius 1, then the circles have radii $\sqrt{\frac{j}{n}}$, for j an integer $0 \le j \le n$, and equations $x^2 + y^2 = \frac{j}{n}$, and the nonoverlapping regions all have area $\frac{\pi}{n}$.

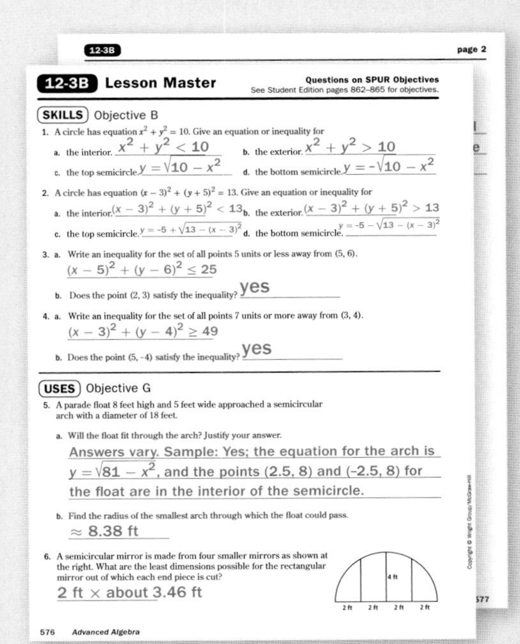

12-3B page 2

12-3B Lesson Master

Questions on SPUR Objectives
See Student Edition pages 862–865 for objectives.

SKILLS Objective B

1. A circle has equation $x^2 + y^2 = 10$. Give an equation or inequality for
   a. the interior. $x^2 + y^2 < 10$
   b. the exterior. $x^2 + y^2 > 10$
   c. the top semicircle. $y = \sqrt{10 - x^2}$
   d. the bottom semicircle. $y = -\sqrt{10 - x^2}$

2. A circle has equation $(x - 3)^2 + (y + 5)^2 = 13$. Give an equation or inequality for
   a. the interior. $(x - 3)^2 + (y + 5)^2 < 13$
   b. the exterior. $(x - 3)^2 + (y + 5)^2 > 13$
   c. the top semicircle. $y = -5 + \sqrt{13 - (x - 3)^2}$
   d. the bottom semicircle. $y = -5 - \sqrt{13 - (x - 3)^2}$

3. a. Write an inequality for the set of all points 5 units or less away from (5, 6).
   $(x - 5)^2 + (y - 6)^2 \le 25$
   b. Does the point (2, 3) satisfy the inequality? yes

4. a. Write an inequality for the set of all points 7 units or more away from (3, 4).
   $(x - 3)^2 + (y - 4)^2 \ge 49$
   b. Does the point (5, -4) satisfy the inequality? yes

USES Objective G

5. A parade float 8 feet high and 5 feet wide approached a semicircular arch with a diameter of 18 feet.
   a. Will the float fit through the arch? Justify your answer.
   Answers vary. Sample: Yes; the equation for the arch is $y = \sqrt{81 - x^2}$, and the points (2.5, 8) and (-2.5, 8) for the float are in the interior of the semicircle.
   b. Find the radius of the smallest arch through which the float could pass.
   ≈ 8.38 ft

6. A semicircular mirror is made from four smaller mirrors as shown at the right. What are the least dimensions possible for the rectangular mirror out of which each end piece is cut?
   2 ft × about 3.46 ft

4 ft
2 ft 2 ft 2 ft 2 ft

576 Advanced Algebra

Copyright © Wright Group/McGraw-Hill

577

Lesson 12-4

GOAL

Introduce a locus definition for an ellipse; from that definition, derive a standard-form equation for an ellipse.

SPUR Objectives

B Write equations for ellipses and inequalities for their interiors and exteriors.

E Identify characteristics of ellipses.

F Classify curves as ellipses using algebraic or geometric properties.

G Use ellipses to solve real-world problems.

I Graph ellipses when given equations for them in standard form, and vice versa.

L Draw a graph or interpret drawings or graphs of ellipses based on their definitions.

Materials/Resources

- Lesson Masters 12-4A and 12-4B
- Resource Masters 1 and 229–232
- Conic graph paper with 8 units between the centers of the circles

HOMEWORK

Suggestions for Assignment

- Questions 1–23
- Question 24 (extra credit)
- Reading Lesson 12-5
- Covering the Ideas 12-5

Local Standards

1 Warm-Up

In 1–3, consider the equation $\frac{x^2}{25} + \frac{y^2}{16} = 1$.

Lesson 12-4 Ellipses

▸ BIG IDEA From the geometric definition of an ellipse, an equation for any ellipse symmetric to the *x*- and *y*-axes can be found.

Vocabulary

ellipse
foci, focal constant of an ellipse
standard position for an ellipse
standard form of an equation for an ellipse
major axis, minor axis
center of an ellipse
semimajor axes, semiminor axes

On the first page of the chapter, we noted that when a plane intersects a cone but is not parallel to the cone's edge, the intersection is a figure called an *ellipse*. Drawing an ellipse freehand is challenging. Identifying several points on the ellipse and connecting them with a smooth curve simplifies the task. The following Activity provides one method for sketching an ellipse.

Mental Math

At the state championship basketball game, the Beatums are beating the Underdogs. The score is 84-52. If the Beatums do not score any more points,

a. how many 2-point shots must the Underdogs make to win? 17

b. how many 3-point shots must they make to win? 11

c. how many 2-point shots must they make to win if they also make five 3-point shots? 9

Activity

Steps 1–4. See the Additional Answers section at the back of the book.

MATERIALS conic graph paper with 8 units between the centers of the circles

Step 1 Label the centers of the circles as F_1 and F_2. Plot the two points of intersection of the circles that are 5 units from both F_1 and F_2.

Step 2 **a.** Mark the two points of intersection between circles that are 4 units from F_1 and 6 units from F_2.
b. Mark the two points of intersection between circles that are 6 units from F_1 and 4 units from F_2.

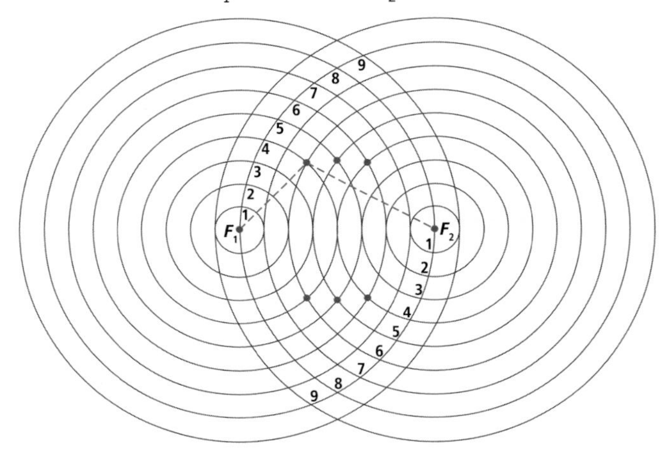

Background

The derivation of an equation for an ellipse from its locus definition on page 818 is perhaps the most difficult algebraic manipulation in this book. We do not expect students to be able to reconstruct it. The goal is that students realize that the equation comes from the definition, applying only properties they already have learned. It is also important that students see some examples of such complicated manipulations.

In Lesson 12-7, a similar derivation is used to obtain equations for some hyperbolas.

Step 3 Repeat the process of Step 2 plotting the intersections of circles that are x units from F_1 and $(10 - x)$ units from F_2 until you have 16 points plotted.

Step 4 Starting on the left and moving clockwise, label the points $P_1, P_2, \ldots, P_{16}$. Connect the dots with a smooth curve to form an ellipse.

What Is an Ellipse?

The ellipse in the Activity is determined by the two points F_1 and F_2, called its *foci* (pronounced "foe sigh," plural of focus), and a number called the *focal constant.* The focal constant is the constant sum of the distances from any point P on the ellipse to the foci. The focal constant of the ellipse in the Activity is 10. That is, $P_nF_1 + P_nF_2 = 10$ for all points P_n on the curve. Every ellipse can be determined in this way.

Definition of Ellipse

Let F_1 and F_2 be any two points in a plane and let d be a constant with $d > F_1F_2$. Then the **ellipse** with **foci** F_1 and F_2 and **focal constant** d is the set of points P in the plane for which $PF_1 + PF_2 = d$.

The equation $PF_1 + PF_2 = d$ is said to define the ellipse. For any point P on the ellipse, the focal constant $PF_1 + PF_2$ has to be greater than F_1F_2 because of the Triangle Inequality. That is why $d > F_1F_2$.

Equations for Some Ellipses

To find an equation for the ellipse in the Activity, consider a coordinate system with $\overleftrightarrow{F_1F_2}$ as the x-axis and with the origin midway between the foci on the axis. Then the foci are $F_1 = (-4, 0)$ and $F_2 = (4, 0)$. This is the *standard position* for the ellipse.

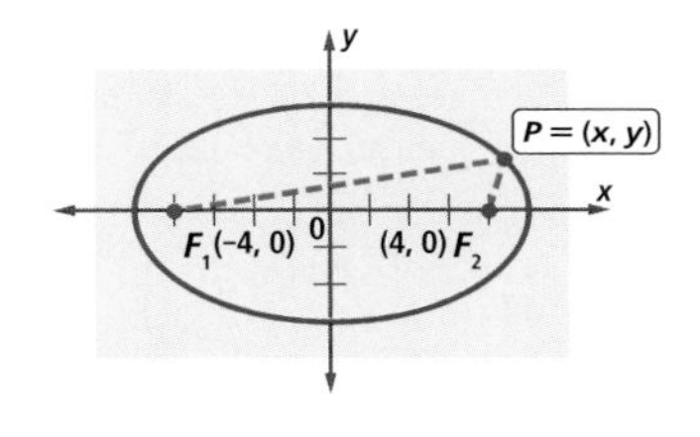

If $P = (x, y)$ is on the ellipse, then because the focal constant is 10,

$$PF_1 + PF_2 = 10.$$

So, by the Distance Formula,

$$\sqrt{(x + 4)^2 + (y - 0)^2} + \sqrt{(x - 4)^2 + (y - 0)^2} = 10,$$

or

$$\sqrt{(x + 4)^2 + y^2} + \sqrt{(x - 4)^2 + y^2} = 10.$$

Accommodating the Learner

An ellipse has equation $\frac{x^2}{100} + \frac{y^2}{25} = 1$. Show that the figure found by connecting consecutive endpoints of the axes is a rhombus. The endpoints of the axes are (-10, 0), (0, 5), (10, 0), and (0, -5). For each pair of consecutive endpoints, the distance between the points is $\sqrt{100 + 25}$. Because all four sides of the figure are congruent, the figure is a rhombus.

ENGLISH LEARNERS
Vocabulary Development

Many students have difficulty with this lesson's vocabulary and in relating the vocabulary to coefficients in the equation for an ellipse. Encourage students to provide their own illustrations for *focus, focal constant,* and *major* and *minor axis.* When students work with specific ellipses, encourage them to write parallel steps using the general equations $\frac{x^2}{a^2} + \frac{y^2}{b^2} = 1$ and $b^2 = a^2 - c^2$ to get a feel for the values of a, b, c, $2a$, and $2b$.

12-4

1. The point (5, 0) satisfies this equation. What are three other points on the axes that satisfy the equation? Graph the four points. (-5, 0), (0, 4), and (0, -4)

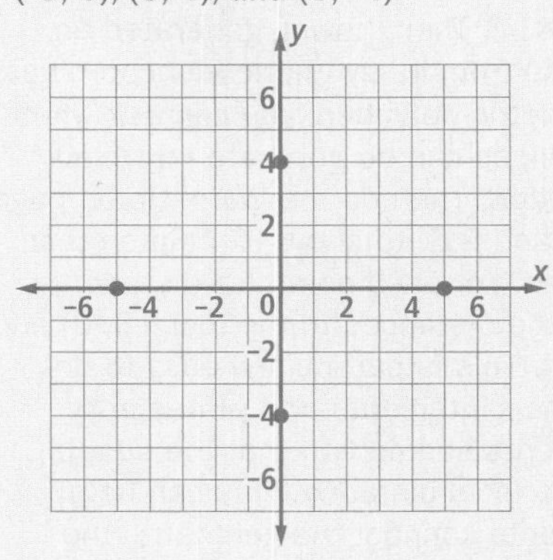

2. Use substitution to show that the point (4, 2.4) satisfies this equation. Use the symmetry of the graph to find three other points on the graph. Graph the four points. (4, -2.4), (-4, 2.4), and (-4, -2.4)

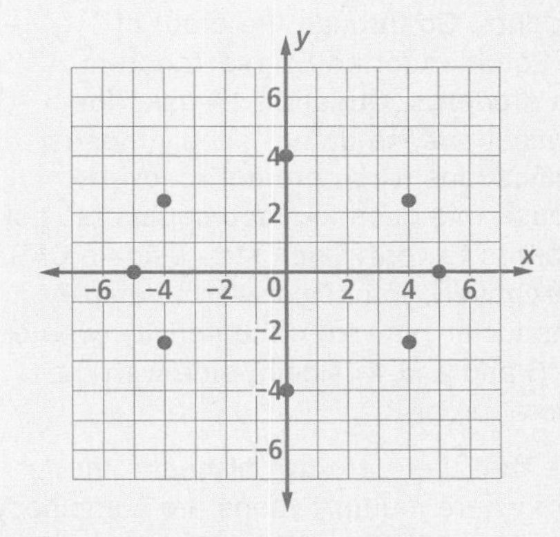

3. When $x = 3$, find the two values of y that satisfy the equation. Repeat with $x = -3$. Graph the four points. (3, 3.2), (3, -3.2), (-3, 3.2), and (-3, -3.2)

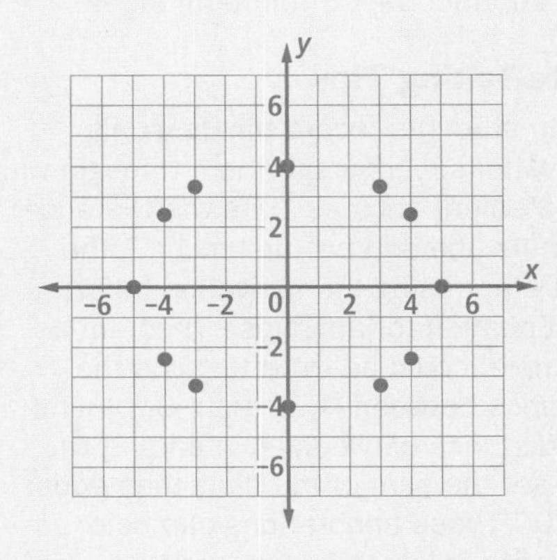

2 Teaching

Notes on the Lesson

Start with the Activity on pages 816 and 817. Then, having generated an ellipse from its synthetic (noncoordinate) geometric definition, you can ask whether an ellipse can be generated from an equation. Then do the Warm-Up on pages 816 and 817 to show 12 points on an ellipse. For each point, have students add the distances to the foci (-3, 0) and (3, 0). This is particularly easy to do for the x-intercepts and y-intercepts. Students should find that the sum is 5, the focal distance. This can help students connect the geometry (the synthetic drawing) and the algebra (the coordinate graph).

Additional Answers can be found in the back of the book.

After completing the Activity, you might wish to read this lesson with your students. Go through the proof of the Equation for an Ellipse Theorem with students. Question 14 asks for justifications, so do not supply those justifications if you are not ready to discuss this question. You could also ask students to verify each step using a CAS. Alternatively, you might wish to display the special case from the Activity (where $c = 5$ and $a = 4$) side-by-side with the general proof.

Note that there are two places in the proof where multiple steps are combined. To go from (3) to (4), students must expand the binomial squares, then subtract $x^2 + c^2 + y^2$ from both sides. To go from (7) to (8), students must expand the binomial square, distribute the a^2, and subtract $2a^2cx$ from both sides.

Note-Taking Tips

When students record this lesson's derivations, encourage them to begin with a statement such as "Use the Distance Formula and add two distances." The next step (using the derivation before the Equation for an Ellipse Theorem as example) could be to write "Find the distance between (x, y) and $(-3, 0)$, find the distance between (x, y) and $(3, 0)$, and set the sum of the distances equal to 10." These annotations can help students follow the derivations.

This equation for the ellipse is quite involved. Surprisingly, to find an equation for this ellipse, and all others with their foci on an axis, it is simpler to begin with a more general case. The resulting equation is well worth the effort it takes to derive it, and so on the next page we state it as a theorem. You are asked to justify the numbered steps in the proof of this theorem in Question 14.

Equation for an Ellipse Theorem

The ellipse with foci $(c, 0)$ and $(-c, 0)$ and focal constant $2a$ has equation $\frac{x^2}{a^2} + \frac{y^2}{b^2} = 1$, where $b^2 = a^2 - c^2$.

Proof Let $F_1 = (-c, 0)$, $F_2 = (c, 0)$, and $P = (x, y)$. By the definition of an ellipse,

$$PF_1 + PF_2 = 2a.$$

1. $\sqrt{(x + c)^2 + y^2} + \sqrt{(x - c)^2 + y^2} = 2a$
2. $\sqrt{(x - c)^2 + y^2} = 2a - \sqrt{(x + c)^2 + y^2}$
3. $(x - c)^2 + y^2 = 4a^2 - 4a\sqrt{(x + c)^2 + y^2} + (x + c)^2 + y^2$
4. $-2cx = 4a^2 - 4a\sqrt{(x + c)^2 + y^2} + 2cx$
5. $4a\sqrt{(x + c)^2 + y^2} = 4a^2 + 4cx$
6. $a\sqrt{(x + c)^2 + y^2} = a^2 + cx$
7. $a^2((x + c)^2 + y^2) = a^4 + 2a^2cx + c^2x^2$
8. $a^2x^2 + a^2c^2 + a^2y^2 = a^4 + c^2x^2$
9. $(a^2 - c^2)x^2 + a^2y^2 = a^2(a^2 - c^2)$

P = (x, y)
$F_1 = (-c, 0)$
$F_2 = (c, 0)$

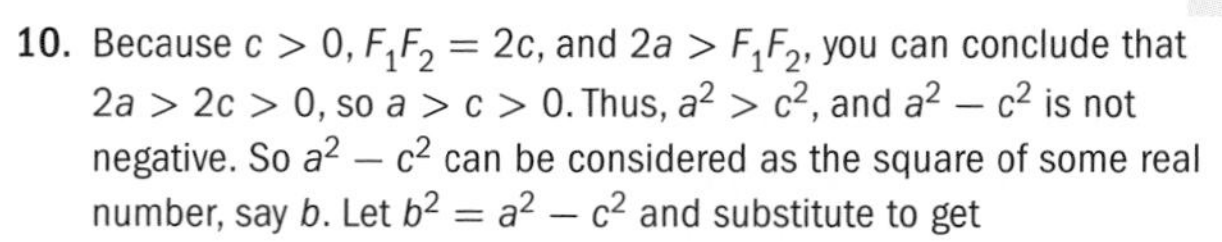

10. Because $c > 0$, $F_1F_2 = 2c$, and $2a > F_1F_2$, you can conclude that $2a > 2c > 0$, so $a > c > 0$. Thus, $a^2 > c^2$, and $a^2 - c^2$ is not negative. So $a^2 - c^2$ can be considered as the square of some real number, say b. Let $b^2 = a^2 - c^2$ and substitute to get

$$b^2x^2 + a^2y^2 = a^2b^2.$$

11. $\frac{x^2}{a^2} + \frac{y^2}{b^2} = 1$

The Standard Form of an Equation for an Ellipse in Standard Position

An ellipse centered at the origin with its foci on an axis is in **standard position**, and $\frac{x^2}{a^2} + \frac{y^2}{b^2} = 1$ is in the **standard form** of an equation for this ellipse. Even without knowing the geometric interpretation of this equation, analyzing the formula can tell you a lot about the shape of its graph.

Accommodating the Learner

A carpenter wants to cut out the largest possible ellipse from a rectangular board. How can the carpenter use the dimensions ℓ and w of the board to identify the foci and the length of string and use the method in Question 16?

The length of string is the length of the major axis of the ellipse, which is ℓ.

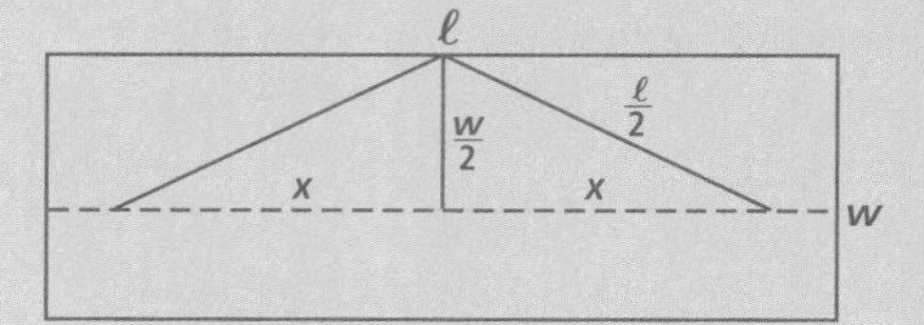

GUIDED

Example 1

Given the equation $\frac{x^2}{9} + \frac{y^2}{4} = 1$, describe

a. the *x*- and *y*-intercepts of its graph.

b. the possible *x*- and *y*-values.

c. the symmetries of the graph, if any.

Solution

a. The *x*-intercepts are the *x*-values for which $y = 0$. Substitute 0 for y to get $\frac{x^2}{9} + \frac{0^2}{4} = 1$. Then solve for *x* to get x = __?__. Similarly, the *y*-intercepts are the *y*-values for which $x =$ __?__. Substitute and solve for *y* to get y = __?__. ± 3; 0; ± 2

b. Now $y^2 \geq 0$ and $\frac{x^2}{9} \leq 1$, so $x^2 \leq 9$. Therefore, $\sqrt{x^2} \leq 3$ and $|x| \leq 3$, so $-3 \leq x \leq 3$. Similarly, $x^2 \geq 0$ and $\frac{y^2}{4} \leq$ __?__, so __?__ $\leq y \leq$ __?__. 1; -2; 2

c. Recall that r_y: $(x, y) \rightarrow (-x, y)$. If you replace *x* with $-x$ in the equation, it becomes $\frac{(-x)^2}{9} + \frac{y^2}{4} = 1$. Because $x^2 = (-x)^2$, this equation is equivalent to the original. Therefore, the graph is symmetric to the __?__. y-axis

To check for symmetry over the *x*-axis, recall that r_x: $(x, y) \rightarrow$ __?__. So, if you replace __?__ with __?__ in the original equation, it becomes __?__, which is equivalent to the original. Therefore, the graph is symmetric to the __?__ as well. $(x, -y)$; y; $-y$; $\frac{x^2}{9} + \frac{(-y)^2}{4} = 1$; *x*-axis

Generalizing from Example 1, the intercepts of the ellipse with equation $\frac{x^2}{a^2} + \frac{y^2}{b^2} = 1$ are $(a, 0)$, $(-a, 0)$, $(0, b)$ and $(0, -b)$. The possible *x*- and *y*-values indicate that the entire ellipse is contained in the rectangle $\{(x, y): -a \leq x \leq a \text{ and } -b \leq y \leq b\}$. These facts can help you sketch a graph of an ellipse by hand.

Consider the ellipse at the right. The segments $\overline{A_1A_2}$ and $\overline{B_1B_2}$ are, respectively, the **major** and **minor axes** of the ellipse. The major axis contains the foci and is always longer than the minor axis. The axes lie on the symmetry lines and intersect at the **center** O of the ellipse. Each segment $\overline{OA_1}$ and $\overline{OA_2}$ is a **semimajor axis** of the ellipse. The segments $\overline{OB_1}$ and $\overline{OB_2}$ are the **semiminor axes** of the ellipse. The diagram illustrates the following theorem. It applies to all ellipses centered at the origin with foci on one of the coordinate axes.

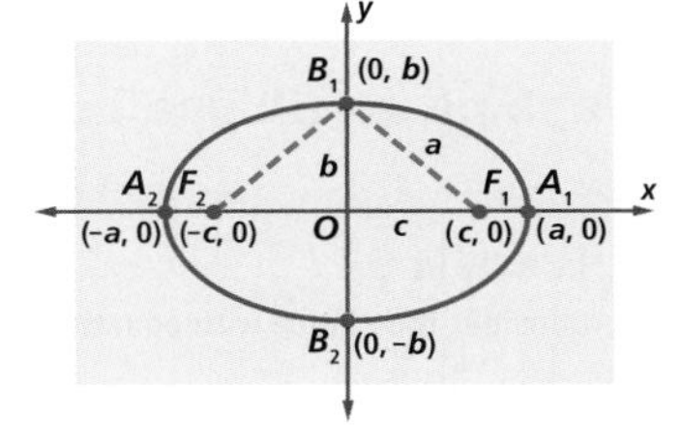

Additional Example

Example 1 Given the equation $\frac{x^2}{49} + \frac{y^2}{64} = 1$, describe the following:

a. *x*- and *y*-intercepts of the graph

b. possible *x*- and *y*-values

c. symmetries of the graph, if any

Solution

a. The *x*-intercepts are the *x*-values for which $y = 0$. Substitute 0 for *y* to get $\frac{x^2}{49} + \frac{0}{64} = 1$. Then solve for *x* to get $x =$ __?__. ± 7 Similarly, the *y*-intercepts are the *y*-values for which $x =$ __?__. 0 Substitute and solve for *y* to get $y =$ __?__. ± 8

b. $y^2 \geq 0$ and $\frac{x^2}{49} \leq 1$, so $x^2 \leq 49$. Therefore, $\sqrt{x^2} \leq 7$ and $|x| \leq 7$, so $-7 \leq x \leq 7$. Similarly, $x^2 \geq 0$ and $\frac{y^2}{64} \leq$ __?__, so __?__ $\leq y \leq$ __?__. 1; -8; 8

c. If you replace *x* with $-x$ in the equation, it becomes $\frac{(-x)^2}{49} + \frac{y^2}{64} = 1$, which is equivalent to the original. Therefore, the graph is symmetric to the __?__. *y*-axis To check for symmetry over the *x*-axis, recall that R_x: $(x, y) \rightarrow$ __?__. $(x, -y)$ So if you replace __?__ with __?__ in the original equation, the equation becomes __?__, which is equivalent to the original. y; $-y$; $\frac{x^2}{49} + \frac{(-y)^2}{64} = 1$ Therefore, the graph is also symmetric to the __?__. *x*-axis

If x represents the distance from the center of the board to each focus, then $x^2 + \left(\frac{w}{2}\right)^2 = \left(\frac{\ell}{2}\right)^2$, so $x = \sqrt{\left(\frac{\ell}{2}\right)^2 - \left(\frac{w}{2}\right)^2} = \frac{1}{2}\sqrt{\ell^2 - w^2}$. The carpenter should use a length ℓ for the string and attach the ends of the string at a distance $\frac{1}{2}\sqrt{\ell^2 - w^2}$ from the center of the board, on a line midway between the long sides of the board.

Additional Example

Example 2 Find the endpoints of the major and minor axes, the foci, and an equation for an ellipse formed when there are 4 units between the centers of the circles. The focal constant is 5. How does this equation relate to the figure constructed in the Activity on page 816?

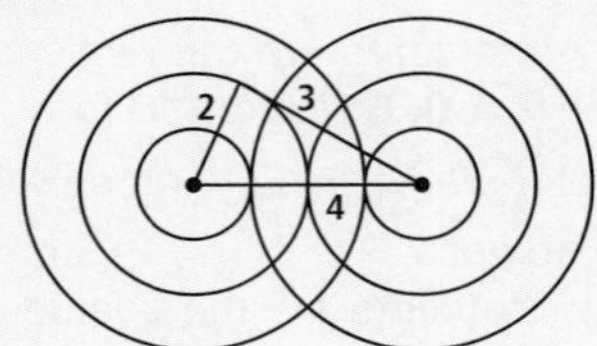

Solution Position a coordinate system on the ellipse with origin at the center of the ellipse and the foci on the x-axis. The radius of the smallest circle is 1 unit. The major axis has length _?_, so $a =$ _?_. 6; 3 The minor axis has length _?_, so $b =$ _?_. 3; 1.5 Therefore, in standard position, the endpoints of the major axis of the ellipse are _?_ and _?_, and the endpoints of the minor axis are _?_ and _?_. (–3; 0); (3, 0); (0, 1.5); (0, –1.5) The foci for the ellipse are _?_ and _?_. (–2; 0); (2, 0) An equation for this ellipse is _?_. $\frac{x^2}{9} + \frac{y^2}{2.25} = 1$. This equation is an equation for the ellipse constructed in the Activity.

Length of Axes of an Ellipse Theorem

In the ellipse with equation $\frac{x^2}{a^2} + \frac{y^2}{b^2} = 1$, $2a$ is the length of the horizontal axis, and $2b$ is the length of the vertical axis.

The length of the major axis is the focal constant. If $a > b$, then the major axis is horizontal and $(c, 0)$ and $(-c, 0)$ are the foci. The focal constant is $2a$, the length of the semimajor axis is a, and by the Pythagorean Theorem $b^2 = a^2 - c^2$ (as in the ellipse on the previous page).

If $b > a$, then the major axis is vertical. So the foci are $(0, c)$ and $(0, -c)$, the focal constant is $2b$, and $a^2 = b^2 - c^2$.

 QY

QY

In the ellipse of Example 1, what are the lengths of the major and minor axes?

GUIDED

Example 2

Find the endpoints of the major and minor axes, the foci, and an equation for the ellipse in the Activity in standard position.

Solution Position a coordinate system on the ellipse, with origin at the center of the ellipse and the foci on the x-axis. Let the radius of the smallest circle on the conic graph paper be 1 unit on the axes scales.

The major axis has length _?_, so a = _?_. 10; 5

The minor axis has length _?_, so b = _?_. 6; 3

Therefore, in standard position, the endpoints of the major axis of the ellipse are (_?_, 0) and (_?_, 0), and the endpoints of the minor axis are (0, _?_) and (0, _?_). –5; 5; –3; 3

Since $a > b$, $b^2 = a^2 - c^2$. So $9 = 25 - c^2$ and $c = 4$.

The foci for the ellipse are (_?_, 0) and (_?_, 0). –4; 4

An equation for this ellipse is $\frac{x^2}{?} + \frac{y^2}{?} = 1$. 25; 9

Graphing an Ellipse in Standard Form

Example 3

Consider the ellipse with equation $\frac{x^2}{9} + \frac{y^2}{10} = 1$.

a. Identify the endpoints and the lengths of the major and minor axes.

b. Graph the ellipse.

Extension

An ellipse with center (p, q) has a horizontal major axis, is in Quadrant I, and is tangent to the two coordinate axes.

1. What are the coordinates of the endpoints of the axes of the ellipse? The endpoints of the horizontal axis are $(0, q)$ and $(2p, q)$, and the endpoints of the vertical axis are $(p, 0)$ and $(p, 2q)$.
2. What is an equation for the ellipse? The length of the major axis is $2p$, and the length of the minor axis is $2q$, so an equation of the ellipse is $\frac{x^2}{p^2} + \frac{y^2}{q^2} = 1$.
3. Name the coordinates of the foci of the ellipse. $c^2 = p^2 - q^2$; the foci are $c = \sqrt{p^2 - q^2}$ units to the left and to the right of (p, q), so the foci are at $\left(p - \sqrt{p^2 - q^2}, q\right)$ and $\left(p + \sqrt{p^2 - q^2}, q\right)$.

12-4A page 2

12-4A Lesson Master

Questions on SPUR Objectives
See Student Edition pages 862–865 for objectives.

SKILLS Objective B

In 1–3, write an equation for an ellipse satisfying the given conditions.

1. The endpoints of the major and minor axes are (12, 0), (-12, 0), (0, 9), and (0, -9). $\frac{x^2}{144} + \frac{y^2}{81} = 1$
2. The endpoints of the major axes are $(u, 0)$ and $(-u, 0)$, and the endpoints of the minor axes are $(0, v)$ and $(0, -v)$. $\frac{x^2}{u^2} + \frac{y^2}{v^2} = 1$
3. The foci are at (0, 6) and (0, -6) and the focal constant is 13. $\frac{x^2}{6.25} + \frac{y^2}{42.25} = 1$

PROPERTIES Objective E

4. For the ellipse with equation $\frac{x^2}{81} + \frac{y^2}{121} = 1$, find
   a. the length of the major axis. 22
   b. the length of the minor axis. 18
   c. the x- and y-intercepts. (9, 0), (–9, 0), (0, 11), (0, –11)
   d. the coordinates of the foci. $(0, \sqrt{40})$, $(0, -\sqrt{40})$
5. Find the focal constant of the ellipse with equation $\frac{x^2}{15} + \frac{y^2}{10} = 1$. $2\sqrt{15}$

PROPERTIES Objective F

In 6–8, determine whether the figure described is a *parabola*, a *circle*, or an *ellipse*.

6. The set of all points whose distance from (x_1, y_1) is a. circle
7. The set of all points whose distances from (x_1, y_1) and (x_2, y_2) sum to a. ellipse
8. The set of all points whose distances from (x_1, y_1) and $y = k$ are equal. parabola

USES Objective G

9. The orbit of the Moon around Earth is an ellipse with major axis 384,400 km long and minor axis 383,800 km long. Give an equation for the Moon's orbit. $\frac{x^2}{192{,}200^2} + \frac{y^2}{191{,}900^2} = 1$
10. The green of a miniature golf hole is in the shape of an ellipse with major axis six feet long and minor axis four feet long.
    a. Give an equation for the ellipse. $\frac{x^2}{9} + \frac{y^2}{4} = 1$
    b. The tee and the hole are the two foci of the ellipse. How far apart are they? $2\sqrt{5}$ ft ≈ 4.47 ft

578 *Advanced Algebra*

Solution

a. $a^2 = 9$ and $b^2 = 10$. So $a = 3$ and $b = \sqrt{10}$. Because $b > a$, the foci of the ellipse are on the y-axis. The endpoints of the major axis are $(0, \sqrt{10})$, and $(0, -\sqrt{10})$. The endpoints of the minor axis are $(3, 0)$, and $(-3, 0)$. The length of the major axis is $2\sqrt{10}$ and the length of the minor axis is 6.

b. Plot the four axis endpoints, then sketch the rest of the ellipse. A graph of the ellipse is at the right.

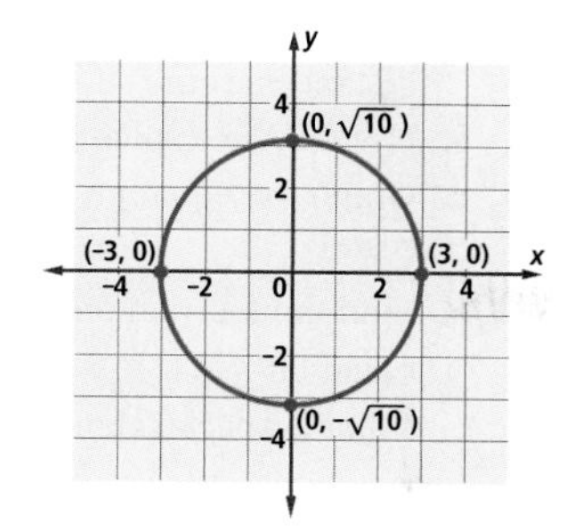

Questions

COVERING THE IDEAS

In 1 and 2, refer to the ellipse in the Activity.

1. What is the focal constant? 10
2. What is the length of each
   a. semimajor axis? 5
   b. semiminor axis? 3
3. On the ellipse at the right, $OA = OB$, $OD = OC$ and $\overline{AB} \perp \overline{CD}$. Identify its
   a. foci. I, J
   b. major axis. $\overline{AB}$
   c. minor axis. $\overline{CD}$

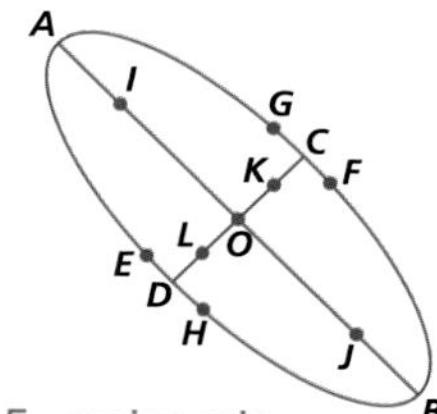

In 4–8, consider the ellipse with equation $\frac{x^2}{a^2} + \frac{y^2}{b^2} = 1$. Assume $b > a$. Identify the following.

4. the center of the ellipse $(0, 0)$
5. the endpoints of the major and minor axes
6. the lengths of the semimajor and semiminor axes
7. the possible values of x and the possible values of y
8. the x- and y-intercepts $(-a, 0), (a, 0); (0, -b), (0, b)$
9. Sketch a graph of the ellipse with equation $\frac{x}{16} + y^2 = 1$. See margin.
10. Write an equation in standard form for the ellipse with focal constant 17 and foci (8, 0) and (-8, 0). $\frac{x^2}{\left(\frac{17}{2}\right)^2} + \frac{y^2}{\left(\frac{\sqrt{33}}{2}\right)^2} = 1$

5. major axis: $(0, -b), (0, b)$; minor axis: $(-a, 0), (a, 0)$
6. semimajor axis: b; semiminor axis: a
7. $-a \le x \le a$; $-b \le y \le b$

APPLYING THE MATHEMATICS

11. Refer to the ellipse graphed at the right.
   a. Find an equation for the ellipse. $\frac{x^2}{64} + \frac{y^2}{16} = 1$
   b. Write an inequality describing the points in the interior of the ellipse. $\frac{x^2}{64} + \frac{y^2}{16} < 1$

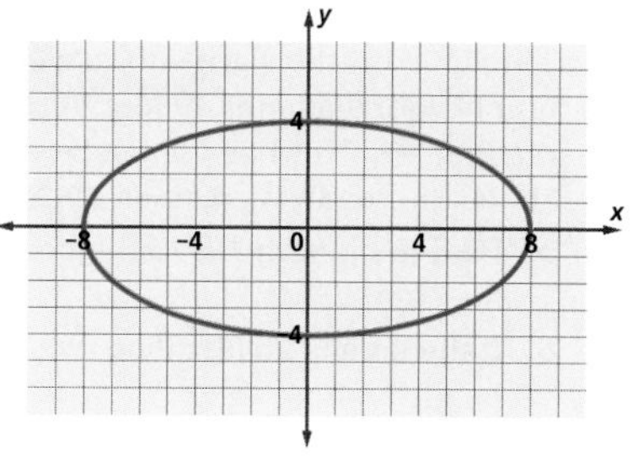

Additional Answers

9.

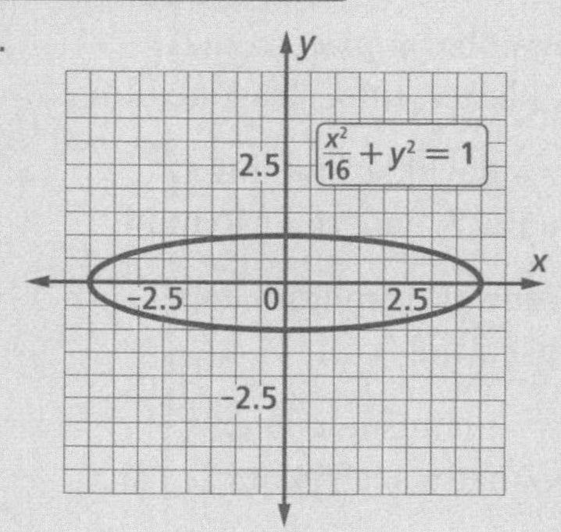

Additional Example

Example 3 Consider the ellipse with equation $\frac{x^2}{8} + \frac{y^2}{16} = 1$.

a. Identify the endpoints and the lengths of the major and minor axes. $a^2 = 8$ and $b^2 = 16$, so $a = 2\sqrt{2}$ and $b = 4$. Because $b > a$, the foci are on the y-axis. The endpoints of the major axis are $(0, 4)$ and $(0, -4)$. The endpoints of the minor axis are $(2\sqrt{2}, 0)$ and $(-2\sqrt{2}, 0)$. The length of the major axis is 8, and the length of the minor axis is $4\sqrt{2}$.

b. Graph the ellipse.

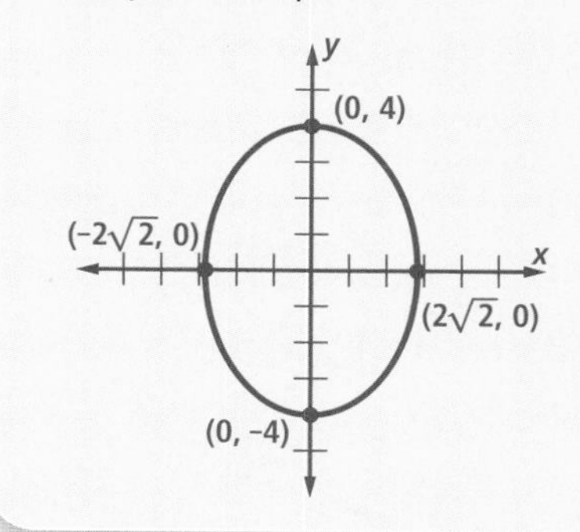

3 Assignment

Recommended Assignment

- Questions 1–23
- Question 24 (extra credit)
- Reading Lesson 12-5
- Covering the Ideas 12-5

Notes on the Questions

Questions 4–8 Because $b \ge a$, the foci are on the y-axis.

Notes on the Questions

Question 15c The two foci are so close together that the second focus is in the interior of the sun.

Additional Answers

12a. $\sqrt{(x-1)^2+(y-1)^2}+\sqrt{(x+1)^2+(y+1)^2}=4$

12b. $y=\frac{2\sqrt{2(3-x^2)}+x}{3}$ or $y=\frac{-2\sqrt{2(3-x^2)}+x}{3}$

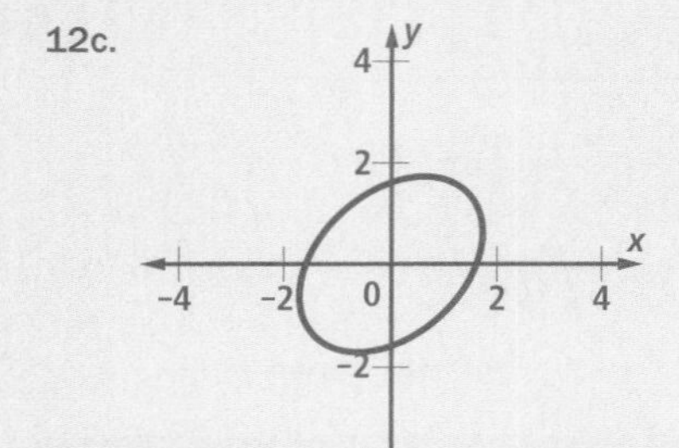

12c.

14. 1. Substitution, Distance Formula
2. Addition Property of Equality
3. Square both sides, Distributive Property
4. Distributive Property, Addition Property of Equality
5. Addition Property of Equality
6. Multiplication Property of Equality
7. Square both sides, Distributive Property
8. Distributive Property, Addition Property of Equality
9. Distributive Property, Addition Property of Equality
10. Substitution
11. Multiplication Property of Equality

12. a. Write an equation describing the set of points (x, y) whose distances from (-1, -1) and (1, 1) add up to 4. 12a–c. See margin.
b. Use a CAS to solve your equation in Part a for y.
c. Graph the equation on a graphing utility and sketch the result.

13. a. Find the foci and focal constant of the ellipse with equation $\frac{x^2}{100}+\frac{y^2}{100}=1$. both foci at (0, 0); focal constant 20
b. What is special about this ellipse? The ellipse is a circle.

14. Write justifications for the statements in the proof of the Equation for an Ellipse Theorem. See margin.

15. The orbits of the planets are nearly elliptical with the Sun at one focus. The shape of Mercury's orbit can be approximated by the equation $\frac{x^2}{1295}+\frac{y^2}{1240}=1$, where x and y are in millions of miles.
a. What is the farthest Mercury gets from the Sun?
b. What is the closest Mercury gets to the Sun?
c. How far apart are the two foci? about 14.8 million mi

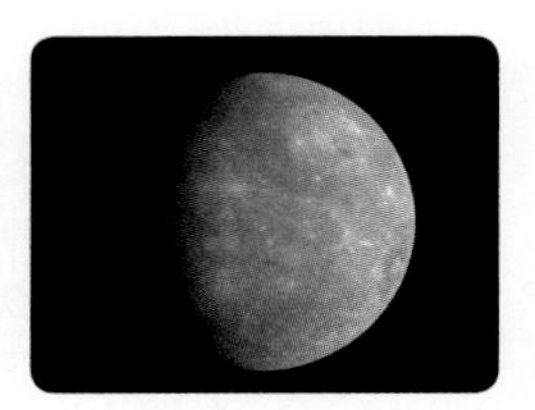

16. a. Using two thumbtacks and a piece of string, draw a curve as shown at the right. 16a–c. See margin.
b. Explain why the curve is an ellipse.
c. What part of your equipment represents the focal constant of the ellipse?

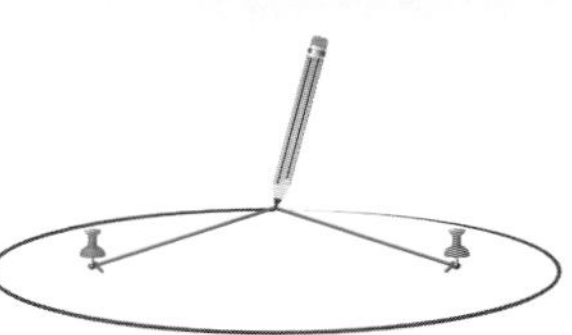

17. A *superellipse* has equation $\left|\frac{x}{a}\right|^n+\left|\frac{y}{b}\right|^n=1$, for nonzero a and b and $n>0$.
a. Sketch a graph of the superellipse for $a=2$, $b=3$, and $n=1$.
b. Identify the major and minor axis on your sketch in Part a.
c. List the x- and y- intercepts of the graph.
d. Repeat Part a when $a=2$, $b=3$, and $n=3$.
e. How are your graphs in Parts a and d related? How are they different?

15a. about 43.4 million mi

15b. about 28.6 million mi

17a–e. See the Additional Answers section at the back of the book.

REVIEW

18. The figure at the right shows a cross section of a tunnel with diameter 40 feet. A rectangular sign reading "Do Not Pass" must be placed at least 16 feet above the roadway. (Lesson 12-3)
a. Find the length BE of the beam that supports the sign. 24 ft
b. If the sign is 16 feet long, what is its maximum height? about 2.33 ft

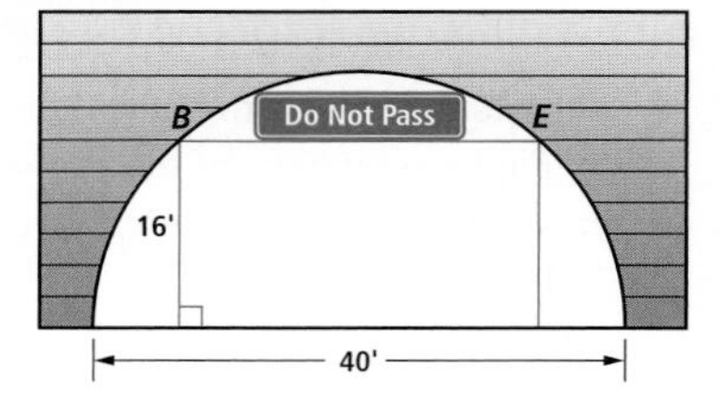

Extension

There are many examples of superellipses in both mathematics and the ordinary world. Superellipses have a long history. Use the Internet or other library resources to learn more about superellipses. Then make a brief presentation to your class. As a start, the following Web sites are recommended.

http://www.oberonplace.com/products/plotter/tutor/lesson2.htm

http://www.daviddarling.info/encyclopedia/S/superellipse.html

http://mathworld.wolfram.com/Superellipse.html

http://www.math.sdu.edu.cn/mathency/math/s/s858.htm

19. Refer to the diagram at the right. Circle A is centered at the origin with radius 3. Circle B is tangent to both axes and has its center on circle A. **(Lessons 12-3, 12-2, Previous Course)**
    a. Write an equation for circle A.
    b. Write an equation for circle B.
    c. Find an inequality describing the interior of circle A.
    d. Find the circumference of each circle.
    e. Find the area of each circle.

19a–e. See the Additional Answers section at the back of the book.

20. Use $\triangle PQR$ at the right. Find the length of $\overline{QR}$ to the nearest tenth. **(Lesson 10-8)** 19.5

In 21 and 22, find *b*. (Lesson 10-7) 21. $b \approx 35.9$ 22. $b \approx 12.2$

21.

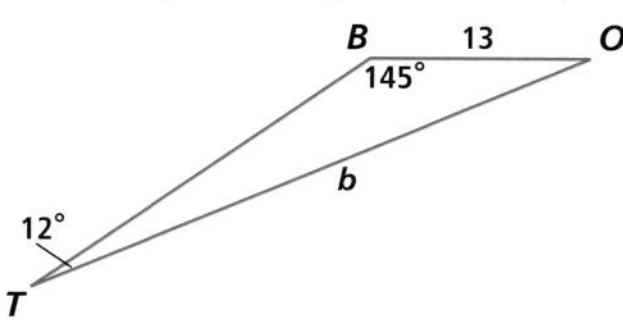

22.

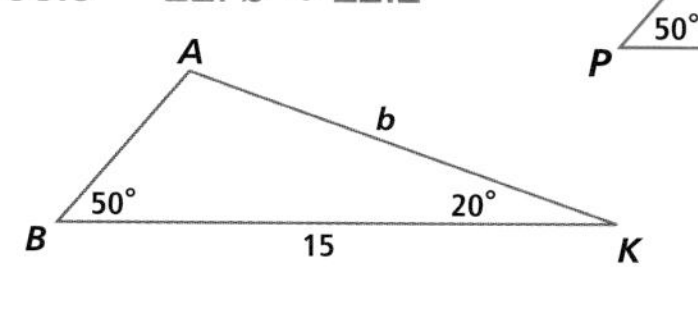

23. What is the image of (x, y) under the scale change $S_{7, 8}$? **(Lesson 4-5)** $(7x, 8y)$

EXPLORATION

24. Over the years, many devices were invented to help drafters draw ellipses by hand. One such tool is the *carpenter's trammel*. Research the carpenter's trammel and explain how it is used to draw an ellipse. See the Additional Answers section at the back of the book.

QY ANSWER

major axis, 6; minor axis, 4

12-4

Notes on the Questions

Additional Answers can be found in the back of the book.

4 Wrap-Up

Ongoing Assessment

Give students the lengths of the major and minor axes of an ellipse and tell them whether the major axis is horizontal or vertical. Then ask students to sketch the ellipse and label the endpoints of its axes. Answers vary. Sample: If the length of the major axis is 12, the length of the minor axis is 6, and the major axis is vertical.

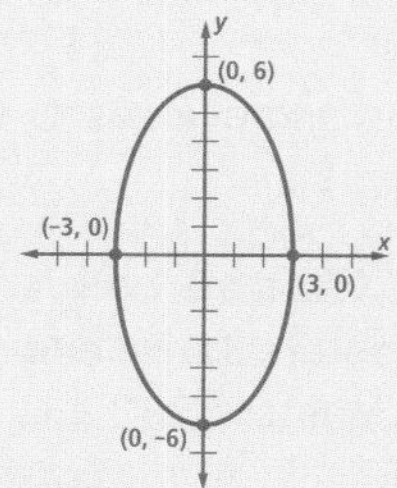

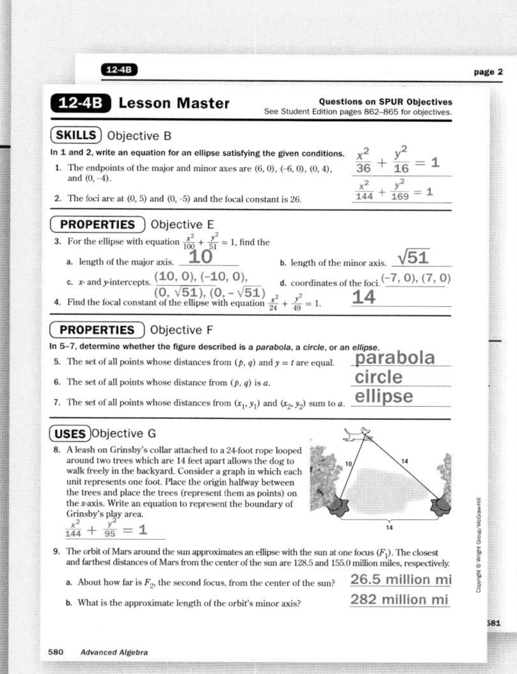

12-4B page 2

12-4B Lesson Master

Questions on SPUR Objectives
See Student Edition pages 862–865 for objectives.

SKILLS Objective B

In 1 and 2, write an equation for an ellipse satisfying the given conditions.

1. The endpoints of the major and minor axes are (6, 0), (-6, 0), (0, 4), and (0, -4). $\frac{x^2}{36} + \frac{y^2}{16} = 1$
2. The foci are at (0, 5) and (0, -5) and the focal constant is 26. $\frac{x^2}{144} + \frac{y^2}{169} = 1$

PROPERTIES Objective E

3. For the ellipse with equation $\frac{x^2}{100} + \frac{y^2}{51} = 1$, find the
   a. length of the major axis. 10
   b. length of the minor axis. $\sqrt{51}$
   c. x- and y-intercepts. (10, 0), (–10, 0), (0, $\sqrt{51}$), (0, –$\sqrt{51}$)
   d. coordinates of the foci. (–7, 0), (7, 0)
4. Find the focal constant of the ellipse with equation $\frac{x^2}{24} + \frac{y^2}{49} = 1$. 14

PROPERTIES Objective F

In 5–7, determine whether the figure described is a *parabola*, a *circle*, or an *ellipse*.

5. The set of all points whose distances from (p, q) and $y = t$ are equal. parabola
6. The set of all points whose distance from (p, q) is a. circle
7. The set of all points whose distances from (x_1, y_1) and (x_2, y_2) sum to a. ellipse

USES Objective G

8. A leash on Grinsby's collar attached to a 24-foot rope looped around two trees which are 14 feet apart allows the dog to walk freely in the backyard. Consider a graph in which each unit represents one foot. Place the origin halfway between the trees and place the trees (represent them as points) on the x-axis. Write an equation to represent the boundary of Grinsby's play area. $\frac{x^2}{144} + \frac{y^2}{95} = 1$
9. The orbit of Mars around the sun approximates an ellipse with the sun at one focus (F_1). The closest and farthest distances of Mars from the center of the sun are 128.5 and 155.0 million miles, respectively.
   a. About how far is F_2, the second focus, from the center of the sun? 26.5 million mi
   b. What is the approximate length of the orbit's minor axis? 282 million mi

Copyright © Wright Group/McGraw-Hill

580 Advanced Algebra

Additional Answers

16a. Answers vary. Sample:

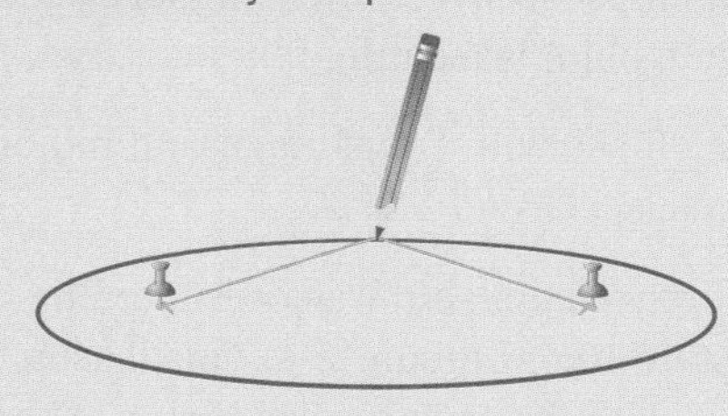

16b. The sum of the distance from the tacks to the pencil's tip is equal to the length of the string. Since the length is constant, by the definition of an ellipse, the curve is an ellipse.

16c. the length of the string

Lesson 12-5

GOAL

Work with ellipses a second day; relate equations and areas of ellipses to equations and areas of circles.

SPUR Objectives

C Find the area of an ellipse.

F Classify curves as circles and/or ellipses using algebraic or geometric properties.

G Use circles and ellipses to solve real-world problems.

Materials/Resources

- Lesson Masters 12-5A and 12-5B
- Resource Masters 233 and 234

HOMEWORK

Suggestions for Assignment

- Questions 1–26
- Question 27 (extra credit)
- Reading Lesson 12-6
- Covering the Ideas 12-6

Local Standards

1 Warm-Up

1. Find the area of a triangle with vertices $A = (-2, 5)$, $B = (8, 5)$, and $C = (8, 9)$. 20 units^2
2. What is the image $\triangle A'B'C'$, of the above triangle under $S_{4,6}$? $S(A) = A' = (-8, 30)$; $S(B) = B' = (32, 30)$; $S(C) = C' = (32, 54)$
3. What is the area of $\triangle A'B'C'$? 480 units^2

Lesson 12-5 Relationships between Ellipses and Circles

Vocabulary

eccentricity of an ellipse

BIG IDEA Ellipses are stretched circles; circles are ellipses whose major and minor axes have the same length.

In some ellipses, the major axis is much longer than the minor axis. In others, the two axes are almost equal in length. The diagrams below illustrate three of the possible cases. All three ellipses have the same focal constant. You can see that when the focal constant stays the same, the positions of the foci in an ellipse affect its shape. The closer the foci are to the origin, the rounder the ellipse appears.

Mental Math

Describe a transformation or composite of transformations that will map (x, y) onto the given point.

a. $(x + 7, y - 2)$ $T_{7,-2}$

b. $(3x, 2.5y)$ $S_{3,2.5}$

c. $(3x + 7, 2.5y - 2)$

d. $(2.5y - 2, 3x + 7)$

c. $T_{7,-2} \circ S_{3,2.5}$

d. $r_{y=x} \circ T_{7,-2} \circ S_{3,2.5}$

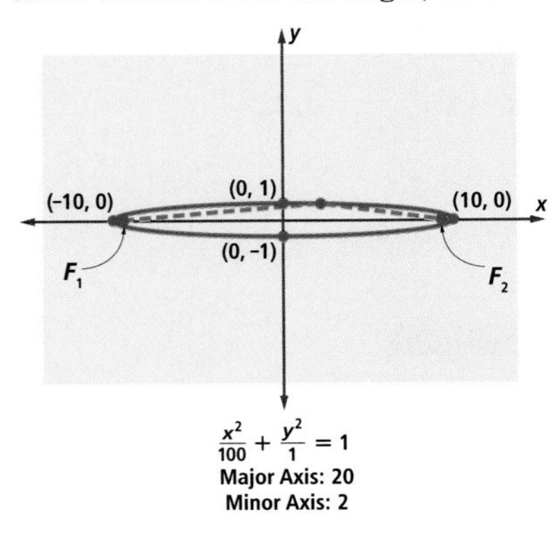

$\frac{x^2}{100} + \frac{y^2}{1} = 1$
Major Axis: 20
Minor Axis: 2

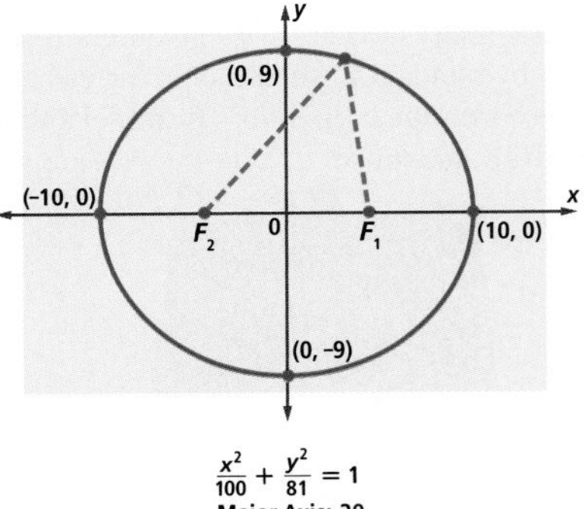

$\frac{x^2}{100} + \frac{y^2}{81} = 1$
Major Axis: 20
Minor Axis: 18

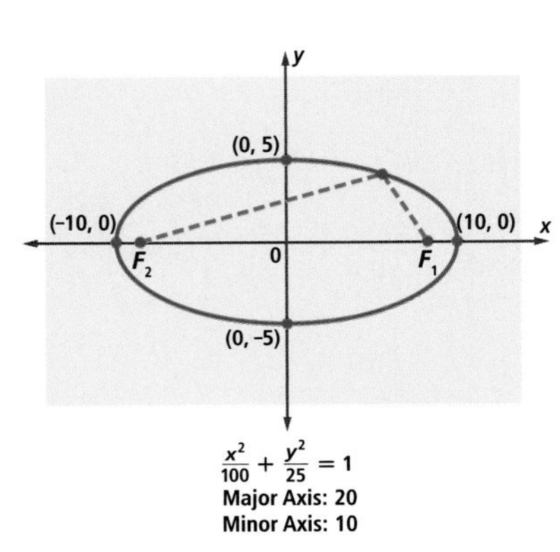

$\frac{x^2}{100} + \frac{y^2}{25} = 1$
Major Axis: 20
Minor Axis: 10

Background

There are many relationships between ellipses and circles, including the following:

1. Until Kepler, it was thought that the orbits of heavenly bodies were circular; now we know that the basic shape of an orbit is elliptical.
2. When a circle is seen at an angle (that is, not from a point directly above its center and not "edge-on"), it is an ellipse.
3. When a circle is stretched uniformly, the result is an ellipse.
4. An ellipse in which the two foci are the same point is a circle.
5. An ellipse with equal major and minor axes is a circle.

The first relationship was presented in Question 15 of Lesson 12-4. This lesson begins with the fourth relationship. Then it mentions the second and fifth relationships. It emphasizes the third relationship because it provides an explanation for the equation of an ellipse and enables us to

Circles as Special Ellipses

A special kind of ellipse results if the major and minor axes are equal. At the right is an ellipse with major axis 20 and minor axis 20. It has equation

$$\frac{x^2}{100} + \frac{y^2}{100} = 1,$$

which can be rewritten as

$$x^2 + y^2 = 100.$$

So this ellipse is a circle.

This can be generalized. Consider the standard form of an equation for an ellipse,

$$\frac{x^2}{a^2} + \frac{y^2}{b^2} = 1.$$

If the major and minor axes each have length $2r$, then $2a = 2r$ and $2b = 2r$, so you may substitute r for both a and b to get $\frac{x^2}{r^2} + \frac{y^2}{r^2} = 1$.

Multiply both sides by r^2 to get $x^2 + y^2 = r^2$.

This is an equation for the circle with center at the origin and radius r. So, a circle is a special kind of ellipse whose major and minor axes are equal in length.

QY1

QY1

Find an equation of the ellipse with center at the origin and major and minor axes of length 14.

Ellipses as Stretched Circles

An ellipse can be thought of as a stretched circle. The transformation that stretches and shrinks figures is the *scale change*, which you studied in Lesson 4-5.

Consider the unit circle with equation $x^2 + y^2 = 1$ and a scale change with horizontal magnitude 4 and vertical magnitude 2. The x- and y-intercepts of the unit circle and their images under this scale change are graphed at the right.

$S_{4,2}$: $(1, 0) \rightarrow (4, 0)$
$S_{4,2}$: $(0, 1) \rightarrow (0, 2)$
$S_{4,2}$: $(-1, 0) \rightarrow (-4, 0)$
$S_{4,2}$: $(0, -1) \rightarrow (0, -2)$

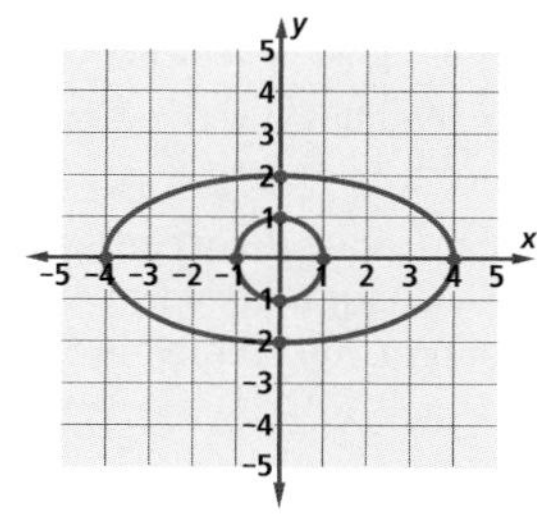

From these four points you can see that the image of the unit circle under this scale change is not a circle. It appears to be an ellipse with foci on the x-axis.

2 Teaching

Notes on the Lesson

This lesson is not very long, and, for most students, it is not difficult. Thus, we suggest you assign the reading and questions without preliminary discussion. Then work through the questions in order. The Example can be covered while discussing Questions 5 and 6.

Ellipses as stretched circles A stretched circle looks like an ellipse, but how can we be sure? Students know that some curves, like parabolas and hyperbolas, look alike until examined more closely. For instance, an egg is oval shaped (the origin of the word *oval* is from the Latin word *ovum*, meaning "egg"), but an oval is not an ellipse because it is not symmetric over the minor axis.

obtain the area of an ellipse from the area of a circle.

Students first encountered scale changes in Lesson 4-5, in conjunction with matrices, where it was shown that the matrix for $S_{a,b}$ is $\begin{bmatrix} a & 0 \\ 0 & b \end{bmatrix}$. The area property of scale changes is a special case of the following theorem: Under a transformation with matrix M, the area of a figure is multiplied by the determinant of M. If the determinant is negative, the orientation of the figure is reversed. The determinant of the above matrix is ab, so $S_{a,b}$ multiplies the area by ab.

Without transformations, it would require calculus to obtain the area of an ellipse. It still requires calculus (specifically, elliptic integrals) to obtain the circumference of an ellipse because scale changes do not affect length uniformly.

Additional Example

Example What is an equation for the image of the unit circle $x^2 + y^2 = 1$ under $S_{9,5}$?

Solution Let (x', y') be the image of (x, y) on the circle. Then $(x', y') = (9x, 5y)$. So $x' = 9x$ and $y' = 5y$. Solve these equations for x and y: $x =$ ___?___ and $y =$ ___?___. $\frac{x'}{9}$; $\frac{y'}{5}$
Because $x^2 + y^2 = 1$, substitute the expressions for x and y involving x' and y' into $x^2 + y^2 = 1$ to get an equation for the image: ___?___ + ___?___ $= 1$. $\left(\frac{x'}{9}\right)^2$; $\left(\frac{y'}{5}\right)^2$ Using x and y for x' and y', the equation is ___?___ + ___?___ $= 1$. $\frac{x^2}{81}$; $\frac{y^2}{25}$
That equation represents an ellipse with a minor axis of length ___?___ and a major axis of length ___?___. 10; 18

GUIDED

Example

Find an equation for the image of the unit circle $x^2 + y^2 = 1$ under $S_{4,2}$.

Solution To find an equation for the image of the circle, let (x', y') be the image of point (x, y) on the circle. Then $(x', y') = (4x, 2y)$.
So, $x' = 4x$ and $y' =$ ___?___. $2y$

Solve these equations for x and y.

$x =$ ___?___ and $y =$ ___?___ $\frac{x'}{4}$; $\frac{y'}{2}$

You know that $x^2 + y^2 = 1$. Substitute the expressions for x and y involving x' and y' into $x^2 + y^2 = 1$ to get an equation for the image.

$(\underline{?})^2 + (\underline{?})^2 = 1.$ $\frac{x'}{4}$; $\frac{y'}{2}$

Now let (x, y) be a point on the image. Rewrite the equation for the image using x and y in place of x' and y'.

$(\underline{?})^2 + (\underline{?})^2 = 1$ $\frac{x}{4}$; $\frac{y}{2}$

The equation you have written is for an ellipse with a minor axis of length ___?___ and a major axis of length ___?___. 4; 8

Check Substitute some points known to be on the image into the equation. Do their coordinates satisfy your equation for the ellipse?

Try $(4, 0)$: $\frac{4^2}{?} + \frac{0^2}{?} =$ ___?___ + ___?___ = ___?___. 4^2; 2^2; 1; 0; 1

Try $(0, -2)$: $\frac{0^2}{?} + \frac{(-2)^2}{?} =$ ___?___ + ___?___ = ___?___. It checks. 4^2; 2^2; 0; 1; 1

The procedure you followed in the Example can be repeated using a in place of 4 and b in place of 2. This shows that any ellipse in standard form can be thought of as a scale-change image of the unit circle.

Circle Scale-Change Theorem

The image of the unit circle with equation $x^2 + y^2 = 1$ under $S_{a,b}$ is the ellipse with equation $\left(\frac{x}{a}\right)^2 + \left(\frac{y}{b}\right)^2 = 1$.

The previous theorem is a special case of a more general Graph Scale-Change Theorem, which is analogous to the Graph-Translation Theorem you studied in Chapter 6.

Accommodating the Learner 

Tell students that the area of an ellipse is p square units and the semimajor and semiminor axes are m and n. Ask them to write an equation for the ellipse in terms of m, n, and p. $A = \pi mn = p$, so $n = \frac{p}{m\pi}$. In the equation $\frac{x^2}{a^2} + \frac{y^2}{b^2} = 1$, replace a with m and b with $\frac{p}{m\pi}$ to get $\frac{x^2}{m^2} + \frac{y^2}{\left(\frac{p}{m\pi}\right)^2} = 1$ or $\frac{x^2}{m^2} + \frac{m^2\pi^2y^2}{p^2} = 1$.

ENGLISH LEARNERS

Vocabulary Development

The paragraph between the Circle Scale-Change Theorem and the Graph Scale-Change Theorem describes a theorem as being *analogous* to another theorem. Be sure students understand that the base word for analogous is "analogy," thus *analogous statements* have the same underlying structure.

Graph Scale-Change Theorem

In a relation described by a sentence in x and y, the following two processes yield the same graph:

1. replacing x by $\frac{x}{a}$ and y by $\frac{y}{b}$;
2. applying the scale change $S_{a,b}$ to the graph of the original relation.

QY2

▸ **QY2**

Find an equation for the image of $x^2 + y^2 = 1$ under $S_{6, 14}$.

A Formula for the Area of an Ellipse

Consider the figure below at the left. If each grid square has area 1, the area of the figure is equal to the number of grid squares inside the figure. Now suppose the scale change $S_{a,b}$ is applied to the figure and the grid. The result is the figure at the right below. Each grid square is transformed into a rectangle with length a, width b, and area ab. Since the area of each rectangle is ab times the area of one grid square, the area of the transformed figure is ab times the area of its preimage.

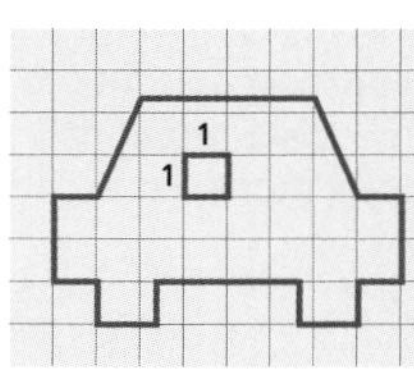

preimage

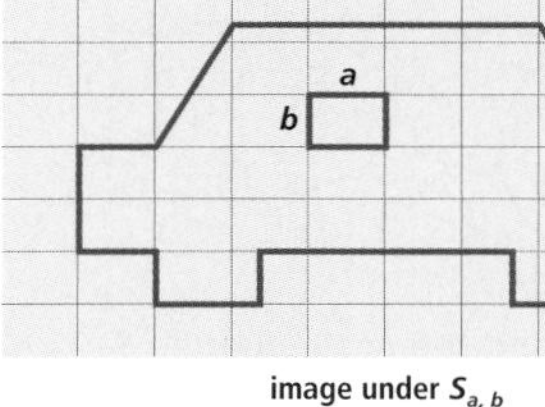

image under $S_{a,b}$

This illustrates that in general, the area of the image of a figure under the scale change $S_{a,b}$ is ab times the area of the preimage. This fact can be used to derive a formula for the area of an ellipse. The area of the unit circle is $\pi(1)^2 = \pi$, and the ellipse with equation $\frac{x^2}{a^2} + \frac{y^2}{b^2} = 1$ is the image of the unit circle under $S_{a,b}$. So, the area of this ellipse is $\pi(ab) = \pi ab$.

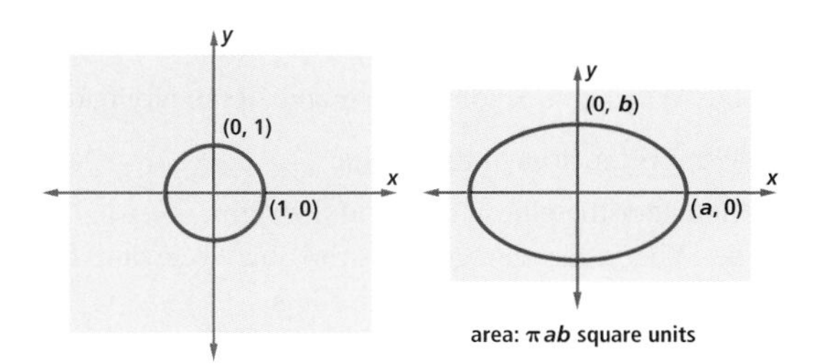

area: π square units

area: πab square units

Notes on the Lesson

Graph Scale-Change Theorem From Lesson 12-4, graphs of certain equations are known to be ellipses. Because a stretch can be described algebraically, the image of a circle can be obtained algebraically. Stress to students that not only can we explain that a stretched circle is an ellipse, but we can also explain the relationship between the equations $\frac{x^2}{a^2} + \frac{y^2}{b^2} = 1$ and $x^2 + y^2 = 1$ (see Question 10).

Note-Taking Tips

When students record the Area of an Ellipse Theorem in their notes, encourage them to include examples when $a = b$ to emphasize how πab is related to πr^2.

Accommodating the Learner

Ask students to find the equations of several ellipses that have area 24π square units. Because $ab = 24$, then any equation of the form $\frac{x^2}{a^2} + \frac{y^2}{b^2} = 1$ with $ab = 24$ will work. Some examples are $\frac{x^2}{4} + \frac{y^2}{144} = 1$ (for $a = 2$ and $b = 12$), $\frac{x^2}{9} + \frac{y^2}{64} = 1$ (for $a = 3$ and $b = 8$), $\frac{x^2}{16} + \frac{y^2}{36} = 1$ (for $a = 4$ and $b = 6$), and so on.

3 Assignment

Recommended Assignment

- Questions 1–26
- Question 27 (extra credit)
- Reading Lesson 12-6
- Covering the Ideas 12-6

Additional Answers

2. false; Answers vary. Sample:

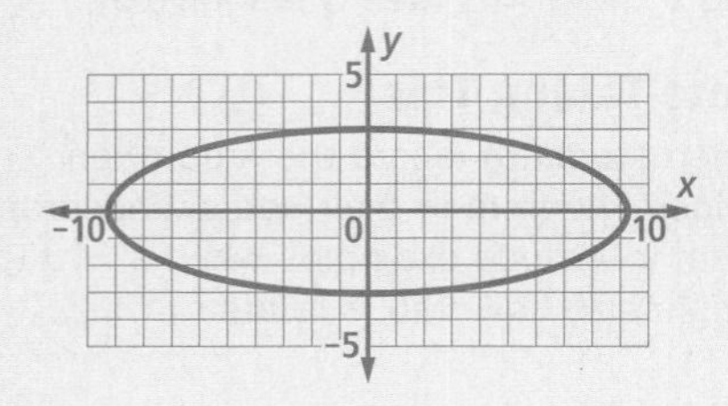

Area of an Ellipse Theorem

An ellipse with semimajor and semiminor axes of lengths a and b has area $A = \pi ab$.

QY3

▸ QY3

The Statuary Hall gallery in the United States Capitol is an elliptical chamber. The gallery is about 83 feet wide and about 96 feet long. Find its floor area.

Questions

COVERING THE IDEAS

1. **Fill in the Blank** A circle is an ellipse in which the major and minor axes C

   A are parallel. B are perpendicular

   C are of equal length. D coincide.

True or False In 2 and 3, indicate whether the statement is true or false. If false, draw a counterexample.

2. All ellipses are circles. See margin. 3. All circles are ellipses. true

4. **Fill in the Blank** All three ellipses below are the same width. In which ellipse are the foci farthest apart? Explain your answer.

   A

   B 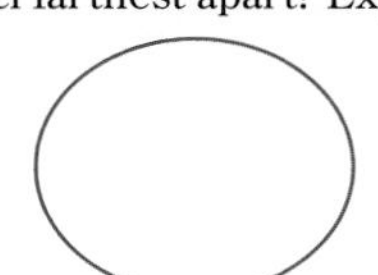

   C 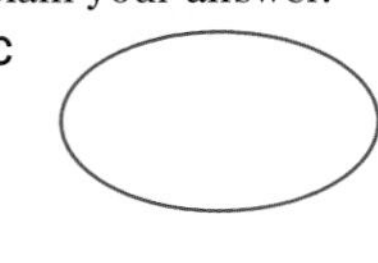

4. A; The closer the foci are to the origin, the rounder the ellipse appears, and A is the least round of the figures.

In 5 and 6, consider the circle $x^2 + y^2 = 1$ and the scale change $S_{5, \frac{1}{2}}$.

5. a. Find the image of (1, 0) under $S_{5, \frac{1}{2}}$. (5, 0)

   b. Find the image of (0, 1) under $S_{5, \frac{1}{2}}$. $\left(0, \frac{1}{2}\right)$

   c. Write an equation of the image of the circle under $S_{5, \frac{1}{2}}$. $\left(\frac{x}{5}\right)^2 + (2y)^2 = 1$

6. What is the area of the image? $\frac{5\pi}{2}$

7. Consider the ellipse drawn at the right.

   a. What scale change maps the unit circle onto this ellipse? $S_{4, 8}$

   b. Write an equation for the ellipse. $\left(\frac{x}{4}\right)^2 + \left(\frac{y}{8}\right)^2 = 1$

   c. Find its area. 32π

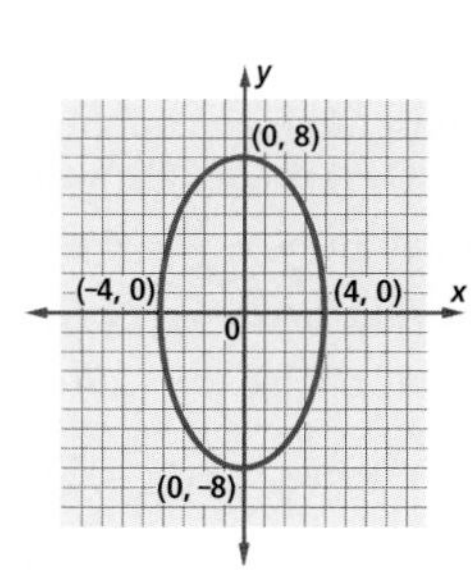

Extension

Ask students to write an equation for a unit circle with center $T = (0, 0)$ and find the coordinates of the point of intersection of the circle with ray $\overrightarrow{TP}$ if $\overrightarrow{TP}$ forms a 45° angle with the positive x-axis. Then ask students to find the image of the circle under a scale change and to find the intersection of the image with the same ray $\overrightarrow{TP}$. If the intersection of $\overrightarrow{TP}$ and $x^2 + y^2 = 1$ is the point (x, y), then $x = y$ and the coordinates of the point are $\left(\frac{\sqrt{2}}{2}, \frac{\sqrt{2}}{2}\right)$. Suppose the scale change is $S_{2, 5}$. Then the image of the circle is the ellipse $\frac{x^2}{4} + \frac{y^2}{25} = 1$. If the intersection is the point (x, y), then $x = y$. So $\frac{x^2}{4} + \frac{x^2}{25} = 1$. Multiplying each side of the equation by 100 gives $25x^2 + 4x^2 = 100$. Then $29x^2 = 100$, and $x = \sqrt{\frac{100}{29}}$. The coordinates of the point are $\left(\sqrt{\frac{100}{29}}, \sqrt{\frac{100}{29}}\right)$.

12-5A Lesson Master

Questions on SPUR Objectives
See Student Edition pages 862–865 for objectives.

SKILLS Objective C

In 1–3, find the area of the given ellipse.

1. the ellipse with equation $\frac{x^2}{144} + \frac{y^2}{400} = 1$ 240π
2. an ellipse with major axis 18 cm and minor axis 12 cm 54π cm^2
3. the image of the unit circle under $S_{10,7}$ 70π

PROPERTIES Objective F

In 4 and 5, under what condition(s) is the described ellipse also a circle?

4. the ellipse with equation $\frac{x^2}{a^2} + \frac{y^2}{b^2} = 1$ when $a = b$
5. the set of all points P where the sum $PF_1 + PF_2$ is constant when F_1 and F_2 are the same point

True or False In 6–10, decide whether each statement is true or false.

6. All circles are ellipses. true
7. All ellipses are circles. false
8. A circle is an ellipse with 2 distinct foci. false
9. An ellipse is an image of a circle under a size transformation. true
10. A circle is an ellipse with congruent major and minor axes. true

USES Objective G

11. June is designing an elliptical flower garden as shown at the right. It will have a major axis of length 6 m and a minor axis of length 4 m. In the center is a fountain with a diameter of 1.5 m. The rest of the space will be used for flowers. Find the area available for flowers, to the nearest tenth of a square meter. 17.1 m^2

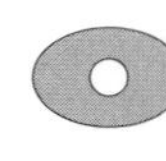

12. The Ellipse (also called the President's Park South) in Washington, D.C. is a park between the Washington Monument and the White House. Its major axis is 1058 feet long and its minor axis is 953 feet long. Find the area of the Ellipse

    a. to the nearest square foot. 791,897 ft^2

    b. to the nearest acre (1 acre = 43,560 ft^2). 18 a.

582 Advanced Algebra

APPLYING THE MATHEMATICS

8. a. Write an equation for an ellipse in which the semimajor and semiminor axes each have length 5 and the distance between the foci is 0. $x^2 + y^2 = 25$
   b. What relationship between ellipses and circles does this illustrate?
9. a. Give an example of a scale change $S_{h,k}$ such that the unit circle and its image under the scale change are similar.
   b. Give an example of a scale change $S_{h,k}$ such that the unit circle and its image under the scale change are not similar.
10. Use the method of the Example to prove that the image of the unit circle under the scale change $S_{a,b}$ is the ellipse $\frac{x^2}{a^2} + \frac{y^2}{b^2} = 1$.
11. The orbit of the planet Mars is in the shape of an ellipse whose minor axis is 282.0 million miles long and whose major axis is 283.3 million miles long. What is the area of this ellipse?

In 12–14, use this definition: The *eccentricity* of an ellipse is the ratio of the distance 2*c* between its foci to the length 2*a* of its major axis.

12. a. Write a formula for the eccentricity *e* of an ellipse. $e = \frac{c}{a}$
    b. What is the eccentricity of the ellipse in the Example? $e = \frac{\sqrt{3}}{2}$
13. An ellipse's major axis is 12 units long. If its eccentricity is $\frac{1}{3}$, how long is its minor axis? $2b = 8\sqrt{2} \approx 11.31$
14. a. What is the eccentricity of a circle? 0
    b. Is there a maximum possible value for the eccentricity of an ellipse? Why or why not?
15. Write the equations of four different ellipses with area 24π.

15–16. See margin.

REVIEW

16. In 1937, a Whispering Gallery was constructed in the Museum of Science and Industry in Chicago. The Gallery was constructed in the form of an *ellipsoid* (an ellipse rotated around its major axis). When a visitor located at one focus whispers, the sound reflects directly to the focus at the other end of the gallery. The width of an ellipse in the plane of the foci is 13 feet 6 inches, and the length of the ellipse is 47 feet 4 inches.
    a. Find an equation that could describe this ellipse.
    b. How far are the foci from the endpoints of the major axis of this ellipse? **(Lesson 12-4)**

8b. Circles are ellipses with major and minor axes of equal length.

9a. Answers vary. Sample: $S_{2,2}$

9b. Answers vary. Sample: $S_{1,2}$

10. The image of a point (x, y) under the scale change $S_{a,b}$ is $(x', y') = (ax, by)$. So, $x = \frac{x'}{a}$ and $y = \frac{y'}{b}$. Substituting these expressions into the equation for a unit circle, we find $\left(\frac{x'}{a}\right)^2 + \left(\frac{y'}{b}\right)^2 = 1$. Thus, the image of the unit circle under the scale change $S_{a,b}$ is $\frac{x^2}{a^2} + \frac{y^2}{b^2} = 1$.

11. $19{,}973\pi \approx 62{,}746$ million mi^2

14b. Ellipses can have eccentricity e such that $0 \le e < 1$; there is no exact maximum value.

Notes on the Questions

Question 10 This question proves the first theorem of the lesson.

Question 16 Whispering galleries can be found elsewhere in the United States, including the gallery in front of the Oyster Bar and Restaurant at Grand Central Station in New York City; the Cincinnati Museum Center at Union Terminal; Statuary Hall in the U.S. Capitol Building in Washington, DC; the Mapparium in the Christian Science complex in Boston; the rotunda of the Texas State Capitol Building in Austin; and the main student center at the University of Wisconsin–Madison.

Additional Answers

15. Answers vary. Sample: $\left(\frac{x}{24}\right)^2 + y^2 = 1$; $\left(\frac{x}{12}\right)^2 + \left(\frac{y}{2}\right)^2 = 1$; $\left(\frac{x}{6}\right)^2 + \left(\frac{y}{4}\right)^2 = 1$; $x^2 + \left(\frac{y}{24}\right)^2 = 1$

16a. $\left(\frac{x}{284}\right)^2 + \left(\frac{y}{81}\right)^2 = 1$, where x and y are in inches.

16b. $248 - \sqrt{74095} \approx 11.8$ in.

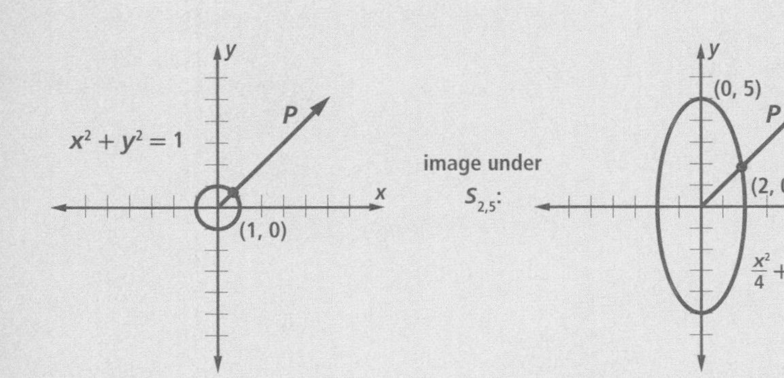

12-5

4 Wrap-Up

Ongoing Assessment

Ask students to find the x- and y-intercepts of the unit circle $x^2 + y^2 = 1$ after each scale change:

a. $S_{3,3}$ $(\pm 3, 0), (0, \pm 3)$

b. $S_{12,4}$ $(\pm 12, 0), (0, \pm 4)$

c. $S_{2,5}$ $(\pm 2, 0), (0, \pm 5)$

Project Update

Project 4, *Orbits of the Planets,* on page 857 relates to the content of this lesson.

12-5B Lesson Master — Questions on SPUR Objectives
See Student Edition pages 862–865 for objectives.

SKILLS Objective C

In 1–11, find the area of the given ellipse.

1. the ellipse with equation $\frac{x^2}{25} + \frac{y^2}{121} = 1$ — 55π
2. an ellipse with major axis 4 cm long and minor axis 3 cm long — 3π cm^2
3. the image of the unit circle under $S_{5,6}$ — 30π
4. the ellipse with equation $\frac{x^2}{100} + \frac{y^2}{700} = 1$ — $100\sqrt{7}\pi$
5. the ellipse with equation $\frac{x^2}{169} + \frac{y^2}{324} = 1$ — 234π
6. an ellipse with major axis 1.5 m long and minor axis 7 m long — 2.625π m^2
7. an ellipse with major axis 4 yd long and minor axis 3 yd long — 3π yd^2
8. the image of the unit circle under $S_{0.4,2.1}$ — 0.84π
9. The endpoints of its major and minor axes are (0, 3) and (0, -3), and (1.5, 0) and (-1.5, 0). — 4.5π
10. It has foci (0, 5) and (0, -5) and focal constant 14. — $14\sqrt{6}\pi$
11. It has foci (-2, 0) and (2, 0) and minor axis length 6. — $3\sqrt{13}\pi$

PROPERTIES Objective F

In 12–14, under what condition(s) is the described set of points not a circle?

12. the image of the unit circle under $S_{a,b}$ — when $a \neq b$
13. the set of all points P, where the sum $PF_1 + PF_2$ is constant — when F_1 and F_2 are not the same point
14. an ellipse with major axis length of $2a$ and minor axis length of $2b$ — when $a \neq b$
15. Explain the relationship between the area formula for a circle, $A = \pi r^2$, and the area formula for an ellipse, $A = \pi ab$.
    Answers vary. Sample: If a figure is an ellipse and not a circle, $a \neq b$. If a figure is a circle, $a = b = r$.

True or False In 16–20, decide whether each statement is true or false.

16. If a figure has two distinct foci, it is a circle. — false
17. If a figure is a circle, it has two distinct foci. — false
18. If a figure is an ellipse, its major and minor axes have different lengths. — false
19. If a figure is a circle, its major and minor axes have the same length. — true

Advanced Algebra 583

Matching In 17–21, match each equation with the best description. A letter may be used more than once. Do not graph. **(Lessons 12-4, 12-3, 12-2)**

17. $(x-2)^2 + y^2 < 36$ iii
18. $\frac{x^2}{48} + \frac{y^2}{64} > 1$ vi
19. $x^2 + 9y^2 = 121$ ii
20. $\frac{x^2}{16} + \frac{y^2}{81} = 4$ ii
21. $x^2 + y^2 = 25$ i

i circle
ii ellipse
iii interior of a circle
iv interior of an ellipse
v exterior of a circle
vi exterior of an ellipse

22. At the right is a top view of a circular fountain surrounded by a circular flower garden. The distance from the center of the fountain to the outside edge of the garden is 65 feet. It is 45 feet from the outside edge of the garden to the fountain. If the center of the fountain is the origin, write a system of inequalities to describe the set of points in the flower garden. **(Lesson 12-3)** $\begin{cases} x^2 + y^2 < 4225 \\ x^2 + y^2 > 400 \end{cases}$

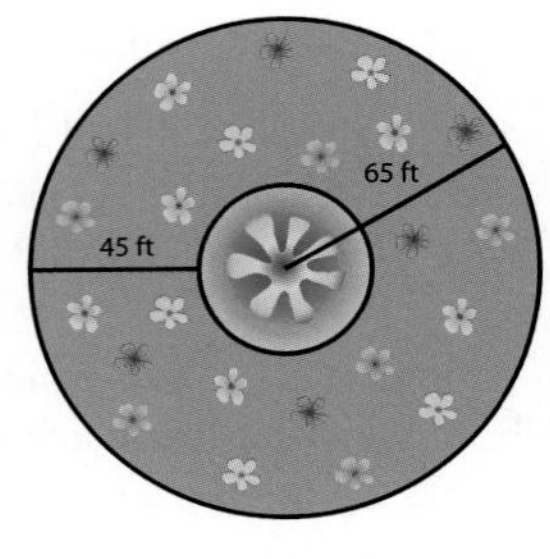

In 23 and 24, solve. **(Lesson 6-2)**

23. $|2n + 1| = 0.5$
24. $\sqrt{x^2} = \sqrt{40}$ $x = \pm 2\sqrt{10}$

23. $n = -0.25$ or $n = -0.75$

In 25 and 26, consider the line ℓ with equation $y = -\frac{3}{7}x + 6$ and the point $P = (5, 2)$. Find an equation for the line through P

25. parallel to ℓ. **(Lesson 4-10)** $y = -\frac{3}{7}x + \frac{29}{7}$
26. perpendicular to ℓ. **(Lesson 4-9)** $y = \frac{7}{3}x - \frac{29}{3}$

EXPLORATION

27. a. Cut out a paper circle and make a dot anywhere in its interior. Fold a point on the circle onto the dot then unfold. Repeat with other points on the circle. What shape is outlined by the crease lines (shown as segments in the diagram)? an ellipse

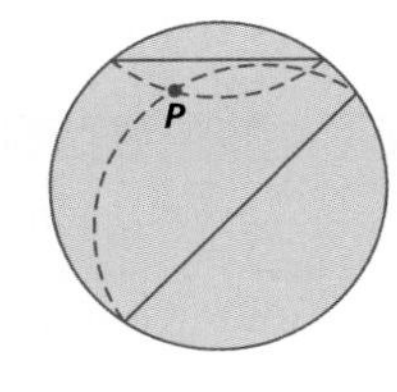

b. Use a new circle. Place the dot at the center of the circle and repeat the activity in Part a. a circle

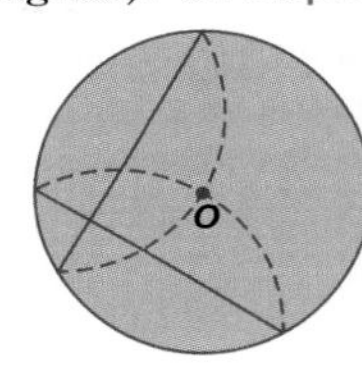

c. Explain your results in Parts a and b.
The point P is a focus of the ellipse. When $P = O$, the two foci coincide and the ellipse is a circle.

QY ANSWERS

1. $\frac{x^2}{49} + \frac{y^2}{49} = 1$ or $x^2 + y^2 = 49$
2. $\frac{x^2}{36} + \frac{y^2}{196} = 1$
3. $1992\pi \approx 6258$ ft^2

Lesson 12-6 Equations for Some Hyperbolas

Vocabulary

hyperbola
foci, focal constant of a hyperbola
vertices of a hyperbola
standard position of a hyperbola
standard form of an equation for a hyperbola

BIG IDEA From the geometric definition of a hyperbola, an equation for any *hyperbola* symmetric to the *x*- and *y*-axes can be found.

The edges of the silhouettes of each of the towers pictured at the right are parts of *hyperbolas*. Structures with this shape are able to withstand higher winds and require less material to build than any other form.

Mental Math

Suppose a function *f* contains the points (4, 17), (9, 12), and (13, 13).

a. Find the rate of change from (4, 17) to (9, 12). −1

b. Find the rate of change from (9, 12) to (13, 13). $\frac{1}{4}$

c. Could the graph of *f* be a line? no

What Is a Hyperbola?

Like an ellipse, a hyperbola is determined by two foci and a focal constant. However, instead of a constant sum of distances from the foci, a point on a hyperbola must be at a *constant difference* of distances from the foci. The following Activity shows one way to find points on a hyperbola.

Activity

MATERIALS conic graph paper with 6 units between the centers of the circles

Step 1 Copy the foci and points P_1 and P_2 at the right. Find P_1F_1, P_2F_1, P_1F_2, and P_2F_2, then calculate $P_1F_1 - P_1F_2$ and $P_2F_1 - P_2F_2$. Do both differences equal the same constant?

Step 2 Plot two more points P_n such that $P_nF_1 = 8$ and $P_nF_2 = 6$, and then two more such that $P_nF_1 = 7$ and $P_nF_2 = 5$. Continue this process to find four more points such that $P_nF_1 - P_nF_2$ is always 2.

(continued on next page) Steps 2–4. See margin.

Step 1
6; 6; 4; 4; 2; 2; yes

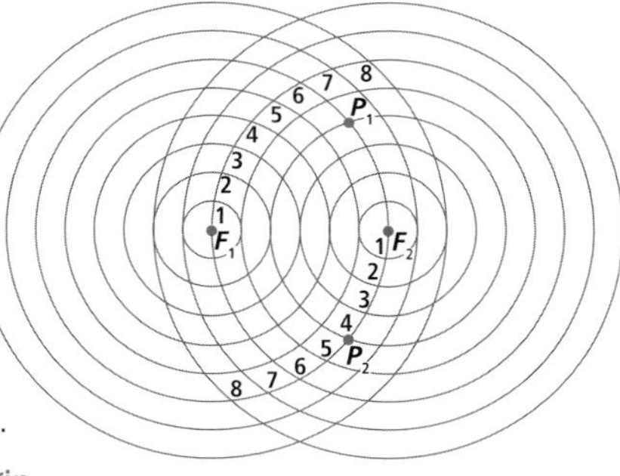

Background

Hyperbolas have two, quite different, standard forms for their equations. For hyperbolas symmetric to the *x*-axis, the form $\frac{y^2}{a^2} - \frac{x^2}{b^2} = 1$ is presented in this lesson. For hyperbolas symmetric to the line $y = x$, the form is $xy = k$, which is presented in Lesson 12-7. Although we could begin with either form, we begin with $\frac{y^2}{a^2} - \frac{x^2}{b^2} = 1$ to take advantage of the hyperbola-ellipse analogy. Just as the locus definitions for ellipses and hyperbolas differ only by the terms *sum* and *difference,* their equations differ only by the signs + and −.

Asymptotes of a hyperbola in standard position The hyperbola with equation $x^2 - y^2 = 1$ is called a *rectangular hyperbola* because its asymptotes are perpendicular to each other. Rectangular hyperbolas are related to all hyperbolas as circles are related to ellipses. Through the scale change $S_{a,b}$, the preimage hyperbola $x^2 - y^2 = 1$ is employed here to obtain equations for the

(continued on next page)

Lesson 12-6

GOAL

Relate hyperbolas to ellipses using the similarities of their definitions.

SPUR Objectives

B Write equations for hyperbolas.

E Identify characteristics of hyperbolas.

F Classify curves as hyperbolas using algebraic or geometric properties.

I Graph hyperbolas when given equations for them in standard form, and vice versa.

L Draw a graph or interpret drawings or graphs of hyperbolas based on their definitions.

Materials/Resources

- Lesson Masters 12-6A and 12-6B
- Resource Masters 1, 235, and 236
- Conic graph paper with 6 units between the centers of the circles

HOMEWORK

Suggestions for Assignment

- Questions 1–18
- Questions 19 and 20 (extra credit)
- Reading Lesson 12-7
- Covering the Ideas 12-7

Local Standards

1 Warm-Up

In 1–3, complete the table of values for each equation.

1. $\frac{x^2}{9} - \frac{y^2}{9} = 1$

x	3	4	5	6
y	0	$\pm\sqrt{7}$	± 4	$\pm 3\sqrt{3}$

(continued on next page)

2. $\frac{x^2}{25} - y^2 = 1$

x	-5	-10	-15	-20
y	0	$\pm\sqrt{3}$	$\pm 2\sqrt{2}$	$\pm\sqrt{15}$

3. $x^2 - \frac{y^2}{4} = 1$

x	-4	-2	2	4
y	$\pm 2\sqrt{15}$	$\pm 2\sqrt{3}$	$\pm 2\sqrt{3}$	$\pm 2\sqrt{15}$

2 Teaching

Notes on the Lesson

Activity Many teachers report that the Activity is helpful for students; it brings home the analogy between ellipses and hyperbolas and shortens the time needed for an explanation.

The standard form of an equation for a hyperbola Continually emphasize to students that these proofs require only the Distance Formula (and algebraic manipulation). Just as in geometry, justifications in the proof are either definitions, previously proved theorems (the Distance Formula, for example), or postulates (such as the properties of real numbers). Discuss the hyperbolas whose standard form equations are $\frac{y^2}{a^2} - \frac{x^2}{b^2} = 1$. Note that these hyperbolas are just like hyperbolas of the form $\frac{x^2}{a^2} - \frac{y^2}{b^2} = 1$ except that x and y have been switched. That should indicate to students what happens and how to graph them: These hyperbolas have branches that open up and down. Their y-intercepts are $\pm a$, and their asymptotes are $\frac{y}{a} = \pm\frac{x}{b}$. If students think of the hyperbola as the union of the graphs of two functions, then the hyperbola whose standard form equation is $\frac{y^2}{a^2} - \frac{x^2}{b^2} = 1$ is the union of the graphs of the inverses of the functions whose union is the graph $\frac{x^2}{a^2} - \frac{y^2}{b^2} = 1$.

Step 3 Repeat Step 2, plotting ten points P_n such that $P_nF_2 - P_nF_1 = 2$.

Step 4 Draw a smooth curve through the points you plotted in Step 2, and another through the points you plotted in Step 3. These are two branches of a hyperbola. The branches do not intersect.

In general, if d is a positive number less than F_1F_2, the set of all points P such that $|PF_1 - PF_2| = d$ is a hyperbola. The absolute value means that the hyperbola has two branches, one from $PF_1 - PF_2 = d$, and the other from $PF_1 - PF_2 = -d$. The absolute value function allows both branches to be described with one equation.

> **Definition of Hyperbola**
>
> Let F_1 and F_2 be any two points and d be a constant with $0 < d < F_1F_2$. Then the **hyperbola** with **foci** F_1 and F_2 and **focal constant** d is the set of points P in a plane that satisfy $|PF_1 - PF_2| = d$.

The **vertices** V_1 and V_2 of the hyperbola are the intersection points of $\overleftrightarrow{F_1F_2}$ and the hyperbola.

While it may look like each branch of the hyperbola is a parabola, this is not the case. Each branch of a hyperbola has *asymptotes*. In the figure at the right, ℓ_1 and ℓ_2 are asymptotes. The farther points on the hyperbola are from a vertex of the hyperbola, the closer they are to an asymptote, without ever touching. In contrast, parabolas do not have asymptotes.

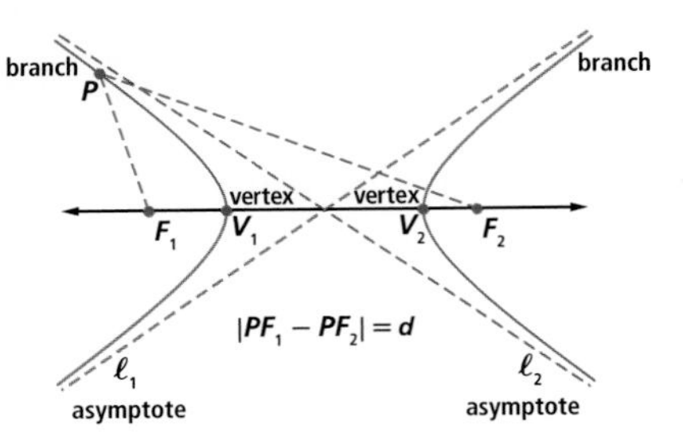

The Standard Form of an Equation for a Hyperbola

A hyperbola is in **standard position** if it is centered at the origin with its foci on an axis. An equation for a hyperbola in standard position resembles the standard form of an equation for an ellipse.

> **Equation for a Hyperbola Theorem**
>
> The hyperbola with foci $(c, 0)$ and $(-c, 0)$ and focal constant $2a$ has equation $\frac{x^2}{a^2} - \frac{y^2}{b^2} = 1$, where $b^2 = c^2 - a^2$.

asymptotes of a hyperbola in standard position, just as applying this transformation to the circle $x^2 + y^2 = 1$ led to equations for ellipses in standard position. There is another analogy between these two equations that students may see in a future math course: Just as the equation $x^2 + y^2 = 1$ is involved in the definition of the circular functions sine, cosine, and so on, the equation $x^2 - y^2 = 1$ is used to define the *hyperbolic sine*, the *hyperbolic cosine*, and so on.

Additional Answers

Activity

Step 2.

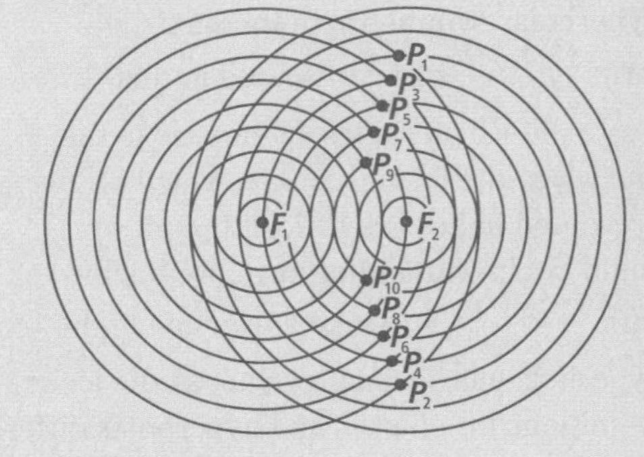

Proof The proof is almost identical to the proof of the Equation for an Ellipse Theorem in Lesson 12-4. Let $P = (x, y)$ be any point on the hyperbola with foci $F_1 = (-c, 0)$ and $F_2 = (c, 0)$ and focal constant $2a$. Then, by the definition of a hyperbola,

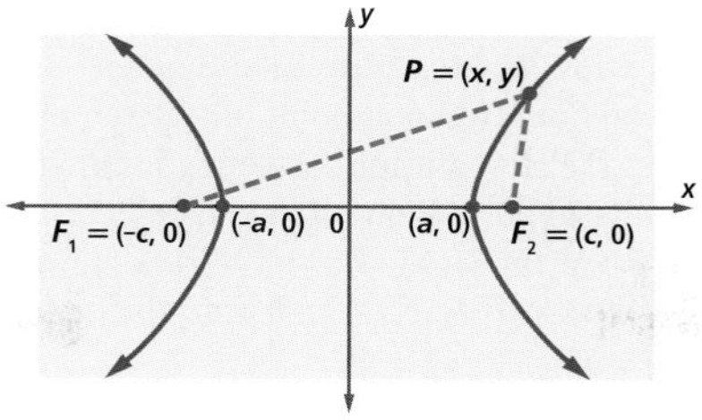

$$|PF_1 - PF_2| = 2a.$$

By the definition of absolute value, you know that this equation is equivalent to

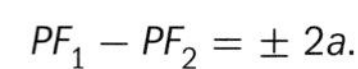

$$PF_1 - PF_2 = \pm 2a.$$

Now substitute $P = (x, y)$, $F_1 = (-c, 0)$, and $F_2 = (c, 0)$ into the Pythagorean Distance Formula to get

$$\sqrt{(x + c)^2 + (y - 0)^2} - \sqrt{(x - c)^2 + (y - 0)^2} = \pm 2a.$$

Do algebraic manipulations similar to those in Steps 1–9 of the proof in Lesson 12-4, and the same equation in Step 9 results.

$$(a^2 - c^2)x^2 + a^2y^2 = a^2(a^2 - c^2)$$

Then in Step 10, for hyperbolas, $c > a > 0$, so $c^2 > a^2$. Thus, $c^2 - a^2$ is positive and you can let $b^2 = c^2 - a^2$. So $-b^2 = a^2 - c^2$. This accounts for the minus sign in the equation.

$$\frac{x^2}{a^2} - \frac{y^2}{b^2} = 1$$

The equation $\frac{x^2}{a^2} - \frac{y^2}{b^2} = 1$ is the **standard form of an equation for a hyperbola**.

Example 1

Find an equation for the hyperbola with foci F_1 and F_2, where $F_1F_2 = 10$ and $|PF_1 - PF_2| = 8$, on a rectangular coordinate system in standard position.

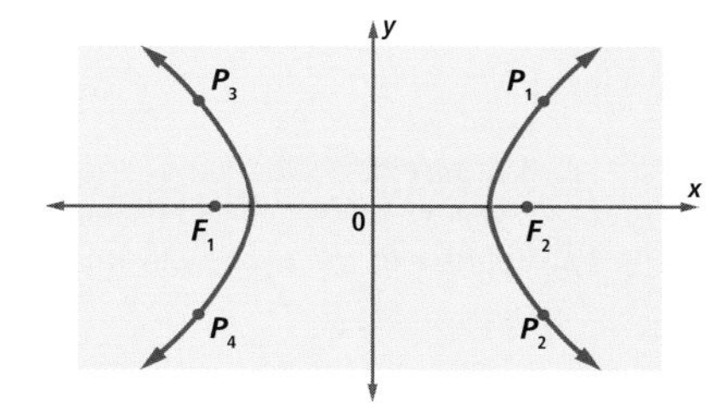

Solution Use the Equation for a Hyperbola Theorem.
You are given $F_1F_2 = 10$, so $2c = 10$, and $c = 5$.
The focal constant is 8, so $2a = 8$, and $a = 4$.
Now, $b^2 = 5^2 - 4^2 = 9$. Thus, an equation for this hyperbola is $\frac{x^2}{16} - \frac{y^2}{9} = 1$.

Asymptotes of a Hyperbola in Standard Position

To find equations for the asymptotes of the hyperbola with equation $\frac{x^2}{a^2} - \frac{y^2}{b^2} = 1$, it helps to examine the special case when a and b both equal 1. (This is like examining the unit circle to learn about ellipses.)

Accommodating the Learner

Ask students to rewrite the equations $\frac{x^2}{16} - \frac{y^2}{9} = 1$ and $\frac{x^2}{a^2} - \frac{y^2}{b^2} = 1$ in the form $Ax^2 + By^2 + C = 0$.

Multiply each side of the first equation by 144 to get $9x^2 - 16y^2 = 144$ or $9x^2 + (-16)y^2 + (-144) = 0$.

Multiply each side of the second equation by a^2b^2 to get $b^2x^2 - a^2y^2 = a^2b^2$ or $b^2x^2 + (-a^2)y^2 + (-a^2b^2) = 0$.

Additional Example

Example 1 Find an equation for the hyperbola with foci F_1 and F_2, where $F_1F_2 = 26$ and $|PF_1 - PF_2| = 10$, on a rectangular system in standard position. It is given that $F_1F_2 = 26$, so $2c = 26$ and $c = 13$. The focal constant is 10, so $2a = 10$ and $a = 5$. Then $b^2 = 13^2 - 5^2 = 144$. Thus an equation for this hyperbola is $\frac{x^2}{169} - \frac{y^2}{144} = 1$.

Notes on the Lesson

Asymptotes of a hyperbola in standard position Have students use a graphing utility to graph the upper half of the hyperbola $x^2 - y^2 = 1$ by graphing $y = \sqrt{x^2 - 1}$ and then graphing the line $y - x$ on the same grid. Have students zoom in on the right part of the graph to see that the hyperbola is getting closer and closer to the line but not reaching it.

Additional Answers

Activity

Step 3.

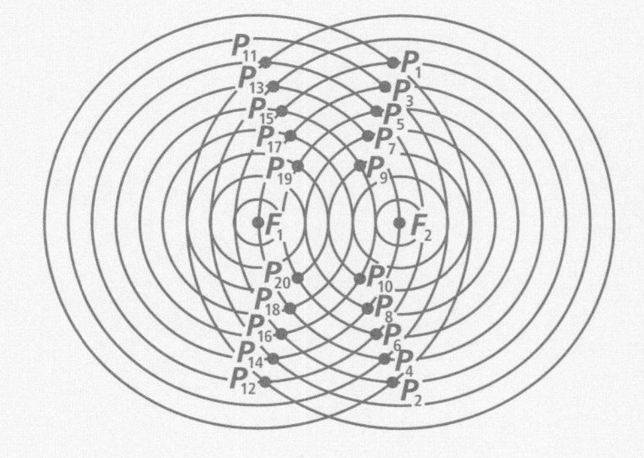

Step 4.

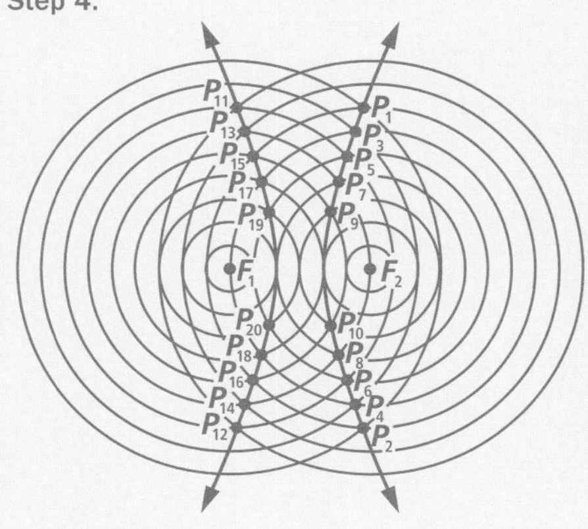

Note-Taking Tips

When students record their notes on the Activity, encourage them to include clear, explicit descriptions of the meaning of P_1F_1, P_2F_2, and so on (for example, P_1F_1 is the distance from a point P_1 on the graph to focus F_1).

Then $x^2 - y^2 = 1$. The hyperbola with this equation is symmetric to both axes. Consequently, each point on the hyperbola in the first quadrant has reflection images on the hyperbola in other quadrants. The graph at the right shows the reflection images of A, B, C, and D over the x-axis and the y-axis.

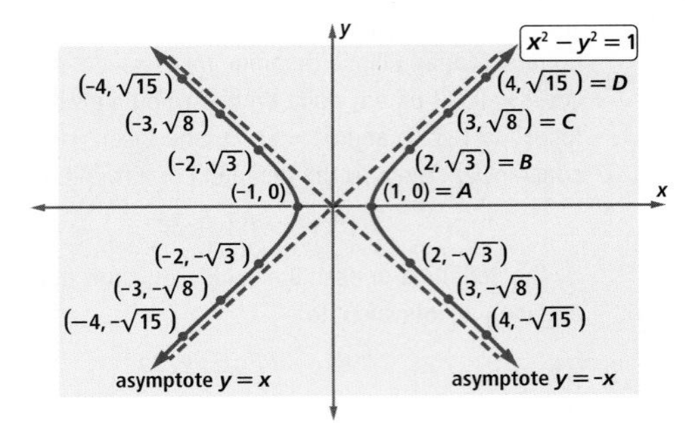

$$A = (1, 0)$$
$$B = (2, \sqrt{3}) \approx (2, 1.73)$$
$$C = (3, \sqrt{8}) \approx (3, 2.83)$$
$$D = (4, \sqrt{15}) \approx (4, 3.87)$$

The lines $y = -x$ and $y = x$ appear to be the asymptotes of $x^2 - y^2 = 1$. We can verify the equations for the asymptotes algebraically.

When $x^2 - y^2 = 1$,

$$y^2 = x^2 - 1.$$

So $\quad y = \pm\sqrt{x^2 - 1}.$

As values of x get larger, $\sqrt{x^2 - 1}$ becomes closer to $\sqrt{x^2}$, which is $|x|$. However, because $\sqrt{x^2 - 1} \neq \sqrt{x^2}$, the curve $x^2 - y^2 = 1$ never intersects the lines with equations $y = x$ or $y = -x$. So, y gets closer to x or $-x$ but never reaches it.

According to the Graph Scale-Change Theorem, the scale change $S_{a,b}$ maps $x^2 - y^2 = 1$ onto $\frac{x^2}{a^2} - \frac{y^2}{b^2} = 1$. Under the same scale change, the asymptotes $y = \pm x$ of $x^2 - y^2 = 1$ are mapped onto the lines with equations $\frac{y}{b} = \pm\frac{x}{a}$. These lines are the asymptotes of $\frac{x^2}{a^2} - \frac{y^2}{b^2} = 1$.

Asymptotes of a Hyperbola Theorem

The asymptotes of the hyperbola with equation $\frac{x^2}{a^2} - \frac{y^2}{b^2} = 1$ are $\frac{y}{b} = \pm\frac{x}{a}$, or $y = \pm\frac{b}{a}x$.

 QY

▶ QY

What are the asymptotes of the hyperbola in Example 1?

Accommodating the Learner

Example 2 uses the hyperbola $\frac{x^2}{16} - \frac{y^2}{36} = 1$. Identify the two foci, F_1 and F_2, of the hyperbola, find any two points P_1 and P_2 on the hyperbola (other than points on one of the axes), and show that $|P_1F_1 - P_1F_2| = |P_2F_1 - P_2F_2|$. Answers vary. Sample: $a^2 = 16$ and $b^2 = 36$. Using $b^2 = c^2 - a^2$ to find c, $36 = c^2 - 16$, so $c^2 = 52$ and $c = \sqrt{52}$; the foci are $F_1 = (-\sqrt{52}, 0)$ and $F_2 = (\sqrt{52}, 0)$. Two points on the hyperbola are $P_1 = (8, \sqrt{108})$ and $P_2 = (-8, \sqrt{108})$. Then $P_1F_1 = \sqrt{(8 + \sqrt{52})^2 + (\sqrt{108} - 0)^2} \approx 18.4222$, $P_1F_2 = \sqrt{(8 - \sqrt{52})^2 + (\sqrt{108} - 0)^2} \approx 10.4222$, $P_2F_1 = \sqrt{(-8 + \sqrt{52})^2 + (\sqrt{108} - 0)^2} \approx 10.4222$, and $P_2F_2 = \sqrt{(-8 - \sqrt{52})^2 + (\sqrt{108} - 0)^2} \approx 18.4222$. Then $|P_1F_1 - P_1F_2| = 8$ and $|P_2F_1 - P_2F_2| = 8$, so $|P_1F_1 - P_1F_2| = |P_2F_1 - P_2F_2|$.

Graphing a Hyperbola with Equation in Standard Form

To graph $\frac{x^2}{a^2} - \frac{y^2}{b^2} = 1$ by hand, notice that $(a, 0)$ and $(-a, 0)$ satisfy the equation. These are the vertices of the hyperbola. When $x = 0$, y is not a real number, so the hyperbola does not intersect the y-axis. Use the asymptotes to make an accurate sketch of the graph. Remember that the asymptotes are not part of the hyperbola.

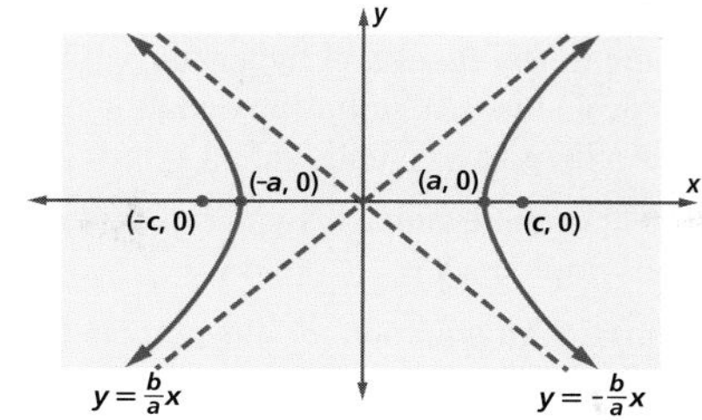

Example 2

Graph the hyperbola with equation $\frac{x^2}{16} - \frac{y^2}{36} = 1$.

Solution The equation is in standard form. So, $a^2 = 16$ and $a = 4$. The vertices are $(4, 0)$ and $(-4, 0)$. The asymptotes are $\frac{y}{6} = \pm\frac{x}{4}$, or $y = \pm\frac{3}{2}x$. Carefully graph the vertices and asymptotes. Then sketch the hyperbola.

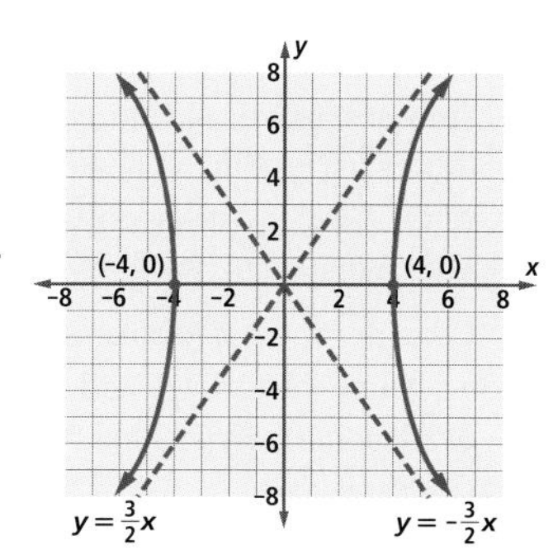

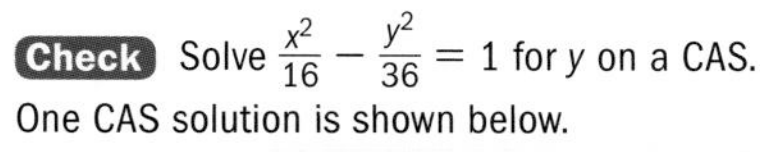

Check Solve $\frac{x^2}{16} - \frac{y^2}{36} = 1$ for y on a CAS.

One CAS solution is shown below.

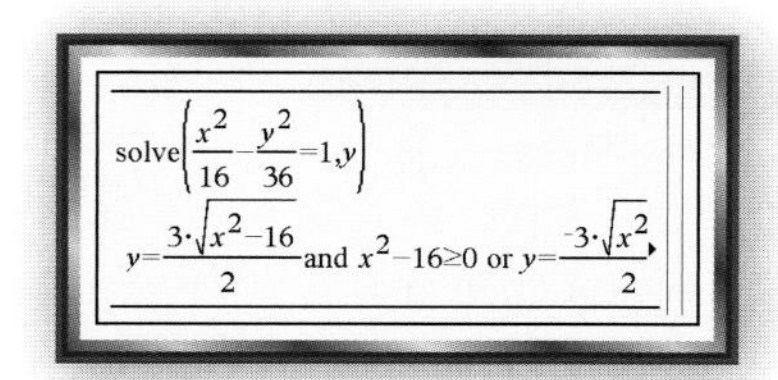

The complete solution is

$$y = \frac{3 \cdot \sqrt{x^2 - 16}}{2} \text{ and } x^2 - 16 \geq 0 \text{ or } y = \frac{-3 \cdot \sqrt{x^2 - 16}}{2} \text{ and } x^2 - 16 \geq 0.$$

So $y = \frac{3\sqrt{x^2 - 16}}{2}$ or $y = -\frac{3\sqrt{x^2 - 16}}{2}$.

Graph both equations on the same axes on a graphing utility.

Although the graphing utility may have trouble graphing values close to the vertices of the hyperbola, the output closely resembles the hand-drawn solution.

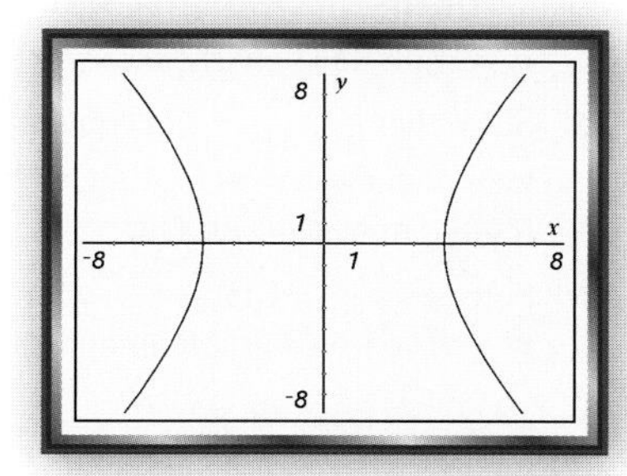

Notes on the Lesson

Example 2 An easy way to sketch the asymptotes is to first make a dotted rectangle with points $(\pm a, 0)$ and $(0, \pm b)$ as the midpoints of its sides. Draw the diagonals of this rectangle and extend them to form the asymptotes. A surprise to many students, when they use two equations to graph a hyperbola, is that the two parts of the graph corresponding to the two equations in y do not correspond to the two branches of the hyperbola but to the tops and the bottoms of each branch. (The Vocabulary Development activity on this page also deals with this idea.)

Additional Example

Example 2 Graph the hyperbola with equation $\frac{x^2}{25} - \frac{y^2}{4} = 1$. The equation is in standard form, so $a^2 = 25$ and $a = 5$; the vertices are $(5, 0)$ and $(-5, 0)$. The asymptotes are $\frac{y}{2} = \pm\frac{x}{5}$ or $y = \pm\frac{2}{5}x$.

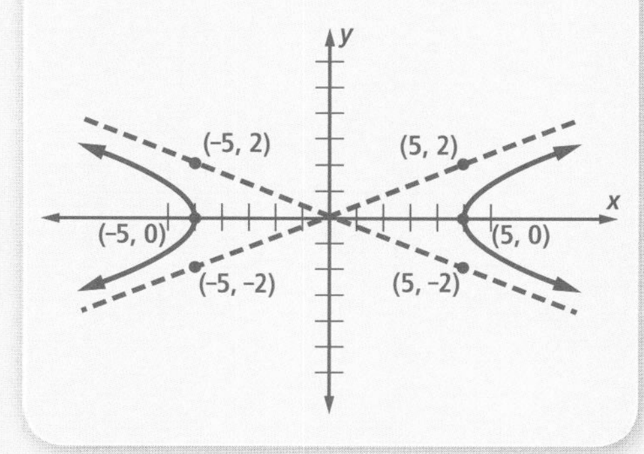

ENGLISH LEARNERS

Vocabulary Development

To help students understand how the branches of a hyperbola are related to its equation, you may want to emphasize the point, mentioned in the Notes on the Lesson for Example 2 on this page that the two branches of a parabola *do not correspond* to the two functions used to graph a hyperbola. Rather, one equation describes the top half of each branch, and the other equation describes the bottom half of each branch.

3 Assignment

Recommended Assignment

- Questions 1–18
- Questions 19 and 20 (extra credit)
- Reading Lesson 12-7
- Covering the Ideas 12-7

Notes on the Questions

Question 12 This question is a preview of an idea that is found in Lesson 12-7 and should be discussed here.

Question 13 On some graphing utilities, the hyperbola $x^2 - y^2 = 1$ can be graphed without solving for y, thus making the first part of this question unnecessary.

Additional Answers

8a. $(-5, 0), (5, 0)$; $y = \pm\frac{8}{5}x$

8b.

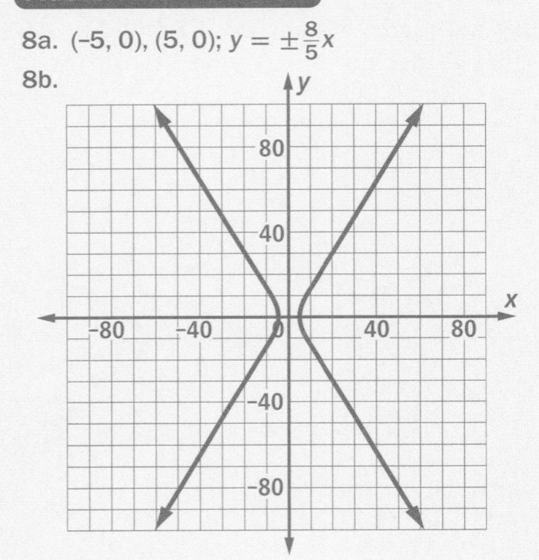

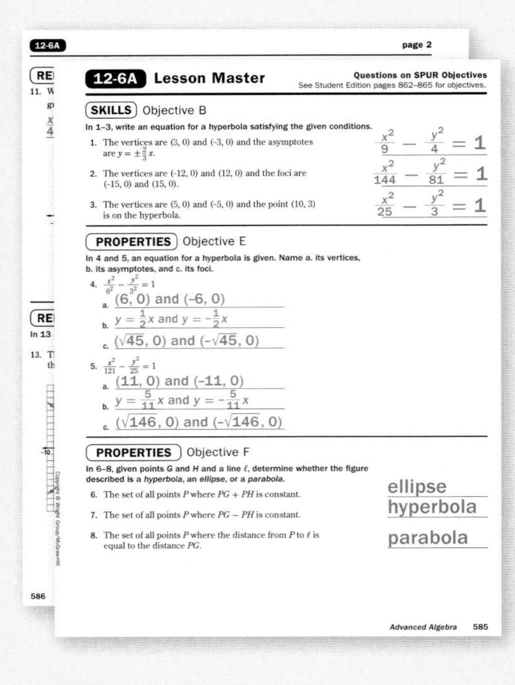
12-6A Lesson Master — Questions on SPUR Objectives. See Student Edition pages 862–865 for objectives.

SKILLS Objective B

In 1–3, write an equation for a hyperbola satisfying the given conditions.

1. The vertices are (3, 0) and (-3, 0) and the asymptotes are $y = \pm\frac{2}{3}x$. $\frac{x^2}{9} - \frac{y^2}{4} = 1$
2. The vertices are (-12, 0) and (12, 0) and the foci are (-15, 0) and (15, 0). $\frac{x^2}{144} - \frac{y^2}{81} = 1$
3. The vertices are (5, 0) and (-5, 0) and the point (10, 3) is on the hyperbola. $\frac{x^2}{25} - \frac{y^2}{3} = 1$

PROPERTIES Objective E

In 4 and 5, an equation for a hyperbola is given. Name a. its vertices, b. its asymptotes, and c. its foci.

4. $\frac{x^2}{6^2} - \frac{y^2}{3^2} = 1$
   a. (6, 0) and (-6, 0)
   b. $y = \frac{1}{2}x$ and $y = -\frac{1}{2}x$
   c. $(\sqrt{45}, 0)$ and $(-\sqrt{45}, 0)$
5. $\frac{x^2}{121} - \frac{y^2}{25} = 1$
   a. (11, 0) and (-11, 0)
   b. $y = \frac{5}{11}x$ and $y = -\frac{5}{11}x$
   c. $(\sqrt{146}, 0)$ and $(-\sqrt{146}, 0)$

PROPERTIES Objective F

In 6–8, given points G and H and a line ℓ, determine whether the figure described is a hyperbola, an ellipse, or a parabola.

6. The set of all points P where PG + PH is constant. ellipse
7. The set of all points P where PG − PH is constant. hyperbola
8. The set of all points P where the distance from P to ℓ is equal to the distance PG. parabola

Advanced Algebra 585

Questions

COVERING THE IDEAS

1. **Fill in the Blanks** A hyperbola with foci $(c, 0)$ and $(-c, 0)$ and focal constant $2a$ has an equation of the form __?__ and vertices at __?__ and __?__.
2. **Fill in the Blanks** A hyperbola with equation $\frac{x^2}{a^2} - \frac{y^2}{b^2} = 1$ has asymptotes $y =$ __?__ and $y =$ __?__. $\frac{b}{a}x$; $-\frac{b}{a}x$

In 3 and 4, an equation for a hyperbola is given. Identify its vertices, its foci, and its asymptotes.

3. $1 = x^2 - y^2$
4. $\frac{x^2}{7^2} - \frac{y^2}{3^2} = 1$
5. **True or False** The focal constant of a hyperbola equals the distance between the foci. false
6. **True or False** If F_1 and F_2 are the foci of a hyperbola, then $\overleftrightarrow{F_1F_2}$ is a line of symmetry for the curve. true
7. What does the phrase "$\sqrt{x^2 - 1}$ is close to $\sqrt{x^2}$ for large values of x" mean?
8. Consider the hyperbola with equation $\frac{x^2}{25} - \frac{y^2}{64} = 1$.
   a. Name its vertices and state equations for its asymptotes.
   b. Graph the hyperbola. 8a–b. See margin.

APPLYING THE MATHEMATICS

9. Explain why $y = |x|$ is not an equation describing the asymptotes of $x^2 - y^2 = 1$.
10. Write an equation for the hyperbola with vertices at (4, 0) and (-4, 0) and one focus at (7, 0). $\frac{x^2}{16} - \frac{y^2}{33} = 1$
11. The point (-6, 3) is on a hyperbola with foci (4, 0) and (-4, 0).
    a. Find the focal constant of the hyperbola. about 6.83
    b. Give an equation for this hyperbola in standard form. (*Hint:* Find b using $b^2 = c^2 - a^2$.) $\frac{x^2}{11.7} - \frac{y^2}{4.3} = 1$
    c. Graph this hyperbola. See margin.
12. Show that $\frac{x^2}{91} - \frac{y^2}{49} = 1$ is equivalent to an equation of the general form $Ax^2 + Bxy + Cy^2 + Dx + Ey + F = 0$ by finding the values of $A, B, C, D, E,$ and F.
13. Solve $x^2 - y^2 = 1$ for y. Use your solution to graph $x^2 - y^2 = 1$ on a graphing utility.

1. $\frac{x^2}{a^2} - \frac{y^2}{b^2} = 1$, where $b^2 = c^2 - a^2$; $(a, 0)$; $(-a, 0)$

3. $(1, 0), (-1, 0)$; $(-\sqrt{2}, 0)$; $(\sqrt{2}, 0)$; $y = x, y = -x$

4. $(7, 0), (-7, 0)$; $(\sqrt{58}, 0)$, $(-\sqrt{58}, 0)$; $y = \pm\frac{3}{7}x$

7. Answers vary. Sample: If x is very large, then the difference between $\sqrt{x^2 - 1}$ and $\sqrt{x^2}$ is very small.

9. Answers vary. Sample: It does not include the asymptotes for the parts of the hyperbola in the second and third quadrants.

12. $A = \frac{1}{91}$, $B = 0$, $C = -\frac{1}{49}$, $D = 0$, $E = 0$, $F = -1$ (or $A = 49$, $B = 0$, $C = -91$, $D = 0$, $E = 0$, $F = -4459$)

13. $y = \pm\sqrt{x^2 - 1}$

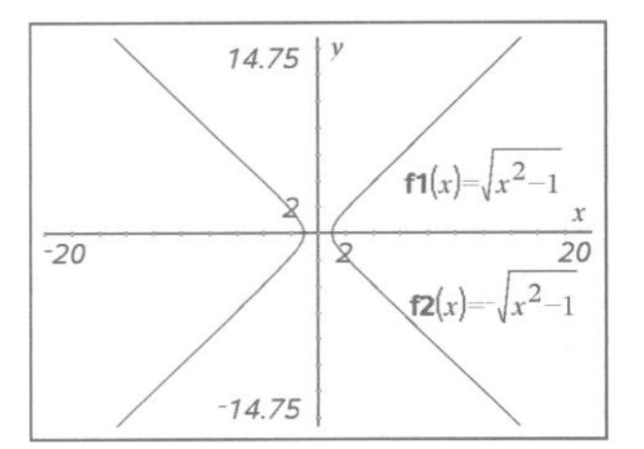

Extension

After defining a hyperbola on page 832, the text describes that each branch of a hyperbola is not a parabola because each branch has asymptotes, and parabolas do not have asymptotes. Ask: Why does a parabola not have an asymptote? (*Note:* The answer is not simple!) Answers vary. Sample: An asymptote is a line that a function approaches. For a parabola, that line cannot be a vertical line with equation $x = a$ because the parabola will cross any vertical line. Consider the parabola with equation $y = x^2$ and any nonvertical line with equation $y = mx$. The line contains the point (x, mx), and the parabola contains the point (x, x^2). So when x reaches and then exceeds the value of m, the parabola crosses $y = mx$. For the parabola with equation $y = ax^2$, students will learn (in calculus) that at every point on the parabola, the slope of the line tangent to the parabola at that point is $2ax$. Because the slope of the tangent line is always changing, there is no single line (i.e., no asymptote) that the graph approaches.

REVIEW

14. In Australia, a type of football is played on elliptical fields. One such field has a major axis of length 185 meters and minor axis of length 155 meters. Surrounding it is an elliptical fence with major axis of length 187 meters and minor axis of length 157 meters. The 1-meter wide track between the fence and the field is to be covered with turf. Find the area of the track. **(Lesson 12-5)** $171\pi \approx 537.21$ m^2

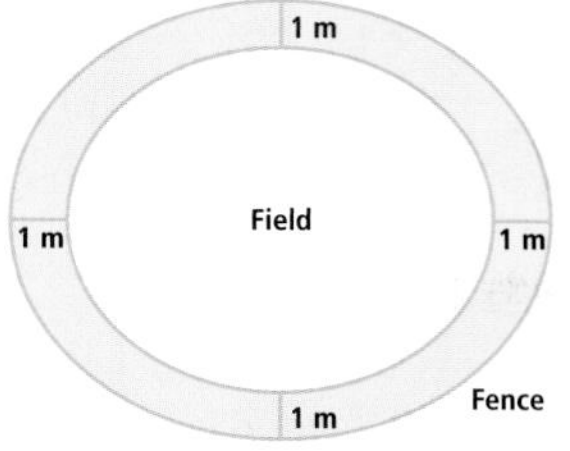

not to scale

In 15 and 16, graph the ellipse with the given equation. (Lesson 12-4)

15. $\frac{x^2}{4} + \frac{y^2}{25} = 1$

16. $\frac{x^2}{9} + y^2 = 1$

15–16. See the Additional Answers section at the back of the book.

17. Standard Quonset huts are semicircular with a diameter of 20 feet and a length of 48 feet. **(Lesson 12-2)**
    a. Inside the hut, how close to either side of the hut could a 6-foot soldier stand upright? no closer than 2 ft
    b. What is the volume of a hut? $2400\pi \approx 7539.82$ ft^3

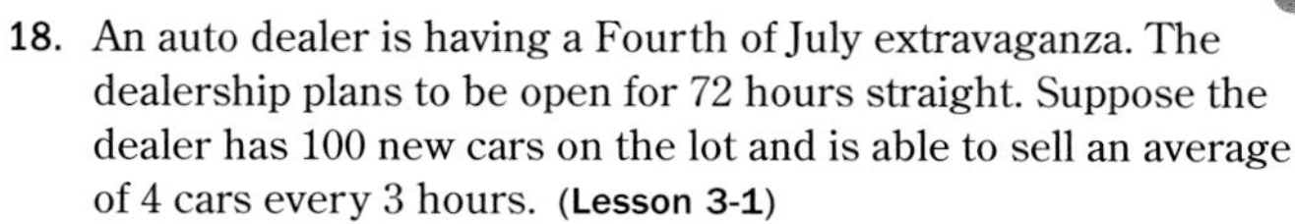

During World War II, easy-to-build Quonset huts were used as barracks for troops.

18. An auto dealer is having a Fourth of July extravaganza. The dealership plans to be open for 72 hours straight. Suppose the dealer has 100 new cars on the lot and is able to sell an average of 4 cars every 3 hours. **(Lesson 3-1)**
    a. Let h be the number of hours the car dealership has been open and let C be the number of cars remaining on the lot. Find three other pairs of values that satisfy this relation and complete the table. Answers vary. Samples given.

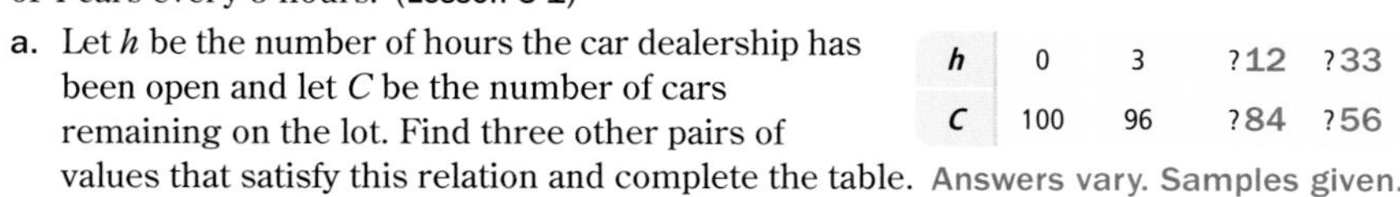

h	0	3	?12	?33	?72
C	100	96	?84	?56	? 4

    b. Write a formula for the number of cars C on the lot as a function of the number of hours h the sale has been on. $C = 100 - \frac{4}{3}h$
    c. After how many hours will there be only 60 cars left? 30
    d. If the dealership is able to maintain the pace of 4 cars sold every 3 hours, will the dealer sell all the cars on the lot during the sale? How can you tell?

18d. No; after 72 hr the dealer will still have 4 cars left. Substituting 72 for h into the formula for C in Part b gives $C = 4$

EXPLORATION

19. The words *ellipsis* and *hyperbole* have literary meanings. What are these meanings?

20. In *Round the Moon*, a novel written by Jules Verne in 1870, a group of men launch a rocket to the Moon. During the journey they argue whether the rocket trajectory is hyperbolic or parabolic. Because each curve is infinite, the men believe they are doomed to travel infinitely through space. Find out on which trajectory modern day rockets travel and whether or not the men had reason to worry.

19–20. See the Additional Answers section at the back of the book.

QY ANSWER

$y = \pm\frac{3}{4}x$

Notes on the Questions

Additional Answers can be found in the back of the book.

4 Wrap-Up

Ongoing Assessment

Ask students to describe how to find the vertices and the asymptotes for a hyperbola whose equation has the form $\frac{x^2}{p^2} - \frac{y^2}{q^2} = 1$. The vertices use the value of p and are $(p, 0)$ and $(-p, 0)$. The asymptotes use the values of p and q and are the lines $\frac{y}{q} = \pm\frac{x}{p}$, which can be rewritten as $y = \pm\frac{q}{p}x$.

Project Update

Project 1, *Reflection Properties of Conics,* on page 856 and Project 5, *Constructing Conic Sections,* on page 857 relate to the content of this lesson.

Additional Answers

11c.

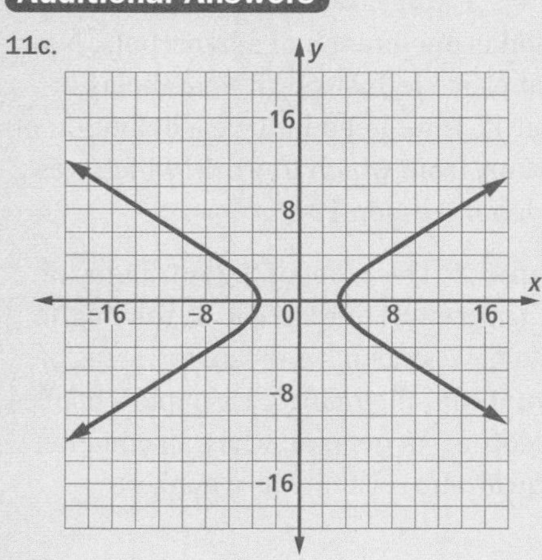

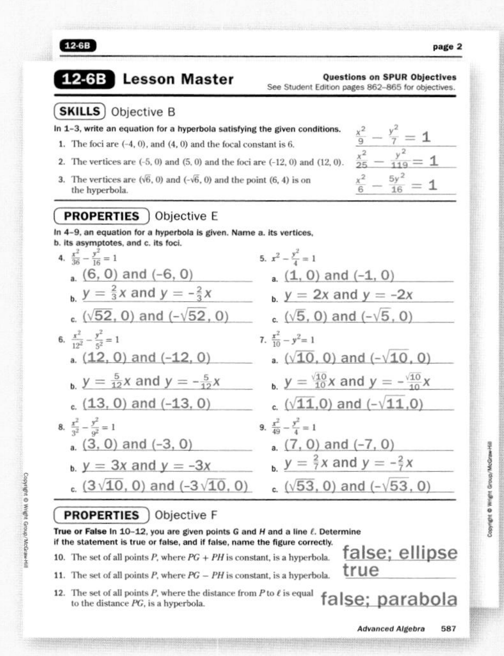

12-6B page 2

12-6B Lesson Master

Questions on SPUR Objectives
See Student Edition pages 862–865 for objectives.

SKILLS Objective B

In 1–3, write an equation for a hyperbola satisfying the given conditions.

1. The foci are (-4, 0), and (4, 0) and the focal constant is 6. $\frac{x^2}{9} - \frac{y^2}{7} = 1$
2. The vertices are (-5, 0) and (5, 0) and the foci are (-12, 0) and (12, 0). $\frac{x^2}{25} - \frac{y^2}{119} = 1$
3. The vertices are $(\sqrt{6}, 0)$ and $(-\sqrt{6}, 0)$ and the point (6, 4) is on the hyperbola. $\frac{x^2}{6} - \frac{5y^2}{16} = 1$

PROPERTIES Objective E

In 4–9, an equation for a hyperbola is given. Name a. its vertices, b. its asymptotes, and c. its foci.

4. $\frac{x^2}{36} - \frac{y^2}{16} = 1$
   a. (6, 0) and (-6, 0)
   b. $y = \frac{2}{3}x$ and $y = -\frac{2}{3}x$
   c. $(\sqrt{52}, 0)$ and $(-\sqrt{52}, 0)$
5. $x^2 - \frac{y^2}{4} = 1$
   a. (1, 0) and (-1, 0)
   b. $y = 2x$ and $y = -2x$
   c. $(\sqrt{5}, 0)$ and $(-\sqrt{5}, 0)$
6. $\frac{x^2}{12^2} - \frac{y^2}{5^2} = 1$
   a. (12, 0) and (-12, 0)
   b. $y = \frac{5}{12}x$ and $y = -\frac{5}{12}x$
   c. (13, 0) and (-13, 0)
7. $\frac{x^2}{10} - y^2 = 1$
   a. $(\sqrt{10}, 0)$ and $(-\sqrt{10}, 0)$
   b. $y = \frac{\sqrt{10}}{10}x$ and $y = -\frac{\sqrt{10}}{10}x$
   c. $(\sqrt{11}, 0)$ and $(-\sqrt{11}, 0)$
8. $\frac{x^2}{3^2} - \frac{y^2}{9^2} = 1$
   a. (3, 0) and (-3, 0)
   b. $y = 3x$ and $y = -3x$
   c. $(3\sqrt{10}, 0)$ and $(-3\sqrt{10}, 0)$
9. $\frac{x^2}{49} - \frac{y^2}{4} = 1$
   a. (7, 0) and (-7, 0)
   b. $y = \frac{2}{7}x$ and $y = -\frac{2}{7}x$
   c. $(\sqrt{53}, 0)$ and $(-\sqrt{53}, 0)$

PROPERTIES Objective F

True or False In 10–12, you are given points G and H and a line ℓ. Determine if the statement is true or false, and if false, name the figure correctly.

10. The set of all points P, where $PG + PH$ is constant, is a hyperbola. false; ellipse
11. The set of all points P, where $PG - PH$ is constant, is a hyperbola. true
12. The set of all points P, where the distance from P to ℓ is equal to the distance PG, is a hyperbola. false; parabola

Advanced Algebra 587

Lesson 12-7

GOAL

Show that different-looking equations, such as $xy = k$ and $\frac{x^2}{a^2} - \frac{y^2}{b^2} = 1$, can lead to similar-looking curves; prove that the inverse-variation function graphs studied in Chapter 2 are hyperbolas.

SPUR Objectives

A Rewrite an equation for a conic section in the standard form of a quadratic equation in two variables.

B Write equations for hyperbolas.

E Identify characteristics of hyperbolas.

I Graph hyperbolas when given equations for them in standard form, and vice versa.

Materials/Resources

- Lesson Masters 12-7A and 12-7B
- Resource Masters 237 and 238
- Quiz 2

HOMEWORK

Suggestions for Assignment

- Questions 1–23
- Question 24 (extra credit)
- Reading Lesson 12-8
- Covering the Ideas 12-8

Local Standards

1 Warm-Up

According to the theorem on page 841, the graph of $xy = 50$ is a hyperbola with foci (10, 10) and (-10, -10) and focal constant 20.

1. Show that the difference between the distances from the point (2, 25) to the two foci is 20. The distance from (2, 25) to (10, 10) is 17; the distance from (2, 25) to (-10, -10) is 37. So the difference of the distances is $37 - 17 = 20$.

Lesson 12-7 A General Equation for Quadratic Relations

Vocabulary

conic section

standard form of an equation for a quadratic relation

BIG IDEA Equations for specific parabolas, ellipses, circles, and hyperbolas are all special cases of one general equation form.

The Conic Sections

On the opening page of this chapter, you read that parabolas, hyperbolas, and ellipses can all be formed when a plane and a double cone intersect. A double cone is formed by rotating a line (in space) about a line it intersects (its axis). Any of the possible images of the line is an *edge* of the cone. The intersection of a plane and a double cone is called a **conic section**. Let k be the measure of the acute angle between the axis of the double cone and its edge. Let θ be the measure of the smallest angle between the axis and the intersecting plane. The following three possible relationships between θ and k determine the three types of conic sections.

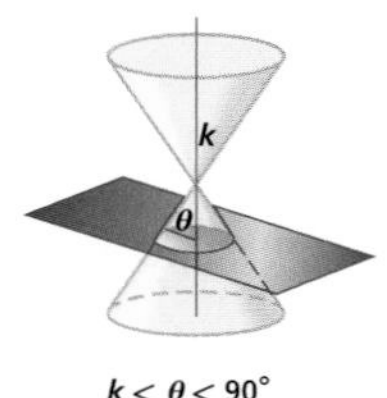

$k < \theta < 90°$
ellipse

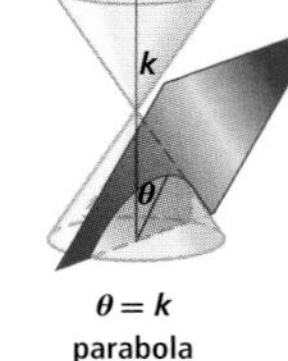

$\theta = k$
parabola

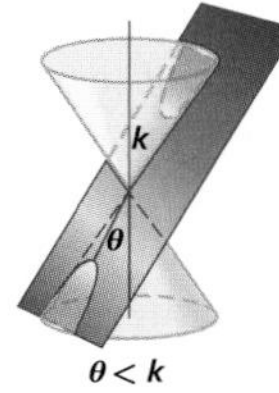

$\theta < k$
hyperbola

Mental Math

Serena is cutting a pie into 8 wedge-shaped pieces.

a. If she wants all the pieces to be the same size, what is the measure in degrees of the angle of each wedge? 45°

b. If she wants each of four of the pieces to be twice as big as each of the other four, what is the measure in degrees of the angle of the larger wedges? 60°

c. If she wants each of two of the pieces to be twice as big as each of the other six, what is the measure in degrees of the angle of the larger wedges? 72°

The Standard Form of an Equation for a Quadratic Relation

You have now seen equations for all three different types of conics. Here are some of these equations in standard form, including the hyperbola form $xy = k$ that you will examine in this lesson.

$y = ax^2 + bx + c$	parabola
$(x - h)^2 + (y - k)^2 = r^2$	circle (special ellipse)
$\frac{x^2}{a^2} + \frac{y^2}{b^2} = 1$	ellipse
$\frac{x^2}{a^2} - \frac{y^2}{b^2} = 1$ or $xy = k$	hyperbola

Background

This lesson has two parts. The lesson begins by discussing the standard form for a quadratic relation, recalling page 796 in which the conic sections were described together. Then the lesson discusses the graphs of inverse variation functions.

Generating more hyperbolas from inverse variation The discussion begins by reviewing a situation students saw in Chapter 2. At that time we *asserted* without proof that the graph of an inverse variation function is one branch of a hyperbola. Now we can prove it. Just as with parabolas in Lesson 12-1, we need to have a definition of hyperbola from which to work, which was provided in Lesson 12-6.

Example 2 The proof of the Attributes of $y = \frac{k}{x}$ Theorem is in Example 2. You might want to have students emulate the steps of the proof with their CASs. Example 3 applies the theorem. In general, when an equation for a quadratic relation has a nonzero

Although the equations for a hyperbola and an ellipse look similar, the others look different. However, all these equations contain only constant terms or terms with x^2, xy, y^2, x, or y. Thus, all the conic sections are special types of relations with polynomial equations of 2nd degree. These are called *quadratic relations*. The **standard form of an equation for a quadratic relation** is

$$Ax^2 + Bxy + Cy^2 + Dx + Ey + F = 0,$$

where A, B, C, D, E, and F are real numbers, and at least one of A, B, or C is nonzero.

Example 1

Show that the circle with equation $(x - 5)^2 + (y - 1)^2 = 12$ is a quadratic relation.

Solution Rewrite the equation in the standard form of an equation for a quadratic relation. First expand the squares of the binomials and combine like terms.

$$x^2 - 10x + y^2 - 2y + 26 = 12$$

Then add -12 to both sides and use the Commutative Property of Addition to reorder the terms so that they are in the order x^2, xy, y^2, x, y, and constants.

$$x^2 + 0xy + y^2 - 10x - 2y + 14 = 0$$

This is in standard form with $A = 1$, $B = 0$, $C = 1$, $D = -10$, $E = -2$, and $F = 14$. Because at least one of A, B, or C is nonzero, this is a quadratic relation.

QY1

QY1

If you put the equation $xy = 25$ for a hyperbola into standard form, what are the values of A, B, C, D, E, and F?

Generating More Hyperbolas from Inverse Variation

Recall Anna and Jenna Lyzer's experiment to verify the Law of the Lever in Lesson 2-7. With Anna seated at a fixed point on one side of a seesaw's pivot, her friends with weights w took turns balancing her while Jenna recorded their distances d feet from the pivot. Anna and Jenna found that the inverse-variation function with equation $d = \frac{119}{w}$ is a good model.

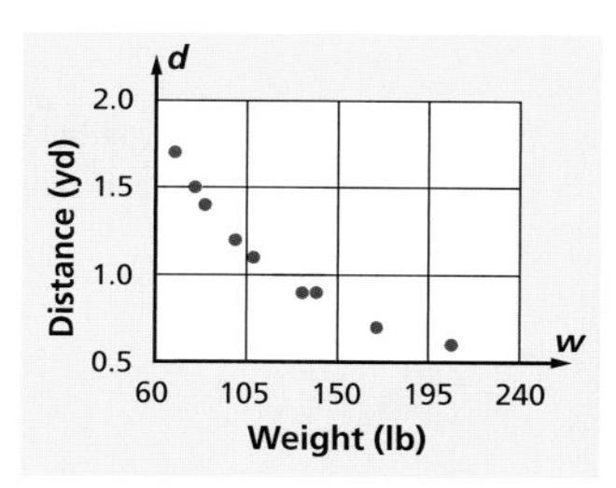

The Lyzers' equation is one instance of the general inverse-variation function, $y = \frac{k}{x}$. In Chapter 2 we claimed that the graph of $y = \frac{k}{x}$ is a hyperbola. Now you can prove it by showing that it satisfies the geometric definition of hyperbola given in the last lesson.

2. Show that the difference between the distances from the point (-1, -50) to the two foci is also 20. The distance from (-1, -50) to (10, 10) is 61; the distance from (-1, -50) to (-10, -10) is 41. So the difference of the distances is 20.

2 Teaching

Notes on the Lesson

The Conic Sections If your students have access to a DGS with 3-dimensional capabilities, you might have them use it to examine the various conic sections. With the DGS, the figures can be rotated for easier viewing.

The standard form of an equation for a quadratic relation Remind students that the term Bxy in the standard form has degree 2. Although the equation $y = \frac{k}{x}$ might not look like a second-degree equation, rewriting it as $xy = k$ shows that it is.

Additional Example

Example 1 Show that the circle with equation $(x + 3)^2 + (y - 5)^2 = 8$ is a quadratic relation. Expanding the equation gives $x^2 + 6x + 9 + y^2 - 10y + 25 = 8$ or $x^2 + 0xy + y^2 + 6x - 10y + 26 = 0$. This is in standard form with $A = 1$, $B = 0$, $C = 1$, $D = 6$, $E = -10$, and $F = 26$. Because at least one of A, B, or C is not zero, this is a quadratic relation.

Note-Taking Tips

When students record their notes on the illustration of conic sections on page 838, you may want to introduce the term *element* as a line on the surface of the cone that contains the vertex. Then students can add the information for the parabola that the plane in the illustration can be considered as being parallel to an element of the cone.

xy-term, then the relation is not symmetric to any horizontal or vertical line. This is why the equations $xy = k$ and $\frac{x^2}{a^2} - \frac{y^2}{b^2} = 1$ are so different even though they lead to the same kind of curve. You may want to inform students that there are other hyperbolas (for example, those whose lines of symmetry are neither the axes nor the lines $y = \pm x$, and those not centered at the origin) that have nonzero x^2-, y^2-, and *xy*-terms.

ENGLISH LEARNERS

Vocabulary Development

This lesson provides a natural opportunity to review the forms for linear equations, including the standard form $Ax + By = C$, the slope-intercept form $y = mx + b$, and the point-slope form $y - y_1 = m(x - x_1)$.

Notes on the Lesson

Example 2 In this example, we substitute k for $\frac{c^2}{2}$ to obtain the equation $xy = k$. If we left the equation as $xy = \frac{c^2}{2}$, the connection with inverse variation might not be as obvious.

Additional Example

Example 2 Find an equation of the form $y = \frac{k}{x}$ for the hyperbola with foci (4, 4) and (-4, -4) and focal constant 8. Let $P = (x, y)$ be a point on the hyperbola. Then

$$\sqrt{(x-4)^2 + (y-4)^2} - \sqrt{(x+4)^2 + (y+4)^2} = 8$$

$$\sqrt{(x-4)^2 + (y-4)^2} = 8 + \sqrt{(x+4)^2 + (y+4)^2}$$

$$(x-4)^2 + (y-4)^2 = 64 + 16\sqrt{(x+4)^2 + (y+4)^2} + (x+4)^2 + (y+4)^2$$

$$x^2 - 8x + 16 + y^2 - 8y + 16 = 64 + 16\sqrt{(x+4)^2 + (y+4)^2} + x^2 + 8x + 16 + y^2 + 8y + 16$$

$$-16x - 16y - 64 = 16\sqrt{(x+4)^2 + (y+4)^2}$$

$$x + y + 4 = -\sqrt{(x+4)^2 + (y+4)^2}$$

$$(x + y + 4)^2 = \left(-\sqrt{(x+4)^2 + (y+4)^2}\right)^2$$

$$(x + y + 4)^2 = (x+4)^2 + (y+4)^2$$

$$x^2 + y^2 + 2xy + 8x + 8y + 16 = x^2 + 8x + 16 + y^2 + 8y + 16$$

$2xy = 16$, so $y = \frac{16}{2x} = \frac{8}{x}$

If $k > 0$, each branch of the graph is reflection-symmetric over the line $y = x$, and so the foci must be on the line $y = x$. Because the graph of $y = \frac{k}{x}$ is rotation-symmetric about the origin, the foci are also rotation-symmetric about the origin. Example 2 shows how an equation of the form $y = \frac{k}{x}$ arises when the foci meet these criteria.

Example 2

Find an equation of the form $y = \frac{k}{x}$ for the hyperbola with foci $F_1 = (c, c)$ and $F_2 = (-c, -c)$ and focal constant $2c$.

Solution Let $P = (x, y)$ be a point on the hyperbola. Then, by the definition of hyperbola, one branch of the curve is the set of points P such that

$$PF_1 - PF_2 = 2c.$$

Use the Distance Formula with $F_1 = (c, c)$, and $F_2 = (-c, -c)$.

$$\sqrt{(x-c)^2 + (y-c)^2} - \sqrt{(x+c)^2 + (y+c)^2} = 2c$$

Now proceed as in Lesson 12-4 with the derivation of an equation for an ellipse. You may find your CAS helpful as you follow the steps. First add $\sqrt{(x+c)^2 + (y+c)^2}$ to both sides.

$$\sqrt{(x-c)^2 + (y-c)^2} = 2c + \sqrt{(x+c)^2 + (y+c)^2}$$

Square both sides. Notice that the right side is a binomial.

$$(x-c)^2 + (y-c)^2 = 4c^2 + 4c\sqrt{(x+c)^2 + (y+c)^2} + (x+c)^2 + (y+c)^2$$

Expand the squares of the binomials, combine like terms, and simplify.

$$-4cx - 4cy - 4c^2 = 4c\sqrt{(x+c)^2 + (y+c)^2}$$

Divide by $-4c$; then square both sides.

$$(x + y + c)^2 = (x+c)^2 + (y+c)^2$$

The other branch of the hyperbola also satisfies this equation. Expand both sides again and simplify.

$$x^2 + 2xy + 2cx + y^2 + 2cy + c^2 = x^2 + 2cx + c^2 + y^2 + 2cy + c^2$$

$$2xy = c^2$$

$$xy = \frac{c^2}{2}$$

$$y = \frac{\frac{c^2}{2}}{x}$$

This is an equation of the form $y = \frac{k}{x}$, where $k = \frac{c^2}{2}$.

Extension

Have students look at the diagram on page 838 showing a plane intersecting a double cone. Ask them to find out the name of the vertical line through the vertex of the double cone (the *axis*) and the name of the line on the surface of the double cone that contains the vertex (the *element;* see the Note-Taking Tips on page 839). Then ask students to use the two terms to describe when the intersection of the plane and the double cone is a circle, an ellipse, a parabola, or a hyperbola.

Answers vary. Sample: Start with the plane perpendicular to the axis. Keeping constant the point of intersection of the plane and the axis, gradually tilt the plane. When the plane is perpendicular to the axis, the intersection is a circle. When the plane is tilted, the intersection is an ellipse. When the tilt is such that the plane is parallel to an element of the double cone, the intersection is a parabola. (Students should notice that the plane intersects only one part of the double cone.) When the tilt is further

The following theorem summarizes attributes of hyperbolas of the form $xy = k$.

Attributes of $y = \frac{k}{x}$ Theorem

The graph of $y = \frac{k}{x}$ or $xy = k$ is a hyperbola. When $k > 0$, this hyperbola has vertices $(\sqrt{k}, \sqrt{k})$ and $(-\sqrt{k}, -\sqrt{k})$, foci $(\sqrt{2k}, \sqrt{2k})$ and $(-\sqrt{2k}, -\sqrt{2k})$, and focal constant $2\sqrt{2k}$. The asymptotes of the graph are $x = 0$ and $y = 0$.

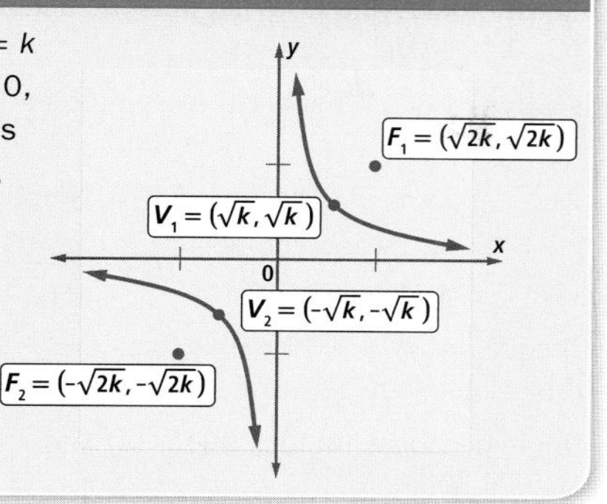

QY2

▶ **QY2**

According to the theorem above, what are the foci and focal constant of the hyperbola that is the graph of $d = \frac{160}{w}$?

GUIDED

Example 3

Find an equation of the form $y = \frac{k}{x}$ for the hyperbola with foci $F_1 = (8, 8)$ and $F_2 = (-8, -8)$, and focal constant 16.

Solution From the Attributes of $y = \frac{k}{x}$ Theorem, you know that the hyperbola has foci $(\sqrt{2k}, \sqrt{2k})$ and (__?__, __?__). $-\sqrt{2k}$; $-\sqrt{2k}$

So (__?__, __?__) = $(\sqrt{2k}, \sqrt{2k})$. Solve for k. 8; 8

__?__ $= \sqrt{2k}$ 8

__?__ $= 2k$ 64

__?__ $= k$ 32

Substitute __?__ for k in $y = \frac{k}{x}$. 32

An equation for the hyperbola is $y =$ __?__. $\frac{32}{x}$

Questions

COVERING THE IDEAS

In 1–4, determine whether the equation is for a quadratic relation. If so, put the equation in standard form of an equation for a quadratic relation. If not, tell why not.

1. $(x - 3)^2 + (y + 7)^2 = 118$
2. $2x^2 + 4x - 7xy + 8y^2 + 3y = -3$
3. $\pi y - 6xy + y^2 + x^2 = \sqrt{11}$
4. $-2x^2y + 2xy + 2x^2 + 6x + 5y = 0$

1. yes; $x^2 + y^2 - 6x + 14y - 60 = 0$
2. yes; $2x^2 - 7xy + 8y^2 + 4x + 3y + 3 = 0$
3. yes; $x^2 - 6xy + y^2 + \pi y - \sqrt{11} = 0$
4. No; there are terms of degree greater than 2.

Notes on the Lesson

You might offer the following observation. The asymptotes of $xy = k$ can be found by solving $xy = 0$; they are always $x = 0$ or $y = 0$. The asymptotes for $\frac{x^2}{a^2} - \frac{y^2}{b^2} = 1$ can always be found by solving $\frac{x^2}{a^2} - \frac{y^2}{b^2} = 0$. From that equation, $\frac{x^2}{a^2} = \frac{y^2}{b^2}$, so $\frac{x^2}{a^2} = \pm\frac{y^2}{b^2}$.

Additional Example

Example 3 Find an equation of the form $y = \frac{k}{x}$ for the hyperbola with foci (3, 3) and (-3, -3) and focal constant 6.

Solution The hyperbola has foci $(\sqrt{2k}, \sqrt{2k})$ and __?__. $(-\sqrt{2k}, -\sqrt{2k})$ So (__?__, __?__) = $(\sqrt{2k}, \sqrt{2k})$. 3; 3 Solve for k: __?__ = $\sqrt{2k}$, __?__ = $2k$, so __?__ = k. 3; 9; 4.5 Substitute __?__ for k in $y = \frac{k}{x}$. 4.5 An equation for the hyperbola is $y =$ __?__. $\frac{4.5}{x}$

3 Assignment

Recommended Assignment

- Questions 1–23
- Question 24 (extra credit)
- Reading Lesson 12-8
- Covering the Ideas 12-8

increased, the plane intersects both parts of the double cone, creating the two branches of a hyperbola.

Accommodating the Learner

Tell students that a graph contains the point (2, -4). Ask them to write at least two equations for the graph if it represents a line, a circle, a parabola, or a hyperbola. Answers vary. Sample: line: $x = 2$, $y = -4$, $y = -x - 2$; circle: $(x - 2)^2 + y^2 = 16$, $x^2 + (y + 4)^2 = 4$, $(x - 2)^2 + (y + 3)^2 = 1$; parabola: $y + 4 = (x - 2)^2$ and $y = x^2 - 8$; hyperbola: $xy = -8$; $\frac{x^2}{2} - \frac{y^2}{16} = 1$

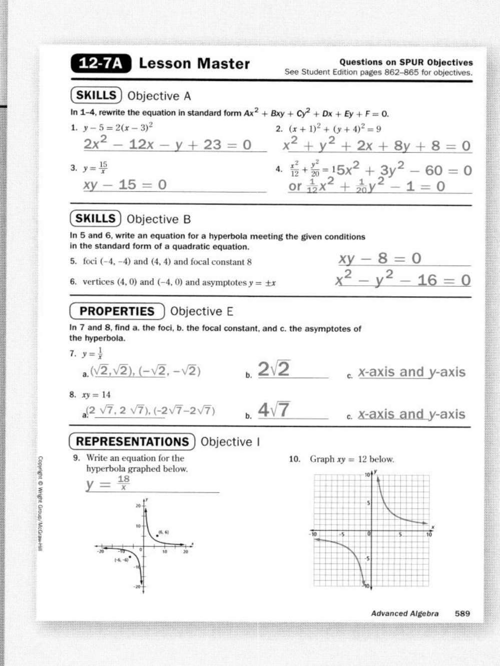

12-7A Lesson Master

Questions on SPUR Objectives
See Student Edition pages 862–865 for objectives.

SKILLS Objective A

In 1–4, rewrite the equation in standard form $Ax^2 + Bxy + Cy^2 + Dx + Ey + F = 0$.

1. $y - 5 = 2(x - 3)^2$ — $2x^2 - 12x - y + 23 = 0$
2. $(x + 1)^2 + (y + 4)^2 = 9$ — $x^2 + y^2 + 2x + 8y + 8 = 0$
3. $y = \frac{15}{x}$ — $xy - 15 = 0$
4. $\frac{x^2}{12} + \frac{y^2}{20} = 1$ — $5x^2 + 3y^2 - 60 = 0$ or $\frac{1}{12}x^2 + \frac{1}{20}y^2 - 1 = 0$

SKILLS Objective B

In 5 and 6, write an equation for a hyperbola meeting the given conditions in the standard form of a quadratic equation.

5. foci (-4, -4) and (4, 4) and focal constant 8 — $xy - 8 = 0$
6. vertices (4, 0) and (-4, 0) and asymptotes $y = \pm x$ — $x^2 - y^2 - 16 = 0$

PROPERTIES Objective E

In 7 and 8, find a. the foci, b. the focal constant, and c. the asymptotes of the hyperbola.

7. $y = \frac{1}{x}$
   a. $(\sqrt{2}, \sqrt{2})$, $(-\sqrt{2}, -\sqrt{2})$ b. $2\sqrt{2}$ c. x-axis and y-axis
8. $xy = 14$
   a. $(2\sqrt{7}, 2\sqrt{7})$, $(-2\sqrt{7} - 2\sqrt{7})$ b. $4\sqrt{7}$ c. x-axis and y-axis

REPRESENTATIONS Objective I

9. Write an equation for the hyperbola graphed below. $y = \frac{18}{x}$
10. Graph $xy = 12$ below.

Notes on the Questions

Question 14 Because the question already indicates that rt is a constant, all one has to do to answer the question is to pick a value of r for which the value of t can be easily calculated (or vice versa).

Question 15 Inequalities are somewhat more difficult for hyperbolas than for other conics because it is not always clear what "side" of a hyperbola a point is on. A hyperbola splits a plane into three parts, not two.

Additional Answers

9.

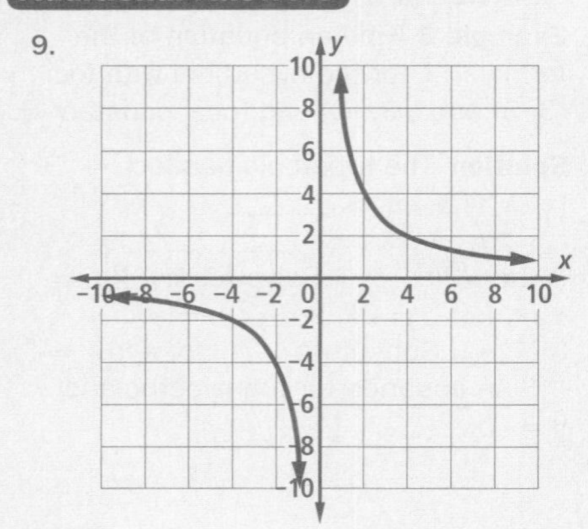

foci: (4, 4), (-4, -4); vertices: $(2\sqrt{2}, 2\sqrt{2})$, $(-2\sqrt{2}, -2\sqrt{2})$; asymptotes: $x = 0, y = 0$; focal constant: 8

11. $\frac{1}{4}x^2 - \frac{1}{9}y^2 - 1 = 0$ (or $9x^2 - 4y^2 - 36 = 0$); $A = \frac{1}{4}, B = 0, C = -\frac{1}{9}, D = 0, E = 0, F = -1$ (or $A = 9, B = 0, C = -4, D = 0, E = 0, F = -36$)

12. $5x^2 + 20x - y + 9 = 0$; $A = 5, B = 0, C = 0, D = 20, E = -1, F = 9$

14b.

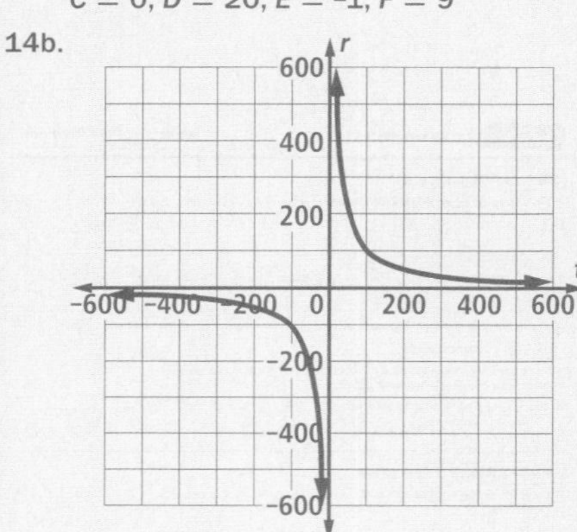

5. Recall Anna and Jenna's equation, $d = \frac{119}{w}$.
   a. What are the foci of the hyperbola with this equation? $(\sqrt{238}, \sqrt{238})$, $(-\sqrt{238}, -\sqrt{238})$
   b. What is the focal constant? $2\sqrt{238} \approx 30.85$

6. At the right is a hyperbola with foci A and B. What must be true about $|Q_1A - Q_1B|$ and $|Q_2A - Q_2B|$?

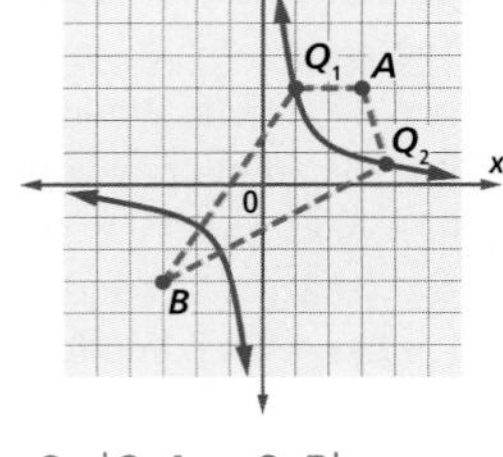

7. The graph of $dw = 240$ is a hyperbola. What are the asymptotes of this hyperbola? $w = 0, d = 0$

8. Consider the hyperbola with equation $xy = k$ where $k > 0$. Name
   a. its foci.
   b. its asymptotes. $x = 0, y = 0$
   c. its focal constant. $2\sqrt{2k}$
   d. its vertices.

9. Graph the hyperbola with equation $xy = 8$. Name its foci, vertices, asymptotes, and focal constant. See margin.

10. a. Find an equation for the hyperbola with foci at (15, 15) and (-15, -15) and focal constant 30. $xy = 112.5$
    b. Verify that the point (5, 22.5) is on the hyperbola in Part a. $5 \cdot 22.5 = 112.5$

6. $|Q_1A - Q_1B| = |Q_2A - Q_2B|$

8a. $(\sqrt{2k}, \sqrt{2k})$, $(-\sqrt{2k}, -\sqrt{2k})$

8d. $(\sqrt{k}, \sqrt{k})$, $(-\sqrt{k}, -\sqrt{k})$

13a. Yes; the asymptotes $x = 0$ and $y = 0$ are perpendicular.

13b. Yes; the asymptotes $y = x$ and $y = -x$ are perpendicular.

13c. No; the asymptotes $y = \frac{3}{2}x$ and $y = -\frac{3}{2}x$ are not perpendicular.

APPLYING THE MATHEMATICS

In 11 and 12, rewrite the equation in the standard form for a quadratic relation, and give the values of A, B, C, D, E, and F.

11. $\frac{x^2}{4} - \frac{y^2}{9} = 1$ 11–12. See margin.

12. $y = 5(x + 2)^2 - 11$

13. A hyperbola with perpendicular asymptotes is called a *rectangular hyperbola*. Explain whether or not each of the following is an equation for a rectangular hyperbola.
    a. $xy = 32$
    b. $x^2 - y^2 = 1$
    c. $\frac{x^2}{4} - \frac{y^2}{9} = 1$

14. A car travels the 2.5 miles around the Indianapolis Motor Speedway in t seconds at an average rate of r mph. Racing fans with stopwatches can calculate how fast the car is traveling if they know the value of the constant rt.
    a. What is that value? (*Hint:* Convert miles per second to miles per hour.) 9000
    b. Graph $rt = k$, where k is your answer to Part a. See margin.
    c. If a driver completes one lap in 45 seconds, how fast is the driver traveling in mph? 200 mph

The Indianapolis Motor Speedway is the largest stadium in the United States. It seats 250,000 people.

15. Sketch a graph of the inequality. See margin.
    a. $xy > 4$
    b. $xy \leq 4$

Accommodating the Learner

Ask students to extend Example 1 by going back through the chapter to identify specific equations for an ellipse, a parabola, and a hyperbola and then showing that each of the specific equations is a quadratic relation.

Answers vary. Sample: For each equation, students should rewrite it in the form $Ax^2 + Bxy + Cy^2 + Dx + Ey + F = 0$; point out that at least one of A, B, and C is not zero; and conclude that the original equation is a quadratic relation.

REVIEW

16. Consider the hyperbola with the equation $\frac{x^2}{64} - \frac{y^2}{121} = 1$.
    a. What are its foci?
    b. Name its vertices.
    c. State equations for its asymptotes. **(Lesson 12-6)**

Multiple Choice In 17–19, choose the set of points that best meets the given condition. **(Lessons 12-6, 12-4, 12-2, 12-1)**

A circle B ellipse C parabola D hyperbola

17. equidistant from a given focus and directrix C
18. satisfy the equation $\left|\sqrt{(x+23)^2 + (y-15)^2} - \sqrt{(x-23)^2 + (y-15)^2}\right| = 7$ D
19. satisfy the equation $9x^2 + 2y^2 = 71$ B
20. **Multiple Choice** Which of the following describes the set of points P whose distances from (7, 2) and (3, 4) add up to 12? **(Lesson 12-4)** C
    A $(x-7)^2 + (y-2)^2 + (x-3)^2 + (y-4)^2 = 12$
    B $(x+7)^2 + (y+2)^2 + (x+3)^2 + (y+4)^2 = 12$
    C $\sqrt{(x-7)^2 + (y-2)^2} + \sqrt{(x-3)^2 + (y-4)^2} = 12$
    D $\sqrt{(x-7)^2 + (y+2)^2} + \sqrt{5(x+3)^2 + (y+4)^2} = 12$
21. To estimate the distance across a river, Sir Vayer marks point A near one bank, sights a tree at point T growing on the opposite bank, and measures off a distance AB of 100 feet along the bank. At B he sights T again. If $m\angle A = 90°$ and $m\angle B = 76°$, how wide is the river? **(Lesson 10-1)** about 401 ft

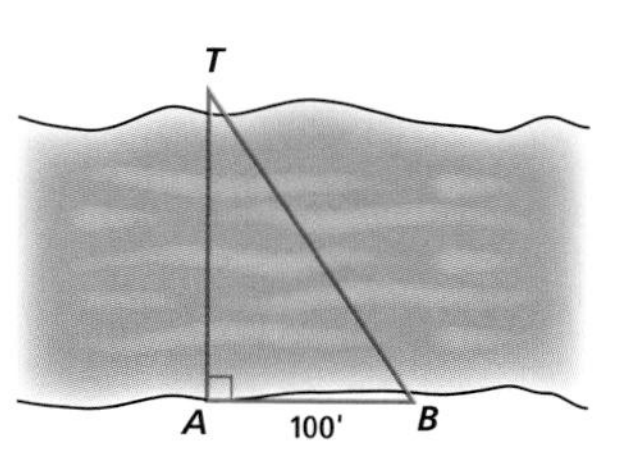

22. a. Evaluate $\log_5 125$ and $\log_{125} 5$ without a calculator.
    b. Evaluate $\log_4 16$ and $\log_{16} 4$ without a calculator.
    c. Generalize Parts a and b. **(Lesson 9-7)**
23. At the zoo, Nigel bought 3 slices of vegetable pizza and 1 small lemonade for \$5.40. Rosa paid \$4.80 for 2 slices of vegetable pizza and 2 small lemonades. What is the cost of a small lemonade? **(Lesson 5-4)** \$0.90

EXPLORATION

24. In the standard form of a quadratic relation equation, there are six coefficients: A, B, C, D, E, and F. Changing these coefficients affects the type and appearance of the conic section. Search the Internet to find interactive websites that allow you to change the appearance of the conics by varying the coefficients. Make at least three conjectures about how certain types of coefficient changes affect the appearance of the graphs.

16a. $(\sqrt{185}, 0)$, $(-\sqrt{185}, 0)$

16b. (8, 0), (-8, 0)

16c. $y = \pm\frac{11}{8}x$

22a. $\log_5 125 = 3$, $\log_{125} 5 = \frac{1}{3}$

22b. $\log_4 16 = 2$, $\log_{16} 4 = \frac{1}{2}$

22c. If a, b, and c are positive real numbers and $\log_a b = c$, then $\log_b a = \frac{1}{c}$.

24. See the Additional Answers section at the back of the book.

QY ANSWERS

1. $A = 0, B = 1, C = 0, D = 0, E = 0, F = -25$
2. The foci are $(\sqrt{320}, \sqrt{320}) = (8\sqrt{5}, 8\sqrt{5})$ and $(-\sqrt{320}, -\sqrt{320}) = (-8\sqrt{5}, -8\sqrt{5})$. The focal constant is $2\sqrt{320} = 16\sqrt{5}$.

12-7

Notes on the Questions

Question 18 If one uses the definition of the various conic sections, this formidable-looking equation is actually not hard to figure out. Once students have determined that the graph of the equation is a hyperbola, you might ask them to indicate the foci and the focal distance of the hyperbola.

4 Wrap-Up

Ongoing Assessment

In the standard form for a quadratic relation $Ax^2 + Bxy + Cy^2 + Dx + Ey + F = 0$, ask students to assume that each coefficient is positive if it is not mentioned. Then ask students what they know about the relation if

a. $B \neq 0$. The relation represents a hyperbola because that is the only relation with a nonzero xy-term.

b. $C < 0$. The relation represents a hyperbola because that is the only one with a negative coefficient for y^2.

c. $B = 0$ and $A = C$. The relation represents a circle because the equation can be written as $(x-h)^2 + (y-k)^2 = r^2$.

Administer Quiz 2 (or a quiz of your own) after students complete this lesson.

Project Update

Project 3, *The General Ellipse and Hyperbola,* on page 856 relates to the content of this lesson.

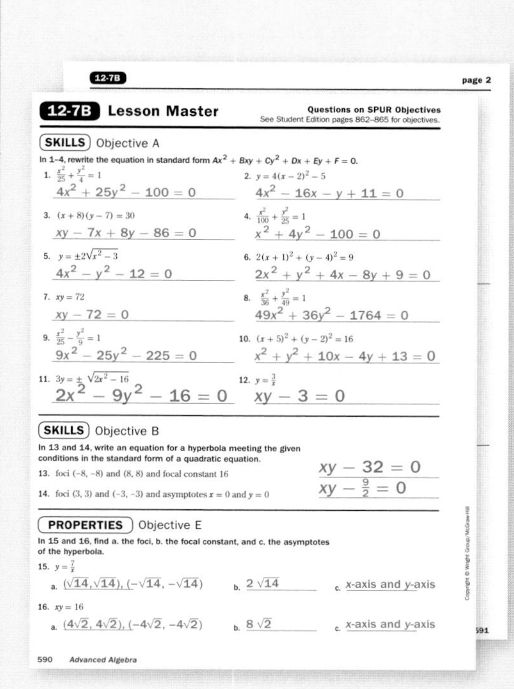

12-7B page 2

12-7B Lesson Master

Questions on SPUR Objectives
See Student Edition pages 862–865 for objectives.

SKILLS Objective A

In 1–4, rewrite the equation in standard form $Ax^2 + Bxy + Cy^2 + Dx + Ey + F = 0$.

1. $\frac{x^2}{25} + \frac{y^2}{4} = 1$ $4x^2 + 25y^2 - 100 = 0$
2. $y = 4(x-2)^2 - 5$ $4x^2 - 16x - y + 11 = 0$
3. $(x+8)(y-7) = 30$ $xy - 7x + 8y - 86 = 0$
4. $\frac{x^2}{100} + \frac{y^2}{25} = 1$ $x^2 + 4y^2 - 100 = 0$
5. $y = \pm 2\sqrt{x^2 - 3}$ $4x^2 - y^2 - 12 = 0$
6. $2(x+1)^2 + (y-4)^2 = 9$ $2x^2 + y^2 + 4x - 8y + 9 = 0$
7. $xy = 72$ $xy - 72 = 0$
8. $\frac{x^2}{36} + \frac{y^2}{49} = 1$ $49x^2 + 36y^2 - 1764 = 0$
9. $\frac{x^2}{25} - \frac{y^2}{9} = 1$ $9x^2 - 25y^2 - 225 = 0$
10. $(x+5)^2 + (y-2)^2 = 16$ $x^2 + y^2 + 10x - 4y + 13 = 0$
11. $3y = \pm\sqrt{2x^2 - 16}$ $2x^2 - 9y^2 - 16 = 0$
12. $y = \frac{3}{x}$ $xy - 3 = 0$

SKILLS Objective B

In 13 and 14, write an equation for a hyperbola meeting the given conditions in the standard form of a quadratic equation.

13. foci (−8, −8) and (8, 8) and focal constant 16 $xy - 32 = 0$
14. foci (3, 3) and (−3, −3) and asymptotes $x = 0$ and $y = 0$ $xy - \frac{9}{2} = 0$

PROPERTIES Objective E

In 15 and 16, find a. the foci, b. the focal constant, and c. the asymptotes of the hyperbola.

15. $y = \frac{7}{x}$
    a. $(\sqrt{14}, \sqrt{14})$, $(-\sqrt{14}, -\sqrt{14})$ b. $2\sqrt{14}$ c. x-axis and y-axis
16. $xy = 16$
    a. $(4\sqrt{2}, 4\sqrt{2})$, $(-4\sqrt{2}, -4\sqrt{2})$ b. $8\sqrt{2}$ c. x-axis and y-axis

590 *Advanced Algebra* 591

Copyright © Wright Group/McGraw-Hill

Additional Answers

15a.

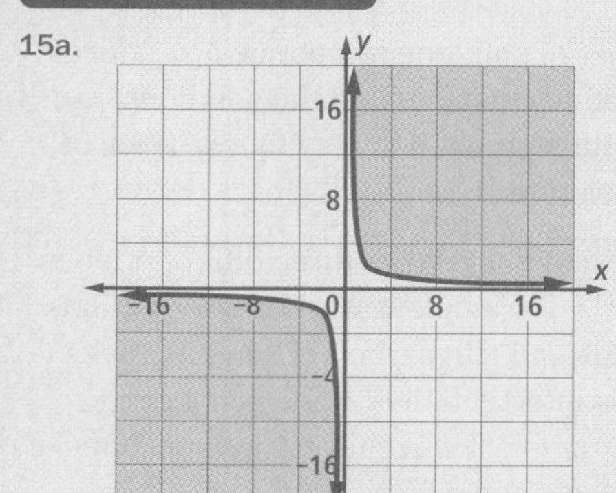

15b.

Lesson 12-8

GOAL

Consider and explore systems of two equations in which one equation is linear and the other is quadratic.

SPUR Objectives

D Solve systems of one linear and one quadratic equation with and without technology.

H Use systems with quadratic equations to solve real-world problems.

K Interpret representations of quadratic-linear systems.

Materials/Resources

- Lesson Masters 12-8A and 12-8B
- Resource Masters 1 and 239–241

HOMEWORK

Suggestions for Assignment

- Questions 1–24
- Question 25 (extra credit)
- Reading Lesson 12-9
- Covering the Ideas 12-9

Local Standards

1 Warm-Up

What are at least two ways to answer the following question? A room in a dance hall is to be a square with area 2500 square feet. A stage needs to be added at one end for musicians, which lengthens the room into a rectangle. If the stage is 15 feet deep and the total area of the room cannot be greater than 2500 square feet, how large (rounded to the nearest inch) can the original square be?

Lesson 12-8 Quadratic-Linear Systems

Vocabulary

quadratic system

quadratic-linear system

BIG IDEA Solutions to systems with one quadratic and one linear equation in x and y can be found by graphing, substitution, using linear combinations, or using a CAS.

A **quadratic system** is a system that involves polynomial sentences of degrees 1 and 2, at least one of which is a quadratic sentence. One way to solve a quadratic system is to examine the points of intersection of the graphs of the equations.

Mental Math

Give all points of intersection of the graph of $y = x^2$ and the graph of the given equation.

a. $y = 0$ (0, 0)

b. $y = 4$ (-2, 4) and (2, 4)

c. $y = x$ (0, 0) and (1, 1)

d. $y = -1.5$ no intersections

Examining Quadratic-Linear Systems Geometrically

A quadratic system with at least one linear sentence is called a **quadratic-linear system**. No new properties are needed to solve quadratic-linear systems. Geometrically, the task is to find the intersection of a conic section and a line. For example, in a system of a parabola and a line, there are three possibilities.

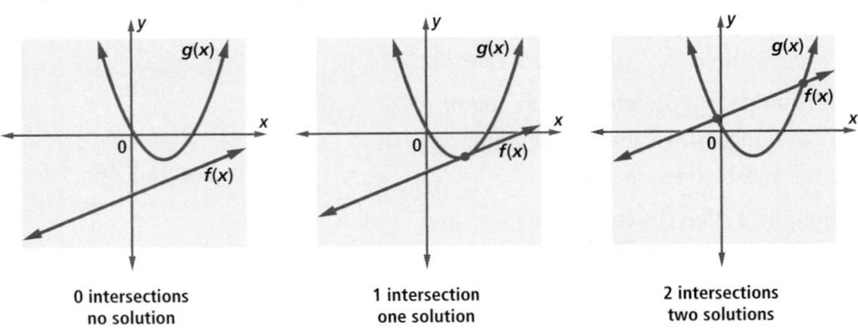

0 intersections no solution | 1 intersection one solution | 2 intersections two solutions

The following Activity will help you determine the possible numbers of intersection points of a line and the other quadratic relations that you have studied.

Background

The content here is standard, and the lesson provides an opportunity to increase student knowledge of conic sections and solving systems. Students should be able to solve simple systems by hand and any system with technology. They should be able to check solutions by graphing and by substitution.

Graphing the equations in a system can usually help a solver quickly determine the number of solutions; algebraic procedures can then be used to find the solutions. Without a graph, it is easy to lose track of one or more solutions.

The examples involve three different types of conics. Example 1 asks for intersections of a line and a hyperbola, Example 2 asks for the intersection of a line and a circle, and Example 3 searches for intersections of a parabola and a line.

Activity

Step 1 Sketch a circle, an ellipse, and a hyperbola on three separate sets of axes. Steps 1–3. See margin.

Step 2 On the graph of the circle, sketch several lines that intersect the circle in various ways. In how many points can a circle and a line intersect?

Step 3 Repeat Step 2 for the ellipse and the hyperbola.

Step 4 Fill in a table like the one at the right with the number of intersections between a line and the indicated quadratic relation. The Line-Parabola cell has been filled in for you.

Quadratic Relation	Number of Intersections with Line
Parabola	0, 1, or 2
Circle	? 0, 1, or 2
Ellipse	? 0, 1, or 2
Hyperbola	? 0, 1, or 2

As you saw in the Activity, a quadratic-linear system may have 0, 1, or 2 solutions. This is because a quadratic equation may have 0, 1, or 2 solutions.

Solving Quadratic-Linear Systems Algebraically

One way to solve a quadratic-linear system is to solve the linear equation for one variable and substitute the resulting expression into the quadratic equation.

Example 1

Find exact solutions to the system $\begin{cases} y + 4x = 10 \\ xy = 4 \end{cases}$.

Solution 1 Geometrically, the solution to this system is the intersection of a line and a hyperbola.

Solve the first sentence for y.

$$y = 10 - 4x$$

Substitute the expression $10 - 4x$ for y in the second sentence.

$$x(10 - 4x) = 4$$

This is a quadratic equation that you can solve by the Quadratic Formula or by factoring. To use the Quadratic Formula, expand the left side and rearrange the equation so one side is zero.

$$10x - 4x^2 = 4$$

$$4x^2 - 10x + 4 = 0$$

$$x = \frac{(-10) \pm \sqrt{100 - 4 \cdot 4 \cdot 4}}{8} = \frac{10 \pm \sqrt{36}}{8}$$

$$x = \frac{10 - 6}{8} \quad \text{or} \quad x = \frac{10 + 6}{8}$$

$$x = \frac{1}{2} \quad \text{or} \quad x = 2$$

(continued on next page)

Answers vary. Sample: (1) Let s be a side of the square. Then solve $s(s + 15) \le 2500$ by graphing $y = s^2 + 15s$ and $y = 2500$. The graphs intersect when $s \approx 43.06$, so the side can be as long as 43'0". (2) Solve $s(s + 15) \le 2500$ by using the Quadratic Formula on the equation $s(s + 15) = 2500$. (3) Solve the system $sL = 2500$ and $L = s + 15$.

(*Note:* Method 3 is the subject of this lesson.)

2 Teaching

Notes on the Lesson

This lesson can be covered rather easily in two ways—either by discussing Examples 1–3 in some detail or by discussing the questions in order. Emphasize that there are no new techniques in this lesson. Every method used here was previously presented in the study of linear systems.

This lesson provides a good illustration of how technology, graphical solutions, and algebraic manipulation can support each other. For instance, in some cases we first estimate solutions graphically and then confirm them algebraically or get exact values. In others, we find an exact solution first and then check it graphically.

For many students, solving a quadratic-quadratic system takes time. Ten systems are given in the questions to solve exactly; that is quite enough for most students. You may wish to use one or two of these for class discussion rather than assigning all of them as homework.

Additional Answers can be found in the back of the book.

Additional Example

Example 1 Find exact solutions to the system $\begin{cases} xy = 6 \\ 2x + y = 8 \end{cases}$. (1, 6) and (3, 2)

Example 2 Solving a system can show you that a line is tangent to a curve. Thus, this system is of a type often seen in calculus courses. Be sure to discuss Solution 2, for it may surprise many students that they can use theorems about circles from geometry in their study of algebra.

Example 3 An algebraic statement can signal that there are no points of intersection.

ENGLISH LEARNERS

Vocabulary Development

In Example 2, students have to know what it means for a line to be tangent to a circle. Students should understand that a line is tangent to a circle if and only if two conditions are met: (1) the line and the circle intersect (that is, there is an ordered pair that satisfies both equations), and (2) the line is perpendicular to a radius at that point (that is, if you multiply the slope of the line times the slope of the radius through the ordered pair from condition (1), the product that results is -1).

Additional Example

Example 2 In this graph of the equations $x^2 + y^2 = 25$ and $y = \frac{4}{3}x + \frac{25}{3}$, it appears that there is only one point of intersection, (-4, 3). Is this so? Justify your answer.

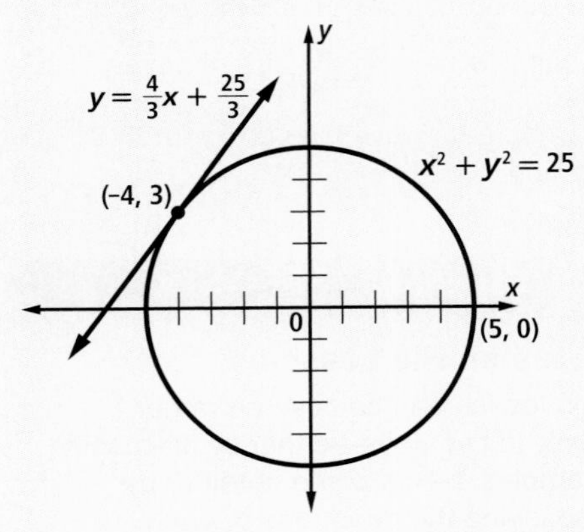

First check that the graphs intersect at (-4, 3). $(-4)^2 + 3^2 = 16 + 9 = 25$ and $\frac{4}{3}(-4) + \frac{25}{3} = \frac{-16}{3} + \frac{25}{3} = \frac{9}{3} = 3$, so the equations represent graphs that intersect at (-4, 3). Using a CAS to solve the system $\begin{cases} x^2 + y^2 = 25 \\ y = \frac{4}{3}x + \frac{25}{3} \end{cases}$, the only solution is $x = -4$, $y = 3$. So (-4, 3) is the only point of intersection.

Note-Taking Tips

When students make a copy of the table for the Activity, you may want to point out that Lesson 12-9 extends that table, adding rows for quadratic-quadratic systems. After Lesson 12-9, encourage students to combine both tables into a single 5-column, 6-row table.

Now substitute each value into $y = 10 - 4x$ to find y.

When $x = \frac{1}{2}$, $y = 10 - 4\left(\frac{1}{2}\right) = 8$. So, one solution is $\left(\frac{1}{2}, 8\right)$.

When $x = 2$, $y = 10 - 4(2) = 2$. The other solution is (2, 2).

So, the solutions are $\left(\frac{1}{2}, 8\right)$ and (2, 2).

Check Solve both equations for y.

$$y = 10 - 4x \quad \text{and} \quad y = \frac{4}{x}$$

Now graph the system with a graphing utility. Zoom in to estimate the coordinates of the intersection points.

The curves intersect at (0.5, 8) and (2, 2). It checks.

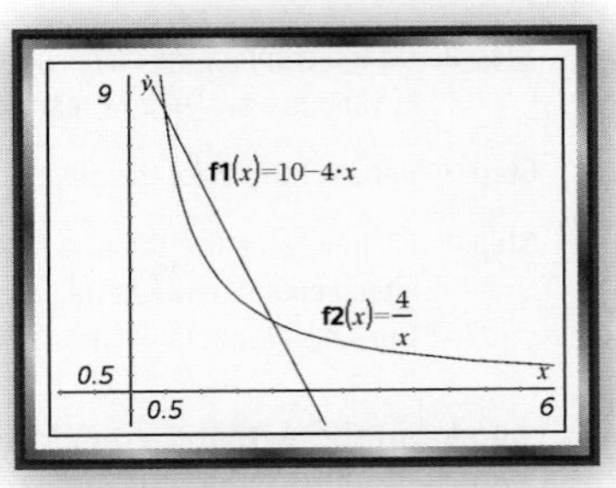

You could also solve Example 1 by using a graphing utility to find the exact coordinates of the intersection points. (See Question 2.)

Example 2 illustrates two solution methods that are quite different from each other. The first solution is algebraic and uses a CAS. The second solution draws on what you have already learned about circles in your study of geometry.

Example 2

At the right are graphs of the equations $x^2 + y^2 = 100$ and $y = -\frac{3}{4}x + \frac{25}{2}$. It appears that they intersect in only one point, (6, 8). (That is, the line is tangent to the circle.) Is this so? Justify your answer.

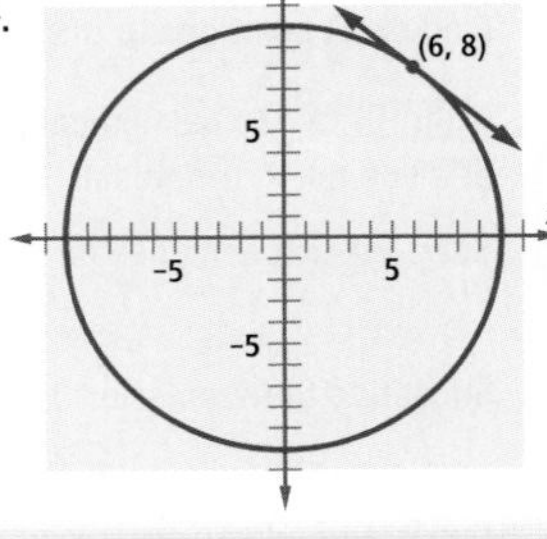

Solution 1 First, check that the graphs intersect at (6, 8).

Does $6^2 + 8^2 = 100$? Yes.

Does $8 = -\frac{3}{4}(6) + \frac{25}{2}$? Yes, because $-\frac{3}{4}(6) + \frac{25}{2} = -\frac{9}{2} + \frac{25}{2} = \frac{16}{2} = 8$.

To find all solutions, solve the system $\begin{cases} x^2 + y^2 = 100 \\ y = -\frac{3}{4}x + \frac{25}{2} \end{cases}$.

Use the solve command on a CAS.

The only solution is $x = 6$ and $y = 8$. So, the only point of intersection is (6, 8).

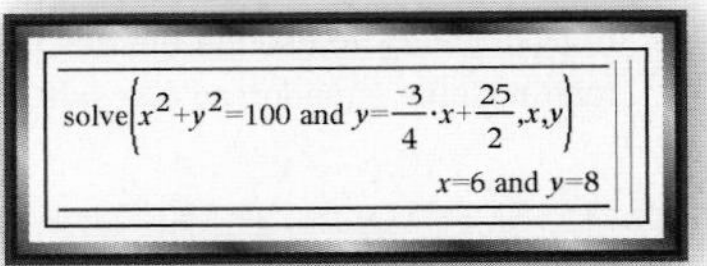

Solution 2 You may remember from your study of geometry that a tangent to a circle is the line perpendicular to the radius at the point of intersection. In this case, a radius from (0, 0) to (6, 8) has slope $\frac{4}{3}$. The line $y = -\frac{3}{4}x + \frac{25}{2}$ has slope $-\frac{3}{4}$. Since the product of the slopes is -1, this line is perpendicular to the radius at (6, 8) and is a tangent.

Accommodating the Learner

Show students a diagram of a square and a circle, each of which has center (0, 0), where one of the vertices of the square is (5, 5) and a point on the circle is (6, 0). Ask: How many points of intersection are there for the square and the circle? Find the exact coordinates of each point.

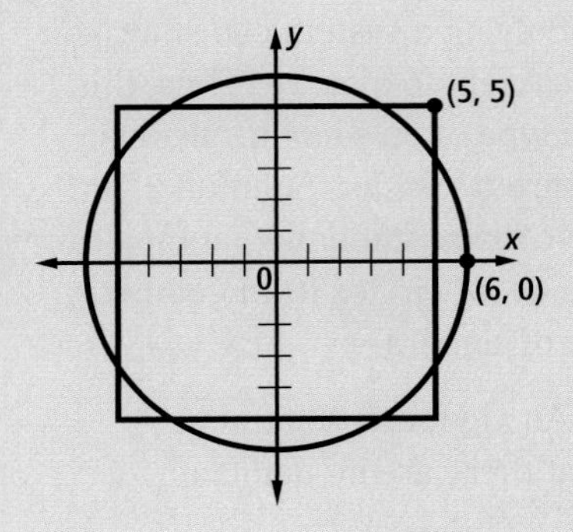

Inconsistent Quadratic Systems

Like linear systems, quadratic systems can be inconsistent. That is, there can be no solution. One signal for inconsistency is that the solutions to the quadratic system are not real. This means that the graphs of the equations in the system do not intersect.

GUIDED

Example 3

Find the points of intersection of the line $y = x$ and the parabola $y = x^2 + 2$.

Solution 1 Graph the line and parabola, as shown at the right. There are __?__ points of intersection. 0

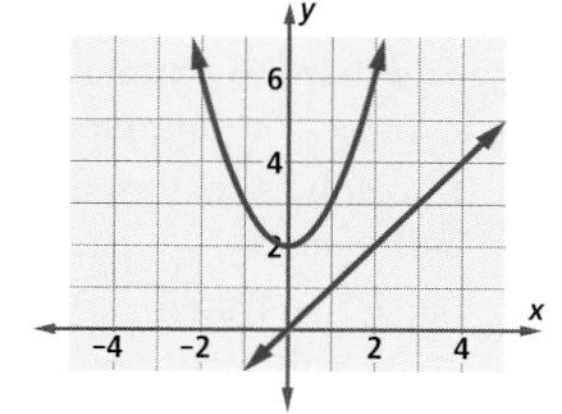

Solution 2 Solve the system 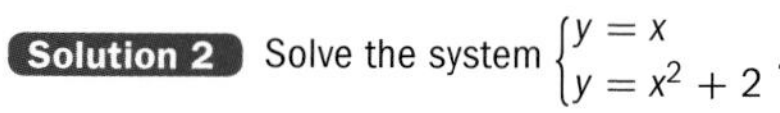 $\begin{cases} y = x \\ y = x^2 + 2 \end{cases}$.

Substitute x for y in the second sentence.

$$\underline{\ ?\ } = x^2 + 2 \quad x$$

Put this equation in standard form so you can use the Quadratic Formula.

$$\underline{\ ?\ } - \underline{\ ?\ } + \underline{\ ?\ } = 0 \quad x^2;\ x;\ 2$$

From that formula, $x = \frac{? \pm \sqrt{?}}{?}$. 1; -7; 2

Both solutions to this equation are nonreal complex numbers. So there are __?__ points of intersection. 0

Questions

COVERING THE IDEAS

1. How many solutions can a system of one linear and one quadratic equation have? 0, 1, or 2
2. Refer to Example 1. Check the solutions by graphing the system on a graphing utility and finding the exact coordinates of the points of intersection. See the Additional Answers section at the back of the book.
3. A graph of the system $\begin{cases} y = 2x \\ 4x^2 + 2y^2 = 48 \end{cases}$ is shown at the right.
   a. How many solutions are there? 2
   b. Use the graph to approximate the solutions. (-2, -4), (2, 4)
   c. Check your answers in Part b.
   $4 = 2 \cdot 2$; $-4 = 2 \cdot -2$; $4(2)^2 + 2(4)^2 = 16 + 32 = 48$; $4(-2)^2 + 2(-4)^2 = 16 + 32 = 48$

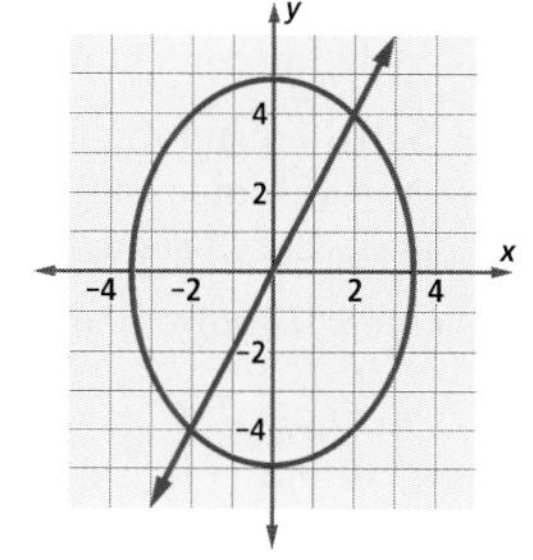

12-8

Additional Example

Example 3 Find the points of intersection of the line $y = \frac{x}{2} + 1$ and the parabola $y = -x^2$.

Solution Solve the system $\begin{cases} y = \frac{x}{2} + 1 \\ y = -x^2 \end{cases}$. Substitute __?__ for y in the second equation:

__?__ $= -x^2$. $\frac{x}{2} + 1$; $\frac{x}{2} + 1$

Put this equation in standard form:

__?__ $= 0$. $2x^2 + x + 2$ From the Quadratic Formula, $x =$ __?__ or __?__. $\frac{-1 \pm \sqrt{1^2 - 4(2)(2)}}{2(2)}$; $\frac{-1 \pm \sqrt{-15}}{4}$ Both solutions are nonreal complex numbers, so there are __?__ points of intersection. 0

3 Assignment

Recommended Assignment

- Questions 1–24
- Question 25 (extra credit)
- Reading Lesson 12-9
- Covering the Ideas 12-9

Notes on the Questions

Additional Answers can be found in the back of the book.

12-8A Lesson Master

Questions on SPUR Objectives
See Student Edition pages 862–865 for objectives.

SKILLS Objective D

1. Solve by hand for all real solutions: $\begin{cases} y = 2x - 1 \\ y = x^2 - 4 \end{cases}$ (3, 5), (-1, -3)

In 2 and 3, a. estimate solutions to the system by graphing on a graphing utility, and b. find the exact solutions. Answers vary for Part a. Samples are given.

2. $\begin{cases} xy = -12 \\ y = -\frac{5}{2}x + 3 \end{cases}$
   a. (-1.7, 7.2), (2.9, -4.2)
   b. $\left(\frac{3 - \sqrt{129}}{5}, \frac{3 + \sqrt{129}}{2}\right), \left(\frac{3 + \sqrt{129}}{5}, \frac{3 - \sqrt{129}}{2}\right)$
3. $\begin{cases} y = 3x - 8 \\ 4x^2 + y^2 = 64 \end{cases}$
   a. (0, -8), (3.7, 3.1)
   b. $(0, -8), \left(\frac{48}{13}, \frac{40}{13}\right)$

USES Objective H

4. A day-care center is fencing off a rectangular area for a playground. They can afford 280 feet of fencing. State licensing requires that the playground be at least 4800 square feet.
   a. Let x be the width of the playground and y be the length. Write an equation stating that the perimeter is 280 feet. $2x + 2y = 280$
   b. Write an equation stating that the area is 4800 ft². $xy = 4800$
   c. Use your answers to Parts a and b to find the dimensions. 60 ft by 80 ft

REPRESENTATIONS Objective K

5. Find two real numbers whose sum is 11 and whose product is 20 or explain why it is impossible. $\frac{11 + \sqrt{41}}{2}$ and $\frac{11 - \sqrt{41}}{2}$
6. On the graph at the right, draw three lines that intersect the hyperbola $xy = 16$ in zero, one, and two points respectively. Graphs vary. Samples are given at the right.
7. Give equations for your lines. Answers vary. Samples: zero intersections: $y = -x$; one intersection: $y = 10$; two intersections: $y = 2x$

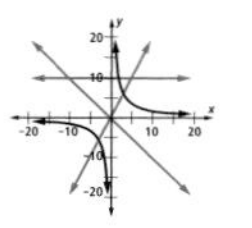

592 *Advanced Algebra*

There are 8 points of intersection. Answers vary. Sample: In the first quadrant, the points of intersection are (5, y) and (x, 5). Using the equation $x^2 + y^2 = 36$, then (5, y) is $(5, \sqrt{11})$ and (x, 5) is $(\sqrt{11}, 5)$. By symmetry, the other 6 points (continuing counterclockwise) are $(-\sqrt{11}, 5)$, $(-5, \sqrt{11})$, $(-5, -\sqrt{11})$, $(-\sqrt{11}, -5)$, $(\sqrt{11}, -5)$, and $(5, -\sqrt{11})$.

Accommodating the Learner

Ask students to sketch two concentric circles, each with center (0, 0) and radii 5 and 8. Ask them to sketch the line that is tangent to the smaller circle at the point (-3, 4) and to find the points of intersection of that line and the larger circle. Answers vary. Sample: A line tangent to the smaller circle at (-3, 4) has equation $y = \frac{3}{4}x + \frac{25}{4}$, so find the solutions to the system $\begin{cases} x^2 + y^2 = 64 \\ y = \frac{3}{4}x + \frac{25}{4} \end{cases}$, which are approximately (-7.996, 0.253) and (1.996, 7.747).

Notes on the Questions

Question 7 Comparing this question with Example 3, students should quickly realize that there are no points of intersection. Stress how algebra (no real-number solution to the system) and geometry (no intersections) support each other.

Questions 12 and 13 Both questions reflect the same idea: Given the sum and product of two numbers, find the numbers. It is not a coincidence that perimeter and area (in Question 12) relate to sum and product, for the origin of these arithmetic operations is as much from geometric applications as from counting applications.

Questions 14 and 15 You might want to have students work in groups of three or four for these questions. After students have completed their work, have a student in each group explain the solutions to others.

Additional Answers

12a.

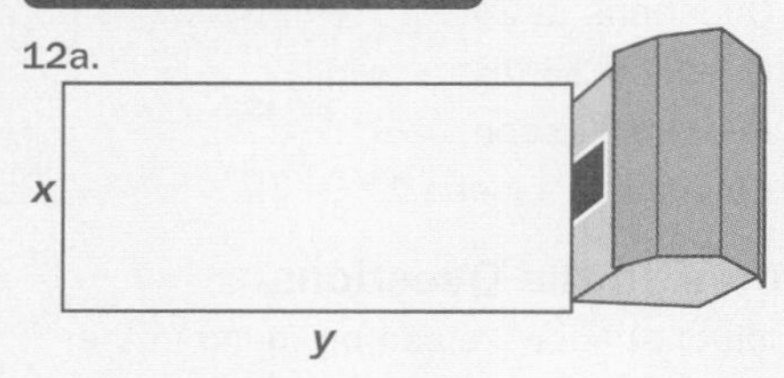

12b. $\begin{cases} xy = 1700 \\ x + 2y = 200 \end{cases}$

12c. From the graph, the dimensions look to be about 180 by 10 or 20 by 90.

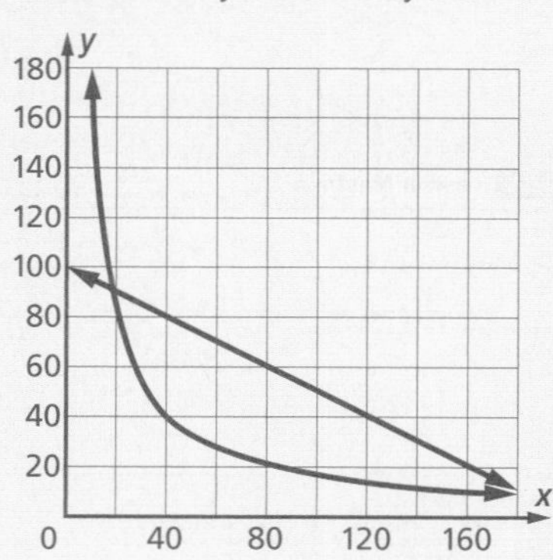

12d. (18.8, 90.6) or (181.2, 9.4); Fencing in a section with dimensions 18.8 m × 90.6 m or 181.2 m × 9.4 m satisfies Phillip's wishes. Note that in both cases, the first dimension is the side that includes the wall of the barn. Since his barn is probably not 180 m long, so he should make the enclosure 18.8 m × 90.6 m.

In 4 and 5, a system is given. Estimate the solutions by graphing. Then find exact solutions by substitution.

4. $\begin{cases} mn = 12 \\ n = -\frac{2}{3}m + 6 \end{cases}$ 4–5. See the Additional Answers section at the back of the book.

5. $\begin{cases} y = 2x^2 + 5x - 1 \\ y = x + 5 \end{cases}$

In 6 and 7, find all intersection points of the line and the parabola.

6. $y = x + 4$ and $y = x^2$

7. $y = 2x^2 - 4$ and $y = x - 3$

8. a. What term is used to describe a system that has no solutions?
   b. Give equations for such a system involving an ellipse and a line.

6. $\left(\frac{1}{2} + \frac{\sqrt{17}}{2}, \frac{9}{2} + \frac{\sqrt{17}}{2}\right)$, $\left(\frac{1}{2} - \frac{\sqrt{17}}{2}, \frac{9}{2} - \frac{\sqrt{17}}{2}\right)$

7. (1, -2), $\left(-\frac{1}{2}, -\frac{7}{2}\right)$

8a. inconsistent

8b. Answers vary. Sample: $y = 2x - 20$, $\frac{x^2}{12} + \frac{y^2}{24} = 1$

In 9 and 10, consider the figure at the right, which suggests that the parabola $y = x^2 + 7x - 10$ and the line $y = -5x - 46$ intersect at or near the point (-6, -16).

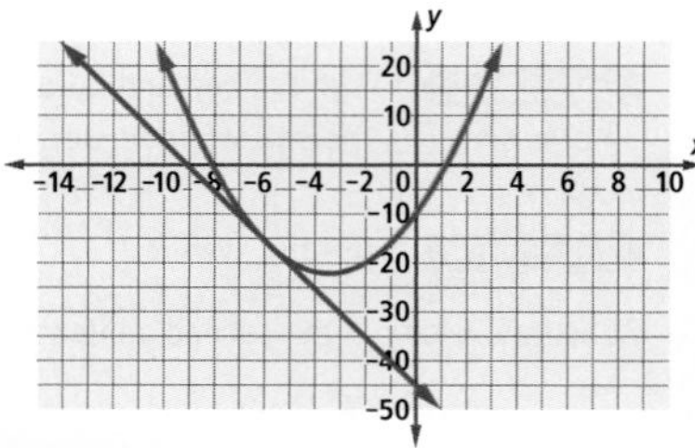

9. Check by substitution that this point is on both curves.

10. Solve the system algebraically to verify that this is the only solution.

APPLYING THE MATHEMATICS

9. $-16 = (-6)^2 + 7 \cdot -6 - 10$; $-16 = -5(-6) - 46$

11. Explain why a quadratic-linear system cannot have an infinite number of solutions. 11. See the Additional Answers section at the back of the book.

12. Phillip has 200 meters of fencing material. Next to his barn, he wants to fence in a rectangular region with area 1700 square meters, using a wall of the barn as one of the sides of the enclosure. See margin.
    a. Let x be the width of the region and y be its length. Draw a picture of the situation.
    b. Assuming Phillip uses all 200 meters of fencing, write a system of equations that can be solved to find x and y.
    c. Graph your system to estimate the dimensions of this region.
    d. Solve your system from Part b and explain your answer in the context of the problem.

10. Solving $-5x - 46 = x^2 + 7x - 10$ gives $x = -6$, so (-6, -16) is the only solution.

13. Solve a quadratic-linear system and use the solution to explain why it is impossible to have two real numbers whose sum is 8 and whose product is 24. 13–15. See the Additional Answers section at the back of the book.

In 14 and 15, solve and check.

14. $\begin{cases} 4r^2 + s^2 = 9 \\ 3r + s = 1 \end{cases}$

15. $\begin{cases} \frac{x^2}{16} + \frac{y^2}{36} = 1 \\ y = \frac{1}{2}x \end{cases}$

Extension

Show students this diagram of two noncongruent circles, externally tangent at point N, with radii a and b.

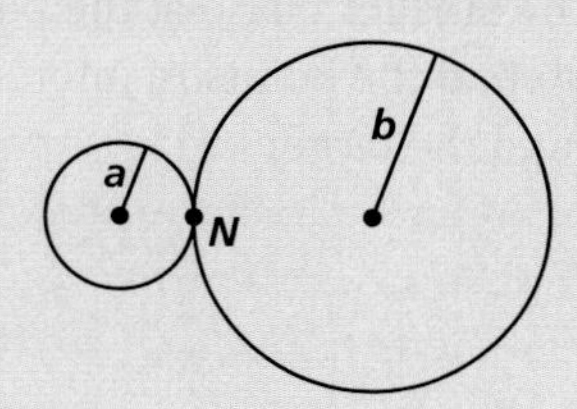

Ask students to copy the diagram, adding to it the two common tangents that do not contain point N, and using M to label the intersection of those two common tangents. Then ask students to express MN in terms of a and b.

REVIEW

16. Consider the hyperbola with equation $xy = k$, where $k > 0$. (Lesson 12-7)
    a. Give the coordinates of its foci. $(\sqrt{2k}, \sqrt{2k}), (-\sqrt{2k}, -\sqrt{2k})$
    b. Identify its asymptotes. $x = 0, y = 0$
    c. Determine the focal constant. $2\sqrt{2k}$

17. Find an equation for the hyperbola with foci at (10, 10) and (-10, -10) and focal constant 20. (Lesson 12-7) $y = \frac{50}{x}$

18. Give an equation for a hyperbola that
    a. is the graph of a function.
    b. is not the graph of a function. (Lessons 12-7, 12-6, 1-4)

18a. Answers vary. Sample: $y = \frac{20}{x}$
18b. Answers vary. Sample: $x^2 - y^2 = 1$

In 19–21, a polynomial is given.
a. Tell whether the polynomial is a binomial square, a difference of squares, or a sum of squares.
b. Factor, if possible, over the integers. (Lesson 11-3)

19. $r^{20} - t^2$ a. difference of squares b. $(r^{10} + t)(r^{10} - t)$
20. $49a^2 - 42ab + 9b^2$ a. binomial square b. $(7a - 3b)^2$
21. $x^2 + 2500$ a. sum of squares b. not possible

In 22 and 23, simplify without a calculator. (Lessons 8-7, 7-8, 6-9)

22. $(2 - \sqrt{-9})(2 + \sqrt{-9})$ 13
23. $\sqrt{-64} + \sqrt[3]{-64} + 64^{-\frac{1}{6}}$ $-\frac{7}{2} + 8i$

24. Suppose a car rental company charges a flat rate of \$25 plus 45 cents for each mile or part of a mile driven. (Lesson 3-9)
    a. Write an equation relating the total charge c to the number m of miles driven. $c = 25 + 0.45\lceil m \rceil$
    b. How much would you pay if you drove 36.3 miles in a rental car? \$41.65
    c. The company also allows you to pay a flat rate of \$65 a day for an unlimited number of miles. How many miles would you have to drive in a day to make this the better deal? more than 88 mi

The first U.S. airport location of a car rental company opened at Chicago's Midway Airport in 1932.

EXPLORATION

25. Find equations for a noncircular ellipse and an oblique (slanted) line that have exactly one point of intersection.

25. Answers vary. Sample: $x^2 + \frac{y^2}{4} = 1$, $y = -x + \sqrt{5}$

Notes on the Questions

Question 25 An elegant solution is to apply a scale change that is not a size change to the circle and line of Example 2.

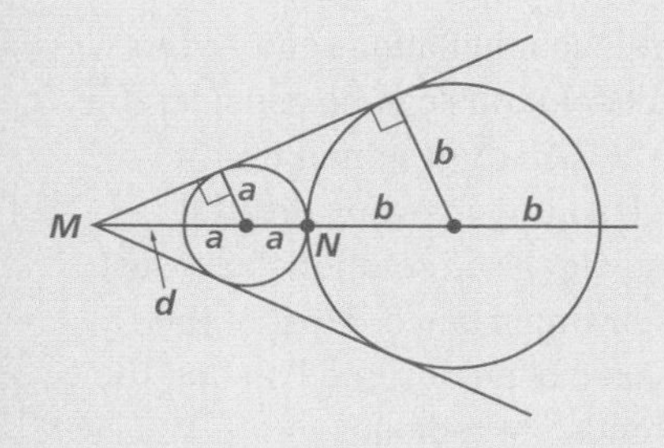

Answers vary. Sample: With d labeled as in the diagram at the left, $MN = d + 2a$. Using similar triangles, $\frac{a}{d + a} = \frac{b}{d + 2a + b}$, so $a(d + 2a + b) = b(d + a)$. Thus $ad + 2a^2 + ab = bd + ba$, $bd - ad = 2a^2$, $d(b - a) = 2a^2$, so $d = \frac{2a^2}{b - a}$. Therefore, $MN = \frac{2a^2}{b - a} + 2a = \frac{2ab}{b - a}$.

4 Wrap-Up

Ongoing Assessment

With students working in small groups, ask them to show two ways that a line can have two points of intersection with a parabola: one with the two points of intersection on the same side of the y-axis and one with the two points of intersection on opposite sides of the y-axis. Then ask students to repeat the exercise for a line and a hyperbola. Answers vary. Sample:

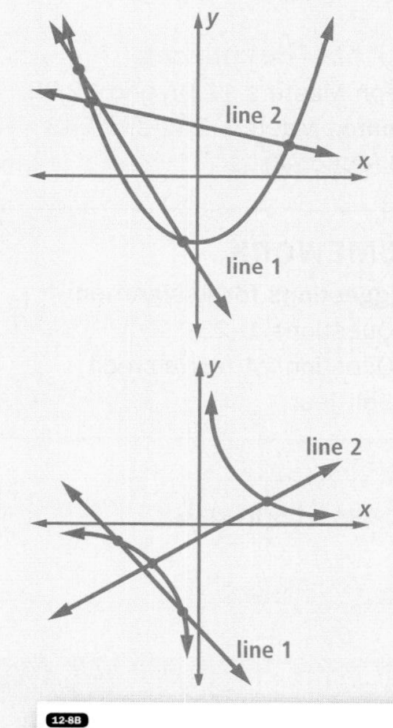

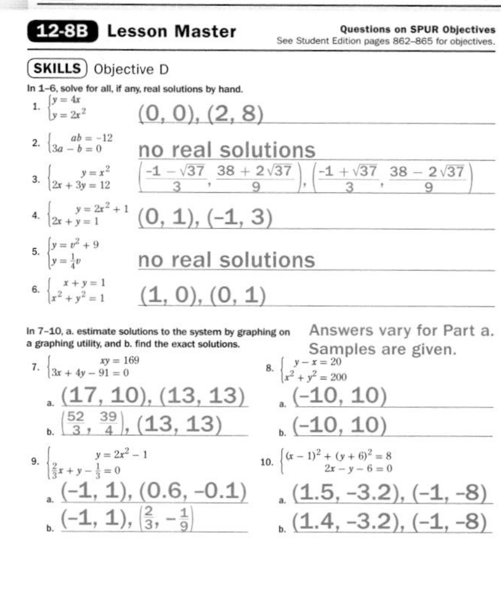

12-8B page 2

12-8B Lesson Master

Questions on SPUR Objectives
See Student Edition pages 862–865 for objectives.

SKILLS Objective D

In 1–6, solve for all, if any, real solutions by hand.

1. $\begin{cases} y = 4x \\ y = 2x^2 \end{cases}$ (0, 0), (2, 8)
2. $\begin{cases} ab = -12 \\ 3a - b = 0 \end{cases}$ no real solutions
3. $\begin{cases} y = x^2 \\ 2x + 3y = 12 \end{cases}$ $\left(\frac{-1 - \sqrt{37}}{3}, \frac{38 + 2\sqrt{37}}{9}\right), \left(\frac{-1 + \sqrt{37}}{3}, \frac{38 - 2\sqrt{37}}{9}\right)$
4. $\begin{cases} y = 2x^2 + 1 \\ 2x + y = 1 \end{cases}$ (0, 1), (–1, 3)
5. $\begin{cases} y = v^2 + 9 \\ y = \frac{1}{4}v \end{cases}$ no real solutions
6. $\begin{cases} x + y = 1 \\ x^2 + y^2 = 1 \end{cases}$ (1, 0), (0, 1)

In 7–10, a. estimate solutions to the system by graphing on a graphing utility, and b. find the exact solutions.

Answers vary for Part a. Samples are given.

7. $\begin{cases} xy = 169 \\ 3x + 4y - 91 = 0 \end{cases}$
   a. (17, 10), (13, 13)
   b. $\left(\frac{52}{3}, \frac{39}{4}\right)$, (13, 13)
8. $\begin{cases} y - x = 20 \\ x^2 + y^2 = 200 \end{cases}$
   a. (–10, 10)
   b. (–10, 10)
9. $\begin{cases} y = 2x^2 - 1 \\ \frac{2}{3}x + y - \frac{1}{3} = 0 \end{cases}$
   a. (–1, 1), (0.6, –0.1)
   b. (–1, 1), $\left(\frac{2}{3}, -\frac{1}{9}\right)$
10. $\begin{cases} (x - 1)^2 + (y + 6)^2 = 8 \\ 2x - y - 6 = 0 \end{cases}$
   a. (1.5, –3.2), (–1, –8)
   b. (1.4, –3.2), (–1, –8)

Advanced Algebra 593

Lesson 12-9

GOAL

Consider graphing, substitution, and linear combination techniques to solve systems of two quadratic equations in two variables.

SPUR Objectives

D Solve systems of two quadratic equations with and without technology.

H Use systems with quadratic equations to solve real-world problems.

K Interpret representations of quadratic-quadratic systems.

Materials/Resources

- Lesson Masters 12-9A and 12-9B
- Resource Masters 242 and 243
- DGS (optional)

HOMEWORK

Suggestions for Assignment

- Questions 1–23
- Question 24 (extra credit)
- Self-Test

Local Standards

1 Warm-Up

1. Solve $4a + 3b = 37$ and $3a - b = 5$. (4, 7) (*Note:* This system is the same as that found in Example 2, with $a = x^2$ and $b = y^2$.)
2. How many pairs of numbers are there so that the sum of the numbers is 11 and the sum of the squares of the numbers is 100? By sketching the graphs of $x + y = 11$ and $x^2 + y^2 = 100$, one sees that the line and circle intersect in two points, but these points are reflection images of each other over the line $y = x$; changing the order of the points does not change the solution, so there is only one solution.

Lesson 12-9 Quadratic-Quadratic Systems

Vocabulary

quadratic-quadratic system

BIG IDEA Solutions to systems with two quadratic equations in x and y can be found by graphing, using linear combinations, by substitution, or using technology.

Recall from Lesson 12-2 that an earthquake sends out seismic waves from its epicenter. A single monitoring station can determine that the epicenter lies on a particular circle with the station as its center, but it takes multiple stations combining their information to locate the epicenter.

Mental Math

Give an inequality that represents the situation.

a. The price n of a gallon of gasoline now is more than 4 times the price t of a gallon 10 years ago. $n > 4t$

b. The life ℓ of a battery is guaranteed to be at least 30 hours. $\ell \geq 30$

c. The average test score s was 86.4 with a 0.5-point margin of error.

d. You can order from the children's menu if your age a is under 7 years. $a < 7$

c. $85.9 \leq s \leq 86.9$, or $|86.4 - s| \leq 0.5$

Example 1

An earthquake monitoring station *A* determines that the center of a quake is 100 km away. A second station *B* 50 km west and 30 km south of the first finds that it is 70 km from the quake's center. Find all possible locations of the epicenter in relation to station *A*.

Solution Let Station A be located at (0, 0). Then Station B is at (–50, –30). Draw the circles with radii 100 and 70. The graph shows two intersections of the circles. These are the possible locations of the epicenter.

Because the epicenter is 100 km from A, the larger circle has equation $x^2 + y^2 = 10{,}000$. Because the epicenter is 70 km from B, the smaller circle has equation $(x + 50)^2 + (y + 30)^2 = 4900$. These two equations form the following *quadratic-quadratic system.*

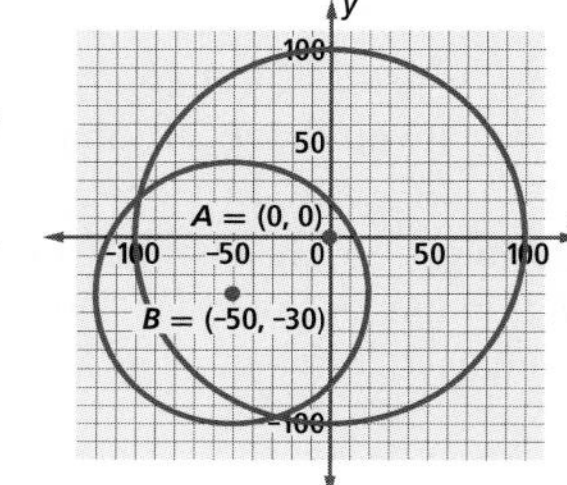

$$\begin{cases} x^2 + y^2 = 10{,}000 \\ (x + 50)^2 + (y + 30)^2 = 4900 \end{cases}$$

In order to find the exact solutions to this system, you can use by-hand methods or a CAS. One CAS solution is partially shown at the right. The full solution, found by scrolling the display, is:

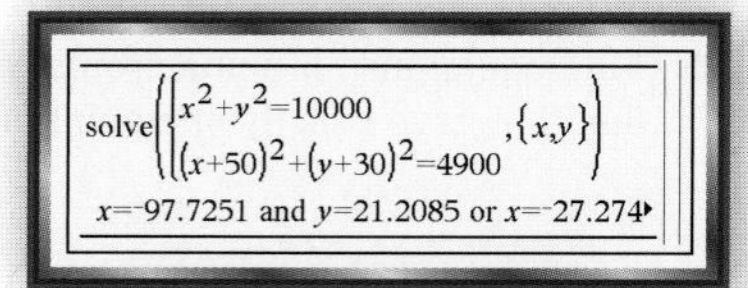


```
x = -97.7251 and y = 21.2085 or
x = -27.2749 and y = -96.2085
```


Background

When a linear-quadratic system cannot be solved by graphing, substitution is usually the only method available. In contrast, any of the methods used in solving linear systems can be appropriate for solving quadratic-quadratic systems: substitution, graphing, or linear combination. No new techniques are needed.

The algebraic manipulation required to obtain exact solutions can be considerable. In practice, a CAS or graphing utility can produce solutions to any desired accuracy, so algebraic solutions have lost some of their importance. Most of the questions have been designed so that the manipulation is not tedious.

The epicenter is located either about 98 kilometers west and 21 kilometers north of Station A, or about 27 kilometers west and 96 kilometers south of Station A. Information from a third station would help you determine which was the actual location.

 QY

> **QY**
> Check both solutions to Example 1 in both equations of the system.

In general, a **quadratic-quadratic system** involves two or more quadratic sentences. Geometrically, a quadratic-quadratic system involves curves represented by quadratic relations: circles, ellipses, hyperbolas, and parabolas.

In Lesson 12-8, you looked at ways a line could intersect the different conic sections. Below are examples of the six different ways that a quadratic-quadratic system of a circle and an ellipse can intersect.

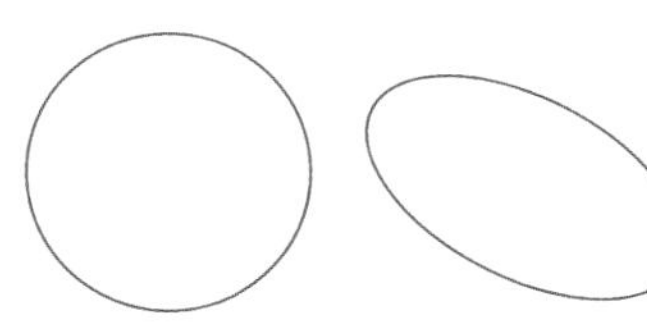

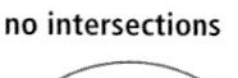

no intersections

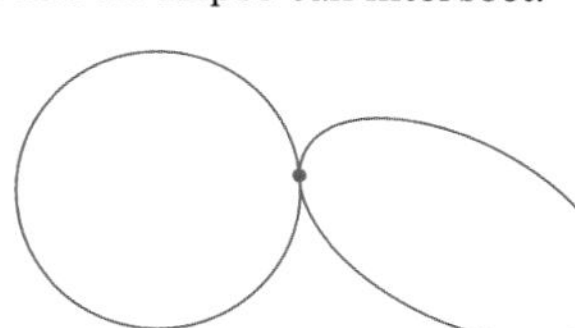

1 intersection

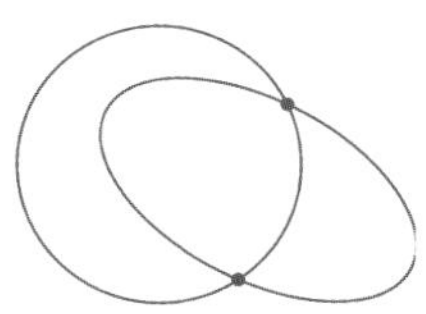

2 intersections

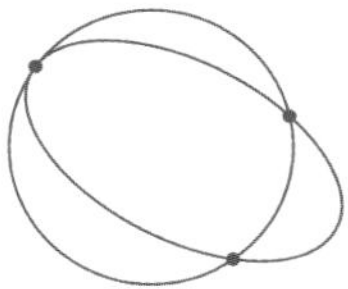

3 intersections

4 intersections

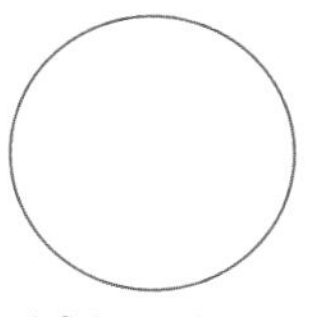

infinite number of intersections

Activity

MATERIALS DGS (optional)

Using the examples above as a guide, fill in a table like the one at the right for the possible numbers of intersections for each quadratic-quadratic system. You may find a DGS helpful.

	Parabola	Circle	Ellipse	Hyperbola
Parabola	?	?	?	?
Circle	?	?	?	?
Ellipse	?	0, 1, 2, 3, 4, or infinitely many	?	?
Hyperbola	?	?	?	?

See the Additional Answers section at the back of the book.

The results of the Activity can be generalized. Quadratic-quadratic systems may have 0, 1, 2, 3, 4, or infinitely many solutions (if the quadratics are equivalent equations).

Some quadratic-quadratic systems are simple enough to be solved by hand.

This lesson reviews many of the ideas of the chapter. Example 1 involves equations of circles, and the Activity involves all the conics. Example 2 involves ellipses and hyperbolas, while Example 3 involves hyperbolas. Discussing the questions in order will cover the lesson.

ENGLISH LEARNERS
Vocabulary Development

The sentence that precedes Example 2 uses the phrase *solved by hand*. Be sure students understand the differences between *solve by hand* (use algebraic methods), *solve by graphing* (use the *trace, list,* or *solution* feature of a graphing calculator), and *solve using a CAS* (use technology to generate a solution).

2 Teaching

Notes on the Lesson

Example 1 Get students in the habit of graphing or thinking about the graphs when solving these systems. Here, it is reasonable from the situation that the two circles will intersect in two points. Notice that Example 1 does not detail a paper-and-pencil solution. Few people can complete a paper-and-pencil solution without making a mistake somewhere, so we strongly encourage the use of technology here. But you might wish to show students what the CAS is probably doing. First expand the second equation to obtain $x^2 + 100x + 2500 + y^2 + 60y + 900 = 4900$. Subtract the first equation from the second to get $100x + 60y = -8500$. Now solve this equation for y to find that $y = -\frac{5x + 425}{3}$. Substituting $-\frac{5x + 425}{3}$ for y in the first equation, the quadratic equation that results is $34x^2 + 4250x + 90{,}625 = 0$. The solutions to this equation are $x = \frac{-4250 \pm\sqrt{4250^2 - 4 \cdot 34 \cdot 90{,}625}}{2 \cdot 34}$, yielding the x-values found by the CAS of approximately –97.7 and –27.3. Substituting those values in the first equation will obtain the corresponding y-values.

Additional Example

Example 1 On a coordinate system, P is 4 units from the origin and 3 units from the point (–2, –1). Find the possible locations for point P.

The system is $\begin{cases} x^2 + y^2 = 16 \\ (x + 2)^2 + (y + 1)^2 = 9 \end{cases}$.

The solutions of the system are approximately (–1.073, –3.84) and (–3.727, 1.453).

Note-Taking Tips

When students complete their copy of the table that appears in the Activity (they started the table in Lesson 12-8), encourage them to illustrate the cells of the table with an appropriate graph for each possible number of solutions.

12-9

Notes on the Lesson

Example 2 The graphs are symmetric about the y-axis because there are x^2 terms but no terms in x. Any solutions will come in pairs of points that are reflection images of each other over the y-axis. If students have difficulty with Example 2 (or the corresponding Question 3), have them substitute a for x^2 and b for y^2, as in the Warm-Up on page 850.

Additional Example

Example 2 Find all solutions (x, y) to $\begin{cases} 2x^2 + y^2 = 41 \\ 4x^2 - 3y^2 = 7 \end{cases}$.

Solution This system represents the intersection of a(n) ___?___ and a(n) ___?___. ellipse; hyperbola There are 0, 1, 2, 3, or 4 possible solutions. Use the linear combination method to find them.

Multiply the first equation by 3 and add the equations to eliminate y:

$6x^2 + 3y^2 = 123$

$\underline{?}\,x^2 - \underline{?}\,y^2 = \underline{?}$ 4; 3; 7

$\underline{?}\,x^2 = \underline{?}$ 10; 130

$x^2 = \underline{?}$ 13

$x = \underline{?}$ $\pm\sqrt{13} \approx \pm3.6056$

Substitute each value of x into one of the given equations.

If $x = \underline{?}$, then $2(\underline{?})^2 + y^2 = 41$, so $y = \pm\underline{?}$. $\sqrt{13}$; $\sqrt{13}$; $\pm\sqrt{15} \approx \pm3.8730$

If $x = \underline{?}$, then $2(\underline{?})^2 + y^2 = 7$, so $y = \pm\underline{?}$. $-\sqrt{13}$; $-\sqrt{13}$; $\pm\sqrt{15} \approx \pm3.8730$

So, this system has four solutions: ___?___, ___?___, ___?___, and ___?___. $(\sqrt{13}, \sqrt{15})$, $(-\sqrt{13}, \sqrt{15})$, $(\sqrt{13}, -\sqrt{15})$, and $(-\sqrt{13}, -\sqrt{15})$

GUIDED

Example 2

Find all solutions (x, y) to $\begin{cases} 4x^2 + 3y^2 = 37 \\ 3x^2 - y^2 = 5 \end{cases}$.

Solution This system represents the intersection of an ___?___ and a ___?___. There are 0, 1, 2, 3, or 4 possible solutions. Use the linear combination method to find them. ellipse; hyperbola

$4x^2 + 3y^2 = 37$

$\underline{?}\,x^2 - \underline{?}\,y^2 = \underline{?}$ Multiply the second equation by 3. 9; 3; 15

$\underline{?}\,x^2 = \underline{?}$ Add the equations to eliminate y. 13; 52

$x^2 = \underline{?}$ 4

$x = \pm\underline{?}$ 2

Substitute each value of x into one of the given equations.

If $x = \underline{?}$, then $4(\underline{?})^2 + 3y^2 = 37$, so $y = \pm\underline{?}$. 2; 2 ; $\sqrt{7}$

If $x = \underline{?}$, then $4(\underline{?})^2 + 3y^2 = 37$, so $y = \pm\underline{?}$. -2; -2; $\sqrt{7}$

So, this system has 4 solutions: $(\underline{?}, \underline{?})$, $(\underline{?}, \underline{?})$, $(\underline{?}, \underline{?})$, and $(\underline{?}, \underline{?})$. 2; $\sqrt{7}$; 2; $-\sqrt{7}$; -2; $\sqrt{7}$; -2; $-\sqrt{7}$

Check Solve on a CAS.

solve$(4x^2+3y^2=37$ and $3x^2-y^2=5, x, y)$

The following quadratic-quadratic system involves the intersection of two rectangular hyperbolas.

Example 3

In one month, Willie's Western Wear took in \$10,500 from boot sales. Although Willie sold 30 fewer pairs of boots the next month, he still sold \$10,800 worth of boots by raising the price \$10 per pair. Find the price of a pair of boots in each month.

Civil War era military boots were not the ideal boot for cowboys. So, in the late 1800s, boots were given pointy toes to help feet get into stirrups and higher heels to help feet stay there.

Solution Let n = the number of pairs of boots sold in the first month. Let p = the price of a pair of boots in the first month.

The equations for total sales in the first and second months, respectively, are:

(1) $np = 10{,}500$

(2) $(n - 30)(p + 10) = 10{,}800$

Accommodating the Learner

Give students the ordered pairs (6, 7) and (14, 3). Ask them to find the equations of two circles that intersect in the given points. Answers vary. Sample: Every circle that contains the given points has its center on the line that is the perpendicular bisector of the segment whose endpoints are the given points. The segment with endpoints (6, 7) and (14, 3) has midpoint (10, 5) and lies on the line whose equation is $y = -\frac{1}{2}x + 10$. So the perpendicular bisector of that segment has equation $y = 2x - 15$. Select any two points on the line, say (0, -15) and (10, 5), as the centers of the two circles. For the circle with center (0, -15), the radius is $\sqrt{(0-6)^2 + (-15-7)^2} = \sqrt{520}$; for the circle with center (10, 5), the radius is $\sqrt{(10-6)^2 + (5-7)^2} = \sqrt{20}$. So the system is $\begin{cases} (x-0)^2 + y - (-15)^2 = 520 \\ (x-10)^2 + (y-5)^2 = 20 \end{cases}$ or $\begin{cases} x^2 + (y+15)^2 = 520 \\ (x-10)^2 + (y-5)^2 = 20 \end{cases}$.

Our goal is to obtain an equation in only one of these variables.

In (1), solve for p. $p = \frac{10{,}500}{n}$

In (2), expand. $np + 10n - 30p - 11{,}100 = 0$

The two forms of equation (1) allow you to make two substitutions into equation (2). Substitute 10,500 for np and $\frac{10{,}500}{n}$ for p to get an equation in one variable.

$$10{,}500 + 10n - 30\left(\frac{10{,}500}{n}\right) - 11{,}100 = 0.$$

Divide both sides by 10.

$$1050 + n - 3\left(\frac{10{,}500}{n}\right) - 1110 = 0$$

Simplify. $n - 60 - \frac{31{,}500}{n} = 0$

Multiply both sides by n. $n^2 - 60n - 31{,}500 = 0$

This is a quadratic equation you can solve in many ways. One CAS solution is shown at the right.

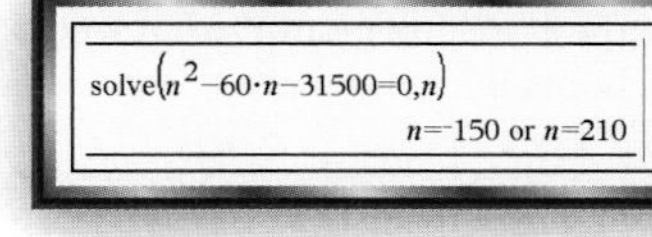

The number n of pairs of boots sold can only be positive.

So, $n = 210.$

Since the price $p = \frac{10{,}500}{n}$, $p = \frac{10{,}500}{210} = 50.$

The boots were priced at \$50 a pair the first month, and $p + 10 = \$60$ a pair the second month.

Check With these numbers, 210 pairs of boots were sold the first month at \$50/pair, so Willie took in \$10,500. That checks. The second month, Willie sold 180 pairs of boots at \$60/pair. So he took in \$10,800. The solution checks.

Questions

COVERING THE IDEAS

1. A system with two quadratic equations in x and y that are not equivalent can have at most how many solutions? 4
2. Without doing any algebra or graphing, tell how many solutions the system $x^2 + y^2 = 9$ and $3x^2 + 3y^2 = 48$ has. Explain your response.
3. Find all solutions (x, y) to $\begin{cases} 9x^2 + 4y^2 = 36 \\ -16x^2 + 4y^2 = 36 \end{cases}$. (0, 3), (0, -3)

2. 0; Both equations represent circles, and the circles have the same center and different radii; thus, they do not intersect.

Extension

Ask students to sketch the system $\begin{cases} y = ax^2 \\ xy = b \end{cases}$, where a and b are positive. Tell students that the vertical line $x = p$ passes through the solution of the system and ask them to express b in terms of a and p. Students' sketches should show a parabola with vertex (0, 0) that opens up, and a hyperbola in Quadrants I and III; the graphs intersect in Quadrant I. By substituting p for x in each equation, the point of intersection can be labeled as (p, ap^2) and as $\left(p, \frac{b}{p}\right)$. So $\frac{b}{p} = ap^2$ and $b = ap^3$.

12-9

Notes on the Lesson

Example 3 The manipulation here is the most complex shown in the lesson and requires a significant amount of time to explain. With some classes, use a CAS solve command after equations (1) and (2) have been set up. With other classes, use a CAS to perform the steps shown in the paper-and-pencil solution on pages 852–853. The screens below show how to use a CAS to substitute 10,500 for np and $\frac{10{,}500}{n}$ for p.

```
n·p+10·n–30·p–11100=0|n·p=10500
                    10·n–30·p–600=0
10·n–30·p–600=0|p=10500/n
                 10·n–315000/n–600=0
```

Divide the result by 10:

```
(10·n–315000/n–600=0)/10
                 (n^2–60·n–31500)/n=0
```

Then multiply by n:

```
((n^2–60·n–31500)/n=0)·n
                 n^2–60·n–31500=0
```

The resulting equation can be solved by factoring, by using the Quadratic Formula, or by using a CAS as shown in the text.

Additional Example

Example 3 Yesterday, a music store took in \$845 from CD sales. Today, they lowered the price of CDs by \$4 each and took in \$855 in CD sales by selling 30 more CDs than yesterday. Find the cost of a CD yesterday and today. If the store sold m CDs yesterday at d dollars each, then (1) $md = 845$ (yesterday) and (2) $(m + 30)(d - 4) = 855$ (today). (1) $d = \frac{845}{m}$ and (2) $md - 4m + 30d - 120 = 855$. Rewriting equation (2) and substituting for md and for d, $4m - \frac{25{,}350}{m} + 130 = 0$; $4m^2 + 130m - 25{,}350 = 0$; so $m = \frac{-130 \pm \sqrt{422{,}500}}{8} = 65$. Thus, yesterday's price was $\frac{845}{65}$ or \$13, and today's price is 13 – 4 or \$9.

3 Assignment

Recommended Assignment

- Questions 1–23
- Question 24 (extra credit)
- Self-Test

Notes on the Questions

Question 5 You might ask what students know about the solutions to this system before they use algebra or graphing. The circle is centered at the vertex of the parabola, so they intersect in two points. Because the circle and parabola are both symmetric to the y-axis, the points of intersection are reflection images of each other.

Questions 7 and 8 These questions are similar; you might assign one for homework and discuss the other one in class.

Additional Answers

6a. Substitute $\frac{10{,}500}{p}$ for n and 10,500 for np.

6b. $10{,}500 + \frac{10{,}500}{p} - 30p - 11{,}100 = 0$

$30p + 600 - \frac{10{,}500}{p} = 0$

$30p^2 + 600p - 10{,}500 = 0$

$30(p + 70)(p - 50) = 0$;

p must be positive, so $p = 50$ and $n = \frac{10{,}500}{50} = 210$; this matches the answer in Example 3.

13a. $\begin{cases} x^2 + y^2 = 1{,}000{,}000 \\ (x - 200)^2 + (y - 800)^2 = 160{,}000 \\ (x - 1000)^2 + (y - 1100)^2 = 250{,}000 \end{cases}$

12-9A Lesson Master

Questions on SPUR Objectives
See Student Edition pages 862–865 for objectives.

SKILLS Objective D

1. Solve by hand for all real solutions: $\begin{cases} x^2 + y^2 = 36 \\ \frac{x^2}{9} + \frac{y^2}{36} = 1 \end{cases}$ (0, 6), (0, –6)

In 2 and 3, a. estimate solutions to the system by graphing on a graphing utility, and b. find the exact solutions. Answers vary for Part a. Samples are given.

2. $\begin{cases} \frac{x^2}{4} + \frac{y^2}{9} = 1 \\ y = x^2 \end{cases}$

   a. (-1.4, 2.1), (1.4, 2.1)

   b. $\left(\frac{\sqrt{-18 + 6\sqrt{73}}}{4}, \frac{-9 + 3\sqrt{73}}{8}\right)$, $\left(-\frac{\sqrt{-18 + 6\sqrt{73}}}{4}, \frac{-9 + 3\sqrt{73}}{8}\right)$

3. $\begin{cases} x^2 + y^2 = 36 \\ xy = 12 \end{cases}$

   a. (2.1, 5.6), (5.6, 2.1), (-2.1, -5.6), (-5.6, -2.1)

   b. $(\sqrt{18 - 6\sqrt{5}}, \sqrt{18 + 6\sqrt{5}})$, $(\sqrt{18 + 6\sqrt{5}}, \sqrt{18 - 6\sqrt{5}})$, $(-\sqrt{18 - 6\sqrt{5}}, -\sqrt{18 + 6\sqrt{5}})$, $(-\sqrt{18 + 6\sqrt{5}}, -\sqrt{18 - 6\sqrt{5}})$

USES Objective H

4. Global Positioning Systems (GPS) use their distance from satellites to locate points on Earth by finding the intersection points of circles. If a GPS only receives information from two satellites, it cannot calculate an exact location. Suppose you know you are 20 miles from point (0, 0) and 31 miles from point (32, 22). Find your two possible positions relative to (0, 0) to the nearest tenth. (1.1, 20.0), (19.0, –6.2)

REPRESENTATIONS Objective K

5. Consider the system $\begin{cases} \frac{x^2}{25} + \frac{y^2}{9} = 1 \\ y = x^2 + 9 \end{cases}$

   a. Sketch the system on the axes at the right.

   b. Determine the number of solutions. no solutions

6. Give an equation for a parabola that intersects the circle $x^2 + y^2 = 16$ in exactly Answers vary. Samples are given.

   a. one point. $y = x^2 + 4$
   b. two points. $y = x^2$
   c. three points. $y = x^2 - 4$
   d. no points. $y = x^2 + 5$

Advanced Algebra 595

4. **True or False** The solutions to the system in Example 2 lie on the symmetry lines of both the hyperbola and the ellipse. false

5. Consider the circle $x^2 + y^2 = 9$ and the parabola $y = x^2$.
   a. How many intersection points do you expect? 2
   b. Check your answer to Part a by finding the points of the intersection. (-1.59, 2.54) and (1.59, 2.54)

In 6 and 7, refer to Example 3.

6. a. What two substitutions could you make to transform the second equation into an equation in terms of p only?
   b. Check the solution by solving the original system using the substitutions in Part a. 6a–b. See margin.

7. In the second month, if Willie had instead raised prices $18 per pair and earned $12,000 from selling 50 fewer pairs of boots than the previous month, what would have been the price of a pair of boots in each month? $42 in the first month and $60 in the second month

APPLYING THE MATHEMATICS

8. The product of two real numbers is 6984. If one number is increased by 4 and the other is decreased by 10, the new product is 6262.
   a. Write a quadratic system that can be solved to find these numbers.
   b. Find the numbers. -28.8 and -242.5 or 97 and 72

In 9–11, solve the system.

9. $\begin{cases} x^2 + y^2 = 25 \\ y = x^2 - 13 \end{cases}$

10. $\begin{cases} \frac{x^2}{16} + \frac{y^2}{9} = 1 \\ x^2 - y^2 = 7 \end{cases}$

11. $\begin{cases} y = x^2 + 3x - 4 \\ y = 2x^2 + 5x - 3 \end{cases}$

12. Draw a graph of the solution set of the system $\begin{cases} y \ge x^2 \\ x^2 + y^2 \le 4 \end{cases}$.

8a. $\begin{cases} xy = 6984 \\ (x + 4)(y - 10) = 6262 \end{cases}$

9. (-4, 3), (4, 3), (-3, -4), (3, -4)

10. $\left(-\frac{16}{5}, -\frac{9}{5}\right), \left(-\frac{16}{5}, \frac{9}{5}\right), \left(\frac{16}{5}, -\frac{9}{5}\right), \left(\frac{16}{5}, \frac{9}{5}\right)$

11. (-1, -6)

12. See margin.

13. A fleet of fishing boats locates its nets by sonar. One boat determines that a net is 1000 meters away. A second boat, 200 meters east and 800 meters north of the first, finds that it is 400 meters from the net. A third boat, 1000 meters east and 1100 meters north of the first, finds that it is 500 meters away from the net.
    a. Suppose the first boat is at the origin of a coordinate system. Write a system of three equations to describe this situation. See margin.
    b. The graphs of the three equations have one intersection point in common. Solve the system and find the location of the net with respect to the first boat. $x = 600$, $y = 800$; The net is 600 m north and 800 m east of the first boat.

Accommodating the Learner

Ask students to sketch a graph of $y = 2x^2 + 3$. Then ask them to find a circle with center (0, 0) that intersects the parabola in exactly one point. The vertex of the parabola is (0, 3), so the circle must touch the parabola at (0, 3). The center of the circle is (0, 0), so the radius is 3. An equation for the circle is $x^2 + y^2 = 9$.

Additional Answers

12.

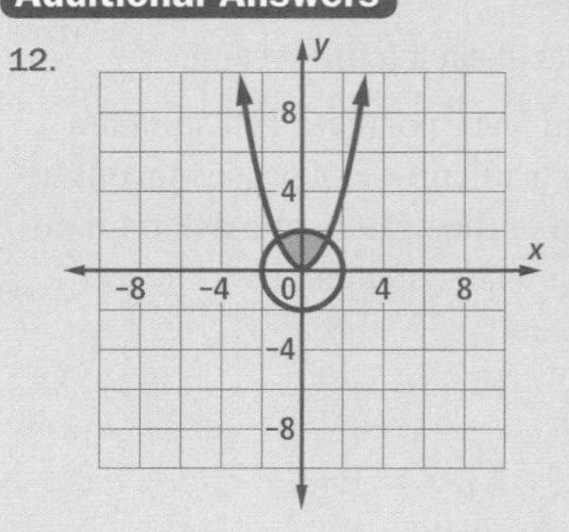

14. The altitude h of the 3-4-5 triangle at the right splits the hypotenuse into segments of length x and $5 - x$.
    a. Use the Pythagorean Theorem to create two quadratic relations in terms of x and h. $h^2 + (5 - x)^2 = 16$, $h^2 + x^2 = 9$
    b. Solve your system of equations in Part a for x and h.
    c. Which solution(s) make(s) sense in the context of this problem? $x = \frac{9}{5}$ and $h = \frac{12}{5}$ (Lengths must be positive.)

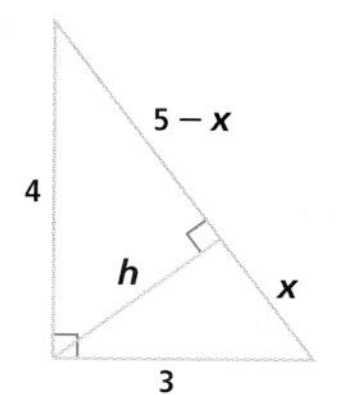

14b. $x = \frac{9}{5}$ and $h = -\frac{12}{5}$ or $x = \frac{9}{5}$ and $h = \frac{12}{5}$

REVIEW

15. The sum of Mr. Hwan's age in years and his baby's age in months is 37. The product of the ages is 300. Solve a system of equations to find their ages. (Lesson 12-8) See margin.

In 16 and 17, an equation is given. Does the equation represent a quadratic relation? If so, put the equation in standard form for a quadratic relation. If not, explain why not. (Lesson 12-7)

16. $x^2 + 5xy^2 = 10$

17. $\frac{1}{2}x - 13y^2 = \sqrt{7}y$

16. No; the equation contains a term with degree 3.

17. yes; $13y^2 - \frac{1}{2}x + \sqrt{7}y = 0$

In 18 and 19, graph the equation. (Lesson 12-6, 12-4)

18. $\frac{x^2}{9} + \frac{y^2}{36} = 1$

19. $\frac{x^2}{9} - \frac{y^2}{36} = 1$ 18–19. See margin.

20. The third and fourth terms of a geometric sequence are 20 and -40. (Lesson 7-5)
    a. What is the constant ratio? -2
    b. What are the first and second terms? 5, -10
    c. Write an explicit formula for the nth term. $g_n = 5(-2)^{n-1}$
    d. What is the 15th term? 81,920

21. Explain why every transformation is a function. (Lesson 4-7)

21. Answers vary. Sample: Transformations map each point of a preimage onto a unique point in the image.

In 22 and 23, multiply the matrices. (Lesson 4-3)

22. $\begin{bmatrix} 3 & 5 & 7 \end{bmatrix}\begin{bmatrix} 1 \\ 0 \\ -2 \end{bmatrix}$ $\begin{bmatrix} -11 \end{bmatrix}$

23. $\begin{bmatrix} 3 & 0 & 5 \\ -1 & 4 & 2 \end{bmatrix}\begin{bmatrix} 2 & -2 \\ 0 & 1 \\ -3 & 4 \end{bmatrix}$ $\begin{bmatrix} -9 & 14 \\ -8 & 14 \end{bmatrix}$

EXPLORATION

24. In 2002, a new method of code breaking called the XSL (eXtended Sparse Linearization) attack was published. The attack is a type of *algebraic cryptanalysis*. Search the Internet to answer these questions.
    a. What is the purpose of the XSL attack? 24a–b. See margin.
    b. How does this system use quadratic systems?

QY ANSWER

$(-97.7)^2 + (21.2)^2 = 9994.73 \approx 10{,}000$;
$(-97.7 + 50)^2 + (21.2 + 30)^2 = 4896.73 \approx 4900$;
$(-27.3)^2 + (-96.2)^2 = 9999.73 \approx 10{,}000$;
$(-27.3 + 50)^2 + (-96.2 + 30)^2 = 4897.73 \approx 4900$

Notes on the Questions

Question 14 Some students may remember that the altitude to the hypotenuse of a right triangle is the geometric mean of the length of the segments into which it divides the hypotenuse. Thus $\frac{5 - x}{h} = \frac{h}{x}$, from which $h^2 = 5x - x^2$. Consider the system with this quadratic equation and the quadratic equation $h^2 + x^2 = 9$ that comes from applying the Pythagorean Theorem to the small right triangle with hypotenuse 3. From these two equations, $5x = 9$, so $x = 1.8$. You can substitute to find $h = 2.4$, or you can realize that all these triangles are similar, so the sides of that small right triangle are in the ratio 3:4:5.

4 Wrap-Up

Ongoing Assessment

Tell students that Q is 5 units from (4, -1) and 6 units from (-2, 3). Ask them to write a system of equations whose solution represents the location of Q.

$$\begin{cases} (x - 4)^2 + (y + 1)^2 = 25 \\ (x + 2)^2 + (y - 3)^2 = 36 \end{cases}$$

Then ask students to solve this system. approximately (-0.638, -2.843) or (3.830, 3.997)

Additional Answers

15. $\begin{cases} x + y = 37 \\ xy = 300 \end{cases}$

The solutions are $x = 12$ and $y = 25$ or $x = 25$ and $y = 12$. Mr. Hwan's age is 25 yr, and his baby's is 12 mo.

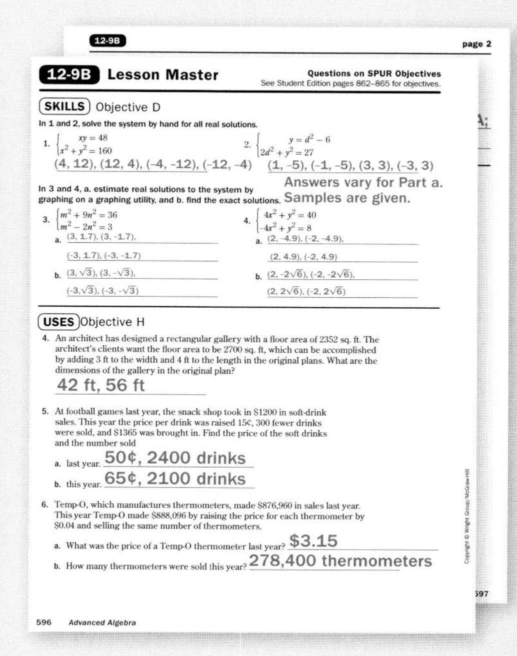

12-9B page 2

12-9B Lesson Master

Questions on SPUR Objectives
See Student Edition pages 862–865 for objectives.

SKILLS Objective D

In 1 and 2, solve the system by hand for all real solutions.

1. $\begin{cases} xy = 48 \\ x^2 + y^2 = 160 \end{cases}$ (4, 12), (12, 4), (-4, -12), (-12, -4)

2. $\begin{cases} y = d^2 - 6 \\ 2d^2 + y^2 = 27 \end{cases}$ (1, -5), (-1, -5), (3, 3), (-3, 3)

In 3 and 4, a. estimate real solutions to the system by graphing on a graphing utility, and b. find the exact solutions. Answers vary for Part a. Samples are given.

3. $\begin{cases} m^2 + 9n^2 = 36 \\ m^2 - 2n^2 = 3 \end{cases}$
   a. (3, 1.7), (3, -1.7), (-3, 1.7), (-3, -1.7)
   b. $(3, \sqrt{3})$, $(3, -\sqrt{3})$, $(-3, \sqrt{3})$, $(-3, -\sqrt{3})$

4. $\begin{cases} 4x^2 + y^2 = 40 \\ -4x^2 + y^2 = 8 \end{cases}$
   a. (2, -4.9), (-2, -4.9), (2, 4.9), (-2, 4.9)
   b. $(2, -2\sqrt{6})$, $(-2, -2\sqrt{6})$, $(2, 2\sqrt{6})$, $(-2, 2\sqrt{6})$

USES Objective H

4. An architect has designed a rectangular gallery with a floor area of 2352 sq. ft. The architect's clients want the floor area to be 2700 sq. ft, which can be accomplished by adding 3 ft to the width and 4 ft to the length in the original plans. What are the dimensions of the gallery in the original plan? 42 ft, 56 ft

5. At football games last year, the snack shop took in $1200 in soft-drink sales. This year the price per drink was raised 15¢, 300 fewer drinks were sold, and $1365 was brought in. Find the price of the soft drinks and the number sold
   a. last year. 50¢, 2400 drinks
   b. this year. 65¢, 2100 drinks

6. Temp-O, which manufactures thermometers, made $876,960 in sales last year. This year Temp-O made $888,096 by raising the price for each thermometer by $0.04 and selling the same number of thermometers.
   a. What was the price of a Temp-O thermometer last year? $3.15
   b. How many thermometers were sold this year? 278,400 thermometers

Copyright © Wright Group/McGraw-Hill

596 Advanced Algebra

Chapter

12

The projects relate to the content of the lessons of this chapter as follows:

Project	Lesson(s)
1	12-6
2	12-2
3	12-7
4	12-5
5	12-6

1 Reflection Properties of Conics

Illustrate for students an elliptical miniature golf "hole" that has a cup at each focus. Ask: How can you sink a ball into a cup after one bounce against the border? To see how a ball "reflects" off the border, identify a point on the ellipse; through that point, imagine the line tangent to the ellipse and another line perpendicular to that tangent. When a ball reflects off the border, the angle of incidence is equal to the angle of reflection (both measured from the perpendicular line). So for a ball in any location in the region (except on the major axis), aim the ball directly away from one cup; it should reflect off the border and go directly toward the other cup.

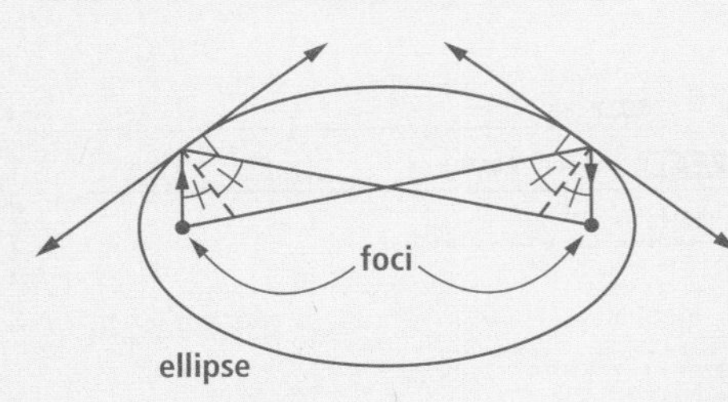

For another perspective on the reflective properties of ellipses, have students visit http://www.ies.co.jp/math/java/conics/focus_ellipse/focus_ellipse.html. This Web site contains a proof that any ray from one focus is reflected to the other focus. It has an applet that demonstrates rays from one focus reflecting to the other focus. The applet lets you change the shape of the ellipse and again show rays from one focus reflecting to the other.

Chapter 12 Projects

1 Reflection Properties of Conics

Parabolas, ellipses, and hyperbolas are used in telescopes, whispering galleries, navigation, satellite dishes, and headlights because they have reflection properties.

a. Explain how the reflection properties of a conic section are used to create whispering galleries. Illustrate your explanation with an accurate drawing.

b. Describe the reflection properties of the remaining conic sections and illustrate them with drawings and examples of their use in the real world.

2 Arches

Semicircular arches were popular with the early Romans. Other kinds of arches have been popular at other times and places. Prepare a brief report on the various kinds of arches that have been used in architecture throughout history. You might include arches from the Roman and Renaissance eras and modern arches such as the Gateway Arch in St. Louis. If possible, give equations for curves that outline these arches.

3 The General Ellipse and Hyperbola

Research the standard, or general, form of a quadratic equation

$$Ax^2 + Bxy + Cy^2 + Dx + Ey + F = 0$$

compared to the standard forms of the equations for the conic sections you studied in this chapter. There are many Internet sites that can help your research.

a. Find out how to interpret $A, B, C, D, E,$ and F to identify which conic section the standard quadratic equation represents.

b. Find out how to transform the standard quadratic equation into the standard forms for ellipses and hyperbolas.

c. Summarize your findings in a report.

Project Rubric

Advanced	Student correctly provides all of the details asked for in the project as well as additional correct independent conclusions.
Proficient	Student correctly provides all of the details asked for in the project.
Partially proficient	Student correctly provides some of the details asked for in the project or provides all details with some inaccuracies.
Not proficient	Student correctly provides few of the details asked for in the project or provides all details with many inaccuracies.
No attempt	Student makes little or no attempt to complete the project.

4 Orbits of the Planets

The orbits of planets around the Sun are ellipses with the Sun at one focus.

a. Describe these ellipses, giving the major and minor axes for the orbit of each planet and indicating the nearest and farthest distances of each planet to the Sun. (These are called the planet's *perihelion* and *aphelion*, respectively.)

b. Draw two accurate pictures of these orbits, one with the inner four major planets, the other with the outer four major planets.

c. Research the orbit of the dwarf planet Pluto. Add its orbit to your drawing of the outer planets' orbits. How does it differ from the orbits of the other planets?

d. The closeness of an ellipse to a circle is measured by the *eccentricity* of the ellipse. Give the eccentricity of each orbit. Which planets' orbits are closest to being circular?

5 Constructing Conic Sections

The Exploration in Lesson 12-1 showed you how to construct a parabola by using paper folding. This project uses a DGS to mimic paper-folding constructions of parabolas and other conic sections.

a. Construct line m and point P not on the line. Construct a line segment from P to point A on the line. Construct the perpendicular bisector of $\overline{PA}$. Set your DGS to trace the path of the perpendicular bisector of $\overline{PA}$ as you vary the location of A on line m. Explain why this construction results in a parabola. Identify the focus and directrix in the construction.

b. Construct circle C and point P in the exterior of the circle. Construct a line segment from P to point A on the circle. Construct the perpendicular bisector $\overline{PA}$. Set your DGS to trace the path of the perpendicular bisector of $\overline{PA}$ as you vary the location of A on circle C. Which conic section does this construction make? Explain why this construction makes the conic section it does.

c. Modify your construction in Part b by moving P to the interior of the circle. Set your DGS to trace the path of the perpendicular bisector of $\overline{PA}$ as you vary the location of A on circle C. Which conic section does this construction make? Explain why this construction makes the conic section it does.

Notes

2 Arches

As an extension, ask students how they could construct part of a circle from this rectangle that maximizes the amount of the rectangle that is used.

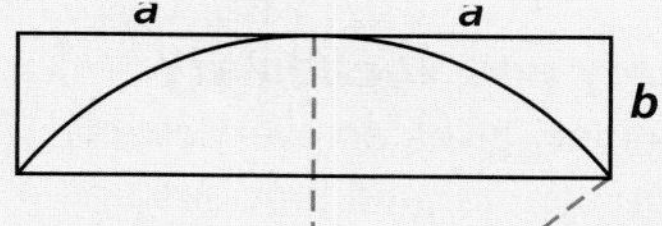

In the diagram, $2a$ is the length of the board to simplify the expression. Using the Pythagorean Theorem, $(r - b)^2 + a^2 = r^2$. So $r^2 - 2br + b^2 + a^2 = r^2$, $-2br = -a^2 - b^2$, and $r = \frac{a^2 + b^2}{2b}$.

3 The General Ellipse and Hyperbola

As an introduction to this project, ask students to write a specific equation for a circle, an ellipse, a parabola, and a hyperbola. Then ask them to rewrite each equation so it is in the general form $Ax^2 + Bxy + Cy^2 + Dx + Ey + F = 0$ and give the values of A, B, C, D, E, and F for their original equation.

4 Orbits of the Planets

In Part a of this project, ask students to express the distance between the foci in terms of the perihelion p and aphelion a. The length of the major axis is $p + a$, so the distance between the foci is $p + a - 2p$ or $a - p$.

5 Constructing Conic Sections

Encourage students to illustrate each of the DGS constructions. For example, they could prepare a diagram such as the following to illustrate the construction in Part a.

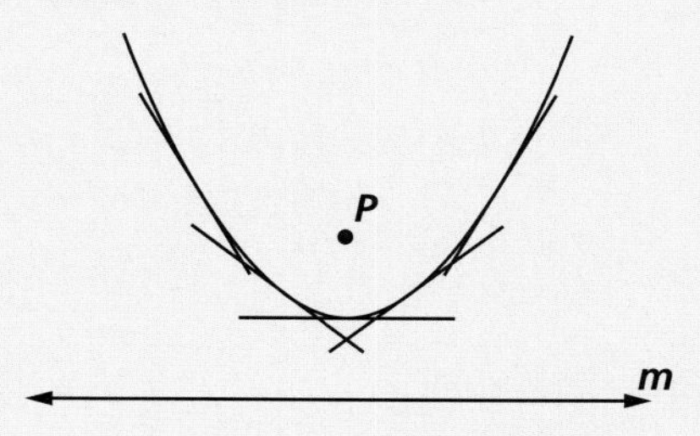

Sample answers for projects are in the Solution Manual in the Electronic Teacher's Edition.

Chapter

12

Summary and Vocabulary

The Summary gives an overview of the entire chapter and provides an opportunity for students to consider the material as a whole. Thus, the Summary can be used to help students relate and unify the concepts presented in the chapter.

Vocabulary words and symbols are listed by lesson to provide a checklist of concepts that students must know. Emphasize to students that they should read the vocabulary list carefully before starting the Self-Test on pages 860–861. If students do not understand the meaning of a vocabulary word, they should refer back to the indicated lesson.

Theorems and Properties covered in the chapter are listed below the Summary with page references included to lead students back to the location in the chapter where the theorem or property is stated.

Chapter 12 Summary and Vocabulary

- In this chapter, you studied **quadratic relations** in two variables, their graphs, and their geometric properties. Equations for all quadratic relations in two variables can be written in the standard form $Ax^2 + Bxy + Cy^2 + Dx + Ey + F = 0$, where not all of A, B, and C are zero. The properties of the various quadratic relations are summarized in the table on the next page
- **Conic sections** appear naturally as orbits of planets and comets, in paths of thrown objects, as energy waves radiating from the epicenter of an earthquake, and in many manufactured objects such as tunnels, windows, and satellite receiver dishes.
- Systems of equations with quadratic sentences can be solved in much the same way as linear systems, that is, by graphing, substitution, using linear combinations, or using a CAS. A system of one linear and one quadratic equation may have 0, 1, or 2 solutions; a system of two quadratic equations may have 0, 1, 2, 3, 4, or infinitely many solutions.

Theorems and Properties

Focus and Directrix of a Parabola Theorem (p. 801)
Circle Equation Theorem (p. 806)
Interior and Exterior of a Circle Theorem (p. 812)
Equation for an Ellipse Theorem (p. 818)
Length of Axes of an Ellipse Theorem (p. 820)
Circle Scale-Change Theorem (p. 826)
Graph Scale-Change Theorem (p. 827)
Area of an Ellipse Theorem (p. 828)
Equation for a Hyperbola Theorem (p. 832)
Asymptotes of a Hyperbola Theorem (p. 834)
Attributes of $y = \frac{k}{x}$ Theorem (p. 841)

Vocabulary

Lesson 12-1
*parabola
focus, directrix
axis of symmetry
vertex of a parabola
paraboloid

Lesson 12-2
*circle, radius, center
*concentric circles
semicircle

Lesson 12-3
*interior, exterior of a circle

Lesson 12-4
*ellipse
foci, focal constant of an ellipse
standard position for an ellipse
standard form of an equation for an ellipse
*major axis, minor axis
center of an ellipse
semimajor axes, semiminor axes

Lesson 12-5
eccentricity of an ellipse

Lesson 12-6
*hyperbola
foci, focal constant of a hyperbola
vertices of a hyperbola
standard position of a hyperbola
*standard form of an equation for a hyperbola

Lesson 12-7
conic section
*standard form of an equation for a quadratic relation

Lesson 12-8
quadratic system
quadratic-linear system

Lesson 12-9
quadratic-quadratic system

	Quadratic Relation			
	Circle	**Ellipse**	**Parabola**	**Hyperbola**
Geometric Definition	given center C and radius r, set of points P such that $PC = r$	given foci F_1 and F_2 and focal constant $2a$, set of points P such that $PF_1 + PF_2 = 2a$	given focus F and directrix ℓ, set of points P equidistant from F and ℓ	given foci F_1 and F_2 and focal constant $2a$, set of points P such that $\lvert PF_1 - PF_2 \rvert = 2a$
Equation(s) in Standard Form	$(x - h)^2 + (y - k)^2 = r^2$	$\frac{x^2}{a^2} + \frac{y^2}{b^2} = 1$	$y = ax^2 + bx + c$ or $y - k = a(x - h)^2$	$\frac{x^2}{a^2} - \frac{y^2}{b^2} = 1$ or $xy = k$
Graph	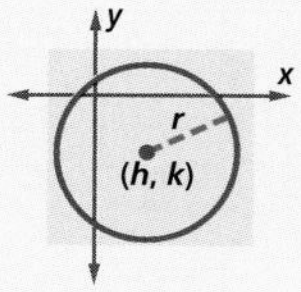 center: (h, k) radius: r	If $a > b$ 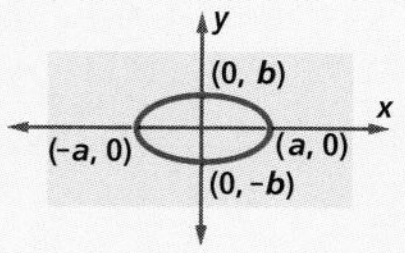 foci: $(-c, 0)$, $(c, 0)$ length of major axis (focal constant): $2a$ length of minor axis: $2b$ $b^2 = a^2 - c^2$	$y = ax^2$ 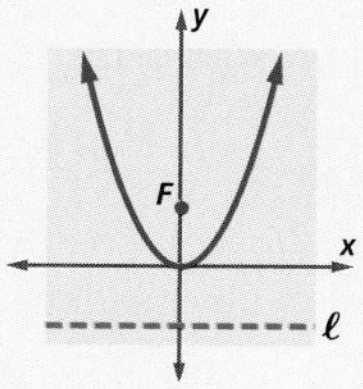 axis of symmetry: $x = 0$ vertex: $(0, 0)$ focus: $\left(0, \frac{1}{4a}\right)$ directrix: $y = -\frac{1}{4a}$	$\frac{x^2}{a^2} - \frac{y^2}{b^2} = 1$ 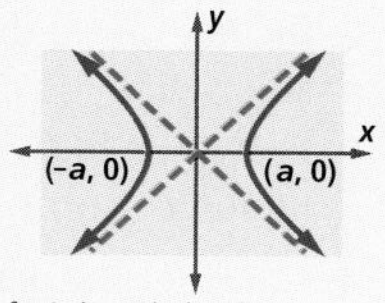 foci: $(-c, 0)$, $(c, 0)$; $b^2 = c^2 - a^2$ asymptotes: $\frac{y}{b} = \pm \frac{x}{a}$
		If $b > a$ 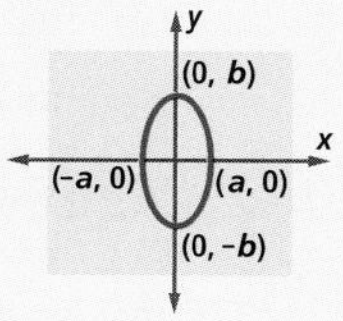 foci: $(0, -c)$, $(0, c)$ length of major axis (focal constant): $2b$ length of minor axis: $2a$ $a^2 = b^2 - c^2$	$y - k = a(x - h)^2$ 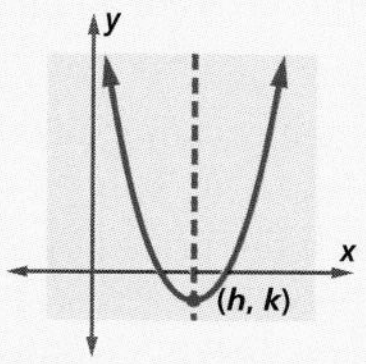 axis of symmetry: $x = h$ vertex: (h, k)	$xy = k$ 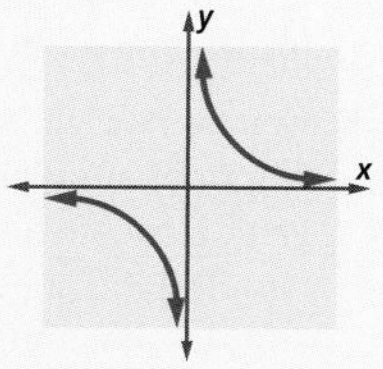 foci: $(\sqrt{2k}, \sqrt{2k})$, $(-\sqrt{2k}, -\sqrt{2k})$ focal constant: $2\sqrt{2k}$ asymptotes: $x = 0, y = 0$
Conic Section		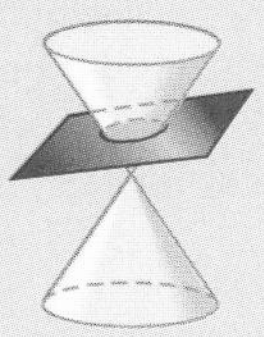		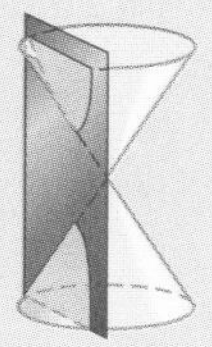

Summary and Vocabulary 859

Self-Test

For the development of mathematical competence, feedback and correction, along with the opportunity for practice, are necessary. The Self-Test provides the opportunity for feedback and correction; the Chapter Review provides additional opportunities for practice. We cannot overemphasize the importance of these end-of-chapter materials. It is at this point that the material gels for many students, allowing them to solidify skills and understanding. In general, student performance should improve after these pages.

Assign the Self-Test as a one-night assignment. Worked-out solutions for all questions are in the Selected Answers section of the student book. Encourage students to take the Self-Test honestly, grade themselves, and then be prepared to discuss the test in class.

Advise students to pay special attention to those Chapter Review questions (pages 862–865) that correspond to the questions they missed on the Self-Test.

Additional Answers

1a. $\frac{1}{25}x^2 - \frac{1}{144}y^2 - 1 = 0$ (or $144x^2 - 25y^2 - 3600 = 0$)

1b. $A = \frac{1}{25}$, $B = 0$, $C = -\frac{1}{144}$, $D = 0$, $E = 0$, $F = -1$ (or $A = 144$, $B = 0$, $C = -25$, $D = 0$, $E = 0$, $F = -3600$)

1c. The equation is of the form $\frac{x^2}{a^2} - \frac{y^2}{b^2} = 1$, so it represents a hyperbola.

2. The interior is the set of points whose distance from (3, –5) is less than 7, so the inequality is $(x - 3)^2 + (y + 5)^2 < 49$.

3. The circle's center shifts to (–2, 5) under the transformation. By the Graph-Translation Theorem, the equation for the image is $(x + 2)^2 + (y - 5)^2 = 1$.

4a. $\left(0, \frac{1}{4 \cdot \frac{1}{11}}\right) = \left(0, \frac{1}{\frac{4}{11}}\right) = \left(0, \frac{11}{4}\right)$

4b. (0, 0)

4c. $y = -\frac{1}{4 \cdot \frac{1}{11}} = -\frac{1}{\frac{4}{11}} = -\frac{11}{4}$

5. The major and minor axes of a circle will be the same length, and the foci will coincide at a single point (the center of the circle).

Chapter 12 Self-Test

Take this test as you would take a test in class. You will need graph paper and a calculator. Use the Selected Answers section in the back of the book to check your work.

1. a. Rewrite $\frac{x^2}{25} - \frac{y^2}{144} = 1$ in the form $Ax^2 + Bxy + Cy^2 + Dx + Ey + F = 0$.
   b. Give the values of A, B, C, D, E, and F.
   c. Identify the conic section represented by the equation in Part a. 1–13. See margin.

In 2 and 3, write an equation or inequality for

2. the interior of the circle with center (3, –5) and radius 7.
3. the image of the graph of $x^2 + y^2 = 1$ under $T_{-2,5}$.
4. Consider the parabola with equation $y = \frac{1}{11}x^2$.
   a. Give the coordinates of its focus.
   b. Give the coordinates of its vertex.
   c. Write an equation for its directrix.
5. Explain what has to be true about the foci and the major and minor axes of an ellipse for it to be a circle.
6. Ernesto's Eye Extravaganza sold \$5600 worth of sunglasses last year. This year, Ernesto's lowered the prices by two dollars, sold seventy more pairs of sunglasses, and took in \$5880. Assuming sunglasses are all the same price,
   a. how much is he selling his sunglasses for now?
   b. how many pairs did he sell this year?

In 7–9, refer to the ellipse below.

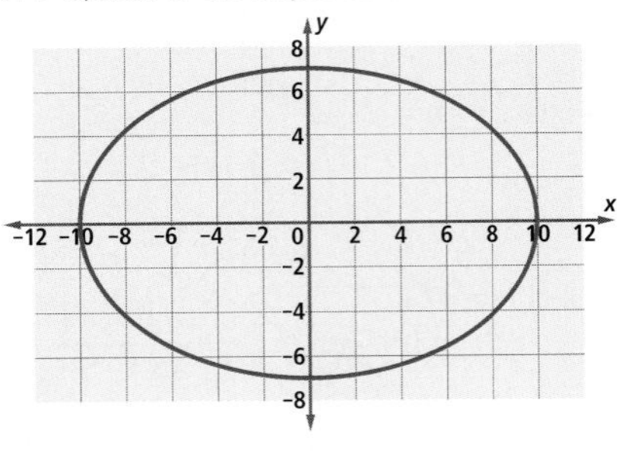

7. Write an equation for the ellipse.
8. Find the area of the ellipse.
9. The ellipse is the image of the circle $x^2 + y^2 = 1$ under what scale change?
10. Graph the conic section with equation $\frac{x^2}{25} - \frac{y^2}{16} = 1$. Identify all its major features.
11. Graph the system $\begin{cases} xy = 2 \\ 2x + 5 = y \end{cases}$ and identify the points of intersection.
12. Solve the system $\begin{cases} y = x^2 - 4x + 3 \\ x^2 + y^2 = 9 \end{cases}$.
13. Consider the equation $xy = -15$.
    a. What type of curve is the graph of this equation?
    b. State the foci and focal constant of the curve.
    c. Does the curve have any lines of symmetry? If so, write an equation for one of them.

Additional Answers

6a. $\begin{cases} (n + 70)(p - 2) = 5880 \\ np = 5600 \end{cases}$

$np + 70p - 2n - 140 = 5880$

$5600 + 70p - 2\frac{5600}{p} - 140 = 5880$

$70p - \frac{11{,}200}{p} = 420$

$70p^2 - 420p - 11{,}200 = 0$

$p^2 - 6p - 160 = 0$

$p = -10$ or $p = 16$, but since price cannot be negative, the original price was $p = 16$. The new price is \$14.

6b. 420; $n = \frac{5600}{p} = \frac{5600}{16} = 350$; this year he sold $n + 70 = 420$ pairs.

7. $a = 10$ and $b = 7$, so an equation is $\frac{x^2}{10} + \frac{y^2}{7^2} = 1$ or $\frac{x^2}{100} + \frac{y^2}{49} = 1$.

8. $A = \pi ab = \pi(10 \cdot 7) = 70\pi$

9. $S_{10,7}$: The image of the circle with equation $x^2 + y^2 = 1$ under $S_{10,7}$ is $\frac{x^2}{100} + \frac{y^2}{49} = 1$ by the Circle Scale-Change Theorem.

14. The elliptically shaped pool shown below is to be surrounded by a tile walkway so that the outer edge of the walkway is also an ellipse. The major axis of the pool has length 15 m, and the minor axis of the pool has length 8 m. The length AB of the major axis of the outer edge of the walkway is 18 m, and the length CD of the minor axis is 11 m. What is the area of the walkway?

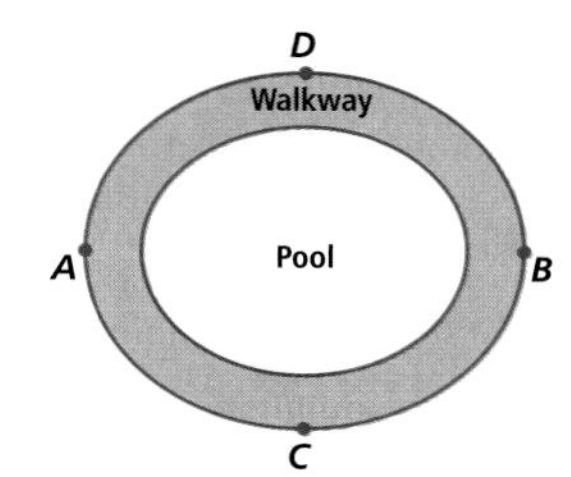

15. Colorado has an area of approximately 104,094 square miles and a perimeter of about 1320 miles. Assuming that Colorado is rectangular, find its dimensions.

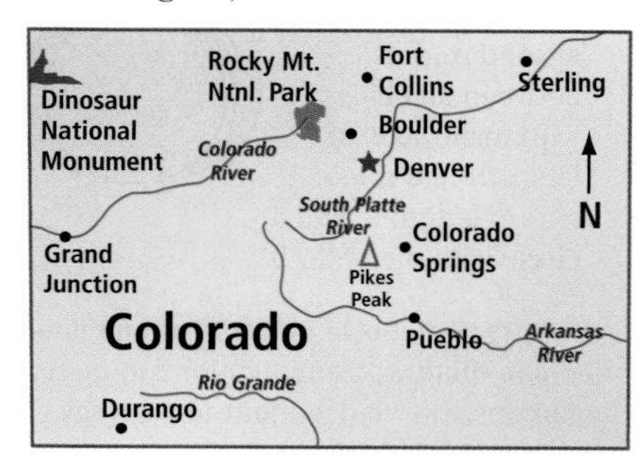

16. Halley's comet has an elliptical orbit with the Sun at one focus. Its closest distance to the Sun is about $9 \cdot 10^7$ km, while its farthest distance is about $5.3 \cdot 10^9$ km.

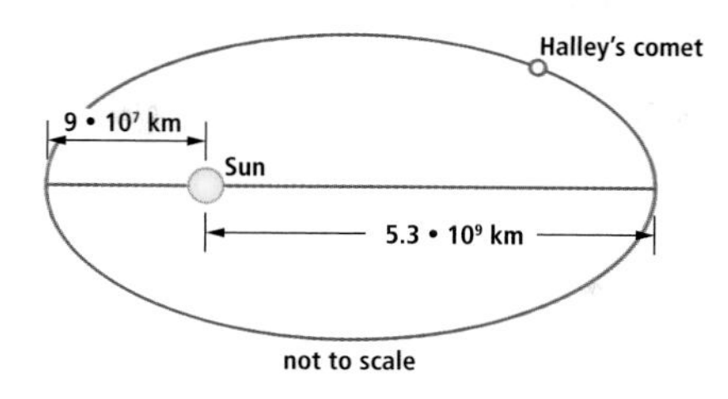

not to scale

Find the length of the major axis of Halley's comet's orbit.

17. Find equations for a quadratic-quadratic system that has exactly three solutions.

18. Graph the set of points that are 8 units from (3, 2.5) and describe the graph with an equation.

19. The entrance to a cave is a semicircular arch that is 14 feet wide at its base. How far from the center of the opening can a 5'8"-tall spelunker stand upright?

20. Graph the set of points that satisfy the inequality $\frac{x^2}{9} + \frac{y^2}{100} \geq 1$.

14. Area of pool: $A = \pi\left(\frac{15}{2} \cdot 4\right) = 30\pi$
Area of walkway and pool:
$A = \pi\left(9 \cdot \frac{11}{2}\right) = 49.5\pi$
Area of walkway:
$49.5\pi - 30\pi = 19.5\pi \approx 61.26 \text{ m}^2$

15. See the Additional Answers section at the back of the book.

16. $(5.3 \cdot 10^9) + (9 \cdot 10^7) = 5.39 \cdot 10^9$ km

17. Answers vary. Sample: A parabola will intersect a circle three times if its vertex is on the highest point of the circle and it opens down. This is the case for the circle and the parabola described by $x^2 + y^2 = 1$ and $y = 1 - x^2$.

18–20. See the Additional Answers section at the back of the book.

Additional Answers

13a. hyperbola

13b. The foci of the hyperbola with equation $xy = 15$ are $\left(\sqrt{2 \cdot 15}, \sqrt{2 \cdot 15}\right) = \left(\sqrt{30}, \sqrt{30}\right)$ and $\left(-\sqrt{2 \cdot 15}, -\sqrt{2 \cdot 15}\right) = \left(-\sqrt{30}, -\sqrt{30}\right)$, and the focal constant is $2\sqrt{30}$. The graph of $xy = -15$ is the reflection image of the graph of $xy = 15$ over the x-axis, so the foci for $xy = -15$ are $\left(\sqrt{30}, -\sqrt{30}\right)$ and $\left(-\sqrt{30}, \sqrt{30}\right)$, and the focal constant is still $2\sqrt{30}$.

13c. Yes; the hyperbola is symmetric over $y = \pm x$.

Additional Answers can be found in the back of the book.

Additional Answers

10.

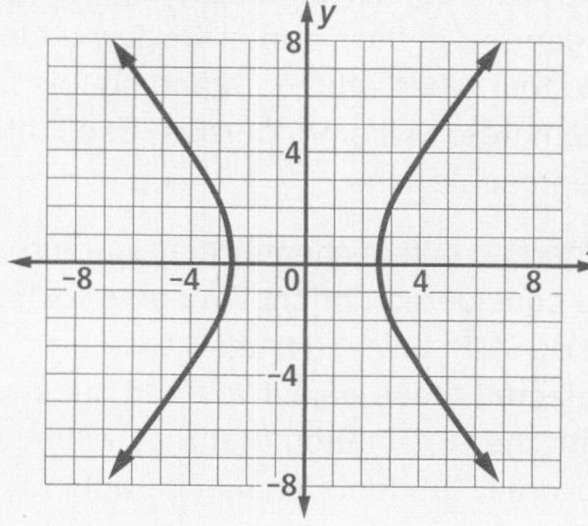

The equation represents a hyperbola with foci at $(\sqrt{41}, 0)$, and $(-\sqrt{41}, 0)$, a focal constant of 10, and vertices at $(-5, 0)$ and $(5, 0)$.

11.

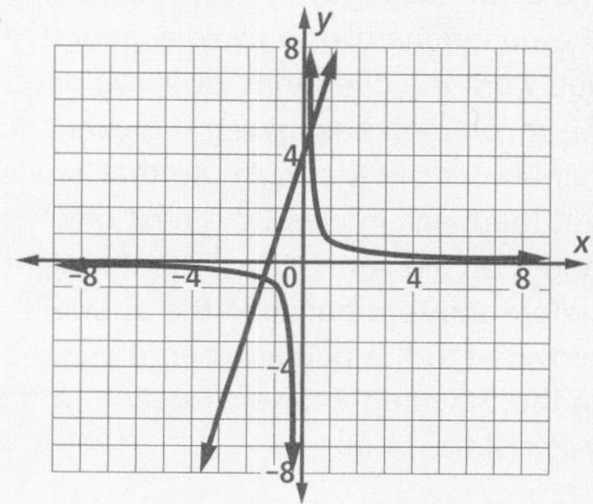

Substitute $2x + 5$ for y in the first equation:
$x(2x + 5) = 2$
$2x^2 + 5x - 2 = 0$
Use the Quadratic Formula to solve for x: $x = \frac{-5 \pm \sqrt{41}}{4}$, or $x \approx 0.35$ or $x \approx -2.85$.
Substitute these values into $xy = 2$ to find the y-values: $y \approx 5.70$ or $y \approx -0.70$.
So, the points of intersection are $(0.35, 5.70)$ and $(-2.85, -0.70)$.

12. Substitute $x^2 - 4x + 3$ for y in the second equation:
$x^2 + (x^2 - 4x + 3)^2 = 9$
$x^2 + x^4 - 8x^3 + 22x^2 - 24x + 9 = 9$
$x^4 - 8x^3 + 23x^2 - 24x = 0$
$x(x^3 - 8x^2 + 23x - 24) = 0$
$x(x - 3)(x^2 - 5x + 8) = 0$
$x = 0$ or $x = 3$ by the Zero-Product Theorem because $x^2 - 5x + 8 = 0$ has no real solutions. When $x = 0$, $y = 0^2 - 4(0) + 3 = 3$. When $x = 3$, $y = 3^2 - 4(3) + 3 = 9 - 12 + 3 = 0$.
So, the solutions to the system are $(0, 3)$ and $(3, 0)$.

Chapter Review

The main objectives for the chapter are organized in the Chapter Review under the four types of understanding this book promotes: Skills, Properties, Uses, and Representations.

Whereas end-of-chapter material may be considered optional in some texts, in UCSMP *Advanced Algebra* we have selected these objectives and questions with the expectation that they will be covered. Students should be able to answer these questions with about 85% accuracy after studying the chapter.

You may assign these questions over a single night to help students prepare for a test the next day or you may assign the questions over a two-day period. If you work the questions over two days, we recommend assigning the evens for homework the first night so that students get feedback in class the next day, and then assigning the odds the night before the test because the answers are provided to the odd-numbered questions in the Selected Answers section at the back of the book.

It is effective to ask students which questions they still do not understand and use the day as a total class discussion of the material that the class finds most difficult.

Resources

- Assessment Resources: Chapter 12 Test Forms A–D; Chapter 12 Test, Cumulative Form

Technology Resources

Teacher's Assessment Assistant, Ch. 12
Electronic Teacher's Edition, Ch. 12

Chapter 12 Chapter Review

SKILLS
PROPERTIES
USES
REPRESENTATIONS

SKILLS Procedures used to get answers

OBJECTIVE A Rewrite an equation for a conic section in the standard form of a quadratic equation in two variables. (Lesson 12-7)

In 1–6, rewrite the equation in the form $Ax^2 + Bxy + Cy^2 + Dx + Ey + F = 0$. Give the values of *A, B, C, D, E,* and *F*. 1–26. See margin.

1. $(x - 7)^2 + (y + 2)^2 = 81$
2. $y = 6(t - 3)^2 + 4$
3. $\frac{x^2}{36} - \frac{y^2}{16} = 1$
4. $\frac{a^2}{8} + \frac{b^2}{5} = 1$
5. $y = \sqrt{169 - x^2}$
6. $y = \frac{30}{x}$

OBJECTIVE B Write equations for quadratic relations and inequalities for their interiors and exteriors. (Lessons 12-1, 12-2, 12-3, 12-4, 12-6, 12-7)

7. Find an equation for the circle with center at the origin and radius 12.
8. Find an equation for the circle with center at (-3, 6) and diameter 7.
9. Give an equation for the upper semicircle of the circle with equation $a^2 + b^2 = 35$.
10. What inequality describes the interior of the circle with equation $x^2 + y^2 = 64$?
11. What sentence describes the exterior of the circle with equation $x^2 + y^2 = 64$?

In 12 and 13, write an equation for the ellipse satisfying the given conditions.

12. foci: (0, 1) and (0, -1); focal constant: 5
13. The endpoints of the major and minor axes are (4, 0), (-4, 0), (0, 7), and (0, -7).
14. Write an equation for the parabola with focus (0, -3) and directrix $y = 3$.

In 15 and 16, find an equation for a hyperbola satisfying the given conditions.

15. vertices: (2, 2) and (-2, -2)
16. foci: (9, 0) and (-9, 0); focal constant: 11

OBJECTIVE C Find the area of an ellipse. (Lesson 12-5)

In 17 and 18, find the area of the ellipse satisfying the given conditions.

17. It has equation $\frac{x^2}{100} + \frac{y^2}{49} = 1$.
18. The endpoints of its axes are (3, 0), (-3, 0), (0, 6), and (0, -6).
19. Which has a larger area and by how much: a circle of radius 15 or an ellipse with major and minor axes of lengths 46 and 20?
20. Find the area of the shaded region between an ellipse with major axis of length 7 and minor axis of length 5, and a circle with diameter 5.

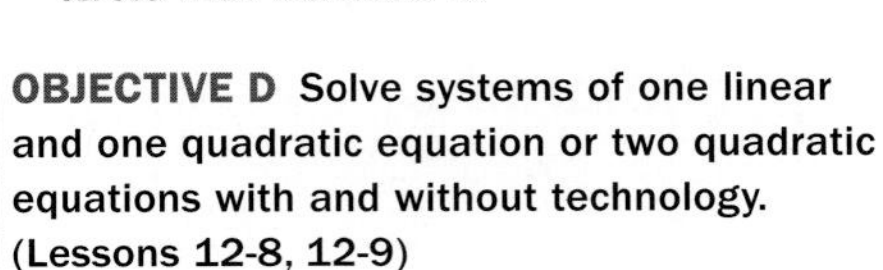

OBJECTIVE D Solve systems of one linear and one quadratic equation or two quadratic equations with and without technology. (Lessons 12-8, 12-9)

In 21–26, solve.

21. $\begin{cases} y = x^2 + 8 \\ y = -x^2 + 7x + 8 \end{cases}$
22. $\begin{cases} 6x + y = 24 \\ y = x^2 + 4x - 5 \end{cases}$
23. $\begin{cases} t = r^2 + 2r - 8 \\ t = 2r^2 + 2r - 6 \end{cases}$
24. $\begin{cases} (x - 1)^2 + y^2 = 3 \\ x^2 + (y + 1)^2 = 3 \end{cases}$
25. $\begin{cases} ab = 4 \\ b = 3a + 1 \end{cases}$
26. $\begin{cases} p^2 - q^2 = 4 \\ \frac{p^2}{16} + \frac{q^2}{9} = 1 \end{cases}$

Additional Answers

1. $x^2 + y^2 - 14x + 4y - 28 = 0$; $A = 1, B = 0, C = 1, D = -14, E = 4, F = -28$
2. $6t^2 - 36t - y + 58 = 0$; $A = 6, B = 0, C = 0, D = -36, E = -1, F = 58$
3. $\frac{1}{36}x^2 - \frac{1}{16}y^2 - 1 = 0$ (or $16x^2 - 36y^2 - 576 = 0$); $A = \frac{1}{36}, B = 0, C = -\frac{1}{16}, D = 0, E = 0, F = -1$ (or $A = 16, B = 0, C = -36, D = 0, E = 0, F = -576$)
4. $\frac{1}{8}a^2 + \frac{1}{5}b^2 - 1 = 0$ (or $5a^2 + 8b^2 - 40 = 0$); $A = \frac{1}{8}, B = 0, C = \frac{1}{5}, D = 0, E = 0, F = -1$ (or $A = 5, B = 0, C = 8, D = 0, E = 0, F = -40$)
5. $x^2 + y^2 - 169 = 0$; $A = 1, B = 0, C = 1, D = 0, E = 0, F = -169$
6. $xy - 30 = 0$; $A = 0, B = 1, C = 0, D = 0, E = 0, F = -30$

27. The product of two numbers is 1073. If one number is increased by 3 and the other is decreased by 7, the new product is 960. 27–32. See margin.
 a. Write a system of equations representing this situation.
 b. Find the numbers.

PROPERTIES Principles behind the mathematics

OBJECTIVE E Identify characteristics of parabolas, circles, ellipses, and hyperbolas. (Lessons 12-1, 12-2, 12-4, 12-6, 12-7)

In 28 and 29, identify the center and radius of the circle with the given equation.

28. $(r + 6)^2 + s^2 = 196$ 29. $x^2 + y^2 = 361$

30. Consider the ellipse with equation $\frac{x^2}{169} + \frac{y^2}{64} = 1$.
 a. Name the endpoints of its axes.
 b. State the length of its minor axis.

31. Consider the parabola with equation $y = \frac{1}{7}x^2$.
 a. Give the coordinates of its focus.
 b. Give the coordinates of its vertex.
 c. State the equation of its directrix.

32. Consider the hyperbola with equation $\frac{p^2}{25} - \frac{q^2}{9} = 1$.
 a. Name its vertices.
 b. State equations for its asymptotes.

33. Consider the ellipse with equation $\frac{x^2}{16} + \frac{y^2}{100} = 1$.
 a. Give the coordinates of its foci F_1 and F_2. $(0, 2\sqrt{21}), (0, -2\sqrt{21})$
 b. Suppose P is on the ellipse. Find the value of $PF_1 + PF_2$. 20

34. Identify the asymptotes of the hyperbola with equation $xy = \frac{23}{5}$. x-axis and y-axis

OBJECTIVE F Classify curves as circles, ellipses, parabolas, or hyperbolas using algebraic or geometric properties. (Lessons 12-1, 12-2, 12-4, 12-5, 12-6)

In 35 and 36, consider two fixed points F_1 and F_2 and a constant d. Name the curve formed by the set of points P satisfying the given conditions. 35–37. See margin.

35. $F_1P + F_2P = d$, where $d > F_1F_2$

36. $|F_1P - F_2P| = d$, where $d < F_1F_2$

37. Each figure below shows a double cone intersected by a plane. In Figure b, the plane is parallel to the edge of the cone; in Figure d, the plane is perpendicular to the axis of the cone. Identify the curve produced by each intersection.

a.
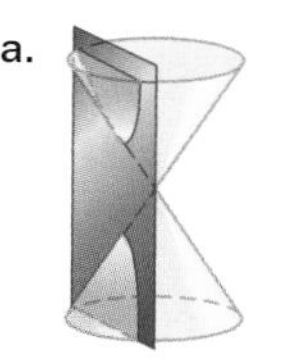

b.

c.
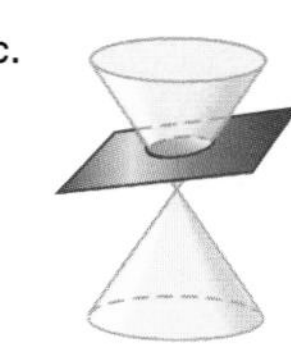

d.
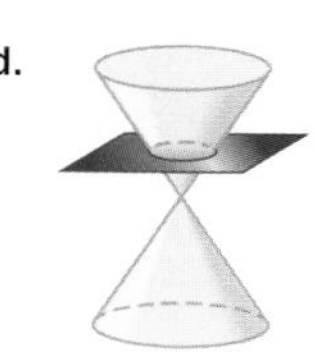

In 38–40, answer true or false.

38. A hyperbola can be considered as the union of two parabolas. false

39. All quadratic relations in two variables can be formed by the intersection of a plane and a double cone. true

40. The image of an ellipse under a scale change can be a circle. true

41. a. What equation describes the image of the circle with equation $x^2 + y^2 = 1$ under the transformation $S: (x, y) \to (5x, 8y)$? $\frac{x^2}{25} + \frac{y^2}{64} = 1$
 b. What kind of curve is the image in Part a? ellipse

Additional Answers

7. $x^2 + y^2 = 144$
8. $(x + 3)^2 + (y - 6)^2 = 12.25$
9. $b = \sqrt{35 - a^2}$
10. $x^2 + y^2 < 64$
11. $x^2 + y^2 > 64$
12. $\frac{x^2}{5.25} + \frac{y^2}{6.25} = 1$
13. $\frac{x^2}{16} + \frac{y^2}{49} = 1$
14. $y = -\frac{1}{12}x^2$
15. $y = \frac{4}{x}$
16. $\frac{x^2}{30.25} - \frac{y^2}{50.75} = 1$
17. $70\pi \approx 219.91$
18. $18\pi \approx 56.55$
19. the ellipse by 5π or 15.71 units^2
20. $2.5\pi \approx 7.85$
21. (0, 8) or $\left(\frac{7}{2}, \frac{81}{4}\right)$
22. (-12.35, 98.1) or (2.35, 9.91)
23. no solutions
24. (-0.62, 0.62) or (1.62, -1.62)
25. $a = \frac{-4}{3}$ and $b = -3$ or $a = 1$ and $b = 4$
26. $p = \frac{4\sqrt{13}}{5}$ and $q = \frac{6\sqrt{3}}{5}$, $p = \frac{4\sqrt{13}}{5}$ and $q = -\frac{6\sqrt{3}}{5}$, $p = -\frac{4\sqrt{13}}{5}$ and $q = \frac{6\sqrt{3}}{5}$, or $p = -\frac{4\sqrt{13}}{5}$ and $q = -\frac{6\sqrt{3}}{5}$

27a. $\begin{cases} ab = 1073 \\ (a + 3)(b - 7) = 960 \end{cases}$

27b. $-\frac{111}{7}$ and $\frac{-203}{3}$ or 29 and 37

28. (-6, 0); 14
29. (0, 0); 19

30a. (-13, 0), (13, 0), (0, 8), (0, -8)

30b. 16

31a. $\left(0, \frac{7}{4}\right)$

31b. (0, 0)

31c. $y = -\frac{7}{4}$

32a. (5, 0) and (-5, 0)

32b. $y = \pm\frac{3}{5}x$

35. ellipse
36. hyperbola

37a. hyperbola

37b. parabola

37c. ellipse

37d. circle

Additional Answers

43. $\begin{cases} x^2 + y^2 \leq 250{,}000 \\ x^2 + y^2 \geq 235{,}225 \end{cases}$

44. The person must be at least 2.19 ft away from either side.

45a. If the moving van is in a lane on a two-way road, it will not be able to pass through the tunnel because the tunnel is only 11.5 ft tall 6 ft from the center. The outer corner of the truck would not fit.

45b. Yes, the tunnel is 12.6 ft tall 3 ft from the center so if the truck drives in the center of the roadway, it will be able to fit through the tunnel with more than 0.5 ft to spare.

46. 8.5 in. by 11 in.

47a. $\begin{cases} x^2 + y^2 = 5{,}625 \\ (x + 30)^2 + (y - 50)^2 = 5{,}625 \end{cases}$

47b. (–74.25, –10.55) or (44.25, 60.55)

48a. $\begin{cases} 2\ell + 2w = 150 \\ \ell w = 1300 \end{cases}$

48b. $\ell = -\frac{5(\sqrt{17} - 15)}{2} \approx 27.2$ m and $w = \frac{5(\sqrt{17} + 15)}{2} \approx 47.8$ m or $\ell = \frac{5(\sqrt{17} + 15)}{2}$ and $w = -\frac{5(\sqrt{17} - 15)}{2}$. Perla can either make a pen that is 27.2 m long and 47.8 m wide or a pen that is 47.8 m long and 27.2 m wide.

49. The price was \$60 in the first month and \$80 in the second month.

USES Applications of mathematics in real-world situations

OBJECTIVE G Use circles and ellipses to solve real-world problems. (Lesson 12-2, 12-3, 12-4, 12-5)

42. An elliptical garden surrounds a circular fountain with diameter 10 feet. The major axis of the garden is 20 feet long, and the minor axis is 10 feet long. What is the area of the garden? $25\pi \approx 78.54$ ft²

43. A castle is surrounded by a circular moat 15 feet wide. The distance from the center of the castle to the outside of the moat is 500 feet. If the center of the castle is considered the origin, write a system of inequalities to describe the set of points on the surface of the moat.

43–49. See margin.

15 ft

500 ft

top view

44. A tent is in the form of half a cylindrical surface. Each cross section is a semiellipse (half an ellipse) with base length 20 feet and height 8 feet. How close to either end can a person 5 feet tall stand straight up?

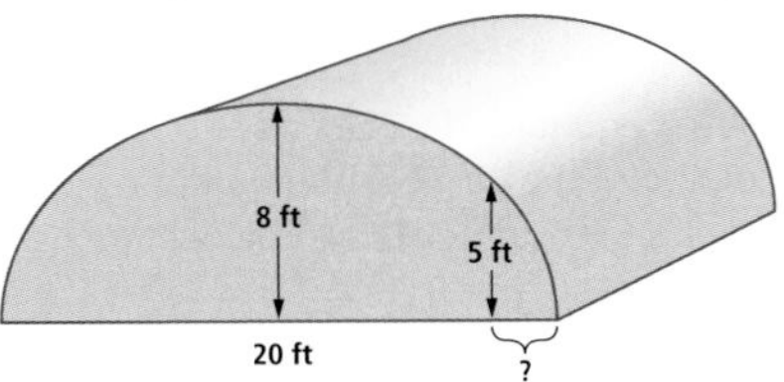

45. A moving van 6 ft wide and 12 ft tall is approaching a semicircular tunnel with radius 13 ft.
   a. Explain why the truck cannot pass through the tunnel if it stays in its lane.
   b. Can the moving van fit through the tunnel if it is allowed to drive anywhere on the roadway? Justify your answer.

OBJECTIVE H Use systems of quadratic equations to solve real-world problems. (Lessons 12-8, 12-9)

46. A piece of paper has an area of 93.5 square inches and a perimeter of 39 inches. Find the dimensions of the piece of paper.

47. Suppose the epicenter of an earthquake is 75 miles away from monitoring stations 1 and 2. Station 2 is 30 miles west and 50 miles north of Station 1. Let Station 1 be at the origin of a coordinate system.
   a. Write a system of equations to describe the location (x, y) of the epicenter.
   b. Find the coordinates of all possible locations of the epicenter relative to Station 1.

48. Perla has 150 meters of fencing material and wants to form a rectangular pen with an area of 1300 square meters.
   a. Let w = the width of the pen and ℓ = its length. Write a system of equations to determine w and ℓ.
   b. Solve the system and interpret your answer in the context of the problem.

49. One month Wanda's Wonderful Wagons took in \$12,000 from sales of wagons. The next month Wanda sold 40 fewer wagons because she had raised the price by \$20. In spite of this, total sales rose to \$12,800. Find the price of wagons in each month.

Additional Answers

50.

51.

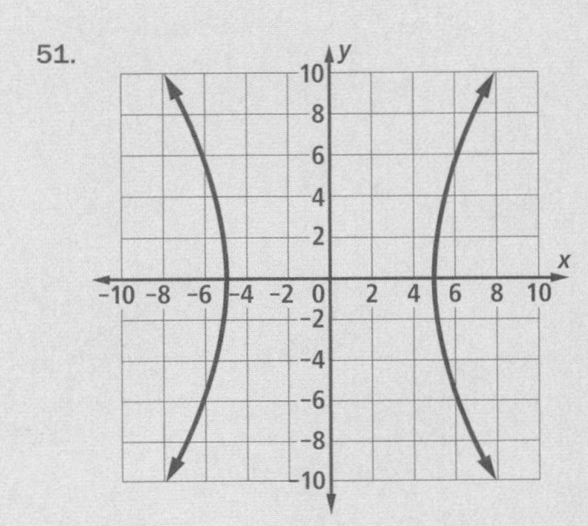

REPRESENTATIONS Pictures, graphs, or objects that illustrate concepts

OBJECTIVE I **Graph quadratic relations when given equations for them in standard form, and vice versa. (Lessons 12-2, 12-4, 12-6, 12-7)** 50–71. See margin.

In 50–53, sketch a graph of the equation.

50. $\frac{x^2}{25} + \frac{y^2}{64} = 1$
51. $\frac{x^2}{25} - \frac{y^2}{64} = 1$
52. $xy - 18 = 0$
53. $x^2 + y^2 = 16$

In 54 and 55, state an equation for the curve.

54.

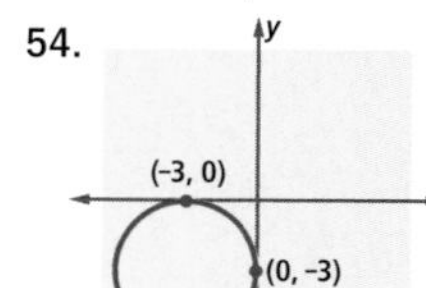

55.

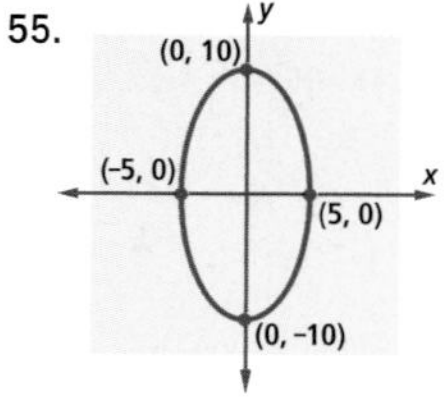

Multiple Choice In 56 and 57, select the equation that best describes each graph.

A $\frac{x^2}{a^2} + \frac{y^2}{b^2} = 1$
B $\frac{x^2}{a^2} - \frac{y^2}{b^2} = 1$
C $y = ax^2$
D $xy = a$

56.

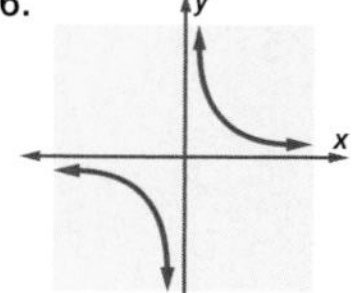

57.

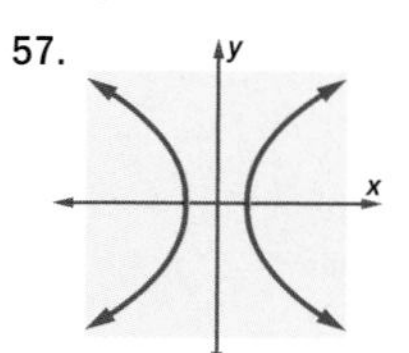

OBJECTIVE J **Graph interiors and exteriors of ellipses when given inequalities for them, and vice versa. (Lesson 12-3)**

58. Write a system of inequalities to represent the points in the shaded region at the right.

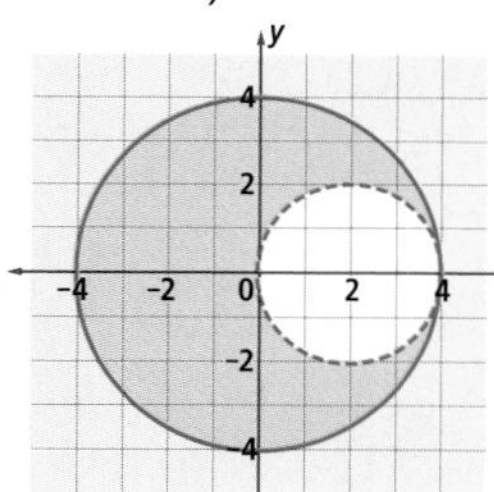

In 59 and 60, sketch a graph of the inequality.

59. $x^2 + (y - 4)^2 > 25$
60. $\frac{x^2}{16} + \frac{y^2}{4} \le 1$

OBJECTIVE K **Interpret representations of quadratic-linear and quadratic-quadratic systems. (Lessons 12-8, 12-9)**

In 61 and 62, give equations for

61. a circle and a hyperbola that intersect in exactly three points.
62. two hyperbolas that intersect exactly twice.
63. Someone claims that the sum of two real numbers is 17 and their product is 73. Use equations and a graph to explain why this is impossible.
64. a. Graph $x^2 + y^2 = 5$ and $y = x^2 - 2$ in the same window.
    b. Find the points of intersection to the nearest tenth.

OBJECTIVE L **Draw a graph or interpret drawings or graphs of conic sections based on their definitions. (Lessons 12-1, 12-2, 12-4, 12-6)**

65. Graph the set of points equidistant from the point (5, 3) and the line $y = -1$.
66. Draw a line ℓ and point F not on ℓ. Sketch 5 points equidistant from F and ℓ.
67. Graph the set of points that are 2.5 units from the origin.
68. Draw two points F_1 and F_2. Sketch 6 more points whose distances from F_1 and F_2 add up to $2F_1F_2$.
69. Graph the set of points whose distances from (0, -3) and (0, 3) add up to 8.
70. Draw two points F_1 and F_2 4 units apart. Sketch 3 points that are 2 units farther from F_1 than from F_2 and 3 points that are 2 units farther from F_2 than from F_1.
71. Graph the set of points whose difference of distances from (-6, 0) and (6, 0) is 5.

Assessment

Evaluation The *Assessment Resources* provide four forms of the Chapter 12 Test. Forms A and B present parallel versions of a short-answer format. Form C consists of four to six short-response questions that cover the SPUR objectives from Chapter 12. Form D offers performance assessment that covers a subset (or even just one) of the SPUR objectives for the chapter. The fifth type of test is a Chapter 12 Test, Cumulative Form. About 50% of this test covers Chapter 12, and the remaining 50% covers the previous chapters evenly.

Feedback After students have taken the test for Chapter 12 and you have scored the results, return the tests to students for discussion. Class discussion on the questions that caused trouble for most students can be very effective in identifying and clarifying misunderstandings. You might want to have them note the items they missed and work either in groups or at home to correct them. It is important for students to receive feedback on every chapter test, and we recommend that students see and correct their mistakes before proceeding too far into the next chapter.

Suggestions for Assignment Assign Lesson 13-1 for homework the evening of the test. It gives students work to do after they have completed the test and keeps the class moving. If you do not do this, you may cover one less chapter over the course of the year.

Additional Answers

52.

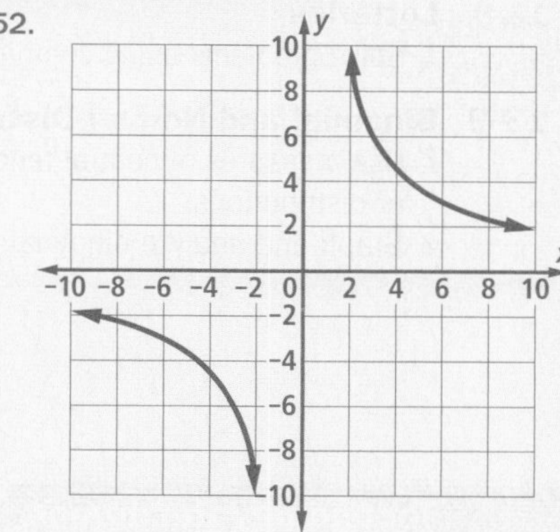

Additional Answers

53.

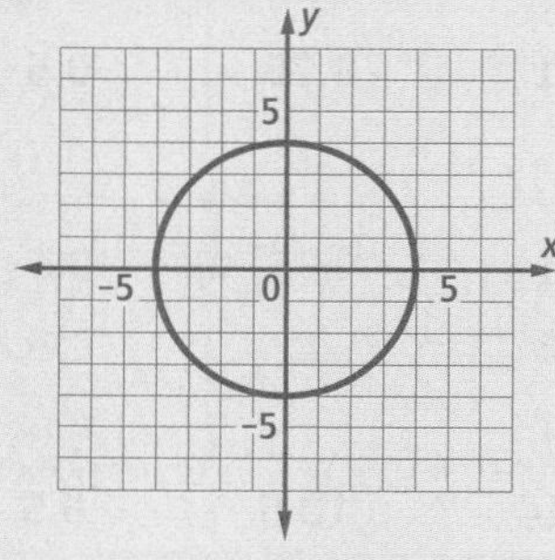

54. $(x + 3)^2 + (y + 3)^2 = 9$

55. $\frac{x^2}{25} + \frac{y^2}{100} = 1$

56. D

57. B

58. $\begin{cases} x^2 + y^2 \le 16 \\ (x - 2)^2 + y^2 > 4 \end{cases}$

59–71. Additional Answers can be found in the back of the book.

Chapter

13 Series and Combinations

Chapter Overview

Lesson	Objectives	Local Standards	Pacing (in days) Average	Advanced	Block
13-1	**Arithmetic Series** A Calculate values of arithmetic series. C Use summation (Σ) and factorial (!) notation. G Solve real-world problems using arithmetic or geometric series.		1	0.75	0.5
13-2	**Geometric Series** B Calculate values of finite geometric series. C Use summation (Σ) and factorial (!) notation. G Solve real-world problems using arithmetic or geometric series.		1	0.75	0.5
13-3	**Using Series in Statistics Formulas** C Use summation (Σ) and factorial (!) notation. I Use measures of central tendency or dispersion to describe data or distributions.		1	0.75	0.5
	QUIZ 1		0.5	0.5	0.25
13-4	**Subsets and Combinations** C Use summation (Σ) and factorial (!) notation. D Calculate permutations and combinations. H Solve real-world counting problems involving permutations or combinations.		1	0.75	0.5
13-5	**Pascal's Triangle** D Calculate permutations and combinations. F Recognize properties of Pascal's Triangle.		1	0.75	0.5
13-6	**The Binomial Theorem** E Use the Binomial Theorem to expand binomials. F Recognize properties of Pascal's Triangle.		1	0.75	0.5
	QUIZ 2		0.5	0.5	0.25
13-7	**Probability and Combinations** J Solve problems using combinations and probability.		1	0.75	0.5
13-8	**Lotteries** J Solve problems using combinations and probability.		1	0.75	0.5
13-9	**Binomial and Normal Distributions** I Use measures of central tendency or dispersion to describe data or distributions. K Graph and analyze binomial and normal distributions.		1	0.75	0.5
		Self-Test	1	0.75	0.5
		Chapter Review	2	1	0.5
		Test	1	1	0.5
		TOTAL	14	10.5	6.5

Technology Resources

Teacher's Assessment Assistant, Ch. 13

Electronic Teacher's Edition, Ch. 13

Differentiated Options  Universal Access

	Accommodating the Learner	Vocabulary Development	Ongoing Assessment	Materials
13-1	pp. 871, 872	p. 870	written, p. 875	
13-2	p. 878	p. 877	group, p. 882	
13-3	p. 886	p. 885	group, p. 888	paper and the first two paragraphs under the Big Idea of Lesson 13-5
13-4	pp. 892, 893	p. 894	group, p. 895	
13-5	pp. 899, 900	p. 898	group, p. 902	
13-6	pp. 905, 906	p. 905	written, p. 908	CAS
13-7	pp. 911, 912	p. 912	group, p. 916	penny or other coin
13-8	p. 919	p. 918	written, p. 921	
13-9	p. 925	p. 924	written, p. 927	

Objectives

	Lessons	Self-Test Questions	Chapter Review Questions
Skills			
A Calculate values of arithmetic series.	13-1	14b	1-5
B Calculate values of finite geometric series.	13-2	15, 16	6–10
C Use summation (Σ) and factorial (!) notation.	13-1, 13-2, 13-3, 13-4	1, 2, 11, 14a	11-19
D Calculate permutations and combinations.	13-4, 13-5	9, 10, 12a	20-27
E Use the Binomial Theorem to expand binomials.	13-6	5, 6	28-34
Properties			
F Recognize properties of Pascal's Triangle.	13-5, 13-6	12b, 22	35-39
Uses			
G Solve real-world problems using arithmetic or geometric series.	13-1, 13-2	13	40-43
H Solve real-world counting problems involving permutations or combinations.	13-4	7, 8	44-48
I Use measures of central tendency or dispersion to describe data or distributions.	13-3, 13-9	3, 4, 19	49-54
J Solve problems using combinations and probability.	13-7, 13-8	17, 18, 20	55-63
Representations			
K Graph and analyze binomial and normal distributions.	13-9	21	64-65

Resource Masters Chapter 13

Resource Master 1, Graph Paper (page 2), can be used with Lesson 13-5.

Resource Master 245 Lesson 13-1

Resource Master 244 Lesson 13-1

Warm-up

1. Find the sum of the integers from 1 to 20 by adding 1 + 20, 2 + 19, and so on.
2. Repeat Warm-Up 1 but find the sum of the integers from 1 to 35.
3. Use the answer to Warm-Up 2 to find the sum of the first 35 even integers, beginning with 2.
4. Use the answer to Warm-Up 3 to find the sum of 35 even integers beginning with 8.

Additional Examples

1. Every birthday, Cathy receives charms for a charm bracelet. She received one charm on her 1st birthday, two charms on her 2nd birthday, three charms on her 3rd birthday, and so on. What was the total number of charms she had received after her 16th birthday?

   Solution Find the sum of consecutive integers from 1 to 16. Substitute 16 for n in the formula for S_n:

   $S_{16} = \frac{\_\_\_}{2}(1 + \_\_\_) = \_\_\_$.

   Cathy had received ___ charms after her 16th birthday.
2. An auditorium has 24 rows, with 10 seats in the front row and 3 more seats in each row thereafter. How many seats are there in all?

Resource Masters for Lesson 13-1

Resource Master 247 Lesson 13-2

Resource Master 246 Lesson 13-2

Warm-up

What are the first five terms of each geometric sequence?

1. first term 1, common ratio 0.5
2. first term 1, common ratio 3
3. first term 144, common ratio $\frac{3}{4}$
4. first term 144, common ratio $-\frac{3}{4}$

Additional Example

1. a. Write the value of S_{12} from the Activity as a sum of the terms in a geometric sequence.
   b. Write S_{12} using Σ-notation.
   c. Compute exact and approximate values of S_{12} with a calculator or a CAS.

   Solution

   a. The terms in the geometric sequence are the first 12 positive integer powers of $\frac{1}{2}$. So, $S_{12} = \frac{1}{2} + \frac{1}{4} + \frac{1}{8} + \_\_\_ + \_\_\_ + \_\_\_ + \_\_\_ + \_\_\_ + \_\_\_ + \_\_\_ + \_\_\_ + \_\_\_$.
   b. There are 12 terms, and an expression for the kth term is $\left(\frac{1}{2}\right)^k$.

   So, $S_{12} = \sum \_\_\_$.
   c. The exact value is ___. An approximate value is ___.

Resource Masters for Lesson 13-2

Resource Master 249 Lesson 13-2

Resource Master 248 Lesson 13-2

Activity

n	g_n (series)	S_n (value)
1	$\frac{1}{2}$	$\frac{1}{2}$
2	$\frac{1}{2} + \frac{1}{4}$	$\frac{3}{4}$
3	$\frac{1}{2} + \frac{1}{4} + \frac{1}{8}$	
4		
5		

Question 11a.

Standard Form	Factored Form
	$(r - 1)(r + 1)$
$r^3 - 1$	
$r^4 - 1$	
$r^5 - 1$	
$r^6 - 1$	

Resource Masters for Lesson 13-2

Resource Master 251 Lesson 13-3

Resource Master 250 Lesson 13-3

Warm-Up

Suppose $x_1 = 8$, $x_2 = 15$, $x_3 = 7$, $x_4 = 10$, and $x_5 = 20$. Calculate the value of each series.

1. $\sum_{i=1}^{4} x_i$
2. $\frac{\sum_{i=1}^{5} x_i}{5}$
3. $\sum_{i=1}^{5} \left(x_i^2\right)$
4. $\sum_{i=1}^{5} (x_i - \mu)^2$, where μ is the value you found in Warm-Up 2
5. $\sum_{i=1}^{5} |x_i - \mu|$, where μ is the value you found in Warm-Up 2

Additional Example

You are offered the chance to play one of two games—Game A or Game B. In each game, you reach into a jar and pull out a slip of paper. You win the dollar amount written on the slip. In both games, there are 8 slips of paper in the jar with a mean value of $100.

Game A Slips			
$99	$99	$100	$100
$100	$100	$101	$101
Game B Slips			
$0	$0	$0	$0
$0	$0	$0	$800

Calculate the *m.a.d.* of the values on the slips for each game. Which game is riskier?

Resource Masters for Lesson 13-3

Resource Master 253 Lesson 13-4

Resource Master 252 Lesson 13-4

Warm-up

1. List all the strings of the four letters O, P, S, and T, such as STOP, that can be made by using each of the letters only once.
2. How many of the strings are words in the English language?

Additional Examples

1. Work in a group of five students. Work with your group to list the permutations beginning with one of the five numbers given.
   a. Write all the possible orders in which a person might choose the numbers 2, 4, 6, 8, and 10 for a lottery ticket.
   b. How many permutations of these five numbers are there?
2. Find $10 \cdot 11 \cdot 12 \cdot 13 \cdot 14 \cdot 15$ using factorials.
3. A committee of 5 people is to be chosen from 12 applicants. In how many different ways can this be done?

Resource Masters for Lesson 13-4

Resource Master 255 Lesson 13-5

Resource Master 254 Lesson 13-5

Warm-up

1. Write or copy the first eight rows of Pascal's Triangle.
2. Let the first row be row 0. Starting with row 1, place alternating − and + signs between the numbers in each row. For example, in row 2 you would have $1 - 2 + 1$.
3. Add the resulting numbers in each row and describe the pattern of sums.
4. Explain the pattern.

Additional Examples

1. Write row 12 of Pascal's Triangle.
2. Solve $\binom{x}{y} = \binom{8}{6} + \binom{8}{7}$.
3. Find $\binom{9}{4}$.

Solution Use Pascal's Triangle Explicit Formula:

$\binom{9}{4} = \frac{\_\_\_!}{\_\_\_!(\_\_\_ - \_\_\_)!} = \_\_\_$.

Resource Masters for Lesson 13-5

Resource Master 257 Lesson 13-6

Resource Master 256 Lesson 13-6

Warm-up

Expand by hand and check with a CAS.

1. $(x - y)^2$
2. $(x - y)^3$
3. $(x - y)^4$

Additional Examples

1. Expand $(a + b)^5$.
2. Expand $(2d + 3f)^4$.
3. Expand $(3x^2 - 2)^3$.

   Solution Think of $3x^2$ as *a* and -2 as *b*. Then follow the form of $(a + b)^3$.

   $(3x^2 - 2)^3 = (\_\_)(3x^2)^{\_\_} + (\_\_)(3x^2)^{\_\_} \cdot (-2)^{\_\_} +$

   $(\_\_)(3x^2)^{\_\_} \cdot (-2)^{\_\_} + (\_\_) \cdot (-2)^{\_\_} = \_\_x^{\_\_} +$

   $\_\_x^{\_\_} + \_\_x^{\_\_} + \_\_$

4. Find the sixth term in the expansion of $(a + b)^{12}$.

Resource Masters for Lesson 13-6

Resource Master 259 Lesson 13-7

Resource Master 258 Lesson 13-7

Warm-up

1. If the probability that an event will occur is the given number, what is the probability that the event will *not* occur?
   a. 35%
   b. $\frac{12}{13}$
   c. 0.95
   d. 0
2. Suppose a stoplight is red for 30 seconds and green for 20 seconds, repeatedly. If you come to this stoplight two days in a row, what is the probability that the stoplight will be
   a. red both days?
   b. red the first day and green the second day?
   c. green the first day and red the second day?
   d. green both days?

Additional Examples

1. Suppose a fair coin is flipped five times. What is the probability of obtaining exactly three heads?
2. In Rhode Island in 2005, the probability that a child would be born with a birth defect was about $\frac{3}{50}$. In the Cass family, there were 5 births, and 1 of the children was born with a birth defect. What is the probability that this would happen if birth defects occur at random?

Resource Masters for Lesson 13-7

Resource Master 260 Lesson 13-7

Activity 1

Trial	Sequence	Number of Heads
1		
2		
⋮		

	0 heads	1 head	2 heads	3 heads	4 heads
Your Tally					
Class Tally					
Relative Frequency					

Resource Master for Lesson 13-7

Resource Master 261 Lesson 13-7

Activity 2

n	0	1	2	3	4
Sequences of 4 Tosses with *n* Heads		THTT HTTT ____	HTTH ____		
y = Number of Sequences with *n* Heads					

Guided Example 3

Number of Successes	Number of Failures	Binomial Expression	Probability
0	3	$\binom{3}{0}p^0q^3$	____ ≈ ____
1	2	$\binom{3}{1}p^1q^{\_\_}$	
2	1	$\_\_p^{\_\_}q^{\_\_}$	
3			

Resource Master for Lesson 13-7

Resource Master 262 Lesson 13-8

Warm-up

1. Does your state have its own state lottery? Does it participate in a multistate lottery?
2. Do you know any people who play the lottery? Have any of them won a major prize?
3. If your state runs lottery games, pick the one with the largest prize. What do you think the chances are that a purchaser of a single ticket will win the grand prize?

Additional Example

1. To win the multistate lottery Hot Lotto you must choose five correct numbers from 1 through 39 and another "hot ball" from 1 through 19. What is the probability of picking the six winning numbers in this lottery game?

   Solution The number of possible combinations for the first five numbers that could be chosen is $\binom{39}{\_\_} = \frac{39!}{(\_\_)(\_\_)} = \_\_$.

   There are 19 choices for the additional ball. So there are ____ · 19 = ____ possible combinations of numbers to choose. Because each combination has the same chance of being drawn, the probability that a particular combination will appear is $\frac{1}{\_\_}$.

   So the probability of picking the five winning numbers is $\frac{1}{\_\_}$ or about ____.

Resource Master for Lesson 13-8

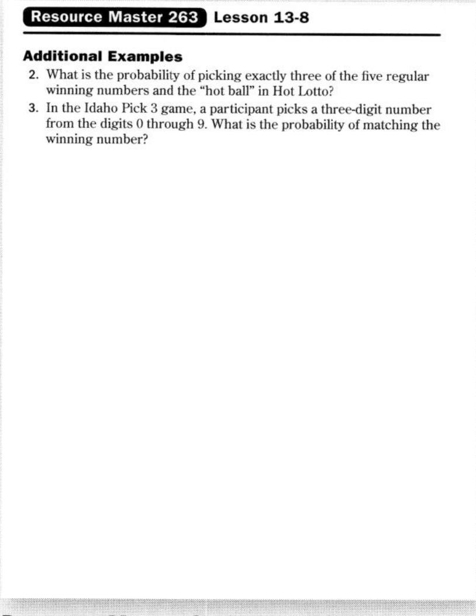

Resource Master 263 Lesson 13-8

Additional Examples

2. What is the probability of picking exactly three of the five regular winning numbers and the "hot ball" in Hot Lotto?
3. In the Idaho Pick 3 game, a participant picks a three-digit number from the digits 0 through 9. What is the probability of matching the winning number?

Resource Master for Lesson 13-8

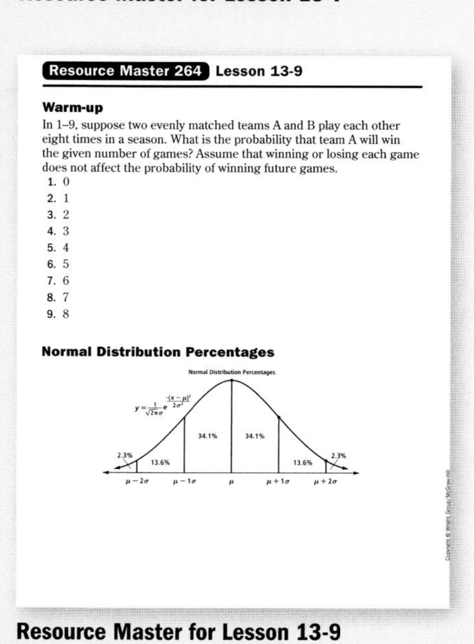

Resource Master 264 Lesson 13-9

Warm-up

In 1–9, suppose two evenly matched teams A and B play each other eight times in a season. What is the probability that team A will win the given number of games? Assume that winning or losing each game does not affect the probability of winning future games.

1. 0
2. 1
3. 2
4. 3
5. 4
6. 5
7. 6
8. 7
9. 8

Normal Distribution Percentages

Resource Master for Lesson 13-9

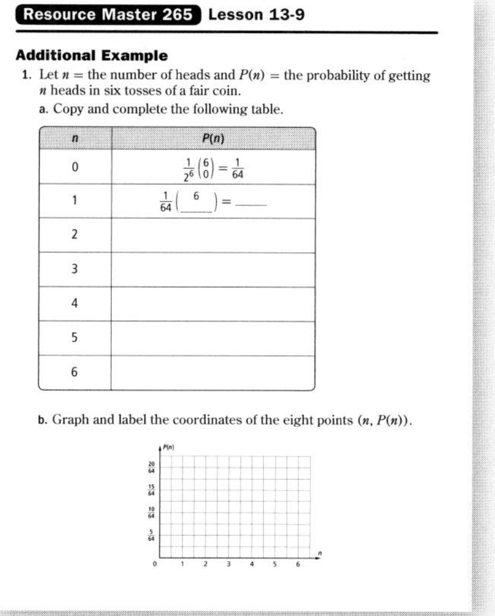

Resource Master 265 Lesson 13-9

Additional Example

1. Let *n* = the number of heads and *P*(*n*) = the probability of getting *n* heads in six tosses of a fair coin.

   a. Copy and complete the following table.

n	*P*(*n*)
0	$\frac{1}{2^6}\binom{6}{0} = \frac{1}{64}$
1	$\frac{1}{64}\binom{6}{\_\_} = \_\_$
2	
3	
4	
5	
6	

   b. Graph and label the coordinates of the eight points (*n*, *P*(*n*)).

Resource Master for Lesson 13-9

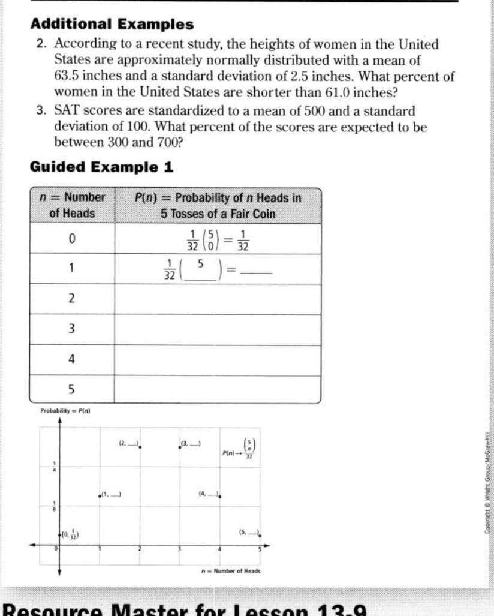

Resource Master 266 Lesson 13-9

Additional Examples

2. According to a recent study, the heights of women in the United States are approximately normally distributed with a mean of 63.5 inches and a standard deviation of 2.5 inches. What percent of women in the United States are shorter than 61.0 inches?
3. SAT scores are standardized to a mean of 500 and a standard deviation of 100. What percent of the scores are expected to be between 300 and 700?

Guided Example 1

n = Number of Heads	*P*(*n*) = Probability of *n* Heads in 5 Tosses of a Fair Coin
0	$\frac{1}{32}\binom{5}{0} = \frac{1}{32}$
1	$\frac{1}{32}\binom{5}{\_\_} = \_\_$
2	
3	
4	
5	

Resource Master for Lesson 13-9

Chapter

13

Pacing

Each lesson in this chapter is designed to be covered in 1 day. At the end of the chapter, you should plan to spend 1 day to review the Self-Test, 1 to 2 days for the Chapter Review, and 1 day for a test. You may wish to spend a day on projects and possibly a day is needed for quizzes. This chapter should therefore take 13–14 days. We strongly advise you not to spend more than 15 days on this chapter.

Overview

These pages present the major applications of combinations that students will encounter and display the array known as Pascal's Triangle.

Using Pages 866–867

Have students write the next four rows of Pascal's Triangle. Then have them find the sum of the elements in each row. The pattern of sums (the nonnegative integer powers of 2) is so simple that they can use that pattern to check whether they have written the correct elements for each row. Row 8: 1, 8, 28, 56, 70, 56, 28, 8, 1; Row 9: 1, 9, 36, 84, 126, 126, 84, 36, 9, 1; Row 10: 1, 10, 45, 120, 210, 252, 210, 120, 45, 10, 1; Row 11: 1, 11, 55, 165, 330, 462, 462, 330, 165, 55, 11, 1; Sum, Row 8: 256; Sum, Row 9: 512; Sum, Row 10: 1024; Sum, Row 11: 2048

Chapter 13 Series and Combinations

Contents

This chapter on series and combinations extends many of the theorems, techniques, and ideas from earlier in the book.

When an employee sets aside a regular portion of wages as savings earning interest, or a ball bounces until it comes to rest, the total amount saved or the total distance traveled is the sum of terms of a sequence. The indicated sum of terms of a sequence is called a *series*. Using the mathematics of polynomials and exponential functions that you have already learned, you can derive formulas related to these series and answer questions about them.

Chapter 13 Overview

This chapter discusses the most important applications of combinations, including Pascal's Triangle and the Binomial Theorem, briefly introducing the ways in which these concepts are used in statistics.

The lessons in this chapter provide only an introduction to each topic; therefore, Chapter 13 is not designed as a chapter in which concept mastery is expected. In the UCSMP series, the ideas presented in this chapter are discussed in much more detail in UCSMP *Functions, Statistics, and Trigonometry* and UCSMP *Precalculus and Discrete Mathematics.* If your students will study from *Functions, Statistics, and Trigonometry* in their next course, this chapter is optional. On the other hand, many students end their formal study of mathematics with Advanced Algebra, and all consumers should know something about lotteries and the normal distribution.

Lessons 13-1 and 13-2 cover arithmetic and geometric series, which are the sums of consecutive terms of arithmetic and

An important pattern with surprising connections is *Pascal's Triangle*. Rows 0–7 of this infinite triangular array of numbers are shown below.

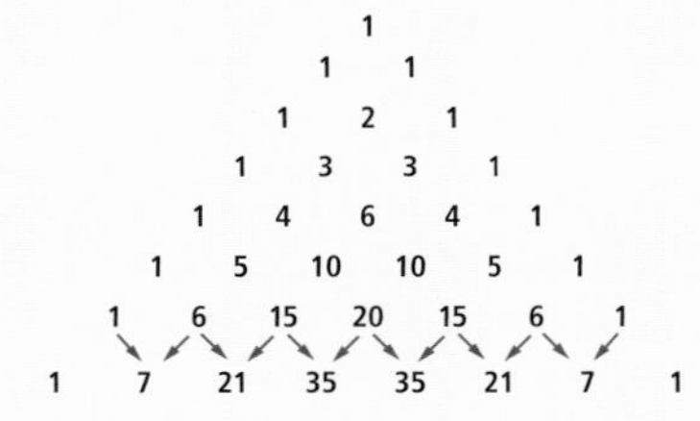

The arrows between rows 6 and 7 show how the *sum* of two elements in one row is an element in the next row. Yet an explicit formula for each element involves *products*.

Pascal's Triangle may have been discovered independently by ancient Chinese, Indian, and Persian mathematicians, who used it to expand the power $(x + y)^n$ of any binomial. The French mathematician Blaise Pascal (1623–1662) later rediscovered the pattern and publicized it as a way to answer questions about probability. The entries in Pascal's Triangle are used to answer counting questions, to compute probabilities, and to help describe statistical distributions.

867

geometric sequences, respectively, using summation notation with the symbol Σ. Summation notation is applied to statistics formulas in Lesson 13-3. The factorial symbol (!) is introduced in Lesson 13-4 to provide the shorthand necessary for formulas involving combinations. In Lesson 13-5, Pascal's Triangle is introduced as a 2-dimensional sequence whose elements can be described with $\binom{n}{r}$ notation, and the familiar factorial formula for $\binom{n}{r}$ is given. In Lesson 13-6, the geometric sequence of powers of $(x + y)$ gives rise to polynomials whose coefficients are found in Pascal's Triangle. The application of Pascal's Triangle to combinations and probability is studied in Lesson 13-7. In Lessons 13-8 and 13-9, these ideas are used to discuss lotteries, one of today's most visible applications of combinations, and the binomial and normal probability distributions, which explain the distributions of scores on college-entrance exams.

Explain the defining pattern of Pascal's Triangle. Find out if any students have previously seen Pascal's Triangle. Because this pattern is found in many mathematics books, even at early elementary levels, you should not be surprised if some have seen it. Ask what students know about it.

Chapter 13 Projects

At the end of each chapter, you will find projects related to the chapter. At this time, you might want to have students look over the projects on pages 928 and 929. You might want to have students tentatively select a project on which to work. Then, as students read and progress through the chapter, they can finalize their project choices.

Sometimes students might work alone. At other times, you might let them collaborate with classmates for a presentation and discussion. We recommend that you allow for diversity and encourage students to use their imaginations when presenting their projects. As students work on projects throughout the year, they should see many uses of mathematics in the real world.

Lesson

13-1

GOAL

Use various methods to find the sum of consecutive terms of an arithmetic sequence and represent this sum using Σ-notation.

SPUR Objectives

A Calculate values of arithmetic series.

C Use summation (Σ) notation.

G Solve real-world problems using arithmetic series.

Materials/Resources

- Lesson Masters 13-1A and 13-1B
- Resource Masters 244 and 245

HOMEWORK

Suggestions for Assignment

- Questions 1–26
- Question 27 (extra credit)
- Reading Lesson 13-2
- Covering the Ideas 13-2

Local Standards

1 Warm-Up

1. Find the sum of the integers from 1 to 20 by adding 1 + 20, 2 + 19, and so on. 21 · 10 = 210
2. Repeat Warm-Up 1 but find the sum of the integers from 1 to 35. 36 · 17 + 18 = 630
3. Use the answer to Warm-Up 2 to find the sum of the first 35 even integers, beginning with 2. 1260
4. Use the answer to Warm-Up 3 to find the sum of 35 even integers beginning with 8. 1470

Lesson 13-1

Arithmetic Series

Vocabulary

series
arithmetic series
Σ, sigma
Σ-notation, sigma notation, summation notation
index variable, index

▸ **BIG IDEA** There are several ways to find sums of the successive terms of an arithmetic sequence.

Mental Math

Consider the arithmetic sequence defined by $a_n = 3n - 12$.

a. Find a_1, a_2, and a_3. −9; −6; −3

b. Find $a_1 + a_2 + a_3$. −18

c. Find a_{101}, a_{102}, and a_{103}. 291; 294; 297

d. Find $a_{101} + a_{102} + a_{103}$. 882

Sums of Consecutive Integers

There is a story the famous mathematician Carl Gauss often told about himself. When he was in third grade, his class misbehaved and the teacher gave the following problem as punishment:

"Add the whole numbers from 1 to 100."

Gauss solved the problem in almost no time at all. His idea was the following. Let S be the desired sum.

$$S = 1 + 2 + 3 + \ldots + 98 + 99 + 100$$

Using the Commutative Property of Addition, the sum can be rewritten in reverse order.

$$S = 100 + 99 + 98 + \ldots + 3 + 2 + 1$$

Now add corresponding terms in the equations above.
The sums 1 + 100, 2 + 99, 3 + 98, ... all have the same value!

So $2S = \underbrace{101 + 101 + 101 + \ldots + 101 + 101 + 101}_{100 \text{ terms}}$.

Thus, $2S = 100 \cdot 101$

and $S = 5050$.

Gauss wrote only the number 5050 on his slate, having done all the figuring in his head. The teacher (who had hoped the problem would keep the students working for a long time) was quite irritated. However, partly as a result of this incident, the teacher did recognize that Gauss was extraordinary and gave him some advanced books to read. (You read about Gauss's work in Lesson 11-6 and may recall that he proved the Fundamental Theorem of Algebra at age 18.)

QY1

▸ **QY1**

Use Gauss's method to add the integers from 1 to 40.

Background

Many people confuse the terms *sequence* and *series,* but the distinction is simple: a series is the sum of the terms in a sequence. If a sequence is $a_1, a_2, a_3, \ldots, a_n$, the corresponding series is $a_1 + a_2 + a_3 + \ldots + a_n$. A series is an *indicated sum,* with many + signs (or possibly + and − signs, if one thinks of subtracting as adding opposites). To distinguish the indicated sum from the number that is the sum of the series, we call the latter number the *value* of the series.

Sums of consecutive integers The story that opens the lesson is one that Gauss told about himself on numerous occasions. The moral is not that Gauss was brilliant (though he was); there is a way of looking at the sum of integers from 1 to n that even an elementary student can understand.

The sum of the terms in a linear sequence written as a quadratic expression repeats an idea found in Chapter 11 when we fitted a polynomial model to a sequence of sums.

What Is an Arithmetic Series?

Recall that an *arithmetic* or *linear sequence* is a sequence in which the difference between consecutive terms is constant. An arithmetic sequence has the form

$$a_1, a_1 + d, a_1 + 2d, ..., a_1 + (n - 1)d, ... ,$$

where a_1 is the first term and d is the constant difference. For example, the odd integers from 1 to 999 form a finite arithmetic sequence with $a_1 = 1$, $n = 500$, and $d = 2$.

A **series** is an indicated sum of terms of a sequence. For example, for the sequence 1, 2, 3, a series is the indicated sum $1 + 2 + 3$. The addends 1, 2, and 3 are the *terms* of the series. The value, or sum, of the series is 6. In general, the sum of the first n terms of a series a is

$$S_n = a_1 + a_2 + a_3 + ... + a_{n-2} + a_{n-1} + a_n.$$

If the terms of a series form an arithmetic sequence, the indicated sum of the terms is called an **arithmetic series**.

If a is an arithmetic series with first term a_1 and constant difference d, you can find a formula for the value S_n of the series by writing the series in two ways:

Start with the first term a_1 and successively add the common difference d.

$$S_n = a_1 + (a_1 + d) + (a_1 + 2d) + ... + (a_1 + (n - 1)d)$$

Start with the last term a_n and successively subtract the common difference d.

$$S_n = a_n + (a_n - d) + (a_n - 2d) + ... + (a_n - (n - 1)d)$$

Now add corresponding pairs of terms of these two formulas, as Gauss did. Then each of the n pairs has the same sum, $a_1 + a_n$.

$$S_n + S_n = \underbrace{(a_1 + a_n) + (a_1 + a_n) + (a_1 + a_n) + ... + (a_1 + a_n)}_{n \text{ terms}}$$

So $\quad 2S_n = n(a_1 + a_n)$.

Thus, $\quad S_n = \frac{n}{2}(a_1 + a_n)$.

This proves that if $a_1 + a_2 + ... + a_n$ is an arithmetic series, then a formula for the value S_n of the series is $S_n = \frac{n}{2}(a_1 + a_n)$.

 QY2

Arithmetic series that involve the sum of consecutive integers from 1 to n lead to a special case of the above formula. In these situations, $a_1 = 1$ and $a_n = n$, so the sum of the integers from 1 to n is $\frac{n}{2}(1 + n)$, or $\frac{n^2 + n}{2}$.

▸ **QY2**

Use the formula for S_n to find the sum of the odd integers from 1 to 999.

2 Teaching

Notes on the Lesson

You might begin with a discussion of the Warm-Up on page 868. Warm-Up 2 uses the 17 sums $1 + 35$, $2 + 34$, ..., $17 + 19$, and then the remaining 18 is added. The answer to Warm-Up 3 is found by doubling the answer to Warm-Up 2. Warm-Up 4's series has terms that are each 6 more than the corresponding terms of Warm-Up 3. Thus, the sum in Warm-Up 4 is $6 \cdot 35$ greater than the sum in Warm-Up 3.

We recommend discussing the lesson in detail and in order, as the examples and theorems follow logically.

What is an arithmetic series? Begin with the story of Gauss and derive a formula for the general sum. The formula $S_n = \frac{n}{2}(a_1 + a_n)$ can be rewritten as $S_n = n\left(\frac{a_1 + a_n}{2}\right)$. (See Question 15.)

It is a discrete analogue to the theorem in calculus that states that the integral of a linear function is a quadratic function. More generally, if an explicit formula for the nth term of a sequence is a polynomial of degree k, then the formula for the sum of consecutive terms of the sequence is a polynomial of degree $k + 1$, again analogous to the situation with integrals.

Summation notation Σ-notation, variously called *sigma* or *summation* notation, is one of those notations that looks difficult but is found to be a natural abbreviation once understood. It is a fundamental notation for both calculus and statistics. We introduce it here and use it continually throughout the chapter.

Notes on the Lesson

Example 1 This simple application of $\frac{n}{2}(a_1 + a_n)$ has a religious holiday counterpart in Question 16.

Discuss the second formula for the sum of an arithmetic series: $S_n = \frac{n}{2}(2a_1 + (n - 1)d)$. It follows immediately from the first formula by substituting for a_n. Example 2 is a straightforward application of that formula.

Additional Examples

Example 1 Every birthday, Cathy receives charms for a charm bracelet. She received one charm on her 1st birthday, two charms on her 2nd birthday, three charms on her 3rd birthday, and so on. What was the total number of charms she had received after her 16th birthday?

Solution Find the sum of consecutive integers from 1 to 16. Substitute 16 for n in the formula for S_n:

$S_{16} = \frac{?}{2}(1 + \_?\_) = \_?\_$. 16; 16; 136

Cathy had received _?_ charms after her 16th birthday. 136

Example 2 An auditorium has 24 rows, with 10 seats in the front row and 3 more seats in each row thereafter. How many seats are there in all? 1068 seats

GUIDED

Example 1

Part of the lyrics of a popular Christmas carol say, "On the 12th day of Christmas my true love gave to me... ." The 12th-day gifts are listed at the right. How many gifts did the singer receive on the 12th day of Christmas?

Solution Find the sum of consecutive integers from 1 to 12. Substitute 12 for n in the formula for S_n.

$S_{12} = \frac{?}{2}(1 + \_?\_)$ 12; 12

$S_{12} = \_?\_$ 78

The singer received _?_ gifts on the 12th day of Christmas. 78

The formula $S_n = \frac{n}{2}(a_1 + a_n)$ is convenient if the first and nth terms of the series are known. If the nth term is not known, you can use another formula. Start with the formula for the nth term of an arithmetic sequence.

$$a_n = a_1 + (n - 1)d$$

Substitute this expression for a_n in the right side of the formula for S_n and simplify.

$$S_n = \frac{n}{2}\left[a_1 + (a_1 + (n - 1)d\right]$$
$$S_n = \frac{n}{2}\left[2a_1 + (n - 1)d\right]$$

This argument proves that if $a_1 + a_2 + \ldots + a_n$ is an arithmetic series with constant difference d, then the value S_n of the series can be found using the formula $S_n = \frac{n}{2}\left[2a_1 + (n - 1)d\right]$.

Example 2

An auditorium has 20 rows, with 14 seats in the front row and 2 more seats in each row thereafter. How many seats are there in all?

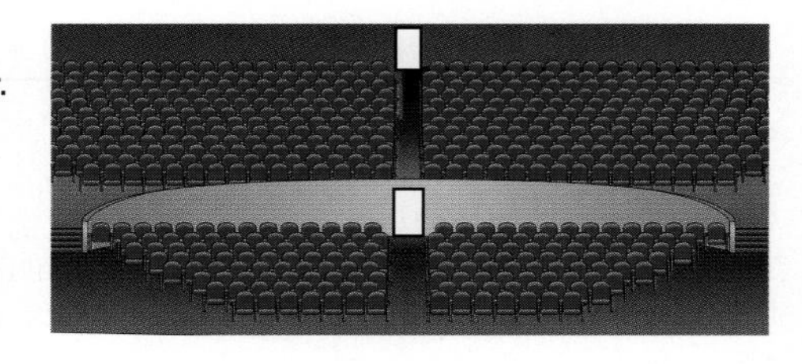

Solution This is an arithmetic-series situation. Because the first term, difference, and number of terms are given, use the formula

$$S_n = \frac{n}{2}(2a_1 + (n - 1)d).$$

In this case, $n = 20$, $a_1 = 14$, and $d = 2$.

So $S_{20} = \frac{20}{2}(2 \cdot 14 + (20 - 1)2)$

$= \frac{20}{2}(28 + 38) = 660.$

There are 660 seats in the auditorium.

ENGLISH LEARNERS

Vocabulary Development

Make sure that students understand the difference between a *series* and a *sequence*. A sequence is a list of terms related by a common difference (*arithmetic sequence*) or a common ratio (*geometric sequence*).

Explain that the Greek letter Σ, or *sigma*, carries the "s" sound and thus stands for the term *sum*. An *arithmetic series* is the indicated *sum* of the terms in an arithmetic sequence. Because an arithmetic series is a sum, we use the term *summation notation*, denoted as *Σ-notation*. On the board, write several examples of Σ-notation. The variable under the Σ is the *index variable*, or *index*. If this variable is *i*, be sure students know that it does *not* represent the complex number *i*. The first value of the index variable is substituted in the expression to the right of the Σ to determine the first term in the series. The next greater integer value of the index is substituted to determine the second term, and so on. The number above the Σ represents the greatest value of the index.

Check Use the formula $S_n = \frac{n}{2}(a_1 + a_n)$. You need to know how many seats are in the first and last row. In this case,
$a_1 = 14$ and $a_n = a_{20} = 14 + 19 \cdot 2 = 52$.
So $S_{20} = \frac{20}{2}(14 + 52) = \frac{20}{2} \cdot 66 = 660$.
There are 660 seats in the auditorium. It checks.

Summation Notation

The sum of the first six terms of a sequence a_n is

$$a_1 + a_2 + a_3 + a_4 + a_5 + a_6.$$

However, when there are many numbers in the series, this notation is too cumbersome. You can shorten this by writing

$$a_1 + a_2 + \cdots + a_6.$$

It is understood that the terms a_3, a_4, and a_5 are included.

This notation can be shortened even further. In a spreadsheet, suppose you have the sum A1 + A2+ A3 + A4 + A5 + A6. That sum can be written as `SUM(A1:A6)`. In algebra, the upper-case Greek letter **Σ (sigma)** indicates a sum. In **Σ-notation,** called **sigma notation** or **summation notation,** the above sum is written

$$\sum_{i=1}^{6} a_i.$$

The expression can be read as "the sum of the values of a sub i, for i equals 1 to 6." The variable i under the Σ sign is called the **index variable,** or **index**. It is common to use the letters $i, j, k,$ or n as index variables. (In summation notation, i is *not* the complex number $\sqrt{-1}$.) In this book, index variables have only integer values.

READING MATH

While you use your index finger to point an object, the *index variable* is used to point to a value. Thus, a_3 points to the third term of the series named a.

Writing Formulas Using Σ-Notation

The two arithmetic series formulas $S_n = \frac{n}{2}(a_1 + a_n)$ and $S_n = \frac{n}{2}(2a_1 + (n - 1)d)$ can be restated using Σ-notation. Notice that i is used as the index variable to avoid confusion with the variable n.

Arithmetic Series Formula

In an arithmetic sequence $a_1, a_2, a_3, \ldots, a_n$ with constant difference d,

$$\sum_{i=1}^{n} a_i = \frac{n}{2}(a_1 + a_n) = \frac{n}{2}(2a_1 + (n - 1)d).$$

Accommodating the Learner

Have students work in pairs or small groups to find the following formulas.

1. The formula for the sum of the first n odd numbers greater than 0
$S_n = \frac{n}{2}(2a_1 + (n - 1)d) =$
$\frac{n}{2}(2 \cdot 1 + (n - 1)2) =$
$n + n^2 - n = n^2$

2. The formula for the sum of the first n even numbers greater than 0
$S_n = \frac{n}{2}(2a_1 + (n - 1)d) =$
$\frac{n}{2}(2 \cdot 2 + (n - 1)2) =$
$2n + n^2 - n = n^2 + n$

Notes on the Lesson

Summation notation Lastly, after students have seen the need for a notation, we introduce Σ-notation for sums. Some students need lots of practice before they are familiar with this notation. To help students, separate the various parts of $\sum_{i=1}^{n} a_i$: Σ denotes sum; a_i represents the terms of the sequence being added. We need to know where we start and where we finish the addition of the terms in the sequence, which is the purpose of $i = 1$ and n. Most students should be familiar with spreadsheets, and you might take advantage of their knowledge of the notation SUM(A1:A6), perhaps using a middle hybrid notation $\Sigma(a_1{:}a_6)$ to point out how the notations are related.

Note-Taking Tips

Have students add to their journal the Arithmetic Series Formula, including an example.

Additional Example

Example 3 Consider $\sum_{i=1}^{200} a_i$ where $a_n = 5n + 8$.

a. Write the series without Σ-notation.

b. Evaluate the sum.

Solution

a. Substitute the expression for a_i and use it to write the terms of the series: $\sum_{i=1}^{200}(5i + 8) =$ $(5 \cdot \underline{?} + 8) +$ $(5 \cdot \underline{?} + \underline{?}) + \underline{?} +$ $\dots + \underline{?} = \underline{?} + \underline{?} + \underline{?} + \dots + \underline{?}$. 1; 2; 8; (5 · 3 + 8); (5 · 200 + 8); 13; 18; 23; 1008

b. This is an arithmetic series. The first term is ___?___. 13 The constant difference is ___?___. 5 There are ___?___ terms in the series. 200 Use the formula $\sum_{i=1}^{n} a_i = \frac{n}{2}(2a_1 + (n - 1)d)$ to evaluate the series: $\sum_{i=1}^{200}(5i + 8) =$

$\frac{?}{2}(2 \cdot \underline{?} + (\underline{?} - 1)\underline{?}) =$ ___?___ 200; 13; 200; 5; 102,100

When $a_i = i$, the sequence is the set of all positive integers in increasing order 1, 2, 3, 4, … . Then

$$\sum_{i=1}^{n} i = \frac{n}{2}(1 + n) = \frac{n(n+1)}{2}.$$

This is a Σ-notation version of Gauss's sum.

 QY3

> **QY3**
> Find $\sum_{i=1}^{40} i$.

One advantage of Σ-notation is that you can substitute an expression for a_i. For instance, suppose $a_n = 2n$, the sequence of even positive integers. Then,

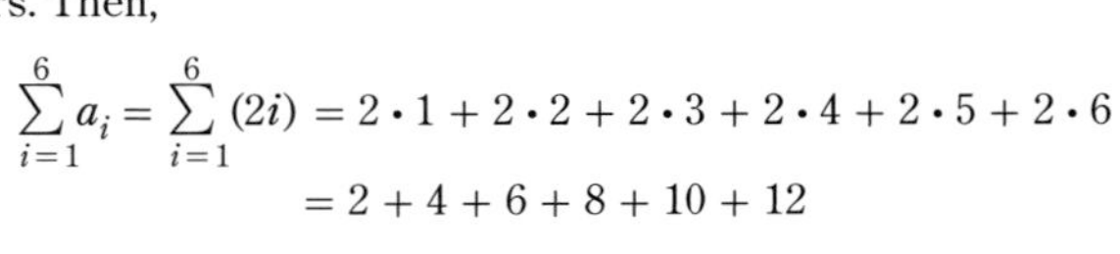

$$\sum_{i=1}^{6} a_i = \sum_{i=1}^{6}(2i) = 2 \cdot 1 + 2 \cdot 2 + 2 \cdot 3 + 2 \cdot 4 + 2 \cdot 5 + 2 \cdot 6$$
$$= 2 + 4 + 6 + 8 + 10 + 12$$
$$= 42.$$

The sum of the first six positive even integers is 42.

GUIDED

Example 3

Consider $\sum_{i=1}^{500} a_i$, where $a_n = 4n + 6$.

a. Write the series without Σ-notation.

b. Evaluate the sum.

Solution

a. Substitute the expression for a_i from the explicit formula and use it to write out the terms of the series.

$\sum_{i=1}^{500}(4i + 6) = (4 \cdot \underline{?} + 6) + (4 \cdot \underline{?} + \underline{?}) + \underline{?} + \dots + \underline{?}$ 1; 2; 6; (4 • 3 + 6) (4 • 500 + 6)

$= \underline{?} + \underline{?} + \underline{?} + \dots + \underline{?}$ 10; 14; 18; 2006

b. This is an arithmetic series. The first term is ___?___. The constant difference is ___?___. There are ___?___ terms in the series. 10 4; 500

Use the formula $\sum_{i=1}^{n} a_i = \frac{n}{2}(2a_1 + (n - 1)d)$ to evaluate the series.

$\sum_{i=1}^{500}(4i + 6) = \frac{?}{2}(2 \cdot \underline{?} + (\underline{?} - 1)\underline{?})$ 500; 10; 500; 4

$= \underline{?}$ 504,000

Accommodating the Learner

Some students might be confused by the ellipsis notation used in this lesson. Explain that rather than writing, for example, 3 + 6 + 9 + 12 + 15 + 18 + 21 + 24 + 27 + 30 for the sum of the multiples of 3 from 3 to 30, we write 3 + 6 + 9 + ... + 30. The first three terms establish the pattern, and the ellipsis indicates that the pattern continues to the last term. A verbal or mathematical description of the sequence will clarify the situation.

Most scientific calculators and CAS have commands to evaluate a series, but the commands and entry styles vary considerably. The entry for one CAS is shown at the right.

 QY4

▸ **QY4**

Check the solution to Example 3 on your calculator or CAS.

Questions

COVERING THE IDEAS

In 1 and 2, tell whether what is given is an arithmetic sequence, an arithmetic series, or neither.

1. $26 + 29 + 32 + 35$
2. $35, 32, 29, 26$
3. What problem was Gauss given in third grade, and what is its answer?
4. Find the sum of the integers from 1 to 500. 125,250
5. **Fill in the Blank** The symbol Σ is the upper-case Greek letter __?__. sigma
6. **Fill in the Blank** In Σ-notation, the variable under the Σ sign is called the __?__. index or index variable
7. Consider the arithmetic sequence with first term a_1 and constant difference d.
   a. Write a formula for the nth term. $a_n = a_1 + (n - 1)d$
   b. Write a formula for the sum S_n of the first n terms using Σ-notation.
   c. Write an equivalent formula to the one you wrote in Part b.
8. Consider the arithmetic series $8 + 13 + 18 + ... + 38$.
   a. Write out all the terms of the series. How many terms are there?
   b. What is the sum of all the terms? 161
   c. Write this series using Σ-notation.
9. Refer to Example 3. Check your answer using the formula $\sum_{i=1}^{n} a_i = \frac{n}{2}(a_1 + a_n)$. $\frac{500}{2}(10 + 2006) = 504{,}000$
10. **Multiple Choice** $\sum_{i=1}^{5} i^2 =$ __?__. A

    A $1 + 4 + 9 + 16 + 25$
    B 5^2
    C $1 + 2 + ... + 5$
    D none of these

1. arithmetic series
2. arithmetic sequence
3. Add the whole numbers from 1 to 100; 5050

7b. $\sum_{i=1}^{n} a_i = \frac{n}{2}(2a_1 + (n - 1)d)$

7c. $\sum_{i=1}^{n} a_i = \frac{n}{2}(a_1 + a_n)$

8a. $8 + 13 + 18 + 23 + 28 + 33 + 38$; 7 terms

8c. $\sum_{i=1}^{7} (5i + 3)$

Notes on the Lesson

Most calculators and CAS use very similar syntax for the sum of a sequence command. The command requires an expression, the variable used, the start value, and the end value. An optional command is the step increment, which usually defaults to 1. Some CAS have a template available where entries are made in locations identical to the text notation. The example in the text is a Casio ClassPad (using a Σ template). The TI-NSpire has a display similar to that of the Casio ClassPad.

3 Assignment

Recommended Assignment

- Questions 1–26
- Question 27 (extra credit)
- Reading Lesson 13-2
- Covering the Ideas 13-2

Notes on the Questions

Question 5 Sigma is the first letter of the Greek word for sum, so it was natural to use it. Western European mathematicians were forced to use letters from other alphabets because they ran out of letters from the Latin alphabet. Many of them knew the Greek letters because they studied Greek in school.

Extension

Ask students to find the value for each expression.

1. $\sum_{k=1}^{7} \left(\sum_{i=1}^{k} 1 \right)$ 28
2. $\sum_{k=1}^{7} \left(\sum_{j=1}^{k} j \right)$ 84

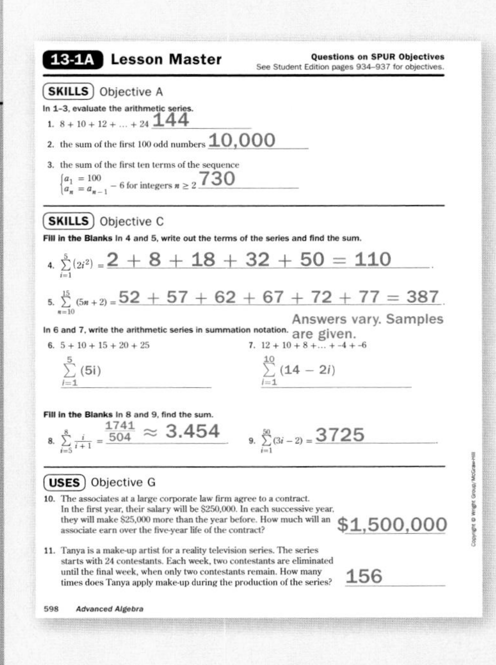
13-1A Lesson Master — Questions on SPUR Objectives. See Student Edition pages 934–937 for objectives.

SKILLS Objective A

In 1–3, evaluate the arithmetic series.

1. $8 + 10 + 12 + ... + 24$ 144
2. the sum of the first 100 odd numbers 10,000
3. the sum of the first ten terms of the sequence $\begin{cases} a_1 = 100 \\ a_n = a_{n-1} - 6 \text{ for integers } n \geq 2 \end{cases}$ 730

SKILLS Objective C

Fill in the Blanks In 4 and 5, write out the terms of the series and find the sum.

4. $\sum_{i=1}^{5} (2i^2) = 2 + 8 + 18 + 32 + 50 = 110$.
5. $\sum_{n=10}^{15} (5n + 2) = 52 + 57 + 62 + 67 + 72 + 77 = 387$.

In 6 and 7, write the arithmetic series in summation notation. Answers vary. Samples are given.

6. $5 + 10 + 15 + 20 + 25$ $\sum_{i=1}^{5} (5i)$
7. $12 + 10 + 8 + ... + -4 + -6$ $\sum_{i=1}^{10} (14 - 2i)$

Fill in the Blanks In 8 and 9, find the sum.

8. $\sum_{i=5}^{8} \frac{i}{i+1} = \frac{1741}{504} \approx 3.454$
9. $\sum_{i=1}^{50} (3i - 2) = 3725$.

USES Objective G

10. The associates at a large corporate law firm agree to a contract. In the first year, their salary will be $250,000. In each successive year, they will make $25,000 more than the year before. How much will an associate earn over the five-year life of the contract? $1,500,000
11. Tanya is a make-up artist for a reality television series. The series starts with 24 contestants. Each week, two contestants are eliminated until the final week, when only two contestants remain. How many times does Tanya apply make-up during the production of the series? 156

598 *Advanced Algebra*

Notes on the Questions

Question 16 It is interesting that for both Christmas and Chanukah (also spelled many different ways, for example, *Hanukkah*), there is a well-known connection with linear sequences. Ask students if similar patterns can be found in other religions.

Question 18b You might ask if any students answered this question without directly using the formula on the sequence of even integers from 50 to 100. For example, one could start with the integers from 1 to 26 (because there are 26 even integers from 50 to 100). That sum is 351. Then double that sum to get 702, the sum of the even integers from 2 to 52. Then add 48 to each of these even integers to get the even integers from 50 to 100; the sum will be $702 + 48 \cdot 26 = 1950$.

11. **Multiple Choice** $7 + 14 + 21 + 28 + 35 + 42 + 49 + 56 + 63 =$ __?__. C

    A $\sum_{i=7}^{63} i$ B $\sum_{i=7}^{63} (7i)$ C $\sum_{i=1}^{9} (7i)$ D none of these

12. In $\sum_{i=100}^{300} (5i)$, how many terms are added? (*Be careful!*) 201

In 13 and 14, evaluate the sum.

13. $\sum_{i=1}^{25} (6i - 4)$ 1850

14. $\sum_{n=-1}^{3} 9 \cdot 3^n$ 363

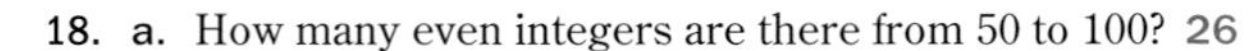

APPLYING THE MATHEMATICS

15. Finish this sentence: The sum of the first n terms of an arithmetic sequence equals the average of the first and last terms multiplied by __?__. the number of terms

16. The Jewish holiday Chanukah is celebrated by lighting candles in a *menorah* for eight nights. On the first night, two candles are lit, one in the center and one on the right. The two candles are allowed to burn down completely. On the second night, three candles are lit (one in the center, and two others) and are allowed to burn down completely. On each successive night, one more candle is lit than the night before, and all are allowed to burn down completely. How many candles are needed for all eight nights? 44 candles

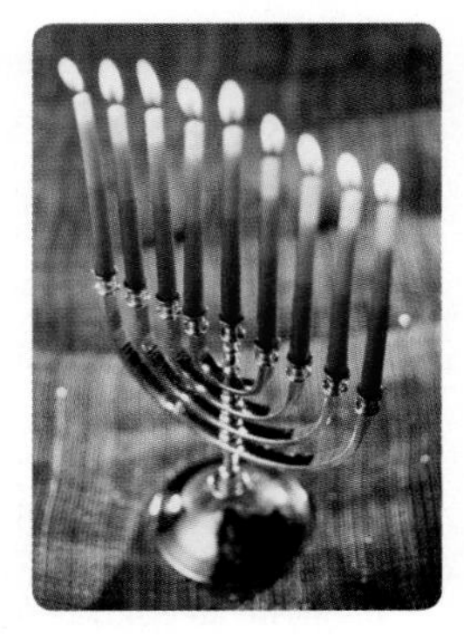

17. Penny Banks decides to start saving money in a Holiday Club account. At the beginning of January she will deposit \$100, and each month thereafter she will increase the deposit amount by \$25. How much will Penny deposit during the year? \$2850

18. a. How many even integers are there from 50 to 100? 26
    b. Find the sum of the even integers from 50 to 100. 1950

19. a. Write the sum of the squares of the integers from 1 to 100 in Σ-notation.
    b. Evaluate the sum in Part a. 338,350

20. a. Translate this statement into an algebraic formula using Σ-notation: The sum of the cubes of the integers from 1 to n is the square of the sum of the integers from 1 to n.
    b. Verify the statement in Part a when $n = 8$

21. Write the arithmetic mean of the n numbers $a_1, a_2, a_3, \ldots, a_n$ using Σ-notation.

19a. $\sum_{i=1}^{100} i^2$

20a. $\sum_{i=1}^{n} i^3 = \left(\sum_{i=1}^{n} i\right)^2$

20b. $\sum_{i=1}^{8} i^3 = 1296$; $\left(\sum_{i=1}^{8} i\right)^2 = 36^2 = 1296$

21. $\frac{1}{n}\sum_{i=1}^{n} a_i$

REVIEW

22. The function with equation $y = k \cdot 2^x$ contains the point (6, 10).
    a. What is the value of k? $k = \frac{5}{32}$
    b. Describe the graph of this function. (Lesson 9-1)

23. Consider the geometric sequence 16, –40, 100, –250, … .
    a. Determine the common ratio. –2.5
    b. Write the 5th term. 625
    c. Write an explicit formula for the nth term. (Lesson 7-5) $a_n = 16(-2.5)^{n-1}$

24. Suppose an account pays 5.75% annual interest compounded monthly. (Lesson 7-4)
    a. Find the annual percentage yield on the account. 5.904%
    b. Find the value of a \$1700 deposit after 5 years if no other money is added or withdrawn from the account. \$2264.69

25. Find an equation for the parabola with a vertical line of symmetry that contains the points (5, 0), (1, 5), and (3, 8). (Lesson 6-6)

26. a. Find the inverse of $\begin{bmatrix} 5 & 2 \\ n & 1 \end{bmatrix}$.
    b. For what value(s) of n does the inverse not exist? (Lesson 5-5) $n = 2.5$

EXPLORATION

27. The number 9 can be written as an arithmetic series: $9 = 1 + 3 + 5$. What other numbers from 1 to 100 can be written as an arithmetic series with three or more positive integer terms?

22b. Answers vary. Sample: The graph has an asymptote at $y = 0$, an x-intercept at $\frac{5}{32}$, and becomes steeper as x increases.

25. $y = -\frac{11}{8}x^2 + 7x - \frac{5}{8}$

26a. $\begin{bmatrix} \frac{1}{5-2n} & \frac{-2}{5-2n} \\ \frac{-n}{5-2n} & \frac{5}{5-2n} \end{bmatrix}$

27. Answers vary. Sample: Many of the nonprime integers can be expressed as arithmetic series. Examples include $15 = 3 + 5 + 7$, $16 = 1 + 3 + 5 + 7$, $22 = 4 + 5 + 6 + 7$, $34 = 4 + 7 + 10 + 13$, and $40 = 7 + 9 + 11 + 13$.

QY ANSWERS

1. $S = 1 + 2 + ... + 40$
   $S = 40 + 39 + ... + 1$
   $2S = \underbrace{41 + 41 + ... + 41}_{40 \text{ terms}}$
   $2S = 40 \cdot 41$
   $S = 820$
2. $S_n = \frac{500}{2}(1 + 999) = 250 \cdot 1000 = 250{,}000$
3. 820
4. Answers vary. Sample:

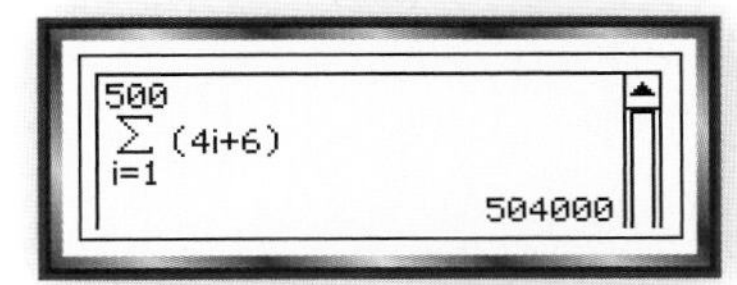

13-1

Notes on the Questions

Question 27 All of the integers from 1 to 100 can be written as an arithmetic series with three or more positive terms EXCEPT for the primes, 4, and 8. This result can be derived as follows. Start with the three-term arithmetic series with the least sum: 1 + 2 + 3. The value of the series is 6. Now add one to each term of the series to get 2 + 3 + 4 = 9. Add one to each term again to get 3 + 4 + 5 = 12, and so on. This shows that all of the multiples of 3, starting with 6, can be written as arithmetic series. If you repeat this process with 1 + 2 + 3 + 4 = 10, you will see that all integers of the form $4n + 2$, starting with 10, can be written as an arithmetic series. Students can continue experimenting in this manner until they have generated all the nonprime integers from 1 to 100 except 4 and 8.

4 Wrap-Up

Ongoing Assessment

Refer students to Questions 13 and 14. Have each student make up three similar questions involving sigma notation. Then have students exchange papers with another student and give the value of the sum for each question. Students should write questions of the requested type and correctly evaluate the sum.

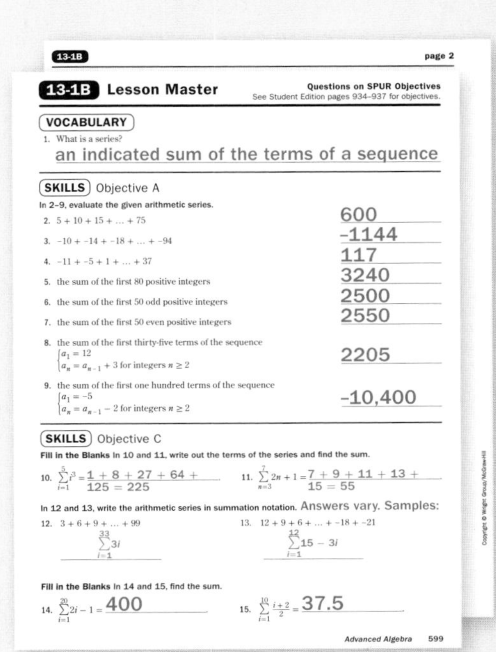

13-1B page 2

13-1B Lesson Master

Questions on SPUR Objectives
See Student Edition pages 934–937 for objectives.

VOCABULARY

1. What is a series? an indicated sum of the terms of a sequence

SKILLS Objective A

In 2–9, evaluate the given arithmetic series.

2. 5 + 10 + 15 + … + 75 — 600
3. –10 + –14 + –18 + … + –94 — –1144
4. –11 + –5 + 1 + … + 37 — 117
5. the sum of the first 80 positive integers — 3240
6. the sum of the first 50 odd positive integers — 2500
7. the sum of the first 50 even positive integers — 2550
8. the sum of the first thirty-five terms of the sequence $\begin{cases} a_1 = 12 \\ a_n = a_{n-1} + 3 \text{ for integers } n \geq 2 \end{cases}$ — 2205
9. the sum of the first one hundred terms of the sequence $\begin{cases} a_1 = -5 \\ a_n = a_{n-1} - 2 \text{ for integers } n \geq 2 \end{cases}$ — –10,400

SKILLS Objective C

Fill in the Blanks In 10 and 11, write out the terms of the series and find the sum.

10. $\sum_{i=1}^{5} i^3 =$ 1 + 8 + 27 + 64 + 125 = 225.
11. $\sum_{n=3}^{7} 2n + 1 =$ 7 + 9 + 11 + 13 + 15 = 55.

In 12 and 13, write the arithmetic series in summation notation. Answers vary. Samples:

12. 3 + 6 + 9 + … + 99 — $\sum_{i=1}^{33} 3i$
13. 12 + 9 + 6 + … + –18 + –21 — $\sum_{i=1}^{12} 15 - 3i$

Fill in the Blanks In 14 and 15, find the sum.

14. $\sum_{i=1}^{20} 2i - 1 =$ 400.
15. $\sum_{i=1}^{10} \frac{i+2}{2} =$ 37.5.

Advanced Algebra 599

Copyright © Wright Group/McGraw-Hill

Lesson 13-2

GOAL

Learn about finite geometric series and how to find the sum of a finite number of consecutive terms in a geometric sequence.

SPUR Objectives

B Calculate values of finite geometric series.

C Use summation (Σ) notation.

G Solve real-world problems using geometric series.

Materials/Resources

- Lesson Masters 13-2A and 13-2B
- Resource Masters 246–249

HOMEWORK

Suggestions for Assignment

- Questions 1–21
- Question 22 (extra credit)
- Reading Lesson 13-3
- Covering the Ideas 13-3

Local Standards

1 Warm-Up

What are the first five terms of each geometric sequence?

1. first term 1, common ratio 0.5
   1, 0.5, 0.25, 0.125, 0.0625
2. first term 1, common ratio 3
   1, 3, 9, 27, 81
3. first term 144, common ratio $\frac{3}{4}$
   144, 108, 81, $\frac{243}{4}$, $\frac{729}{16}$
4. first term 144, common ratio $-\frac{3}{4}$
   144, −108, 81, $-\frac{243}{4}$, $\frac{729}{16}$

Lesson 13-2 Geometric Series

Vocabulary

geometric series

▸ **BIG IDEA** There are several ways to find the sum of the successive terms of a finite geometric sequence.

Activity Steps 1–6. See the Additional Answers section at the back of the book.

Step 1 Draw a large square on a sheet of paper.

Step 2 Divide the square into two equal parts and shade one of the regions. How much of the square has been shaded?

Step 3 Divide the unshaded half into two equal parts and shade one of the regions. How much of the original square does this region represent? How much of the total square have you shaded? The figure at the right shows one possible result of Steps 1–3.

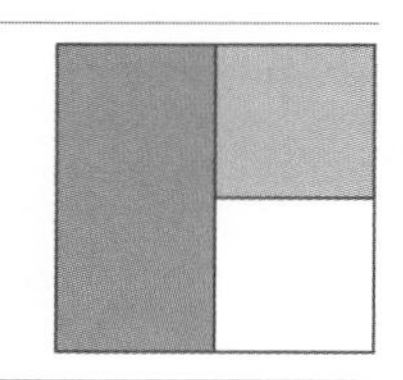

Step 4 Repeat Step 3 three more times. Fill in a table like the one below where n represents the number of shaded regions and S_n is the total fraction of the original large square that is shaded.

n	1	2	3	4	5
g_n (series)	$\frac{1}{2}$	$\frac{1}{2}+\frac{1}{4}$	$\frac{1}{2}+\frac{1}{4}+\frac{1}{8}$	?	?
S_n (value)	$\frac{1}{2}$	$\frac{3}{4}$	?	?	?

Step 5 What is the value of S_6? Describe the nth term of the series and the value of S_n.

Step 6 Will the original square ever be entirely shaded? Explain why or why not.

In the Activity, the terms in the series g form a geometric sequence with first term $\frac{1}{2}$ and constant ratio $\frac{1}{2}$. So the kth term in the sequence is $\left(\frac{1}{2}\right)^k$. For instance, the 5th term in the sequence is $\left(\frac{1}{2}\right)^5 = \frac{1}{32}$, and

$$S_5 = \frac{1}{2} + \frac{1}{4} + \frac{1}{8} + \frac{1}{16} + \frac{1}{32} = \sum_{k=1}^{5} \frac{1}{2^k} = \frac{31}{32}.$$

Mental Math

Is the point (2, 1) included in the set?

a. the circle with equation $x^2 + y^2 = 5$ yes

b. the interior of the circle with equation $x^2 + y^2 = 5$ no

c. the exterior of the circle with equation $x^2 + y^2 = 3$ yes

d. the interior of the circle with equation $(x - 1)^2 + (y + 1)^2 = 3$ no

Background

A formula for the value of any finite geometric series The proof is ingenious but not atypical of the kind of reasoning used in deriving formulas.

Geometric series have a number of important applications. For finite series, the most common application is to annuities, as illustrated in Example 3. In general, if an amount A is deposited (or paid) periodically and the periodic yield is r, then the scale factor x is $1 + r$. Suppose this continues for n payments. Then the total amount is given by $Ax^{n-1} + Ax^{n-2} + \ldots + Ax + A$. This is a finite geometric series with first term A and constant ratio x, whose sum is given by $S_n = \frac{A(x^n - 1)}{x - 1}$. Substituting $1 + r$ for x yields the following formula, found in some finance books and books of tables: $S_n = \frac{A((1 + r)^n - 1)}{r}$.

GUIDED

Example 1

a. Write the value of S_{10} from the Activity as a sum of terms of a geometric sequence.

b. Write S_{10} using Σ-notation.

c. Compute exact and approximate values of S_{10} using a calculator or CAS.

Solution

a. The terms in the geometric sequence are the first ten positive integer powers of $\frac{1}{2}$. So, $S_{10} = \frac{1}{2} + \frac{1}{4} + \frac{1}{8} + \underline{\ ?\ } + \underline{\ ?\ } + \underline{\ ?\ } + \underline{\ ?\ } + \underline{\ ?\ } + \underline{\ ?\ } + \underline{\ ?\ }$. $\frac{1}{16}; \frac{1}{32}; \frac{1}{64}; \frac{1}{128}; \frac{1}{256}; \frac{1}{512}; \frac{1}{1024}$

b. There are 10, terms and an expression for the kth term is $\left(\frac{1}{2}\right)^k$.

So $S_{10} = \sum_{?}^{?} \underline{\ ?\ }$. $10; k = 1; \left(\frac{1}{2}\right)^k$

c. The exact value is $\underline{\ ?\ }$. An approximate value is $\underline{\ ?\ }$. $\frac{1023}{1024}$; 0.999

An indicated sum of successive terms of a geometric sequence, like the one for S_{10} in Part a of Example 1, is called a **geometric series**. As with arithmetic series, there are formulas for the values of geometric series.

A Formula for the Value of Any Finite Geometric Series

In Example 1, notice that if each term of the sequence is halved, many values are identical to those in the original series:

$$S_{10} = \frac{1}{2} + \frac{1}{4} + \frac{1}{8} + \frac{1}{16} + \dots + \left(\frac{1}{2}\right)^9 + \left(\frac{1}{2}\right)^{10}$$

$$\frac{1}{2}S_{10} = \frac{1}{4} + \frac{1}{8} + \frac{1}{16} + \dots + \left(\frac{1}{2}\right)^9 + \left(\frac{1}{2}\right)^{10} + \left(\frac{1}{2}\right)^{11}.$$

Subtracting the second equation from the first yields

$$\frac{1}{2}S_{10} = \frac{1}{2} + \left(\frac{1}{4} - \frac{1}{4}\right) + \left(\frac{1}{8} - \frac{1}{8}\right) + \dots + \left(\left(\frac{1}{2}\right)^{10} - \left(\frac{1}{2}\right)^{10}\right) - \left(\frac{1}{2}\right)^{11}.$$

That is, $\frac{1}{2}S_{10} = \frac{1}{2} - \left(\frac{1}{2}\right)^{11}$,

and so $S_{10} = 2\left(\frac{1}{2} - \left(\frac{1}{2}\right)^{11}\right) = 1 - \left(\frac{1}{2}\right)^{10} = 1 - \frac{1}{1024} = \frac{1023}{1024}$.

This procedure can be generalized to find the value S_n of any finite geometric series. Let S_n be the geometric series with first term g_1, constant ratio $r \neq 1$, and n terms.

ENGLISH LEARNERS

Vocabulary Development

On the board, write both an arithmetic sequence and a geometric sequence. Have students discuss the differences between the two sequences and stress that the terms of a geometric sequence are related by a constant *ratio* rather than a constant *difference* as in an arithmetic sequence.

Review that a series is a sum of terms, and that a *geometric series* is the sum of a given number of terms in a geometric sequence. Then have students write several geometric series with six terms and then compute their values. Answers vary. Check students' work.

2 Teaching

Notes on the Lesson

Activity and Example 1 This geometric series is special because it can be easily pictured geometrically.

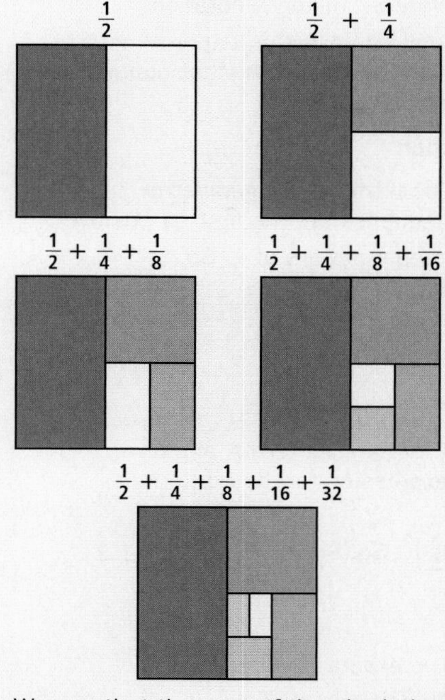

We see that the sum of the shaded areas is all but $\frac{1}{2}, \frac{1}{4}, \frac{1}{8}, \frac{1}{16}$, and $\frac{1}{32}$ of these rectangles. So the sums are, from left to right, top to bottom: $\frac{1}{2}, \frac{3}{4}, \frac{7}{8}, \frac{15}{16}$, and $\frac{31}{32}$. Now the result of Example 1 makes sense because it is what would be found in the 10th term of this truly "geometric" series.

A formula for the value of any finite geometric series Plan on discussing both a specific case and the general formula on page 878. You might wish to place the two side by side (rather than one after the other as in the lesson).

Note-Taking Tips

Have students add to their journals the Finite Geometric Series Formula, including an example.

Additional Example

Example 1

a. Write the value of S_{12} from the Activity as a sum of the terms in a geometric sequence.

b. Write S_{12} using Σ-notation.

c. Compute exact and approximate values of S_{12} with a calculator or a CAS.

Solution

a. The terms in the geometric sequence are the first 12 positive integer powers of $\frac{1}{2}$. So, $S_{12} = \frac{1}{2} + \frac{1}{4} + \frac{1}{8} + \underline{\ ?\ } + \underline{\ ?\ } + \underline{\ ?\ } + \underline{\ ?\ } + \underline{\ ?\ } + \underline{\ ?\ } + \underline{\ ?\ } + \underline{\ ?\ } + \underline{\ ?\ }$. $\frac{1}{16}$; $\frac{1}{32}$; $\frac{1}{64}$; $\frac{1}{128}$; $\frac{1}{256}$; $\frac{1}{512}$; $\frac{1}{1024}$; $\frac{1}{2048}$; $\frac{1}{4096}$

b. There are 12 terms, and an expression for the kth term is $\left(\frac{1}{2}\right)^k$. So, $S_{12} = \sum_{?}^{?} \underline{\ ?\ }$.

12; k=1; $\left(\frac{1}{2}\right)^k$

c. The exact value is $\underline{\ ?\ }$. $\frac{4095}{4096}$

An approximate value is $\underline{\ ?\ }$.

0.999756

Notes on the Lesson

Example 2 This series is called an alternating series because addition and subtraction alternate. It also involves complex fractions, which are difficult for many students. You should go through the arithmetic of the solution to Part b. Not only is it instructive, but many students are quite surprised that the Finite Geometric Series Formula works when the common ratio is negative. You might start with a simpler example, such as $144 - 108 + 81 - \frac{243}{4}$. Here $g_1 = 144$, $r = -0.75$, and $n = 4$. Substitution into the formula yields $\frac{144(1 - (-0.75)^4)}{1 - (-0.75)}$, or 56.25, which is easily checked by adding and subtracting the original terms.

$$S_n = g_1 + g_1 r + g_1 r^2 + \ldots + g_1 r^{n-1}$$

$$rS_n = g_1 r + g_1 r^2 + \ldots + g_1 r^{n-1} + g_1 r^n \quad \text{Multiply by } r.$$

$$S_n - rS_n = g_1 - g_1 r^n \quad \text{Subtract the second equation from the first.}$$

$$(1 - r)S_n = g_1(1 - r^n) \quad \text{Use the Distributive Property.}$$

$$S_n = \frac{g_1(1 - r^n)}{1 - r} \quad \text{Divide each side by } 1 - r.$$

This proves the following theorem.

Finite Geometric Series Formula

Let S_n be the sum of the first n terms of the geometric sequence with first term g_1 and constant ratio $r \neq 1$. Then $S_n = \frac{g_1(1 - r^n)}{1 - r}$.

The constant ratio r cannot be 1 in this formula. (Do you see why?) But that is not a problem. If $r = 1$, the series is $g_1 + g_1 + g_1 + \ldots + g_1$, with n terms, and its sum is ng_1.

 QY

The formula for a geometric series works even when the constant ratio is negative.

QY

Find the sum of the first 10 terms of a geometric series sequence with common ratio $\frac{3}{4}$ and first term 16.

GUIDED

Example 2

a. Write the indicated sum given by $\sum_{k=1}^{5} 27\left(-\frac{1}{3}\right)^{k-1}$.

b. Compute the value of the series in Part a.

Solution

a. The indicated sum is $27(\underline{\ ?\ })^0 + 27(\underline{\ ?\ })^1 + 27(\underline{\ ?\ })^{\underline{?}} + 27(\underline{\ ?\ })^{\underline{?}} + \underline{\ ?\ }(\underline{\ ?\ })^{\underline{?}} = \underline{\ ?\ } + \underline{\ ?\ } + \underline{\ ?\ } + \underline{\ ?\ } + \underline{\ ?\ }$. $-\frac{1}{3}$; $-\frac{1}{3}$; $-\frac{1}{3}$; 2 $-\frac{1}{3}$; 3; 27; $-\frac{1}{3}$; 4; 27; -9; 3 -1; $\frac{1}{3}$

b. Use the Finite Geometric Series Formula.

$S_5 = \frac{?(1 - ?^?)}{1 - ?} = \underline{\ ?\ }$ 27; $-\frac{1}{3}$; 5; $-\frac{1}{3}$; $\frac{61}{3}$

Check Compute the sum by hand to check that the formula works for negative values of r.

$\underline{\ ?\ } + \underline{\ ?\ } + \underline{\ ?\ } + \underline{\ ?\ } + \underline{\ ?\ } = \underline{\ ?\ }$. It checks. 27; −9; 3; −1; $\frac{1}{3}$; $\frac{61}{3}$

Accommodating the Learner ↑

Have students work in pairs or small groups to find the sum of the first n terms in each geometric series.

1. $1 + x^3 + x^6 + x^9 + \ldots$ $\frac{1 - x^{3n}}{1 - x^3}$
2. $1 - x^3 + x^6 - x^9 + \ldots$ $\frac{1 - (-x^3)^n}{1 + x^3}$

Accommodating the Learner ↓

Have students draw a large square on a sheet of paper and then use the procedure described in the Activity to verify the solution in Example 1.

Geometric Series and Compound Interest

Geometric series arise in compound-interest situations when the equal amounts of money are deposited or invested at regular intervals. The total value of such investments can be found using the Finite Geometric Series Formula.

Example 3

On the day her granddaughter Savanna was born, Mrs. Kash began saving for Savanna's college education by depositing $1000 in an account earning an annual percentage yield of 5.2%. She continued to deposit $1000 each year on Savanna's birthday into the same account at the same interest rate. How much money will be in Savanna's account on her 18th birthday, not including that birthday's payment?

Solution Make a table showing each deposit and its value on Savanna's 18th birthday.

Birthday	Deposit	Value on 18th Birthday
0	$1000	$\$1000(1.052)^{18}$
1	$1000	$\$1000(1.052)^{17}$
2	$1000	$\$1000(1.052)^{16}$
⋮	⋮	⋮
17	$1000	$\$1000(1.052)^{1}$

The amount in the account is the value of the geometric series $1000(1.052) + 1000(1.052)^2 + ... + 1000(1.052)^{18}$.

The first term is $a = 1000(1.052)$, the ratio is $r = 1.052$, and there are 18 terms. Therefore, the sum is

$$\frac{1000(1.052)(1 - 1.052^{18})}{1 - 1.052} \approx 30{,}153.58.$$

Savanna will have $30,153.58 in the account on her 18th birthday.

Questions

COVERING THE IDEAS

1. Refer to the Activity. What fraction of the square is shaded when $n = 8$? $\frac{255}{256}$
2. a. State a formula for the sum of the first n terms of a geometric sequence with first term g_1 and constant ratio r.
   b. In the formula in Part a, what value can r not have? 1
   c. Why can r not have the value in Part b? In this situation, what is the value of the series?

2a. $S_n = \frac{g_1(1-r^n)}{1-r}$

2c. If $r = 1$, then the expression on the right side of the formula above is undefined. In this case, $S_n = ng_1$.

13-2

Notes on the Lesson

Example 3 Notice that this geometric series is a polynomial of degree 18 with individual terms that are quite messy, but the calculation of the sum is not particularly difficult.

Additional Examples

Example 2

a. Write the indicated sum given by $\sum_{k=1}^{8} 32\left(-\frac{1}{2}\right)^{k-1}$.

b. Compute the value of the series in Part a.

Solution

a. The indicated sum is $32(\underline{?})^0 + 32(\underline{?})^1 + 32(\underline{?})^{\underline{?}} + 32(\underline{?})^{\underline{?}} + 32(\underline{?})^{\underline{?}} + 32(\underline{?})^{\underline{?}} + 32(\underline{?})^{\underline{?}} + 32(\underline{?})^{\underline{?}} = \underline{?} + \underline{?} + \underline{?} + \underline{?} + \underline{?} + \underline{?} + \underline{?} + \underline{?}$. $-\frac{1}{2}; -\frac{1}{2}; -\frac{1}{2}; 2; -\frac{1}{2}; 3; -\frac{1}{2}; 4; -\frac{1}{2}; 5; -\frac{1}{2}; 6; -\frac{1}{2}; 7; 32; -16; 8; -4; 2; -1; \frac{1}{2}; -\frac{1}{4}$

b. Use the Finite Geometric Series Formula.

$S_n = \frac{\underline{?}\left(1 - \underline{?}^{\underline{?}}\right)}{1 - \underline{?}} \approx \underline{?}$

$32; -\frac{1}{2}; 8; -\frac{1}{2}; \frac{85}{4}$

Example 3 On the day she was born, Cindy Ducat's parents began saving for her college education by depositing $500 in an account earning an annual percentage yield of 4.5%. They continued to deposit $500 each year on her birthday into the same account at the same interest rate. How much money will be in Cindy's account on her 17th birthday, not including that birthday's payment? $12,927.54

3 Assignment

Recommended Assignment

- Questions 1–21
- Question 22 (extra credit)
- Reading Lesson 13-3
- Covering the Ideas 13-3

Notes on the Questions

Questions 3–6 A common error is to think that the number of terms is the exponent in the coefficient of the last term. Note that there are 8 terms in Question 3 and 17 terms in Question 6.

Additional Answers

7b.

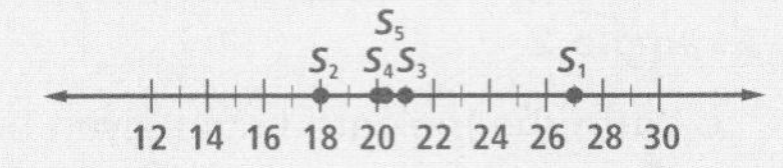

S_n is between S_{n-1} and S_{n-2}

11a.

Standard Form	Factored Form
$r^2 - 1$	
	$(r - 1)(r^2 + r + 1)$
	$(r - 1)(r + 1)(r^2 + 1)$
	$(r - 1)(r^4 + r^3 + r^2 + 1)$
	$(r - 1)(r + 1) \cdot (r^2 + r + 1)(r^2 - r + 1)$

11b. 1; 0; Suppose $P(r) = r^n - 1$, then $P(1) = 1^n - 1 = 0$ for all n. Thus, by the Factor Theorem, $r - 1$ is a factor of $P(r) = r^n - 1$ for all n.

11c. $n = 2$: $\frac{r^n - 1}{r - 1} = r + 1$; $n = 3$: $\frac{r^n - 1}{r - 1} = r^2 + r + 1$; $n = 4$: $\frac{r^n - 1}{r - 1} = (r + 1)(r^2 + 1)$; $n = 5$: $\frac{r^n - 1}{r - 1} = r^4 + r^3 + r^2 + 1$; $n = 6$: $\frac{r^n - 1}{r - 1} = (r + 1)(r^2 + r + 1) \cdot (r^2 - r + 1)$

13-2A Lesson Master Questions on SPUR Objectives
See Student Edition pages 934–937 for objectives.

SKILLS Objective B

In 1–3, a geometric series is given. Find a. the first term, b. the common ratio, c. the number of terms, and d. the sum using the Finite Geometric Series Sum Theorem.

1. $5 + 10 + 20 + 40 + 80$
   a. 5 b. 2 c. 5 d. 155
2. $4 - 12 + 36 - 108 + 324$
   a. 4 b. −3 c. 5 d. 244
3. $v + \frac{1}{5}v + \frac{1}{25}v + \ldots + \frac{1}{3125}v$
   a. v b. $\frac{1}{5}$ c. 6 d. $\frac{3906}{3125}v$
4. Find the sum of the first fifteen terms of the sequence $\begin{cases} g_1 = 20 \\ g_n = 0.9g_{n-1} \text{ for integers } n \geq 2 \end{cases}$ ≈ 158.822

SKILLS Objective C

In 5 and 6, a. write the geometric series in summation notation and b. find the sum.

5. $5 + 5r + 5r^2 + \ldots + 5r^{19}$ a. $\sum_{i=1}^{20} 5 \cdot r^{i-1}$ b. $5 \cdot \frac{1 - r^{20}}{1 - r}$
6. $8 - 4 + 2 - 1 + \frac{1}{2} - \ldots - \frac{1}{1024}$ a. $\sum_{i=1}^{14} \left(\frac{8}{(-2)^{i-1}}\right)$ b. $\frac{5461}{1024} \approx 5.333$

In 7 and 8, a. determine whether the summation is an arithmetic or a geometric series, and b. find the value of the series.

7. $\sum_{i=1}^{12} (3 + 2i)$ a. arithmetic b. 192
8. $\sum_{i=1}^{12} (3 \cdot 2^i)$ a. geometric b. 24,570

USES Objective G

9. A labor union agrees to a six-year contract. Workers will be paid $60,000 in the first year and receive a 5% raise each successive year. How much will a worker make in total over the six years? $\approx$ $408,115
10. Mr. Buescher pushes his two-year-old daughter on a swing set. On one swing, she travels forward 8 feet from back to front. Then he stops pushing, and she gradually slows down with each swing traveling 94% as far as the previous swing. Find the total distance traveled forward in ten swings. ≈ 61.5 ft

Advanced Algebra 601

In 3–6, a geometric series is given.
   a. **How many terms does the series have?**
   b. **Write the series in Σ-notation.**
   c. **Use the Finite Geometric Series Formula to evaluate the series.**

3. $5 + 10 + 20 + 40 + \ldots + 5 \cdot 2^7$
4. $170 + 17 + 1.7 + 0.17 + 0.017 + 0.0017$
5. $170 - 17 + 1.7 - 0.17 + 0.017 - 0.0017$
6. $a + \frac{1}{2}a + \frac{1}{4}a + \frac{1}{8}a + \ldots + \left(\frac{1}{2}\right)^{16}a$
7. Consider the geometric series in Example 2.
   a. Calculate the following sums.
      i. S_2 18 ii. S_3 21 iii. S_4 20 iv. S_5 $\frac{61}{3}$
   b. Plot the sums S_1 (which is 27), S_2, S_3, S_4, and S_5 on a number line. How is S_n related to S_{n-1} and S_{n-2}? See margin.
8. Find the sum of the first 17 terms of the geometric sequence with first term 20 and constant ratio 1. 340
9. Suppose $500 is deposited into a bank account on July 17 for seven consecutive years and earns an annual percentage yield of 4%.
   a. Write a geometric series that represents the value of this investment on July 17 of the eighth year (before that year's deposit).
   b. Rewrite your answer to Part a in Σ-notation.
   c. How much is in the account on July 17 of the eighth year? $4107.11

3a. 8
3b. $\sum_{k=1}^{8} 5(2)^{k-1}$
3c. 1275
4a. 6
4b. $\sum_{k=1}^{6} 170\left(\frac{1}{10}\right)^{k-1}$
4c. ≈ 188.89
5a. 6
5b. $\sum_{k=1}^{6} 170\left(-\frac{1}{10}\right)^{k-1}$
5c. ≈ 154.55
6a. 17
6b. $\sum_{k=1}^{17} a\left(\frac{1}{2}\right)^{k-1}$
6c. $\approx 1.99998a$
9a. $500(1.04) + 500(1.04)^2 + \ldots + 500(1.04)^7$
9b. $\sum_{k=1}^{7} 500(1.04)^k$

APPLYING THE MATHEMATICS

10. a. A worker deposits $2000 at the end of each year into a retirement account earning an annual percentage yield of 5.1%. Assume no other deposits or withdrawals from the account. To the nearest dollar, how much will the worker have after 40 years, assuming no deposit is made at the end of the 40th year?
    b. A second worker waits ten years before starting to save money for retirement. Assume that this worker saves $A per year for thirty years, also earning an APY of 5.1%. Write an expression for the total amount of money this worker will have saved, including interest, over thirty years, assuming no deposit is made at the end of the 30th year.
    c. How much does the second worker have to save each year in order to have the same amount after 30 years as the first worker has after 40 years? $3687.84

10a. $245,577
10b. $\frac{A(1.051)(1 - 1.051^{29})}{1 - 1.051}$

11. a. Complete the table below by expanding or factoring each polynomial on a CAS. a–c. See margin.

Standard Form	Factored Form
?	$(r - 1)(r + 1)$
$r^3 - 1$	?
$r^4 - 1$	?
$r^5 - 1$	?
$r^6 - 1$	?

b. **Fill in the Blanks** According to the Factor Theorem, $r - 1$ is a factor of a polynomial $P(r)$ if and only if $P(\underline{\ ?\ }) = \underline{\ ?\ }$. Use this fact to prove that $r - 1$ is a factor of $r^n - 1$ for all n.

c. Use the results of Parts a and b to simplify $\frac{r^n - 1}{r - 1}$ for $n = 2, 3, 4, 5,$ and 6.

12. A ball is dropped from a height of 10 feet. Each bounce returns it to $\frac{4}{5}$ of the height of the previous bounce.

a. Draw a diagram showing the ball's path until it touches the ground for the fourth time. See margin.

b. Find the total vertical distance the ball has traveled when it touches the ground for the fourth time. 49.04 ft

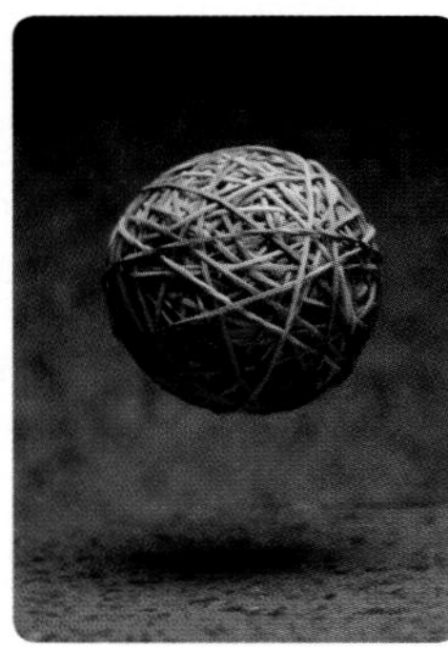

13. Consider the geometric series $x^7 + x^{12} + x^{17} + \ldots + x^{77}$.

a. What is the common ratio? x^5

b. Use the Finite Geometric Series Formula to find a formula for the value of the series.

c. Verify your result in Part b with a CAS. See margin.

13b. $S_{15} = \frac{x^7(1-x^{75})}{1-x^5}$

14. The number $\frac{1}{3}$ can be approximated by the finite geometric series $0.3 + 0.03 + 0.003 + 0.0003 + \ldots + g_1 r^{n-1}$.

a. Identify g_1 and r for the series. $g_1 = 0.3$, $r = \frac{1}{10}$

b. What approximation to $\frac{1}{3}$ occurs when $n = 6$? 0.333333

c. How far from $\frac{1}{3}$ is the approximation in Part b? 0.000000333...

REVIEW

15. Find the sum of the integers from 101 to 200. (Lesson 13-1) 15,050

16. a. How many odd integers are there from 25 to 75? 26

b. Find the sum of the odd integers from 25 to 75. (Lesson 13-1) 1300

17. A math club mails a monthly newsletter. In January, the club mailed newsletters to each of its 325 members. If membership increases by 5 members each month, how many newsletters will it mail for the entire year? (Lesson 13-1) 4230

Notes on the Questions

Question 12 Students often do not realize that the ball has traveled up only three times when it touches the ground for the fourth time.

Question 14 Any infinite repeating decimal can be written as an infinite geometric series.

Additional Answers

12a.

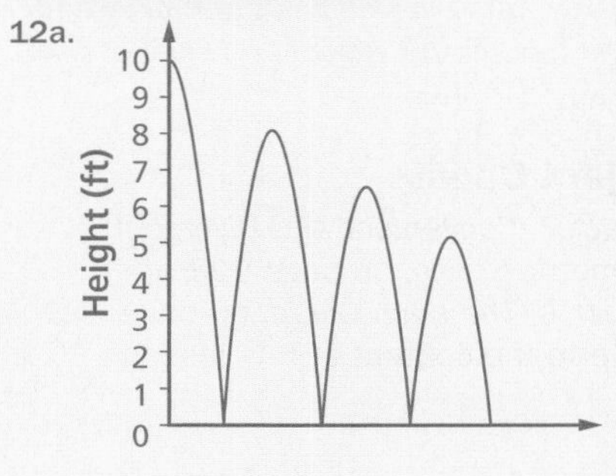

13c.

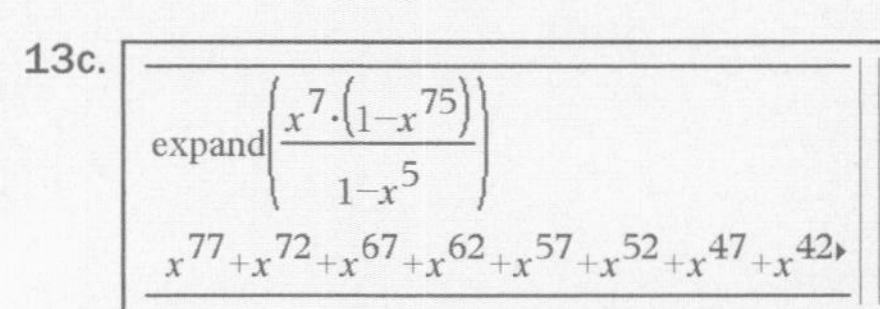

4 Wrap-Up

Ongoing Assessment

Have students work in pairs. Then have each student write the first 4 terms of a geometric series on a sheet of paper. Have students exchange papers and determine the sum of the first 10 terms in the given series. Students should provide a geometric series and then correctly apply the formula in this lesson to find the sum of a given number of terms.

Project Update

Project 2, *Convergent and Divergent Geometric Series,* on page 928 and Project 3, *The Koch Curve,* on page 929 relate to the content of this lesson.

13-2B page 2

13-2B Lesson Master — Questions on SPUR Objectives
See Student Edition pages 934–937 for objectives.

SKILLS Objective B

In 1–6, a geometric series is given. Find a. the first term, b. the common ratio, c. the number of terms, and d. the sum using the Finite Geometric Series Sum Theorem.

1. $81 + 27 + 9 + 3 + 1 + \frac{1}{3} + \frac{1}{9}$
   a. 81 b. $\frac{1}{3}$ c. 7 d. ≈ 121.4
2. $1 + 2 + 4 + 8 + \ldots + 512$
   a. 1 b. 2 c. 10 d. 1023
3. $6 + 24 + 96 + \ldots + 6 \cdot 4^{11}$
   a. 6 b. 4 c. 12 d. 33,554,430
4. $0.005 + 0.01 + 0.02 + 0.04 + \ldots + 0.005 \cdot 2^8$
   a. 0.005 b. 2 c. 9 d. 2.555
5. $1 - 1.5 + 2.25 - \ldots + 1.5^{10}$
   a. 1 b. -1.5 c. 11 d. ≈ 35.0
6. $1 + m + m^2 + m^3 + \ldots + m^{17}$
   a. 1 b. m c. 18 d. $\frac{1 - m^{18}}{1 - m}$
7. Find the sum of the first ten terms of the sequence $\begin{cases} g_1 = 32 \\ g_n = 0.75g_{n-1}, \text{ for integers } n \geq 2 \end{cases}$. ≈ 120.79
8. Find the sum of the first nine terms of the sequence $\begin{cases} g_1 = -10 \\ g_n = -g_{n-1}, \text{ for integers } n \geq 2 \end{cases}$. -10

SKILLS Objective C

In 9 and 10, a. write the geometric series in summation notation and b. find the sum.

9. $3 + 3a + 3a^2 + \ldots + 3a^{12}$ a. $\sum_{i=1}^{13} 3 \cdot a^{i-1}$ b. $3 \cdot \frac{1 - a^{13}}{1 - a}$
10. $1 - 3 + 9 - 27 + 81 - 243$ a. $\sum_{i=1}^{6} (-3)^{i-1}$ b. -182

In 11 and 12, a. determine whether the summation is an arithmetic or a geometric series, and b. find the value of the series.

11. $\sum_{i=1}^{12} 2^i$ a. geometric b. 8190
12. $\sum_{i=1}^{12} (i + 2)$ a. arithmetic b. 102

602 *Advanced Algebra*

18. Suppose $t_n = -2n + 9$. Find $t_1 + t_2 + t_3 + \ldots + t_{19}$. **(Lessons 13-1, 3-8)** -209

19. Let $f(x) = 27^x$. **(Lessons 9-7, 7-7, 7-3, 7-2, 7-1)**
    a. Evaluate $f(-3)$, $f(0)$, and $f\left(\frac{2}{3}\right)$.
    b. Identify the domain and range of f.
    c. Give an equation for the reflection image of the graph of $y = f(x)$ over the line $y = x$. $f(x) = \log_{27} x$

20. a. Identify the type of quadrilateral graphed at the right.
    b. Prove or disprove that the diagonals of this quadrilateral have the same length. **(Lesson 4-4, Previous Course)** See margin.

21. Write an equation for the line parallel to $7x + 2y = 13$ and containing the point $(6, 5)$. **(Lessons 3-4, 3-2)** $y - 5 = -\frac{7}{2}(x - 6)$

19a. $f(-3) = 27^{-3} = \frac{1}{19{,}683}$; $f(0) = 27^0 = 1$; $f\left(\frac{2}{3}\right) = 27^{\frac{2}{3}} = 9$

19b. domain: set of all real numbers; range: set of positive real numbers

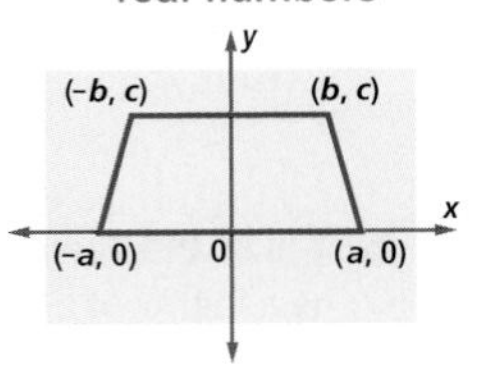

20a. isosceles trapezoid

EXPLORATION

22. Suppose that, because of inflation, a payment of P dollars n years from now is estimated to be worth $P(0.96)^n$ today. This worth is called the ***present value*** of a future payment.
    a. A lottery advertising $10,000,000 in winnings actually plans to pay the winner $500,000 each year for 20 years, starting the day the winner wins the lottery. Write the sum of the present values of these payments as a geometric series.
    b. Evaluate the geometric series in Part a. How does the sum compare to the advertised jackpot of $10,000,000?

22a. $500{,}000(0.96)^{19} + 500{,}000(0.96)^{18} + \ldots + 500{,}000(0.96)^0$

22b. $6,974,969.58; about $\frac{7}{10}$ of the advertised jackpot.

QY ANSWERS

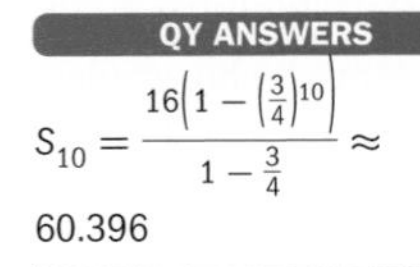

$S_{10} = \frac{16\left(1 - \left(\frac{3}{4}\right)^{10}\right)}{1 - \frac{3}{4}} \approx 60.396$

Additional Answers

20b. The diagonal with endpoints $(-b, c)$ and $(a, 0)$ has length $\sqrt{(a - (-b))^2 + (0 - c)^2} = \sqrt{(a + b)^2 + c^2}$, and the diagonal with endpoints $(-a, 0)$ and (b, c) has length $\sqrt{(b - (-a))^2 + (c - 0)^2} = \sqrt{(a + b)^2 + c^2}$. Thus, the diagonals are the same length.

Lesson 13-3 Using Series in Statistics Formulas

Vocabulary

mean
measure of center, measure of central tendency
absolute deviation
mean absolute deviation, *m.a.d.*
standard deviation, *s.d.*

Mental Math

Roderick has averaged 87 on two advanced algebra tests. What is the minimum score he can receive on the final test if he wants to finish the course with an average test score of at least

a. 90? 96
b. 70? 36
c. 95? 111

BIG IDEA Formulas for certain statistics, such as the *mean*, *mean absolute deviation*, and *standard deviation*, involve sums.

When you used Σ-notation in the previous two lessons, there was a formula for the numbers being added. In many situations, and particularly in statistics, data may be represented with an index variable and no formula. You can think of the data as terms of a sequence. We also say that each datum is an element of a data set. In data sets, different elements can have the same value. For instance, suppose that you have to read 10 short stories this semester in your English class and they have the following numbers of pages:

6, 14, 3, 8, 8, 9, 4, 11, 10, 23.

Let L_i be the length of the ith story, so $L_1 = 6$, $L_2 = 14$, $L_3 = 3$, and so on. The sum of these 10 numbers can be represented as $\sum_{i=1}^{10} L_i$. In this case, $\sum_{i=1}^{10} L_i = 96$, and so the mean of the lengths L_i is $\frac{\sum_{i=1}^{10} L_i}{10} = \frac{96}{10} = 9.6$. That is, the mean length of a story is 9.6 pages.

In general, when S is a data set of n numbers $x_1, x_2, x_3, ..., x_n$, then the **mean** of $S = \frac{\sum_{i=1}^{n} x_i}{n} = \frac{1}{n}\sum_{i=1}^{n} x_i$.

The Greek letter μ (mu, pronounced "mew") is customarily used to represent the mean of a data set.

Deviations and Absolute Deviations

Recall from Lesson 3-5 that the difference between an element of a data set and the mean of the set is called the element's deviation from the mean. If the mean is μ and the element is x_i, then the deviation is

$$x_i - \mu.$$

Background

Measures such as the mean, median, mode, and range are *descriptive statistics*. Two types of descriptive statistics are measures of *center* (*central tendency*) and measures of *spread* (*dispersion*). This lesson uses summation notation for three statistics. The mean is a measure of center. The mean absolute deviation and the standard deviation are measures of spread.

All students will have seen formulas for the mean, but it is likely they have never used Σ-notation in those formulas. To understand these formulas, students must realize that, unlike the use of the index i in describing an arithmetic or geometric series, there is no algebraic formula for a data value x_i in terms of i; it is simply the ith element of the data set. Here i is an integer; it bears no relation to the nonreal complex number i whose square is -1.

Deviations and absolute deviations Measures of spread are important in describing a data set and can be seen as measures of volatility or risk in data.

(continued on next page)

Lesson 13-3

GOAL

Review the mean and mean absolute deviation and learn about the standard deviation of a data set, describing them all with summation notation.

SPUR Objectives

C Use summation (Σ) notation.

I Use measures of central tendency or dispersion to describe data or distributions.

Materials/Resources

- Lesson Masters 13-3A and 13-3B
- Resource Masters 250 and 251
- Quiz 1
- Paper and the first two paragraphs under the Big Idea of Lesson 13-5

HOMEWORK

Suggestions for Assignment

- Questions 1–25
- Question 26 (extra credit)
- Reading Lesson 13-4
- Covering the Ideas 13-4

Local Standards

1 Warm-Up

Suppose $x_1 = 8$, $x_2 = 15$, $x_3 = 7$, $x_4 = 10$, and $x_5 = 20$. Calculate the value of each expression.

1. $\sum_{i=1}^{4} x_i$ 40
2. $\frac{\sum_{i=1}^{5} x_i}{5}$ 12
3. $\sum_{i=1}^{5} (x_i^2)$ 838
4. $\sum_{i=1}^{5} (x_i - \mu)^2$, where μ is the value you found in Warm-Up Question 2 118
5. $\sum_{i=1}^{5} |x_i - \mu|$, where μ is the value you found in Warm-Up 2 22

(continued on next page)

Note: If the answer to Warm-Up 4 is divided by 5 and then the square root is taken, the result ($\sqrt{23.6} \approx 4.86$) is the standard deviation of the five values. If the answer to Warm-Up 5 is divided by 5, the result (4.4) is the mean absolute deviation of the five values.

2 Teaching

Notes on the Lesson

An important broad point to make to students is that they should try to not be psyched out by strange notations or symbols such as Σ or μ. They should ask themselves why the notation is used. In this lesson's formulas, the reason for the notation is the same—the notation provides a useful shorthand.

To make this point, you might ask for the formula for the mean μ of two numbers x_1 and x_2 without summation notation. $\mu = \frac{x_1 + x_2}{2}$ Then ask for the formula for the mean μ of three numbers. $\mu = \frac{x_1 + x_2 + x_3}{2}$ These are different formulas, and the formula for the mean of four numbers would be different still. By using summation notation, we can express all these formulas in the same way.

We suggest you go over the Example with the class. Then discuss Questions 1 and 2, followed by the Activity. Lastly, discuss the other questions. The questions use data from real situations and from abstract sets. We use descriptive statistics from real situations to gain information about the situation. We use descriptive statistics from abstract sets for quick practice or concept building.

For instance, in the data set of story lengths, the deviation of the 6-page story from the mean of 9.6 pages is 6 – 9.6, or -3.6. That is, the story is 3.6 pages shorter than the mean length. In general, deviation is positive if an element is larger than the mean and negative if an element is smaller than the mean.

The sum of the deviations of the elements of a set from the mean of the set is 0. That is,

$$\sum_{i=1}^{n}(x_i - \mu) = 0.$$

This suggests that the mean is a number on which the data set "balances." For this reason, the mean is a called a **measure of center,** or a **measure of central tendency,** of a data set.

 QY1

Suppose you are estimating the number of beans in a jar and you want to know how close your estimate E is to the actual number A. Then you do not care whether E is larger or smaller than A. You want to know the *absolute deviation* of your estimate from A, or $|E - A|$. The **absolute deviation** of an element of a data set from the mean of the set is

$$|x_i - \mu|.$$

For instance, the absolute deviation of the element 6 from the mean 9.6 is $|6 - 9.6| = |-3.6| = 3.6$.

 QY2

The mean of the absolute deviations is a statistic called the **mean absolute deviation**, or ***m.a.d.*** The *m.a.d.* is a measure of the *spread* or *dispersion* of a data set. In Σ-notation,

$$m.a.d. = \frac{1}{n}\sum_{i=1}^{n}|x_i - \mu|.$$

▸ **QY1**

a. Find the deviations of all 10 elements of the data set of story lengths from the mean of the lengths.

b. Find the mean of the deviations.

▸ **QY2**

a. Find the absolute deviations of all 10 elements of the data set of story lengths from the mean of the lengths.

b. Find the mean of these absolute deviations.

Example

You are offered the chance to play one of two games, Game A or Game B. In each game you reach into a jar and pull out a slip of paper. You win the dollar amount written on the slip. In both games there are 10 slips of paper in the jar with a mean value of $50.

Calculate the *m.a.d.* of the values on the slips for each game. Which game gives more spread out results?

Game A Slips				
$49	$49	$49	$49	$50
$50	$51	$51	$51	$51

Game B Slips				
$0	$0	$0	$0	$0
$0	$0	$0	$0	$500

The American Statistical Association's (2005) curriculum framework suggests that the first measure of spread introduced to students be the mean absolute deviation. Students who studied from the Third Edition of UCSMP *Transition Mathematics* and UCSMP *Algebra* will have seen this statistic.

The standard deviation The standard deviation has properties that make it the preferred statistic of spread in most statistical applications. It is likely, however, that students have never seen it before.

Few people today calculate standard deviations by hand; you should make sure that students know how to obtain standard deviations by using calculators or spreadsheet programs.

Some statistics books have $n - 1$, also known as the degrees of freedom, in the denominator of the formula for standard deviation. Some distinguish the *population* standard deviation from a *sample* standard deviation. We make no such distinction here because the idea is more important than the detail.

Solution For each game, the mean dollar amount μ is \$50. For Game A, there are 8 slips whose amounts deviate by \$1 from the mean, and the other two slips have no deviation from the mean. So,

$$\text{m.a.d. for Game } A = \frac{1}{n}\sum_{i=1}^{n}|x_i - \mu| = \frac{1}{10}(8 \cdot 1 + 2 \cdot 0) = 0.8.$$

In Game B, there are 9 amounts that deviate by \$50 from the mean, and 1 amount that deviates by \$450. So,

$$\text{m.a.d. for Game } B = \frac{1}{n}\sum_{i=1}^{n}|x_i - \mu| = \frac{1}{10}(9 \cdot 50 + 1 \cdot 450) = 90.$$

There is quite a difference in the spread of dollar amounts in the games. The more the values are spread out from the mean, the less likely you are to win an amount of money close to the mean amount. Since 90 is greater than 0.8, the results of Game B are more spread out.

The Standard Deviation

The *m.a.d.* of a data set is relatively easy to calculate, but it does not have as many useful properties as a second measure of spread, the *standard deviation*. The lower-case Greek letter sigma (σ) is often used to denote the standard deviation, as in the following definition.

Definition of Standard Deviation

Let S be a data set of n numbers $\{x_1, x_2, ..., x_n\}$. Let μ be the mean of S. Then the **standard deviation,** or **s.d.**, of S is given by

$$s.d. = \sigma = \sqrt{\frac{1}{n}\sum_{i=1}^{n}(x_i - \mu)^2}.$$

This formula looks complicated, so it may help to describe it in words. To use the formula, find the mean of the data set and then square each element's deviation from the mean. Then find the mean of these squared deviations. The square root of this mean is the standard deviation. The mean of the squared deviations is also called the *variance* of the data set. So, the standard deviation of a set is the square root of the variance of the set.

Standard deviation is used in a wide variety of statistical analyses. For example, a readability index is a measure of how difficult written text is to understand. To find one index, a computer program analyzes random paragraphs to find the mean and standard deviation of the number of words per sentence.

ENGLISH LEARNERS

Vocabulary Development

Discuss the definitions of the vocabulary terms in this lesson and review the definitions of *median* and *mode*. Then explain that a *measure of center,* or *measure of central tendency,* gives a number that in some sense is at the "center" of the set. Then write on the board a set of six or eight numbers and work with students to find the *mean,* median, mode, *mean absolute deviation,* and *standard deviation* for the set of numbers.

Additional Example

Example You are offered the chance to play one of two games—Game A or Game B. In each game, you reach into a jar and pull out a slip of paper. You win the dollar amount written on the slip. In both games, there are 8 slips of paper in the jar with a mean value of \$100.

Game A Slips			
\$99	\$99	\$100	\$100
\$100	\$100	\$101	\$101
Game B Slips			
\$0	\$0	\$0	\$0
\$0	\$0	\$0	\$800

Calculate the *m.a.d.* of the values on the slips for each game. Which game is riskier? For each game, the mean dollar amount μ is \$100. For Game A, there are four slips whose amounts deviate by \$1 from the mean, and the other four slips have no deviation from the mean. So, $\frac{1}{n}\sum_{i=1}^{n}|x_i - \mu| = \frac{1}{8}(4 \cdot 1 + 4 \cdot 0) = 0.5$. In Game B, there are seven amounts that deviate by \$100 from the mean, and one amount that deviates by \$700. So $\frac{1}{n}\sum_{i=1}^{n}|x_i - \mu| = \frac{1}{8}(7 \cdot 100 + 1 \cdot 700) = 175$. The values for Game B are more spread out from the mean than the values for Game A.

Notes on the Lesson

Some calculators can keep sums of squares in memory. Usually these calculators can also automatically calculate standard deviations. But if not, the alternate form of the standard deviation formula is useful:

$$s.d. = \sqrt{\frac{\sum_{i=1}^{n} x_i^2 - \frac{\left(\sum_{i=1}^{n} x_i\right)^2}{n}}{n}}.$$

Note-Taking Tips

Have students add to their journals the definitions of mean absolute deviation (*m.a.d.*) and standard deviation (*s.d.*) and include appropriate examples.

Additional Answers

Activity

Step 3

1.96, 0.16, 0.36, 0.16, 2.56; 31.36, 29.16, 5.76, 92.16, 54.76

Step 5

Answers vary. Sample: Paragraph 1: It has fewer words per sentence on average, and since the standard deviation is much lower, each sentence does not differ much from the average sentence length.

3 Assignment

Recommended Assignment

- Questions 1–25
- Question 26 (extra credit)
- Reading Lesson 13-4
- Covering the Ideas 13-4

13-3A Lesson Master

Questions on SPUR Objectives
See Student Edition pages 934–937 for objectives.

SKILLS Objective C

In 1–4, a data set contains 20 elements, d_1 through d_{20}. Tell what each expression represents.

1. $\sum_{i=1}^{20} d_i$ the sum of the elements
2. $\frac{1}{20}\sum_{i=1}^{20} d_i$ the mean
3. $\frac{1}{20}\sum_{i=1}^{20} |d_i - \mu|$ the mean absolute deviation
4. $\sqrt{\frac{1}{20}\sum_{i=1}^{20} (d_i - \mu)^2}$ the standard deviation

In 5 and 6, a data set contains n elements, a_1 through a_n. Give an expression for each measure.

5. the mean $\frac{1}{n}\sum_{i=1}^{n} a_i$
6. the standard deviation $\sqrt{\frac{1}{n}\sum_{i=1}^{n} (a_i - \mu)^2}$

USES Objective I

7. Tess's percentage scores on her math tests for the semester are 78, 91, 84, 87, and 85.
   a. Find the mean. 85
   b. Find the deviations from the mean. −7, 6, −1, 2, 0
   c. Find the mean absolute deviation. 3.2
   d. Find the standard deviation. $\sqrt{18} \approx 4.243$
   e. What score does she need on the last test to earn an 86.5% average for the semester? 94
8. The table at the right shows the mean income of U.S. households when divided into fifths. For example, the mean income of the lowest fifth of households was $9714 in 1985 and $10,655 in 2005. The numbers are adjusted for inflation so they can be compared.

	1985	2005
Lowest Fifth	$9714	$10,655
Second Fifth	$24,618	$27,357
Third Fifth	$40,863	$46,301
Fourth Fifth	$61,466	$72,825
Highest Fifth	$114,816	$159,583

Source: http://www.census.gov

   a. Find the mean of each year's data for all households. 1985: $50,295.40; 2005: $63,344.20
   b. Find the standard deviation of each year's data. 1985: $36,559.10; 2005: $52,370.78
   c. Explain how income and distribution changed from 1985 to 2005. Answers vary. Sample: Incomes went up from 1985 to 2005, and they became less evenly distributed. OR, Percent increases over 20 years were greatest for higher incomes.

604 *Advanced Algebra*

Activity

MATERIALS Paper and the first two paragraphs under the Big Idea of Lesson 13-5

Step 1 Make a table like the one at the right and record the number of words in each sentence of each paragraph. When counting words, note that a "word" is any character or group of characters with a space before and after it.

	Number of words	
Sentence Number	Paragraph 1	Paragraph 2
1	? 12	? 27
2	? 11	? 16
3	? 10	? 19
4	? 11	? 31
5	? 9	? 14

Step 2 Calculate the mean number of words per sentence in each paragraph. 10.6; 21.4

Step 3 Calculate the square of the deviation of each element in the Paragraph 1 data set from its mean. Repeat for the Paragraph 2 data set. See margin.

Step 4 Find the mean of the squared deviations for each data set in Step 3. Then calculate the standard deviation for each. 1.04; 42.64; 1.02; 6.53

Step 5 Which paragraph from Lesson 13-5 do you think is easier to read and understand? Support your conclusion with your statistics from Steps 2–4. See margin.

Most spreadsheet programs and calculators calculate standard deviations. One CAS shows the results at the right for the standard deviations of the data sets in the Activity.

stDevPop({12,11,10,11,9})	1.0198
stDevPop({27,16,19,31,14})	6.52993

Questions

COVERING THE IDEAS

1. Find the mean absolute deviation of the data set {2, 3, 3, 4, 5, 6, 6, 6, 6, 7}. 1.44

2. In 2006, the Miami Heat salaries, in millions of dollars, were approximately 0.4, 0.74, 2.88, 0.15, 0.07, 5.53, 0.41, 0.075, 1.19, 2.5, 20, 0.74, 6.39, 0.41, 0.93, 3.84, 7.61, 8.25, and 1.33. Find the *m.a.d.* of these salaries. 3.325 million dollars

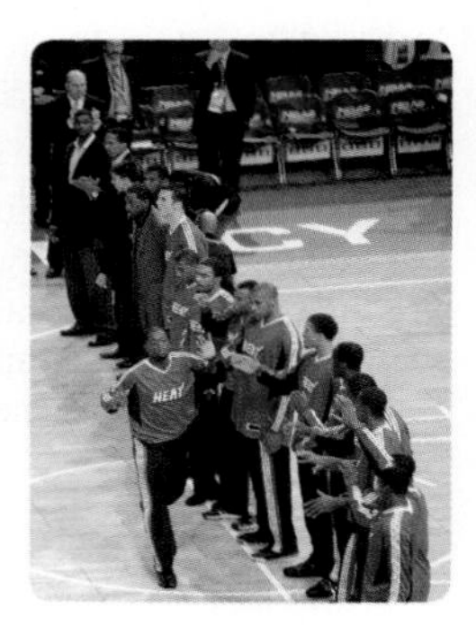

3. Calculate the standard deviation of the data set of story lengths on the first page of this lesson. about 5.43

4. A person bowls games of 158, 201, 175, and 134. For these scores, calculate
   a. the *m.a.d.* 21
   b. the *s.d.* about 24.44

Accommodating the Learner

The algorithm for calculating the mean absolute deviation of a data set is easy to remember from the letters *m.a.d.* First calculate the deviations (d) from the mean of the data set. These are positive or negative, but their sum is 0. Then take the absolute values (a) of the deviations. Finally take the mean (m) of those absolute values.

Accommodating the Learner

Divide students into three or four equal-sized groups. Within each group, have students list their heights in inches. Groups should find the measures of central tendency and dispersion for their data, including median, mode, and standard deviation. Then have the groups describe ways in which the groups are alike and ways in which the groups are different.

In 5–9, suppose that 100 scores are identified as $s_1, s_2, \ldots, s_{100}$. What does each expression represent?

5. $\sum_{i=1}^{100} s_i$
6. $\frac{1}{100}\sum_{i=1}^{100} s_i$
7. $\frac{1}{100}\sum_{i=1}^{100} (s_i - \mu)$
8. $\frac{1}{100}\sum_{i=1}^{100} |s_i - \mu|$
9. $\sqrt{\frac{1}{100}\sum_{i=1}^{100} (s_i - \mu)^2}$

10. Refer to the two games described in the Example.
    a. Calculate the standard deviation of the amounts in each game 0.89, 150
    b. Why would someone want to play Game B?

11. Fundraisers sell 10,000 raffle tickets for $5 each. The raffle officials need to decide whether to have several winners of small amounts or just a few winners of large amounts. One option is to have two prizes worth $10,000 each and two prizes worth $5000 each. A second option is to have two prizes worth $15,000 apiece. In which option are the results more spread out? (Consider any non-winning ticket as a $0 prize.)

5. the sum of all of the scores
6. the mean
7. the average deviation from the mean
8. the mean absolute deviation
9. the standard deviation

10b. Answers vary. Sample: Game B has a chance for a much bigger payout than is possible with Game A.

11. The results are more spread out in the first option. It has a lower *m.a.d.* and the chances of winning something close to the mean are greater.

APPLYING THE MATHEMATICS

12. **Multiple Choice** A store has two managers and nine employees. Each manager earns $40,000 a year, six employees earn $25,000 a year, and three employees earn $15,000 a year. If each person gets a $1000 raise next year, the standard deviation of the salaries C
    A will increase by $1000.
    B will increase by $3000.
    C will not change.
    D will increase by about 3%.

13. a. Let $x_i = 2i$, for $i = 1, 2, 3, \ldots, 10$. Find the mean and standard deviation of the x_i values. 11, 5.74
    b. Let $y_i = 2i + 1$, for $i = 1, 2, 3, \ldots, 10$. Find the mean and standard deviation of the y_i values. 12, 5.74

14. Below are the ages of the Democratic and Republican United States Presidents when they were first inaugurated into office, as of 2008.

    Democrats: 43, 46, 47, 48, 49, 51, 52, 54, 55, 55, 56, 60, 61, 65

    Republicans: 42, 46, 49, 50, 51, 51, 51, 52, 54, 54, 54, 55, 55, 56, 61, 62, 64, 69

    Compare the ages at inauguration of Democrats and Republicans by calculating means and standard deviations. See margin.

15. Give an example, different from the one in the lesson, of two different data sets that have the same mean but different standard deviations. Answers vary. Sample: {0, 150, 300} and {100, 150, 200}

While John F. Kennedy was the youngest person elected president, Theodore Roosevelt was the youngest person to become president when William McKinley was assassinated.

Notes on the Questions

Question 11 Here, standard deviation acts as a measure of risk. The greater the standard deviation, the greater the risk.

Question 12 Students should think about the idea of spread and perhaps visualize the old and new salaries on a number line. Will the spread of the data increase? No

Question 13 It should be obvious to your students that the mean in Part b should be 1 greater than the mean in Part a, but the standard deviations are the same.

Additional Answers

14. means: 53 (D), 54.2 (R); standard deviations: 6.01 (D), 6.34 (R): Republican presidents are on average older at inauguration but their ages at inauguration also vary more than those of the Democratic presidents.

4 Wrap-Up

Ongoing Assessment

Have students work in small groups. Have each student write a data set of four numbers. Have students exchange papers and determine both the mean absolute deviation and the standard deviation for the numbers they have been given. Have group members check and discuss their work. Students should demonstrate that they can find the mean absolute deviation and the standard deviation for a set of data.

Administer Quiz 1 (or a quiz of your own) after students complete this lesson.

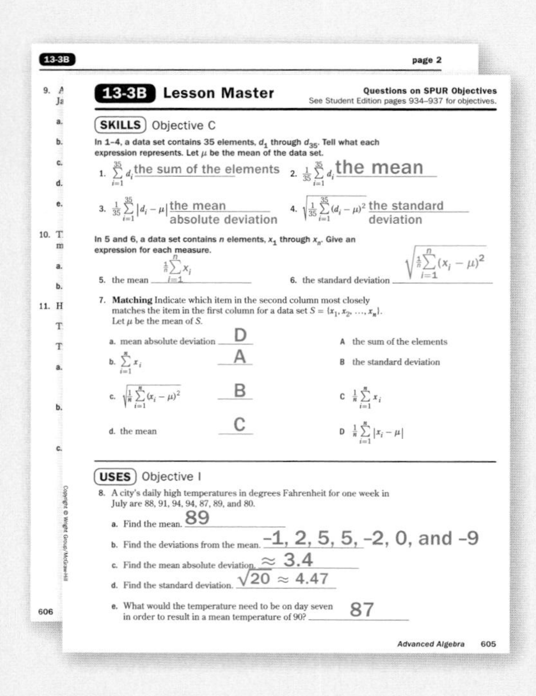
13-3B page 2

13-3B Lesson Master

Questions on SPUR Objectives
See Student Edition pages 934–937 for objectives.

SKILLS Objective C

In 1–4, a data set contains 35 elements, d_1 through d_{35}. Tell what each expression represents. Let μ be the mean of the data set.

1. $\sum_{i=1}^{35} d_i$ the sum of the elements
2. $\frac{1}{35}\sum_{i=1}^{35} d_i$ the mean
3. $\frac{1}{35}\sum_{i=1}^{35} |d_i - \mu|$ the mean absolute deviation
4. $\sqrt{\frac{1}{35}\sum_{i=1}^{35} (d_i - \mu)^2}$ the standard deviation

In 5 and 6, a data set contains n elements, x_1 through x_n. Give an expression for each measure.

5. the mean $\frac{1}{n}\sum_{i=1}^{n} x_i$
6. the standard deviation $\sqrt{\frac{1}{n}\sum_{i=1}^{n} (x_i - \mu)^2}$
7. **Matching** Indicate which item in the second column most closely matches the item in the first column for a data set $S = \{x_1, x_2, \ldots, x_n\}$. Let μ be the mean of S.

a. mean absolute deviation D
b. $\sum_{i=1}^{n} x_i$ A
c. $\sqrt{\frac{1}{n}\sum_{i=1}^{n} (x_i - \mu)^2}$ B
d. the mean C

A the sum of the elements
B the standard deviation
C $\frac{1}{n}\sum_{i=1}^{n} x_i$
D $\frac{1}{n}\sum_{i=1}^{n} |x_i - \mu|$

USES Objective I

8. A city's daily high temperatures in degrees Fahrenheit for one week in July are 88, 91, 94, 94, 87, 89, and 80.
   a. Find the mean. 89
   b. Find the deviations from the mean. -1, 2, 5, 5, -2, 0, and -9
   c. Find the mean absolute deviation. ≈ 3.4
   d. Find the standard deviation. $\sqrt{20} \approx 4.47$
   e. What would the temperature need to be on day seven in order to result in a mean temperature of 90? 87

606

Advanced Algebra 605

16. What would a data set with standard deviation equal to 0 look like?

16. Every element in the set would have the same value.

REVIEW

17. Lotta Moola invests \$350 on the first day of every month in an account that earns an annual interest rate of 6% compounded monthly. Assume no other deposits or withdrawals are made.
    a. How much interest will the first \$350 deposit earn in 6 months? \$10.63
    b. How much will be in Lotta's account just after she makes her 7th deposit? **(Lessons 13-2, 11-1, 7-4)** \$2487.05

In 18 and 19, suppose a tennis ball is released from a height of 1 meter above the floor. Each time it hits the floor it bounces to 40% of its previous height. (Lessons 13-2, 7-5)

18. Suppose the ball has hit the floor four times. How high will it get on the next bounce? 2.56 cm
19. If the ball hits the floor eight times, find the vertical distance it will have traveled. 2.33 m
20. Beginning with 1, how many consecutive positive integers do you have to add in order to total 2701? **(Lesson 13-1)** 73

In 21–23, evaluate and write your answer in $a + bi$ form. (Lessons 6-9, 6-8)

21. $(1 + i)^2$ $2i$
22. $\frac{-8 + 2i}{i}$ $2 + 8i$
23. $i^4 + i^5 + i^6 + i^7$ 0
24. If 4 thingies and 3 somethings weigh 190 lb, and 6 thingies and 7 somethings weigh 350 lb, what will 2 thingies and 4 somethings weigh? **(Lesson 5-4)** 160 lb
25. Ivan has test scores of 80, 97, 90, and 88. What must Ivan score on the next test to have
    a. a mean of 90 for the five tests? 95
    b. a median of 90 for the five tests? at least 90
    c. a mode of 90 for the five tests? **(Previous Course)** 90

EXPLORATION

26. You have used your calculator's statistical regression functions to find equations to model sets of data points. To do this, the regression procedure minimizes the sum of the squares of the deviations of the points from the curve. Search the Internet (for example, search for "sum of squares applet") to find interactive websites that allow you to graphically explore how to minimize a sum of squares. See margin.

QY ANSWERS

1. a. –3.6, 4.4, –6.6, –1.6, –1.6, –0.6, –5.6, 1.4, 0.4, 13.4
   b. 0
2. a. 3.6, 4.4, 6.6, 1.6, 1.6, 0.6, 5.6, 1.4, 0.4, 13.4
   b. 3.92

Additional Answers

26. Answers vary. Sample: There are many examples of sums of squares applets. One example is at http://www.math.duke.edu/education/webfeatsII/gdrive/Team%20E/Web/LeastSquares.htm.

Lesson 13-4 Subsets and Combinations

Vocabulary

permutation

!, factorial symbol

$n!$

combination

▸ **BIG IDEA** Given a set of n objects, there are formulas for the number of ways of choosing r objects where the order or the objects matters, and for the number of ways of choosing r objects without regard to their order.

Permutations

An arrangement of objects where order matters is called a **permutation.** With 3 objects A, B, and C, there are 6 possible permutations: ABC, ACB, BAC, BCA, CAB, and CBA. You can think of these 6 permutations in many ways, such as ways to arrange 3 objects on a shelf or orders in which runners could win medals in an Olympic race.

Example 1

a. Write all the possible orders in which 4 runners A, B, C, and D might finish a race.

b. How many permutations of 4 runners are there?

Solution

a. Make a list as shown below. Assume A finishes first. The left column lists the 6 possible orders of B, C, and D finishing behind A. The next column has B first followed by the 6 possible orders of A, C, and D. The third and fourth columns begin with C and D, respectively.

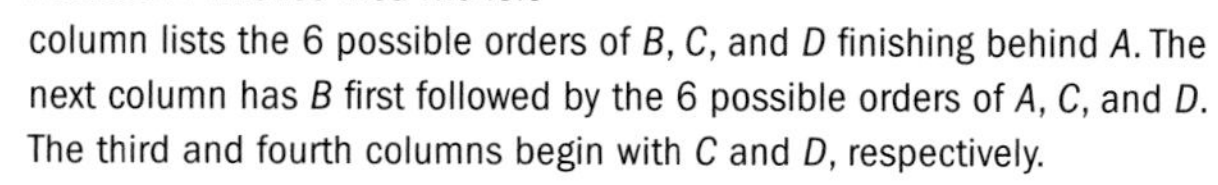

ABCD	BACD	CABD	DABC
ABDC	BADC	CADB	DACB
ACBD	BCAD	CBAD	DBAC
ACDB	BCDA	CBDA	DBCA
ADBC	BDAC	CDAB	DCAB
ADCB	BDCA	CDBA	DCBA

b. Count the permutations you listed. There are 24 permutations. Notice that the number of permutations of 4 objects is 4 times the number of permutations of 3 objects, or $4 \cdot 6$.

Special Olympics serves people with intellectual disabilites in over 180 countries.

a. the set of all real numbers

b. $\{p \mid p \text{ is divisible by } 6\}$

c. the set of all ellipses

Mental Math

Simplify.

a. $\{n \mid n < 3\} \cup \{n \mid n \geq -8\}$

b. $\{p \mid p \text{ is divisible by } 2\} \cap \{p \mid p \text{ is divisible by } 3\}$

c. the set of all circles $\cup$ the set of all ellipses

d. the set of all rectangles with perimeter 50 $\cap$ the set of all squares with area 225 $\emptyset$

Background

Permutations of n distinct objects are covered here as a vehicle to introduce factorials and to assist with the proof of the formula for the number of combinations of n objects taken r at a time. Combinations are used throughout the rest of the chapter. For some students, all of the material in this lesson will be new. For students who have had studied from previous UCSMP courses, factorial notation and the number of permutations of n distinct objects should be a review.

Permutations It is typical for students to initially confuse permutations and combinations. To permute is to switch the order of, so permutations involve the number of ways of switching orders. When you combine, as in combining like terms, the order does not make a difference, so combinations ignore order.

(continued on next page)

Lesson 13-4

GOAL

Review permutations and factorial notation and investigate combinations.

SPUR Objectives

C Use factorial (!) notation.

D Calculate permutations and combinations.

H Solve real-world counting problems involving permutations or combinations.

Materials/Resources

- Lesson Masters 13-4A and 13-4B
- Resource Masters 252 and 253

HOMEWORK

Suggestions for Assignment

- Questions 1–21
- Question 22 (extra credit)
- Reading Lesson 13-5
- Covering the Ideas 13-5

Local Standards

1 Warm-Up

1. List all the strings of the four letters O, P, S, and T, such as STOP, that can be made by using each of the letters only once. Check students' lists. There are 24 strings.
2. How many of the strings are words in the English language? 6: OPTS, POST, POTS, SPOT, STOP, and TOPS

To list the possible ways in which 5 people could finish a race, you could begin with the list in Example 1. Call the fifth racer E. In each permutation in the list, you can insert E in 5 places: at the beginning, in one of the three middle spots, or at the end. For instance, inserting E into $ABCD$ yields $EABCD$, $AEBCD$, $ABECD$, $ABCED$, or $ABCDE$. This means that the number of permutations of 5 objects is 5 times the number of permutations of 4 objects, or $5 \cdot 24$.

The Factorial Symbol

You may have noticed a pattern. The number of permutations of 2 objects A and B is 2, AB and BA, and $2 = 2 \cdot 1$. The number of permutations of 3 objects A, B, and C is 6, which is $3 \cdot 2$, or $3 \cdot 2 \cdot 1$. The number of permutations of 4 objects is $4 \cdot 6$, or $4 \cdot 3 \cdot 2 \cdot 1$. The number of permutations of 5 objects is $5 \cdot 4 \cdot 3 \cdot 2 \cdot 1$, or 120.

These products of the integers n through 1 are represented by a special symbol, called the *factorial symbol*. The **factorial symbol, !,** is an exclamation point, and $n!$ is read "n factorial."

Definition of Factorial

Let n be any integer ≥ 2. Then $n!$ is the product of the integers from 1 through n.

A generalization of Example 1 can be described using factorials.

Number of Permutations Theorem

There are $n!$ permutations of n distinct objects.

In the order of operations, factorials are calculated before multiplications or divisions. That is, $2 \cdot 5! = 2 \cdot 120 = 240 \neq 10!$.

Activity Steps 1 and 2. See margin.

Step 1 Copy and fill in the table at the right.

Step 2 Describe the pattern you see in the table. Use the pattern to write a recursive formula for the sequence $f_n = n!$.

n	3	4	5	6	7	8	9	10
$n!$	?	?	120	?	?	?	362,880	?
$(n-1)!$	2	?	?	?	720	?	?	?
$\frac{n!}{(n-1)!}$	?	?	?	?	?	?	?	?

The pattern in the Activity is a fundamental property of factorials.

Factorial Product Theorem

For all $n \geq 1$, $n! = n \cdot (n-1)!$.

2 Teaching

Notes on the Lesson

For Warm-Up 1, many students will say, "How many ways can you combine the four letters?" or "How many combinations can you make with the four letters?" In so doing, these people are using combination language for permutation problems, thus making it easier for students to confuse permutations and combinations. Warm-Up 1 and Example 1 each have a single combination but 24 permutations of that combination.

Permutations Emphasize that permutations are arrangements of objects in order, whereas combinations are selections of objects without regard to order. Compare and contrast the solutions to the following problems about Veneda, Wanda, Xander, Yolanda, and Zelda.

1. The five women enter a 10-kilometer race. In how many orders can they finish? VWXYZ; VXWYZ; VYWXZ; VZWXY; VWXZY; VXWZY; VYWZX; VZWYX; VWYXZ; VXYWZ; VYXWZ; VZYWX; VWYZX; VXYZW; VYXZW; VZXYW; VWZXY; VXZWY; VYZWX; VZXWY; VWZYX; VXZYW; VYZXW; VZYXW; There are 4! with Veneda winning, so $5 \cdot 4!$ or $5! = 120$ orders in all.
2. Two of the five women will be chosen for $7500 scholarships. In how many ways can the scholarships be awarded? Note that in contrast to situation 1, the order in which the names are chosen here does not matter. $C(5, 2) = \frac{5!}{2!(5-2)!} = 10$: VW; VX; VY; VZ; WX; YX; WY; YZ; WZ; XZ

In this lesson, we give a formula for only the number of permutations of n objects. We do not identify the formula for the number of permutations of r of these objects, although that formula is found in the proof of the theorem on page 893. We leave that discussion of permutations for a later course. The emphasis here is on combinations. Examples 3–5 all involve combinations.

The factorial symbol $k!$, the *product* of integers from 1 to k, is analogous to $\sum_{i=1}^{k} n$, the *sum* of integers from 1 to k. From this, the *quotient of factorials* describes the product of integers from a to b and is directly analogous to the *difference of sums* that describes the sum of integers from a to b. Specifically, $\frac{b!}{(a-1)!}$ is the product of integers from a to b, and $\sum_{i=1}^{b} n - \sum_{i=1}^{a-1} n$ is the sum of integers from a to b.

When $n \geq 3$, the theorem follows from the definition of factorial. For the theorem to hold when $n = 2$, we must have $2! = 2 \cdot (2 - 1)! = 2 \cdot 1!$. This means that 1! has to equal 1. This makes sense with permutations. If there is only one object, there is only one order. If the theorem is to hold when $n = 1$, then it must be that $1! = 1 \cdot (1 - 1)! = 1 \cdot 0!$. This means that we must have $0! = 1$.

Many calculators and CAS give exact values of $n!$ for small values of n, but for larger values, they give approximations in scientific notation. For instance, when 20! is entered, one calculator displays

2432902008176640000

while another displays 2.4329 E 18, which means 2,432,900,000,000,000,000.

Products of Consecutive Integers

Factorials help you calculate products of consecutive integers, starting at any number.

Example 2

Find 7 • 8 • 9 • 10 • 11 • 12 • 13 • 14 • 15 • 16 using factorials.

Solution 1 Multiply the given product by a factorial so that the final product is a factorial.

Let $x = 7 \cdot 8 \cdot 9 \cdot 10 \cdot 11 \cdot 12 \cdot 13 \cdot 14 \cdot 15 \cdot 16$.

Notice that $6! \cdot x = 1 \cdot 2 \cdot 3 \cdot 4 \cdot 5 \cdot 6 \cdot x = 16!$.

Solving for x, $x = \frac{16!}{6!} = 29{,}059{,}430{,}400$.

Solution 2 Multiply the given product by $\frac{6!}{6!}$. This does not change its value.

$$7 \cdot 8 \cdot 9 \cdot 10 \cdot 11 \cdot 12 \cdot 13 \cdot 14 \cdot 15 \cdot 16$$
$$= \frac{6!}{6!} \cdot 7 \cdot 8 \cdot 9 \cdot 10 \cdot 11 \cdot 12 \cdot 13 \cdot 14 \cdot 15 \cdot 16$$
$$= \frac{16!}{6!} = 29{,}059{,}430{,}400$$

QY1

▸ QY1
Write $22 \cdot 23 \cdot 24$ as a quotient of two factorials.

Subsets and Combinations

You can apply the technique in Example 2 to problems where you are choosing subsets and order does not matter.

Additional Answers

Activity

Step 1

Top row: 6; 24; 720; 5040; 40,320; 3,628,800

Middle row: 6; 24; 120; 5040; 40,320; 362,880

Bottom row: 3; 4; 5; 6; 7; 8; 9; 10

Step 2

The pattern is $n = \frac{n!}{(n-1)!}$, $\begin{cases} f_1 = 1 \\ f_n = n \cdot f_{n-1} \end{cases}$, for $n \geq 2$

Additional Examples

Example 1 Have students work in groups of five. Have each group list the permutations beginning with one of the four numbers given. Assign each starting number to at least one group.

a. Write all the possible orders in which a person might choose the numbers 2, 4, 6, and 8 for a lottery ticket. 2, 4, 6, 8; 2, 4, 8, 6; 2, 6, 4, 8; 2, 6, 8, 4; 2, 8, 4, 6; 2, 8, 6, 4; 4, 2, 6, 8; 4, 2, 8, 6; 4, 6, 2, 8; 4, 6, 8, 2; 4, 8, 2, 6; 4, 8, 6, 2; 6, 2, 4, 8; 6, 2, 8, 4; 6, 4, 2, 8; 6, 4, 8, 2; 6, 8, 2, 4; 6, 8, 4, 2; 8, 2, 4, 6; 8, 2, 6, 4; 8, 4, 2, 6; 8, 4, 6, 2; 8, 6, 2, 4; 8, 6, 4, 2

b. How many permutations of these four numbers are there? 24

Example 2 Find $10 \cdot 11 \cdot 12 \cdot 13 \cdot 14 \cdot 15$ using factorials. Multiply the given product by a factorial so that the final product is a factorial. Let $x = 10 \cdot 11 \cdot 12 \cdot 13 \cdot 14 \cdot 15$. Notice that $9! \cdot x = 1 \cdot 2 \cdot 3 \cdot 4 \cdot 5 \cdot 6 \cdot 7 \cdot 8 \cdot 9 \cdot x = 15!$. Solving for x, $x = \frac{15!}{9!} = 3{,}603{,}600$.

Notes on the Lesson

Subsets and combinations

Combinations are subsets of a set. It is very helpful to point out to students the variety of notations used for the number of subsets of size r from a set of size n. In this lesson, we use ${}_nC_r$ or $C(n, r)$. In the next lesson, we show that these are the same as $\binom{n}{r}$, an element in Pascal's Triangle.

Whenever possible, enumerate the combinations. This not only checks answers but also makes the idea more understandable for students.

Additional Example

Example 3 A committee of 5 people is to be chosen from 12 applicants. In how many different ways can this be done? Think of the applicants as the set {A, B, C, D, E, F, G, H, I, J, K, L}. Each possible committee is a 5-element subset of this set. It seems that there are 12 · 11 · 10 · 9 · 8 possible committees. However, this assumes that the order in which the people are chosen makes a difference, which it does not: {A, B, C, D, E} and {A, B, C, E, D} are the same committee. In fact, there are 5! = 120 different orders of A, B, C, D, and E that form the same committee. So 12 · 11 · 10 · 9 · 8 is 5! times what you need. The number of committees with 5 people is $\frac{12 \cdot 11 \cdot 10 \cdot 9 \cdot 8}{5!}$. Multiply both the numerator and denominator by 7!: $\frac{12 \cdot 11 \cdot 10 \cdot 9 \cdot 8}{5!} \cdot \frac{7!}{7!} = \frac{12!}{(5! \cdot 7!)} = 792$. There are 792 ways to choose a committee of 5 from a set of 12 people.

Example 3

A committee of 4 people is to be chosen from 10 applicants. In how many different ways can this be done?

Solution Think of the applicants as the set {A, B, C, D, E, F, G, H, I, J}. Each possible committee is a 4-element subset of this set. For instance, two possible committees are {D, C, A, B} and {C, D, F, J}.

Form the committees one person at a time. There are 10 possibilities for the first person. After selecting the first person, there are 9 possibilities for the second person. After selecting the first two people, there are 8 possibilities for the third person. After selecting the first three people, there are 7 possibilities for the fourth person. So it seems that there are 10 • 9 • 8 • 7 possible committees.

However, this assumes that the order in which the people are chosen makes a difference, but the order of people in a committee does not matter: {B, E, H, I} and {H, B, E, I} are the same committee. In fact, there are 4! = 24 different orders of the elements B, E, H, and I, all of which form the same committee. So, the answer 10 • 9 • 8 • 7 is 4! times what you need.

The number of committees with 4 people is $\frac{10 \cdot 9 \cdot 8 \cdot 7}{4!}$.

Multiply both the numerator and denominator by 6!.

$$\frac{10 \cdot 9 \cdot 8 \cdot 7}{4!} \cdot \frac{6!}{6!} = \frac{10!}{4! \cdot 6!} = 210$$

So, there are 210 ways to choose a committee of 4 from a set of 10 people.

 QY2

QY2

How many committees of 3 people can be chosen from 10 applicants?

Example 3 can be viewed as a problem in counting subsets. How many subsets of 4 elements are possible from a set of 10 elements? It also can be viewed as a problem in counting *combinations* of objects. How many combinations of 4 objects are possible from 10 different objects?

Any choice of r objects from n objects *when the order of choice does not matter* is called a **combination.** The number of combinations of r objects that can be created from n objects is denoted ${}_nC_r$. The following theorem connects combinations with counting subsets.

Combination Counting Formula

The number ${}_nC_r$ of subsets, or combinations, of r elements that can be formed from a set of n elements is given by the formula ${}_nC_r = \frac{n!}{r!(n-r)!}$.

Accommodating the Learner

Some students may have trouble distinguishing between permutations and combinations. Emphasize that a permutation and a combination, while similar, are not the same.

Show that a permutation is an arrangement of objects in a particular order. For example, for the letters A, B, and C, the arrangements ABC, ACB, BAC, BCA, CAB, and CBA are all different arrangements. There are six permutations of the three letters taken three at a time. In combinations, on the other hand, order is not important. Each permutation listed is the *same combination* of the three letters taken three at a time, so there is only one combination.

Proof There are n choices for the first element in a subset. Once that element has been picked, there are $n - 1$ choices for the second element, and $n - 2$ choices for the third element. This continues until all r elements have been picked. There are $(n - r + 1)$ choices for the rth element.

So, if all possible orders are considered different, there are

$$\underbrace{n(n-1)(n-2)\ldots(n-r+1)}_{r \text{ factors}}$$

ways to choose them. But each subset is repeated $r!$ times with the same elements in various orders. So the number of different subsets is

$${}_nC_r = \frac{n(n-1)(n-2)\ldots(n-r+1)}{r!}.$$

Multiplying both numerator and denominator by $(n - r)!$ gives the Combination Counting Formula.

${}_nC_r$ is sometimes read "n choose r." Another notation for the number of combinations is $C(n, r)$. Both have the same meaning and are equal to $\frac{n!}{r!(n-r)!}$. Example 3 shows that ${}_{10}C_4 = C(10, 4) = 210$. Many calculators have keys that enable you to calculate ${}_nC_r$ directly.

GUIDED

Example 4

How many subsets of 11 elements are possible from a set of 13 elements?

Solution Evaluate $C(13, 11)$. Use the Combination Counting Formula with $n = \underline{\ ?\ }$ and $r = \underline{\ ?\ }$. 13; 11

Then $\frac{n!}{r!(n-r)!} = \frac{?}{? \cdot ?} = \underline{\ ?\ }$. 13!; 11!; 2!; 78

Check Use a calculator or CAS. At the right is one way to enter the combination.

Example 5

Given 7 points in a plane, with no 3 of them collinear, how many different triangles can have 3 of these points as vertices?

Solution 1 Because no 3 points are collinear, any choice of 3 points from the 7 points determines a triangle. Use the Combination Counting Formula with $n = 7$ and $r = 3$.

The number of possible triangles is ${}_7C_3 = \frac{7!}{3!(7-3)!} = \frac{7!}{3!4!} = 35$.

Solution 2 Use the idea of the proof of the Combination Counting Formula.

(continued on next page)

Accommodating the Learner

Refer students to Example 5. Have them work in groups to first draw the situation to verify the number of triangles. Then have them solve a similar problem involving eight noncollinear points with three points forming different triangles. With 7 points, students should draw 35 triangles. With 8 points, students should find that there are 56 different triangles, which corresponds to the total found using the combination formula.

Additional Examples

Example 4 How many subsets of 8 elements are possible from a set of 12 elements?

Solution Evaluate $C(12, 8)$. Use the Combination Counting Formula with $n = \underline{\ ?\ }$ and $r = \underline{\ ?\ }$. 12; 8 Then $\frac{n!}{r!(n-r)!} = \underline{\ ?\ } = \underline{\ ?\ }$. $\frac{12!}{8!(12-8)!}$; 495

Example 5 Six points are in a plane, with no three collinear. How many different triangles can have three of these points as vertices? Because no three points are collinear, any choice of three points from the six points determines a triangle. Use the Combination Counting Formula with $n = 6$ and $r = 3$. The number of possible triangles is ${}_6C_3 = \frac{6!}{3!(6-3)!} = 20$.

Note-Taking Tips

Have students add to their journal the definition, theorems, and formula from this lesson and include appropriate examples.

3 Assignment

Recommended Assignment

- Questions 1–21
- Question 22 (extra credit)
- Reading Lesson 13-5
- Covering the Ideas 13-5

Notes on the Questions

Question 3 These are the first seven elements of the *factorial sequence*. That sequence is defined explicitly as $a_n = n!$ and can be defined recursively as $\begin{cases} a_1 = 1 \\ a_n = na_{n-1}, \text{ for } n \geq 2 \end{cases}$ (as per the Activity). When this sequence is defined recursively, then the theorem in this lesson is no longer a theorem but a definition. Question 12 is related.

13-4A Lesson Master — Questions on SPUR Objectives. See Student Edition pages 934–937 for objectives.

SKILLS Objective C

1. Write as a factorial: $1 \cdot 2 \cdot 3 \cdot 4 \cdot 5 \cdot 6 \cdot 7 \cdot 8$ $8!$
2. Write as a quotient of factorials: $12 \cdot 13 \cdot 14 \cdot 15$ $\frac{15!}{11!}$
3. Write $\frac{20!}{16!}$ as a product of four numbers. $20 \cdot 19 \cdot 18 \cdot 17$
4. For what value of n does $20 \cdot n! = 20!$? $n = 19$

SKILLS Objective D

5. **Multiple Choice** Which of the following is equal to ${}_{12}C_9$? D
   A $\frac{12!}{9 \cdot 3}$ B $\frac{12!}{9!}$ C $\frac{12!}{3!}$ D $\frac{12!}{9!3!}$
6. If $d \leq 20$, write ${}_{20}C_d$ using factorials. $\frac{20!}{d!(20-d)!}$
7. Evaluate:
   a. ${}_{100}C_{98}$ 4950 b. ${}_{72}C_{10}$ 536,211,932,256

USES Objective H

8. A high school class has 120 students.
   a. They want to choose a four-person committee to plan a dance. How many different committees are possible? 8,214,570
   b. They want to choose a president, vice-president, secretary, and treasurer for the dance committee. How many different ways can this be done? 197,149,680
9. In a standard deck of cards, there are thirteen hearts: A, 2, 3, 4, 5, 6, 7, 8, 9, 10, J, Q, K. In how many ways can five hearts be selected? 1287
10. a. How many permutations are there of the letters in the word "MEAT"? 24
    b. List those that are also words in English. MEAT, TEAM, MATE, TAME, META

Advanced Algebra 607

The first vertex of the triangle can be chosen in 7 ways. The second vertex can then be chosen in 6 ways. And the third vertex can then be chosen in 5 ways. So, if order mattered, there would be $7 \cdot 6 \cdot 5 = 210$ different triangles. But order doesn't matter and each triangle is counted $3! = 6$ times. So divide 210 by 6, giving 35 different triangles.

Questions

COVERING THE IDEAS

1. a. Write all permutations of the three symbols P, R, M.
   b. Write all combinations of the three symbols P, R, M. PRM
2. How many permutations are there for the 5 vowels A, E, I, O, and U? 120
3. Give the values of 1!, 2!, 3!, 4!, 5!, 6!, and 7!.
4. Explain why $23! = 23 \cdot 22!$.
5. Explain, in words, the difference between a permutation and a combination.
6. Write $100 \cdot 101 \cdot 102 \cdot 103$ as the quotient of two factorials. $\frac{103!}{99!}$
7. How many combinations of r objects can you make from n different objects? $\frac{n!}{r!(n-r)!}$
8. What is another way to represent ${}_nC_r$? $C(n, r)$ $\left(\text{or } \frac{n!}{r!(n-r)!}\right)$
9. A cone of 3 different scoops of ice cream is to be chosen from 5 different flavors. In how many ways can this be done? 10
10. How many subcommittees of 6 people are possible in a committee of 15? 5005
11. Refer to Example 5. How many different line segments can have 2 of the 7 points as endpoints? 21

APPLYING THE MATHEMATICS

12. Prove that $(n + 1)! = n!(n + 1)$.
13. Recall that the U.S. Congress consists of 100 senators and 435 representatives.
    a. How many four-person senatorial committees are possible?
    b. How many four-person house committees are possible?
    c. A "conference committee" of 4 senators and 4 representatives is chosen to work out differences in bills passed by the two houses. How many different conference committees are possible? about 5.770 quadrillion

1a. *PRM, PMR, RPM, RMP, MPR, MRP*

3. 1, 2, 6, 24, 120, 720, 5040

4. For $n \geq 1$, $n! = n \cdot (n-1)!$. Therefore, $23! = 23 \cdot 22!$.

5. Answers vary. Sample: A permutation is a choice of objects where order matters. A combination is a choice of objects where order does not matter.

12. By the Factorial Product Theorem, for an integer $p \geq 1$, $p! = p \cdot (p-1)!$. Let $p = n + 1$. Then, by substitution, $(n + 1)! = (n + 1) \cdot n!$.

13a. 3,921,225

13b. 1,471,429,260

ENGLISH LEARNERS

Vocabulary Development

Spend some time with the definitions of *permutation* and *combination*. Stress that order is important with permutations but not with combinations. You might reinforce the meanings using small slips of paper with numbers or letters written on them, having students actually form the different arrangements. Then define the term and symbol for *factorial* and discuss the Factorial Product Theorem, which is basically a definition of $n!$: For all $n \geq 1$, $n! = n \cdot (n-1)!$ Have volunteers give the value of $n!$ for various values of n. Finally, explain that both 0! and 1! must equal 1 for the definition of $n!$ to be valid for $n \geq 1$.

14. Consider a set of n elements.
    a. How many subsets of any number of elements are possible when $n = 1, 2, 3, 4, 5$? 1, 3, 7, 15, 31
    b. Based on your answers to Part a, make a conjecture about the number of subsets for a set with k elements. $2^k - 1$

15. Dyana sells custom-made tie-dyed T-shirts. A customer chooses 6 dyes from 25 possibilities. Dyana advertises that she offers 150,000 different dye combinations.
    a. Assuming a customer chooses 6 dyes, how many dye combinations are possible? Is the advertisement correct?
    b. How many choices does a customer have if the order of color choice matters? 127,512,000

15a. 177,100; she offers more dye combinations than advertised.

REVIEW

16. Find the standard deviation of the data set {4, 11, 25, 39, 39, 25, 11, 4}. **(Lesson 13-3)** 13.44

17. If two sets of scores have the same mean but the standard deviation of the first set is much larger than that of the second set, what can you conclude? **(Lesson 13-3)**

17. The scores in the first set are more spread out.

18. In $\triangle SPX$, $m\angle S = 75°$, $s = 11$, and $x = 9$. Find $m\angle X$. **(Lesson 10-7)** 52.21°

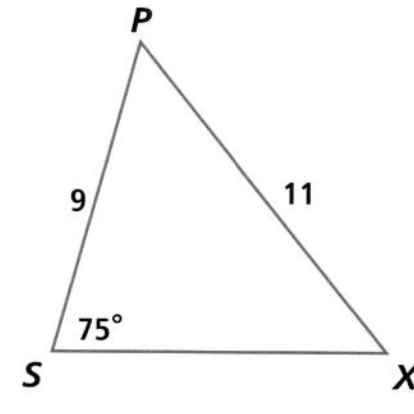

19. a. Find an equation for the inverse of the linear function with equation $y = mx + b$. $y = \frac{1}{m}x - \frac{b}{m}$
    b. How are the slopes of a linear function and its inverse related? They are reciprocals.
    c. When is the inverse not a function? **(Lessons 8-2, 1-4)** when $m = 0$

20. Suppose y varies inversely as the cube of w. If y is 6 when w is 5, find y when w is 11. **(Lesson 2-2)** $\frac{750}{1331} \approx 0.5635$

21. Give a set of integers whose mean is 12, whose mode is 14, and whose median is 13. **(Previous Course)**

21. Answers vary. Sample: {8, 12, 14, 14}

EXPLORATION

22. a. Consider the state name MISSISSIPPI. In how many different ways can you rearrange the letters, if you do not distinguish between letters that are the same? $\frac{11!}{4!4!2!} = 34{,}650$
    b. Repeat Part a using WOOLLOOMOOLOO, the name of a town near Sydney, Australia. $\frac{13!}{8!3!} = 25{,}740$

QY ANSWERS

1. $22 \cdot 23 \cdot 24 = \frac{24!}{21!}$
2. $\frac{10 \cdot 9 \cdot 8}{3!} \cdot \frac{7!}{7!} = \frac{10!}{3! \cdot 7!} = 120$

Notes on the Questions

Question 15b This problem involves finding the number of permutations of r elements from n different elements, often written as ${}_nP_r$. A general formula is that ${}_nP_r = \frac{n!}{(n - r)!}$.

4 Wrap-Up

Ongoing Assessment

Have students work in pairs. Have each student write a problem similar to that in Example 3. Have students exchange papers and solve the problem they have been given. Students should write meaningful problems involving combinations and solve the problems correctly.

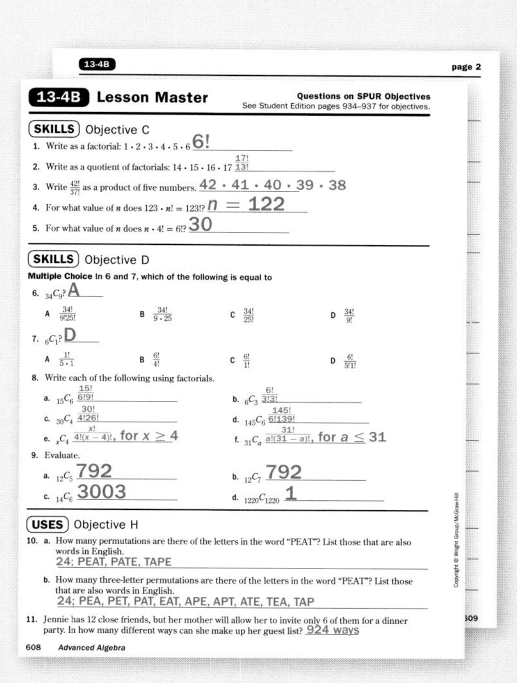

13-4B page 2

13-4B Lesson Master

Questions on SPUR Objectives
See Student Edition pages 934–937 for objectives.

SKILLS Objective C

1. Write as a factorial: $1 \cdot 2 \cdot 3 \cdot 4 \cdot 5 \cdot 6$ 6!
2. Write as a quotient of factorials: $14 \cdot 15 \cdot 16 \cdot 17$ $\frac{17!}{13!}$
3. Write $\frac{42!}{37!}$ as a product of five numbers. $42 \cdot 41 \cdot 40 \cdot 39 \cdot 38$
4. For what value of n does $123 \cdot n! = 123!$? $n = 122$
5. For what value of n does $n \cdot 4! = 6!$? 30

SKILLS Objective D

Multiple Choice In 6 and 7, which of the following is equal to

6. ${}_{34}C_9$? A

   A $\frac{34!}{9!25!}$ B $\frac{34!}{9 \cdot 25}$ C $\frac{34!}{25!}$ D $\frac{34!}{9!}$

7. ${}_6C_1$? D

   A $\frac{1!}{5 \cdot 1}$ B $\frac{6!}{4!}$ C $\frac{6!}{1!}$ D $\frac{6!}{5!1!}$

8. Write each of the following using factorials.
   a. ${}_{15}C_6$ $\frac{15!}{6!9!}$
   b. ${}_6C_3$ $\frac{6!}{3!3!}$
   c. ${}_{30}C_4$ $\frac{30!}{4!26!}$
   d. ${}_{145}C_6$ $\frac{145!}{6!139!}$
   e. ${}_xC_4$ $\frac{x!}{4!(x-4)!}$, for $x \geq 4$
   f. ${}_{31}C_a$ $\frac{31!}{a!(31-a)!}$, for $a \leq 31$

9. Evaluate.
   a. ${}_{12}C_5$ 792
   b. ${}_{12}C_7$ 792
   c. ${}_{14}C_6$ 3003
   d. ${}_{1220}C_{1220}$ 1

USES Objective H

10. a. How many permutations are there of the letters in the word "PEAT"? List those that are also words in English.
    24; PEAT, PATE, TAPE
    b. How many three-letter permutations are there of the letters in the word "PEAT"? List those that are also words in English.
    24; PEA, PET, PAT, EAT, APE, APT, ATE, TEA, TAP

11. Jennie has 12 close friends, but her mother will allow her to invite only 6 of them for a dinner party. In how many different ways can she make up her guest list? 924 ways

608 *Advanced Algebra*

609

Lesson

13-5

GOAL

Learn about Pascal's Triangle and the two ways in which it is generated—(1) by a recursive pattern in which two elements from one row are added to get an element in the next; (2) by an explicit formula involving factorials—and connect the elements with the combinations studied in Lesson 13-4.

SPUR Objectives

D Calculate combinations.

F Recognize properties of Pascal's Triangle.

Materials/Resources

- Lesson Masters 13-5A and 13-5B
- Resource Masters 1, 254, and 255

HOMEWORK

Suggestions for Assignment

- Questions 1–30
- Question 31 (extra credit)
- Reading Lesson 13-6
- Covering the Ideas 13-6

Local Standards

1 Warm-Up

1. Write or copy the first eight rows of Pascal's Triangle. See triangle in lesson.
2. Let the first row be row 0. Starting with row 1, place alternating – and + signs between the numbers in each row. For example, in row 2 you would have $1 - 2 + 1$. $1 - 1$; $1 - 2 + 1$; $1 - 3 + 3 - 1$; $1 - 4 + 6 - 4 + 1$; $1 - 5 + 10 - 10 + 5 - 1$; $1 - 6 + 15 - 20 + 15 - 6 + 1$; $1 - 7 + 21 - 35 + 35 - 21 + 7 - 1$
3. Add the resulting numbers in each row and describe the pattern of sums. The sums are all 0.

Lesson

13-5 Pascal's Triangle

Vocabulary

Pascal's Triangle

BIG IDEA The *n*th row of Pascal's Triangle contains the number of ways of choosing *r* objects out of *n* objects without regard to their order, that is, the number of combinations of *r* objects out of *n*.

Mental Math

Let *D* be a relation that maps any polynomial onto its degree.

a. Name three ordered pairs in *D*.

b. Is *D* a function? yes

c. What is the range of *D*?

d. Is the inverse of *D* a function? no

a. Answers vary. Samples: $(x^2 + 3, 2)$, $(h + hk^3, 4)$, $(\pi, 0)$

c. the set of nonnegative integers

Very often a single idea has applications to many parts of mathematics. On the first page of this chapter, we mentioned *Pascal's Triangle*. Pascal's Triangle is not a triangle in the geometric sense. It is an infinite array of numbers in a triangular shape. The top rows of the triangle are shown below.

1	row 0
1 1	row 1
1 2 1	row 2
1 3 3 1	row 3
1 4 6 4 1	row 4
1 5 10 10 5 1	row 5
1 6 15 20 15 6 1	row 6
1 7 21 35 35 21 7 1	row 7

Pascal's Triangle

This array seems to have first appeared in the 11th century in the works of Abu Bakr al-Karaji, a Persian mathematician, and Jia Xian, a Chinese mathematician. The works of both of these men are now lost, but 12th-century writers refer to them. Versions of the array were discovered independently by the Europeans Peter Apianus in 1527 and Michael Stifel in 1544. But in the western world the array is known as Pascal's Triangle after Blaise Pascal (1623–1662), the French mathematician and philosopher who discovered many properties relating the numbers in the array. Pascal himself called it the *triangle arithmetique*, which literally translates as the "arithmetical triangle."

Background

The array of numbers known as Pascal's Triangle is 2-dimensional, both geometrically and algebraically. As a triangle, it grows in two directions. As a sequence, its description requires two variables. A recursive definition for the sequence is the definition on page 897. An explicit formula for the terms of the sequence is the theorem on page 899.

It is theorized that Pascal's Triangle was discovered independently by individuals in many cultures, which shows that mathematical ideas are universal. One reason that this particular array has so many origins is that it codifies answers to a variety of problems, including problems involving combinations, powers of binomials, and probability that are discussed in the next three lessons. However, it is also possible that there was communication between peoples along ancient trade routes such as the Silk Road. Furthermore, recent discoveries of artifacts suggest that thousands of years ago humans moved great distances.

How Is Pascal's Triangle Formed?

Pascal's Triangle is formed in a very simple way. You can think of Pascal's Triangle as a two-dimensional sequence in which each element is determined by a row and its position in that row.

Here is a recursive definition for the sequence: The only element in the top row (row 0) is 1. The first and last elements of all other rows are also 1. If x and y are located next to each other in a row, the element just below and directly between them is $x + y$, as illustrated at the right.

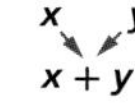

For instance, from row 7 you can get row 8 as follows.

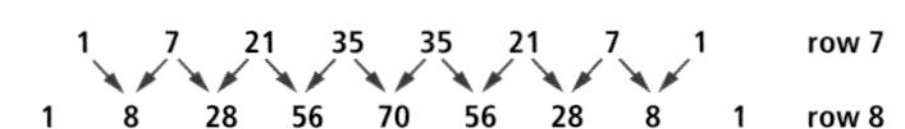

From this recursive definition, you can obtain any row in the array if you know the preceding row.

Example 1

Write row 9 of Pascal's Triangle.

Solution Begin by listing row 8, as shown above. Apply the recursive definition to generate row 9. Remember that the first and last elements of each row are 1.

1 8 28 56 70 56 28 8 1

1 9 36 84 126 126 84 36 9 1

 QY1

▶ QY1

Write row 10 of Pascal's Triangle.

The elements in the nth row of Pascal's triangle are identified as $\binom{n}{0}$, $\binom{n}{1}$, $\binom{n}{2}$, ..., $\binom{n}{n}$. The top row of the array is called row 0, so in this row $n = 0$. It has one element, its first element, $\binom{0}{0}$. So, $\binom{0}{0} = 1$. The two elements of row 1 are $\binom{1}{0}$ and $\binom{1}{1}$. The three elements of row 2 are $\binom{2}{0}$, $\binom{2}{1}$, and $\binom{2}{2}$. In general, the $(r + 1)$st element in row n of Pascal's triangle is denoted by $\binom{n}{r}$.

 QY2

▶ QY2

Write row 8 of Pascal's Triangle using $\binom{n}{r}$ notation.

4. Explain the pattern. Answers vary. Sample: When n is odd, row n has an even number of elements in it and is symmetric, so each number is added and then subtracted to yield 0. When n is even, the center number is the additive inverse of the sum of the remaining numbers.

2 Teaching

Notes on the Lesson

Pascal was a remarkable individual. Students in your class who are studying French are likely to have read some of his *Pensées* (Thoughts), which is among the most famous writings in French. The *Pensées* were published eight years after his death at age 39. He tended to do mathematics in spurts of incredible creativity.

How is Pascal's Triangle formed? Pascal's Triangle can be generated by anyone who can add whole numbers. The point of this lesson is to use algebra to generalize the process. Thinking of Pascal's Triangle as a 2-dimensional sequence, we seek a simple recursive definition and a simple explicit definition.

Additional Example

Example 1 Write row 12 of Pascal's Triangle. Write row 9 of the triangle as shown in the text. Then generate rows 10, 11, and 12. Row 9: 1, 9, 36, 84, 126, 126, 84, 36, 9, 1; Row 10: 1, 10, 45, 120, 210, 252, 210, 120, 45, 10, 1; Row 11: 1, 11, 55, 165, 330, 462, 462, 330, 165, 55, 11, 1; and Row 12: 1, 12, 66, 220, 495, 792, 924, 792, 495, 220, 66, 12, 1

Although we give Pascal's Triangle in its familiar "isosceles-triangle" form, in many parts of the world, students learn a "right-triangle form," as shown at the right.

1
1 1
1 2 1
1 3 3 1
1 4 6 4 1
1 5 10 10 5 1
1 6 15 20 15 6 1
.
.
.

Notes on the Lesson

We use the common symbol $\binom{n}{r}$ to represent an element of the triangle. The most difficult aspect of this is that each row must begin with $\binom{n}{0}$, not $\binom{n}{1}$, and the general symbol $\binom{n}{r}$ represents the $(r + 1)$st element of the nth row, not the rth element.

The recursive definition on page 897 comes directly from the arithmetic way in which Pascal's Triangle is generated. It is often difficult for students to understand because it involves two variables. The explicit formula, which is sometimes used as an explicit definition for the sequence, $\binom{n}{r} = \frac{n!}{r!(n-r)!}$, is often easier for students to understand.

Additional Example

Example 2 Find a solution to the equation $\binom{x}{y} = \binom{8}{6} + \binom{8}{7}$. Apply Part 2 of the definition of Pascal's Triangle. Here $n = 8$ and $r = 6$. Substituting these values into the definition, we have $\binom{8}{6} + \binom{8}{7} = \binom{9}{7}$. So, $x = 9$ and $y = 7$.

Note-Taking Tips

Have students add to their journals the definition of Pascal's Triangle and the explicit formula for the triangle, along with an appropriate example.

On the previous page, we wrote a recursive definition of Pascal's Triangle in words. Now, we can write a recursive definition using the $\binom{n}{r}$ symbol. The recursive rule involves two variables because Pascal's Triangle is a two-dimensional sequence, that is, a sequence in two directions: down and across.

Definition of Pascal's Triangle

Pascal's Triangle is the sequence satisfying

1. $\binom{n}{0} = \binom{n}{n} = 1$, for all integers $n \geq 0$ and
2. $\binom{n+1}{r+1} = \binom{n}{r} + \binom{n}{r+1}$, for $0 \leq r < n$.

Part 1 of the definition gives the "sides" of the triangle. Part 2 is a symbolic way of stating that adding two adjacent elements in one row gives an element in the next row.

Example 2

Find a solution to the equation $\binom{x}{y} = \binom{7}{5} + \binom{7}{6}$.

Solution 1 Apply Part 2 of the definition of Pascal's Triangle.
Here $n = 7$ and $r = 5$. Substituting these values into Part 2, we have

$$\binom{7}{5} + \binom{7}{6} = \binom{8}{6}.$$

So, $x = 8$ and $y = 6$.

Solution 2 Find $\binom{7}{5}$ and $\binom{7}{6}$ in Pascal's triangle and add the results.

$\binom{7}{5}$ is the 6th element in row 7. So $\binom{7}{5} = 21$. $\binom{7}{6}$ is the 7th element in row 7, so $\binom{7}{6} = 7$. $21 + 7 = 28$.

Locate where 28 appears in Pascal's Triangle.

28 is the 3rd element in row 8 and the 7th element in row 8. So, $x = 8$ and $y = 2$ is one solution, and $x = 8$ and $y = 6$ is another solution.

Entries in Pascal's Triangle

There is a very close connection between combinations and the elements in the rows of Pascal's Triangle.

ENGLISH LEARNERS

Vocabulary Development

Review with students the composition of Pascal's Triangle. Have them note that odd-numbered rows have an even number of elements and vice versa. Also have them note that in odd-numbered rows, the middle two elements are the same. You might also draw the triangle on the board, using the right-triangle format as shown in the Background on page 897. You might also give students some interesting facts about Pascal's life, for example, that as a young man he invented an adding machine and that he and Fermat worked together on laws of chance.

Activity

Steps 1–5. See margin.

Step 1 Calculate ${}_4C_0$, ${}_4C_1$, ${}_4C_2$, ${}_4C_3$, and ${}_4C_4$.

Step 2 How are the results of Step 1 related to Pascal's Triangle?

Step 3 Find ${}_7C_0$, ${}_7C_1$, ${}_7C_2$, ${}_7C_3$, ${}_7C_4$, ${}_7C_5$, ${}_7C_6$, and ${}_7C_7$.

Step 4 How are the results of Step 3 related to Pascal's Triangle?

Step 5 Generalize Steps 1–4.

The generalization of the Activity is stated below. It was first proved by the famous English mathematician and physicist Isaac Newton in the 17th century.

Pascal's Triangle Explicit Formula

If n and r are integers with $0 \leq r \leq n$, then $\binom{n}{r} = {}_nC_r = \frac{n!}{r!(n-r)!}$.

Proof To show that $\binom{n}{r} = \frac{n!}{r!(n-r)!}$, it is enough to show that the factorial expression $\frac{n!}{r!(n-r)!}$ satisfies the relationships involving $\binom{n}{r}$ in the recursive definition of Pascal's Triangle.

(1) When $n \geq 0$, does the expression $\frac{n!}{0!(n-0)!}$ equal the expression $\frac{n!}{n!(n-n)!}$ and equal 1? Yes, since $\frac{n!}{0!(n-0)!} = \frac{n!}{0!n!} = \frac{n!}{1 \cdot n!} = 1$, and $\frac{n!}{n!(n-n)!} = \frac{n!}{n!0!} = \frac{n!}{n! \cdot 1} = 1$.
Thus, the formula works for the "sides" of Pascal's triangle.

(2) To prove that the expression $\frac{(n+1)!}{(r+1)!(n-r)!}$ is the sum of the expressions $\frac{n!}{r!(n-r)!}$ and $\frac{n!}{(r+1)!(n-r-1)!}$, use a calculator or CAS. Enter ${}_nC_r + {}_nC_{r+1}$.
This CAS displays $\frac{(n+1) \cdot n!}{(r+1) \cdot r! \cdot (n-r)!}$.
Using the definition of factorial,
$\frac{(n+1) \cdot n!}{(r+1) \cdot r! \cdot (n-r)!} = \frac{(n+1)!}{(r+1)!(n-r)!}$.
The right side is an expression for $\binom{n+1}{r+1}$. So, this explicit formula gives the same sequence as the recursive formula that defines Pascal's Triangle.

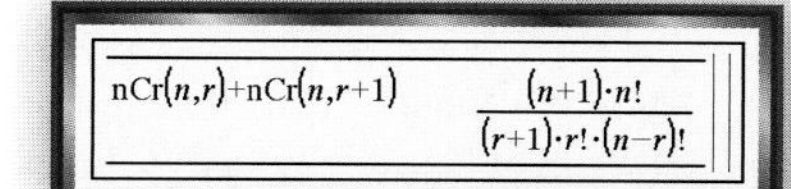

Notes on the Lesson

Pascal's Triangle Explicit Formula The proof of the explicit formula from the recursive definition is subtle. We show that the sequence generated by the formula is the same as the sequence defined by the recursive relation involving $\binom{n}{r}$. The second part is shown using a CAS. Here are the steps in a paper-and-pencil proof: We need to show that $\binom{n}{r} + \binom{n}{r+1} = \binom{n+1}{r+1}$.

$$\binom{n}{r} + \binom{n}{r+1} = \frac{n!}{(n-r)!r!} + \frac{n!}{(r+1)!(n-(r+1))!}$$
$$= \frac{n!}{(n-r)!r!} + \frac{n!(n-r)}{(r+1)!(n-r)!}$$
$$= \frac{n!(r+1)}{(n-r)!(r+1)!} + \frac{n!(n-r)}{(r+1)!(n-r)!}$$
$$= \frac{n![(r+1)+(n-r)]}{(r+1)!(n-r)!}$$
$$= \frac{n!(n+1)}{(r+1)!(n-r)!}$$
$$= \frac{(n+1)!}{(r+1)!(n-r)!}$$
$$= \binom{n+1}{r+1}$$

Additional Answers

Activity

Step 1

${}_4C_0 = 1$, ${}_4C_1 = 4$, ${}_4C_2 = 6$, ${}_4C_3 = 4$, ${}_4C_4 = 1$

Step 2

These are the 5 elements in row 4 of Pascal's Triangle.

Step 3

${}_7C_0 = 1$, ${}_7C_1 = 7$, ${}_7C_2 = 21$, ${}_7C_3 = 35$, ${}_7C_4 = 35$, ${}_7C_5 = 21$, ${}_7C_6 = 7$, ${}_7C_7 = 1$

Step 4

These are the 8 elements in row 7 of Pascal's Triangle.

Step 5

${}_nC_r$ is the $(r+1)$st element in row n of Pascal's Triangle.

Accommodating the Learner

Have groups of students outline a 4-by-4 square on a grid and mark one corner of the square "start." Have students imagine they are walking along the grid lines from "start" to every other intersection of the grid lines, including those along the edges. Have them determine the number of different paths they can take to get to each intersection, considering only the shortest routes. Have them write the total number of paths at each intersection. Ask what pattern is shown by the numbers at the intersections. Students should find that the pattern of numbers corresponds to the pattern of numbers in Pascal's Triangle. Then have students predict the number of paths if they extend the diagram to a 5-by-5 square and check by counting the routes.

Additional Example

Example 3 Find $\binom{9}{4}$.

Solution Use the Pascal's Triangle Explicit Formula:

$\binom{9}{4} = \dfrac{\underline{\ ?\ }!}{\underline{\ ?\ }!(\underline{\ ?\ } - \underline{\ ?\ })!} = \underline{\ ?\ }$.

9; 4; 9; 4; 126

The result of all this is an exceedingly useful fact: *The elements in row n of Pascal's triangle are the numbers of combinations possible from n things taken 0, 1, 2, …, n at a time.* So, you do not need to calculate all the rows of Pascal's triangle to get the next row. You can use your knowledge of combinations.

GUIDED

Example 3

Find $\binom{8}{5}$.

Solution 1 Use the Pascal's Triangle Explicit Formula.

$$\binom{8}{5} = \frac{?!}{?!(?-?)!} = \underline{\ ?\ } \quad 8; 5; 8; 5; 56$$

Solution 2 $\binom{8}{5}$ is the _?_th element in row _?_ of Pascal's triangle. From the second page of the lesson, it is _?_. 6; 8; 56

3 Assignment

Recommended Assignment

- Questions 1–30
- Question 31 (extra credit)
- Reading Lesson 13-6
- Covering the Ideas 13-6

Notes on the Questions

Question 4 To obtain row 11, students need to compute row 10. Suggest to students that they might want to keep a copy of these rows for reference. They may have already done this if you used Additional Example 1.

Questions

COVERING THE IDEAS

1. When and where did the array known as Pascal's Triangle first appear? See margin.
2. When and where did Pascal live? See margin.
3. Explain how entries in a row of Pascal's Triangle can be used to obtain entries in the next row. See margin.
4. Write row 11 of Pascal's Triangle.
5. Write row 5 of Pascal's Triangle using $\binom{n}{r}$ notation.
6. **Fill in the Blanks** The element $\binom{16}{8}$ is the _?_ element in row _?_ of Pascal's Triangle. 9th; 16

In 7–12, calculate the element of Pascal's Triangle and give its location in the triangle.

7. $\binom{6}{4}$
8. $\binom{12}{3}$
9. ${}_{10}C_0$
10. $\binom{8}{8}$
11. $\binom{7}{5}$
12. ${}_{18}C_{10}$
13. Calculate the 3rd element in the 100th row of Pascal's triangle. 4950

4. 1 11 55 165 330 462 462 330 165 55 11 1

5. $\binom{5}{0}$ $\binom{5}{1}$ $\binom{5}{2}$ $\binom{5}{3}$ $\binom{5}{4}$ $\binom{5}{5}$

7. 15; 5th element, row 6

8. 220; 4th element, row 12

9. 1; 1st element, row 10

10. 1; 9th element, row 8

11. 21; 6th element, row 7

12. 43,758; 11th element, row 18

13-5A Lesson Master

Questions on SPUR Objectives
See Student Edition pages 934–937 for objectives.

SKILLS Objective D

In 1–3, evaluate the expression.

1. $\binom{10}{8}$ = 45
2. $\binom{13}{5}$ = 1287
3. $\binom{n}{1}$ = n

PROPERTIES Objective F

4. Rows 0 through 4 of Pascal's Triangle are given. Fill in the next three rows.

Row 0: 1
Row 1: 1 1
Row 2: 1 2 1
Row 3: 1 3 3 1
Row 4: 1 4 6 4 1
Row 5: 1 5 10 10 5 1
Row 6: 1 6 15 20 15 6 1
Row 7: 1 7 21 35 35 21 7 1

5. Write row 7 of Pascal's Triangle in $\binom{n}{r}$ notation.
$\binom{7}{0}$ $\binom{7}{1}$ $\binom{7}{2}$ $\binom{7}{3}$ $\binom{7}{4}$ $\binom{7}{5}$ $\binom{7}{6}$ $\binom{7}{7}$

6. **Fill in the Blanks** $\binom{12}{2}$ is the third element in row 12 of Pascal's Triangle.

7. Where in Pascal's Triangle is the element $\binom{21}{12}$? 13th element, 21st row

8. Use your completed triangle from Question 4 to find $\binom{6}{3}$. 20

9. Solve for a and b: $\binom{8}{5} + \binom{8}{6} = \binom{a}{b}$. $a = 9, b = 6$

Accommodating the Learner

Some students may have trouble evaluating expressions like the one in Example 3. Have them work in pairs and give them expressions such as $\binom{11}{8}$, $\binom{12}{6}$, and so on. Have them apply the Pascal's Triangle Explicit Formula to evaluate each expression, making sure that they are substituting correctly and that they can evaluate the factorials correctly.

Additional Answers

1. The array that later became known as Pascal's Triangle first appeared in the 11th century in the works of Abu Bakr al-Karaji, a Persian mathematician, and Jia Xian, a Chinese mathematician.
2. Blaise Pascal was a French mathematician who lived from 1623–1662.
3. Pascal's Triangle is generated as follows: The only element in the top row is 1, and every other row begins and ends with a 1. If x and y are adjacent elements in a row, then $x + y$ is the element immediately beneath and between them.

APPLYING THE MATHEMATICS

14. Simplify $\binom{n}{n-1}$. $\binom{n}{n-1} = \frac{n!}{(n-1)!(n-(n-1))!} = \frac{n \cdot (n-1)!}{(n-1)!1!} = n$

In 15 and 16, find a solution to the equation.

15. $\binom{9}{4} + \binom{9}{5} = \binom{x}{y}$ $\binom{x}{y} = \binom{10}{5}$

16. $\binom{11}{5} + \binom{a}{b} = \binom{12}{5}$ $\binom{a}{b} = \binom{11}{4}$

17. a. Find the sum of the elements in each of the rows 1 through 6 of Pascal's triangle. 2, 4, 8, 16, 32, 64
    b. Based on the results of Part a, what do you think is the sum of the elements in row 7? 128
    c. Write an expression for the sum of the elements in row n of Pascal's Triangle. 2^n

18. What sequence is defined by the second element of each row in Pascal's Triangle? $a_n = n$

19. Where in Pascal's Triangle can the sequence of triangular numbers 1, 3, 6, 10, 15, ... $\frac{n(n+1)}{2}$, ... be found?

20. Where in Pascal's Triangle can the sequence of series with terms the first n triangular numbers 1, 1 + 3, 1 + 3 + 6, 1 + 3 + 6 + 10, ... be found?

REVIEW

21. How many golf foursomes can be formed from twelve people? **(Lesson 13-4)** 495

22. Consider drawing cards at random from a standard 52-card deck.
    a. In how many ways can you draw one card? 52
    b. How many different pairs of cards can you draw if order does not matter? 1326
    c. What are the chances of drawing the four aces on your first 4 draws? **(Lesson 13-4)** $\frac{1}{270{,}725}$

23. Will had a mean of 86 on five tests. After the lowest test score was dropped, his mean was 93. What was the score that was dropped? **(Lesson 13-3)** 58

24. Give the first 8 terms of the sequence $a_n = \sin(n \cdot 45°)$. **(Lessons 10-1, 1-8)** $\frac{\sqrt{2}}{2}, 1, \frac{\sqrt{2}}{2}, 0, -\frac{\sqrt{2}}{2}, -1, -\frac{\sqrt{2}}{2}, 0$

25. A square has double the area of a circle. The square has side length 10. What is the radius of the circle? **(Lesson 6-2)** about 3.99

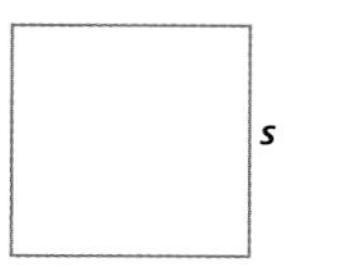

19. This sequence is formed by the 3rd elements of consecutive rows, beginning with row 2.

20. This sequence is formed by the 4th elements of consecutive rows, beginning with row 3.

Notes on the Questions

Questions 19 and 20 You can connect Pascal's Triangle with series. The triangular numbers are the sums of the integers from 1 to n, which can be seen by going down the diagonal that has these integers in order. Suppose you go from 1 to 6 (going down to the left). Then the sum, 21, is found just to the right and below the 6. This pattern holds regardless of the diagonal being used. Thus, the sum of the first six triangular numbers (1 + 3 + 6 + 10 + 15 + 21) is found by going down their diagonal until you reach 21 and then moving to the right and below to read 56. This property is called the "hockey stick" property because if the numbers and their sum are surrounded by a simple closed curve, the figure resembles a hockey stick. This property is illustrated at the bottom of this page.

Question 22 Students from different cultures, particularly if they did not grow up in the United States, may not be familiar with a 52-card deck of cards.

Question 23 This is a reversed statement of the problem of having a mean of 93 after 4 tests and wondering what score it would take to have a mean of 86 after 5 tests. Did any students realize this?

Question 25 Students have seen a similar problem in which the areas are equal.

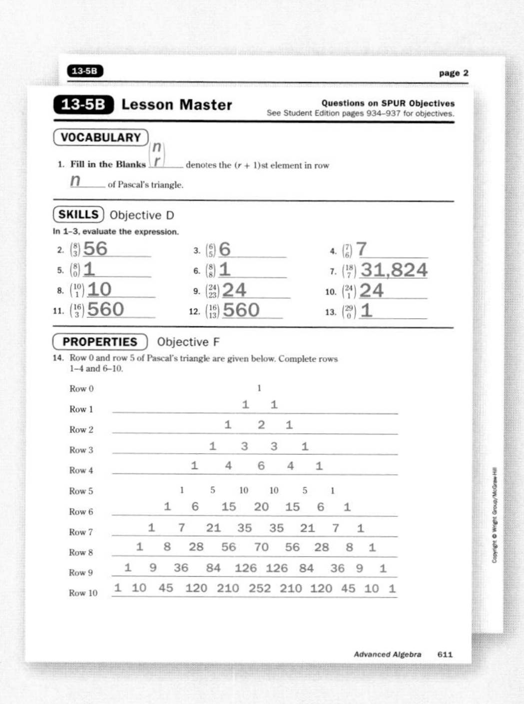

13-5B page 2

13-5B Lesson Master

Questions on SPUR Objectives
See Student Edition pages 934–937 for objectives.

VOCABULARY

1. **Fill in the Blanks** $\binom{n}{r}$ denotes the $(r + 1)$st element in row n of Pascal's triangle.

SKILLS Objective D

In 1–3, evaluate the expression.

2. $\binom{8}{3}$ 56	3. $\binom{6}{5}$ 6	4. $\binom{7}{6}$ 7
5. $\binom{8}{0}$ 1	6. $\binom{8}{8}$ 1	7. $\binom{18}{7}$ 31,824
8. $\binom{10}{1}$ 10	9. $\binom{24}{23}$ 24	10. $\binom{24}{1}$ 24
11. $\binom{16}{3}$ 560	12. $\binom{16}{13}$ 560	13. $\binom{29}{0}$ 1

PROPERTIES Objective F

14. Row 0 and row 5 of Pascal's triangle are given below. Complete rows 1–4 and 6–10.

Row 0 1
Row 1 1 1
Row 2 1 2 1
Row 3 1 3 3 1
Row 4 1 4 6 4 1
Row 5 1 5 10 10 5 1
Row 6 1 6 15 20 15 6 1
Row 7 1 7 21 35 35 21 7 1
Row 8 1 8 28 56 70 56 28 8 1
Row 9 1 9 36 84 126 126 84 36 9 1
Row 10 1 10 45 120 210 252 210 120 45 10 1

Copyright © Wright Group/McGraw-Hill

Advanced Algebra 611

Notes on the Questions

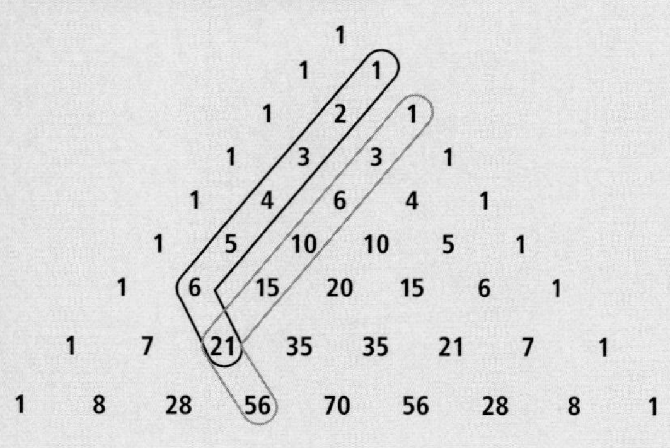

Notes on the Questions

Question 26 This question anticipates Lesson 13-6. You might want to generalize Part c: For all a and b, $(a + b)^2 - (a - b)^2 = 4ab$.

Question 31 This property is known as the "Star of David Property" of Pascal's Triangle. The products of the two sets of alternating vertices are equal. When these alternating vertices are connected, the result looks like the Star of David. Because virtually every mathematics student for the past 200 years has been taught Pascal's Triangle, Hoggatt's and Hansell's discovery of this property relatively recently is dramatic proof that there are still simple properties to be discovered in mathematics. In 1973, one of the authors of this text (Usiskin) extended Hoggatt's and Hansell's work to find other patterns that yield perfect squares, perfect cubes, fourth powers, and so on.

4 Wrap-Up

Ongoing Assessment

Have students work in pairs. Have one partner write a problem similar to that in Example 2 and the other partner write a problem similar to that in Example 3. Have students exchange papers and solve the problem each has been given. Then have students repeat the activity by reversing roles. Students should write and solve meaningful problems involving Pascal's Triangle.

Project Update

Project 4, *Famous Mathematical Triangles*, on page 929 relates to the content of this lesson.

26. Expand. **(Lesson 6-1)**
    a. $(a + b)^2$ $a^2 + 2ab + b^2$
    b. $3(x - 7)^2$ $3x^2 - 42x + 147$
    c. $(3p + 6q)^2 - (3p - 6q)^2$ $72pq$

27. Explain why $\begin{bmatrix} 3 & 1 \\ 6 & 2 \end{bmatrix}$ does not have an inverse. **(Lesson 5-5)**

27. $\det\begin{bmatrix} 3 & 1 \\ 6 & 2 \end{bmatrix} = 0$, so its inverse is undefined.

In 28–30 solve. (Lesson 1-6)

28. $3y + 60 = 5y + 42$ $y = 9$
29. $\frac{4}{y} + \frac{8}{y} = 5$ $y = \frac{12}{5}$
30. $0.05x + 0.1(2x) + 0.25(100 - 3x) = 20$ $x = 10$

EXPLORATION

31. There are six elements surrounding each element not on a side of Pascal's Triangle. For instance, around 15 in row 6 are the elements 5, 10, 20, 35, 21, and 6. In 1969, an amazing property about the product of these six elements was discovered by Verner Hoggatt and Walter Hansell of San Jose State University.

```
      1   5  10  10   5   1        row 5
    1   6  15  20  15   6   1      row 6
  1   7  21  35  35  21   7   1    row 7
```

    a. Find the product of all the elements surrounding the number 15 in row 6. 4,410,000
    b. Repeat for the number 3 in row 3. 144
    c. Find the surrounding product for each element not on a side of row 5 of the triangle. 3600; 360,000; 360,000; 3600
    d. Describe the pattern you see in your products in Parts a through c. They are all perfect squares.
    e. Support your answer to Part d by calculating the product for two elements in row 8 of the triangle.

31e. Answers vary. Sample: Two of the surrounding products of elements in row 8 are $63{,}504 = 252^2$ and $199{,}148{,}544 = 14{,}112^2$.

QY ANSWERS

1. 1 10 45 120 210 252 210 120 45 10 1

2. $\binom{8}{0}$ $\binom{8}{1}$ $\binom{8}{2}$ $\binom{8}{3}$ $\binom{8}{4}$ $\binom{8}{5}$ $\binom{8}{6}$ $\binom{8}{7}$ $\binom{8}{8}$

Extension

Give students the following problems to solve.

1. Show that $\binom{n}{1} = \binom{n}{n-1} = n$.
   $\binom{n}{1} = \frac{n!}{1!(n-1)!} = n$ and $\binom{n}{n-1} = \frac{n!}{(n-1)!(1!)} = n$
2. Show that $\binom{n}{r} = \binom{n}{n-r}$. $\binom{n}{r} = \frac{n!}{r!(n-r)!}$ and $\binom{n}{n-r} = \frac{n!}{(n-r)!(r!)}$

Lesson 13-6 The Binomial Theorem

Vocabulary

binomial coefficients

a. $r^2 - 2rs + s^2$
b. $49p^2 + 126p + 81$
c. $4a^2b^2 - 12abc + 9c^2$
d. $25m^4k^4 + 10m^2n^3k^4 + n^6k^4$

Mental Math

Expand.

a. $(r - s)^2$
b. $(7p + 9)^2$
c. $(2ab - 3c)^2$
d. $k^4(5m^2 + n^3)^2$

BIG IDEA The nth row of Pascal's Triangle contains the coefficients of the terms of $(a + b)^n$.

You have seen patterns involving squares of binomials in many places in this book. In this lesson we examine patterns involving the coefficients of higher powers.

Activity Steps 1–7. See margin.

MATERIALS CAS

Step 1 Expand the binomials in column 1 on a CAS and record the results in column 2 of a table like the one below.

Power of $(a + b)$	Expansion of $(a + b)^n$	Sum of Exponents of the Variables in Each Term
$(a + b)^0$	1	0
$(a + b)^1$	$a + b$	1
$(a + b)^2$	$a^2 + 2ab + b^2$	2
$(a + b)^3$	?	?
$(a + b)^4$	?	?
$(a + b)^5$	?	?
$(a + b)^6$	?	?

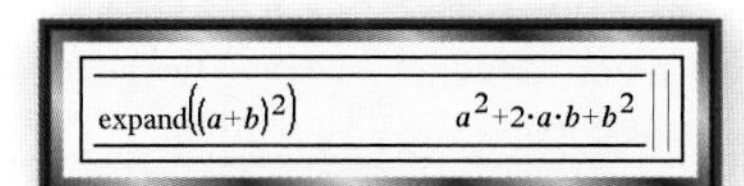

Step 2 In column 3 of the table above, record the sum of the exponents of the variables in each term of the expansion of $(a + b)^n$.

Step 3 Set up a table like the one at the right. Record the coefficients of the terms in each expansion in column 2.

Power of $(a + b)$	Coefficients in the Expansion of $(a + b)^n$	Exponents of a in the Expansion	Exponents of b in the Expansion
$(a + b)^0$	1	0	0
$(a + b)^1$	1, 1	1, 0	0 ,1
$(a + b)^2$	1, 2, 1	2, 1, 0	0, 1, 2
$(a + b)^3$	?	?	?
$(a + b)^4$	?	?	?
$(a + b)^5$	?	?	?
$(a + b)^6$	?	?	?

(continued on next page)

Background

This lesson first expands binomials without using Pascal's Triangle. Otherwise, students might not realize what is happening and view the exponent n as another new notation, not similar to anything they have studied previously. Having expanded the binomials, they will see that Pascal's Triangle is hidden among the coefficients.

The remainder of the lesson is devoted to examples. It takes practice and lots of concentration to do these problems by hand without error. However, these calculations are easily accomplished with a CAS.

If the factorials in the Binomial Theorem are expanded and simplified, for example, $\binom{n}{2} = \frac{n(n-1)}{2}$, then it is possible to interpret the Binomial Theorem when n is not an integer. This was first done by Newton, who is credited with the first proof of the Binomial Theorem.

Lesson 13-6

GOAL

Learn how powers of binomials can be expanded and relate these expansions to Pascal's Triangle.

SPUR Objectives

E Use the Binomial Theorem to expand binomials.

F Recognize properties of Pascal's Triangle.

Materials/Resources

- Lesson Masters 13-6A and 13-6B
- Resource Masters 256 and 257
- Quiz 2
- CAS

HOMEWORK

Suggestions for Assignment

- Questions 1–24
- Question 25 (extra credit)
- Reading Lesson 13-7
- Covering the Ideas 13-7

Local Standards

1 Warm-Up

Expand by hand and check with a CAS.

1. $(x - y)^2$ $x^2 - 2xy + y^2$
2. $(x - y)^3$ $x^3 - 3x^2y + 3xy^2 - y^3$
3. $(x - y)^4$
$x^4 - 4x^3y + 6x^2y^2 - 4xy^3 + y^4$

(*Note:* Point out that the expansion of $(x - y)^3$ can be found by multiplying the expansion of $(x - y)^2$ by $(x - y)$. Similarly, the expansion of $(x - y)^4$ can be found by multiplying the expansion of $(x - y)^3$ by $(x - y)$.)

2 Teaching

Notes on the Lesson

You might wish to work through this lesson paragraph by paragraph, example by example. Note that the words *expand* and *expansion* arise from the written expanded form being an expression with more terms than the binomial power. Emphasize that both $(a + b)^n$ and its expansion have equal value for given values of *a*, *b*, and *n*.

Emphasize that students should always check first by letting each variable equal a simple number, even 1. This will help to check the coefficients. Then they should check with a value of the variable other than 1. This will help to check the exponents.

Note-Taking Tips

Have students add the Binomial Theorem to their journals.

Additional Answers

Activity

Step 2

$n(n + 1)$

Step 4

The coefficients form Pascal's Triangle.

Step 5

$\binom{5}{0}, \binom{5}{1}, \binom{5}{2}, \binom{5}{3}, \binom{5}{4}, \binom{5}{5}$

Step 7

The exponents of *a* start at *n* and decrease by 1 with each term, and the exponents of *b* start at 0 and increase by 1 with each term.

Step 4 What do you notice about the coefficients of the expansions of $(a + b)^n$?

Step 5 Write the coefficients of the expansion of $(a + b)^5$ using $\binom{n}{r}$ notation.

Step 6 Record the exponents of the powers of *a* and *b* in each term in the binomial expansions in the rightmost two columns of the table in Step 3.

Step 7 What do you notice about the exponents of *a* in each expansion of $(a + b)^n$? What do you notice about the exponents of *b* in each expansion of $(a + b)^n$?

The Activity reveals several properties of the expansion of $(a + b)^n$. Knowledge of these properties makes expanding $(a + b)^n$ easy.

- In each term of the expansion, the sum of the exponents of *a* and *b* is *n*.
- All powers of *a* occur in decreasing order from *n* to 0, while all powers of *b* occur in increasing order from 0 to *n*.
- If the power of *b* is *r*, then the coefficient of the term is $\binom{n}{r} = {}_nC_r$.

As a consequence of these properties, binomial expansions can be written using the $\binom{n}{r}$ symbol.

$$(a + b)^0 = \binom{0}{0}$$

$$(a + b)^1 = \binom{1}{0}a + \binom{1}{1}b$$

$$(a + b)^2 = \binom{2}{0}a^2 + \binom{2}{1}ab + \binom{2}{2}b^2$$

$$(a + b)^3 = \binom{3}{0}a^3 + \binom{3}{1}a^2b + \binom{3}{2}ab^2 + \binom{3}{3}b^3$$

$$\vdots \qquad \qquad \vdots$$

The information above is summarized in a famous theorem that was known to Omar Khayyam, the Persian poet, mathematician, and astronomer, who died around the year 1123. Of course, he did not have the notation we use today. Our notation makes it clear that the *n*th row of Pascal's triangle contains the coefficients of $(a + b)^n$.

Omar Khayyam

Additional Answers

Activity

Steps 1–2

$a^3 + 3a^2b + 3ab^2 + b^3$	13
$a^4 + 4a^3b + 6a^2b^2 + 4ab^3 + b^4$	24
$a^5 + 5a^4b + 10a^3b^2 + 10a^2b^3 + 5ab^4 + b^5$	35
$a^6 + 6a^5b + 15a^4b^2 + 20a^3b^3 + 15a^2b^4 + 6ab^5 + b^6$	46

Steps 3 and 6

1, 3, 3, 1	3, 2, 1, 0	0, 1, 2, 3
1, 4, 6, 4, 1	4, 3, 2, 1, 0	0, 1, 2, 3, 4
1, 5, 10, 10, 5, 1	5, 4, 3, 2, 1, 0	0, 1, 2, 3, 4, 5
1, 6, 15, 20, 15, 6, 1	6, 5, 4, 3, 2, 1, 0	0, 1, 2, 3, 4, 5, 6

Binomial Theorem

For all complex numbers a and b, and for all integers n and r with $0 \le r \le n$,

$$(a + b)^n = \sum_{r=0}^{n} \binom{n}{r} a^{n-r} b^r.$$

A proof of the Binomial Theorem requires mathematical induction, a powerful proof technique beyond the scope of this book. You will see this proof in a later course.

Example 1

Expand $(a + b)^7$.

Solution First, write the powers of a and b in the form of the answer. Leave spaces for the coefficients.

$$(a + b)^7 = \_\_\_a^7 + \_\_\_a^6b + \_\_\_a^5b^2 + \_\_\_a^4b^3 + \_\_\_a^3b^4 + \_\_\_a^2b^5 + \_\_\_ab^6 + \_\_\_b^7$$

Second, fill in the coefficients using $\binom{n}{r}$ notation.

$$(a + b)^7 = \binom{7}{0}a^7 + \binom{7}{1}a^6b + \binom{7}{2}a^5b^2 + \binom{7}{3}a^4b^3 + \binom{7}{4}a^3b^4 + \binom{7}{5}a^2b^5 + \binom{7}{6}ab^6 + \binom{7}{7}b^7$$

Finally, evaluate the coefficients, either by referring to row 7 of Pascal's Triangle or by using the formula $\binom{n}{r} = \frac{n!}{r!(n-r)!}$.

$$(a + b)^7 = a^7 + 7a^6b + 21a^5b^2 + 35a^4b^3 + 35a^3b^4 + 21a^2b^5 + 7ab^6 + b^7$$

The Binomial Theorem can be used to expand a variety of expressions.

Example 2

Expand $(3x - 4y)^3$.

Solution 1 The expansion follows the form of $(a + b)^3$.

$$(a + b)^3 = \binom{3}{0}a^3 + \binom{3}{1}a^2b + \binom{3}{2}ab^2 + \binom{3}{3}b^3.$$

(continued on next page)

Notes on the Lesson

Example 1 Students should be able write the coefficients automatically by using Pascal's Triangle.

Examples 2 and 3 These examples involve chunking, the idea of thinking of an entire expression as an individual object.

Additional Examples

Example 1 Expand $(a + b)^5$. $a^5 + 5a^4b + 10a^3b^2 + 10a^2b^3 + 5ab^4 + b^5$

Example 2 Expand $(2d + 3t)^4$. $16d^4 + 96d^3t + 216d^2t^2 + 216dt^3 + 81t^4$

ENGLISH LEARNERS

Vocabulary Development

Review with students the composition of Pascal's Triangle. You might also write 11 or 12 rows of the triangle on the board. Show how the numbers in each row are related to the Binomial Theorem. As these numbers affect the coefficients in a binomial expansion, they are called *binomial coefficients.*

Accommodating the Learner

In the sigma notation for the Binomial Theorem, the index variable is r, where r is one less than the number of the term of the expansion and n is the power of $(a + b)$. Point out that because we start at $r = 0$, there will be $n + 1$ terms summed.

Notes on the Lesson

Example 4 The order of terms is from the highest power of a to the lowest power of a because a is the first variable in the expression in the base. The eighth term in the expansion of $(b + a)^{20}$ does not equal the eighth term in the expansion of $(a + b)^{20}$ even though the polynomials are equal by the Commutative Property of Addition.

Additional Examples

Example 3 Expand $(3x^2 - 2)^3$.

Solution Think of $3x^2$ as a and -2 as b. Then follow the form of $(a + b)^3$.

$(3x^2 - 2)^3 = (\underline{?})(3x^2)^{\underline{?}} + (\underline{?})(3x^2)^{\underline{?}} \cdot (-2)^{\underline{?}} + (\underline{?})(3x^2)^{\underline{?}} \cdot (-2)^{\underline{?}} + (\underline{?}) \cdot (-2)^{\underline{?}} = \underline{?}\,x^{\underline{?}} + \underline{?}\,x^{\underline{?}} + \underline{?}\,x^{\underline{?}} + \underline{?}$

1; 3; 3; 2; 1; 3; 1; 2; 1; 3; 27; 6; –54; 4; 36; 2; –8

Example 4 Find the sixth term in the expansion of $(a + b)^{12}$. $\binom{12}{5}a^{12-5}b^5 = 792a^7b^5$, which is the sixth term in the expansion of $(a + b)^{12}$.

Think of $3x$ as a and $-4y$ as b and substitute.

$$(3x - 4y)^3 = 1(3x)^3 + 3(3x)^2(-4y) + 3(3x)(-4y)^2 + 1(-4y)^3$$
$$= 27x^3 - 108x^2y + 144xy^2 - 64y^3$$

Solution 2 Expand the binomial on a CAS.

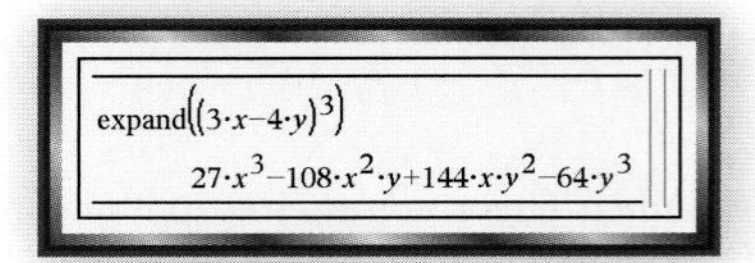

GUIDED

Example 3

Expand $(2x^2 + 1)^4$.

Solution Think of $2x^2$ as a and 1 as b. Then follow the form of $(a + b)^4$.

$(2x^2 + 1)^4 = (\underline{?})(2x^2)^{\underline{?}} + (\underline{?})(2x^2)^{\underline{?}} \cdot (1)^{\underline{?}} +$ 1; 4; 4; 3; 1

$(\underline{?})(2x^2)^{\underline{?}} \cdot (1)^{\underline{?}} + (\underline{?})(2x^2)^{\underline{?}} \cdot (1)^{\underline{?}} +$ 6; 2; 2; 4; 1; 3

$(\underline{?}) \cdot (1)^{\underline{?}}$ 1; 4

$= \underline{?}\,x^{\underline{?}} + \underline{?}\,x^{\underline{?}} + \underline{?}\,x^{\underline{?}} + \underline{?}\,x^{\underline{?}} + \underline{?}$ 16; 8; 32; 6; 24; 4; 8; 2; 1

Check Substitute a value for x in the binomial power and in the expansion. The two results should be equal.

You can also use the Binomial Theorem to quickly find any term in the expansion of a binomial power without writing the full expansion.

Example 4

Find the 8th term in the expansion of $(a + b)^{20}$.

Solution The formula $(a + b)^{20} = \sum_{r=0}^{20} \binom{20}{r} a^{20-r}b^r$ gives the full expansion of the binomial. Because r starts at 0, the 8th term is when $r = 7$.

$$\binom{20}{7}a^{20-7}b^7 = 77{,}520a^{13}b^7$$

The 8th term in the expansion is $77{,}520a^{13}b^7$.

 **QY**

> **QY**
> Find the 13th term in the expansion of $(x + 2)^{15}$.

Due to their use in the Binomial Theorem, the numbers in Pascal's Triangle are sometimes called **binomial coefficients.** The Binomial Theorem has a surprising number of applications in estimation, counting problems, probability, and statistics. You will study these applications in the remainder of this chapter.

Extension

Have students prove this conjecture: $\binom{n}{0} + \binom{n}{1} + \ldots + \binom{n}{n} = 2^n$. (*Hint:* Tell students to use the binomial expansion of $(x + 1)^n$.) $(x + 1)^n = \binom{n}{0}x^n + \binom{n}{1}x^{n-1} + \ldots + \binom{n}{n}x^0$; substituting 1 for x gives the result $2^n = \binom{n}{0} + \binom{n}{1} + \ldots + \binom{n}{n}$.

Accommodating the Learner

Have pairs of students expand $(ax + by)$ and $(ax - by)$ to the second through sixth powers for values of their choice for a and b. Then have them find the differences and the similarities between the same powers of the two binomials. Answers vary. Check students' work.

Questions

COVERING THE IDEAS

1. a. Expand $(x + y)^2$. $x^2 + 2xy + y^2$
   b. What are the coefficients of the terms in the expansion of $(x + y)^3$? 1, 3, 3, 1

In 2–4, expand each binomial power.

2. $(a - 3b)^3$
3. $\left(\frac{1}{2} - m^2\right)^4$
4. $(2x + 5y)^3$

In 5 and 6, find the 5th term in the binomial expansion.

5. $(x + y)^{10}$ $210x^6y^4$
6. $(a - 3b)^8$ $5670a^4b^4$

In 7 and 8, find the second-to-last term in the binomial expansion. (This term is called the *penultimate* term.)

7. $(5 - 2n)^9$ $11{,}520n^8$
8. $(3j + k)^{12}$ $36jk^{11}$

APPLYING THE MATHEMATICS

In 9 and 10, convert to an expression in the form $(a + b)^n$.

9. $\sum_{r=0}^{14} \binom{14}{r} x^{14-r} 2^r$ $(x + 2)^{14}$
10. $\sum_{i=0}^{n} \binom{n}{i} y^{n-i} (-3w)^i$ $(y - 3w)^n$

11. Multiply the binomial expansion for $(a + b)^3$ by $a + b$ to check the expansion for $(a + b)^4$. See margin.

12. a. Multiply and simplify $(a^2 + 2ab + b^2)(a^2 + 2ab + b^2)$.
    b. Your answer to Part a should be a power of $a + b$. Which one? Explain your answer.

In 13 and 14, use this information. The Binomial Theorem can be used to approximate some powers quickly without a calculator. Here is an example.

$$\begin{aligned}(1.002)^3 &= (1 + 0.002)^3 \\ &= 1^3 + 3 \cdot 1^2 \cdot (0.002) + 3 \cdot 1 \cdot (0.002)^2 + (0.002)^3 \\ &= 1 + 0.006 + 0.000012 + 0.000000008 \\ &= 1.006012008\end{aligned}$$

Because the last two terms in the expansion are so small, you may ignore them in an approximation. So $(1.002)^3 \approx 1.006$ to the nearest thousandth.

13. Show how to approximate $(1.003)^3$ to the nearest thousandth without a calculator. Check your answer with a calculator.

14. Show how to approximate $(1.001)^4$ to nine decimal places without a calculator.

2. $a^3 - 9a^2b + 27ab^2 - 27b^3$

3. $\frac{1}{16} - \frac{1}{2}m^2 + \frac{3}{2}m^4 - 2m^6 + m^8$

4. $8x^3 + 60x^2y + 150xy^2 + 125y^3$

12a. $a^4 + 2a^3b + a^2b^2 + 2a^3b + 4a^2b^2 + 2ab^3 + a^2b^2 + 2ab^3 + b^4 = a^4 + 4a^3b + 6a^2b^2 + 4ab^3 + b^4$

12b. 4th; Explanations vary. Sample: the coefficients of the terms in the expression have the pattern 1, 4, 6, 4, 1, and the exponents add up to 4 in each term.

13. $(1 + 0.003)^3 \approx 1^3 + 3 \cdot 1^2 \cdot (0.003) = 1 + 0.009 = 1.009$

14. $(1 + 0.001)^4 \approx 1^4 + 4 \cdot 1^3 \cdot (0.001) + 6 \cdot 1^2 \cdot (0.001)^2 + 4 \cdot 1 \cdot (0.001)^3 = 1 + 0.004 + 0.000006 + 0.000000004 = 1.004006004$

Additional Answers

11. $(a + b)(a^3 + 3a^2b + 3ab^2 + b^3) = a^4 + 3a^3b + 3a^2b^2 + ab^3 + a^3b + 3a^2b^2 + 3ab^3 + b^4 = a^4 + 4a^3b + 6a^2b^2 + 4ab^3 + b^4 = \sum_{r=0}^{4} \binom{4}{r} a^{4-r} b^r$

3 Assignment

Recommended Assignment

- Questions 1–24
- Question 25 (extra credit)
- Reading Lesson 13-7
- Covering the Ideas 13-7

Notes on the Questions

Questions 5–8 Without a CAS, it is perhaps easiest to answer these questions by finding the exponents first. These will determine n and r in $\binom{n}{r}$.

Questions 9 and 10 These questions can be difficult for many students. Write the Binomial Theorem above the summation expressions so students can see what has been substituted.

Questions 13 and 14 In general, if x is very close to zero, then a good approximation of $(1 + x)^n$ is $1 + nx$. The reason is that if x is small, then x^2 is even smaller. For instance, in Question 13, $x = 0.003$ and $n = 3$, and the approximation 1.009 is within 28 millionths of the actual value.

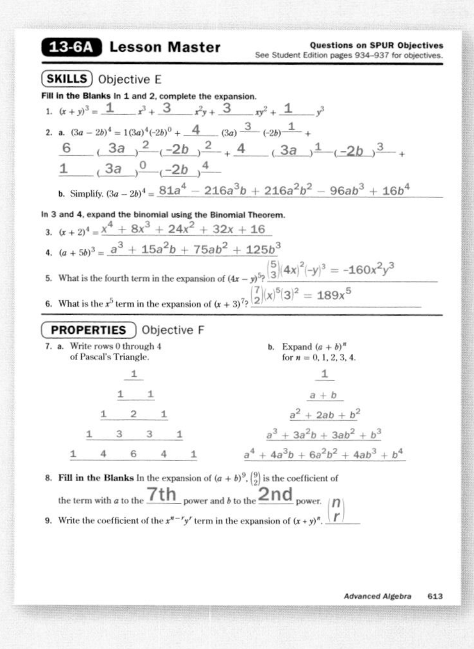

13-6A Lesson Master

Questions on SPUR Objectives
See Student Edition pages 934–937 for objectives.

SKILLS Objective E

Fill in the Blanks In 1 and 2, complete the expansion.

1. $(x + y)^3 =$ 1 $x^3 +$ 3 $x^2y +$ 3 $xy^2 +$ 1 y^3
2. a. $(3a - 2b)^4 = 1(3a)^4(-2b)^0 +$ 4 $(3a)^3(-2b)^1 +$ 6 $(3a)^2(-2b)^2 +$ 4 $(3a)^1(-2b)^3 +$ 1 $(3a)^0(-2b)^4$
   b. Simplify. $(3a - 2b)^4 = 81a^4 - 216a^3b + 216a^2b^2 - 96ab^3 + 16b^4$

In 3 and 4, expand the binomial using the Binomial Theorem.

3. $(x + 2)^4 = x^4 + 8x^3 + 24x^2 + 32x + 16$
4. $(a + 5b)^3 = a^3 + 15a^2b + 75ab^2 + 125b^3$
5. What is the fourth term in the expansion of $(4x - y)^5$? $\binom{5}{3}(4x)^2(-y)^3 = -160x^2y^3$
6. What is the x^5 term in the expansion of $(x + 3)^7$? $\binom{7}{2}(x)^5(3)^2 = 189x^5$

PROPERTIES Objective F

7. a. Write rows 0 through 4 of Pascal's Triangle.
   1
   1 1
   1 2 1
   1 3 3 1
   1 4 6 4 1
   b. Expand $(a + b)^n$ for $n = 0, 1, 2, 3, 4$.
   1
   $a + b$
   $a^2 + 2ab + b^2$
   $a^3 + 3a^2b + 3ab^2 + b^3$
   $a^4 + 4a^3b + 6a^2b^2 + 4ab^3 + b^4$
8. **Fill in the Blanks** In the expansion of $(a + b)^9$, $\binom{9}{2}$ is the coefficient of the term with a to the 7th power and b to the 2nd power.
9. Write the coefficient of the $x^{n-r}y^r$ term in the expansion of $(x + y)^n$. $\binom{n}{r}$

Advanced Algebra 613

Notes on the Questions

Question 18 This is the sum of the terms in row 9 of Pascal's Triangle. This sum can also be found by evaluating $(1 + 1)^9$. If 1 is substituted for both a and b in $(a + b)^9$, then the value of the expression is the sum of its coefficients. Because of the symmetry of Pascal's Triangle, students can also find the sum of the first 5 terms and then multiply by 2.

4 Wrap-Up

Ongoing Assessment

On the board, write a binomial expression similar to those in Questions 2–4. Then have students take turns writing terms in the expansion of the expression. Repeat this process until all students have participated. Students should correctly apply the Binomial Theorem to expand binomial expressions.

Administer Quiz 2 (or a quiz of your own) after students complete this lesson.

13-6B page 2

13-6B Lesson Master

Questions on SPUR Objectives
See Student Edition pages 934–937 for objectives.

SKILLS Objective E

Fill in the Blanks In 1 and 2, complete the expansion.

1. $(x + y)^6 = \underline{1}\,x^6 + \underline{6}\,x^5y + \underline{15}\,x^4y^2 + \underline{20}\,x^3y^3 + \underline{15}\,x^2y^4 + \underline{6}\,xy^5 + \underline{1}\,y^6$

2. a. $(2m + 3n^2)^6 = 1(2m)^6(3n^2)^0 + \underline{6}\,(2m)^{\underline{5}}(3n^2)^{\underline{1}} + \underline{15}\,(\underline{2m})^{\underline{4}}(\underline{3n^2})^{\underline{2}} + \underline{20}\,(\underline{2m})^{\underline{3}}(\underline{3n^2})^{\underline{3}} + \underline{15}\,(\underline{2m})^{\underline{2}}(\underline{3n^2})^{\underline{4}} + \underline{6}\,(\underline{2m})^{\underline{1}}(\underline{3n^2})^{\underline{5}} + \underline{1}\,(\underline{2m})^{\underline{0}}(\underline{3n^2})^{\underline{6}}$

b. Simplify.
$(2m + 3n^2)^6 = 64m^6 + 576m^5n^2 + 2160m^4n^4 + 4320m^3n^6 + 4860m^2n^8 + 2916mn^{10} + 729n^{12}$

In 3–11, expand the binomial using the Binomial Theorem.

3. $(x^4 + 5)^3$
$x^{12} + 15x^8 + 75x^4 + 125$

4. $(5p^2 - q)^3$
$125p^6 - 75p^4q + 15p^2q^2 - q^3$

5. $(3a - 7b)^4$
$81a^4 - 756a^3b + 2646a^2b^2 - 4116ab^3 + 2401b^4$

6. $(m - n^4)^5$
$m^5 - 5m^4n^4 + 10m^3n^8 - 10m^2n^{12} + 5mn^{16} - n^{20}$

7. $(5p^2 - q)^6$
$15{,}625p^{12} - 18{,}750p^{10}q + 9375p^8q^2 - 2500p^6q^3 + 375p^4q^4 - 30p^2q^5 + q^6$

8. $(a^4 - 1)^8$
$a^{32} - 8a^{28} + 28a^{24} - 56a^{20} + 70a^{16} - 56a^{12} + 28a^8 - 8a^4 + 1$

614 Advanced Algebra

15. a. Evaluate 11^0, 11^1, 11^2, 11^3, and 11^4. How are these numbers related to Pascal's Triangle? a–c. See margin.
b. Expand $(10 + 1)^4$ using the Binomial Theorem.
c. Use the Binomial Theorem to calculate 11^5.

REVIEW

True or False In 16 and 17, explain your reasoning.

16. $\binom{99}{17}$ is an integer. **(Lesson 13-5)**

17. $\frac{n!}{(n-2)!}$ is always an integer when $n \geq 2$. **(Lesson 13-4)**

18. Simplify: ${}_9C_0 + {}_9C_1 + {}_9C_2 + {}_9C_3 + {}_9C_4 + {}_9C_5 + {}_9C_6 + {}_9C_7 + {}_9C_8 + {}_9C_9$. **(Lesson 13-4)** 512

19. Consider the ellipse with equation $\frac{x^2}{15} + \frac{y^2}{26} = 1$. **(Lessons 12-5, 12-4)**
a. Give the length of its major axis. $2\sqrt{26}$
b. Give the coordinates of the endpoints of its major and minor axes. $(0, -\sqrt{26})$, $(0, \sqrt{26})$; $(-\sqrt{15}, 0)$, $(\sqrt{15}, 0)$
c. Find the coordinates of its foci F_1 and F_2.
d. If P is a point on this ellipse, find $PF_1 + PF_2$. $2\sqrt{26}$
e. Find the area of the ellipse. $\pi\sqrt{390} \approx 62.04$

20. Paola has been saving to buy a condo for five years. At the beginning of the first year, she placed \$2200 in a savings account that pays 3.7% interest annually. At the beginning of the second, third, fourth, and fifth years, she deposited \$2350, \$2125, \$2600, and \$2780, respectively, into the same account. At the end of the five years, does Paola have enough money in the account to make a \$15,000 down payment? If not, how much more does she need? **(Lesson 11-1)**

In 21–24, solve. **(Lessons 9-9, 9-7, 9-5)**

21. $\log_7 y = 2 \log_7 13$ $y = 169$
22. $2 \ln 13 = \ln x$ $x = 169$
23. $\log z = 5$ $z = 100{,}000$
24. $\ln(3x) = \ln 2 + \ln 18$ $x = 12$

EXPLORATION

25. The expansion of $(a + b)^3$ has 4 terms.
a. How many terms are in the expansion of $(a + b + c)^3$? 10
b. How many terms are in the expansion of $(a + b + c + d)^3$? 20
c. Generalize these results.

16. True; Explanations vary. Sample: $\binom{99}{17}$ is an element of Pascal's triangle, which is made up of integers.

17. True; $\frac{n!}{(n-2)!} = \frac{n(n-1)(n-2)!}{(n-2)!} = n^2 - n$; this is the difference of two integers, which will be an integer.

19c. $(0, \sqrt{11})$, $(0, -\sqrt{11})$

20. No; she still needs \$1595.63 more.

25c. There are $\binom{n+2}{3}$ terms in the expansion of $(x_1 + x_2 + \ldots + x_n)^3$.

QY ANSWER

$\binom{15}{12}x^{15-12} \cdot 2^{12} = 1{,}863{,}680x^3$

Additional Answers

15a. 1; 11; 121; 1331; 14,641; The digits in each term form a row of Pascal's Triangle.

15b. $\sum_{r=0}^{4} \binom{4}{r} 10^{4-r} 1^r =$
$10{,}000 + 4000 + 600 + 40 + 1 = 14{,}641$

15c. $\sum_{r=0}^{5} \binom{5}{r} 10^{5-r} 1^r =$
$100{,}000 + 50{,}000 + 10{,}000 + 1{,}000 + 50 + 1 = 161{,}051$

Lesson 13-7 Probability and Combinations

Vocabulary

trial

binomial experiment

▶ **BIG IDEA** The probability of an event occurring *r* times in *n trials* of a *binomial experiment* can be found by calculating combinations.

Mental Math

Calculate

a. ${}_{1000}C_{999}$ 1000

b. ${}_{1000}C_{1000}$ 1

c. ${}_{1000}C_{1}$ 1000

d. ${}_{1000}C_{2}$ 499,500

Pascal originally conceived of the triangle named in his honor in the context of probability problems. Activity 1 can help you connect Pascal's Triangle and probabilities.

Activity 1 Steps 1–3. See the Additional Answers section at the back of the book.

MATERIALS penny or other coin

The task is to estimate the probability of getting exactly 2 heads in 4 tosses of the coin by repeating an experiment a large number of times.

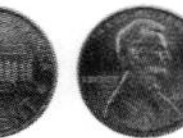

Step 1 Make a table with headings as shown at the right. Include ten rows for trials 1 through 10. Flip a coin 4 times and record the results. For example, if the coin came up heads, then tails, then tails, and then heads, write HTTH in the Sequence column and 2 in the Number of Heads column.

Trial	Sequence	Number of Heads
1	?	?
2	?	?
⋮	?	?

Step 2 Repeat Step 1 nine more times until you have filled the entire table. Then tally the number of times you got 0 heads, 1 head, 2 heads, 3 heads, and 4 heads.

Step 3 Combine your results with others in your class. Then compute relative frequencies of each number of heads for the class as a whole. Graph the five ordered pairs, where each ordered pair is of this form: (number of heads in 4 flips, relative frequency of that number of heads). What is your class's relative frequency for getting 2 heads in 4 flips?

Many people are surprised to find out that the relative frequency of getting 2 heads in 4 flips is usually not too close to 50%. But it is not difficult to compute the probability if the coins are fair. Activity 2 explores that computation.

Background

We assume students are familiar with the idea of probability, as it was covered in detail in previous UCSMP courses. Specifically, students should have tossed coins (as in Activity 1) and should have seen the difference between relative frequency and probability. They should understand that relative frequencies are based on actual experiments and fluctuate, while probabilities are based on assumptions such as the equal likelihood of outcomes and do not vary unless the assumptions are changed. In Example 1, we are careful to say that the coin is fair. Without an assumption like this, we have no way of calculating the probability that the coin might land on heads. Being "fair" must be an assumption rather than a fact because no experiment can determine for certain that a coin is equally balanced.

(continued on next page)

Lesson 13-7

GOAL

Connect binomial coefficients and numbers of combinations by considering the probability that an event occurs *r* times in *n* repetitions, given that it occurs with probability *p* on each trial.

SPUR Objectives

J Solve problems using combinations and probability.

Materials/Resources

- Lesson Masters 13-7A and 13-7B
- Resource Masters 258–261
- Penny or other coin

HOMEWORK

Suggestions for Assignment

- Questions 1–24
- Question 25 (extra credit)
- Reading Lesson 13-8
- Covering the Ideas 13-8

Local Standards

1 Warm-Up

1. If the probability that an event will occur is the given number, what is the probability that the event will *not* occur?
   a. 35% 65%
   b. $\frac{12}{13}$ $\frac{1}{13}$
   c. 0.95 0.05
   d. 0 1
2. Suppose a stoplight is red for 30 seconds and green for 20 seconds, repeatedly. If you come to this stoplight two days in a row, what is the probability that the stoplight will be
   a. red both days? 0.36
   b. red the first day and green the second day? 0.24
   c. green the first day and red the second day? 0.24
   d. green both days? 0.16

2 Teaching

Notes on the Lesson

This lesson can be taught from the Questions but proceed slowly so that students follow you throughout. Carefully explaining one situation, such as that in Questions 1, 2, or 7, is worth a good deal of time.

Additional Answers can be found in the back of the book.

Additional Example

Example 1 Suppose a fair coin is flipped five times. What is the probability of obtaining exactly three heads? ${}_5C_3 \cdot P(H)^3 \cdot P(T)^2 = 10 \cdot \frac{1}{8} \cdot \frac{1}{4} = \frac{5}{16}$

Additional Answers

Activity 2

Step 1

n	0	1	2	3	4
Sequences of 4 Tosses with n Heads	TTTT	HTTT THTT TTHT TTTH	HHTT HTHT HTTH THHT THTH TTHH	HHHT HHTH HTHH THHH	HHHH
y = Number of Sequences with n Heads	1	4	6	4	1

Step 2

Number of Sequences y with n Heads

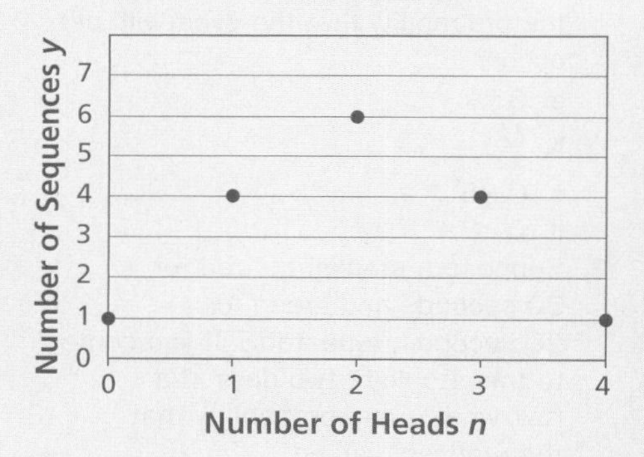

Step 3

Answers vary. Sample: The two graphs are nearly identical in shape.

Activity 2

Steps 1–3. See margin.

Step 1 Write every possible sequence of four H's and T's. Organize the sequences in a table like the one at the right. Three sequences have been written in the table to get you started. Then count the number of sequences in each cell and write the counts in the bottom row of the table.

n	0	1	2	3	4
Sequences of 4 Tosses with n Heads	?	THTT HTTT ?	HTTH ?	?	?
y = Number of Sequences with n Heads	?	?	?	?	?

Step 2 Graph the five points (n, y), where y is the number of sequences of 4 H's and T's that have n heads.

Step 3 Compare the shape of your graph in Step 2 with the shape of the graph in Step 3 of Activity 1.

You should find that the shapes of the graphs in the Activities are quite similar. In Activity 2 you should have found 6 different sequences of 2 heads and 2 tails:

HHTT, HTHT, HTTH, THHT, THTH, TTHH.

If the coin is fair, for a single toss, the probability $P(H)$ of heads and the probability of $P(T)$ tails each equal $\frac{1}{2}$. So, each of these 6 sequences has the same probability, $\frac{1}{2} \cdot \frac{1}{2} \cdot \frac{1}{2} \cdot \frac{1}{2} = \frac{1}{16}$, regardless of the order of the heads and tails. Therefore, the probability of getting 2 heads in 4 tosses of a fair coin is $6 \cdot \frac{1}{16} = \frac{3}{8} = 0.375$. This should be close to your class's relative frequency from Step 3 of Activity 1.

You can use the same idea to find the probability of obtaining any number of heads in any number of tosses of a fair coin.

Example 1

Suppose a fair coin is flipped 6 times. What is the probability of obtaining exactly 2 heads?

Solution 1 First count the number of sequences of 6 flips with exactly 2 heads. You could list the sequences by hand, but the Combination Counting Formula gives a faster way to count. Number the six flips 1, 2, 3, 4, 5, and 6. Then choosing two flips to be heads is equivalent to choosing a two-element subset of {1, 2, 3, 4, 5, 6}. The number of two-element subsets of a six-element set is

$${}_6C_2 = \binom{6}{2} = \frac{6!}{2!(6-2)!} = 15.$$

Among the most powerful of all theorems of elementary mathematics is the Binomial Probability Theorem, which gives the probability of throwing r heads in n tosses of a coin or the probability of guessing r questions correct in a test of n true-false questions. That these probabilities can even be calculated will surprise some students. One of the wonders of mathematics is that these calculations are related to combinations, the Binomial Theorem, and Pascal's Triangle.

Binomial Probability Theorem It is possible to state this theorem without introducing the variable q, by replacing q with $1 - p$. So, if a coin has a probability p of heads, then the probability of r heads in n tosses is $\binom{n}{r}p^r(1-p)^{n-r}$.

Now compute the probability of each sequence occurring. (Remember, each sequence has the same probability.)

$$P(H) \cdot P(H) \cdot P(T) \cdot P(T) \cdot P(T) \cdot P(T)$$
$$= P(H)^2 \cdot P(T)^4$$
$$= \left(\tfrac{1}{2}\right)^2\left(\tfrac{1}{2}\right)^4 = \tfrac{1}{64}.$$

So, the probability of getting exactly 2 heads in 6 tosses of a fair coin is ${}_6C_2 \cdot P(H)^2 \cdot P(T)^4 = 15 \cdot \frac{1}{64} = \frac{15}{64}$.

Solution 2 The 15 sequences with two heads are shown below.

HHTTTT	HTHTTT	HTTHTT	HTTTHT	HTTTTH
THHTTT	THTHTT	THTTHT	THTTTH	TTHHTT
TTHTHT	TTHTTH	TTTHHT	TTTHTH	TTTTHH

There are two outcomes for each of the flips (*H* or *T*), so the total number of sequences is $2 \cdot 2 \cdot 2 \cdot 2 \cdot 2 \cdot 2 = 2^6 = 64$. Thus, the probability of getting exactly two heads is $\frac{15}{64}$.

Connecting Probabilities with Combinations

Notice that the number of sequences of 2 heads in 6 flips equals the binomial coefficient $\binom{6}{2}$, which is the third number in row 6 of Pascal's Triangle. This is no accident: If an experiment is repeated n times , the number of possible sequences with r successes (and $n - r$ failures) is $\binom{n}{r}$, because determining such a sequence is equivalent to picking an r-element subset from $\{1, 2, \ldots, n\}$.

What happens if the two outcomes are not equally likely? Example 2 addresses this issue.

Example 2

Two generations ago, around 1950, the probability that a birth would be a multiple birth (twins, triplets, etc.) was about $\frac{1}{87}$. Mrs. Pereskier gave birth five times. Three of the births resulted in twins. What is the probability of this happening if multiple births occur at random?

Solution Let *M* be a multiple birth and *S* be a single birth. In this case, $P(M) = \frac{1}{87}$, so $P(S) = \frac{86}{87}$.

(continued on next page)

The Multiple Birth Family Reunion in Mexico is an annual event for families of multiples.

Additional Example

Example 2 In Rhode Island in 2005, the probability that a child would be born with a birth defect was about $\frac{3}{50}$. In the Cass family, there were 5 births, and 1 of the children was born with a birth defect. What is the probability that this would happen if birth defects occur at random? Let *D* denote a birth defect and *N* denote no birth defect. In this case, $P(D) = \frac{3}{50}$, so $P(N) = \frac{47}{50}$. There are $\binom{5}{1} = 5$ ways that 1 of the 5 births could involve a birth defect, such as the sequence NNNND. The probability of this sequence is $P(N) \cdot P(N) \cdot P(N) \cdot P(N) \cdot P(D) = (P(N))^4 \cdot (P(D)) = \left(\frac{47}{50}\right)^4 \cdot \left(\frac{3}{50}\right) \approx 0.04684$. There are 5 such sequences possible, so the probability of 1 birth defect in 5 births is about $5 \cdot 0.04684 = 0.234$ or about 23 in 100.

Accommodating the Learner

Give pairs of students a blank spinner. Have them color the spinner so that it has only two regions that are not the same size, for example, $\frac{3}{4}$ red and $\frac{1}{4}$ blue. Have them spin their spinner 50 times and note the relative frequency of getting each color. Have them compare these frequencies with the probabilities they would expect by calculating them mathematically. Have students share their results with the class. Answers vary. Check students' work.

There are $\binom{5}{3} = 10$ ways that 3 of the 5 births could be multiple births.

One of these ways yields the sequence SSMMM, which is what happened in the Pereskier family. The probability of this sequence is

$$\begin{aligned} P(S) \cdot P(S) \cdot P(M) \cdot P(M) \cdot P(M) &= (P(S))^2 \cdot (P(M))^3 \\ &= \left(\frac{86}{87}\right)^2 \cdot \left(\frac{1}{87}\right)^3 \\ &= \frac{7396}{4{,}984{,}209{,}207} \\ &\approx 0.00000148. \end{aligned}$$

There are 10 such sequences possible, so the probability of 3 multiple births in 5 births at that time was about $10 \cdot (0.00000148)$, or 0.0000148, or about 15 in a million.

This is a very low probability, and the actual occurrence of multiple births in some families is much higher than would be expected if they occurred randomly. This is how doctors realized that a tendency towards multiple births runs in some families.

 QY

> **QY**
> Refer to Example 2. What was the probability of exactly 1 multiple birth in 5 births?

Binomial Experiments

The situations of Examples 1 and 2 satisfy four criteria.

1. A task, called a **trial,** is repeated n times, where $n \geq 2$.
2. Each trial has outcomes that can be placed in one of only two categories, sometimes called "success" and "failure."
3. The trials are independent, that is, the probability of success on one trial is not affected by the results of earlier trials.
4. Each trial has the same probability of success.

When these four criteria are satisfied, the situation is called a **binomial experiment.** In a binomial experiment, the following properties hold:

- In n trials, there are $\binom{n}{r}$ possible sequences of r successes and $n - r$ failures.
- If the probability of success in any one trial is p, then the probability of failure is $q = 1 - p$ because success and failure are the only possible outcomes and they are mutually exclusive. Recall that categories are mutually exclusive if it is impossible for an element to belong to more than one of the categories.

ENGLISH LEARNERS

Vocabulary Development

Refer students to the criteria for a *binomial experiment* on page 912. Stress that the number of *trials,* in this lesson tosses of a coin, must be two or greater. Emphasize that all outcomes of trials in binomial experiments must be in one of two categories—success and failure—in contrast to some experiments that involve spinning a spinner.

Accommodating the Learner 

The fourth item in the list of criteria for a binomial experiment on page 912 might be misinterpreted by some students. Explain that saying that each trial has the same probability of success does not automatically mean that each of the two possible outcomes in the trial has the same probability. This might occur, but many times it does not. The statement means that the probability for each possible outcome remains the same from one trial to another.

- Because each trial has the same probability of success, the probability of any particular sequence of r successes and $n - r$ failures is $p^r q^{n-r}$.
- Because the trials are independent, the order in which successes and failures occur does not affect their probabilities. Therefore, the probability of *each* sequence of r successes and $n - r$ failures is $p^r q^{n-r}$, and their combined probability is $\binom{n}{r} p^r q^{n-r}$.

This argument proves the following theorem.

Binomial Probability Theorem

Suppose an experiment has an outcome with probability p, so that the probability the outcome does not occur is $q = 1 - p$. Then in n independent repetitions of the experiment, the probability that the outcome occurs r times is $\binom{n}{r} p^r q^{n-r}$.

These probabilities are often called ***binomial probabilities*** because of their connection with binomial coefficients.

GUIDED

Example 3

Suppose you roll two dice on each of three successive turns in a game. Compute the probability of rolling two sixes 0 times, 1 time, 2 times, and 3 times in those turns.

Solution Organize the computations in a table. Let rolling two sixes be a success and rolling anything else be a failure. If the die is fair, P(success) = probability of rolling a six on one die • probability of rolling a six on the other die = $\frac{1}{6}$ • _?_ = _?_. To compute the final result, substitute _?_ for p and 1 − _?_ = _?_ for q into the Binomial Probability Theorem.

$\frac{1}{6}$; $\frac{1}{36}$

$\frac{1}{36}$; $\frac{1}{36}$; $\frac{35}{36}$

Number of Successes	Number of Failures	Binomial Expression	Probability
0	3	$\binom{3}{0}p^0q^3$	_?_ ≈ _?_
1	2	$\binom{3}{1}p^1q^{?}$	_?_
2	1	_?_ $p^{?}q^{?}$	_?_
3	_?_	_?_	_?_

See margin.

Additional Answers

Example 3

			Probability
			$\left(\frac{35}{36}\right)^3$; 0.919
		2	$3 \cdot \frac{1}{36} \cdot \left(\frac{35}{36}\right)^2 \approx 0.0788$
		$\binom{3}{2}$; 2; 1	$3 \cdot \left(\frac{1}{36}\right)^2 \cdot \frac{35}{36} \approx 0.00225$
	0	$\binom{3}{3}p^3q^0$	$\left(\frac{1}{36}\right)^3 \approx 0.0000214$

Note-Taking Tips

Have students add the Binomial Probability Theorem to their journals.

Additional Example

Example 3 Suppose you roll two dice on each of four successive turns in a game. Compute the probability of rolling two 4s zero times, one time, two times, three times, and four times.

Solution Let rolling two 4s be a success and rolling anything else be a failure. If the die is fair, P(success) = the probability of rolling a 4 on one die • the probability of rolling a 4 on the other die = $\frac{1}{6}$ • _?_ = _?_. To compute the final result, substitute _?_ for p and 1 − _?_ = _?_ for q into the Binomial Probability Theorem. $\frac{1}{6}$; $\frac{1}{36}$; $\frac{1}{36}$; $\frac{1}{36}$; $\frac{35}{36}$

Number of Successes	Number of Failures	Binomial Expression	Probability
0	4	$\binom{4}{0}p^0q4$	$\left(\frac{35}{36}\right)^{?}$ ≈ _?_ 4; 0.893
1	3	$\binom{4}{1}p^1q^{?}$ 3	_?_ $4 \cdot \frac{1}{36} \cdot \left(\frac{35}{36}\right)^3 \approx 0.102$
2	2	_?_ $p^{?}q^{?}$ $\binom{4}{2}$; 2; 2	_?_ $6 \cdot \left(\frac{1}{36}\right)^2 \cdot \left(\frac{35}{36}\right)^2 \approx 0.00438$
3	1	_?_ $\binom{4}{3}p^3q^1$	_?_ $4 \cdot \left(\frac{1}{36}\right)^3 \cdot \left(\frac{35}{36}\right) \approx 0.00008$
4	_?_ 0	_?_ $\binom{4}{4}p^4q^0$	_?_ $\left(\frac{1}{36}\right)^4 \approx 0.0000006$

3 Assignment

Recommended Assignment

- Questions 1–24
- Question 25 (extra credit)
- Reading Lesson 13-8
- Covering the Ideas 13-8

Notes on the Questions

Questions 1, 2, 4, and 5 You might run a computer simulation of coin tossing. Have the computer repeat an experiment thousands of times to see how close the results come to those that would be predicted by probability theory.

Questions 9 and 10 The ratio of times the light is red and green equals that in Warm-Up 2, so the probabilities are consistent with what is there.

13-7A Lesson Master

Questions on SPUR Objectives
See Student Edition pages 934–937 for objectives.

USES Objective J

1. If the probability that an event occurs is p, what is the probability that the event does not occur? $1 - p$
2. If the probability that an event occurs is p, what is the probability that the event occurs exactly r times in n independent trials? $\binom{n}{r} \cdot p^r \cdot (1-p)^{n-r}$
3. Suppose you flip six fair coins. Find the probability of getting
   a. all six heads. $\frac{1}{64}$
   b. exactly one head. $\frac{6}{64}$
   c. exactly three heads. $\frac{20}{64}$
   d. at least five heads. $\frac{7}{64}$
4. The AA Minor League Baseball team Akron Aeros is playing a three-game series with the Bowie Baysox. Suppose there is a 60% probability that Akron will win any particular game. Find the probability that Akron wins
   a. all three games. 0.216
   b. exactly two games. 0.432
   c. exactly one game. 0.288
   d. none of the games. 0.064
5. Airlines routinely sell more tickets for a flight than they have seats, expecting some people to not arrive. Suppose an airline sells 52 tickets for a regional jet flight with 50 seats. From previous data, they expect that each passenger has a 90% chance of showing up for the flight. Find the probability that more than 50 people show up. ≈ 0.0283

In 6 and 7, consider a standardized test like the SAT where there is a penalty for wrong answers in the multiple-choice section. Your math teacher recommends that you reason if you can eliminate some answers. Suppose you do not know the answers to 5 of the questions, but you have narrowed each of them down to three possibilities, so your chance of guessing correctly on any one question is $\frac{1}{3}$.

6. Find the probability that you get the given number of the five questions correct.
   a. none $\frac{32}{243}$
   b. one $\frac{80}{243}$
   c. two $\frac{80}{243}$
   d. three $\frac{40}{243}$
   e. four $\frac{10}{243}$
   f. five $\frac{1}{243}$
7. You gain one point for each question answered correctly, and lose $\frac{1}{4}$ point for each question answered incorrectly. Use your answers to question 6 to find the probability that you gain or lose points overall by guessing from among three possibilities on these five questions.
   a. lose points $\frac{32}{243} \approx 13\%$
   b. gain points $\frac{131}{243} \approx 54\%$
   c. break even $\frac{80}{243} \approx 33\%$

616 *Advanced Algebra*

In Example 3, notice that the expressions in the Binomial Expression column are also the terms in the expansion of $(p + q)^3$. In general, the probability of r successes in n trials is the $p^r q^{n-r}$ term in the expansion of $(p + q)^n$. Because $p + q = 1$, $(p + q)^n = 1^n = 1$. That is, the sum of the probabilities of all possible outcomes computed using the Binomial Probability Theorem is 1.

Questions

COVERING THE IDEAS

In 1 and 2, a fair coin is flipped 5 times. A sequence of 5 H's (heads) and T's (tails) is recorded.

1. a. How many different sequences are possible with exactly 2 H's? 10
   b. How many different sequences are possible with exactly 2 T's? 10
   c. What is the probability of flipping exactly 2 heads? $\frac{10}{32} = 0.3125$
2. a. How many different sequences are possible with exactly 4 T's? 5
   b. What is the probability of flipping exactly 4 tails? $\frac{5}{32} = 0.15625$
3. About 1 in 35 births today is a multiple birth. Suppose there are 4 births in a family. What is the probability that exactly 1 of them is a multiple birth? $\binom{4}{1}\left(\frac{1}{35}\right)\left(\frac{34}{35}\right)^3 \approx 0.1048$

In 4 and 5, a fair coin is flipped 8 times. Give the probability of each event.

4. getting exactly 8 heads
5. getting exactly 4 heads

4. $\frac{1}{256} \approx 0.0039$

5. $\frac{35}{128} \approx 0.2734$

6. What is the probability of getting exactly r heads in n tosses of a fair coin? $\binom{n}{r}\left(\frac{1}{2}\right)^n$
7. Suppose that a coin is biased so that there is a 55% chance that the coin will show tails when tossed. Find the probability of each event.
   a. The coin shows heads when tossed. 0.45
   b. When tossed twice, the coin shows heads the first time and tails the second time. 0.2475
   c. When tossed twice, the coin shows heads once and tails once. 0.495
8. Use the information in Question 3. What is the probability that, of the 3 births in a family today, at least 1 is a multiple birth? about 0.08329

In 9 and 10, suppose a stoplight is red for 45 seconds and green for 30 seconds. Suppose, also, that every day for a full week you get to this stoplight at a random time. What is the probability that the stoplight will be red

9. every day of the full week? about 0.02799
10. 3 of the 5 days of the work week? about 0.3456

The stoplight was invented by Garrett Augustus Morgan, Sr., an African-American born in Paris, Kentucky. He received a patent for the stoplight on November 20, 1923.

APPLYING THE MATHEMATICS

11. An O-ring is a circular mechanical seal (usually made of rubber) that generally prevents leakage between two compressed objects. A manufacturer of 14-mm diameter O-rings claims that 97.5% of the O-rings he manufactures are less than 14.5 mm in diameter. In a sample of 10 such O-rings, you find that three O-rings have a diameter greater than 14.5 mm. If the manufacturer's claim is correct, what is the probability of this outcome? about 0.0016

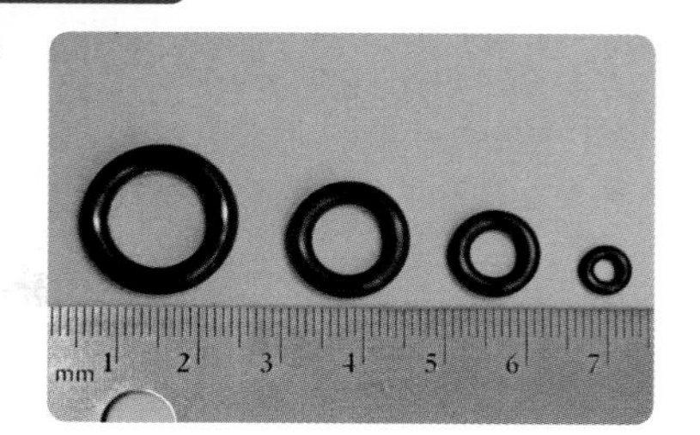

12. Slugger Patty McBattie has a batting average of 0.312. Use this average as her probability of getting a hit in a particular time at bat. In a game where she bats 5 times, what is the probability she gets exactly 2 hits? about 0.3170

In 13 and 14, suppose you have two minutes left to fill in the last 8 questions on a multiple-choice test. You can eliminate enough answers so that your probability of guessing the correct answer to any question is $\frac{1}{4}$.

13. What is the probability you get exactly 5 questions correct? about 0.0231
14. What is the probability you get 2 or more questions correct? about 0.6329

In 15 and 16, a student is given the quiz at the right.

15. Using R for right and W for wrong, list all possible ways the quiz might be answered. For example, getting all four right is coded RRRR. Assume an unanswered question is wrong.
16. Assuming that the student guesses on each item, and that the probability of guessing the right answer is $\frac{1}{2}$, calculate each probability.
    a. The student gets all 4 correct.
    b. The student gets exactly 2 correct.
    c. The student gets at least 2 correct.

QUIZ
1. Which is farther north, Anchorage, Alaska or Helsinki, Finland?
2. Is the 1,000,000th decimal place of π 5 or greater?
3. Is the area of Central Park in New York greater than 5 times the area of Hyde Park in London?
4. Did Euler die before or after Gauss was born?

15. RRRR, RRRW, RRWR, RWRR, WRRR, RRWW, RWRW, RWWR, WRRW, WRWR, WWRR, RWWW, WRWW, WWRW, WWWR, WWWW

16a. $\frac{1}{16} = 0.0625$

16b. $\frac{3}{8} = 0.375$

16c. $\frac{3}{8} + \frac{1}{4} + \frac{1}{16} = \frac{11}{16} = 0.6875$

REVIEW

17. Expand $(a + b)^5$. **(Lesson 13-6)** $a^5 + 5a^4b + 10a^3b^2 + 10a^2b^3 + 5ab^4 + b^5$
18. Use the Binomial Theorem to approximate $(1.001)^{10}$ to fifteen decimal places. **(Lesson 13-6)** 1.010045120210252
19. The mean of three numbers in a geometric sequence is 35. The first number is 15. What might the other numbers be? **(Lessons 13-3, 7-5)** 30, 60

Notes on the Questions

Questions 13 and 14 On some multiple-choice tests where there are 5 choices, a test-taker loses $\frac{1}{4}$ of a point for each wrong answer. You might have students explain why this means that a test-taker who guesses on a lot of questions would neither gain nor lose points. 1 point for the right answer balances $\frac{1}{4}$ point for each of 4 wrong answers, given that they are equally likely. Ask: What would be appropriate to lose if there were 4 choices? $\frac{1}{3}$ of a point

Question 18 You might ask how many decimal places the *exact* value of $(1.001)^{10}$ would have in base 10. 30 decimal places

13-7

4 Wrap-Up

Ongoing Assessment

Refer groups to Example 1. Have them find the probability of tossing three heads in six tosses. Have them use both solution methods.

P(3 heads in 6 tosses) = 0.3125. Students should be able to determine probabilities involving coin tosses in two ways.

13-7B page 2

13-7B Lesson Master — Questions on SPUR Objectives. See Student Edition pages 934–937 for objectives.

VOCABULARY

1. Define *independent events*.
   Events are independent if the probability of success on one trial is not affected by the results of earlier trials.
2. Give an example of two independent events.
   Answers vary. Sample: Roll 6 on a die; roll 4 on a die.
3. Give an example of two events that are not independent.
   Answers vary. Sample: Pick a card from a deck; keep the card and pick another card.
4. State the four criteria for a binomial experiment.
   1. A trial is repeated *n* times, where $n \geq 2$. 2. Each trial has only 2 outcomes, "success" or "failure." 3. The trials are independent. 4. Each trial has the same probability of success.

USES Objective J

5. If $\binom{n}{r} \cdot p^r \cdot (1-p)^{n-r}$ represents the probability that an event occurs exactly *r* times in *n* independent trials,
   a. what does the quantity *p* represent? It represents the probability that the event occurs.
   b. what does the quantity $1 - p$ represent? It represents the probability that the event does not occur.
6. Suppose a fair coin is tossed 5 times. Answers vary. Samples are given.
   a. What could the quantity $\binom{5}{4}$ represent? the number of ways 4 heads could occur
   b. What could the quantity 2^5 represent? the number of possible outcomes
   c. What could the quantity $\binom{5}{4}(0.5)^4(0.5)^1$ represent? the probability of getting exactly 4 heads

In 7 and 8, consider a 5-question multiple-choice quiz with three possible answers per question. If each question is answered by guessing, the probability of correctly answering any one question is $\frac{1}{3}$.

7. What is the probability of correctly answering exactly 3 questions? ≈ 0.165
8. What is the probability of scoring at least 75% on the quiz? ≈ 0.041

Advanced Algebra 617

20. A snail is crawling straight up a wall. The first hour it climbs 16 inches, the second hour it climbs 12 inches, and each succeeding hour it climbs $\frac{3}{4}$ the distance it climbed the previous hour. Assume this pattern holds indefinitely.
    a. How far does the snail climb during the 7th hour? about 2.85 in.
    b. What is the total distance the snail has climbed in 7 hours? **(Lesson 13-2)** about 55.46 in.

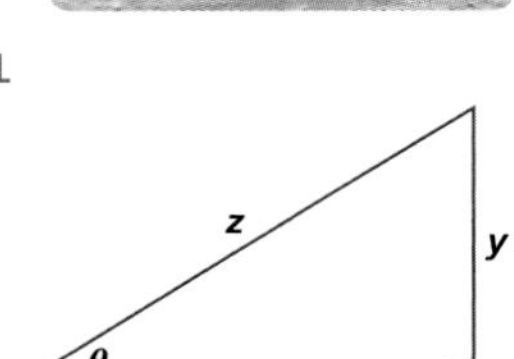

In 21 and 22, expand and simplify. (Lesson 11-2)

21. $(t^2 - r^2)(t^2 + r^2)$ $t^4 - r^4$
22. $(4a^2 + 2a + 1)(2a - 1)$ $8a^3 - 1$
23. In the triangle at the right, find $\frac{\sin\theta}{\cos\theta}$. **(Lesson 10-1)** $\frac{y}{x}$
24. Suppose an experiment begins with 120 bacteria and that the population of bacteria doubles every hour.
    a. About how many bacteria will there be after 3 hours? 960
    b. Write a formula for the number *y* of bacteria after *x* hours. **(Lesson 9-1)** $y = 120(2)^x$

EXPLORATION

25. a. Use a random-number generator in a spreadsheet to simulate 50 trials of tossing 4 coins simultaneously. Record your results.
    b. Calculate the relative frequency of each of the following outcomes: 0 heads, exactly 1 head, exactly 2 heads, exactly 3 heads, 4 heads.
    c. How closely do your results agree with predictions based on the Binomial Probability Theorem? Do your think your random number generator program is a good one? Explain why or why not.

	A coin1	B coin2	C coin3	D
◆	=randint(0,1,50)			
1	1			
2	1			
3	0			
4	1			
5	0			
6	1			

B coin2

25. Answers vary. Sample:
a–b.

Number of Heads	Occurrences	Relative Frequency
0	1	0.02
1	14	0.28
2	19	0.38
3	10	0.20
4	6	0.12

c. The Binomial Probability Theorem predicts relative frequencies of 0.0625, 0.25, 0.375, 0.25, and 0.0625, respectively. My results agree fairly well with the predictions of the Binomial Probability Theorem. This suggests that my random number generator is fair.

QY ANSWER

$\binom{5}{1} \cdot \left(\frac{1}{87}\right)^1 \cdot \left(\frac{86}{87}\right)^4 \approx 0.055$, or about 1 in 18

Lesson 13-8 Lotteries

Vocabulary

lottery

unit fraction

▶ **BIG IDEA** The probability of winning a lottery prize can be calculated using permutations and combinations.

A **lottery** is a game or procedure in which prizes are distributed by pure chance. The simplest lotteries are raffles in which you buy tickets that are put in a bin, and winning tickets are picked from that bin. In recent years, however, more complicated lotteries have been designed. These lotteries pay out large amounts of money to a few individuals in order to attract participants. Today, several countries run lotteries themselves or allow private lotteries. In the United States, about 94% of people live in states that run lotteries, and participants must be 18 years of age or older.

Lotteries are designed to make money, so they always take in more than they pay out. This means that many more people will lose money in a lottery than will win. Still, the possibility, however remote, of winning a huge amount of money is very attractive.

Consider a typical lottery. To participate in the Mega Millions game, which is played across several states, a participant pays $1 and picks five numbers out of the set of consecutive integers {1, 2, 3, ..., 56} and one number (called the "Mega Ball") from the set of consecutive integers {1, 2, 3, ..., 46}. Twice a week, five balls are picked at random from balls numbered 1 through 56, and one Mega Ball is randomly picked from a different set of 46 balls. These balls show the winning numbers. For instance, the winning numbers in one Mega Millions game were 1, 5, 13, 18, 33, and 30. The people who pick all six winning numbers split the grand prize, which is always at least $12 million.

Mental Math

Given that sin 52° ≈ 0.788, find

a. sin(−52°) −0.788

b. sin 232° −0.788

c. sin 128° 0.788

d. cos 38° 0.788

GUIDED

Example 1

What is the probability of picking the six winning numbers in the Mega Millions lottery?

Solution The number of possible combinations for the first five numbers that could be chosen is $\binom{56}{?} = \frac{56!}{? \cdot ?} = \underline{\ ?\ }$. 5; 5!; 51!; 3,819,816

(continued on next page)

Background

Until the 1970s, lotteries were unknown in the United States, though raffle games like the Irish Sweepstakes were well known abroad. As of 2008, the District of Columbia and all states except Alabama, Alaska, Arkansas, Hawaii, Mississippi, Nevada, Utah, and Wyoming participated in lotteries. In most states, there are many different games, with different odds, available on various days of the week.

Lotteries proliferate because they provide revenue not from sales taxes or property taxes. Often, the funds are to be used for education or other social services, but increasingly in practice, this only means that only less money from other sources is used for those services.

In general, the more a person knows about the odds of winning, the less likely he or she might be to enter a lottery. One possible reason for this is that those people realize that the odds against winning are

(continued on next page)

Lesson 13-8

GOAL

Apply the ideas of combinations to calculate the probability of winning various lottery games.

SPUR Objectives

J Solve problems using combinations and probability.

Materials/Resources

- Lesson Masters 13-8A and 13-8B
- Resource Masters 262 and 263

HOMEWORK

Suggestions for Assignment

- Questions 1–19
- Question 20 (extra credit)
- Reading Lesson 13-9
- Covering the Ideas 13-9

Local Standards

1 Warm-Up

1. Does your state have its own state lottery? Does it participate in a multistate lottery? Answers vary.
2. Do you know any people who play the lottery? Have any of them won a major prize? Answers vary.
3. If your state runs lottery games, pick the one with the largest prize. What do you think the chances are that a purchaser of a single ticket will win the grand prize? Answers vary.

There are 46 choices for the Mega Ball number. So there are a total of _?_ • 46 = _?_ possible combinations of numbers to choose. Because each combination has the same chance of being drawn, the probability that a particular combination will appear is $\frac{1}{?}$. So, the probability of picking the six winning numbers is $\frac{1}{?}$ or about _?_. 3,819,816; 175,711,536 175,711,536 175,711,536; $5.69 \cdot 10^{-9}$

The answer to Example 1 explains why there is often no winner in a lottery. The chance of choosing all the winning numbers is quite small.

Because the probability of winning the grand prize is so low, most lotteries give smaller prizes to participants who pick almost all of the numbers. For instance, in Mega Millions, there is a *much* smaller prize for picking the five regular winning numbers but not the Mega Ball number. There is an even smaller prize given for picking four of the five regular winning numbers.

Example 2

What is the probability of picking exactly four of the five regular winning numbers in Mega Millions?

Solution Of the five regular numbers, four must be picked from the five winning regular numbers, one must be picked from the 51 incorrect regular numbers that remain, and the Mega Ball number must be chosen incorrectly.

There are $\binom{5}{4}$ different sets of 4 numbers from the 5 winning regular numbers.

There are 51 ways to choose one incorrect number from the remaining regular numbers.

There are 45 non-winning Mega Ball numbers.

Winners are chosen from the 175,711,536 possible combinations found in Example 1. So, the probability of picking four of the five regular winning numbers is

$$\frac{\binom{5}{4} \cdot 51 \cdot 45}{175{,}711{,}536} = \frac{11{,}475}{175{,}711{,}536} \approx 0.000065 \approx \frac{1}{15{,}385}.$$

A **unit fraction** is a simple fraction with 1 in its numerator. In Example 2, the probability 0.000065 is approximated by the unit fraction $\frac{1}{15{,}385}$ to make it easier to interpret the answer as "about 1 chance in 15,385" of picking four winning balls. This fraction was found by calculating the reciprocal of 0.000065. That reciprocal is about 15,385. The reciprocal of the reciprocal equals the original number.

2 Teaching

Notes on the Lesson

The calculations of the probability of winning most lotteries take time, and you should proceed very slowly in your explanations. You can discuss Examples 1–3 or pick examples from your state's lottery or from a lottery in a nearby state. (Unless you are in Alaska or Hawaii, there is a neighboring state with a lottery.)

Example 1 Because there is a special ball (the Mega Ball) that is independent of the others, after the number of combinations of the first five numbers is calculated, the Mega Ball must be factored into the overall probability of winning.

very strong. The purpose of this lesson is to teach students how to calculate the probability of winning a lottery so that they will realize how low the probability of winning is and thus be able to make a wiser decision regarding entering such games.

In this lesson, we ignore the amount that is bet and the amount that is paid out because these change from time to time. We calculate the probability only.

Additional Example

Example 1 To win the multi-state lottery Hot Lotto, you must choose five correct numbers from 1 through 39 and another "hot ball" from 1 through 19. What is the probability of picking the six winning numbers in this lottery?

Solution The number of possible combinations for the first five numbers that could be chosen is $\binom{39}{?} = \frac{39!}{(?)(?)} = ?$. 5; 5!; 34!; 575,757 There are 19 choices for the hot ball. So there are _?_ • 19 = _?_ possible combinations of numbers to choose. 575,757; 10,939,383 Because each combination has the same chance of being drawn, the probability that a particular combination will appear is $\frac{1}{?}$. 10,939,383 So the probability of picking the five winning numbers is $\frac{1}{?}$ or about _?_. 10,939,383; 0.00000009

ENGLISH LEARNERS

Vocabulary Development

Review with students that the word *lottery* refers to a game or procedure in which prizes are awarded solely by chance, or *lot*. If you have not already discussed the Warm-Up, do so now.

Students should also be familiar with the term *unit fraction,* a fraction with 1 as its numerator. Students should relate *unit* to *one*.

 QY

Because probabilities of winning are so low in many lotteries, people can get discouraged from entering repeatedly. Consequently, states also have lotteries with fewer numbers to match in which more people win, but the payouts are much lower. Some of these lotteries require that three or four digits (from 0 to 9) be matched exactly, in order. Because the order matters, the probability of winning cannot be calculated using combinations.

Example 3

To play Florida's basic "Play 4" lottery, a participant picks four digits, each from 0 to 9, and must match a 4-digit number. What is the probability of matching the four winning digits?

Solution 1 There is a probability of $\frac{1}{10}$ that each digit will be matched. Because these events are independent, the probability of matching all four numbers is $\frac{1}{10} \cdot \frac{1}{10} \cdot \frac{1}{10} \cdot \frac{1}{10}$, or $\frac{1}{10{,}000}$.

Solution 2 Think of the four digits as forming one number. There are ten thousand numbers from 0000 to 9999. The probability of matching one of these is $\frac{1}{10{,}000}$.

Some people have computers pick lottery numbers for them. Others study past winning numbers to look for patterns. Still others use their "lucky" numbers or their birthdays. None of these strategies changes the probability of winning. The probability is always tiny, and there is no systematic way to win lotteries like these.

▶ **QY**

A probability of 0.0028 means "about 1 in __?__."

Questions

COVERING THE IDEAS

1. What is a lottery? *a game or procedure in which prizes are distributed by pure chance*

In 2 and 3, consider the Mega Millions game.

2. What must a participant do in order to win the grand prize in this lottery? *Pick 5 winning numbers from the integers from 1 to 56 and the winning Mega Ball number from the integers from 1 to 46.*
3. What is the probability of picking only the five regular winning numbers in this lottery? $\frac{5}{19{,}523{,}504} \approx 0.00000026 \approx \frac{1}{3{,}846{,}154}$
4. New York's "Take 5" lottery gives participants a chance to win a jackpot by matching five numbers (in any order) from a set of 39. What is the probability of winning this lottery? $\frac{1}{575{,}757}$

Notes on the Lesson

Example 2 We do not discuss how much is paid out, but generally much less is paid out for matching 4 of 5 numbers than for matching all 5.

Note that students may get different unit fractions for the probability if they take the reciprocal of their written decimal approximation than if they take the reciprocal of their calculator's stored value by entering "ans^{-1}". The text below Example 2 and the answers given to the Questions reflect the former procedure.

Emphasize the last sentence before the Questions. There is no system for winning. There cannot be a system for winning this type of game. The more you play, the more you can expect to lose. You should play only if you can afford to lose the money that you are betting.

Additional Examples

Example 2 What is the probability of picking exactly three of the five regular winning numbers and the "hot ball" in Hot Lotto? $\frac{\binom{5}{3} \cdot \binom{34}{2} \cdot 1}{10{,}939{,}383} = \frac{5610}{10{,}939{,}383} \approx 0.0005 \approx \frac{1}{2000}$

Example 3 In the Idaho Pick 3 game, a player picks a three-digit number from the digits 0 through 9. What is the probability of matching the winning number? There is a probability of $\frac{1}{10}$ that each digit will be matched. Because these events are independent, the probability of matching three digits is $\frac{1}{10} \cdot \frac{1}{10} \cdot \frac{1}{10} = \frac{1}{1000}$.

3 Assignment

Recommended Assignment

- Questions 1–19
- Question 20 (extra credit)
- Reading Lesson 13-9
- Covering the Ideas 13-9

Accommodating the Learner ↑

Have students compare the probabilities of winning a lottery in which the winner chooses six numbers from 1 to 36 in any order and six numbers in a given order. Each number can be chosen only once. In order: $\frac{1}{36} \cdot \frac{1}{35} \cdot \frac{1}{34} \cdot \frac{1}{33} \cdot \frac{1}{32} \cdot \frac{1}{31} = \frac{1}{1{,}402{,}410{,}240}$; In any order: There are ${}_{36}C_6 = 1{,}947{,}792$ ways to choose 6 numbers, so the probability of winning is $\frac{1}{1{,}947{,}792}$.

Accommodating the Learner ↓

Review Examples 1–3 with students to help them see the difference between permutations and combinations. Point out that in Examples 1 and 2, order does not matter, so these are combinations. In Example 3, however, a winner must select five numbers that match the order of the five numbers in the winning number, so this is a permutation.

5. Refer to Example 3. If Florida's "Play 4" lottery had an option where a participant must match the first three of four numbers (each of which can be any digit from 0 through 9) in exact order, what would be the probability of winning? $\frac{1}{1000}$

APPLYING THE MATHEMATICS

6. Another multi-state lottery, Powerball, is played by picking five numbers from balls numbered 1 to 55 and one additional Powerball number from balls numbered 1 to 42. A smaller prize is awarded to participants who match four of the regular winning numbers and the Powerball number.
   a. In how many ways can a participant win the smaller prize? 250
   b. What is the probability of winning the smaller prize?

6b. $\frac{125}{73,053,981} \approx 0.0000017 \approx \frac{1}{588,235}$

7. The European lottery "Euro Millions" is played by choosing five numbers from a set of 50 and two "star" numbers from a set of nine (the digits 1 to 9). What is the probability of picking all seven winning numbers? $\frac{1}{76,275,360}$
8. Consider New York's "Take 5" lottery in Question 4.
   a. How many different tickets are possible for this lottery? Remember that order does not matter, so all tickets listing the numbers 12, 32, 11, 19, and 6, for instance, are considered the same. 575,757
   b. How many tickets from your answer to Part a are losers? 575,756
   c. A special promotion advertises that a participant with a losing ticket can enter for a second chance prize. What is the probability of being eligible for this drawing? $\frac{575,756}{575,757} \approx 0.999998$
9. To play the "Cash 5" lottery in Connecticut, a participant pays \$1 and picks five numbers from a set of 35. For 50¢ more, the participant can add a "kicker" number picked from the remaining 30 numbers not already picked. One way to win a kicker prize is to match the kicker number and four out of five of the regular numbers. What is the probability of winning a kicker prize in this way? $\frac{5}{324,632} \approx 0.0000154 \approx \frac{1}{64,935}$
10. In the Quinto lottery formerly played in Washington state, a participant picked five cards from a standard 52-card deck. The lottery paid \$1000 for a ticket matching four of the five cards, and \$20 for a ticket matching three of the five. Does this mean that participants were $\frac{1000}{20} = 50$ times as likely to match three of five winning cards as to match four of five winning cards? Explain your answer. See margin.

Additional Answers

10. No; Answers vary. Sample: There are $\binom{5}{3} \cdot 47 \cdot 46 = 21,620$ ways to match 3 cards, but only $\binom{5}{4} \cdot 47 = 235$ ways to match 4 cards. So, you are actually $\frac{21,620}{235} = 92$ times as likely to match 3 cards as you are to match 4.

13-8A Lesson Master

Questions on SPUR Objectives
See Student Edition pages 934–937 for objectives.

USES Objective J

1. Since 1997, in the Powerball Lottery, a participant wins the jackpot by choosing five numbers from 1 to 55 (in any order) and also matching a red Powerball number from 1 to 42.
   a. Find the probability of winning the jackpot. $\frac{1}{146,107,962}$
   b. How many times as likely are you to win a simpler lottery where six numbers are chosen from 1 to 55 than you are to win this lottery? about 5 times as likely
2. In the Connecticut Lottery before 2008, participants chose six numbers from 1 to 40, in any order. In 2008, the game expanded to use 44 numbers.
   a. In how many ways can a player choose six numbers out of 40? 3,838,380
   b. Find the probability of winning the pre-2008 lottery. $\frac{1}{3,838,380}$
   c. In how many ways can a participant choose six numbers out of 44? 7,059,052
   d. Find the probability of winning the post-2008 lottery. $\frac{1}{7,059,052}$
   e. Find the probability of winning a much smaller prize by choosing five of the numbers correctly before 2008. $\frac{204}{3,838,380} \approx \frac{1}{18,816}$ after 2008. $\frac{208}{7,059,052} \approx \frac{1}{30,961}$
   f. This lottery expanded in order to increase the size of the jackpots, which roll over from week to week if there is no winner. Explain how this change could increase the jackpots. Answers vary. Sample: The probability of winning the jackpot under the new system is about 61% of what it was under the old system, so it is more likely that no one will win and the jackpot will roll over.
3. In the Virginia Lottery's "Pick 3" game, a three-digit number is chosen from 000 to 999.Participants can choose one of two versions: "Exact Match" where you must pick the exact three-digit number, or "Any Order" in which you win if yourthree digits come up in any order. For instance, if you play "Any Order" withthe number "123," you win if the number chosen is 123, 132, 213, 231, 312, or 321.
   a. Find the probability of winning the "Any Order" game. Assume you picked three different digits (like the example above). $\frac{6}{1000}$
   b. Tickets for this lottery cost one dollar. In the "Exact Match" game, a winning ticket pays \$500. In "Any Order," a winning ticket pays \$80. Which game is more beneficial financially for the state? Explain. Answers vary. Sample: "Any Order" is better for the state; they pay out $\$80 \cdot 6 = \$480$ for each 1000 tickets purchased; "Exact Match" pays \$500 for each 1000 tickets sold because only 1 in 1000 tickets is a winner.

Advanced Algebra 619

REVIEW

11. A golden retriever has a litter of 8 puppies. If males and females are equally likely to be in the litter, what is the probability that 4 of the puppies are male and 4 are female? **(Lesson 13-7)** $\frac{35}{128} \approx 0.2734$

12. Sam Dunk makes 75% of the free throws he attempts. What is the probability that he will make at least 7 out of 10 free throws? **(Lesson 13-7)** ≈ 0.7759

13. You pick four numbers out of a set of 30. If four numbers are selected at random from this set, what is the probability that the four numbers you picked are selected? **(Lesson 13-7)** $\frac{1}{27{,}405}$

14. Solve ${}_nC_3 = 84$. **(Lessons 13-4, 11-6)** $n = 9$

In 15 and 16, do not solve the equation.
a. State the number of roots each equation has.
b. State the number of positive roots the equation has. (Lesson 11-6)

15. $x^5 + 8x^3 + x = 0$ a. 5; b. 0

16. $13t^2 + 6t^7 + it^3 = 14$ a. 7; b. 0

17. **Multiple Choice** Choose the equation for an exponential decay function and explain why it is that kind of function. **(Lesson 9-2)**

    A $f(x) = \frac{1^x}{5}$ B $f(x) = 5^{-x}$ C $f(x) = 5^x$ D $f(x) = \left(\frac{1}{5}\right)^{-x}$

17. B; it is equivalent to the equation $f(x) = \left(\frac{1}{5}\right)^x$, which has a growth factor between 0 and 1.

18. Write the reciprocal of $2 + i$ in $a + bi$ form. **(Lesson 6-9)** $\frac{2}{5} - \frac{1}{5}i$

19. Assume that the cost of a spherical ball bearing varies directly as the cube of its diameter. What is the ratio of the cost of a ball bearing 6 mm in diameter to the cost of a ball bearing 3 mm in diameter? **(Lesson 2-3)** $\frac{8}{1}$

EXPLORATION

20. The term "odds" is often used interchangeably (and often incorrectly) with the term "probability" when discussing probability. Look up information about odds and find out how odds are related to, but are not the same thing as, probability. See margin.

QY ANSWER

357

Additional Answers

20. Answers vary. Sample: If p is the probability of an event occurring, and $1 - p$ is the probability that it does not occur, then the odds in the event's favor are $\frac{p}{1-p}$ and against it are $\frac{1-p}{p}$. Odds are actually ratios of probabilities. In gambling, odds do not represent real probabilities of various outcomes, but they represent the payout for winning bets. Displayed odds, therefore, often already include profit for the bet-taker, dealer, or casino.

13-8

Notes on the Questions

Question 11 This question assumes males and females in the litter are equally likely. This may be true for golden retrievers. Humans, on the other hand, are more likely to have males than females, but the difference has been shrinking since the 1970s.

Question 12 This question assumes that making one free throw does not affect the probability of making the next, nor does missing a free throw affect the probability of making the next.

Question 20 Lottostrategies.com advertises that the odds of winning the New York game "Take 5" (see Questions 4 and 8) are 1:575,757. Thus they equate odds with probability. But most sources do not consider them to be the same.

4 Wrap-Up

Ongoing Assessment

Have students write a paragraph explaining some of the pitfalls of lottery games and why they are so popular. Answers vary. Students should recognize that lottery games are set up so that the states take in more money than they pay out.

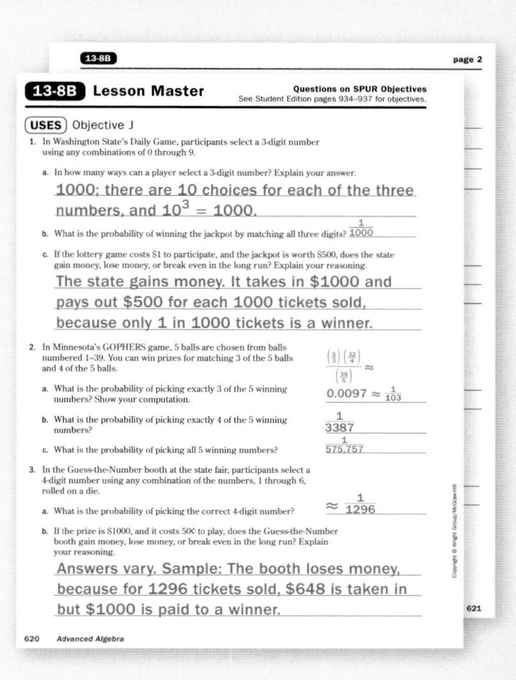

13-8B page 2

13-8B Lesson Master

Questions on SPUR Objectives
See Student Edition pages 934–937 for objectives.

USES Objective J

1. In Washington State's Daily Game, participants select a 3-digit number using any combinations of 0 through 9.
   a. In how many ways can a player select a 3-digit number? Explain your answer.
   1000; there are 10 choices for each of the three numbers, and $10^3 = 1000$.
   b. What is the probability of winning the jackpot by matching all three digits? $\frac{1}{1000}$
   c. If the lottery game costs \$1 to participate, and the jackpot is worth \$500, does the state gain money, lose money, or break even in the long run? Explain your reasoning.
   The state gains money. It takes in \$1000 and pays out \$500 for each 1000 tickets sold, because only 1 in 1000 tickets is a winner.

2. In Minnesota's GOPHERS game, 5 balls are chosen from balls numbered 1–39. You can win prizes for matching 3 of the 5 balls and 4 of the 5 balls.
   a. What is the probability of picking exactly 3 of the 5 winning numbers? Show your computation. $\frac{\binom{5}{3}\binom{32}{4}}{\binom{39}{5}} \approx 0.0097 \approx \frac{1}{103}$
   b. What is the probability of picking exactly 4 of the 5 winning numbers? $\frac{1}{3387}$
   c. What is the probability of picking all 5 winning numbers? $\frac{1}{575{,}757}$

3. In the Guess-the-Number booth at the state fair, participants select a 4-digit number using any combination of the numbers, 1 through 6, rolled on a die.
   a. What is the probability of picking the correct 4-digit number? $\approx \frac{1}{1296}$
   b. If the prize is \$1000, and it costs 50¢ to play, does the Guess-the-Number booth gain money, lose money, or break even in the long run? Explain your reasoning.
   Answers vary. Sample: The booth loses money, because for 1296 tickets sold, \$648 is taken in but \$1000 is paid to a winner.

Copyright © Wright Group/McGraw-Hill

620 Advanced Algebra 621

Lesson

13-9

GOAL

Introduce the normal distribution by beginning with binomial distributions and examples of how the normal distribution is used.

SPUR Objectives

I Use measures of central tendency or dispersion to describe data or distributions.

K Graph and analyze binomial and normal distributions.

Materials/Resources

- Lesson Masters 13-9A and 13-9B
- Resource Masters 264–266

HOMEWORK

Suggestions for Assignment

- Questions 1–24
- Question 25 (extra credit)
- Self-Test

Local Standards

1 Warm-Up

In 1–9, suppose two evenly matched teams A and B play each other eight times in a season. What is the probability that team A will win the given number of games? Assume that winning or losing each game does not affect the probability of winning future games.

1. 0 $\frac{1}{256}$
2. 1 $\frac{8}{256} = \frac{1}{32}$
3. 2 $\frac{28}{256} = \frac{7}{64}$
4. 3 $\frac{56}{256} = \frac{7}{32}$
5. 4 $\frac{70}{256} = \frac{35}{128}$
6. 5 $\frac{56}{256} = \frac{7}{32}$
7. 6 $\frac{28}{256} = \frac{7}{64}$
8. 7 $\frac{8}{256} = \frac{1}{32}$
9. 8 $\frac{1}{256}$

(*Note:* Graphing this distribution (number of games won, *P*(winning that many games)) yields a set of points that begin to look somewhat like a normal distribution.)

Lesson

13-9 Binomial and Normal Distributions

Vocabulary

probability function, probability distribution
binomial probability distribution, binomial distribution
normal distribution
normal curve
standard normal curve
standardized scores

▸ **BIG IDEA** As the number of trials of a binomial experiment increases, the graphs of the probabilities of each event and the relative frequencies of each event approaches a distribution called a *normal distribution*.

Mental Math

Tell whether each graph is the graph of a function.

a. the image of $y = \sin x$ under R_{90} no

b. the image of $y = \cos x$ under $r_{x\text{-axis}}$ yes

c. the image of $x = 12$ under $T_{2,8}$ no

d. the image of $x = 12$ under R_3 yes

A Binomial Distribution with Six Points

Let $P(n)$ = the probability of n heads in 5 tosses of a fair coin. Then the domain of P is $\{0, 1, 2, 3, 4, 5\}$. By the Binomial Probability Theorem, and because the probability of heads = the probability of tails = $\frac{1}{2}$,

$$P(n) = \left(\frac{1}{2}\right)^5\binom{5}{n} = \frac{1}{32}\binom{5}{n}.$$

GUIDED

Example 1

a. Copy and complete the table shown below.

b. Graph and label the coordinates of the six points $(n, P(n))$.

Solution See the Additional Answers section at the back of the book.

a. Use the formula for $P(n)$ given above to fill in the second row.

n = Number of Heads	0	1	2	3	4	5
P(n) = Probability of n Heads in 5 Tosses of a Fair Coin	$\frac{1}{32}\binom{5}{0} = \frac{1}{32}$	$\frac{1}{32}\binom{5}{?} = \underline{\ ?\ }$	?	?	?	?

b. The points are graphed below. Fill in the missing coordinates with values from the table in Part a.

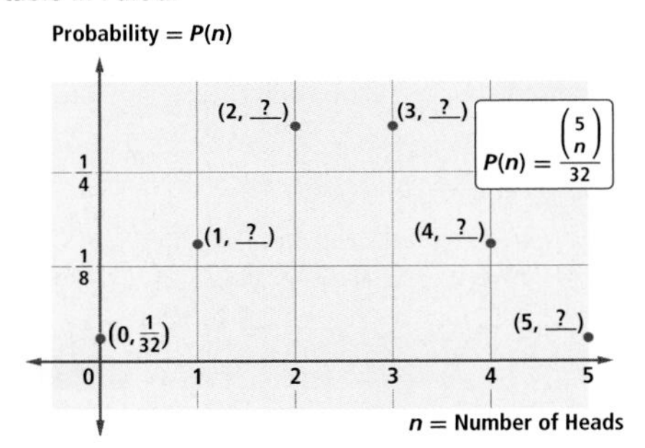

Background

A binomial distribution is a probability function that arises from binomial coefficients, so it is a natural extension of Lesson 13-7. The normal distribution is the limit of the binomial.

This lesson should be considered more as a reading lesson than as a lesson for mastery. It provides an opportunity for students to learn how relatively advanced mathematics is used in applications that may affect their everyday lives. But there is not enough practice here to master these ideas. The next course, UCSMP *Functions, Statistics, and Trigonometry,* has much more detail.

A binomial distribution with six points The shape of a binomial distribution, which comes from graphing binomial probabilities, is discussed first. Notice that the graph of the distribution in Example 1 has only the semblance of the shape of the normal curve because there are only 5 tosses. But with 10 tosses, as

P is a *probability function*. A **probability function**, or **probability distribution**, is a function that maps a set of events onto their probabilities. Because the function P results from calculations of binomial probabilities, it is called a **binomial probability distribution,** or simply a **binomial distribution.**

A Binomial Distribution with Eleven Points

If a fair coin is tossed 10 times, the possible numbers of heads are 0, 1, 2, ..., 10, so there are 11 points in the graph of the corresponding probability function. Again, by the Binomial Probability Theorem with equally likely events, the probability $P(x)$ of tossing x heads is given by

$$P(x) = \left(\frac{1}{2}\right)^{10}\binom{10}{x} = \frac{1}{1024}\binom{10}{x}.$$

The 11 probabilities are easy to calculate because the numerators in the fractions are the numbers in the 10th row of Pascal's triangle. That is, they are binomial coefficients.

n = Number of Heads	0	1	2	3	4	5	6	7	8	9	10
$P(x)$ = Probability of x Heads	$\frac{1}{1024}$ ≈ 0.001	$\frac{10}{1024}$ ≈ 0.01	$\frac{45}{1024}$ ≈ 0.04	$\frac{120}{1024}$ ≈ 0.12	$\frac{210}{1024}$ ≈ 0.21	$\frac{252}{1024}$ ≈ 0.25	$\frac{210}{1024}$ ≈ 0.21	$\frac{120}{1024}$ ≈ 0.12	$\frac{45}{1024}$ ≈ 0.04	$\frac{10}{1024}$ ≈ 0.01	$\frac{1}{1024}$ ≈ 0.001

The binomial distribution in the table is graphed at the right. Closely examine this 11-point graph of $P(x) = \frac{1}{1024}\binom{10}{x}$, along with the table of values. The individual probabilities are all less than $\frac{1}{4}$. Notice how unlikely it is to get 0 heads or 10 heads in a row. (The probability for each is less than $\frac{1}{1000}$.) Even for 9 heads in 10 tosses, the probability is less than $\frac{1}{1000}$. Like the graph of the 6-point probability function $P(n) = \frac{1}{32}\binom{5}{n}$ on the previous page, this 11-point graph has a vertical line of symmetry.

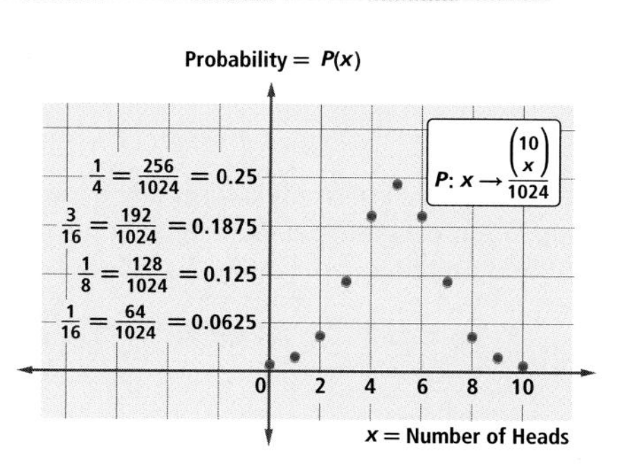

Normal Distributions

As the number of tosses of a fair coin is increased, the points on the graph more closely outline a curve shaped like a bell. On the next page, this bell-shaped curve is positioned so that it is reflection-symmetric to the y-axis and its equation is simplest. Its equation is $y = \frac{1}{\sqrt{2\pi}}e^{\left(\frac{-x^2}{2}\right)}$.

2 Teaching

Notes on the Lesson

We suggest reading the lesson and discussing the Questions simultaneously. Read the first section and then discuss Question 1. Read the section "A Binomial Distribution with Eleven Points" and then discuss Questions 2–4. Then read about the normal curve and the graph of test scores and then discuss Questions 5–7. Finally, work through Example 3 and discuss Questions 8–10.

on page 923, we see the bell shape of the normal curve begin to appear. That shape is then extended to the normal distribution.

In the equation for the standard normal distribution, $y = \frac{1}{\sqrt{2\pi}}e^{\left(\frac{-x^2}{2}\right)}$, students may not realize that $\left(\frac{-x^2}{2}\right)$ is an exponent. The appearance of x^2 rather than x ensures that the distribution is symmetric to the y-axis. The exponent is always negative, which means that the distribution will act somewhat like the graph of $y = e^x$ in Quadrant II; that is, it will hug the x-axis after a short while. The x-axis is an asymptote at both ends of the curve. The coefficient $\frac{1}{\sqrt{2\pi}}$ scales the graph so that the area under the curve is 1.

Additional Example

Example 1 Let n = the number of heads and $P(n)$ = the probability of getting n heads in six tosses of a fair coin.

a. Copy and complete the following table.

n	$P(n)$
0	$\frac{1}{64}\binom{6}{0} = \frac{1}{64}$
1	$\frac{1}{64}\binom{6}{?} = \underline{\ ?\ }$ 1; $\frac{3}{32}$
2	? $\frac{1}{64}\binom{6}{2} = \frac{15}{64}$
3	? $\frac{1}{64}\binom{6}{3} = \frac{5}{16}$
4	? $\frac{1}{64}\binom{6}{4} = \frac{15}{64}$
5	? $\frac{1}{64}\binom{6}{5} = \frac{3}{32}$
6	? $\frac{1}{64}\binom{6}{6} = \frac{1}{64}$

b. Graph and label the coordinates of the seven points $(n, P(n))$.

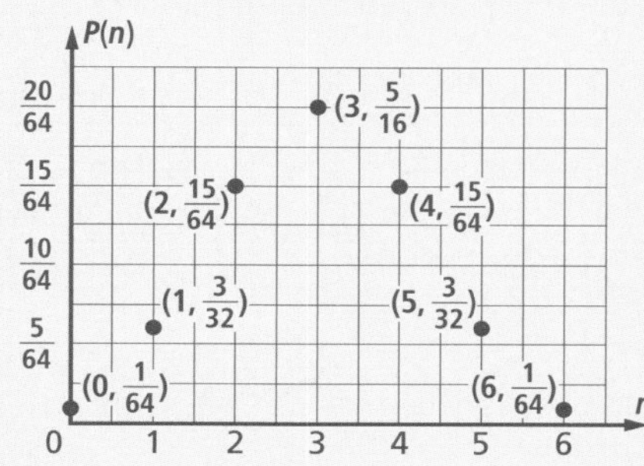

Additional Examples

Example 2 According to a recent study, the heights of women in the United States are approximately normally distributed with a mean of 63.5 inches and a standard deviation of 2.5 inches. What percent of women in the United States are shorter than 61.0 inches? 15.9%

Example 3 SAT scores are standardized to a mean of 500 and a standard deviation of 100. What percent of the scores is expected to be between 300 and 700? 95.4%

The function that determines this graph is called a **normal distribution**, and the curve is called a **normal curve**. Notice that its equation involves the famous constants $e \approx 2.718$ and $\pi \approx 3.14$. Every normal curve is the image of the graph at the right under a composite of translations and scale changes. Thus, the graph of $y = \frac{1}{\sqrt{2\pi}} e^{\left(\frac{-x^2}{2}\right)}$  is sometimes called the **standard normal curve**.

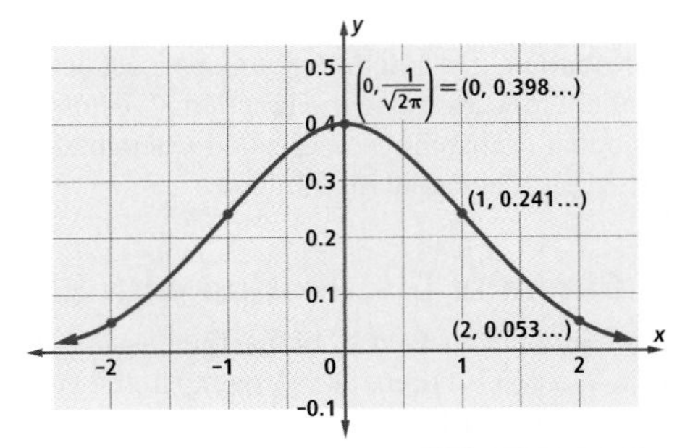

STOP QY1

In any distribution whose graph is a normal curve, the values fall in certain intervals based on the mean μ and standard deviation σ as shown in the graph below. For example, 34.1% of the function values fall between the mean and 1 standard deviation above the mean.

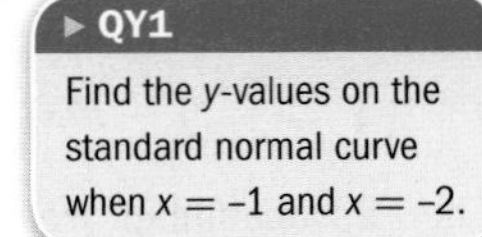

QY1

Find the y-values on the standard normal curve when $x = -1$ and $x = -2$.

Normal Distribution Percentages

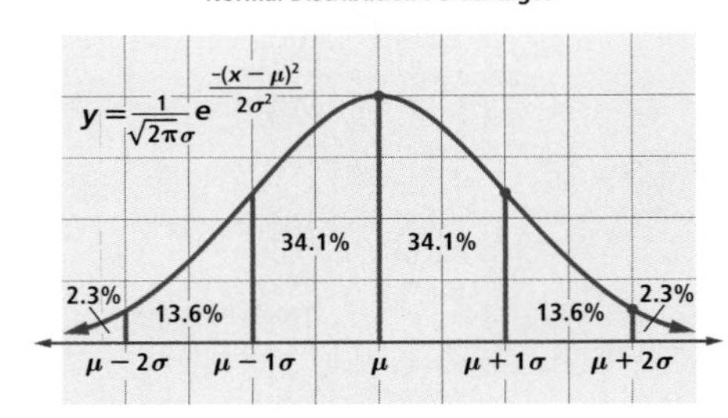

Normal curves are models for many natural phenomena. If you know the mean and standard deviation, you can determine other information about a normally distributed data set.

Example 2

The heights of men in the United States are approximately normally distributed with a mean of 69.2 inches and a standard deviation of 2.8 inches. What percent of men in the U.S. are taller than 72.0 inches?

Solution The difference between the mean height 69.2 inches and the given height 72.0 inches is 2.8 inches. This value is exactly one standard deviation for these data. So, 72.0 inches is 1 standard deviation above the mean, or $\mu + 1\sigma$. From the graph above, notice that to the right of $\mu + 1\sigma$ are 13.6% + 2.3% = 15.9% of the normally-distributed heights. So, about 15.9% of men are taller than 72.0 inches.

STOP QY2

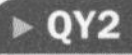

QY2

It is estimated that 2.3% of the men in the U.S. are less than a certain height in inches. What is that height?

ENGLISH LEARNERS

Vocabulary Development

There are more than the usual number of new terms in this lesson and many of them are similar, so be sure to cover them very carefully. Have students note that *probability function* and *probability distribution* mean the same thing—a function that maps a set of events onto their probabilities. When the values of a probability function are proportional to binomial coefficients, it is called a *binomial probability distribution*, or *binomial distribution*. The normal distribution, or normal curve, is so named because it has the same symmetrical shape in every case. In any distribution that yields a normal curve, the values fall in certain intervals based on the mean and standard deviation. Be sure to emphasize the three diagrams of normal curves in the lesson. *Standardized scores,* as the name suggests, are based on the number of standard deviations scored above or below a mean score.

Normal curves are often good mathematical models for the distribution of scores on an exam. The graph at the right shows an actual distribution of scores on a 40-question test given to 209 geometry students. (It was a hard test!) A possible corresponding normal curve is shown.

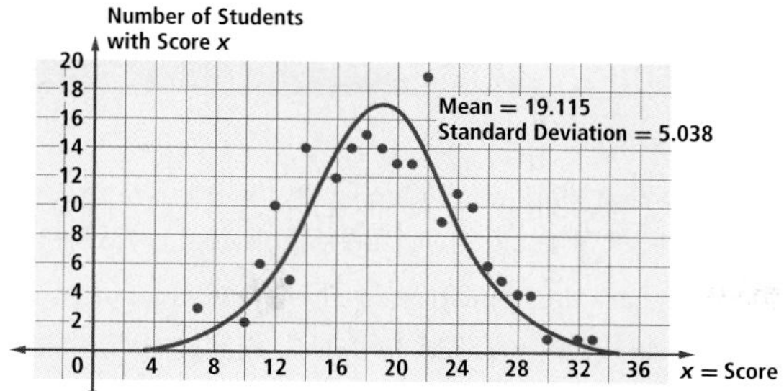

On some tests, scores are **standardized**. This means that a person's score is not the number of correct answers, but is converted so that it lies in a normal distribution with a predetermined mean and standard deviation. Standardized tests make it easy to evaluate an individual score relative to the mean, but not to other individual scores.

Example 3

SAT scores are standardized to a historic mean of 500 and a standard deviation of 100. What percent of the scores are expected to be between 400 and 700?

Solution Find out how many standard deviations each score, 400 and 700, is from the mean, 500.

$$500 - 400 = 100 \text{ and } 700 - 500 = 200$$

So, a score of 400 is 1 standard deviation below the mean and a score of 700 is 2 standard deviations above the mean.

Refer to the Normal Distribution Percentages graph on the previous page. The percent of scores between $\mu - 1\sigma$ and $\mu + 2\sigma$ is $34.1\% + 34.1\% + 13.6\% = 81.8\%$.

About 81.8% of SAT scores are expected to be between 400 and 700.

The normal distribution is an appropriate topic with which to end this book, because it involves so many of the ideas you have studied in it. The distribution is a function. Its equation involves squares, square roots, π, e, and negative exponents. Its graph is the composite of a translation and scale change image of the curve with equation $y = \frac{1}{\sqrt{2\pi}} e^{\left(\frac{-x^2}{2}\right)}$. It models real data and shows a probability distribution that is used on tests that help to determine which colleges some people will attend. It shows how interrelated and important the ideas of mathematics are.

Accommodating the Learner ↑

With students working in groups, give each group six dice. Have them toss the dice and count the even numbers that appear. Have them run the experiment at least 100 times. Let $P(e)$ be the relative frequency that e even numbers appears in a toss of the six dice. Then have them graph $(e, P(e))$ and tell how close the graph is to a normal distribution. Answers vary. Check students' work.

Accommodating the Learner ↓

Review with students the Binomial Probability Theorem and discuss with them how the theorem is used to calculate the entries in the two tables in the lesson.

Notes on the Lesson

Some states in the United States are "SAT (Scholastic Aptitude Test) states." Others are "ACT (American College Testing) states." Often, people in each type of state are surprised to learn that the test most of their students take is not taken by students in all states. Generally, the center of the United States relies more on the ACT, while the coasts rely more on the SAT. About 1,422,000 students in the high school graduating class of 2008 took the ACT. The table below shows the distribution of composite scores. You might have students graph this distribution and see how close it looks to a normal distribution. It is quite close to a normal distribution with mean between 20 and 21 and standard deviation of about 5; the actual mean was about 21.1. See Question 14 for a summary of similar data.

Score	Number of Students	Score	Number of Students
36	428	18	99,925
35	2,872	17	91,454
34	6,358	16	81,654
33	10,583	15	70,135
32	15,555	14	56,097
31	21,423	13	39,305
30	28,948	12	22,021
29	35,725	11	8,263
28	44,964	10	2,152
27	54,298	9	678
26	63,329	8	226
25	74,021	7	84
24	84,038	6	28
23	92,044	5	12
22	99,676	4	3
21	105,855	3	1
20	106,902	2	0
19	102,884	1	0

3 Assignment

Recommended Assignment

- Questions 1–24
- Question 25 (extra credit)
- Self-Test

Notes on the Questions

Question 11 The equation for a normal curve with mean μ and standard deviation σ is $y = \frac{1}{\sigma\sqrt{2\pi}} e^{\frac{-(x-\mu)^2}{2\sigma^2}}$. Students can look this equation up on the Internet, or you can refer them to Project 1 on page 928, where the equation is given in Part f.

Question 13 Because of the ways in which grade-level tests are standardized, they do not usually give an accurate reading. For example, a 7th grader who is scoring at the 11th-grade level in mathematics would likely do very poorly on a test of 11th-grade mathematics. The score of the 7th grader means only that this 7th grader is in a high percentile of all 7th graders of those students on whom the test was standardized.

Question 14 Point out to students that ACT scores are always whole numbers.

Additional Answers

1b. $\frac{5}{32}$; Answers vary. Sample: $P(4)$ could represent the pobability of getting 4 heads in 5 tosses of a fair coin.

13-9A Lesson Master

Questions on SPUR Objectives
See Student Edition pages 934–937 for objectives.

USES Objective I

1. The PSAT is a standardized test taken by high school sophomores and juniors. The mean and standard deviation of scores for one particular year are shown in the table at the right.

	10th	11th
Mean	44.1	49.3
S.D.	11.1	11.3

   a. The top 2.3% of juniors are 2 standard deviations or more above the mean. What scores did they get? 71.9 and higher

   b. What was the range of scores for the middle 68.2% of sophomores? 33.0 to 55.2

2. On a particular section of interstate, the traffic is moving with a mean speed of 69 miles per hour and a standard deviation of 2 miles per hour.

   a. If the speed limit is 65 mph, about what percentage of the traffic is moving faster than the speed limit? 97.7%

   b. A police officer is targeting the fastest 16% of cars. How fast are these cars traveling? 71 mph and faster

REPRESENTATIONS Objective K

3. Consider an experiment where a fair coin is flipped eight times.

   a. Find the probability $P(n)$ of getting n heads for $n = 0, 1, 2, ..., 8$. Complete the table below.

n	0	1	2	3	4	5	6	7	8
$P(n)$	$\frac{1}{256}$	$\frac{8}{256}$	$\frac{28}{256}$	$\frac{56}{256}$	$\frac{70}{256}$	$\frac{56}{256}$	$\frac{28}{256}$	$\frac{8}{256}$	$\frac{1}{256}$

   b. Graph the function P at the right.

   c. Explain why P is a *binomial distribution*.
   Answers vary. Sample: The function values of P are binomial probabilities.

4. The scores of 242 students on a standardized test are shown in the graph at the right.
   Answers vary. Samples are given.

   a. Sketch a normal curve through the data.

   b. Use your curve to approximate the mean. 20.5

P(n)
0.5
0.25
0 1 2 3 4 5 6 7 8 9 10 n

Number of Students
30 25 20 15 10 5 0
5 10 15 20 25 30 35 40 45 50
Score

622 Advanced Algebra

Questions

COVERING THE IDEAS

1. Let $P(n) = \frac{1}{32} \cdot \binom{5}{n}$.
   a. What kind of function is P? binomial probability distribution
   b. Find $P(4)$ and describe what it could represent. See margin.
2. What are the domain and range of the function $P: x \to \frac{1}{1024} \cdot \binom{10}{x}$?
3. If a fair coin is tossed 10 times, what is the probability of getting exactly 4 heads? $\frac{210}{1024} \approx 0.21$
4. Let $P(n)$ = the probability of getting n heads in 7 tosses of a fair coin. See margin.
   a. Make a table of values for P.
   b. Graph P.
5. Write an equation for the standard normal curve. $y = \frac{1}{\sqrt{2\pi}} e^{\left(\frac{-x^2}{2}\right)}$
6. Describe one application of normal curves.
7. a. What does it mean for scores to be standardized?
   b. What is one advantage of doing this?
8. Approximately what percent of scores on a normal curve are within 2 standard deviations of the mean? 95.4%
9. Refer to Example 2. What percent of men in the U.S. are between 66.4 and 72.0 inches tall? 68.2%
10. Approximately what percent of people score below 300 on an SAT test with mean 500 and standard deviation 100? 2.3%

2. domain: {0, 1, 2, 3, 4, 5, 6, 7, 8, 9, 10}; range: {0.001, 0.01, 0.04, 0.12, 0.21, 0.25}

6. Answers vary. Sample: A normal curve could represent the distribution of class grades on the most recent math test.

7a. Standardized scores are adjusted so they lie in a normal distribution with a predetermined mean and standard deviation.

7b. Standardized scores make it easy to evaluate an individual score relative to the mean.

APPLYING THE MATHEMATICS

11. Graph the normal curve with mean 50 and standard deviation 10. See margin.
12. If you repeatedly toss 8 fair coins, about what percent of the time do you expect to get from 4 to 6 heads? 60.16%
13. Some tests are standardized so that the mean is the grade level at which the test is taken and the standard deviation is 1 grade level. So, for students who take a test at the beginning of 10th grade, the mean is 10.0 and the standard deviation is 1.0.
    a. On such a test taken at the beginning of 10th grade, what percent of students are expected to score below 9.0 grade level? 15.9%
    b. If a test is taken in the middle of 8th grade (grade level 8.5), what percent of students are expected to score between 7.5 and 9.5? 68.2%
14. For the graduating class of 2004, total ACT scores for seniors ranged from 1 to 36 with a mean of 20.9 and a standard deviation of 4.8. What percent of students had an ACT score above 25? 15.9%

Additional Answers

4a.

n	$P(n)$
0	0.0078
1	0.0547
2	0.1641
3	0.2734
4	0.2734
5	0.1641
6	0.0547
7	0.0078

4b. **The Probability $P(n)$ of Getting n Heads in 7 Tosses of a Fair Coin**

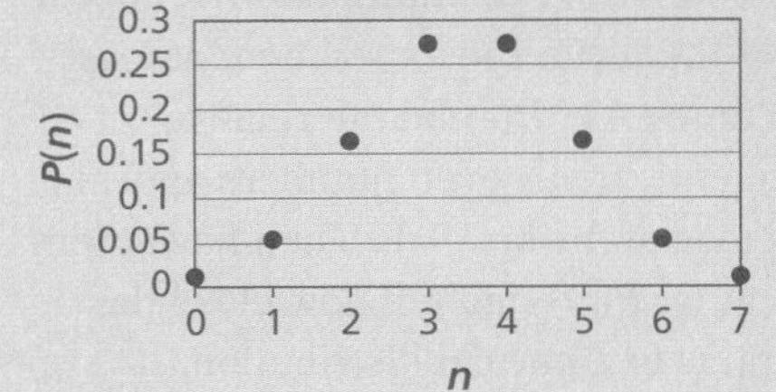

15. **Fill in the Blanks** Assume that the lengths of jumps of boys on a track team are normally distributed with a mean of 18 feet and a standard deviation of 1 foot. In a normal distribution, 0.13% of the jumps lie more than 3 standard deviations away from the mean in each direction. This implies that about 1 out of __?__ boys will have a jump over __?__. 770; 21 ft

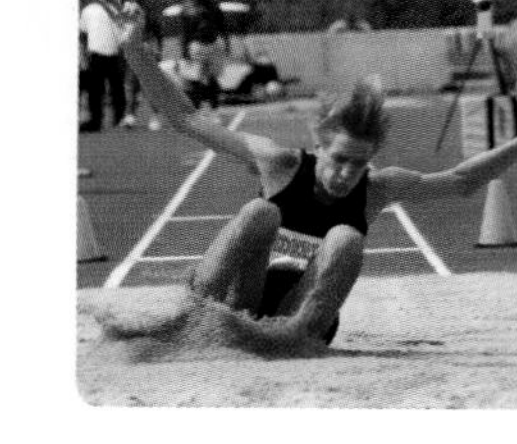

16. Let $y = \frac{1}{\sqrt{2\pi}} e^{\left(\frac{-x^2}{2}\right)}$. Estimate y to the nearest thousandth when $x = 1.5$. 0.130

17. A game has prizes distributed normally with a mean of \$60 and a standard deviation of \$20. If you play the game 10 times, what is the probability that you win more than \$100 at least 3 times? 0.00129

REVIEW

18. In the Texas Lotto, a participant picks 6 numbers from 1 to 54 to win. What is the probability of *not* winning the Texas Lotto? **(Lesson 13-8)**

19. **True or False** The probability of getting exactly 50 heads in 100 tosses of a fair coin is less than 5%. Justify your answer. **(Lesson 13-7)**

20. Evaluate ${}_nC_0$. **(Lesson 13-6)** 1

21. Expand $\left(6 - \frac{x}{2}\right)^5$. **(Lesson 13-6)**

22. A hot air balloon is sighted from two points on level ground at the same elevation on opposite sides of the balloon. From point P the angle of elevation is 21°. From point Q the angle of elevation is 15°. If points P and Q are 10.2 kilometers apart, how high is the balloon? **(Lessons 10-7, 10-1)** 1.61 km

23. Simplify $\sqrt{16} \cdot \sqrt{25} + \sqrt{-16} \cdot \sqrt{25} + \sqrt{-16} \cdot \sqrt{-25} + \sqrt{16} \cdot \sqrt{-25}$. **(Lessons 6-8, 6-2)** $40i$

24. Give an equation for the right angle AOB graphed at the right. **(Lesson 6-2)** $x = -|y|$

18. $\frac{25{,}827{,}164}{25{,}827{,}165} \approx 0.999999$

19. false; $\binom{100}{50}\left(\frac{1}{2}\right)^{100} \approx 0.0796 \approx 8\%$

21. $7776 - 3240x + 540x^2 - 45x^3 + \frac{15}{8}x^4 - \frac{1}{32}x^5$

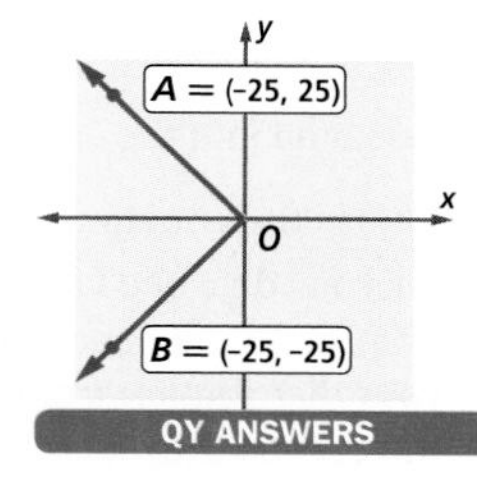

EXPLORATION

25. Together with some other students or using a random number generator, simulate the tossing of 12 coins and count the number of heads. Run the simulation at least 200 times. Let $P(h)$ = the number of times h heads appear out of 12.
    a. Graph the points $(h, P(h))$. How close is $P(h)$ to a normal distribution? See margin.
    b. What is the mean number of heads of the distribution? about 6
    c. Estimate the standard deviation of the distribution. about 1.5

QY ANSWERS

1. ≈ 0.24; ≈ 0.05
2. 2.3% of men are two standard deviations below the mean, and because one standard deviation equals 2.8 in., then the height is $69.2 - 5.6 = 63.6$ in.

Notes on the Questions

Question 23 Be sure that students do not get the right answer for the wrong reason.

Question 25 You might arrange the class into groups of four or five students. The results of all groups can be combined to answer the questions. It also could be simulated on a computer.

4 Wrap-Up

Ongoing Assessment

Have students refer to the graph of the normal curve on page 924. Then give students this problem: 600 students are given a test in which the mean score is 70 and the standard deviation is 15. Have students write at least three conclusions that can be drawn. Students should provide reasonable conclusions based on the normal curve.

Project Update

Project 1, *A Skewed Probability Distribution,* on page 928 relates to the content of this lesson.

Additional Answers

11.

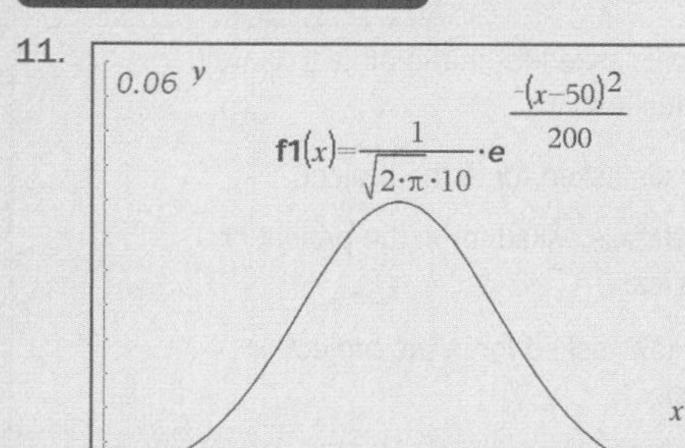

25a. Answers vary. Sample:

The Probability $P(h)$ of Obtaining h Heads When Tossing 12 Coins

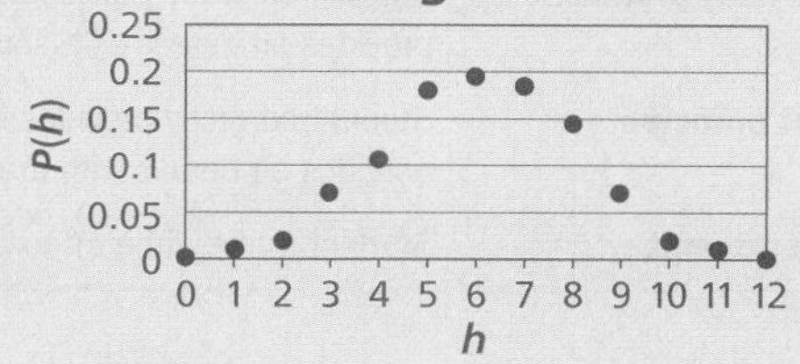

The graph is very close to a normal distribution.

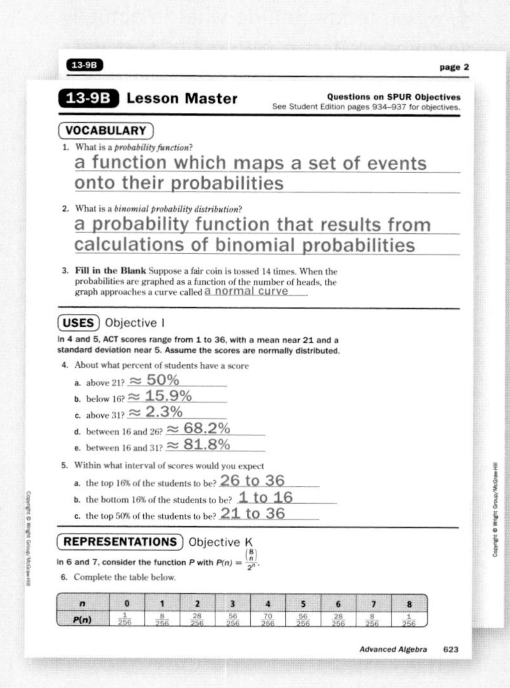

13-9B page 2

13-9B Lesson Master

Questions on SPUR Objectives
See Student Edition pages 934–937 for objectives.

VOCABULARY

1. What is a *probability function*?
a function which maps a set of events onto their probabilities

2. What is a *binomial probability distribution*?
a probability function that results from calculations of binomial probabilities

3. **Fill in the Blank** Suppose a fair coin is tossed 14 times. When the probabilities are graphed as a function of the number of heads, the graph approaches a curve called a normal curve.

USES Objective I

In 4 and 5, ACT scores range from 1 to 36, with a mean near 21 and a standard deviation near 5. Assume the scores are normally distributed.

4. About what percent of students have a score
   a. above 21? ≈ 50%
   b. below 16? ≈ 15.9%
   c. above 31? ≈ 2.3%
   d. between 16 and 26? ≈ 68.2%
   e. between 16 and 31? ≈ 81.8%

5. Within what interval of scores would you expect
   a. the top 16% of the students to be? 26 to 36
   b. the bottom 16% of the students to be? 1 to 16
   c. the top 50% of the students to be? 21 to 36

REPRESENTATIONS Objective K

In 6 and 7, consider the function P with $P(n) = \frac{\binom{8}{n}}{2^n}$.

6. Complete the table below.

n	0	1	2	3	4	5	6	7	8
$P(n)$	$\frac{1}{256}$	$\frac{8}{256}$	$\frac{28}{256}$	$\frac{56}{256}$	$\frac{70}{256}$	$\frac{56}{256}$	$\frac{28}{256}$	$\frac{8}{256}$	$\frac{1}{256}$

Advanced Algebra 623

Chapter 13

The projects relate to the content of the lessons of this chapter as follows:

Project	Lesson(s)
1	13-9
2	13-2
3	13-2
4	13-5

1 A Skewed Probability Distribution

If students do not know the meaning of *skewed,* explain that a skewed distribution is one that is distorted, or misshapen.

2 Convergent and Divergent Geometric Series

Many students will gain more insight by using paper-and-pencil calculations rather than technology in Parts a and b. For example, in Part b with $r = \frac{1}{2}$,

$$S_{100} = \frac{2\left(1 - \frac{1}{2^{100}}\right)}{1 - \frac{1}{2}} = 4\left(1 - \frac{1}{2^{100}}\right).$$

By examining the form of the last expression, students will see that S_{100} is very close to 4 but not quite equal to 4. If students use technology, the answers for both S_{50} and S_{100} will be rounded to 4, which tends to hide what is actually going on in Part a. You might suggest calculating S_{35} and S_{75} so that students observe how the sign of S_n can vary when r is negative. In both Parts and b, check that students use both positive and negative values for r.

Chapter 13 Projects

1 A Skewed Probability Distribution

Use random numbers and technology to simulate the tossing of a fair six-sided die. Call an outcome of 6 a success and an outcome of any number less than 6 a failure.

a. Simulate tossing the die 100 times. How many outcomes were successful?

b. Repeat Part a 100 times. Record the number successes in each set of 100 tosses.

c. Calculate the relative frequency of each number of successes. For example, if you had 30 successes in 12 of the trials, the relative frequency of 30 successes would be $\frac{12}{100}$ or 0.12.

d. Plot the points (number of successes, relative frequency of that number of successes) and draw a smooth curve that roughly models all the points.

e. Compute the mean μ and standard deviation σ of your data set from Part b.

f. Substitute your mean and standard deviation into the equation $y = \frac{1}{\sigma\sqrt{2\pi}}e^{\frac{-(x-\mu)^2}{2\sigma^2}}$.

This is the equation for the normal curve for your data set. Graph this equation on a graphing utility and sketch the graph onto your distribution from Part d. Compare the curves. How close did you come to sketching the normal curve?

2 Convergent and Divergent Geometric Series

In Lesson 13-2, you were given a formula for the sum of a geometric series.

a. Choose five different values for r such that $|r| > 1$. For each of these ratios, consider the geometric series with constant ratio r and first term $g_1 = 2$. Determine the value of each of these geometric series for 10 terms, 50 terms, and 100 terms. Organize you data into a chart.

b. Repeat Part a for five different values for r such that $|r| < 1$.

c. A sequence whose elements approach or draw near to a particular value is said to *converge*. For example, the sequence p with $p_n = \frac{1}{n}$ converges to 0. The word *diverge* means "does not converge." For example, the sequence $S_n = n^2$ diverges, as n^2 becomes larger than any particular value. Using your answers to Parts a and b, make a conjecture about the values of r for which a geometric series will converge.

d. Think about the formulas for geometric series. Write a mathematical argument to support your conjecture in Part c.

Project Rubric

Advanced	Student correctly provides all of the details asked for in the project as well as additional correct independent conclusions.
Proficient	Student correctly provides all of the details asked for in the project.
Partially proficient	Student correctly provides some of the details asked for in the project or provides all details with some inaccuracies.
Not proficient	Student correctly provides few of the details asked for in the project or provides all details with many inaccuracies.
No attempt	Student makes little or no attempt to complete the project.

3 The Koch Curve

The snowflake curve called a *Koch curve* results from the following recursive process.

Begin with an equilateral triangle. To create the $(n + 1)$st figure, take each segment on the nth figure, trisect it, and replace it with the four congruent segments shown at the right below.

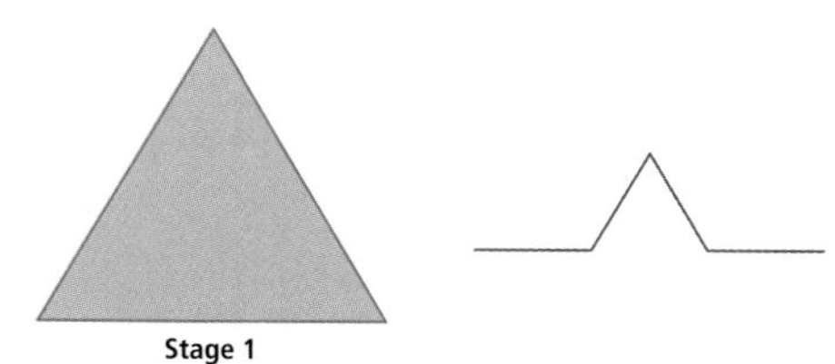

Stage 1

a. Draw the first four stages of the Koch snowflake curve. (*Hint:* The second stage looks like a six-pointed star.)

b. Count the number of segments in the figure at each stage and record this number in a table like the one below. Imagine repeating this process forever. How many segments would the nth figure have? Visualize and describe how the figure changes at each stage.

Stage	1	2	3	4	...	n
Number of Segments	3	?	?	?	...	?

c. Let the length of a side of the first triangle be 1. Find the perimeter of the Koch curve at each stage and record it in a table like the one below. Generalize the pattern to find the perimeter of the figure at the nth stage.

Stage	1	2	3	4	...	n
Perimeter	3	?	?	?	...	?

d. How does the area of the snowflake grow? Fill in a table like the one below to find out. To be able to generalize the pattern, leave the answers in radical form.

Stage	1	2	3	4	...	n
Area	$\frac{\sqrt{3}}{4}$	?	?	?	...	?

e. Suppose the process for creating the Koch curve is repeated infinitely many times. Is the perimeter of the snowflake finite or infinite? Why? Is the area finite or infinite? Why?

f. The Koch curve is an example of a *fractal*. Look in other books and copy an example of another fractal.

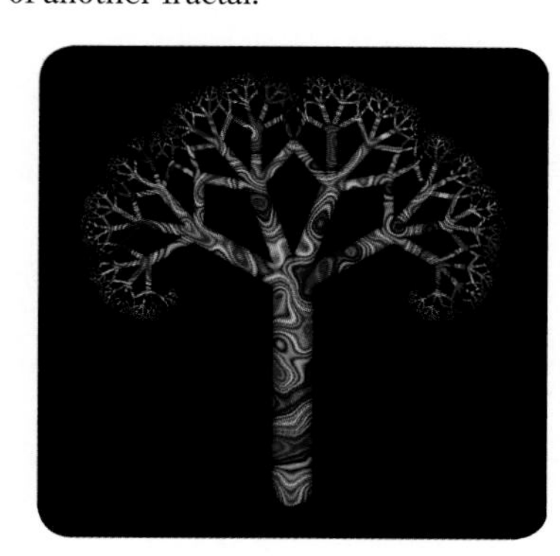

4 Famous Mathematical Triangles

Pascal's Triangle is not the only interesting mathematical triangular array. Two others are Euler's Triangle and the Leibniz Harmonic Triangle. Research each triangle. Write the first five rows of each triangle and find out its rule for writing additional rows. Compare and contrast each triangle to Pascal's Triangle.

Notes

3 The Koch Curve

Be sure to provide dot paper for the drawing activity in Part a. If students want to see what the figures look like without all the dots, they can use tracing paper to copy the paper figures. Most students will be surprised by the results in Parts c, d, and e. It is fairly easy to see how the construction can be modified to yield other similar results. The conclusions in Part e use ideas of convergence, which are considered in Project 2.

4 Famous Mathematical Triangles

Students will find many sites on the Internet to help them research these two triangles. You might have them prepare a poster to show the triangles and include the rules for writing additional rows.

Sample answers for projects are in the Solution Manual in the Electronic Teacher's Edition.

Chapter 13

Summary and Vocabulary

The Summary gives an overview of the entire chapter and provides an opportunity for students to consider the material as a whole. Thus, the Summary can be used to help students relate and unify the concepts presented in the chapter.

Vocabulary words and symbols are listed by lesson to provide a checklist of concepts that students must know. Emphasize to students that they should read the vocabulary list carefully before starting the Self-Test on pages 932–933. If students do not understand the meaning of a vocabulary word, they should refer back to the indicated lesson.

Theorems and Properties covered in the chapter are listed below the Summary with page references included to lead students back to the location in the chapter where the theorem or property is stated.

Chapter 13 Summary and Vocabulary

- Some sums and products are denoted by special symbols. For instance, the sum $x_1 + x_2 + \ldots + x_n$ is represented by $\sum_{i=1}^{n} x_i$. The product $n(n-1)(n-2) \cdot \ldots \cdot 2 \cdot 1$ is represented by ***n*! (*n* factorial)**.

- A **series** is an indicated sum of terms of a sequence. Values of finite arithmetic or geometric series may be calculated from the following formulas:

  For an **arithmetic sequence** $a_1, a_2, \ldots, a_n$ with common difference d:

  $$\sum_{i=1}^{n} a_i = \frac{1}{2}n(a_1 + a_n) = \frac{n}{2}(2a_1 + (n-1)d).$$

  For a finite **geometric sequence** $g_1, g_2, \ldots, g_n$ with common ratio r:

  $$\sum_{i=1}^{n} g_i = g_1\frac{(1-r^n)}{1-r} = g_1\frac{(r^n-1)}{r-1}.$$

- The **mean absolute deviation** and the **standard deviation** of a data set are measures of the spread, or dispersion, of the data in the set. For the data set $\{x_1, \ldots, x_n\}$, the mean μ is $\frac{1}{n}\sum_{i=1}^{n} x_i$, the mean absolute deviation is $\frac{1}{n}\sum_{i=1}^{n} |x_i - \mu|$, and the standard deviation is $\sqrt{\frac{1}{n}\sum_{i=1}^{n}(x_i - \mu)^2}$.

- **Pascal's Triangle** is a 2-dimensional sequence. The $(r+1)$st element in row n of Pascal's Triangle is denoted by $\binom{n}{r} = \frac{n!}{r!(n-r)!}$. The expression $\binom{n}{r}$, also denoted ${}_nC_r$, appears in several other important applications. It is the coefficient of $a^{n-r}b^r$ in the binomial expansion of $(a+b)^n$. It is the number of subsets, or **combinations**, with r elements taken from a set with n elements. If a situation consists of n trials with two outcomes, and the probability of one of these outcomes is p, then the probability of that outcome occurring exactly r times is $\binom{n}{r}p^r(1-p)^{n-r}$. This is a **binomial probability.**

Vocabulary

Lesson 13-1
*series
*arithmetic series
Σ, sigma
Σ-notation, sigma notation, summation notation
index variable, index

Lesson 13-2
*geometric series

Lesson 13-3
*mean
measure of center, measure of central tendency
absolute deviation
*mean absolute deviation, *m.a.d.*
*standard deviation, *s.d.*

Lesson 13-4
permutation
!, factorial symbol
n!
*combination

Lesson 13-5
*Pascal's Triangle

Lesson 13-6
*binomial coefficients

Lesson 13-7
trial
binomial experiment

Lesson 13-8
lottery
unit fraction

Lesson 13-9
probability function, probability distribution
binomial probability distribution, binomial distribution
normal distribution
normal curve
standard normal curve
standardized scores

- The number of **permutations** of n objects is $n!$. By using permutations and combinations, the probabilities of winning many games of pure chance, such as **lotteries**, can be calculated.
- Distributions of binomial probabilities are related to Pascal's Triangle. As the number of the row of Pascal's Triangle increases, the graph of the distribution takes on a shape more and more like a **normal curve**. Some tests are standardized so that graphs of their scores fit that shape. In a **normal distribution**, about 68% of the data are within 1 standard deviation of the mean, and about 95% are within 2 standard deviations. The equation $y = \frac{1}{\sigma\sqrt{2\pi}}e^{\frac{-(x-\mu)^2}{2\sigma^2}}$ for a normal distribution with mean μ and standard deviation σ combines many of the ideas of this book in one place.

Theorems

Arithmetic Series Formula (p. 871)
Finite Geometric Series Formula (p. 878)
Number of Permutations Theorem (p. 890)
Factorial Product Theorem (p. 890)
Combination Counting Formula (p. 892)
Pascal's Triangle Explicit Formula (p. 899)
Binomial Theorem (p. 905)
Binomial Probability Theorem (p. 913)

Summary and Vocabulary 931

Self-Test

For the development of mathematical competence, feedback and correction, along with the opportunity for practice, are necessary. The Self-Test provides the opportunity for feedback and correction; the Chapter Review provides additional opportunities for practice. We cannot overemphasize the importance of these end-of-chapter materials. It is at this point that the material gels for many students, allowing them to solidify skills and understanding. In general, student performance should improve after these pages.

Assign the Self-Test as a one-night assignment. Worked-out solutions for all questions are in the Selected Answers section of the student book. Encourage students to take the Self-Test honestly, grade themselves, and then be prepared to discuss the test in class.

Advise students to pay special attention to those Chapter Review questions (pages 934–937) that correspond to the questions they missed on the Self-Test.

Additional Answers

1. This is a series with 17 terms where each term is the fourth power of the index variable: $\sum_{i=1}^{17} i^4$.

2. $\sum_{j=0}^{100} 5j + 1 = \frac{n}{2}(a_1 + a_n) =$ $50.5(1 + 501) = 25{,}351$

3. $\mu = \frac{68 + 69 + 70 + 71 + 71 + 74 + 74}{7} =$ 71; m.a.d. $= \frac{1}{7}\sum_{i=1}^{7} |x_i - \mu| =$ $\frac{1}{7}(|68 - 71| + |69 - 71| + |70 - 71| + |71 - 71| + |71 - 71| + |74 - 71| + |74 - 71|) = \frac{12}{7}$;
$\sigma = \sqrt{\frac{1}{7}\sum_{i=1}^{7}(x_i - 71)^2} =$ $\sqrt{\frac{1}{7}(9 + 4 + 1 + 0 + 0 + 9 + 9)} =$ $\sqrt{\frac{32}{7}} \approx 2.14$

4. The mean team weight is 71 kg. If the standard deviation is 0, then $\sqrt{\frac{1}{7}\sum_{i=1}^{n}(x_i - 71)^2} = 0$, which means that each of the seven team members weighs 71 kg.

Chapter 13 Self-Test

Take this test as you would take a test in class. You will need a calculator. Then use the Selected Answers section in the back of the book to check your work.

1. Write using summation notation: $1^4 + 2^4 + 3^4 + \ldots + 17^4$. See margin.

2. Evaluate $\sum_{j=0}^{100}(5j + 1)$. See margin.

In 3 and 4, seven members of the Stern Rowing Team weigh in before a race. In kilograms, their weights are 68, 69, 70, 71, 71, 74, 74. 3–6. See margin.

3. Find the mean absolute deviation and the standard deviation of the Stern Team's weights.

4. Suppose the Jolly Rowing Team has seven members with a mean team weight identical to the Stern Team's. However, Jolly's standard deviation is 0. What are the seven weights of Jolly's team members?

5. Expand $(x^2 + 2)^5$ using the Binomial Theorem.

6. Find the coefficient of x^3 in the expansion of $(x + 3)^4$.

7. To celebrate the end of the school year, you buy a bowl with three scoops of ice cream from a shop that sells 17 different flavors. How many combinations of three different flavors are possible?

8. Tyler buys 9 different textbooks his freshman year of college. In how many ways can they be arranged on his bookshelf? By the Number of Permutations Theorem, there are 9! = 362,880 arrangements

7. $\binom{17}{3} = \frac{17!}{3!14!} = 680$ combinations

9. Evaluate. 9–12. See margin.
   a. $\binom{7}{4}$
   b. ${}_{164}C_4$

10. Calculate ${}_{37}C_{36}$ and explain why your answer makes sense.

11. Rewrite $117 \cdot 116 \cdot 115 \cdot 114 \cdot 113$ as a quotient of factorials.

12. a. Calculate $\binom{6}{3}$ and describe its position in Pascal's Triangle.
    b. Calculate the coefficient of p^5q^2 in the expansion of $(p + q)^7$ and describe its position in Pascal's Triangle.

13. Francisco gets a summer job on a trial basis. The first day he is paid \$30, the second day he is paid \$32, and he continues to get a \$2 raise each day. How much will Francisco be paid for 30 days of work?

14. a. Write the arithmetic series $3 + 7 + 11 + \ldots + 87$ using Σ-notation.
    b. Calculate the sum in Part a.

15. Find the sum of the integer powers of 5 from 5^0 to 5^{19}.

16. Find the sum of the first 20 terms of the sequence $\begin{cases} a_1 = 50 \\ a_n = \frac{4}{5}a_{n-1}, \text{ for integers } n \geq 2 \end{cases}$ to the nearest hundredth.

17. A fair coin is flipped five times. Find the probability of each outcome: 0 heads, 1 head, 2 heads, and so on to 5 heads.

13, 14a, 15–17. See the Additional Answers section at the back of the book.

14b. $\sum_{i=1}^{22}(4i - 1) = \frac{22}{2}(3 + 87) = 990$

Additional Answers

5. $(x^2 + 2)^5 = \sum_{r=0}^{5}\binom{5}{r}(x^2)^{5-r}2^r = x^{10} + 10x^8 + 40x^6 + 80x^4 + 80x^2 + 32$

6. The second term in the expansion is $\binom{4}{1}x^3(3)^1$, so the coefficient is $\binom{4}{1}(3) = 12$.

9a. $\binom{7}{4} = \frac{7!}{4!(7-4)!} = 35$

9b. ${}_{164}C_4 = \binom{164}{4} = 29{,}051{,}001$

10. ${}_{37}C_{36} = \binom{37}{36} = \frac{37!}{36!1!} = 37$. This makes sense because each subset of 36 elements is created by removing one element, and there are 37 possibilities.

11. $\frac{117 \cdot 116 \cdot 115 \cdot 114 \cdot 113}{1} \cdot \frac{112!}{112!} = \frac{117!}{112!}$

12a. $\binom{6}{3} = \frac{6!}{3!(6-3)!} = \frac{6 \cdot 5 \cdot 4}{6} = 20$; This number is the 4th element in row 6 of Pascal's Triangle.

12b. This is the 3rd term of the expansion with eight terms, so its coefficient is $\binom{7}{2} = \frac{7!}{2!(7-2)!} = \frac{7 \cdot 6}{2} = 21$. This value is the 3rd element in row 7 of Pascal's Triangle.

13, 14a, 15–17. Additional answers can be found at the back of the book.

18. In Lottery A, you need to match six numbers picked at random from the integers 1 to 50. In Lottery B, you need to match five numbers picked at random from the integers 1 to 70. Order does not matter in either lottery. In which lottery do you have a higher probability of winning? Explain your reasoning. See margin.

19. On a recent administration of the SAT test, the mean mathematics score was 515, and the standard deviation was 114.
    a. If test scores are normally distributed, about what percent of scores are within 1 standard deviation of the mean?
    b. To what range of scores on this test does your answer in Part a correspond?
    c. About what percent of scores are at or above 743?

19a. According to the Normal Distribution Percentages graph, 34.1% + 34.1% = 68.2% of scores are in this range.

19b. $\mu - \sigma = 515 - 114 = 401$ and $\mu + \sigma = 515 + 114 = 629$. So, the scores range from 401 to 629.

19c. $743 = 515 + 228 = \mu + 2\sigma$; therefore, about 2.3% of scores are at or above 743.

20. Suppose a coin is biased so that there is a 65% chance that the coin will show tails when tossed. Find the probability that there will be 2 heads in 3 tosses.

21. Let $P(n) = \frac{1}{2^6}\binom{6}{n}$. a–c. See margin.
    a. Make a table of values for this function.
    b. Graph this function.
    c. Describe in words what $P(n)$ represents in the context of a coin toss.

22. Find a value of x such that $\binom{n}{2} = \binom{n}{n-x}$ for all integers $n \geq 2$.

20. The probability of r heads in n tosses is $\binom{n}{r}p^r q^{n-r}$. Here, $p = 0.35$, $q = 0.65$, $n = 3$, and $r = 2$; $\binom{3}{2}(0.35)^2(0.65)^1 \approx 0.239$.

22. $\binom{n}{2} = \binom{n}{n-2}$ because $\binom{n}{2} = \frac{n!}{2!(n-2)!} = \frac{n!}{(n-2)!2!} = \frac{n!}{(n-2)!(n-(n-2))!} = \binom{n}{n-2}$. Therefore, $x = 2$. This value of x can also be deduced from the symmetry of Pascal's Triangle.

Additional Answers

18. The number of possible combinations of six numbers in Lottery A is $\binom{50}{6} =$ 15,890,700. Since the probability of picking each combination is the same, the probability of winning is $\frac{1}{15{,}890{,}700} \approx 6.29 \cdot 10^{-8}$. The number of possible combinations of five numbers in Lottery B is $\binom{70}{5} = 12{,}103{,}014$, so similarly, the probability of winning is $\frac{1}{12{,}103{,}014} \approx 8.26 \cdot 10^{-8}$. Therefore, you have a higher probability of winning in Lottery B.

21a.

n	$P(n)$
0	$\frac{1}{64}$
1	$\frac{3}{32}$
2	$\frac{15}{64}$
3	$\frac{5}{16}$
4	$\frac{15}{64}$
5	$\frac{3}{32}$
6	$\frac{1}{64}$

21b.

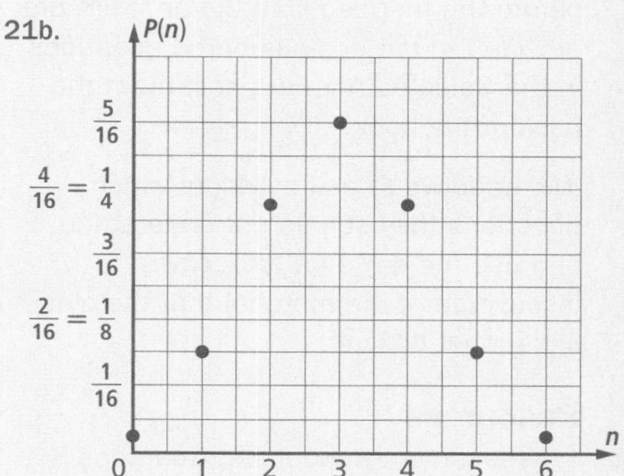

21c. Answers vary. Sample: $P(n)$ represents the probability of a certain number of heads in 6 tosses. For example, $P(5)$ represents the probability that there will be exactly 5 heads in 6 tosses.

Chapter 13 Review

Chapter Review

The main objectives for the chapter are organized in the Chapter Review under the four types of understanding this book promotes: Skills, Properties, Uses, and Representations.

Whereas end-of-chapter material may be considered optional in some texts, in UCSMP *Advanced Algebra* we have selected these objectives and questions with the expectation that they will be covered. Students should be able to answer these questions with about 85% accuracy after studying the chapter.

You may assign these questions over a single night to help students prepare for a test the next day or you may assign the questions over a two-day period. If you work the questions over two days, we recommend assigning the evens for homework the first night so that students get feedback in class the next day, and then assigning the odds the night before the test because the answers are provided to the odd-numbered questions in the Selected Answers section at the back of the book.

It is effective to ask students which questions they still do not understand and use the day as a total class discussion of the material that the class finds most difficult.

Resources

- Assessment Resources: Chapter 13 Test Forms A–D; Chapter 13 Test, Cumulative Form; Comprehensive Test, Chapters 1–13

Technology Resources

Teacher's Assessment Assistant, Ch. 13
Electronic Teacher's Edition, Ch. 13

Chapter 13 Chapter Review

SKILLS
PROPERTIES
USES
REPRESENTATIONS

SKILLS Procedures used to get answers

OBJECTIVE A Calculate values of arithmetic series. (Lesson 13-1)

In 1–4, evaluate the arithmetic series.

1. $1 + 2 + 3 + \ldots + 123$ 7626
2. $2 + 8 + 14 + \ldots + 92$ 752
3. the sum of the smallest 49 positive integers that are divisible by 7 8575
4. the sum of the first 9 terms of the sequence $\begin{cases} a_1 = 120 \\ a_n = a_{n-1} - 6 \text{ for integers } n \geq 2 \end{cases}$ 864
5. If $1 + 2 + 3 + \ldots + k = 1653$, what is the value of k? 57

OBJECTIVE B Calculate values of finite geometric series. (Lesson 13-2)

In 6–9, evaluate the geometric series.

6. $7 + 2.1 + 0.63 + \ldots + 7(0.3)^7$ ≈9.999
7. $3 - 12 + 48 - 192 + \ldots + 196{,}608$ 157,287
8. the sum of integer powers of 4 from 4^0 to 4^{17} 22,906,492,245
9. the sum of the first 11 terms of the sequence $\begin{cases} g_1 = 21 \\ g_n = \frac{3}{7}g_{n-1}, \text{for integers } n \geq 2 \end{cases}$ ≈36.75
10. A geometric series has 18 terms. The constant ratio is 1.037, and the first term is 1313. Estimate the value of the series to the nearest integer. 32,760

OBJECTIVE C Use summation (Σ) and factorial (!) notation. (Lesson 13-1, 13-2, 13-3, 13-4)

In 11 and 12, write the terms of the series, and then evaluate the series.

11. $\sum_{n=1}^{5} (3n - 6)$
12. $\sum_{i=-3}^{2} 5 \cdot 7^i$
13. **Multiple Choice** Which equals the sum $1 + 8 + 27 + \ldots + 1{,}000{,}000$? C
    A $\sum_{n=1}^{10} n^6$
    B $\sum_{n=1}^{100} 3^n$
    C $\sum_{n=1}^{100} n^3$
    D $\sum_{n=1}^{1000} n^2$
14. Suppose $a_1 = 23$, $a_2 = 24$, $a_3 = 25$, $a_4 = 26$, $a_5 = 27$. Evaluate $\frac{1}{5}\sum_{i=1}^{5} a_i$. 25

In 15 and 16, rewrite using Σ-notation.

15. $3 + 6 + 9 + \ldots + 123$ $\sum_{i=1}^{41} 3i$
16. $\mu = \frac{y_1 + y_2 + y_3 + \ldots + y_n}{n}$ $\mu = \frac{1}{n}\sum_{i=1}^{n} y_i$
17. If $g(n) = n! - n$, calculate $g(3) - g(8)$. -40,309
18. Rewrite $41 \cdot 42 \cdot 43 \cdot 44$ as a quotient of factorials. $\frac{44!}{40!}$
19. **Multiple Choice** $\frac{(n-1)!}{n!} =$ D
    A -1
    B n
    C $n - 1$
    D $\frac{1}{n}$

11. -3, 0, 3, 6, 9; 15

12. $\frac{5}{343}, \frac{5}{49}, \frac{5}{7}$, 5, 35, 245; $\frac{98{,}040}{343} \approx 285.831$

OBJECTIVE D Calculate permutations and combinations. (Lessons 13-4, 13-5)

20. Interpret the symbol $\binom{n}{r}$ in terms of Pascal's Triangle. See margin.

21. **Multiple Choice** Which of the following is equal to $\frac{13!}{10! \cdot 3!}$? B

A $_{10}C_3$ B $\binom{13}{3}$

C $\binom{10}{3}$ D $13 \cdot 12 \cdot 11$

In 22 and 23, consider the set {V, E, R, T, I, C, A, L}.

22. How many permutations of the letters in VERTICAL are possible? 40,320

23. a. How many subsets have 3 elements? 56

b. What is the total number of subsets that can be formed? 256

In 24–27, evaluate.

24. $\binom{13}{6}$ 1716 25. $\binom{432}{432}$ 1

26. $_7C_5$ 21 27. $_{532}C_{531}$ 532

OBJECTIVE E Use the Binomial Theorem to expand binomials. (Lesson 13-6)

In 28–31, expand using the Binomial Theorem. See margin.

28. $(x + y)^4$ 29. $(t - 3)^5$

30. $(2a^2 - 3)^3$ 31. $\left(\frac{p}{2} + 2q\right)^4$

True or False In 32 and 33, if the statement is false, change the statement to make it true.

32. One term of the binomial expansion of $(17x + z)^8$ is $17x^8$. See margin.

33. One term of the binomial expansion of $(43a - b)^{15}$ is $\binom{15}{2}(43a)^{13}(-b)^2$. true

34. **Multiple Choice** Which equals $\sum_{r=0}^{n} \binom{n}{r} x^{n-r} 7^r$? D

A $(x + n)^7$ B $(x + r)^n$

C $(x + 7)^r$ D $(x + 7)^n$

PROPERTIES Principles behind the mathematics

OBJECTIVE F Recognize properties of Pascal's Triangle. (Lesson 13-5, 13-6)

In 35 and 36, consider the top row in Pascal's Triangle to be row 0. See margin.

	row
1	0
1 1	1
1 2 1	2
	.
	.
	.

35. Write row 7 of Pascal's Triangle.

36. What is the sum of the numbers in row n?

37. Find a solution to $\binom{10}{6} + \binom{10}{7} = \binom{x}{y}$ $\binom{x}{y} = \binom{11}{7}$

38. **True or False** For all positive integers n, $\binom{n}{1} = \binom{n}{n-1}$. Justify your answer. See margin.

39. Describe the coefficient of r^2s^{13} in the expansion of $(r + s)^{15}$ in terms of Pascal's Triangle. See margin.

USES Applications of mathematics in real-world situations

OBJECTIVE G Solve real-world problems using arithmetic or geometric series. (Lessons 13-1, 13-2)

40. A bank stacks rolls of quarters in the following fashion: one roll on top, two rolls in the next layer, three rolls in the next layer, and so on.

a. If there are 10 layers of quarters, how many rolls are in the stack? 55 rolls

b. If you want to stack 120 rolls as described above, how many rolls will you need to put on the bottom layer? 15 rolls

Additional Answers

20. $\binom{n}{r}$ is the $(r + 1)$st element in row n of Pascal's Triangle.

28. $x^4 + 4x^3y + 6x^2y^2 + 4xy^3 + y^4$

29. $t^5 - 15t^4 + 90t^3 - 270t^2 + 405t - 243$

30. $8a^6 - 36a^4 + 54a^2 - 27$

31. $\frac{p^4}{16} + p^3q + 6p^2q^2 + 16pq^3 + 16q^4$

32. False; one term is $(17x)^8 = 6{,}975{,}757{,}441x^8$.

35. 1 7 21 35 35 21 7 1

36. 2^n

38. True; by the Commutative Property of Multiplication, $\binom{n}{1} = \frac{n!}{1!(n-1)!} = \frac{n!}{(n-1)!1!} = \frac{n!}{(n-1)!(n-(n-1))!} = \binom{n}{n-1}$.

39. The coefficient is the 14th element of row 15 of Pascal's Triangle.

Additional Answers

51. the 1989 freshman class
52. between 602.4 and 727.4

41. In a non-leap year, Kevin saved $1 on January 1, $2 on January 2, and $3 on January 3. Each day Kevin saved one dollar more than the previous day.
    a. How much did Kevin save on February 15? $46
    b. How much did he save in total by February 15? $1081
    c. How many days will it take Kevin to save a total of $10,000? 141 days

42. A ball is dropped from a height of 2 meters and bounces to 90% of its previous height on each bounce. When it hits the ground the eighth time, how far has it traveled? 20.78 m

43. A concert hall has 30 rows. The first row has 12 seats. Each row thereafter has 2 more seats than the preceding row. How many seats are in the concert hall? 1230 seats

OBJECTIVE H Solve real-world counting problems involving permutations or combinations. (Lesson 13-4)

44. The visible spectrum is associated with the acronym ROY G BIV (red, orange, yellow, green, blue, indigo, violet). How many ways can these letters be rearranged (ignoring spaces)? 5040

45. A used car dealer has 10 cars that he can line up next to the street. How many different ways can he arrange his cars? 3,628,800

46. There are 25 students in a class. How many handshakes will take place if every student shakes hands with everyone else exactly once? 300

In 47 and 48, use the fact that the Senate of the 110th Congress had 49 Republicans, 49 Democrats, and 2 Independents.

47. How many choices were there for forming a 5-member committee of Senators? 75,287,520

48. How many 7-member committees could be formed with Independents and Democrats? 115,775,100

OBJECTIVE I Use measures of central tendency or dispersion to describe data or distributions. (Lessons 13-3, 13-9)

In 49 and 50, consider these 2007 profits of the ten largest companies in the United States.

Company	Profit (millions of $)
Wal-Mart Stores	12,731
Exxon Mobil	40,610
Chevron	18,688
General Motors	−38,732
ConocoPhillips	11,891
General Electric	22,208
Ford Motor	−2,723
Citigroup	3,617
Bank of America Corp.	14,982
AT&T	11,951

49. Find the mean absolute deviation for this data set. 13,280.98

50. Find the standard deviation. 19,432.69

In 51–53, use this information: Johns Hopkins University compared the SAT math scores for the incoming 1989 freshman class to the scores for the incoming 2006 freshman class. Some of the data are presented below.

Year	Number of Students in Class	Mean	Standard Deviation
1989	831	662.6	68.2
2006	1211	664.9	62.5

51–52. See margin.

51. Which class shows a greater spread of scores?

52. Assume that the scores for the 2006 class are normally distributed. Within what interval would you expect the middle 68% of the class scores to occur?

53. When the scores for both classes are pooled into one data set, the mean SAT math score is 664.0, which is not the average of the means of the two classes when considered separately. Explain why. See margin.

54. Consider the test scores {93, 71, 78, 83, 93, 72, 99, 85}. Give the range of possible values for the mean if a ninth score ranging from 50 to 100 is added to the data set. $80.44 \le \mu \le 86$

OBJECTIVE J Solve problems using combinations and probability. (Lessons 13-7, 13-8)

In 55 and 56, suppose that a fair coin is tossed 6 times. Calculate the probability of each event.

55. getting exactly 1 head

56. getting exactly 3 heads

55–56. See margin.

In 57–59, suppose a coin is biased so there is a 70% chance that the coin shows tails when tossed. Find the probability of each event to the nearest thousandth.

57. There are 3 heads in 3 tosses. 0.027

58. When tossed twice, the coin shows heads the first time and tails the second time. 0.21

59. When tossed twice, the coin shows heads once and tails once. 0.42

60. If 7 out of 10 is a passing score on a true-or-false quiz with 10 questions and a student guessed at every answer, what is the probability that he passed the test? 0.172

61. If 70 out of 100 is a passing score on a true-or-false test and a student guesses at every answer, will he have the same probability of passing the test as the quiz in Question 60? Explain your reasoning. See margin.

62. In Illinois' Lotto game, a participant chooses six numbers from 1 to 52. To win the jackpot, the participant must match all six winning numbers. (Order does not matter.) What is the probability of this occurring? See margin.

63. The Virginia "Pick 3" lottery requires that a participant choose three numbers, each a digit from 0 to 9. To win the grand prize, the participant must match all three numbers in the order drawn. What is the probability of winning this lottery? See margin.

REPRESENTATIONS Pictures, graphs, or objects that illustrate concepts

OBJECTIVE K Graph and analyze binomial and normal distributions. (Lesson 13-9)

64. Consider the function $P(n) = \frac{1}{2^8}\binom{8}{n}$. a–c. See margin.
   a. Evaluate $P(n)$ for integers 0, 1, …, 8.
   b. Graph this function.
   c. What name is given to this function?

65. Below is pictured a normal distribution with mean μ and standard deviation σ.

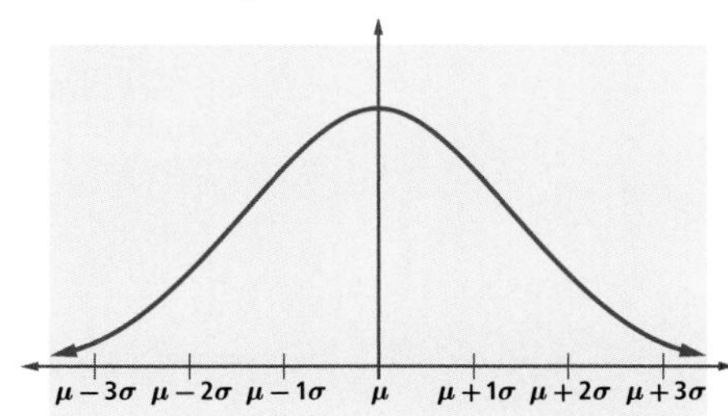

   a. What percent of the data are greater than or equal to μ? 50%
   b. About what percent of the data are between $\mu - 1\sigma$ and $\mu + 1\sigma$? 68.2%
   c. About what percent of the data are more than 2 standard deviations away from μ? 4.6%

Assessment

Evaluation The *Assessment Resources* provide four forms of the Chapter 13 Test. Forms A and B present parallel versions of a short-answer format. Form C consists of four to six short-response questions that cover the SPUR objectives from Chapter 13. Form D offers performance assessment that covers a subset (or even just one) of the SPUR objectives for the chapter. The fifth type of test is a Chapter 13 Test, Cumulative Form. About 50% of this test covers Chapter 13, and the remaining 50% covers the previous chapters evenly.

Feedback After students have taken the test for Chapter 13 and you have scored the results, return the tests to students for discussion. Class discussion on the questions that caused trouble for most students can be very effective in identifying and clarifying misunderstandings. You might want to have them note the items they missed and work either in groups or at home to correct them. It is important for students to receive feedback on every chapter test, and we recommend that students see and correct their mistakes.

Additional Answers

53. Answers vary. Sample: The two classes have different numbers of students, which means that the mean score of incoming 1989 freshmen is weighted less than the mean score of 2006 freshmen.

55. $\frac{3}{32} = 0.09375$

56. $\frac{5}{16} = 0.3125$

61. No; $\left(\frac{1}{2}\right)^{100} \sum_{k=70}^{100} {}_{100}C_k \neq \left(\frac{1}{2}\right)^{10} \sum_{i=7}^{10} {}_{10}C_i$

62. $\frac{1}{20{,}358{,}520}$

63. $\frac{1}{1000} = 0.001$

64a. $\frac{1}{256}, \frac{1}{32}, \frac{7}{64}, \frac{7}{32}, \frac{35}{128}, \frac{7}{32}, \frac{7}{64}, \frac{1}{32}, \frac{1}{256}$

Additional Answers

64b.

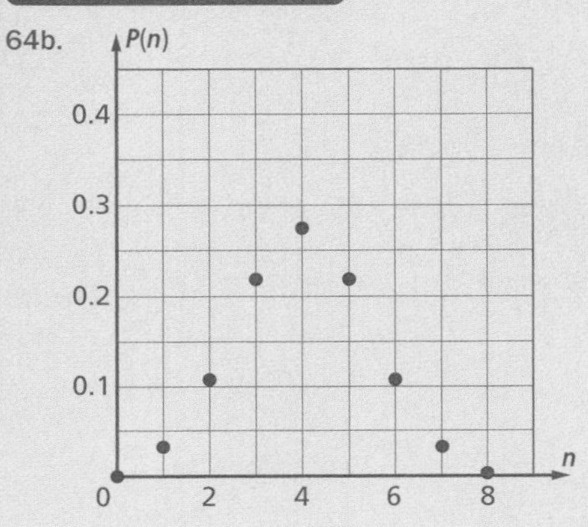

64c. binomial probability distribution or binomial distribution

Properties

Algebra Properties from Earlier Courses

Selected Properties of Real Numbers

For any real numbers a, b, and c:

Postulates of Addition and Multiplication (Field Properties)

	Addition	*Multiplication*
Closure property	$a + b$ is a real number.	ab is a real number.
Commutative property	$a + b = b + a$	$ab = ba$
Associative property	$(a + b) + c = a + (b + c)$	$(ab)c = a(bc)$
Identity property	There is a real number 0 with $0 + a = a + 0 = a$.	There is a real number 1 with $1 \cdot a = a \cdot 1 = a$.
Inverse property	There is a real number $-a$ with $a + -a = -a + a = 0$.	If $a \neq 0$, there is a real number $\frac{1}{a}$ with $a \cdot \frac{1}{a} = \frac{1}{a} \cdot a = 1$.
Distributive property	$a(b + c) = ab + ac$	

Postulates of Equality

Reflexive property	$a = a$
Symmetric property	If $a = b$, then $b = a$.
Transitive property	If $a = b$ and $b = c$, then $a = c$.
Substitution property	If $a = b$, then a may be substituted for b in any arithmetic or algebraic expression.
Addition property	If $a = b$, then $a + c = b + c$.
Multiplication property	If $a = b$, then $ac = bc$.

Postulates of Inequality

Trichotomy property	Either $a < b$, $a = b$, or $a > b$.
Transitive property	If $a < b$ and $b < c$, then $a < c$.
Addition property	If $a < b$, then $a + c < b + c$.
Multiplication property	If $a < b$ and $c > 0$, then $ac < bc$. If $a < b$ and $c < 0$, then $ac > bc$.

Postulates of Powers

For any nonzero bases a and b and integer exponents m and n:

Product of Powers property	$b^m \cdot b^n = b^{m+n}$
Power of a Power property	$(b^m)^n = b^{mn}$
Power of a Product property	$(ab)^m = a^m b^m$
Quotient of Powers property	$\frac{b^m}{b^n} = b^{m-n}$
Power of a Quotient property	$\left(\frac{a}{b}\right)^m = \frac{a^m}{b^m}$

Selected Theorems of Graphing

The set of points (x, y) satisfying $Ax + By = C$, where A and B are not both 0, is a line.

The line with equation $y = mx + b$ has slope m and y-intercept b.

Two nonvertical lines are parallel if and only if they have the same slope.

Two nonvertical lines are perpendicular if and only if the product of their slopes is -1.

The set of points (x, y) satisfying $y = ax^2 + bx + c$ is a parabola.

Selected Theorems of Algebra

For any real numbers a, b, c, and d (with denominators of fractions not equal to 0):

Multiplication Property of Zero	$0 \cdot a = 0$
Multiplication Property of -1	$-1 \cdot a = -a$
Opposite of an Opposite Property	$-(-a) = a$
Opposite of a Sum	$-(b + c) = -b + -c$
Distributive Property of Multiplication over Subtraction	$a(b - c) = ab - ac$
Addition of Like Terms	$ac + bc = (a + b)c$
Addition of Fractions	$\frac{a}{c} + \frac{b}{c} = \frac{a+b}{c}$
Multiplication of Fractions	$\frac{a}{b} \cdot \frac{c}{d} = \frac{ac}{bd}$
Equal Fractions	$\frac{ac}{bc} = \frac{a}{b}$
Means-Extremes	If $\frac{a}{b} = \frac{c}{d}$, then $ad = bc$.
Binomial Square	$(a + b)^2 = a^2 + 2ab + b^2$
Extended Distributive Property	To multiply two polynomials, multiply each term in the first polynomial by each term in the second, and then add the products.
Zero Exponent	If $b \neq 0$, then $b^0 = 1$.
Negative Exponent	If $b \neq 0$, then $b^{-n} = \frac{1}{b^n}$.
Zero Product	$ab = 0$ if and only if $a = 0$ or $b = 0$.
Absolute Value-Square Root	$\sqrt{a^2} = \lvert a \rvert$
Product of Square Roots	If $a \geq 0$ and $b \geq 0$, then $\sqrt{ab} = \sqrt{a} \cdot \sqrt{b}$.
Quadratic Formula	If $ax^2 + bx + c = 0$ and $a \neq 0$, then $x = \frac{-b \pm \sqrt{b^2 - 4ac}}{2a}$.

Geometry Properties from Earlier Courses

In this book, the following symbols are used:

Symbol	Meaning
a, b, c	sides
A	area
B	area of base
b_1, b_2	bases
C	circumference
d	diameter
d_1, d_2	diagonals
h	height
ℓ	length
ℓ	slant height (in conics)
L.A.	lateral area
n	number of sides
p	perimeter
r	radius
s	side
S.A.	surface area
V	volume
w	width

Two-Dimensional Figures

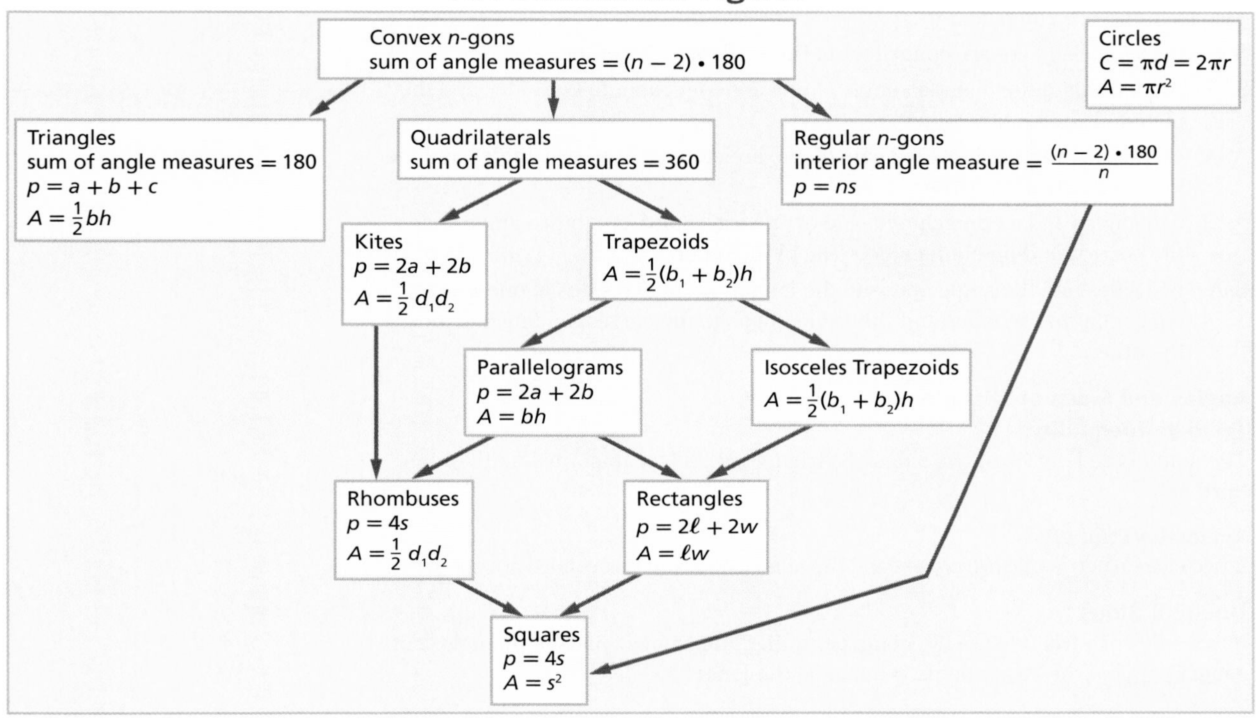

Three-Dimensional Figures

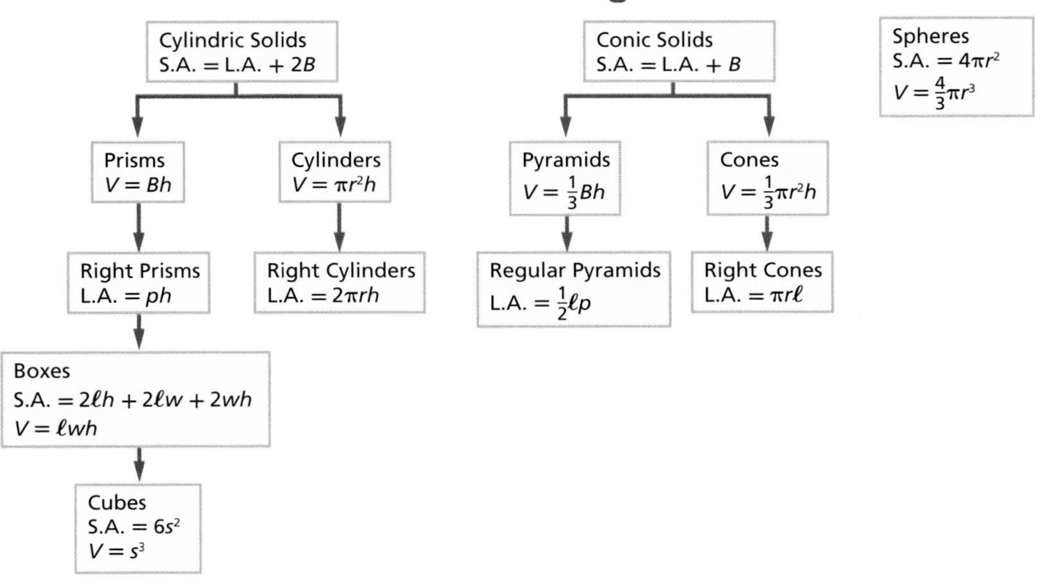

Selected Theorems of Geometry

Parallel Lines

Two lines are parallel if and only if:

1. corresponding angles have the same measure.
2. alternate interior angles are congruent.
3. alternate exterior angles are congruent.
4. they are perpendicular to the same line.

Triangle Congruence

Two triangles are congruent if:

SSS three sides of one are congruent to three sides of the other.

SAS two sides and the included angle of one are congruent to two sides and the included angle of the other.

ASA two angles and the included side of one are congruent to two angles and the included side of the other.

AAS two angles and a nonincluded side of one are congruent to two angles and the corresponding nonincluded side of the other.

SsA two sides and the angle opposite the longer of the two sides of one are congruent to two sides and the angle opposite the corresponding side of the other.

Angles and Sides of Triangles

Triangle Inequality

The sum of the lengths of two sides of a triangle is greater than the length of the third side.

Isosceles Triangle

If two sides of a triangle are congruent, the angles opposite those sides are congruent.

Unequal Sides

If two sides of a triangle are not congruent, then the angles opposite them are not congruent, and the larger angle is opposite the longer side.

Unequal Angles

If two angles of a triangle are not congruent, then the sides opposite them are not congruent, and the longer side is opposite the larger angle.

Pythagorean Theorem

In any right triangle with legs a and b and hypotenuse c, $a^2 + b^2 = c^2$.

30-60-90 Triangle

In a 30-60-90 triangle, the sides are in the extended ratio $x : x\sqrt{3} : 2x$.

45-45-90 Triangle

In a 45-45-90 triangle, the sides are in the extended ratio $x : x : x\sqrt{2}$.

Parallelograms

A quadrilateral is a parallelogram if and only if:

1. one pair of sides is both parallel and congruent.
2. both pairs of opposite sides are congruent.
3. both pairs of opposite angles are congruent.
4. its diagonals bisect each other.

Quadrilateral Hierarchy
If a figure is of any type in the hierarchy pictured at the right, it is also of all types above it to which it is connected.

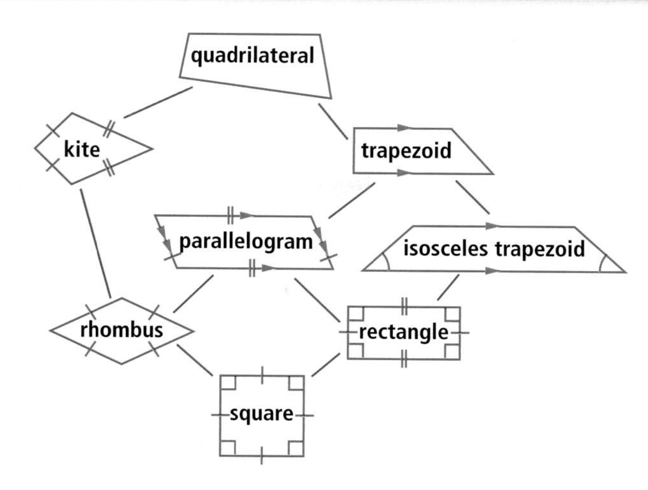

Properties of Transformations

A-B-C-D
Every isometry preserves angle measure, betweenness, collinearity, and distance.

Two-Reflection for Translations
If $m \parallel n$, the translation $r_n \circ r_m$ has magnitude two times the distance between m and n in the direction from m perpendicular to n.

Two-Reflection for Rotations
If m intersects ℓ, the rotation $r_m \circ r_\ell$ has a center at the point of intersection of m and ℓ, and has a magnitude twice the measure of an angle formed by these lines, in the direction from ℓ to m.

Isometry
Every isometry is a transformation that is a reflection or a composite of reflections.

Size-Change
Every size change with magnitude k preserves angle measure, betweenness, and collinearity; a line is parallel to its image; distance is multiplied by k.

Fundamental Theorem of Similarity
If two figures are similar with ratio of similitude k, then:

1. corresponding angle measure are equal.
2. corresponding lengths and perimeters are in the ratio k.
3. corresponding areas and surface areas are in the ratio k^2.
4. corresponding volumes are in the ratio k^3.

Triangle Similarity
Two triangles are similar if:

1. three sides of one are proportional to three sides of the other (SSS).
2. the ratios of two pairs of corresponding sides are equal and the included angles are congruent (SAS).
3. two angles of one are congruent to two angles of the other (AA).

Coordinate Plane Formulas
For all $A = (x_1, y_1)$ and $B = (x_2, y_2)$:

Distance formula	$AB = \sqrt{(x_2 - x_1)^2 + (y_2 - y_1)^2}$
Midpoint formula	The midpoint of $\overline{AB}$ is $\left(\frac{x_1 + x_2}{2}, \frac{y_1 + y_2}{2}\right)$.

For all points (x, y):

reflection over the x-axis	$(x, y) \rightarrow (x, -y)$
reflection over the y-axis	$(x, y) \rightarrow (-x, y)$
reflection over $y = x$	$(x, y) \rightarrow (y, x)$
size change of magnitude k, center $(0, 0)$	$(x, y) \rightarrow (kx, ky)$
translation h units horizontally, k units verically	$(x, y) \rightarrow (x + h, y + k)$

Theorems

Advanced Algebra Theorems

Chapter 1

Rules for Order of Operations *(Lesson 1-1, p. 8)*

1. Perform operations within parentheses or other grouping symbols from the innermost group out.
2. Within grouping symbols or if there are no grouping symbols:
   a. Take powers from left to right.
   b. Multiply and divide in order from left to right.
   c. Add and subtract in order from left to right.

Distributive Property *(Lesson 1-6, p. 41)*
For all real numbers a, b, and c, $c(a + b) = ca + cb$.

Opposite of a Sum Theorem *(Lesson 1-6, p. 44)*
For all real numbers a and b, $-(a + b) = -a + -b = -a - b$.

Chapter 2

The Fundamental Theorem of Variation
(Lesson 2-3, p. 88)

1. If $y = kx^n$, that is, y varies *directly* as x^n, and x is multiplied by c, then y is multiplied by c^n.
2. If $y = \frac{k}{x^n}$, that is, y varies *inversely* as x^n, and x is multiplied by a nonzero constant c, then y is divided by c^n.

Slope of $y = kx$ Theorem *(Lesson 2-4, p. 95)*
The graph of the direct-variation function with equation $y = kx$ has constant slope k.

Converse of the Fundamental Theorem of Variation *(Lesson 2-8, p. 122)*

a. If multiplying every x-value of a function by c results in multiplying the corresponding y-values by c^n, then y varies directly as the nth power of x, that is, $y = kx^n$.
b. If multiplying every x-value of a function by c results in dividing the corresponding y-values by c^n, then y varies inversely as the nth power of x, that is, $y = \frac{k}{x^n}$.

Chapter 3

Parallel Lines and Slope Theorem
(Lesson 3-1, p. 154)
Two non-vertical lines are parallel if and only if they have the same slope.

Standard Form of an Equation of a Line Theorem *(Lesson 3-3, p. 163)*
The graph of $Ax + By = C$, where A and B are not both zero, is a line.

Point-Slope Theorem *(Lesson 3-4, p. 170)*
If a line contains the point (x_1, y_1) and has slope m, then it has the equation $y - y_1 = m(x - x_1)$.

***n*th Term of an Arithmetic Sequence Theorem** *(Lesson 3-8, p. 197)*
The nth term a_n of an arithmetic (linear) sequence with first term a_1 and constant difference d is given by the explicit formula $a_n = a_1 + (n - 1)d$.

Constant-Difference Sequence Theorem
(Lesson 3-8, p. 198)
The sequence defined by the recursive formula

$$\begin{cases} a_1 \\ a_n = a_{n-1} + d, \text{ for integers } n \geq 2 \end{cases}$$

is the arithmetic sequence with first term a_1 and constant difference d.

Chapter 4

Size Change Theorem *(Lesson 4-4, p. 244)*
$\begin{bmatrix} k & 0 \\ 0 & k \end{bmatrix}$ is the matrix for S_k.

Pythagorean Distance Formula *(Lesson 4-4, p. 245)*
If $A = (x_1, y_1)$ and $B = (x_2, y_2)$, then
$AB = \sqrt{|x_2 - x_1|^2 + |y_2 - y_1|^2}$.

Scale Change Theorem *(Lesson 4-5, p. 251)*
$\begin{bmatrix} a & 0 \\ 0 & b \end{bmatrix}$ is a matrix for $S_{a,b}$.

Matrix for r_y Theorem *(Lesson 4-6, p. 256)*
$\begin{bmatrix} -1 & 0 \\ 0 & 1 \end{bmatrix}$ is the matrix for r_y.

Matrix Basis Theorem *(Lesson 4-6, p. 257)*
Suppose A is a transformation represented by a 2×2 matrix. If $A : (1, 0) \rightarrow (x_1, y_1)$ and $A : (0, 1) \rightarrow (x_2, y_2)$, then A has the matrix $\begin{bmatrix} x_1 & x_2 \\ y_1 & y_2 \end{bmatrix}$.

Matrices for r_x, $r_{y=x}$, and $r_{y=-x}$ Theorem
(Lesson 4-6, p. 259)
1. $\begin{bmatrix} 1 & 0 \\ 0 & -1 \end{bmatrix}$ is the matrix for r_x.
2. $\begin{bmatrix} 0 & 1 \\ 1 & 0 \end{bmatrix}$ is the matrix for $r_{y=x}$.
3. $\begin{bmatrix} 0 & -1 \\ -1 & 0 \end{bmatrix}$ is the matrix for $r_{y=-x}$.

Matrices and Composites Theorem
(Lesson 4-7, p. 265)
If $M1$ is the matrix for transformation T_1, and $M2$ is the matrix for transformation T_2, then $M2M1$ is the matrix for $T_2 \circ T_1$.

Composite of Rotations Theorem
(Lesson 4-8, p. 270)
A rotation of $b°$ following a rotation of $a°$ with the same center results in a rotation of $(a + b)°$. In symbols, $R_b \circ R_a = R_{a+b}$.

Matrix for R_{90} Theorem *(Lesson 4-8, p. 270)*
$\begin{bmatrix} 0 & -1 \\ 1 & 0 \end{bmatrix}$ is the matrix for R_{90}.

Perpendicular Lines and Slopes Theorem
(Lesson 4-9, p. 276)
Two lines with slopes m_1 and m_2 are perpendicular if and only if $m_1 m_2 = -1$.

Parallel Lines and Translations Theorem
(Lesson 4-10, p. 282)
Under a translation, a preimage line is parallel to its image.

Chapter 5

Addition Property of Inequality *(Lesson 5-1, p. 303)*
For all real numbers a, b, and c, if $a < b$, then $a + c < b + c$.

Multiplication Property of Inequality
(Lesson 5-1, p. 303)
For all real numbers a, b, and c, if $a < b$ and $c > 0$, then $ac < bc$; if $a < b$ and $c < 0$, then $ac > bc$.

Substitution Property of Equality
(Lesson 5-3, p. 314)
If $a = b$, then a may be substituted for b in any arithmetic or algebraic expression.

Inverse Matrix Theorem *(Lesson 5-5, p. 329)*
If $ad - bc \neq 0$ and $M = \begin{bmatrix} a & b \\ c & d \end{bmatrix}$,

then $M^{-1} = \begin{bmatrix} \frac{d}{ad - bc} & \frac{-b}{ad - bc} \\ \frac{-c}{ad - bc} & \frac{a}{ad - bc} \end{bmatrix}$.

System-Determinant Theorem *(Lesson 5-6, p. 338)*
An $n \times n$ system of linear equations has exactly one solution if and only if the determinant of the coefficient matrix is *not* zero.

Linear-Programming Theorem *(Lesson 5-9, p. 356)*
The feasible region of every linear-programming problem is convex, and the maximum or minimum quantity is determined at one of the vertices of this feasible region.

Chapter 6

Binomial Square Theorem *(Lesson 6-1, p. 376)*
For all real numbers x and y,
$(x + y)^2 = x^2 + 2xy + y^2$ and
$(x - y)^2 = x^2 - 2xy + y^2$.

Absolute Value-Square Root Theorem
(Lesson 6-2, p. 381)
For all real numbers x, $\sqrt{x^2} = |x|$.

Graph-Translation Theorem *(Lesson 6-3, p. 387)*
In a relation described by a sentence in x and y, the following two processes yield the same graph:
1. replacing x by $x - h$ and y by $y - k$;
2. applying the translation $T_{h,k}$ to the graph of the original relation.

Parabola-Translation Theorem *(Lesson 6-3, p. 388)*
The image of the parabola with equation $y = ax^2$ under the translation $T_{h,k}$ is the parabola with the equation

$$y - k = a(x - h)^2$$
or
$$y = a(x - h)^2 + k.$$

Parabola Congruence Theorem *(Lesson 6-4, p. 395)*
The graph of the equation $y = ax^2 + bx + c$ is a parabola congruent to the graph of $y = ax^2$.

Completing the Square Theorem *(Lesson 6-5, p. 402)*
To complete the square on $x^2 + bx$, add $\left(\frac{b}{2}\right)^2$.

Quadratic Formula Theorem *(Lesson 6-7, p. 414)*
If $ax^2 + bx + c = 0$ and $a \neq 0$, then $x = \frac{-b \pm \sqrt{b^2 - 4ac}}{2a}$.

Square Root of a Negative Number Theorem
(Lesson 6-8, p. 422)
If $k < 0$, $\sqrt{k} = i\sqrt{-k}$.

Properties of Complex Numbers Postulate
(Lesson 6-9, p. 428)
In the set of complex numbers:
1. Addition and multiplication are commutative and associative.
2. Multiplication distributes over addition and subtraction.
3. $0 = 0i = 0 + 0i$ is the additive identity; $1 = 1 + 0i$ is the multiplicative identity.
4. Every complex number $a + bi$ has an additive inverse $-a + -bi$ and a multiplicative inverse $\frac{1}{a + bi}$ provided $a + bi \neq 0$.
5. The addition and multiplication properties of equality hold.

Discriminant Theorem *(Lesson 6-10, p. 437)*
Suppose a, b, and c are real numbers with $a \neq 0$. Then the equation $ax^2 + bx + c = 0$ has:
(i) two real solutions if $b^2 - 4ac > 0$.
(ii) one real solution if $b^2 - 4ac = 0$.
(iii) two complex conjugate solutions if $b^2 - 4ac < 0$.

Chapter 7

Probability of Repeated Independent Events
(Lesson 7-1, p. 454)
If an event has probability p, and if each occurrence of the event is independent of all other occurrences, then the probability that the event occurs n times in a row is p^n.

Product of Powers Postulate *(Lesson 7-2, p. 459)*
For any nonnegative base b and nonzero real exponents m and n, or any nonzero base b and integer exponents m and n, $b^m \cdot b^n = b^{m+n}$.

Quotient of Powers Theorem *(Lesson 7-2, p. 460)*
For any positive base b and real exponents m and n, or any nonzero base b and integer exponents m and n, $\frac{b^m}{b^n} = b^{m-n}$.

Power of a Product Postulate *(Lesson 7-2, p. 460)*
For any nonnegative bases a and b and nonzero real exponent m, or any nonzero bases a and b and integer exponent m, $(ab)^m = a^m b^m$.

Power of a Quotient Theorem *(Lesson 7-2, p. 461)*
For any positive bases a and b and real exponent n, or any nonzero bases a and b and integer exponent n, $\left(\frac{a}{b}\right)^n = \frac{a^n}{b^n}$.

Zero Exponent Theorem *(Lesson 7-2, p. 461)*
If b is a nonzero real number, $b^0 = 1$.

Power of a Power Postulate *(Lesson 7-2, p. 462)*
For any nonnegative base b and nonzero real exponents m and n, or any nonzero base b and integer exponents m and n, $(b^m)^n = b^{mn}$.

Negative Exponent Theorem *(Lesson 7-3, p. 467)*
For any positive base b and real exponent n, or any nonzero base b and integer exponent n, $b^{-n} = \frac{1}{b^n}$.

Annual Compound Interest Formula
(Lesson 7-4, p. 473)
Let P be the amount of money invested at an annual interest rate r compounded annually. Let A be the total amount after t years. Then $A = P(1 + r)^t$.

General Compound Interest Formula
(Lesson 7-4, p. 473)
Let P be the amount invested at an annual interest rate r compounded n times per year. Let A be the amount after t years. Then $A = P\left(1 + \frac{r}{n}\right)^{nt}$.

Recursive Formula for a Geometric Sequence
(Lesson 7-5, p. 479)
Let r be a nonzero constant. The sequence g defined by the recursive formula $\begin{cases} g_1 = x \\ g_n = rg_{n-1}, \text{ for integers } n \geq 2 \end{cases}$ is the geometric, or exponential, sequence with first term x and constant multiplier r.

Explicit Formula for a Geometric Sequence
(Lesson 7-5, p. 481)
In the geometric sequence g with first term g_1 and constant ratio r, $g_n = g_1(r)^{n-1}$, for integers $n \geq 1$.

Number of Real Roots Theorem *(Lesson 7-6, p. 488)*
Every positive real number has:
2 real nth roots when n is even.
1 real nth root when n is odd.
Every negative real number has:
0 real nth roots when n is even.
1 real nth root when n is odd.
Zero has:
1 real nth root.

$\frac{1}{n}$ Exponent Theorem *(Lesson 7-6, p. 489)*
When $x \geq 0$ and n is an integer greater than 1, $x^{\frac{1}{n}}$ is an nth root of x.

Rational Exponent Theorem *(Lesson 7-7, p. 493)*
For any nonnegative real number x and positive integers m and n,
$x^{\frac{m}{n}} = \left(x^{\frac{1}{n}}\right)^m$, the mth power of the positive nth root of x, and
$x^{\frac{m}{n}} = (x^m)^{\frac{1}{n}}$, the positive nth root of the mth power of x.

Chapter 8

Inverse-Relation Theorem *(Lesson 8-2, p. 524)*
Suppose f is a relation and g is the inverse of f. Then:
1. If a rule for f exists, a rule for g can be found by switching x and y in the rule for f.
2. The graph of g is the reflection image of the graph of f over the line with equation $y = x$.
3. The domain of g is the range of f, and the range of g is the domain of f.

Inverse Functions Theorem *(Lesson 8-3, p. 530)*
Two functions f and g are inverse functions if and only if:
1. For all x in the domain of f, $g(f(x)) = x$, and
2. For all x in the domain of g, $f(g(x)) = x$.

Power Function Inverse Theorem
(Lesson 8-3, p. 532)
If $f(x) = x^n$ and $g(x) = x^{\frac{1}{n}}$ and the domains of f and g are the set of *nonnegative* real numbers, then f and g are inverse functions.

Root of a Power Theorem *(Lesson 8-4, p. 539)*
For all positive integers $m \geq 2$ and $n \geq 2$, $\sqrt[n]{x^m} = (\sqrt[n]{x})^m = x^{\frac{m}{n}}$ when $x \geq 0$.

Root of a Product Theorem *(Lesson 8-5, p. 546)*
For any nonnegative real numbers x and y, and any integer $n \geq 2$, $(xy)^{\frac{1}{n}} = x^{\frac{1}{n}} \cdot y^{\frac{1}{n}}$ (power form) and $\sqrt[n]{xy} = \sqrt[n]{x} \cdot \sqrt[n]{y}$ (radical form).

***n*th Root of a Product Theorem** *(Lesson 8-7, p. 559)*
When $\sqrt[n]{x}$ and $\sqrt[n]{y}$ are defined and are real numbers, then $\sqrt[n]{xy}$ is also defined and $\sqrt[n]{xy} = \sqrt[n]{x} \cdot \sqrt[n]{y}$

Chapter 9

Exponential Change Model *(Lesson 9-2, p. 589)*
If a positive quantity a is multiplied by b ($b > 0$, $b \neq 1$) in each unit period, then after a period of length x, the amount of the quantity is ab^x.

Continuously Compounded Interest Formula
(Lesson 9-3, p. 597)
If an amount P is invested in an account paying an annual interest rate r compounded continuously, the amount A in the account after t years is $A = Pe^{rt}$.

Log_b of b^n Theorem *(Lesson 9-9, p. 636)*
For every positive base $b \neq 1$, and any real number n, $\log_b b^n = n$.

Logarithm of 1 Theorem *(Lesson 9-9, p. 636)*
For every positive base $b \neq 1$, $\log_b 1 = 0$.

Logarithm of a Product Theorem *(Lesson 9-9, p. 637)*
For any positive base $b \neq 1$ and positive real numbers x and y, $\log_b(xy) = \log_b x + \log_b y$.

Logarithm of a Quotient Theorem *(Lesson 9-9, p. 638)*
For any positive base $b \neq 1$ and for any positive real numbers x and y, $\log_b\left(\frac{x}{y}\right) = \log_b x - \log_b y$.

Logarithm of a Power Theorem *(Lesson 9-9, p. 639)*
For any positive base $b \neq 1$ and for any positive real number x and any real number n, $\log_b(x^n) = n \log_b x$.

Change of Base Theorem *(Lesson 9-10, p. 646)*
For all positive real numbers a, b, and t, $b \neq 1$ and $t \neq 1$, $\log_b a = \frac{\log_t a}{\log_t b}$.

Chapter 10

Pythagorean Identity Theorem *(Lesson 10-5, p. 688)*
For all θ, $(\cos \theta)^2 + (\sin \theta)^2 = 1$.

Supplements Theorem *(Lesson 10-7, p. 701)*
For all θ in degrees, $\sin \theta = \sin(180° - \theta)$.

Law of Sines Theorem *(Lesson 10-7, p. 702)*
In any triangle ABC, $\frac{\sin A}{a} = \frac{\sin B}{b} = \frac{\sin C}{c}$.

Law of Cosines Theorem *(Lesson 10-8, p. 706)*
In any triangle ABC, $c^2 = a^2 + b^2 - 2ab \cos C$.

Chapter 11

Extended Distributive Property *(Lesson 11-2, p. 739)*
To multiply two polynomials, multiply each term in the first polynomial by each term in the second and add the products.

Difference of Squares Factoring Theorem
(Lesson 11-3, p. 747)
For all a and b, $a^2 - b^2 = (a + b)(a - b)$.

Binomial Square Factoring Theorem
(Lesson 11-3, p. 747)
For all a and b, $a^2 + 2ab + b^2 = (a + b)^2$ and
$a^2 - 2ab + b^2 = (a - b)^2$.

Zero-Product Theorem *(Lesson 11-4, p. 752)*
For all a and b, $ab = 0$ if and only if $a = 0$ or $b = 0$.

Factor Theorem *(Lesson 11-4, p. 753)*
$x - r$ is a factor of $P(x)$ if and only if $P(r) = 0$, that is, r is a zero of P.

Rational-Root (or Rational-Zero) Theorem
(Lesson 11-5, p. 761)
Suppose that all the coefficients of the polynomial function described by $f(x) = a_n x^n + a_{n-1}x^{n-1} + ... + a_2x^2 + a_1x + a_0$ are integers with $a_n \neq 0$ and $a_0 \neq 0$. If $\frac{p}{q}$ is a root of $f(x)$ in lowest terms, then p is a factor of a_0 and q is a factor of a_n.

The Fundamental Theorem of Algebra
(Lesson 11-6, p. 766)
Every polynomial equation $P(x) = 0$ of any degree ≥ 1 with complex number coefficients has at least one complex number solution.

Number of Roots of a Polynomial Equation Theorem *(Lesson 11-6, p. 768)*
Every polynomial equation of degree n has exactly n roots, provided that multiple roots are counted according to their multiplicities.

Polynomial-Difference Theorem *(Lesson 11-7, p. 773)*
$y = f(x)$ is a polynomial function of degree n if and only if, for any set of x-values that form an arithmetic sequence, the nth differences of corresponding y-values are equal and the $(n - 1)$st differences are not equal.

Chapter 12

Focus and Directrix of a Parabola Theorem
(Lesson 12-1, p. 801)
For any nonzero real number a, the graph of $y = ax^2$ is the parabola with focus at $\left(0, \frac{1}{4a}\right)$ and directrix at $y = -\frac{1}{4a}$.

Circle Equation Theorem *(Lesson 12-2, p. 806)*
The circle with center (h, k) and radius r is the set of points (x, y) that satisfy $(x - h)^2 + (y - k)^2 = r^2$.

Interior and Exterior of a Circle Theorem
(Lesson 12-3, p. 812)
Let c be the circle with center (h, k) and radius r. Then the interior of c is described by $(x - h)^2 + (y - k)^2 < r^2$ and the exterior of c is described by $(x - h)^2 + (y - k)^2 > r^2$.

Equation for an Ellipse Theorem
(Lesson 12-4, p. 818)
The ellipse with foci $(c, 0)$ and $(-c, 0)$ and focal constant $2a$ has equation $\frac{x^2}{a^2} + \frac{y^2}{b^2} = 1$, where $b^2 = a^2 - c^2$.

Length of Axes of an Ellipse Theorem *(Lesson 12-4, p. 820)*
In the ellipse with equation $\frac{x^2}{a^2} + \frac{y^2}{b^2} = 1$, $2a$ is the length of the horizontal axis and $2b$ is the length of the vertical axis.

Circle Scale-Change Theorem *(Lesson 12-5, p. 826)*
The image of the unit circle with equation $x^2 + y^2 = 1$ under $S_{a,b}$ is the ellipse with equation $\left(\frac{x}{a}\right)^2 + \left(\frac{y}{b}\right)^2 = 1$.

Graph Scale-Change Theorem *(Lesson 12-5, p. 827)*
In a relation described by a sentence in x and y, the following two processes yield the same graph:
1. replacing x by $\frac{x}{a}$ and y by $\frac{y}{b}$;
2. applying the scale change $S_{a,b}$ to the graph of the original relation.

Area of an Ellipse Theorem *(Lesson 12-5, p. 828)*
An ellipse with semimajor and semiminor axes of lengths a and b has area $A = \pi ab$.

Equation for a Hyperbola Theorem *(Lesson 12-6, p. 832)*
The hyperbola with foci $(c, 0)$ and $(-c, 0)$ and focal constant $2a$ has equation $\frac{x^2}{a^2} - \frac{y^2}{b^2} = 1$, where $b^2 = c^2 - a^2$.

Asymptotes of a Hyperbola Theorem *(Lesson 12-6, p. 834)*
The asymptotes of the hyperbola with equation $\frac{x^2}{a^2} - \frac{y^2}{b^2} = 1$ are $\frac{y}{b} = \pm\frac{x}{a}$, or $y = \pm\frac{b}{a}x$.

Attributes of $y = \frac{k}{x}$ Theorem *(Lesson 12-7, p. 841)*
The graph of $y = \frac{k}{x}$ or $xy = k$ is a hyperbola. When $k > 0$, this hyperbola has vertices $\left(\sqrt{k}, \sqrt{k}\right)$ and $\left(-\sqrt{k}, -\sqrt{k}\right)$, foci $\left(\sqrt{2k}, \sqrt{2k}\right)$ and $\left(-\sqrt{2k}, -\sqrt{2k}\right)$, and focal constant $2\sqrt{2k}$. The asymptotes of the graph are $x = 0$ and $y = 0$.

Chapter 13

Arithmetic Series Formula *(Lesson 13-1, p. 871)*
In an arithmetic sequence $a_1, a_2, a_3, ..., a_n$ with constant difference d, $\sum_{i=1}^{n} a_i = \frac{n}{2}(a_1 + a_n) = \frac{n}{2}(2a_1 + (n-1)d)$.

Finite Geometric Series Formula *(Lesson 13-2, p. 878)*
Let S_n be the sum of the first n terms of the geometric sequence with first term g_1 and constant ratio $r \neq 1$. Then $S_n = \frac{g_1(1 - r^n)}{1 - r}$.

Number of Permutations Theorem *(Lesson 13-4, p. 890)*
There are $n!$ permutations of n distinct objects.

Factorial Product Theorem *(Lesson 13-4, p. 890)*
For all $n \geq 1$, $n! = n \cdot (n-1)!$.

Combination Counting Formula *(Lesson 13-4, p. 892)*
The number ${}_nC_r$ of subsets, or combinations, of r elements that can be formed from a set of n elements is given by the formula ${}_nC_r = \frac{n!}{r!(n-r)!}$.

Pascal's Triangle Explicit Formula *(Lesson 13-5, p. 899)*
If n and r are integers with $0 \leq r \leq n$, then $\binom{n}{r} = {}_nC_r = \frac{n!}{r!(n-r)!}$.

Binomial Theorem *(Lesson 13-6, p. 905)*
For all complex numbers a and b, and for all integers n and r with $0 \leq r \leq n$, $(a + b)^n = \sum_{r=0}^{n} \binom{n}{r} a^{n-r} b^r$.

Binomial Probability Theorem *(Lesson 13-7, p. 913)*
Suppose an experiment has an outcome with probability p, so that the probability the outcome does not occur is $q = 1 - p$. Then in n independent repetitions of the experiment, the probability that the outcome occurs r times is $\binom{n}{r} p^r q^{n-r}$.

CAS Commands

The Computer Algebra System (CAS) commands used in this course and examples of their use are given below. Each command must be followed by a number, variable, expression, or equation, usually enclosed in parentheses.

Command	Description	Example
Define	A rule for a function is stored under the name indicated. Values of that function can then be calculated by entering the function's name followed by the value of the independent variable in parentheses.	Define $f(n)=2000\cdot n-1400$ *Done*; $f(4)$ 6600
| (such that)	Variable values that appear after the symbol are substituted into an expression, inequality, or equation that appears before the symbol.	$r=\frac{\sqrt{v}}{\sqrt{h\cdot\pi}}\|v=500000$ → $r=\frac{500\cdot\sqrt{2}}{\sqrt{h\cdot\pi}}$
solve	An equation, inequality, or system is solved for an indicated variable or variables. All real solutions are given.	$\text{solve}\left(y=\frac{1}{2}\cdot x-5 \text{ and } y=2\cdot x-1,\{x,y\}\right)$ → $x=\frac{-8}{3}$ and $y=\frac{-19}{3}$
expand	The Distributive Property is applied to products and powers of mathematical expressions.	$\text{expand}((72+w)\cdot(24+2\cdot w))$ → $2\cdot w^2+168\cdot w+1728$
DelVar	Any stored values for the indicated variable are deleted from memory.	DelVar *a* *Done*
cSolve	An equation or inequality is solved for an indicated variable. All complex solutions are given.	$\text{cSolve}(z^4=81,z)$ → $z=3\cdot i$ or $z=-3\cdot i$ or $z=-3$ or $z=3$
factor	A polynomial is factored over the rational numbers. On some CAS, if ",x" is added to the end of the polynomial, it is factored over the real numbers.	$\text{factor}(x^4-14\cdot x^2+45)$ → $(x-3)\cdot(x+3)\cdot(x^2-5)$; $\text{factor}(x^4-14\cdot x^2+45,x)$ → $(x-3)\cdot(x+3)\cdot(x+\sqrt{5})\cdot(x-\sqrt{5})$
cFactor	A polynomial is factored over the complex numbers.	$\text{cFactor}(x^2+36,x)$ → $(x+-6\cdot i)\cdot(x+6\cdot i)$
rfactor	On some CAS, a polynomial is factored over the real numbers.	$\text{rfactor}(x^2-14)$ → $(x+\sqrt{14})\cdot(x-\sqrt{14})$

Chapter 7

Lesson 7-1 (pp. 452–458)

Mental Math **a.** Answers vary. Sample: –13 **b.** does not exist **c.** Answers vary. Sample: $12 + 6i$ **d.** does not exist

Activity **Step 1:** For even powers, see graph in Activity. Odd powers: functions are in Quadrants I and III and they are symmetric about the origin.

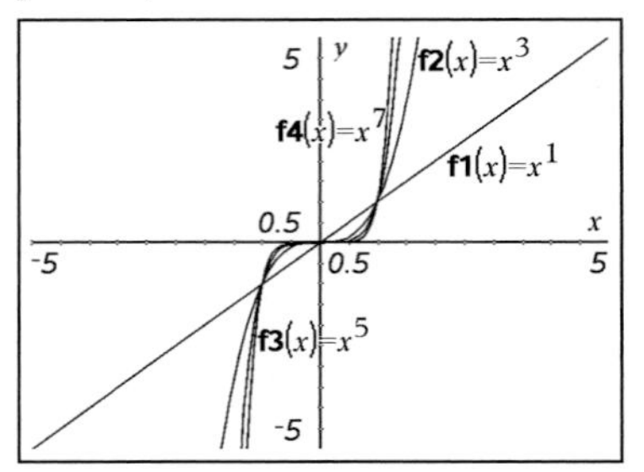

Step 2: Even powers: The domain is the set of all real numbers and the range is $\{y \mid y \geq 0\}$; Odd powers: The domain is the set of all real numbers and the range is the set of all real numbers. **Step 3:** Answers vary. Sample: The graphs of even-power functions are in Quadrants I and II, and they are symmetric to the *y*-axis. The graphs of odd-power functions are in Quadrants I and III, and they are symmetric about the origin.

Questions

1. 2048; 4096 **3.** the probability of an independent event with probability $p = 0.3$ happening four times in a row is 0.0081. **5. a.** 0.00098 **b.** 0.00000095 **c.** p^{10}

7. a.

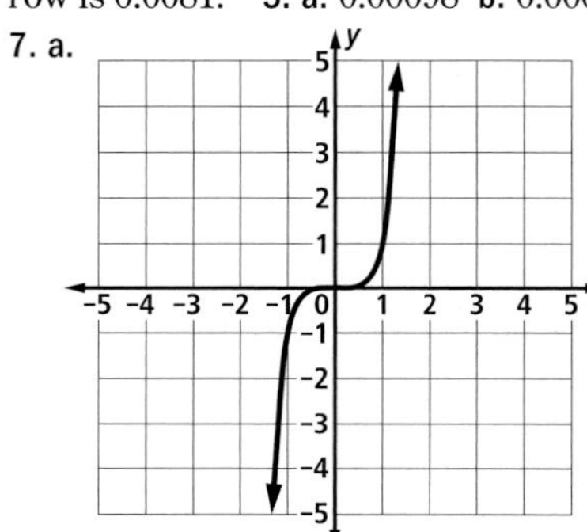

b. domain: all real numbers; range: all real numbers **c.** rotation symmetry about the origin

9. $\{y \mid y \geq 0\}$; I; II

11. B; The graph should pass through the origin and be symmetric over the *y*-axis. B is the only graph that meets both of these requirements. **13. a.** 0.5 **b.** 0.25 **c.** about 2.98×10^{-8} or 0.0000000298 **15. a.** $x > 0; x < 0$ **b.** all real numbers x such that $x \neq 0$; none **17.** $y = x^{13}$

19. a.

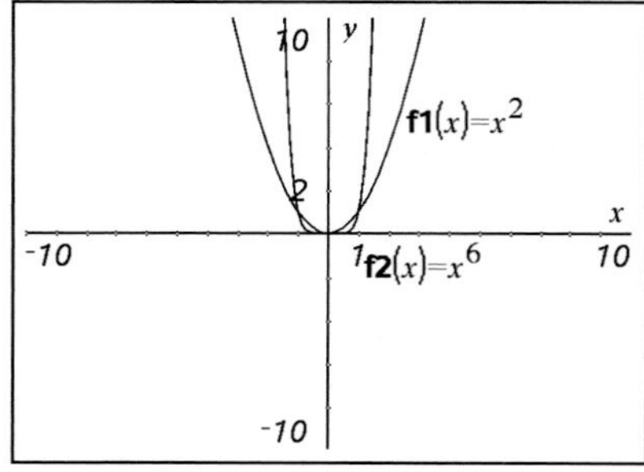

b. $x = -1, 0, 1$ **c.** $\{x \mid -1 < x < 1, x \neq 0\}$ **d.** The difference between $f(x)$ and $g(x)$ increases, then decreases as x increases from 0 to 1. **21. a.** 2 **b.** $4 + 6i$ **23.** $x = \frac{3}{4}, y = -\frac{27}{8}, z = \frac{1}{2}$ **25.** $\frac{3}{2}x^3$

Lesson 7-2 (pp. 459–465)

Mental Math **a.** false **b.** true **c.** true **d.** true

Activity 1 **Step 1:** **a.** x^2 **b.** x^{10} **c.** x^{15} **Step 2:** x^{m+n} **Step 3:** **a.** $x^5 \cdot y^5$ **b.** $x^2 \cdot y^2$ **c.** $x^{15} \cdot y^{15}$ **Step 4:** $x^m \cdot y^m$

Guided Example 1 3; 10; 7

Activity 2 **Step 1:** **a.** x^6 **b.** y^{20} **c.** z^{18} **d.** 1 **Step 2:** x^{mn}

Guided Example 5 $2r$; $4r^2$; $4r^2$; 4; 0.785; 78.5

Questions

1. Answers vary. Sample: $3^2 \cdot 3^3 = 3^5$ **3.** Answers vary. Sample: $(7^2)^3 = 7^6$ **5.** Answers vary. Sample: $\left(\frac{3}{5}\right)^4 = \frac{3^4}{5^4}$ **7.** 5^6; $(5^2)^3 = (5 \cdot 5)^3 = (5 \cdot 5)(5 \cdot 5)(5 \cdot 5) = 5 \cdot 5 \cdot 5 \cdot 5 \cdot 5 \cdot 5 = 5^6$ **9.** Power of a Quotient Theorem **11.** n^{70} **13.** $27x^{12}$ **15.** v^a **17.** 6 **19.** about 5417 times

21. a.

b. 6 **23.** $5^5 \cdot 7^4$ **25.** Answers vary. Sample: $x^2 \cdot x^5$; $x^1 \cdot x^6$; $x^0 \cdot x^7$ **27.** $\frac{-2}{3x^2}$ **29.** 1 **31.** even

Lesson 7-3 (pp. 466–471)

Mental Math **a.** 4 **b.** 11 **c.** $\left(\frac{b}{2}\right)^2$ **d.** $\left(\frac{b}{2}\right)^2 - c$

Activity **Step 1:** **a.** $\frac{1}{x^3}$ **b.** $\frac{1}{x^8}$ **c.** $\frac{1}{x^{11}}$ **Step 2:** $\frac{1}{x^n}$

Guided Example 1 2^5; 0.03125

Guided Example 3 **a.** 5; 12; –7 **b.** –3; 5; 2 **c.** 4; 6; 6; 6; 6; 4

Questions

1. t^{-7} **3.** $\frac{1}{x^4}$ **5.** 7 **7. a.** 1 **b.** $\frac{5}{9}$ **c.** $\frac{25}{81}$ **9. a.** 0.001953125 **b.** $1.953125 \cdot 10^{-3}$ **11.** $\frac{2y^3}{3}$ **13.** $\frac{2}{a^3b^4}$ **15.** 1 **17.** D **19.** $A = khg^{-5}$ **21.** $\frac{4x^{38}}{9y^{26}z^{34}}$ **23. a.** $\frac{28}{10^5}$; $\frac{49}{10^5}$; $\frac{126}{10^5}$ **b.** $2.8 \cdot 10^{-4}$; $4.9 \cdot 10^{-4}$; $1.26 \cdot 10^{-3}$ **25.** $4x^2y^{-3}$ **27.** $20a^4$ **29.** A; the range contains no negative numbers. **31. a.** domain: all real numbers except 0; range: all negative real numbers **b.** domain: all real numbers except 0; range: all real numbers except 0

Lesson 7-4 (pp. 472–478)

Mental Math **a.** $\frac{1}{81}$ **b.** $\frac{1}{8}$ **c.** $\frac{1}{648}$

Guided Example 2 **a.** 0.055; 1.0561; 1.0561; 0.0561; 5.61 **b.** 0.055, 365; 365 • 1, 1.0565; 1.0565, 0.0565; 5.65

Questions

1. \$2593.79; \$2691.10; \$2792.06; \$2896.81; \$3005.49 **3. a.** $A = P\left(1 + \frac{r}{12}\right)^{12t}$ **b.** $A = P\left(1 + \frac{r}{366}\right)^{366t}$ **5.** 4.08% **7.** False; because the starting balance gets larger each year, the interest earned each year increases. **9. a.** \$3405 **b.** \$3423.49 **c.** No; when interest is compounded, the starting balance increases each year and thus the amount of interest earned each year also increases, but with simple interest, the principal used to calculate the amount of interest earned does not increase during the investment period. **11.** \$91.36 **13.** $\frac{1}{729}$ **15.** False; Answers vary. Sample: $(2^3)^5$ is not the same as 2^{3^5}. $(2^3)^5 = 2^{15}$ but $2^{3^5} = 2^{243}$. **17.** $T_{-3,-8}$ **19. a.** 4, 12, 36, 108, 324 **b.** No; the terms do not increase by a constant amount.

Lesson 7-5 (pp. 479–485)

Mental Math **a.** no **b.** yes; 11 **c.** yes; -0.1 **d.** no

Guided Example 2 1; 4; 5 – 1; 81; 324; $4(-3)^{10-1}$; 4(-19,683)

Questions

1. adding; multiplying **3.** no **5. a.** 200, 0.02, $2 \cdot 10^{-17}$, $2 \cdot 10^{-47}$ **b.** The first 15 terms are 200, 20, 2, 0.2, 0.02, 0.002, 0.0002, $2 \cdot 10^{-4}, \ldots, 2 \cdot 10^{-12}$.

	A n	B	C	D	E
◆		=200*(.1)^('n−1)			
1	1	200.			
2	2	20.			
3	3	2.			
4	4	.2			
5	5	.02			

B =200·(.1)^'n−1

7. a. $r = \frac{g_{n+1}}{g_n}$ **b.** $g_{n+1} = x(r)^n$ **9. a. i.** 0.38 **ii.** 0.38 **iii.** 0.38 **iv.** 0.38 **b.** They are all equal. **11. a.** $g_n = 6.6(0.6)^{n-1}$ **b.** 1 in. **13. a.** $g_t = 5000(1.0225)^t$ **b.** \$7802.55 **c.** No; there is not a constant ratio between amounts. **15.** 224, 448; $g_n = 14(2)^{n-1}$

17. a. $\begin{cases} g_1 = 23 \\ g_n = -g_{n-1}, \text{ for integers } n \geq 2 \end{cases}$

b. $g_n = 23(-1)^{n-1}$ **19. a.** $\frac{1}{8}$ **b.** $A_n = \frac{1}{8}\left(\frac{1}{2}\right)^n$ **21.** $N = kab^{-2}c^{-3}$ **23.** longer

Lesson 7-6 (pp. 486–492)

Mental Math **a.** positive, two **b.** positive, two **c.** negative, none **d.** zero, one

Guided Example 2 5th; 77; $\frac{1}{5}$; 2.384; 2.384; 2.384; odd

Questions

1. $2^{\frac{1}{12}}$ **3.** 228.6 Hz **5.** 3 **7.** 2 **9.** 1 **11.** 1.26 **13.** $x = 12, -12, 12i, -12i$ **15.** false **17.** D; The exponent is negative, so it cannot be an nth root. **19.** 6% **21.** Answers vary. Sample: $x = \frac{1}{4}$ **23.** > **25.** $\frac{1}{4}$ **27.** geometric; $5 \cdot 2^{n-1}$ **29.** true

Lesson 7-7 (pp. 493–499)

Mental Math **a.** 2 qt **b.** 4 qt

Activity 1 **Step 1:** $8^{0.5}$; $8^{1.25}$; $8^{1.5}$; $8^{1.\overline{6}}$; 2; 2.83; 4.76; 13.45; 22.63; 32 **Step 2:** It is between 1 and 8. **Step 3:** It is between 8 and 64. **Step 4:** It gets larger. **Step 5:** Answers vary. Sample: It will be between 32 and 64, since the exponent is between $\frac{5}{3}$ and 2.

Activity 2 **Step 1: a.** No; because there is no real 6th root of a negative number, so the first graph will only be defined for nonnegative numbers.

b.

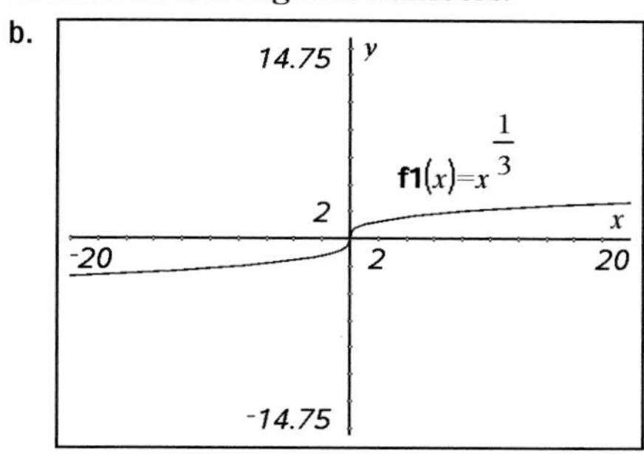

c.

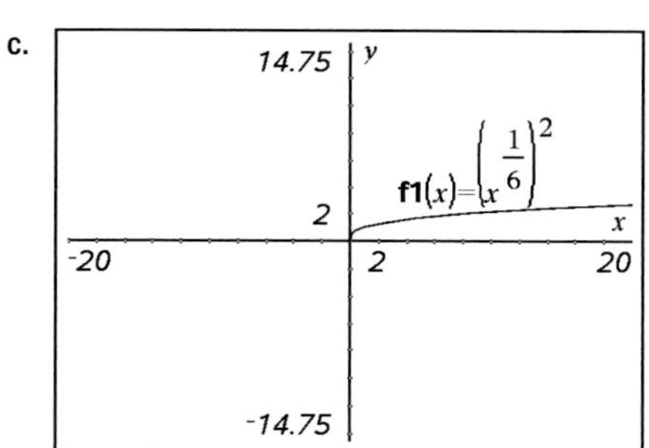

Step 2: aa. No; the 5th power of a negative number is negative, but the square root of the 10th power of a negative number is a positive number.

ab.

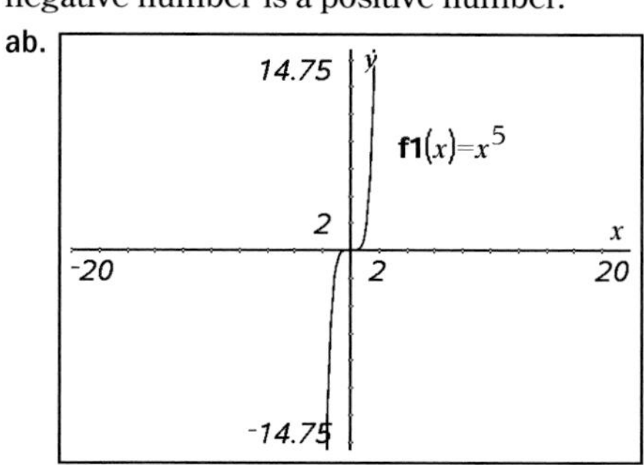

ac.

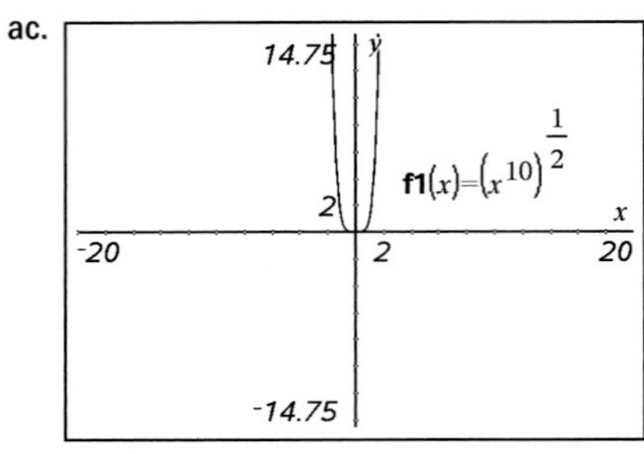

b. Answers vary. Sample: I predict the graph will look like the sections of the graphs in Part a that are in Quadrant I.

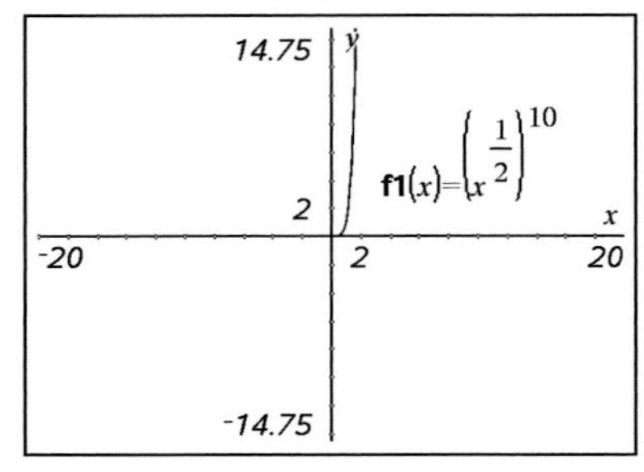

Step 3: Answers vary. Sample: I predict the graph will be a ray in Quadrant I.

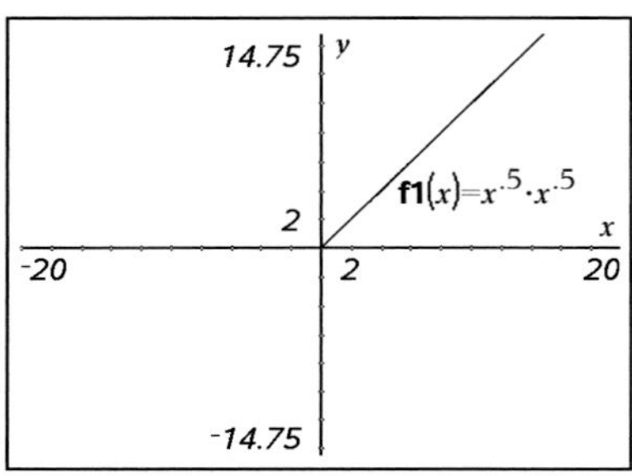

Step 4: The Power of a Power and Power of a Product Postulates do not hold for noninteger rational exponents with negative bases.

Questions

1. $x^{\frac{3}{7}}$ **3. a.** $(10{,}000{,}000^4)^{\frac{1}{7}}, \left(10{,}000{,}000^{\frac{1}{7}}\right)^4$ **b.** $\left(10{,}000{,}000^{\frac{1}{7}}\right)^4$ **c.** 10,000 **5.** 32 **7.** 27 **9.** 2197 **11.** $c^{\frac{25}{12}}$ **13.** $R = 100{,}000$ **15.** $s = 10^{\frac{7}{4}}$ **17.** $<$

19. a.

Rational Power	$\left(\frac{1}{4}\right)^0$	$\left(\frac{1}{4}\right)^{\frac{1}{4}}$	$\left(\frac{1}{4}\right)^{\frac{1}{2}}$	$\left(\frac{1}{4}\right)^{\frac{2}{3}}$	$\left(\frac{1}{4}\right)^1$
Decimal Power	$\left(\frac{1}{4}\right)^0$	$\left(\frac{1}{4}\right)^{0.25}$	$\left(\frac{1}{4}\right)^{0.5}$	$\left(\frac{1}{4}\right)^{0.\overline{6}}$	$\left(\frac{1}{4}\right)^1$
Value	1	0.707	0.5	0.397	0.25
Rational Power	$\left(\frac{1}{4}\right)^{\frac{4}{3}}$	$\left(\frac{1}{4}\right)^{\frac{3}{2}}$	$\left(\frac{1}{4}\right)^{\frac{7}{4}}$	$\left(\frac{1}{4}\right)^2$	
Decimal Power	$\left(\frac{1}{4}\right)^{1.\overline{3}}$	$\left(\frac{1}{4}\right)^{1.5}$	$\left(\frac{1}{4}\right)^{1.75}$	$\left(\frac{1}{4}\right)^2$	
Value	0.157	0.125	0.088	0.063	

b. $\left(\frac{1}{4}\right)^n$ gets smaller as n gets larger. **c.** Answers vary. Sample: Since $\frac{3}{2} < \frac{5}{3} < \frac{7}{4}$, $0.125 < \left(\frac{1}{4}\right)^{\frac{5}{3}} < 0.088$. **d.** smaller **21.** 2^n **23.** $\frac{8}{27}$ **25.** 0.008 **27.** 1374.6 times as heavy; it is less than the original estimate. **29.** $\left(-1 - \sqrt{3}i\right)^3$ **31. a.** nonnegative numbers **b.** nonpositive numbers **33.** $T = s_{\frac{2}{3}, \frac{1}{12}}$

Lesson 7-8 (pp. 500–504)

Mental Math a. 64 **b.** 8 **c.** 8

Guided Example 1 1. $\frac{625}{16}$; $\frac{5}{2}$; $\frac{125}{8}$; $\frac{2}{5}$; $\frac{8}{125}$; $\frac{125}{8}$; $\frac{4096}{244{,}140{,}625}$; $\frac{8}{125}$; $\frac{125}{8}$

Questions

1. $\frac{1}{10}$ **3.** $\frac{27}{125}$ **5.** 0.115 **7.** 0.890 **9.** about 4165 kg **11.** $w = \frac{1}{32}$ **13.** $x \approx 0.010$ **15.** 4.5% **17.** True; $\left(x^{-\frac{1}{5}}\right)^{-5} = x$. **19.** $t = \frac{1}{2}$ **21.** x; Let $x = 2$: $(2^{-4})^{-\frac{1}{4}} = \left(\frac{1}{16}\right)^{-\frac{1}{4}} = 16^{\frac{1}{4}} = 2$. **23.** $\frac{1}{2}x^{\frac{8}{3}}$; Let $x = 27$: $\frac{27}{6(27)^{-\frac{4}{3}}}\left(3(27)^{\frac{1}{3}}\right) = \frac{27}{6 \cdot \frac{1}{81}}(9) = \frac{6561}{2}$, $\frac{1}{2}(27)^{\frac{8}{3}} = \frac{1}{2} \cdot 3^8 = \frac{6561}{2}$. **25.** 100,000 **27.** 0.16 **29.** Since $y = k$ does not intersect $y = x^n$ for $k < 0$ and n even, there are no real solutions.

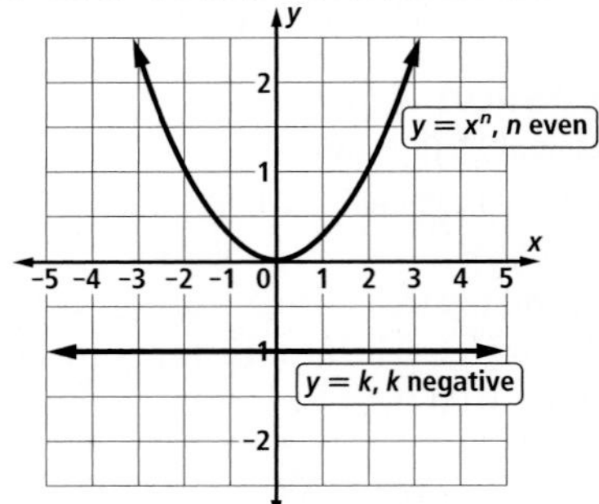

31. $\frac{a^3}{4b^6}$

Self-Test (p. 509)

1. Exponents do not distribute across addition. $(3 + 4)^{\frac{1}{2}} = 7^{\frac{1}{2}} \approx 2.65$, while $3^{\frac{1}{2}} + 4^{\frac{1}{2}} \approx 3.73$. **2.** $7^{-2} = \frac{1}{7^2} = \frac{1}{49}$ **3.** $(214{,}358{,}881)^{\frac{1}{8}} = 11$ because $11^8 = 214{,}358{,}881$. **4.** $\left(\frac{343}{27}\right)^{-\frac{4}{3}} = \left(\frac{27}{343}\right)^{\frac{4}{3}} = \left(\frac{3}{7}\right)^4 = \frac{81}{2041}$ **5.** $\frac{7.3 \cdot 10^3}{10^{-4}} = 7.3 \cdot 10^3 \cdot 10^4 = 7.3 \cdot 10^7 = 73{,}000{,}000$ **6.** $\left(1728x^9y^{27}\right)^{\frac{1}{3}} = 1728^{\frac{1}{3}}x^{\frac{9}{3}}y^{\frac{27}{3}} = 12x^3y^9$ **7.** $\frac{84x^{21}y^5}{6x^3y^7} = \frac{84}{6}x^{21-3}y^{5-7} = 14x^{18}y^{-2}$, or $\frac{14x^{18}}{y^2}$ **8. a.** True; $-5^{\frac{1}{3}}$ is negative and $5^{-\frac{1}{3}}$ is positive. **b.** False; $3^{-6.4} = \frac{1}{3^{6.4}}$, $3^{-6.5} = \frac{1}{3^{6.5}}$, and $\frac{1}{3^{6.4}} > \frac{1}{3^{6.5}}$. **9.** $\left(x^{\frac{3}{2}}\right)^{\frac{2}{3}} = 0.8^{\frac{2}{3}}$; $x = 0.8^{\frac{2}{3}}$; $x \approx 0.862$ **10.** 1.27 **11.** n is even because the graph has reflection symmetry about the y-axis. **12. a.** $h_1 = 5$; $h_2 = 0.85 \cdot 5 = 4.25$; $h_3 = 0.85 \cdot 4.25 \approx 3.61$; $h_4 \approx 0.85 \cdot 3.61 \approx 3.07$. **b.** $h_n = 5(0.85)^{n-1}$ **13.** False; the range of $y = x^2$ is all real numbers great der than or equal to zero, so $y = x^2$ is a counterexample. **14. a.** $r = \frac{0.6}{3} = 0.2$; $r = 0.2$; $0.024 \cdot 0.2 = 0.0048$, $0.0048 \cdot 0.2 = 0.00096$

b. $\begin{cases} h_1 = 3 \\ h_n = 0.2h_{n-1}, \text{ for integers } n \geq 2 \end{cases}$ **c.** $h_n = 3(0.2)^{n-1}$

15. a. $r = \frac{-12}{-4} = 3$; $-108 \cdot 3 = -324$, $-324 \cdot 3 = -972$

b. $\begin{cases} h_1 = -4 \\ h_n = 3h_{n-1}, \text{ for integers } n \geq 2 \end{cases}$ **c.** $h_n = -4(3)^{n-1}$

16. $\left(\frac{1}{3}\right)^{10} \approx 0.000017$ 17. $1.23 \cdot (1.2)^2 \approx 1.77$ minutes = 1 minute 46.2 seconds 18. Solve $x^{10} = 1024$ for x. A CAS in real-number mode shows that $x = 2$ or $x = -2$, so the real 10th roots of 1024 are 2 and -2. 19. False; $-4(3)^{n-1}$ represents only the positive 4th root of 625, which is 5.

20. a. $500(1+0.0425)^6 \approx \$641.84$ b. $\left(1+\frac{0.0425}{4}\right)^4 \approx 1.0432$, so the APY is about 4.32%.
21. $7854 = P\left(1+\frac{0.068}{12}\right)^{12 \cdot 7}$, so $P \approx \$4{,}885.96$.

Self-Test Correlation Chart

Question	1	2	3	4	5	6	7
Objective(s)	E	A	A	A	B	B	B
Lesson(s)	7-2, 7-6, 7-7, 7-8	7-2, 7-3, 7-6, 7-7, 7-8	7-2, 7-3, 7-6, 7-7, 7-8	7-2, 7-3, 7-6, 7-7, 7-8	7-2, 7-3, 7-7, 7-8	7-2, 7-3, 7-7, 7-8	7-2, 7-3, 7-7, 7-8
Question	**8**	**9**	**10**	**11**	**12**	**13**	**14**
Objective(s)	E	D	A	I	H	I	C
Lesson(s)	7-2, 7-6, 7-7, 7-8	7-6, 7-7, 7-8	7-2, 7-3, 7-6, 7-7, 7-8	7-1	7-5	7-1	7-5
Question	**15**	**16**	**17**	**18**	**19**	**20**	**21**
Objective(s)	C	F	F	D	E	G	G
Lesson(s)	7-5	7-1, 7-6, 7-7, 7-8	7-1, 7-6, 7-7, 7-8	7-6, 7-7, 7-8	7-2, 7-6, 7-7, 7-8	7-4	7-4

Chapter Review (pp. 510–513)

Questions

1. 1 3. $\frac{3}{5}$ 5. 16 7. 24.73 9. 18.52 11. $y = 9$
13. $4x^6$ 15. $\frac{125p^4}{27q^4}$ 17. $-4x^6y^2$ 19. a. $g_n = 4(-3)^{n-1}$
b. $\begin{cases} g_1 = 4 \\ g_n = -3g^{n-1}, \text{ for } n \geq 2 \end{cases}$ c. $g_{16} = -57{,}395{,}628$
21. a. $4(1.075)^{24}$ b. 22.691 23. 7, 21, 63, 189 25. 6, 4, $\frac{8}{3}$, $\frac{16}{9}$
27. $x = \pm 6$ 29. $y = \pm 2$ 31. $y = 216$ 33. $x \approx 268.01$
35. $m \approx 13.87$ 37. False; $\pi^{5.4} > \pi^{5.3}$, thus $\frac{1}{\pi^{5.4}} < \frac{1}{\pi^{5.3}}$.
39. a. ± 11 b. 11 41. true 43. A 45. B, C
47. a. odd numbers b. 2 49. $\frac{1}{n}$th 51. 61% 53. $\left(\frac{T}{t}\right)^{\frac{2}{3}}$
55. $\frac{3\sqrt[3]{6}}{2\sqrt[3]{36}} \approx 0.825$ 57. \$3465.09 59. a. \$3357.34 b. \$629.15
61. \$436.45 63. a. 18.1 cm × 22.6 cm b. 15.2 cm× 12.2 cm
65. $y = x^8$ 67. a.

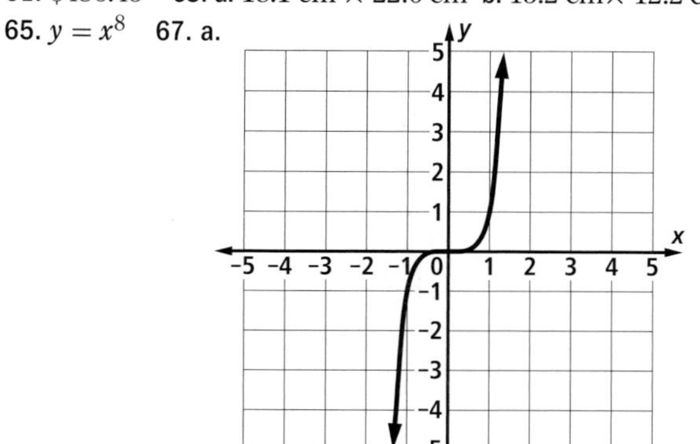

b. domain: all real numbers; range: all real numbers
c. rotation symmetry about the origin

69.

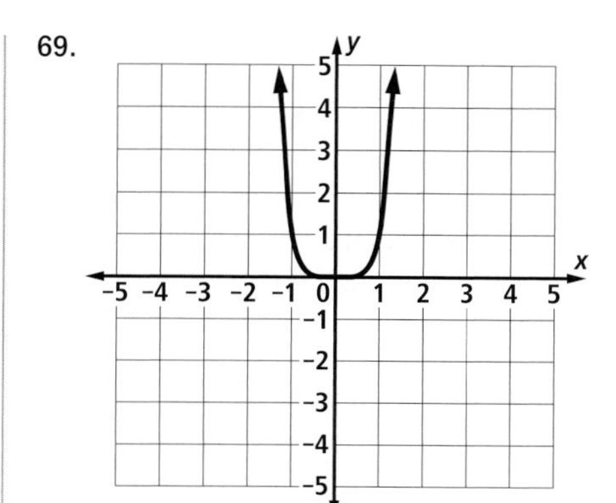

The range $y \geq 0$ does not include $y = -5$.

Chapter 8

Lesson 8-1 (pp. 516–521)

Mental Math a. $\frac{3}{2} + i$ b. $-10 - 5i$ c. 13 d. $k^2 + r^2$
Activity Step 1 \$27,040 **Step 2** \$27,280 **Step 3** discount first and then rebate; \$240
Guided Example 2 a. $3x^2$; $3x^2$ b. $x - 2$; $x - 2$; $x^2 - 4x + 4$; $3x^2 - 12x + 12$
Questions
1. a. \$20,240 b. \$20,000 3. a. -21,296 b. -21,296 5. Yes; $f(g(x)) = (x - 3) + 1 = x - 2$, $g(f(x)) = (x + 1) - 3 = x - 2$.
7. a. $-4a^2 - 4a - 4$ b. $16a^2 - 4a + 1$ 9. a. the set of real numbers other than 0 b. no 11. the set of real numbers other than 0 13. $f(x) = 0.6x$; $g(x) = x - 300$; $f(g(x)) = 0.6(x - 300) = 0.6x - 180$; $g(f(x)) = 0.6x - 300$;

He should take Executive Rental's offer. **15. a.** $w = \frac{k_1}{z}$; $f: z \rightarrow \frac{k_1}{z}$ **b.** $z = k_2x^4$; $g: x \rightarrow k_2x^4$ **c.** $w = \frac{k_1}{k_2x^4} = \frac{k_3}{x^4}$; $h: x \rightarrow \frac{k_3}{x^4}$ **d.** w varies inversely as the fourth power of x. **e.** $h = f \circ g$ **17. a.** x^4 **b.** when $x = 0$

19. $\begin{bmatrix} \frac{1}{a} & \frac{7}{18a} \\ 0 & \frac{1}{18} \end{bmatrix}$ **21.** false **23. a.** $\frac{13}{4}$ **b.** $-\frac{4}{13}$

Lesson 8-2 (pp. 522-528)

Mental Math a. $\frac{1}{100}$ **b.** $\frac{20}{100}$ or $\frac{1}{5}$ **c.** $\left(\frac{4}{10}\right)^n \cdot \left(\frac{5}{10}\right)^m$, or $\left(\frac{2}{5}\right)^n \cdot \left(\frac{1}{2}\right)^m$

Guided Example 2 a. x; y^2 **b.** $y = x^2$; $y = x$

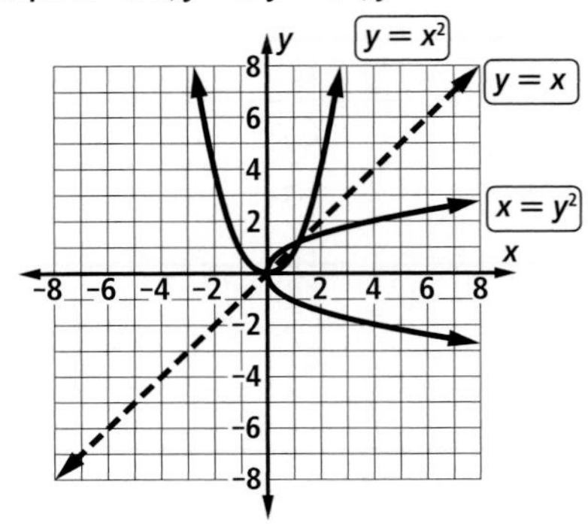

c. is not; Answers vary. Sample: The graph of the inverse contains the points (1, 1) and (1, -1), which have the same first coordinate.

Questions

1. by switching the coordinates of the points in the relation **3. a.** $g = \{(-9, -4), (-7, -3), (-1, 0), (5, 3), (7, 4), (11, 6)\}$

b.

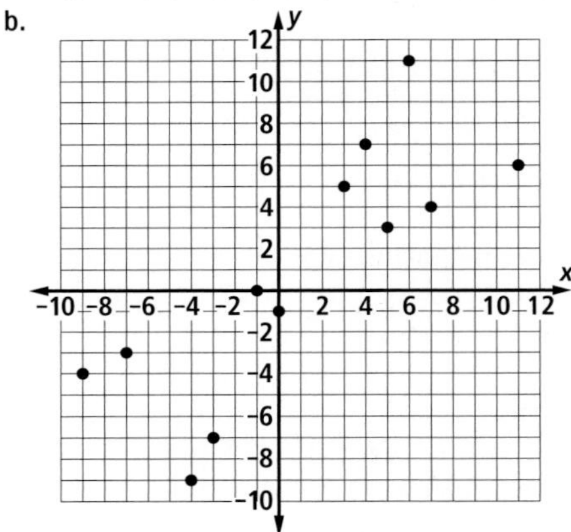

c. The graph of the inverse is the graph of f reflected over the line with equation $y = x$. **d.** $f(x) = 2x - 1$ **e.** $g(x) = \frac{x+1}{2}$ **5.** The graph of the inverse of any relation f is the reflection of the graph of f over the line with equation $y = x$. **7.** $y = 5x + 10$ **9.** The inverse of q is not a function because the graph of q does not pass the horizontal-line test. **11.** No; the graph of the function does not pass the horizontal-line test. **13.** $H: x \rightarrow \frac{x}{2}$

15. a, c.

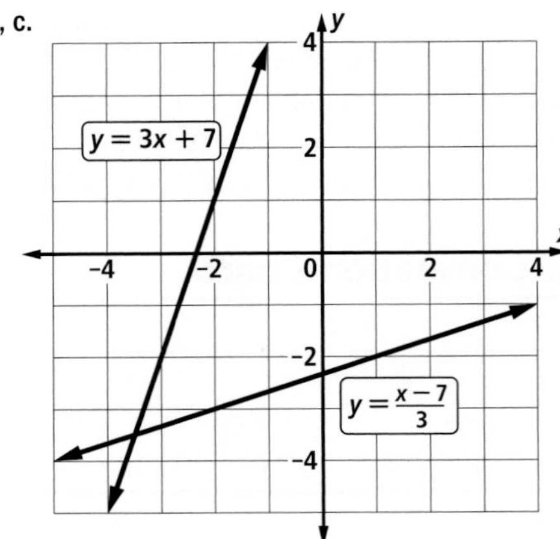

b. $y = \frac{x-7}{3}$

d. Yes; the graph of the inverse satisfies the vertical-line test. **e.** The slope of the inverse function is the reciprocal of the slope of the function. **17. a.** $U = \frac{25}{16}E$ **b.** $E = 0.64U$ **c.** Yes; the points in the first function are of the form (price in euros, price in dollars), and the points in the second function are of the form (price in dollars, price in euros). **19. a.** 8 **b.** 4 **c.** x **d.** the identity function **21.** False; $|-3(-1)| = 3$, but $3(-1) = -3$. **23.** $BC = 9$; $CE = 8$

Lesson 8-3 (pp. 529-536)

Mental Math a. $y - 3 = -2(x - 1)^2$ **b.** $y + 2 = -2(x + 2)^2$ **c.** $y - 5.4 = 2(x - 0.3)^2$

Activity 1 Step 1 $g(x) = 12x - 4$; $g(x) = \frac{1}{3} + \frac{x}{12}$ **Step 2** $f(g(x)) = x$; $g(f(x)) = x$ **Step 3** The results are the same.

Guided Example $8x$, 11; $\frac{8x-11}{3}$; $\frac{8y-11}{3}$; $8y$, 11; 11, $8y$; $\frac{3x+11}{8}$; $\frac{3x+11}{8}$

Activity 2 f^{-1} is a function if the domain of f is $x \geq 0$, or the domain of f is $x \leq 0$.

Questions

1. the inverse of f; f inverse **3.** Yes; $f(g(x)) = 5 - 2\left(\frac{x-5}{-2}\right) = 5 + x - 5 = x$; $g(f(x)) = \frac{(5-2x)-5}{-2} = \frac{-2x}{-2} = x$ **5. a.** $A(x) = x + 15$ **b.** $A^{-1}(x) = x - 15$ **c.** subtracting 15 **d.** 63 **7.** No; an equation for the inverse would be $x = 21$, which does not represent a function. **9.** $f^{-1}(x) = x^{\frac{1}{7}}$ **11. a.** $f^{-1}(x) = -12 - (2x)^{\frac{1}{3}}$ **b.** yes; all real numbers **13.** CODES ARE COOL

15. a.

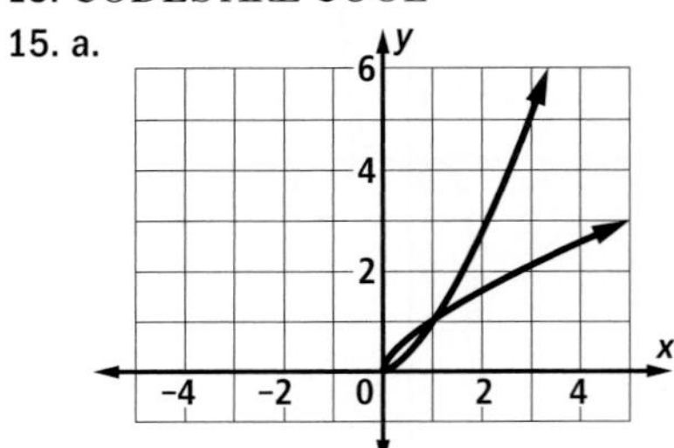

b. The graph of h is the graph of g reflected over the line with equation $y = x$. **c.** Each is equal to x. **d.** $64 = 512^{\frac{2}{3}}$

e. Yes, over the restricted domain $x \geq 0$, they are inverses because the graph of g is the reflection image of the graph of h over the line with equation $y = x$. **17.** $y = 2x - 14$ **19.** f; the inverse of the inverse of a function is the original function. **21.** B **23. a.** $\frac{11}{2}$ **b.** 1 **c.** $2x^{-2} + 5$ **d.** $(2x + 5)^{-2}$ **25. a.** $\frac{1}{4}$ **b.** all real numbers

Lesson 8-4 (pp. 537-544)

Mental Math **a.** \$4.50 **b.** \$6.75 **c.** 12 **d.** 20

Guided Example 2 **a.** 6561; positive; 4th; 9; 9; 9 **b.** $x^4 = 6561$; 9; -9; $9i$; $-9i$; 4th

Questions

1. René Descartes **3.** false **5.** about 3.77 **7.** 1.69 **9.** $\sqrt[n]{x^m}$, or $\left(\sqrt[n]{x}\right)^m$ **11. a.** 11, -11, $11i$, $-11i$ **b.** 11 **13.** c^3 **15.** $x^{\frac{1}{16}}$ **17.** A **19. a.** 1.62, 1.43, 2.78, 1.68, 1.51 **b.** about 1.856; about 85.6% **21. a.** $r = \sqrt[3]{\frac{3}{4\pi}V}$ **b.** $\left(\frac{3}{4\pi}V\right)^{\frac{1}{3}}$ **23. a.** $\left(43{,}046{,}721z^{48}\right)^{\frac{1}{16}}$ **b.** $\sqrt[16]{43{,}046{,}721z^{48}}$ **c.** 24 **25.** $\frac{\sqrt[4]{k}}{\sqrt[4]{k}} = 1$ **27. a.** $h(w(x))$ **b.** $h(w(x)) = -0.0010692x^2 + 0.4905x + 4$ **c.** about 420.1 ft **d.** about 466.8 ft **29.** -125 **31.** $t = -1$, 2, and -3 are not in the domain of g. **33. a.** 1.55 **b.** 1.60 **c.** 1.61 **d.** $\frac{\sqrt{5}+1}{2}$ **e.** Answers vary. Sample: As the approximations of $\sqrt{1 + \sqrt{1 + \ldots}}$ get more exact, they get closer to $\frac{\sqrt{5}+1}{2}$.

Lesson 8-5 (pp. 545-550)

Mental Math **a.** w^5 **b.** x^2 **c.** $\frac{36}{y^5}$ or $36y^{-5}$ **d.** $8w^4z^2 + \frac{wz^3}{2}$

Activity **Step1: a.** $(a \cdot b)^{\frac{1}{3}} - a^{\frac{1}{3}} \cdot b^{\frac{1}{3}} \mid a>0 \text{ and } b>0$ 0

b. $(a \cdot b)^{\frac{1}{12}} - a^{\frac{1}{12}} \cdot b^{\frac{1}{12}} \mid a>0 \text{ and } b>0$ 0

c. $a^{\frac{1}{4}} \cdot b^{\frac{1}{4}} - (a \cdot b)^{\frac{1}{4}} \mid a>0 \text{ and } b>0$ 0

d. $a^{\frac{1}{7}} \cdot b^{\frac{1}{7}} - (a \cdot b)^{\frac{1}{7}} \mid a>0 \text{ and } b>0$ 0

Step 2: 0 **Step 3:** $a^{\frac{1}{n}} \cdot b^{\frac{1}{n}}$

Guided Example 2 **Solution 1** $625x^4$; 625, x^4; $5x$ **Solution 2** $125x^3$; $625x^4$; x^4

Questions

1. For any nonnegative real numbers x and y, and any integer $n \geq 2$, $(xy)^{\frac{1}{n}} = x^{\frac{1}{n}} \cdot y^{\frac{1}{n}}$. **3.** 100 **5.** Answers vary. Sample: $\sqrt[3]{25} \cdot \sqrt[3]{10}$; $\sqrt[3]{50} \cdot \sqrt[3]{5}$; $\sqrt[3]{125} \cdot \sqrt[3]{2}$ **7.** $a = 27$, $b = 3$ **9.** $14\sqrt{7}$ **11. a.** $4y^6$ **b.** $\frac{y^8}{2}\sqrt[3]{y}$ **13.** 6 **15.** $\sqrt[3]{5} + \sqrt[3]{5}$ **17. a.** The Root of a Product Theorem does not apply when multiplying two different nth roots. **b.** $n = 80$ **19.** $2\sqrt{x^2 + y^2}$ **21. a.** about 0.189 **b.** about 0.040 **23. a.** $L^{-1}(x) = \frac{x-b}{m}$ **b.** They are reciprocals. **c.** when $m = 0$ **25.** $-\frac{4}{85} + \frac{33}{85}i$

Lesson 8-6 (pp. 551-555)

Mental Math **a.** 12 ft **b.** 4.5 ft **c.** 6 ft

Activity **Step1: a.** $\frac{\sqrt{2}}{2}$ **b.** $\frac{3\sqrt{5}}{5}$ **c.** $-\frac{13\sqrt{7}}{7}$ **Step 2:** yes **Step 3:** $\frac{\sqrt{a}}{a}$

Guided Example 1 **Solution 1** $\sqrt{3x}$; $\sqrt{3x}$; 4; x; 2; $3x$; $\sqrt{3x}$; $2x$ **Solution 2** $\sqrt{12x}$; $3\sqrt{12x}$; $\sqrt{3x}$; $\sqrt{12x}$; $2x$

Questions

1. a. 316,800 inches $\cdot \frac{1 \text{ foot}}{12 \text{ inches}} \cdot \frac{1 \text{ yard}}{3 \text{ feet}} = 8800$ yards **b.** 8800 yards $\cdot \frac{1 \text{ mile}}{1760 \text{ yards}} = 5$ miles **3.** 0.7 **5.** $\frac{b\sqrt{a}}{a}$ **7.** $\frac{11\sqrt{3}}{3}$ **9. a.** $\frac{3+\sqrt{5}}{3+\sqrt{5}}$ **b.** $\frac{21}{4} + \frac{7\sqrt{5}}{4}$ **11.** $\frac{\sqrt{3}}{2}$ **13.** $\frac{\sqrt{x}}{x^2}$ **15.** $\frac{4\sqrt{n}+24}{n-36}$ **17. a.** $\frac{16\sqrt{3}}{3}$ **b.** $\frac{a\sqrt{3}}{3}$; $\frac{2a\sqrt{3}}{3}$ **c.** $\frac{5\sqrt{3}}{3}$ **19.** $3a^2\sqrt[3]{2a}$ **21.** True; by the Power of a Power Postulate, each side is equivalent to $x^{\frac{1}{2}}y^{\frac{1}{8}}$. **23. a.** $g^{-1}(x) = x^3$ **b.** $(2x)^{\frac{1}{3}}$ **25.** No; the inverse contains two points, (5, 3) and (5, 8), with the same first coordinates. **27.** $\frac{1}{p^{\frac{5}{3}}}$ **29.** Gd

Lesson 8-7 (pp. 556-561)

Mental Math **a.** 10 min **b.** 9 min, 20 sec **c.** 8 min, 40 sec

Activity **Step 1:**

x	f1(x):...	f2(x):...
	(-2)^x	(-7)^x
2	4.	49.
4	16.	2.4E3
6	64.	1.18E5
8	256.	5.76E6
10	1.02E3	2.82E8
12	4.1E3	1.38E10
2		

x	f1(x):...	f2(x):...
	(-6)^x	(-5)^x
2	36.	25.
4	1.3E3	625.
6	4.67E4	1.56E4
8	1.68E6	3.91E5
10	6.05E7	9.77E6
12	2.18E9	2.44E8
2		

Step 2: Answers vary. Sample: Every even power of a negative number is positive; every even power of an even number is even; every even power of an odd number is odd.

Step 3:

x	f1(x):...	f2(x):...
	(-2)^x	(-7)^x
1	-2.	-7.
3	-8.	-343.
5	-32.	-1.68E4
7	-128.	-8.24E5
9	-512.	-4.04E7
11	-2.05E3	-1.98E9
1		

x	f1(x):...	f2(x):...
	(-6)^x	(-5)^x
1	-6.	-5.
3	-216.	-125.
5	-7.78E3	-3.13E3
7	-2.8E5	-7.81E4
9	-1.01E7	-1.95E6
11	-3.63E8	-4.88E7
1		

Every odd power of a negative number is negative; every odd power of an even number is even; and every odd power of an odd number is odd. **Step 4:** Even; positive; odd; negative

Guided Example 1 5; -2; 3; -27

Questions

1. a. Answers vary. Sample: 2, 4, 6 **b.** Answers vary. Sample: 1, 3, 5 **3. a.** positive **b.** negative **c.** negative **d.** negative **5.** $(-2)^3$ **7.** -6 **9.** -1 **11.** $-\frac{4}{3}y^9$ **13.** $2q^3\sqrt[7]{10q^2}$ **15.** The intersection point is (-3, -27). This shows that $(-3)^3 = -27$, or $\sqrt[3]{-27} = -3$. **17.** Answers vary. Sample: If $x < 0$, then $\sqrt[18]{x^6} = -\sqrt[3]{x}$. **19. a.** $(2 + 2i)^4 = (2(1 + i))^4 = 2^4((1 + i)^2)^2 = 2^4 \cdot (2i)^2 = 16 \cdot (-4) = -64$ **b.** $(-2 - 2i)^4 = (-(2 + 2i))^4 = (-1)^4(2 + 2i)^4 = 1(-64) = -64$ **c.** $(2 - 2i)^4 = (2(1 - i))^4 = 2^4((1 - i)^2)^2 = 2^4 \cdot (-2i)^2 = 16 \cdot (-4) = -64$ **d.** The other fourth root is $-2 + 2i$. $(-2 + 2i)^4 = (-(2 - 2i))^4 = (-1)^4(2 - 2i)^4 = 1(-64) = -64$ **e.** $\sqrt[4]{-64}$ is not defined because none of the 4th roots of -64 are real numbers. **21.** $7 - 4\sqrt{3}$ **23.** 4 **25.** $r = 512$ **27.** 85

Lesson 8-8 (pp. 562-567)

Mental Math a. $y = \frac{1}{7}x$; yes **b.** $x + y = 4.5$; yes **c.** $x = 13$; no

Guided Example 2 Solution 1 $-\sqrt[6]{x}$, -5; $-\sqrt[6]{x}$; 729, 6th **Check** 729; 729; 3; $x = 729$; no **Solution 2** $\sqrt[6]{x} \geq 0$; no

Questions

1. 1.28 m **3.** $m = 1296$ **5.** $w = 16{,}777{,}216$ **7.** $x = 2.375$ **9.** $(1 - \sqrt{15}, -2)$, $(1 + \sqrt{15}, -2)$ **11. a.** about 1.62 ft **b.** 1.275 ft **c.** $18.2 = 4hs + 2s^2$; $18.2 = 2(2hs + s^2)$; $9.1 = 2hs + s^2$; $9.1 + h^2 = 2hs + s^2 + h^2$; $\sqrt{9.1 + h^2} = s + h$; $s = -h + \sqrt{9.1 + h^2}$ **13. a.** 36, 226, 52, 38; 1.36, 3.26, 1.52, 1.38

b. The geometric mean of the size-change factors is about 1.70, indicating an average increase of about 70% per decade. **c.** about \$157,575 **15.** $x = -1$ **17.** $-2y^3$ **19.** Answers vary. Sample: $((-1)^4)^{\frac{1}{4}} = 1 \neq -1$ **21.** true; $\frac{\sqrt{3t}}{\sqrt{t}} = \frac{\sqrt{3t}}{\sqrt{t}} \cdot \frac{\sqrt{3}}{\sqrt{3}} = \frac{3\sqrt{t}}{\sqrt{3t}}$ **23. a.** $u(v(x)) = \sqrt[3]{x^6} = x^2$; domain: all real numbers **b.** $v(u(x)) = (\sqrt[3]{x})^6 = x^2$; domain: all real numbers

25. $\begin{cases} x \geq -2 \\ y \geq -4 \\ y \leq 4 \\ y \leq 4 - 2x \end{cases}$

Self-Test (pp. 572-573)

1. $4 - (3(-1) + 7)^2 = 4 - 16 = -12$
2. $f(g(x)) = 4 - (3x + 7)^2 = -9x^2 - 42x - 45$
3. $g \circ f(x) = 3(4 - x^2) + 7 = 19 - 3x^2$
4. no; from Question 3, $g(f(x)) = 19 - 3x^2 \neq x$
5. a. $x = \frac{1}{2}y + 3$; $x - 3 = \frac{1}{2}y$; $y = 2x - 6$
b. Yes; Answers vary. Sample: It is a line in slope-intercept form.
6.

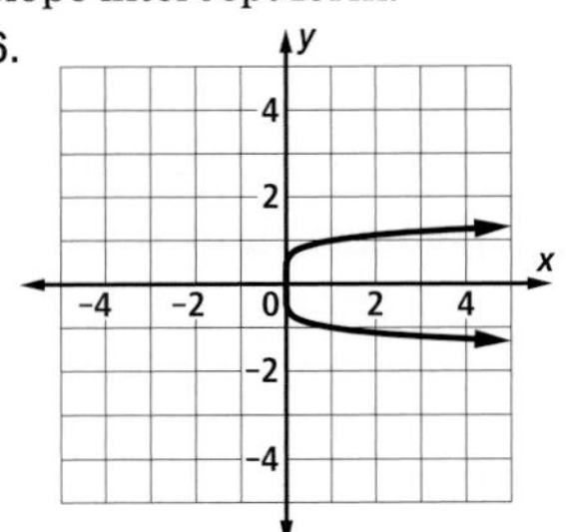

7. Restrict it to either only positive numbers or only negative numbers. That way, the graph of the original function will pass the horizontal-line test. **8.** False; While $(-2)^4 = 16$, the use of the radical symbol indicates the positive real 4th root of 16, which is 2. **9.** Substitute $r = 12$ into the formula and solve for S: $12 = \sqrt{\frac{S}{4\pi}}$; $144 = \frac{S}{4\pi}$; $S = 1810 \text{ cm}^2$ **10.** $\sqrt[3]{-216x^{12}y^3} = \sqrt[3]{-216} \cdot \sqrt[3]{x^{12}} \cdot \sqrt[3]{y^3} = -6x^4y$ **11.** $\sqrt[4]{\frac{32x^{12}}{x^4}} = \frac{\sqrt[4]{16} \cdot \sqrt[4]{2} \cdot \sqrt[4]{x^{12}}}{\sqrt[4]{x^4}} = \frac{2x^3\sqrt[4]{2}}{x} = 2x^2\sqrt[4]{2}$ **12.** $\frac{3x^2}{\sqrt{81x}} = \frac{3x^2}{9\sqrt{x}} \cdot \frac{\sqrt{x}}{\sqrt{x}} = \frac{3x^2\sqrt{x}}{9x} = \frac{x^2\sqrt{x}}{3}$ **13.** Deon and Carmen; Construct an isosceles right triangle with legs of length h and a hypotenuse of length 15. By the Pythagorean Theorem, $2h^2 = 15^2$. So $h = \sqrt{\frac{225}{2}} = \frac{15\sqrt{2}}{2}$. **14.** $\sqrt[5]{\sqrt[3]{13}} = (13^{\frac{1}{3}})^{\frac{1}{5}} = 13^{\frac{1}{15}}$ **15.** $\frac{24}{8 - 2\sqrt{3}} \cdot \frac{8 + 2\sqrt{3}}{8 + 2\sqrt{3}} = \frac{192 + 48\sqrt{3}}{52} = \frac{48 + 12\sqrt{3}}{13}$ **16.** $r = \sqrt[3]{\frac{3(268)}{4\pi}} = \sqrt[3]{\frac{201}{\pi}} \approx 4.00$ in. **17.** $25 = \sqrt[4]{7x}$; $\left(\frac{25}{4}\right)^2 = 7x$; $x = \frac{625}{112}$ **18.** $17 + \sqrt[3]{2x + 7} = 20$; $\sqrt[3]{2x + 7} = 3$; $2x + 7 = 27$; $x = 10$ **19.** odd integers **20.** domain: $x \geq 0$; range: $y \geq 0$
21. $\sqrt[6]{1092 \cdot 597 \cdot 46 \cdot 144 \cdot 32 \cdot 27} \approx 125$ bacteria per mL
22. None; The price when the coupon is used first is $0.7(P - 45) = 0.7P - 31.5$, and the price when the discount is taken first is $0.7P - 45$. For all values of P, $0.7P - 31.5 > 0.7P - 45$.

Self-Test Correlation Chart

Question	1	2	3	4	5	6	7	8
Objective(s)	A	A	A	F	B	J	J	G
Lesson(s)	8-1	8-1	8-1	8-2, 8-3	8-2, 8-3	8-2, 8-3	8-2, 8-3	8-4, 8-5, 8-7
Question	**9**	**10**	**11**	**12**	**13**	**14**	**15**	**16**
Objective(s)	I	D	D	D	I	D	D	C
Lesson(s)	8-4, 8-8	8-5, 8-6, 8-7	8-5, 8-6, 8-7	8-5, 8-6, 8-7	8-4, 8-8	8-5, 8-6, 8-7	8-5, 8-6, 8-7	8-4, 8-7
Question	**17**	**18**	**19**	**20**	**21**	**22**		
Objective(s)	E	E	F	J	I	H		
Lesson(s)	8-8	8-8	8-2, 8-3	8-2, 8-3	8-4, 8-8	8-1		

Chapter Review (pp. 574–577)

1. f **3. a.** 25 **b.** $x^2 + x - 5$ **5.** yes; $f \circ g(x) = x = g \circ f(x)$ **7.** $h(h(x)) = x^{\frac{4}{9}}$ **9.** $y = \frac{1}{6}x + \frac{1}{2}$ **11.** $\frac{x-13}{7}$ **13.** $-\sqrt{-t}$ **15.** 3 **17.** $\frac{16}{49}$ **19.** 1.44 **21.** -16.87 **23.** b^4 **25.** 2 **27.** $-u^2v^4$ **29.** $\sqrt[8]{k}$ **31.** $\sqrt{13}$ **33.** $\frac{7\sqrt{3}+7}{2}$ **35.** $y = 15.625$ **37.** $y = -2288$ **39.** no solution **41.** true **43.** domain: $\{x \mid x \geq -6\}$; range: $\{y \mid y \leq 0\}$ **45.** The range of f is the set of all positive integers. **47.** D **49.** all real numbers **51.** False; the Root of a Product Theorem does not hold for negative a and b and even n. **53. a.** \$981 **b.** \$981 **c.** The deal is the same because both the discount and the sales tax involve multiplication, which is commutative. **55.** about 1.33 times farther **57.** 151.25 ft **59.** the diameter of the first balloon is about 1.91 times larger

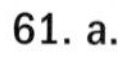
61. a.

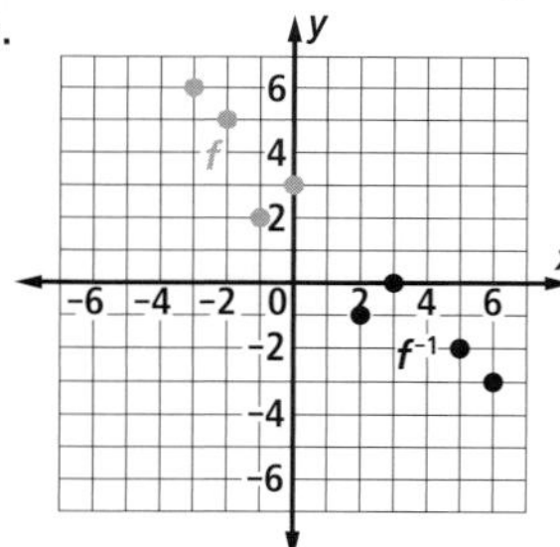

b. reflection over the line with equation $y = x$

63. a.

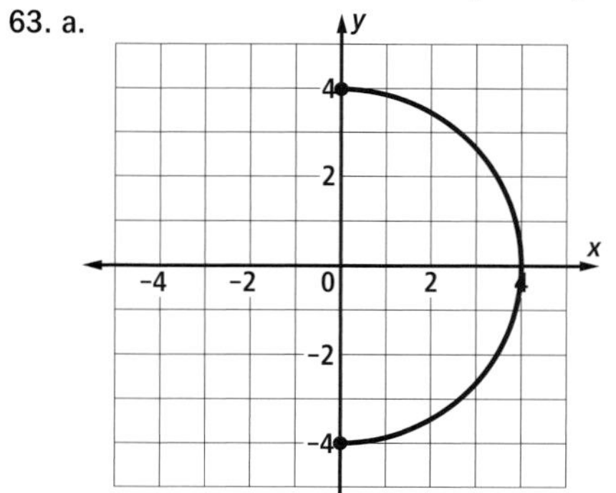

b. No; Explanations vary. Sample: The graph of the original function does not pass the horizontal-line test.

65. a.

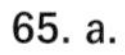
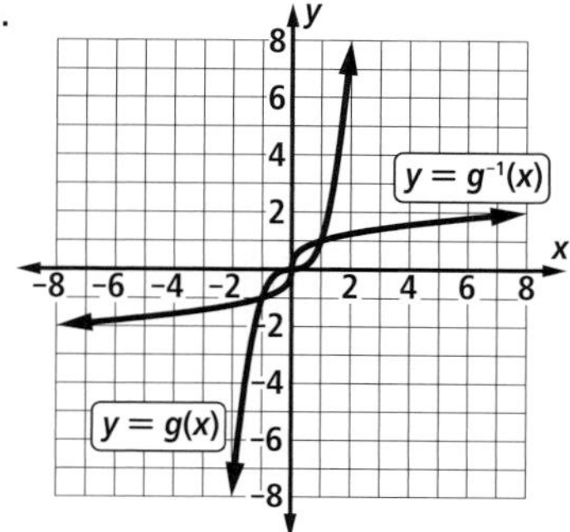

b. the set of all real numbers

67. a.

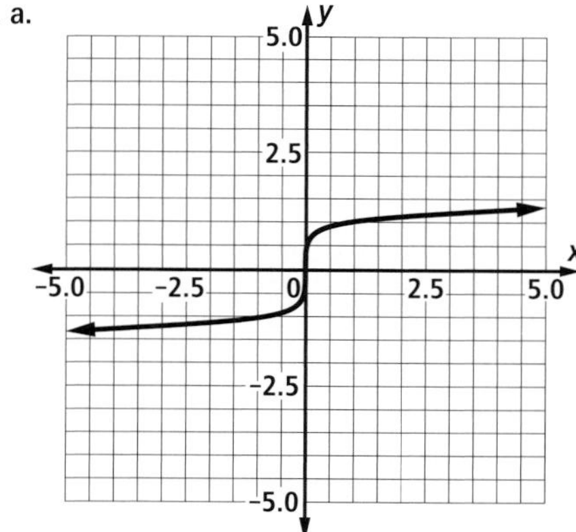

b. domain: all real numbers; range: all real numbers

Chapter 9

Lesson 9-1 (pp. 580–586)

Mental Math 1 hr 21 min

Guided Example 2 a. 280.6; 1.78; $280.6(1.78)^x$ **b.** 280.6; 1.78; 1.2; 1.2 **c.** $280.6(1.78)^x$; 2.4; 2.4; 1.2 1.2

Questions

1. 56,680 rabbits **3.** 5252 rabbits **5.** C

7. a.

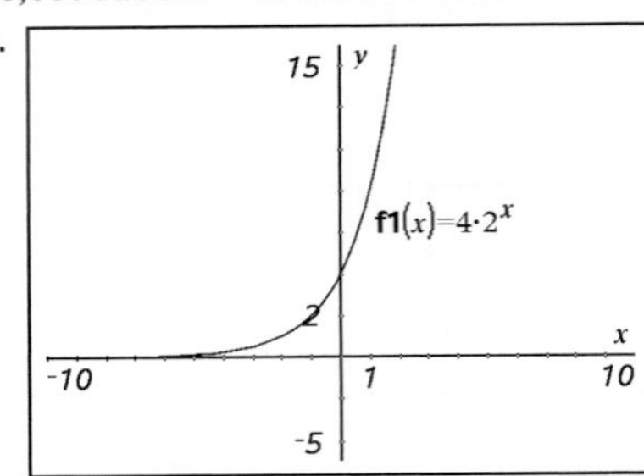

b. 1.52 **c.** True; the function satisfies the definition of an exponential function. **9. a.** 0.88 **b.** the speed in teraflops of the fastest computer in 1995 **11. a.** independent: t; dependent: A **b.** $(1 + r)$ **13. a.** $a = 31.1$, $b = 1.0116$, $c = 30.2$, $d = 1.0238$; $C(x) = 31.1(1.0116)^x$, $M(x) = 30.2(1.0238)^x$ **b.** 29.36 million, 26.85 million

c.

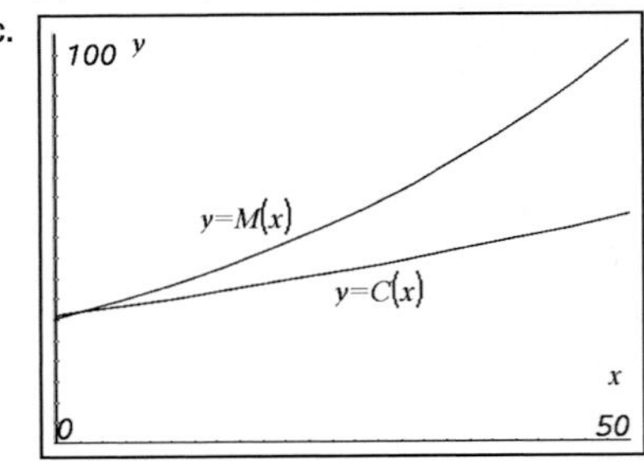

d. Answers vary. Sample: Morocco's population will outgrow Canada's population in the long run. **15. a.** 1 **b.** 1.94 **c.** 1,106,207 bighead carp

17. a. $\begin{bmatrix} 4 & 4 & -2 \\ -3 & -4 & 1 \end{bmatrix}$

b.

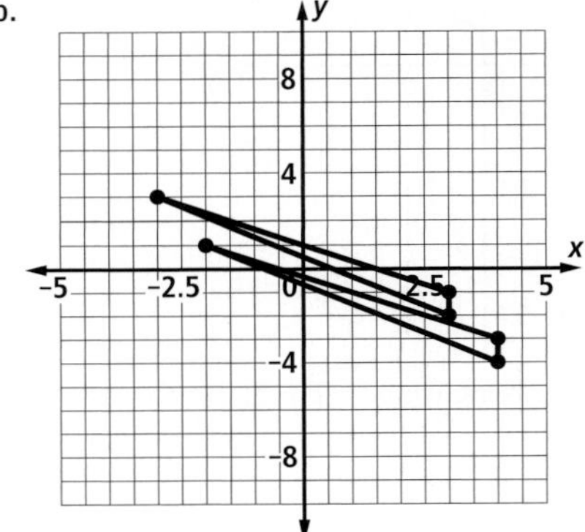

19. a. \$22,960 **b.** \$22,400 **c.** $28{,}000^{\frac{(100 - r)}{100}}$

Lesson 9-2 (pp. 587–594)

Mental Math a. 0 **b.** 1 **c.** infinitely many **d.** infinitely many **e.** 1

Guided Example 1 a. 88; 36,025; 0.88; $36{,}025(0.88)^t$ **b.** 4; 4; 36,025; 4; 21,604.03; \$21,604.03

Guided Example 3 a. 100; 1; 1; $\left(\frac{1}{2}\right)$ **b.** 0.8; 0.3; 0.3; 1700

Activity Step 1: a. As b is increases, the steepness at the right side of the graph increases. **b.** All of these functions are increasing over their whole domain.

Step 2: a. As b decreases, the graphs drop more sharply. **b.** All of these functions are decreasing over their whole domain **Step 3: a.** For $0 < b < 1$, the graph decreases for all x; for $b > 1$, the graph increases for all x. **b.** The shapes of the two kinds of graphs are reflections of each other over the y-axis.

Step 4: The y-intercept changes with a because $y = a$ at $x = 0$.

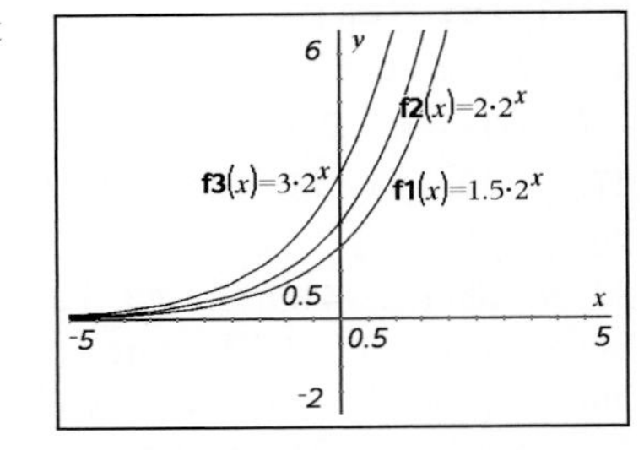

Step 5:

Property	Exponential Decay: $a > 0, 0 < b < 1$	Exponential Growth: $a > 0, b > 1$
Domain	all real numbers	all real numbers
Range	$y > 0$	$y > 0$
y-intercept	a	a
x-intercept	none	none
Horizontal asymptote	$y = 0$	$y = 0$
As x increases, y ...	decreases	increases

Step 6:

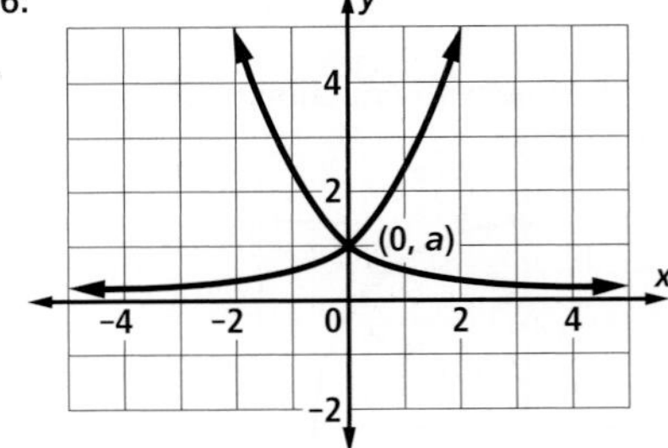

Questions

1. \$10,033.00 **3.** The *half-life* of a substance is the amount of time it takes for half of the atoms in that substance to decay into other matter. **5.** about 7400 BCE

7. a.

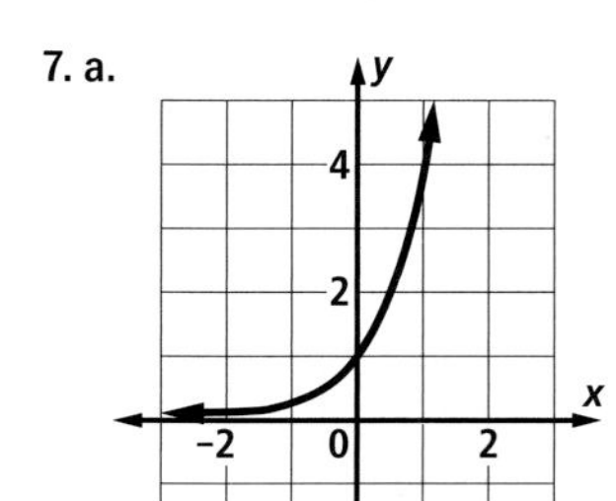

b.

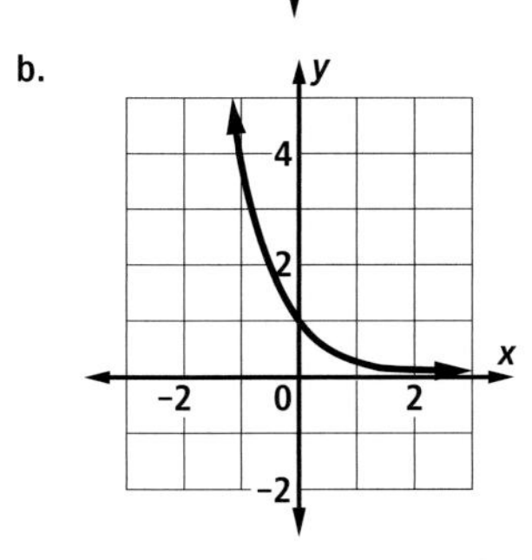

c. The graph of $y = 4^x$ is the reflection of the graph of $y = \left(\frac{1}{4}\right)^x$ over the y-axis, and vice versa. **9.** True; $ab^x \neq 0$ for all x, when $a \neq 0$ and $b > 0$.

11. a.

Year (t)	Value (N)
1	\$18,000
2	\$16,200
3	\$14,580
4	\$13,122

b.

Year (t)	Value (N)
1	\$18,000
2	\$16,000
3	\$14,000
4	\$12,000

c. With the exponential model, $N = 20{,}000(0.9)^t$, so after 6 months, the car is worth $20{,}000(0.9)^{\frac{1}{2}} \approx \$18{,}974$. With the linear model, $N = 20{,}000 - 2000t$, so after 6 months, the car is worth $20{,}000 - 2000\left(\frac{1}{2}\right) = \$19{,}000$. Thus, the exponential depreciation is preferred for this situation. **13. a.** $P(x) = 340\left(\frac{1}{2}\right)^x$ **b.** \$1360; \$680; \$340; \$170; \$85; \$42.50 **c.** 32.5 half-lives; $P(32) \approx \$0.06$ per terabyte (1 terabyte = 1,000,000 megabytes) **d.** after 25 half-lives, that is, in 2011 **e.** Answers vary. Sample: Yes; this just means that a larger quantity of memory, such as the terabyte, would become the basis for the price of memory. **15. a.** D **b.** all real numbers **c.** $\{y \mid y > 0\}$ **17. a.** about 50 **b.** $g(w) = 12(1.33)^{\frac{w}{2}}$ **19. a.** 125 **b.** 55.9 **c.** 70.7 **21.** tr^n

Lesson 9-3 (pp. 595-601)

Mental Math a. 36π **b.** 8

Activity $1\left(1 + \frac{1}{4}\right)^4$; 12, $1\left(1 + \frac{1}{12}\right)^{12}$, \$2.61304; 365, $1\left(1 + \frac{1}{365}\right)^{365}$, \$2.71457; 8760, $1\left(1 + \frac{1}{8760}\right)^{8760}$, \$2.71813; 525,600, $1\left(1 + \frac{1}{525{,}600}\right)^{525{,}600}$, \$2.71828

Guided Example 2 0.448; –10.0055; 0.448, –10.0055, 0.08; 0.448, 0.449; 0.998

Questions

1. irrational **3. a.** about \$2.7146 **b.** e **5. a.** \$1061.83 **b.** \$1233.67 **7.** about 81.6% **9. a. i.** increasing **ii.** increasing **iii.** decreasing

b. i.

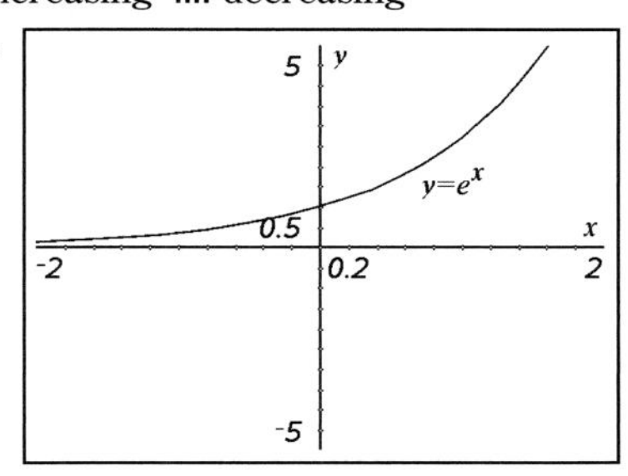

ii.

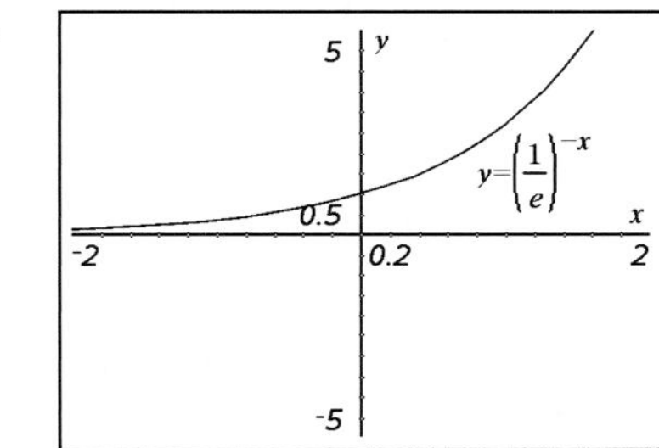

iii.

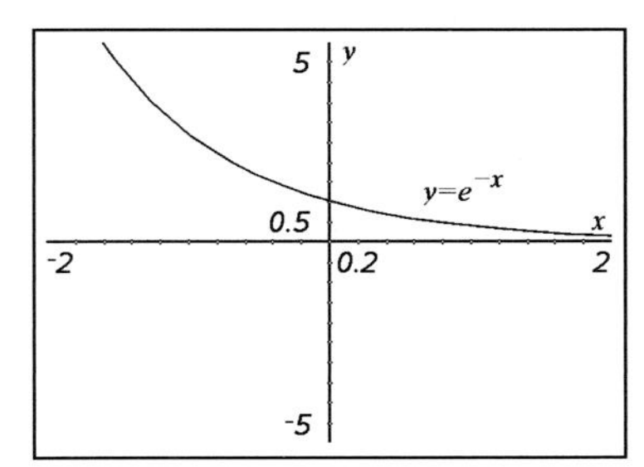

c. The graphs of y_1 and y_2 coincide because $y_2 = \left(\frac{1}{e}\right)^{-x} = (e^{-1})^{-x} = e^x = y_1$. **d.** i, ii **e.** iii **11. a.** about 29.5% **b.** about \$364,968 **13. a.** about 352.2 million **b.** about 862.4 million **c.** The answer for Part b; Reasons vary. Sample: The newer model uses a faster rate of population growth. **d.** Answers vary. Sample: As of July 2007, the U.S. population was about 301 million. The first model predicts the 2007 U.S. population would be 280.1 million, and the second model predicts 304.3 million. **15. a.** $\frac{1}{4096}$; 1; 64 **b.** domain: all real numbers; range: all positive real numbers **c.** $x = 16^y$ **17.** $k = \frac{3}{\sqrt[3]{5}}$ **19.** $a > \frac{16}{7}$ **21. a.** $y = 6.6x + 73.6$ **b.** 152.8 cm

Lesson 9-4 (pp. 602–607)

Mental Math **a.** yes **b.** no **c.** yes

Activity Step 1: $y = 991.709 \cdot (0.890071)^x$

Step 2: $y = 992 \cdot (0.890)^x$ **Step 3:** The model from Step 2 yields 553.939; the one from Example 1 yields 539.835. Therefore, the Step 2 model fits better.

Step 4.

Hours Since Administration	Amount of Drug in Body	Example 1	Activity Step 2
0	1000	1000	991.7
5	550	539.8	554.0
10	316	291.4	309.5
15	180	157.3	172.9
20	85	84.93	96.6
25	56	45.85	54.0
30	31	24.75	30.1

The model from Step 2 appears more accurate overall, especially as the number of hours since the drug was taken increase.

Questions

1. a. $y = 1000 \cdot (0.891)^x$ **b.** after approximately 39.9 hr
3. No, the initial condition is not given.
5. a. Answers vary. Sample: $y = 126.8 \cdot (1.127)^x$, where x is the number of years after 2001. **b.** 2009
7. a. $y = 3887 \cdot (0.4934)^x$ **b.** (2, 946), (6, 56) **c.** Tyler is correct because approximately half of the coins land heads on every drop.
9. a. (–1, 0.0067), (0, 1), (0.25, 3.49)

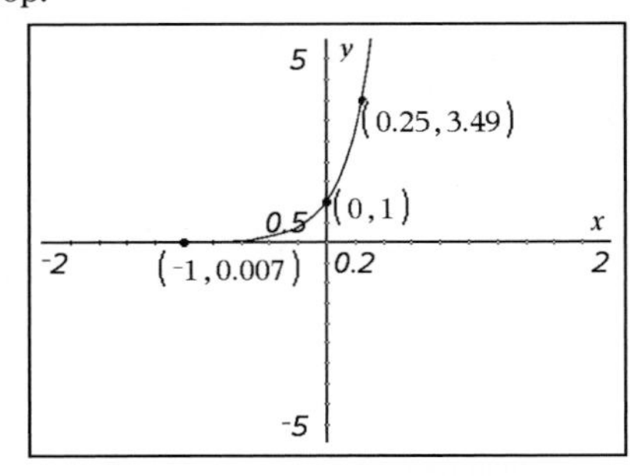

b. domain: all real numbers; range: all positive real numbers
11. a. \$5428.71 **b.** \$5439.08 **c.** \$5439.11 **13.** 16 **15.** $4xy$

Lesson 9-5 (pp. 608–614)

Mental Math $\sqrt[3]{4.8}$

Guided Example 1 **a.** 2; 2 **b.** -5; –5 **c.** 1; 0

Activity Step 1: 0.01, 0.1, 0.178, 0.316, 0.562, 1, 1.778, 3.162, 5.623, 10, 100

Step 4:

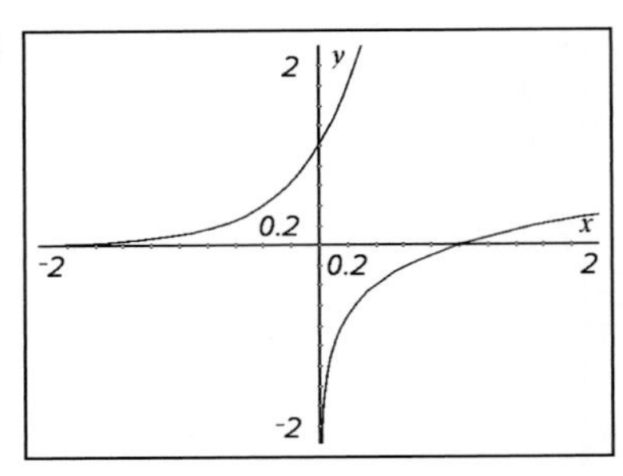

These graphs are the same as those from Steps 2 and 3.

Questions

1. $10^m = n$ **3.** 7 **5.** -7 **7.** -1 **9.** 8 and 9 **11.** -2.510
13. 100,000 **15. a.** x-intercept: 1; there is no y-intercept.
b. Answers vary. Sample: (1, 0), (10, 1), (100, 2)
c. Answers vary. Sample: (0, 1), (1, 10), (2, 100) **17.** $\log_{10} x$
19. 1 and 2 **21.** 3.765 **23.** x; f and g are inverse functions.
25. about 64% **27.** \$1,632,986 **29.** 13^{-6}

Lesson 9-6 (pp. 615–621)

Mental Math **a.** 10^4 or 10,000 **b.** 10^{11} **c.** $2 \cdot 10^9$ **d.** $\frac{a}{b} \cdot 10^{m-n}$

Guided Example 4 6.9, 9.3; 9.3, 6.9, 2.4; 2.4, 251.189, 251, 1989

Questions

1. 73.89 dB **3.** between 10^{-4} and 10^{-3} **5.** 100 times as intense **7.** about 15.8 times as loud **9.** 31.6 times as much force **11.** 7.69 **13.** 19.95 **15.** 5.5 **17.** -8.14
19. $1{,}000{,}000 = 10^6$; thus, $\log_{10} 1{,}000{,}000 = 6$.
21. $x = 10{,}000{,}000$ **23.** $y = \log x, x = 10^y$
25. exponential decay; Explanations vary. Sample: y will decrease as x increases. **27.** $\frac{p^2q^4}{m^3}$

Lesson 9-7 (pp. 622–628)

Mental Math **a.** (-3, 5) **b.** (9, 15) **c.** (-6, –5) **d.** (1, 4)

Guided Example 2 **a.** 2; 2 **b.** definition of logarithm; 1; $3x$, 1; $3x$, 1; $\frac{1}{3}$, Division Property of Equality; $\frac{1}{3}$ **c.** 4^x; 4^x, -3; x, -3; -3

Activity Step 1: Answers vary. Sample: $b = 2$;

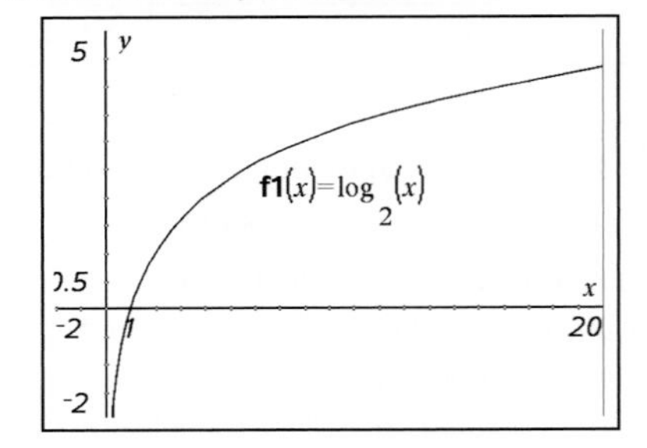

Step 2:

b	Domain	Range	x-intercepts	y-intercepts	Asymptotes
2	all positive real numbers	all real numbers	1	none	$x = 0$

Step 3:

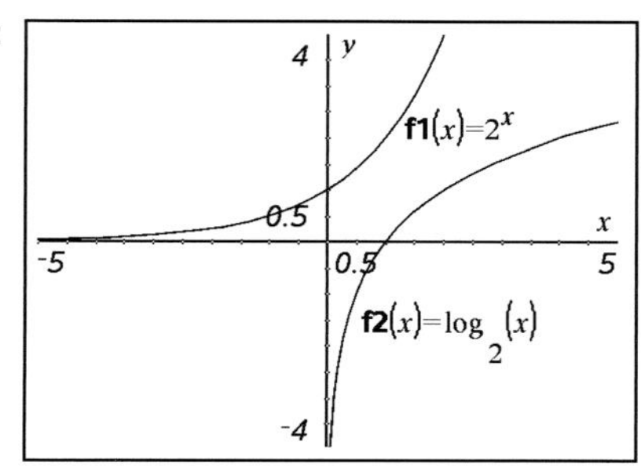

They are reflection images of one another over the line $y = x$.
Step 4: Answers vary.
Step 5: Answers vary. Sample: The functions all have an x-intercept of 1 and an asymptote of $x = 0$. They all have the same domain and range.

Questions

1. $b^x = a$ when b is any positive value other than 1
3. $\log_{6\sqrt{3}} 136{,}048{,}896 = 8$ **5.** $b^c = a$ **7.** domain: $x > 0$; range: all real numbers
9.

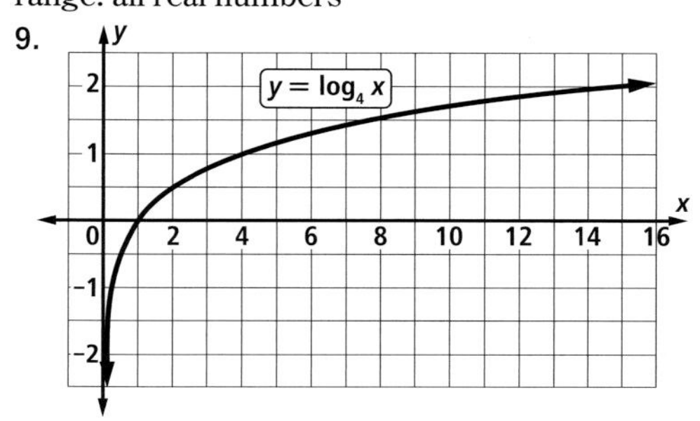

11. $\left(\frac{1}{4}\right)^y = \frac{1}{64}$; $y = 3$ **13.** $a^{\frac{1}{3}} = 8$; $a = 512$ **15.** $47^{-0.2} = d$; $d \approx 0.463$ **17.** $w^1 = w$; $w > 0$, $w \neq 1$ **19. a.** 1 **b.** 2 **c.** about 0.203 **21. a.** 3; $\frac{1}{3}$ **b.** 2; $\frac{1}{2}$ **c.** $\log_a b = \frac{1}{\log_b a}$ **23.** 10^{10} **25.** $4.5 \cdot 10^{-9}$ **27.** -4 **29. a.** x^{12} **b.** x^{-6} **c.** x^{27} **d.** x^3

Lesson 9-8 (pp. 629-634)

Mental Math a. x^8 **b.** x^8 **c.** $\sqrt{6x} - 3$ **d.** $6\sqrt{x} - 3$
Guided Example 2 6; -34, 6; 17.4; 17.4

Questions

1. natural logarithms **3.** $e^0 = 1$ **5.** $\ln 148.41 \approx 5$ **7.** ln 1000; because $e < 10$, e must be raised to a greater power to get 1000. **9.** about 27.1 ft **11.** 1 **13.** -2 **15.** about 20 minutes longer **17.** about 26 decibels **19. a.** no y-intercept **b.** no y-intercept **c.** Graphs of equations of the form $y = \log_b x$, where $b > 0$ and $b \neq 1$ have no y-intercept. This is because $b^y \neq 0$ for all y. **21.** 0.896 **23.** $x = \sqrt{37}$ **25.** B; this equation can be written in the the form $f(x) = ab^x$, where $a = 1$ and $b = \frac{1}{7}$. Since $0 < b < 1$, this equation describes exponential decay.

Lesson 9-9 (pp. 635-642)

Mental Math a. $2 \cdot 10$, 10^2, 2^{10} **b.** e^{16}, 3^{16}, π^{16} **c.** 0.5, $\sqrt{0.5}$, $\sqrt[3]{0.5}$

Activity 1 Step 1: a. 0; 0; 0; 0 **b.** 1; 1; 1; 1 **c.** -2, -1, 0, 1 **Step 2:** For set a, for any base $b > 0$, $b \neq 1$, $\log_b 1 = 0$. For set b, for any base $b > 0$, $b \neq 1$, $\log_b b = 1$. For set c, for any base $b > 0$, $b \neq 1$, and any real number n, $\log_b b^n = n$.
Activity 2 Step 1: log 6, log 6; 2 log 6, 2 log 6; $\log_5\left(\frac{175}{2}\right)$, $\log_5\left(\frac{175}{2}\right)$; 7 ln 2, 7 ln 2 **Step 2:** $\log_b x + \log_b y$
Guided Example 3 N, 10^{-12}; N, 12; N, 12
Activity 3 Step 1: a. 0.477 **b.** 0.954 **c.** 1.431 **d.** 1.908 **e.** 2.303 **f.** 4.605 **g.** 6.908 **h.** 9.210 **Step 2:** $n \cdot \log_b(x)$
Step 3: The Product Property of Logarithms supports this conclusion.

Questions

1. 15.4 **3.** 0 **5. a.** $\log_2 7$ **b.** Logarithm of a Quotient Theorem **7. a.** 3 **b.** Answers vary. Sample: Logarithm of a Power Theorem **9.** $\log(64) = \log(2^6) = 6 \log 2$ **11.** $\log_b\left(\frac{x\sqrt{z}}{y}\right)$ **13.** true **15.** False; Answers vary. Sample: For $M = 3$ and $N = 7$, $\log(10) \neq \log 3 + \log 7$; $\log(MN) = \log M + \log N$. **17.** true **19.** $y = \left(\frac{x}{w}\right)^{\frac{1}{4}}$ **21.** $\log_{10} 5 + \log_{10} 2 = \log_{10}(5 \cdot 2) = \log_{10} 10 = 1$ and $\log_{10}(a \cdot b) = \log_{10} a + \log_{10} b$; therefore,
$$\frac{\log_{10} a}{\log_{10} 5 + \log_{10} 2} + \frac{\log_{10} b}{\log_{10} 5 + \log_{10} 2} = \frac{\log_{10}(a \cdot b)}{\log_{10} 5 + \log_{10} 2} = \log_{10}(a \cdot b)$$
23. a. b^m **b.** $(b^m)^n$ **c.** b^{mn} **d.** b^{nm} **e.** nm **25.** $x = 12$
27. a.

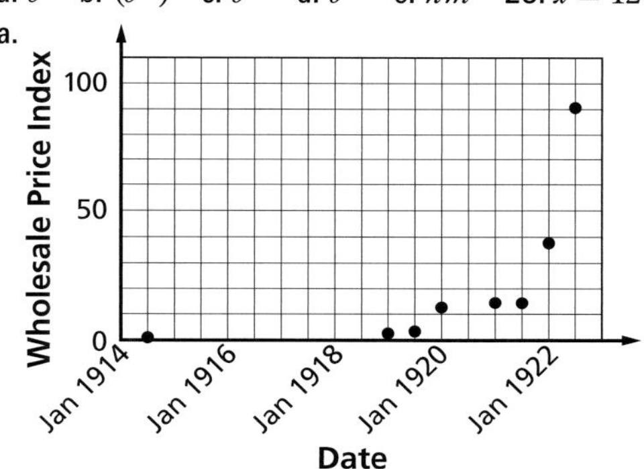

b. Answers vary. Sample: The data seem to roughly lie on an exponential curve. **c.** Answers vary. Sample: $y \approx 0.533 \cdot 1.30x$ **d.** 46.11 **e.** under predicts
29. a. $\frac{19}{3}$ **b.** $\frac{19}{3}$ is the slope of the line segment connecting the points (-3, -9) and $\left(-2, -\frac{8}{3}\right)$.

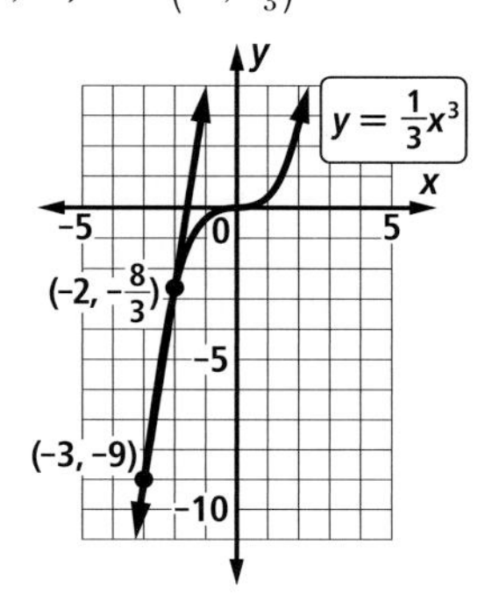

Lesson 9-10 (pp. 643-649)

Mental Math **a.** $x = 4$ **b.** $y = 3$ **c.** $z = 2$ **d.** $w = 2$

Guided Example 2 $Ce^{-\frac{\ln 2}{5730}t}$; $e^{-\frac{\ln 2}{5730}t}$; $\ln\left(e^{-\frac{\ln 2}{5730}t}\right)$; $-\frac{\ln 2}{5730}t$; $-\frac{5730}{\ln 2}$; 2182.11; 2182

Questions

1. a. 5 **b.** 5 **c.** 5 **3.** about 3.565; $4^{3.565} \approx 140$ **5.** $r = \frac{\log 2}{12 \log e} \approx 0.0578$ **7.** about 6067 yr old **9.** -6.322; $0.5^{-6.322} \approx 80$ **11.** about 5.61 yr **13.** $y \approx 0.879$ **15. a.** about 1.27% **b.** in 2011; $5{,}995{,}000{,}000 \cdot (1.0127)^{12.28} \approx 7{,}000{,}000{,}000$ **c.** in 2054 **d.** Answers vary. Sample: 2008: 6,706,992,932; 2007: 6,627,548,985; growth rate: 1.20; in 2057 **17.** 2 and 3 **19.** -3 and -2 **21.** $x = 3$ **23.** about $3409.7 \frac{\text{m}}{\text{sec}}$ **25.** -2

27. a.

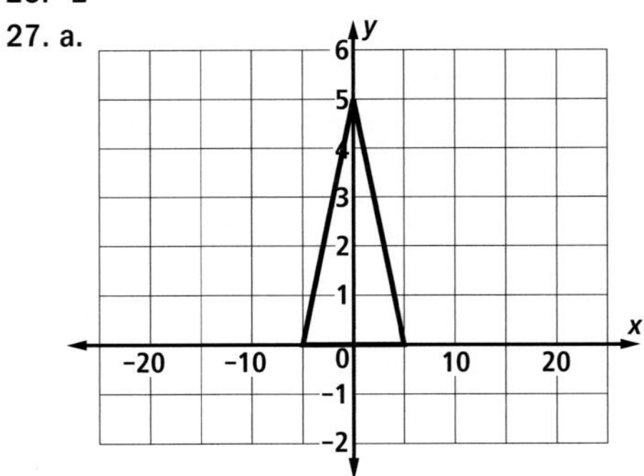

b. isosceles **c.**

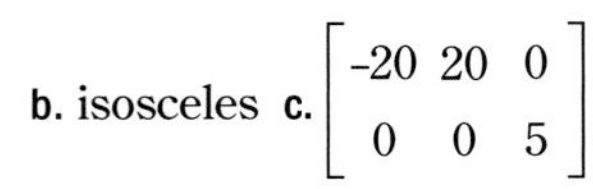

$\begin{bmatrix} -20 & 20 & 0 \\ 0 & 0 & 5 \end{bmatrix}$

d.

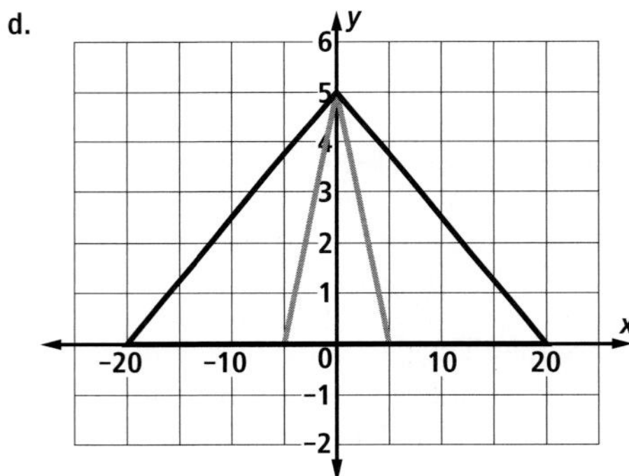

e. no

Self-Test (pp. 654-655)

1. domain: $x > 0$; range: all real numbers **2.** The fraction of uranium remaining in an artifact after x half-lives is $U(x) = \left(\frac{1}{2}\right)^x$. Since in this case one half-life is about a week, the fraction remaining after three half-lives is $U(3) = 0.125$. So, there is 12.5% of the original amount of uranium remaining in an artifact after 3 weeks.

3. a.

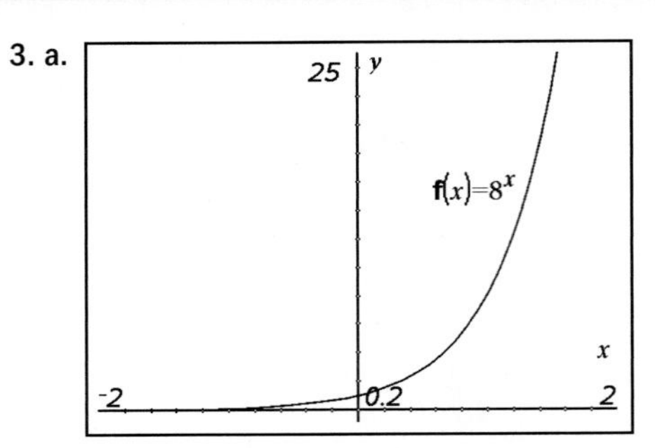

b. $f(\pi) = 8^{\pi} \approx 687.3$ **c.** yes; $y = 0$ **4. a.** any b with $0 < b < 1$; example: $b = 0.5$ **b.** domain: all real numbers; range: $y > 0$ if $a > 0$, $y < 0$ if $a < 0$ **5.** $\log 100{,}000{,}000 = \log(10^8) = 8$ by the Log_b of b^n Theorem. **6.** $\log_2\left(\frac{1}{16}\right) = \log_2 2^{-4} = -4$ by the Log_b of b^n Theorem. **7.** $\ln e^{-4} = -4$ because $\ln e^x = x$. **8.** $\log a + 2\log t - \log s = \log a + \log(t^2) - \log s = \log(at^2) - \log s = \log\left(\frac{at^2}{s}\right)$ **9.** The initial population is 50 and the yearly growth factor is 1.12; so the number of birds after t years is given by $N(t) = 50(1.12)^t$. $N(3) = 70.2464$; thus, after 3 years, there will be about 70 birds. **10.** $\log_x 27 = \frac{3}{4}$; $x^{\frac{3}{4}} = 27$; $x = 27^{\frac{4}{3}}$; $x = 81$ **11.** $5^y = 40$; $y \log 5 = \log 40$; $y = \frac{\log 40}{\log 5} \approx 2.29$ **12.** $\ln(7z) = \ln 3 + \ln 21$; $\ln(7z) = \ln(3 \cdot 21) = \ln 63$; $7z = 63$; $z = 9$ **13.** False; if $a = 5$ and $b = 3$, $\log_5 a + \log_3 b = 1 + 1 = 2$, but $\log_{15}(ab) = 1$. **14.** The inverse of a logarithmic function is an exponential function with the same base, so an equation for the inverse is $y = 4^x$. **15.** $7.3 = 6.1 + \log\left(\frac{23}{C}\right)$; $1.2 = \log 23 - \log C$; $\log C = \log 23 - 1.2 \approx 0.162$; $C \approx 10^{0.162} \approx 1.45$. **16.** $\log_{14} 24.72 = \frac{\log 24.72}{\log 14} = 1.215$ **17.** $\log_b b^n = n$, $b > 0$, $b \neq 1$ **18. a.** Answers vary. Sample: (1, 0); (5, 1); (25, 2) **b.** Powers of 5 must be positive, so the domain is $x > 0$; all real numbers can be exponents, so the range is all real numbers.

c.

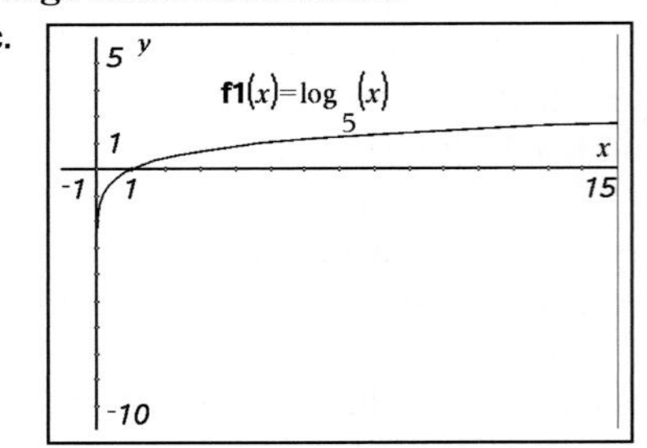

d. $y = 5^x$ **e.**

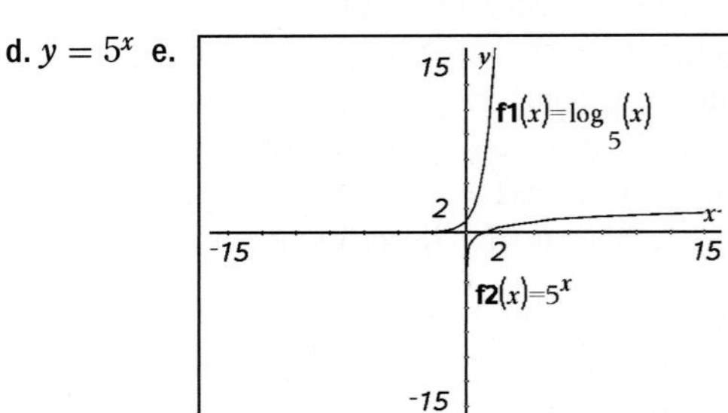

19. A; graphs of exponential growth have this shape and a *y*-intercept of 1. **20. a.** In 2025, $t = 18$, and so $P = 302{,}200{,}000\ e^{0.006(18)} \approx 336{,}665{,}229 \neq 349{,}400{,}000$ **b.** $349{,}400{,}000 = 302{,}200{,}000e^{18r}$; $1.156188 = e^{18r}$; $18r = \ln 1.156188 \approx 0.145128$; $r = 0.00806$. So a growth rate of about 0.8% would give the reported projected population. **21. a.** $27^x = 14$; $x \cdot \ln 27 = \ln 14$; $x = \frac{\ln 14}{\ln 27}$ **b.** $x = 0.801$ **22. a.** Exponential regression shows that an exponential model for these data is $y = 572.6123(1.022)^x$, where x is the number of months after March 2007 and y is the number of articles in thousands. **b.** $1000 = 572.6123(1.022)^x$; $1.74638 = 1.022^x$; $x = \ln 1.022 = \ln 1.74638$, $x = \frac{\ln 1.74638}{\ln 1.022} \approx 25.6$. This model predicts that there will be 1 million German *Wikipedia* articles about 26 months after March 2007, or in April 2010.

Self-Test Correlation Chart

Question	**1**	**2**	**3**	**4**	**5**	**6**	**7**	**8**
Objective(s)	E	G	D, J	D	A	A	A	F
Lesson(s)	9-5, 9-7, 9-8	9-1, 9-2, 9-3, 9-10	9-1, 9-2, 9-3	9-1, 9-2, 9-3	9-5, 9-7, 9-8, 9-10	9-5, 9-7, 9-8, 9-10	9-5, 9-7, 9-8, 9-10	9-9, 9-10
Question	**9**	**10**	**11**	**12**	**13**	**14**	**15**	**16**
Objective(s)	G	C	B	C	F	E	I	A
Lesson(s)	9-1, 9-2, 9-3, 9-10	9-5, 9-6, 9-7, 9-9	9-10	9-5, 9-6, 9-7, 9-9	9-9, 9-10	9-5, 9-7, 9-8	9-6, 9-8	9-5, 9-7, 9-8, 9-10
Question	**17**	**18**	**19**	**20**	**21**	**22**		
Objective(s)	F	A, E, J, K	J	G	B	H		
Lesson(s)	9-9, 9-10	9-1, 9-2, 9-5, 9-7, 9-8, 9-10	9-1, 9-2	9-1, 9-2, 9-3, 9-10	9-10	9-4		

Chapter Review (pp. 656–659)

1. 4 **3.** 8 **5.** 15 **7.** -3 **9.** 4.99 **11.** undefined **13.** 1.65 **15.** $t = 0.90$ **17.** $n = 18.85$ **19.** $z = 3.78$ **21.** $a = 1.89$ **23.** $x = 11$ **25.** $z = 10^{18}$ **27.** $x = 125$ **29.** $x = 7.03$ **31.** domain: all real numbers; range: positive real numbers **33.** when $a > 1$ **35.** $y = 0$ **37.** $f^{-1}(x) = -\ln x$ **39.** true **41.** $3^{-5} = \frac{1}{243}$ **43.** $10^n = m$ **45.** $\log 0.01585 \approx -1.8$ **47.** $\log_x z = y, x > 0, x \neq 1$ **49.** $\ln(204)$; Logarithm of a Product Theorem **51.** $\log_{12}\left(\frac{1}{121}\right)$; Logarithm of a Power Theorem **53.** 79; Logarithm of a Power Theorem, $\log_b$ of b^n Theorem **55.** $\log\left(\frac{a}{b^3}\right)$; Logarithm of a Power Theorem, Logarithm of a Quotient Theorem **57.** about 37.675 million **59.** 2048 **61.** 16.53% **63.** \$11,327.88 **65. a.**

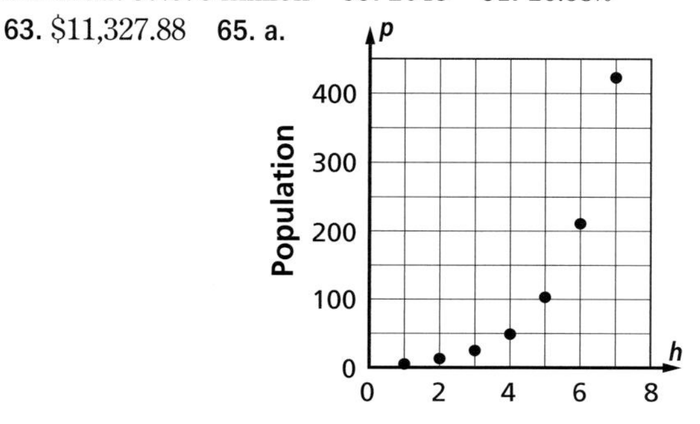

b. $P = 2.72(2.06)^h$ **c.** about 771,100 **67.** 215.89 decibels **69.** 10,000 **71.** 206.96°F

73.

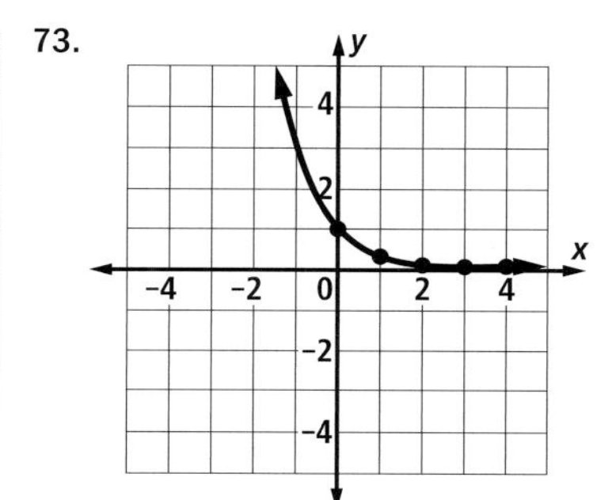

75. a. $y = 3^x$ **b.** $y = 2^x$ **c.** The graph of e^x shares the same *y*-intercept and falls between the graphs of f and g for all other values of x.

77. a.

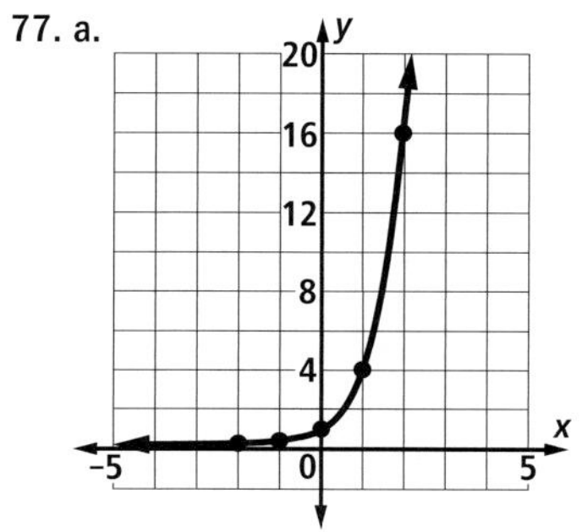

b. 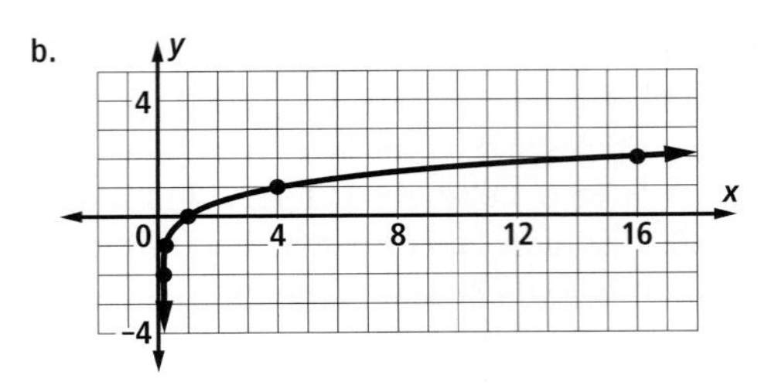

79. a. 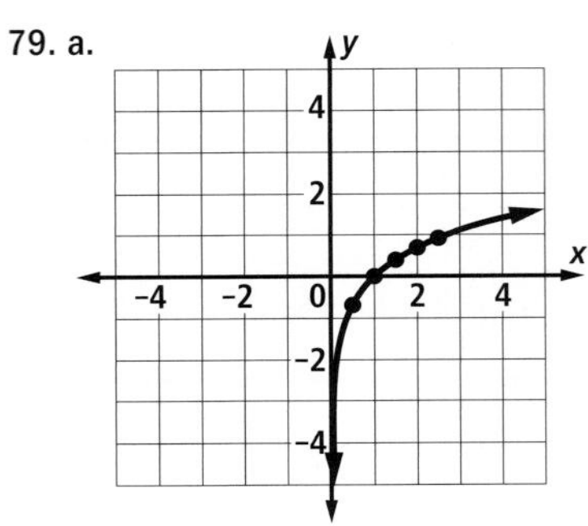

b. $y = e^x$ **81.** 1

Chapter 10

Lesson 10-1 (pp. 662–669)

Mental Math a. yes **b.** no **c.** yes

Activity Steps 1–2:

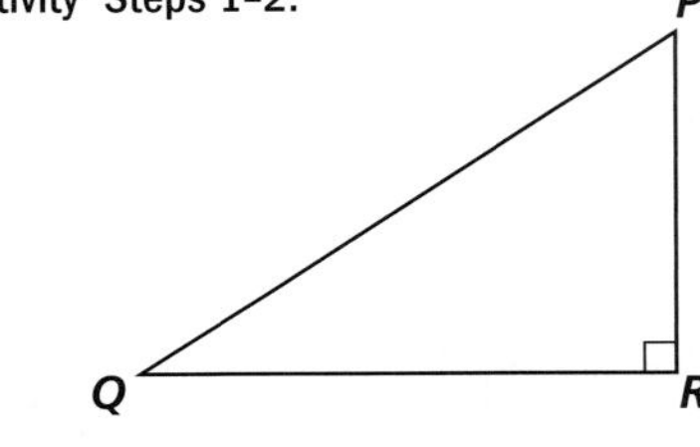

Step 3: Answers vary. Sample: $PQ = 8.4$ cm, $QR = 6.5$ cm, $RP = 5.3$ cm **Step 4:** $\sin 39° \approx 0.631$, $\cos 39° \approx 0.774$, $\tan 39° \approx 0.815$ **Step 5:** $\sin 39° \approx 0.629$, $\cos 39° \approx 0.777$, $\tan 39° \approx 0.810$ **Step 6:** 0.3%, –0.3%, 0.6%

Guided Example 2 16.7°; 490; 490, sin 16.7°; 1705.2; 1705; 1705, 490, 1633; 16.7°, 0.958, 0.958

Questions

1. D **3. a.** $\frac{a}{c}$ **b.** $\frac{b}{c}$ **c.** $\frac{a}{b}$ **5.** about 98.9 m **7.** 4.58 cm
9. a. about 24.1 ft **b.** about 24.0 ft

11. a.

$\sin 30° = 0.5$ $\cos 60° = 0.5$	$\sin 40° = 0.643$ $\cos 50° = 0.643$
$\sin 15° = 0.259$ $\cos 75° = 0.259$	$\sin 90° = 1$ $\cos 0° = 1$

b. They are complementary. **c.** They are equal.

d. The cosine of an angle is equal to the sine of its complement (and, equivalently, the sine of an angle is equal to the cosine of its complement). **e.** Answers vary. Sample: $\cos 85° = \sin 5° \approx 0.087$ **13.** about 1.85 units
15. a. $\sin C = \frac{h}{a}$; $h = a \sin C$; $A = \frac{1}{2}bh = \frac{1}{2}ba \sin C$
b. 936.73 **17.** $z = 32$ **19. a.** π **b.** π **21.** false, $\angle 1 \cong \angle 5$
23. a. $(90 - x)°$ **b.** $x°$

Lesson 10-2 (pp. 670–674)

Mental Math a. 7 and 8 **b.** 8 and 9 **c.** 0 and 1 **d.** 5 and 6

Guided Example 2 $\angle A$; Answers vary. Sample: sin, 5, 13; sin; sin, sin, sin, 5, 13; 22.62°; 22.62°; 67.38°

Guided Example 4 elevation β; cosine; β, 110.56, 125.75; β, 0.8792; 28.45°; 28.45

Questions

1. Answers vary. Sample: `2nd SIN.475)ENTER` **3.** 45°
5. a. $\tan^{-1}\left(\frac{5}{12}\right) \approx 22.62°$ **b.** $\sin^{-1}\left(\frac{12}{13}\right) \approx 67.38°$ **7.** horizontal
9. The line of sight is a transversal for parallel horizontal lines, so the angles of elevation and depression are alternate interior angles and therefore congruent.
11. a. 0.015 **b.** 0.015 **c.** about 0.86° **13.** about 23.20°
15. about 16.33° **17.** $\frac{11\sqrt{2}}{4}$ **19.** $x = \frac{-s \pm \sqrt{s^2 - 4rt}}{2r}$
21. $\sqrt{13} \approx 3.606$

Lesson 10-3 (pp. 675–681)

Mental Math a. isometry **b.** neither **c.** isometry

Activity 1 Step 1: Answers vary. Sample: My thumb moves more than my partner. The background doesn't seem to jump. After stepping back, only my thumb seems to jump.
Step 2: Apparent position of star from A: 6; apparent position of star from B: 4
Step 3: a. Answers vary. Sample:

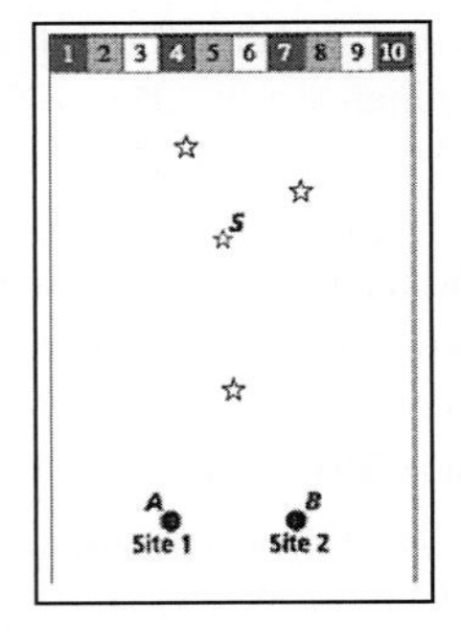

b. 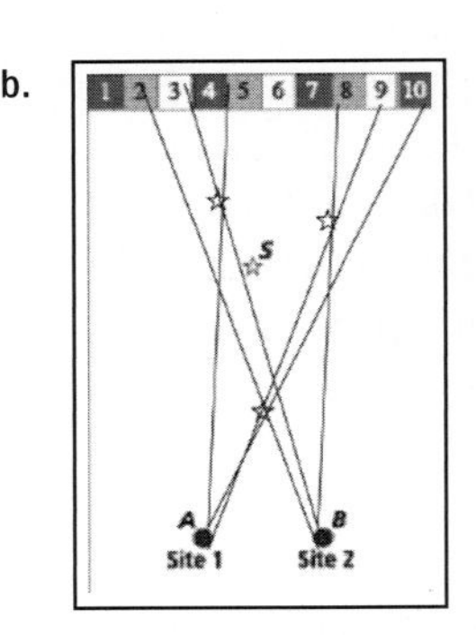

c. Answers vary. Sample: 3, 5; 8, 9; 2, 10; the larger the jump, the larger the angle. **d.** Close objects seem to jump more than distant objects because the angle between the two segments connecting the object to both eyes is greater when the object is closer.

Activity 2 **Step 2:** Answers vary. Sample: 3 spaces
Step 3: Answers vary. Sample: Par $\angle$: 7.5°
Step 4: Answers vary. Sample: 7.5°, 82.5°, 82.5°
Step 5: Answers vary. Sample: 15.2 feet
Activity 3 **Step 1:** 89.89°, 89.89° **Step 2:** 179,700 miles
Activity 4 **Step 1:**

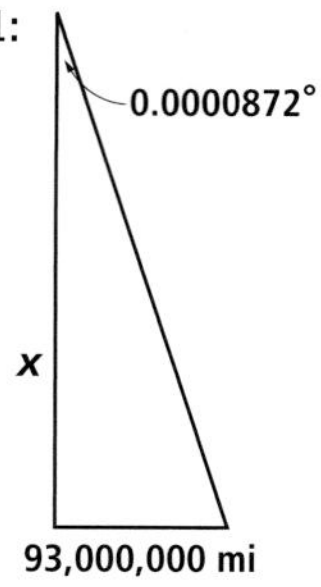

$6.11 \cdot 10^{13}$ miles **Step 2:** about 10.4 light-years
Activity 5
Step 1.

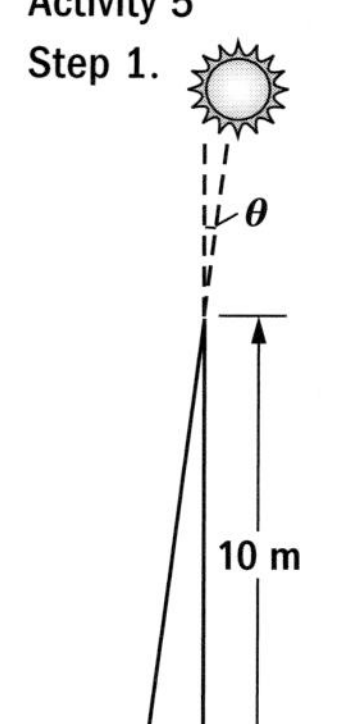

$\theta = 7.24°$

Step 2:

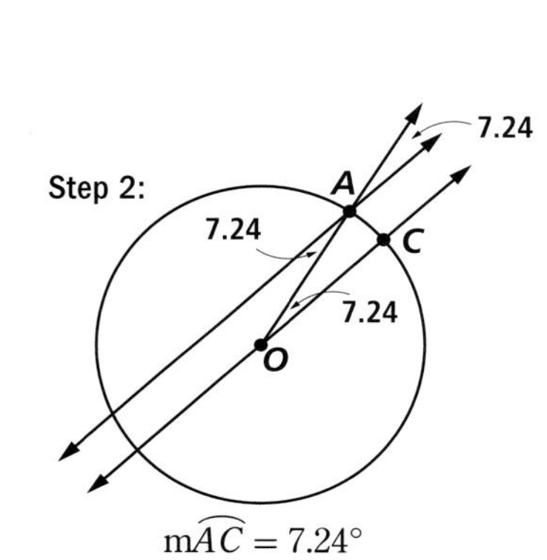

$m\widehat{AC} = 7.24°$

Step 3: 797.45 km **Step 4:** $x \approx 39{,}652$ km
Questions
1. the illusion of motion created by changing viewing positions **3.** We assumed the Moon was equidistant from the two cities. This assumption is justified because the variation is very small compared to the distances being measured. **5.** 14.32 ft **7.** 1708.6 meters
9. a. $\frac{s}{5r}$ **b.** $\frac{1}{5}$ **c.** $\frac{s}{r}$ **11. a.** (0, 1) **b.** (-1, 0) **c.** (0, -1) **d.** (0, -1)
13. a. III **b.** II **c.** I, III

Lesson 10-4 (pp. 682-686)

Mental Math **a.** 90 **b.** 16 ft **c.** no
Activity **Step 1:** Check students' work. **Step 2: a.** Check students' work. $A_{20} = (\cos 20°, \sin 20°)$ **b.** Answers vary. Sample: $A_{20} \approx (0.95, 0.35)$ **c.** $A_{20} = (\cos 20°, \sin 20°) \approx (0.940, 0.342)$ **Step 3: a.** Check students' work. $A_{40} = (\cos 40°, \sin 40°)$ **b.** Answers vary. Sample: $A_{40} \approx (0.77, 0.64)$ **c.** $A_{40} = (\cos 40°, \sin 40°) \approx (0.766, 0.643)$
Step 4: a. Check students' work. $A_{75} = (\cos 75°, \sin 75°)$ **b.** Answers vary. Sample: $A_{75} \approx (0.97, 0.26)$
c. $A_{75} = (\cos 75°, \sin 75°) = (0.966, 0.259)$

Step 5: a. For any θ, the coordinates of a rotation R_θ centered at (0, 0) of magnitude θ is $(\cos \theta, \sin \theta)$. **b.** Answers vary. Sample: $A_{61} \approx (0.49, 0.68)$ **c.** Answers vary. Sample: $\cos 61° \approx 0.48$; $\frac{0.49-0.48}{0.48} \approx 0.02$; $\sin 61° \approx 0.87$; $\frac{0.86-0.87}{0.87} \approx -0.01$; both were within 3% of the actual values.
Questions
1. a. x **b.** y **3.** (1, 0); 1; 0 **5.** 0 **7.** 0 **9. a.** a rotation of 180° **b.** (-1, 0) **c.** 0 **11.** C **13.** 0; 1 **15.** c **17.** c **19.** a
21. $x = 32°$; $\cos 392° = \cos 32° \approx 0.848$ **23. a.** 1 **b.** -1
25. $\sin(-270°) = \sin 450° = 1$ **27.** Because stars are extremely far away, you need to use very distant sites in order to have manageable parallax angles.
29. about 3003 ft away

Lesson 10-5 (pp. 687-692)

Mental Math **a.** 32 **b.** 7 **c.** 0
Activity **Step 1:**

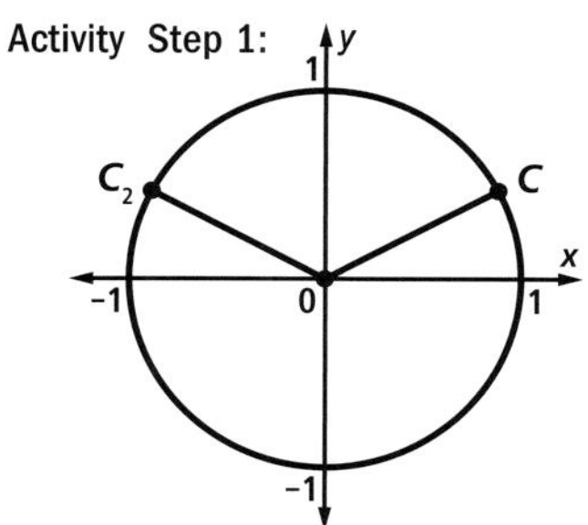

$C_2 \approx (-0.883, 0.469)$ **Step 2:** The acute angles that C and C_2 make with the x-axis are congruent, so they both measure 28°. Thus, the magnitude of the rotation that maps (1, 0) onto C_2 is $180° - 28° = 152°$.
$\cos 152° \approx -0.883$, $\sin 152° \approx 0.469$
Step 3:

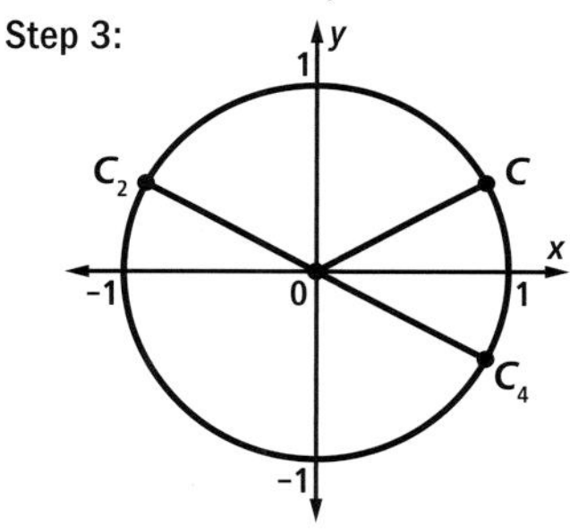

$C_4 \approx (0.883, -0.469)$ **Step 4:** $\theta = -28° = 332°$; $\sin 332° \approx -0.469$, $\cos 332° \approx 0.883$

Step 5:

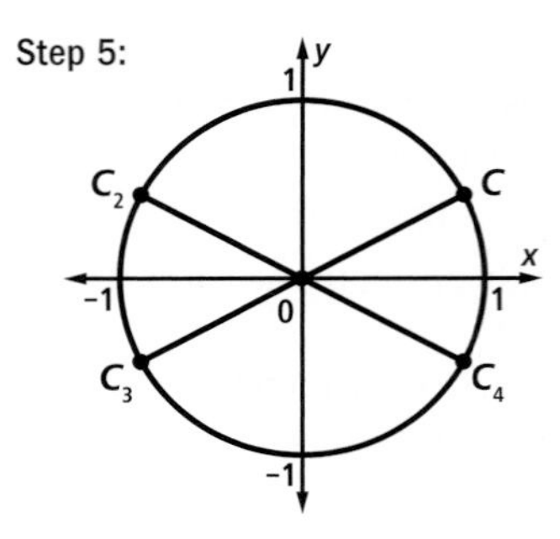

$C_3 = (\cos 208°, \sin 208°) \approx (-0.883, -0.469)$

Questions

1. is always negative **3.** is always positive

5. negative

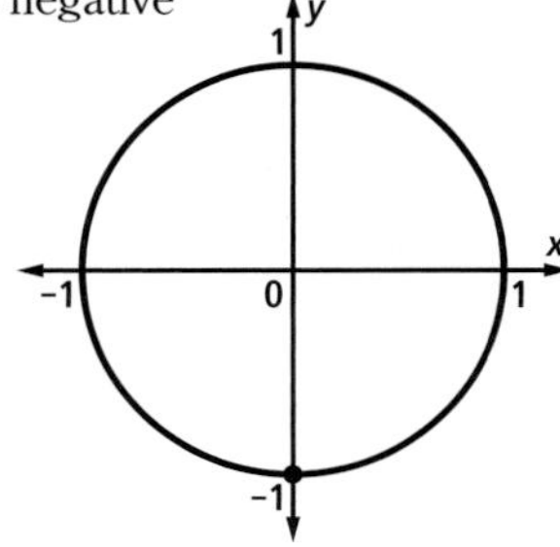

7. a. $\frac{12}{13}, -\frac{12}{13}$ **b.** $\sin x$ is the y-coordinate of $R_x(1, 0)$, and $\sin(-x)$ is the y-coordinate of $R_{-x}(1, 0)$. Because $R_{-x}(1, 0)$ is the reflection image of $R_x(1, 0)$ over the x-axis, the y-coordinates of these points are oppostites. Therefore, $\sin(-x) = -\frac{5}{13}$.

9.

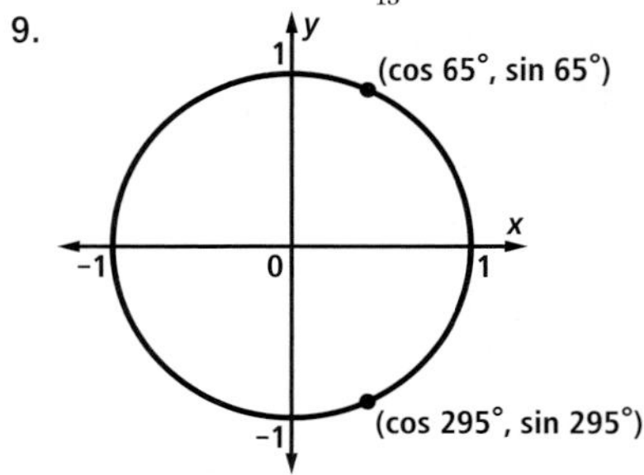

Since (cos 295°, sin 295°) is the image of (cos 65°, sin 65°) reflected over the y-axis, we know $\sin 295° = -\sin 65°$. $\sin 295° = -\sin 65° \approx -0.906$ **11.** $\frac{\sqrt{2}}{2}$ **13.** $-\frac{\sqrt{3}}{2}$ **15.** 233°

17. a. $\sin 300° \approx -0.866$; $\cos 300° = 0.5$; $\tan 300° \approx -1.732$ **b.** $\frac{-0.866}{0.5} = -1.732$ **19.** 0 **21.** The y-coordinates of $R_\theta(1, 0)$ and $R_{180°-\theta}(1, 0)$ are the same, and $\sin \theta$ is the y-coordinate of points on the unit circle. **23.** false **25. a.** about 10 degrees **b.** Answers vary. Sample: The stairs will now be less steep. **27.** $x = 9$ or $x = 1$

Lesson 10-6 (pp. 693–699)

Mental Math a. the shortest diagonal **b.** the other leg **c.** the diagonal **d.** They are the same length.

Activity Step 1:

θ	$\cos \theta$
0°	1.00
15°	0.97
30°	0.87
45°	0.71
60°	0.50
75°	0.26
90°	0.00
105°	-0.26
120°	-0.50
135°	-0.71
150°	-0.87
165°	-0.97
180°	-1.00
195°	-0.97
210°	-0.87
225°	-0.71
240°	-0.50
255°	-0.26
270°	0.00
285°	0.26
300°	0.50
315°	0.71
330°	0.87
345°	0.97
360°	1.00

Step 2:

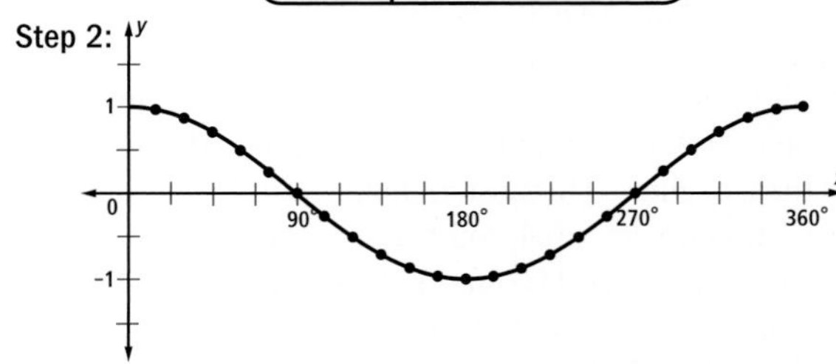

Step 3: The graph is bounded such that $-1 \le \cos \theta \le 1$ and has intercepts that are odd multiples of 90°.

Step 4: The largest value is 1 and the smallest value is -1.

Questions

1. the cosine function **3. a.** 1; 0 **b.** 0; -1 **c.** increase **5.** 8 **7.** -180°, 0°, 180° **9.** false **11.** true **13. a.** Answers vary. Sample: -90°, 270° **b.** Answers vary. Sample: 45°, 225° **15.** yes; 360° **17.** No; this is a polynomial function. **19. a.** Answers vary. Sample: Temperatures are annually affected by the seasons; therefore, the data are periodic with period 1 year. **b.** domain: all real numbers; range: $66 \le T \le 105$

21. a. Yes; period: 360°

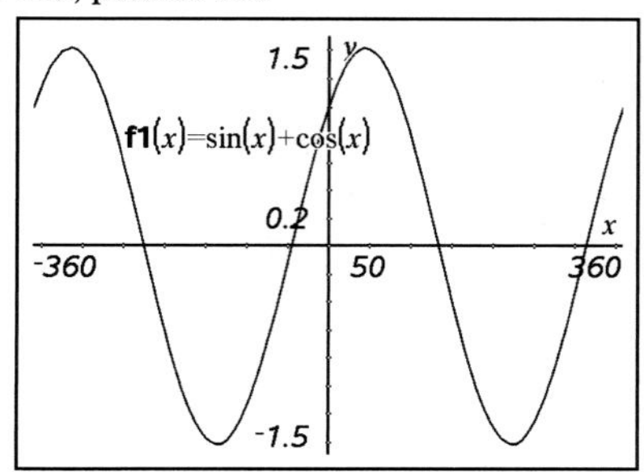

b. domain: all real numbers; range: $-\sqrt{2} \leq y \leq \sqrt{2}$ **23.** 0
25. a. $h = -1.86t^2 + 15t + 47$
b.

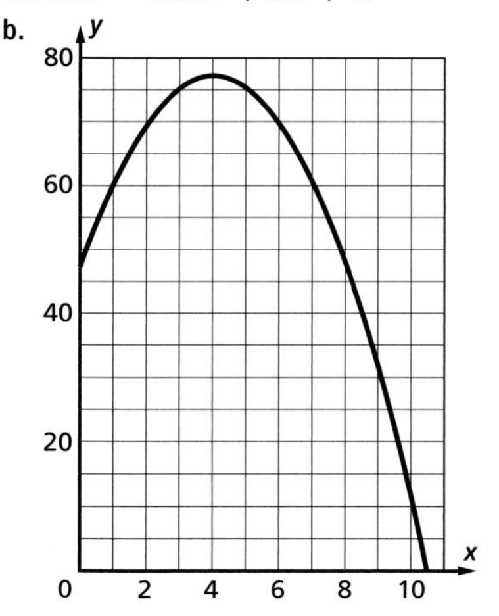

c. 77 m **d.** 10.5 sec **27. a.** $y = -\frac{1}{9}x$ **b.** direct

Lesson 10-7 (pp. 700-705)

Mental Math a. 1 **b.** 0 **c.** infinitely many (any line parallel to $y = x$)
Activity Step 1:

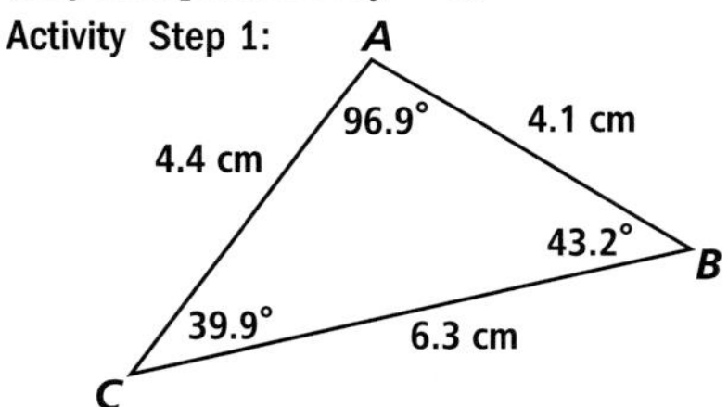

Step 2: $\frac{\sin A}{a} = \frac{\sin B}{b} = \frac{\sin C}{c} \approx 0.158$ **Step 3:** The ratios of the sines of $\triangle ABC$'s angles to the lengths of its sides opposite them are equal, but these ratios are not equal to the corresponding ratios of my partner's triangle.
Guided Example 3 $\frac{\sin 55°}{7}$, $\frac{\sin 17°}{g}$; 2.5
Questions
1. For any value of k between 0 and 1 and for $0° < \theta < 180°$, the graph of $y = k$ intersects $y = \sin\theta$ in two points.
3. 135° **5.** In any triangle, the ratios of the sines of its angles to the lengths of the sides opposite them are equal.
7. $r \approx 6.63$ **9. a.** The statement is incorrect because $\triangle BSG$ is not a right triangle. **b.** No, the Law of Sines can be used only when either the AAS condition or the ASA condition is satisfied. **11. a.** about $1.24 \cdot 10^8$ m/sec **b.** about 2.42 **c.** about $1.36 \cdot 10^8$ m/sec **13.** Transitive Property of Equality; $\triangle ABC$; $ab \sin C = ac \sin B = bc \sin A$; $\frac{ab \sin C}{abc} = \frac{ac \sin B}{abc} = \frac{bc \sin A}{abc}$ **15.** 90°, 270°, 450° **17.** $\pm\sqrt{1 - \sin^2\theta}$

Lesson 10-8 (pp. 706-711)

Mental Math a. true **b.** false **c.** true
Guided Example 3 14, 12, 20; 20, 14, 12, 14, 12; 400, 340, 336; 60, -336; -0.1786; 100.29°; 100°
Questions
1. q^2 **3.** $p^2 + q^2 - 2pq \cos R$
5. $BC = \sqrt{x^2 + 100 - 20x \cos 27.5°}$
7. Step 1 $m\angle C = \sin^{-1}\left(\frac{c}{a} \sin A\right) \approx 22.02°$
Step 2 $m\angle B \approx 180° - 30° - 22.02° = 127.98°$
Step 3 $b = \frac{\sin B}{\sin A} \cdot a \approx 12.6$ cm **9.** Consider $\triangle ABC$ with $\angle C$ acute. By the Law of Cosines, $c^2 - a^2 - b^2 = -2ab \cos C$. Since C is acute, $\cos C > 0$, so $-2ab \cos C < 0$. Thus, $c^2 - a^2 - b^2 < 0$, and $c^2 < a^2 + b^2$.
11. $\cos A = \frac{a^2 - b^2 - c^2}{-2bc}$ **13. a.** ≈ 54.35 m **b.** $\approx 12.51°$
15. 59.49° **17.** 50.12 m **19.** Yes. Equations vary. Sample: $x = 90°$. **21.** By the Pythagorean Identity, we have $D = \sqrt{r^2 \cos^2\theta + r^2 \sin^2\theta} = \sqrt{r^2(\cos^2\theta + \sin^2\theta)} = \sqrt{r^2} = |r|$.
23. $\frac{85}{360} = \frac{17}{72}$

Lesson 10-9 (pp. 712-717)

Mental Math a. 24 **b.** 11.33 **c.** 16
Guided Example 2 a. $\frac{\pi \text{ radians}}{180 \text{ degrees}}$, $\frac{45\pi}{180}$, $\frac{\pi}{4}$, $\frac{\pi}{4}$
b. $\frac{180 \text{ degrees}}{\pi \text{ radians}}$, $\frac{360}{3}$ degrees; 120°; 120°
Guided Example 3 2, 2, -0.416; $\frac{3\pi}{4}$, $\frac{3\pi}{4}$, -1; 57.3°, 114.6°; 114.6°, -0.416; 135°, 135°, -1
Questions
1. a. 2π **b.** π **c.** $\frac{\pi}{2}$ **d.** $\frac{11\pi}{2}$ **3.** 1440° **5.** 56° **7.** $\frac{\pi}{2}$ **9.** $\frac{5\pi}{4}$
11. a. sin 6 is the sine of 6 radians; sin 6° is the sine of 6 degrees. **b.** -0.279, 0.105 **13. a.** 0 **b.** cos 270° = 0
15. 2π **17.** B and D **19.** 1 **21. a.** $\frac{5\pi}{2}$ **b.** 5π **23.** $\frac{16\pi}{3}$ feet
25. $\sin\theta = \sin(180° - \theta)$; thus, if you use the Law of Sines, you know $\theta \approx 49.46°$ or 130.54°. **27.** 1
29. The stones form a right triangle, with legs of 2 and 1, and $\tan^{-1}\left(\frac{1}{2}\right) = 26.57°$. Thus, using this technique will always give a 26.57° angle.

Self-Test (pp. 722-723)

1. a. $\cos(17.4°) \approx 0.954$ **b.** $\sin(17.4°) \approx 0.299$
2. $\tan^{-1}(\tan\theta) = \tan^{-1}(0.64)$; $\theta \approx 32.619°$ **3. a.** $\cos\theta = \frac{\text{adj.}}{\text{hyp.}} = \frac{40}{41}$ **b.** $\tan\theta = \frac{\text{opp.}}{\text{adj.}} = \frac{9}{40}$ **4.** $1 - \sin^2\theta = \cos^2\theta$; $1 - (0.280)^2 = \cos^2\theta$; $\cos^2\theta = 0.9216$; $\cos\theta = \pm 0.96$.
Since $90° < \theta < 180°$, $\cos\theta = -0.96$. **5. a.** (cos(-423°), sin(-423°)) **b.** According to the unit-circle definitions of cosine and sine, for any θ, the point $(\cos\theta, \sin\theta)$ is the image of (1, 0) under R_θ. **6.** $x = 163°$; since $\sin\theta = \sin(180° - \theta)$, $\sin(180° - 17°) = \sin 163° = \sin 17°$.

7. a, because the angle that the radius through (a, b) makes with the x-axis measures about 70°, and cosine is the x-coordinate of points on the unit circle. **8.** f, because (e, f) is in the third quadrant, and sine is the y-coordinate of points on the unit circle. **9.** According to the Law of Cosines, $c^2 = a^2 + b^2 - 2ab \cos C$. Therefore, $c^2 = 250^2 + 175^2 - 2(250)(175)\cos 35°$; $c^2 \approx 21{,}449.2$; $c \approx 146.455$; he is about 146 m away. **10.** According to the Law of Sines, $\frac{\sin S}{s} = \frac{\sin L}{\ell}$. Therefore, $\frac{\sin S}{425} = \frac{\sin 12°}{321}$; $m\angle S = \sin^{-1}\left(425 \cdot \left(\frac{\sin 12°}{321}\right)\right) \approx 16.0°$ **11.** $\sin(\theta + 360°) = \sin\theta$ for all values of θ; therefore, the period is 360°. **12.** Answers vary. Sample: $-360° < \theta < -270°$ and $-90° < \theta < 90°$. **13.** $15^2 = 20^2 + 30^2 - 2(20)(30)\cos\theta$; $\cos\theta = \frac{43}{48}$; $\cos^{-1}\left(\frac{43}{48}\right) = 26.38°$; The sum of the measures of the angles of a parallelogram is 360°, and opposite angles are equal. Therefore, $360 - 2(26.38) = 2\theta$; $\theta = 153.62$. The angles of the parallelogram have measures 153.62°, 26.38°, 153.62°, and 26.38°. **14.** Convert 0.008 arc-second to degrees: 0.008 arc-second $\cdot \frac{1 \text{ degree}}{3600 \text{ arc-seconds}} \approx 0.000002°$. Let d be the distance from Earth to Betelgeuse. $\tan(0.000002°) = \frac{93{,}000{,}000}{d}$; $d \approx 2.66 \cdot 10^{15}$ miles. Convert miles to light-years. $d \approx 2.66 \cdot 10^{15}$ miles $\cdot \frac{1 \text{ light-year}}{5.88 \cdot 10^{12} \text{ mi}} \approx 452.4$ light-years **15. a.** $60° \cdot \frac{\pi}{180°} = \frac{\pi}{3}$ **b.** $25° \cdot \frac{\pi}{180°} = \frac{5\pi}{36}$ **16. a.** $4\pi \cdot \frac{180°}{\pi} = 720°$ **b.** $\frac{\pi}{7} \cdot \frac{180°}{\pi} \approx 25.7°$ **17. a.** $\sin 36° = \frac{1500}{d}$; $d = \frac{1500}{\sin 36°} \approx 2552$ ft **b.** $\tan 36° = \frac{1500}{a}$; $a = \frac{1500}{\sin 36°} \approx 2065$ ft

Self-Test Correlation Chart

Question	1	2	3	4	5	6	7	8	9
Objective(s)	A	B	E	F	E	F	I	I	H
Lesson(s)	10-1, 10-9	10-2, 10-7	10-1, 10-4, 10-5	10-5, 10-7	10-1, 10-4, 10-5	10-5, 10-7	10-4, 10-5	10-4, 10-5	10-7, 10-8
Question	**10**	**11**	**12**	**13**	**14**	**15**	**16**	**17**	
Objective(s)	C	J	J	C	G	D	D	G	
Lesson(s)	10-7, 10-8	10-6	10-6	10-7, 10-8	10-1, 10-2, 10-3	10-9	10-9	10-1, 10-2, 10-3	

Chapter Review (pp. 724-727)

1. 0.559 **3.** -0.383 **5.** -0.951 **7.** $\theta = 30°$ or $150°$ **9.** $\theta = 90°$ **11.** $a = 13.4$ **13.** $c = 86.9°$ **15.** $e = 14.1$ **17.** $-\frac{7\pi}{12}$ **19.** $\frac{9\pi}{4}$ **21.** 270° **23.** 210° **25.** D **27.** C **29.** $\frac{5}{13}$ **31.** true; $\tan x \cdot \cos x = \frac{\sin x}{\cos x} \cdot \cos x = \sin x$ as long as x is not an odd multiple of $\frac{\pi}{2}$. **33.** -0.292; -0.956 **35.** false; $\cos\theta - \cos(180° - \theta) = \cos\theta + \cos\theta \neq 0$ **37.** $\cos x \approx \pm 0.968$ **39.** 4.8° **41.** 11,000 km **43.** about 309 cm **45.** 84°

47. $\frac{\sqrt{2} - \sqrt{6}}{4}$

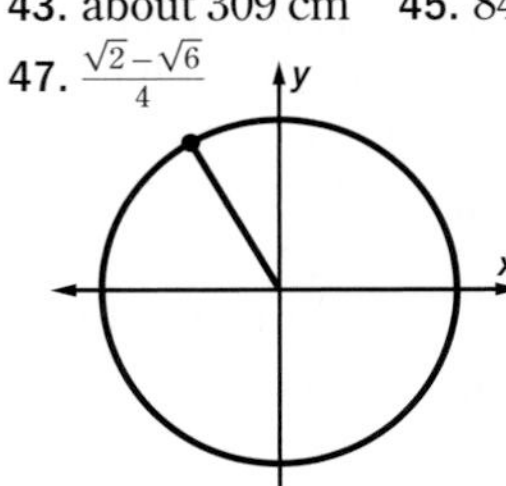

49. $\frac{-\sqrt{2} - \sqrt{6}}{4}$

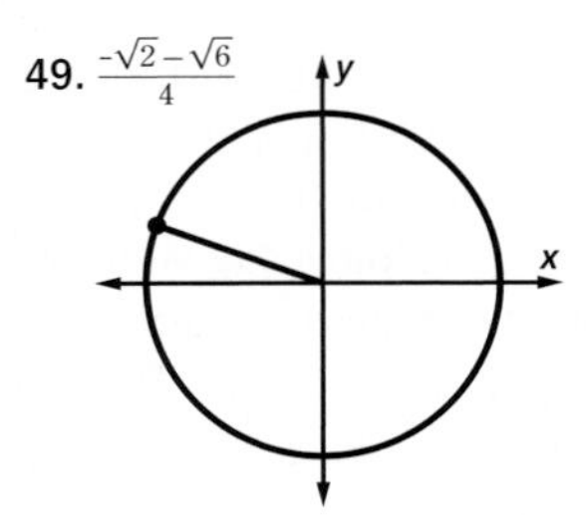

51. $\frac{\sqrt{6} - \sqrt{2}}{4}$

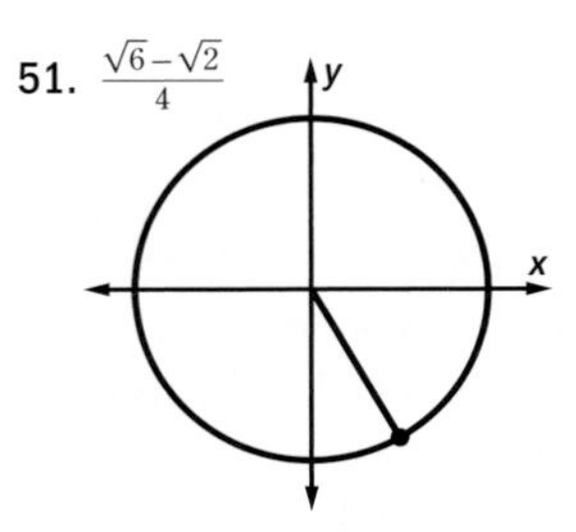

53. 4 radians **55.** e

57. a.

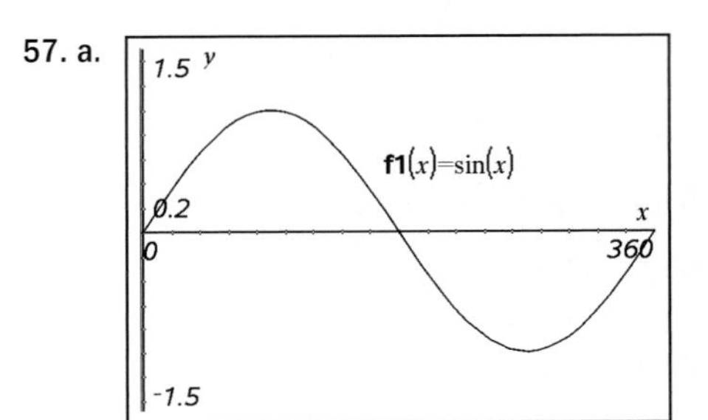

b. domain: all real numbers; range: $-1 \le y \le 1$ **59.** Answers vary. Sample: $T: (x, y) \to (x - 90°, y)$ **61.** No; this graph cannot be mapped onto the graph of the sine function $s: \theta \to \sin\theta$ by any composite of translations, scale changes, or reflections.

Chapter 11

Lesson 11-1 (pp. 730-737)

Mental Math a. 0 **b.** Answers vary. Sample: $\begin{bmatrix} 2 & 1 \\ 6 & 3 \end{bmatrix}$ **c.** does not exist **d.** Answers vary. Sample: $f: x \to 1$

Guided Example 1 a. 1; 3; 16; 96; 4; 16; 96; -16; 0; 4; 0; 96 **b.** 4; 4; -16; -16 **c.** -16; 4; 96

Activity 1 Step 1: a. $f(x) + g(x) = 5x^3 + 2x^2 + 3x + 5$; degree 3 **b.** $f(x) - g(x) = -5x^3 + 2x^2 + 3x + 3$; degree 3 **Step 2: a.** 5 **b.** 10 **Step 3: a.** $10x^5 + 15x^4 + 20x^3 + 2x^2 + 3x + 4$ **b.** Answers vary. They are the same. **Step 4:** sum; product

Activity 2 Step 1: $f(g(x)) = 2(5x^3 + 1)^2 + 3(5x^3 + 1) + 4$ **a.** Answers vary. Sample: 6 **b.** Answers vary. Sample: 50 **Step 2: a.** $50x^6 + 35x^3 + 9$ **b.** Answers vary. Sample: They are the same. **Step 3:** Answers vary. Sample: The degree of the composite of two polynomial functions is the product of the degrees of the polynomial functions. The leading coefficient of $f(g(x))$ is the leading coefficient of $g(x)$ to the power of the degree of $f(x)$ multiplied by the leading coefficient of $f(x)$.

Guided Example 3 a. 2; 1; 3 **b.** 3; 4; 12 **c.** 2; 1; 2 **d.** 3; 4; 48

Questions

1. Yes; its degree is 1 and its leading coefficient is 8.
3. Yes; its degree is 5 and its leading coefficient is 6.
5. $a_4t^4 + a_3t^3 + a_2t^2 + a_1t + a_0$ **7. a.** -10
b.

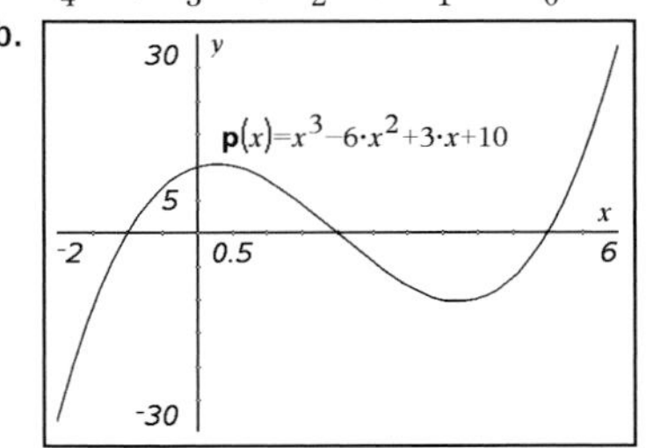

9. a. 8 **b.** 6 **c.** $6x^8 + 2x^4 - \frac{5}{2}$ **11. a.** 5 **b.** 8 **c.** 15 **13. a.** 2 **b.** $-\frac{1}{2}g$ or -16 **c.** 47.04 ft **15. a.** 40,000 + 5000 + 700 + 2 = 45,702 **b.** 19,394 **17. a.** $\frac{1}{49}$, $\frac{1}{343}$; 3, -8 **b.** $A_n = 49 \cdot \left(\frac{1}{7}\right)^{n-1}$ **c.** $B_n = 47 - 11(n - 1)$ **d.** A

19.

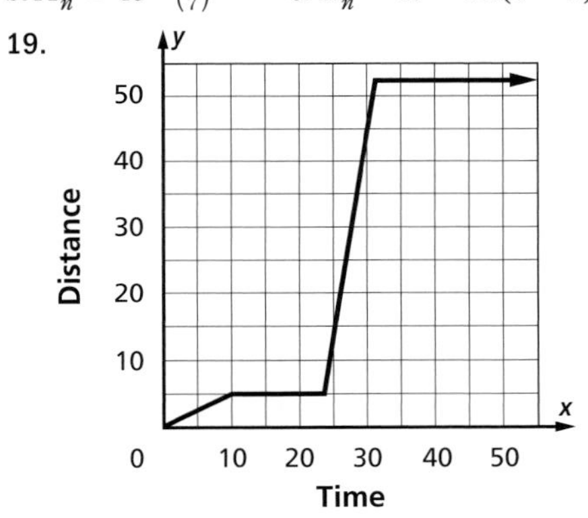

21. B **23. a.** 3 **b.** 128°

Lesson 11-2 (pp. 738-744)

Mental Math $2\sqrt{2} \approx 2.8$ blocks

Guided Example 3 $5x^2$; $4x^2$; $11x$; $220x^5$; 2; 8; -3; -48; $4x^2$; $11x$; 440; 88

Questions

1. a. trinomial **b.** 8 **3. a.** binomial **b.** 3 **5. a.** monomial **b.** 0 **7.** Answers vary. Sample: $2xy^4 + y$ **9.** $10b^4 - 15b^3 + 10b^2 - 15b$ **11. a.** 384; 384; 300; 84; 0; 0 **b.** $x = 3$ **13. a.** $x^4 - 3x^2 + 9$ **b.** $x^4 - 8x^2 + 16$ **c.** $x^4 - 15x^2 + 25$ **d.** $x^4 - 24x^2 + 36$ **e.** $x^4 - (n^2 - 2n)x^2 + n^2$ **15. a.** $V(x) = x\left(\frac{15\sqrt{3} - 6x}{4}\right)(15 - 2x\sqrt{3})$ **b.** $V(x) = 3\sqrt{3}x^3 - 45x^2 + \frac{225\sqrt{3}x}{4}$ **c.** $V(4) = 417\sqrt{3} - 720 \approx 2.27$ **d.** 62.5 in³ **17.** $(75 - 2b) \cdot (150 - a - c) = 11{,}250 + 2ab + 2bc - 75a - 300b - 75c$ **19.** $2y + 1$ and $y + 7$ **21. a.** 5 **b.** \$5119.36

23. a.

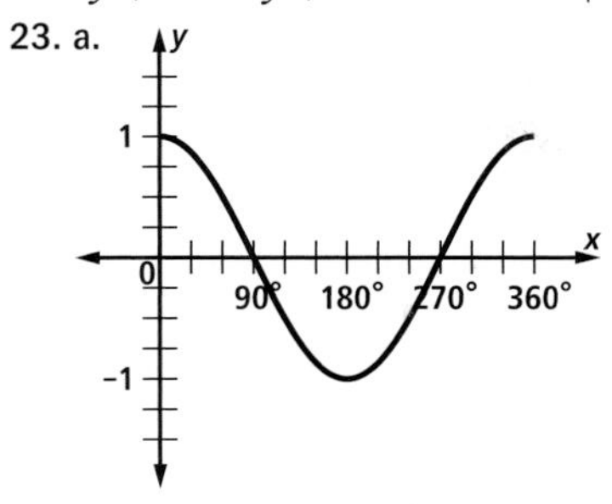

b. $x = 90°, x = 270°$ **25.** $x^2 + 14x + 49$

Lesson 11-3 (pp. 745-751)

Mental Math a. -0.15 **b.** 0.15 **c.** -0.15 **d.** 0.15

Activity Step 1: a.

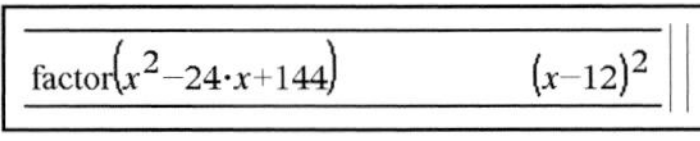

b. factor(x^2-49) $(x-7)\cdot(x+7)$

c. factor(x^2-64) $(x-8)\cdot(x+8)$

d. factor($x^2+8\cdot x+16$) $(x+4)^2$

e. factor($4\cdot x^2-81$) $(2\cdot x-9)\cdot(2\cdot x+9)$

f. factor($x^2-6\cdot x+9$) $(x-3)^2$

g. factor($x^2+10\cdot x+25$) $(x+5)^2$

h. factor($36\cdot x^2-1$) $(6\cdot x-1)\cdot(6\cdot x+1)$

Step 2: (d) and (g) have the form $(a + b)^2$, (a) and (f) have the form $(a - b)^2$, and (b), (c), (e), and (h) have the form $(a - b)(a + b)$. **Step 3: a.** $(x + y)(x - y)$ **b.** $(x - y)^2$ **c.** $(x + y)^2$

Guided Example 2 a. $3x^3$; $10y$; $3x^3$; $10y$; $3x^3$; $10y$ **b.** p; 9; 9; $p - 9$

Questions

1. $3m^2$; $5m$; $-2n$ **3.** $90xy^2(x^2 + 3 + 2x)$ **5. a.** binomial square **b.** $(x - y)^2$ **7. a.** difference of squares **b.** $(7x - 12b)(7x + 12b)$ **9. a.** neither **b.** not possible **11. a.** $12t(t + 1)(t - 1)$ **b.** $(12t^2 + 12t)(t - 1) = 12t^3 - 12t^2 + 12t^2 - 12t = 12t^3 - 12t$ **13.** $(x + 3)(x - 3) \cdot (x + 1)(x - 1)$; For $x = -3$, $(-3)^4 - 10(-3)^2 + 9 = 0$ and $(-3 + 3)(-3 - 3)(-3 + 1)(-3 - 1) = 0(-6)(-2)(-4) = 0$. **15.** $-1(1 + 5y)^2$; common monomial factoring, binomial square factoring **17.** $3x(2x + 5)(2x - 5)$;

common monomial factoring, difference of squares
19. a. yes **b.** no; $(x - \sqrt{30})(x + \sqrt{30})$ **21.** A **23.** $4x + 7$
25. $2(q + 1)(3q - 2)$ **27. a.** $5x(x^2 - 2x - 35) = 5x(x - 7)(x + 5)$ **b.** $(5x^2 - 35x)(x + 5) = 5x^3 + 25x^2 - 35x^2 - 175x = 5x^3 - 10x^2 - 175x$ **29. a.** $\frac{(2x + 3)(2x - 3)}{(2x + 3)(x - 1)}$
b. $\frac{(2x - 3)}{(x - 1)}$ **c.** The domain includes all real numbers x such that $x \neq$ -1.5 and $x \neq 1$. If x took these values, the denominator of the expression would equal zero.
31. $4h^3 + 14h^2 + 12h$ **33. a.** $V = \frac{1}{3}\pi r^2 h$ **b.** $r = \sqrt{81 - h^2}$
c. $V = \frac{1}{3}\pi h\left(\sqrt{81 - h^2}\right)^2 = \frac{1}{3}\pi(81h - h^3)$ **d.** true **35.** -1

Lesson 11-4 (pp. 752-759)

Mental Math a. never **b.** never **c.** always **d.** never
Activity 1 Step 1:

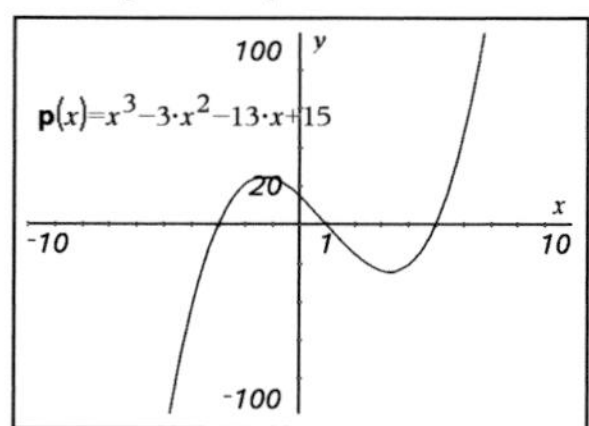

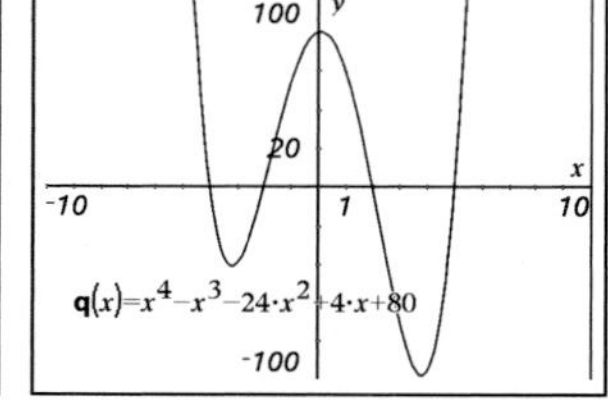

Step 2: $p(x) = x^3 - 3x^2 - 13x + 15$: -3, 1, 5;
$q(x) = x^4 - x^3 - 24x^2 + 4x + 80$: -4, -2, 2, 5

Step 3:

factor$(x^3-3\cdot x^2-13\cdot x+15)$
$(x-5)\cdot(x-1)\cdot(x+3)$

factor$(x^4-x^3-24\cdot x^2+4\cdot x+80)$
$(x-5)\cdot(x-2)\cdot(x+2)\cdot(x+4)$

Step 4: If r is an x-intercept of the graph of $P(x)$, then $x - r$ is a factor of $P(x)$. **Step 5:** Answers vary. Sample:
$r(x) = (x + 1)(x - 4)(x - 5) = x^3 - 8x^2 + 11x + 20$
Guided Example 3 $x - (-2); x - (-1); x + 2; x + 1$; **Check:** Graph should match the one in Guided Example 3.
Activity 2 Step 1: a. -4, 0, 3 **b.** -4, 0, 3 **c.** -4, 0, 3 **d.** -4, 0, 3
Step 2:

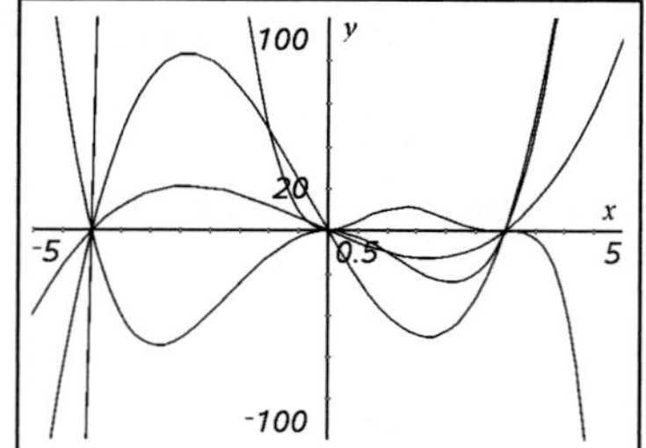

The four graphs have the same x-intercepts. The function paths between the x-intercepts are different.
Step 3: Answers vary. Sample: $m(x) = x(x + 4)^2(x - 3)$

Questions
1. For all a and b, $ab = 0$ if and only if $a = 0$ or $b = 0$.
3. $-\sqrt{2}, -1, \sqrt{2}, 20$ **5.** C **7. a.** $r(t) = t(t + 3)(2t - 7)$
b. $-3, 0, \frac{7}{2}$ **9. a.** $p(x) = k(x - 5.6)^a(x + 2.9)^b$, where $k \neq 0$ and a and b are positive integers.
b. Answers vary. Sample:

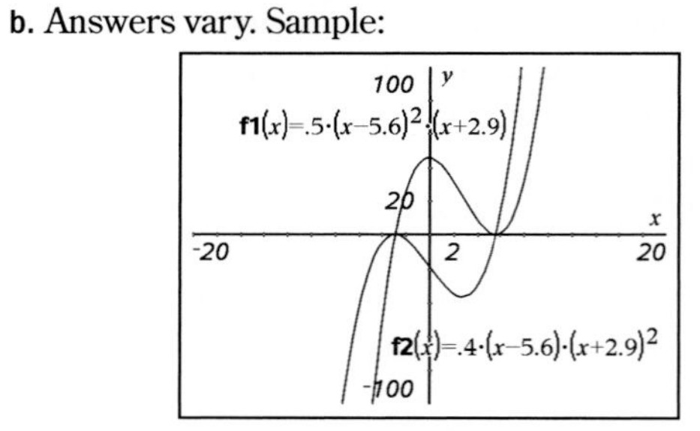

11. $y = \frac{1}{2}(x + 2)(x - 1)(x - 3)^2$ **13. a.** $P(x) = x(x^2 + 5x + 3)$
b. $x = 0, x = \frac{-5 \pm \sqrt{13}}{2}$ **c.** $P(x) = x\left(x + \frac{5 - \sqrt{13}}{2}\right)\left(x + \frac{5 + \sqrt{13}}{2}\right)$; the second factor in Part a has been factored.
15. $x^2 + 1 \neq 0$ for all real numbers x. **17. a.** -3, 2 **b.** $k = \frac{1}{4}$
19. a. $f(n) = -0.1n^2(n - \sqrt{800})(n + \sqrt{800})$ **b.** $-\sqrt{800} \approx$ -28.2843, 0, $\sqrt{800} \approx 28.2843$ **c.** The zeros represent the number of employees that results in 0 units produced per month.
d.

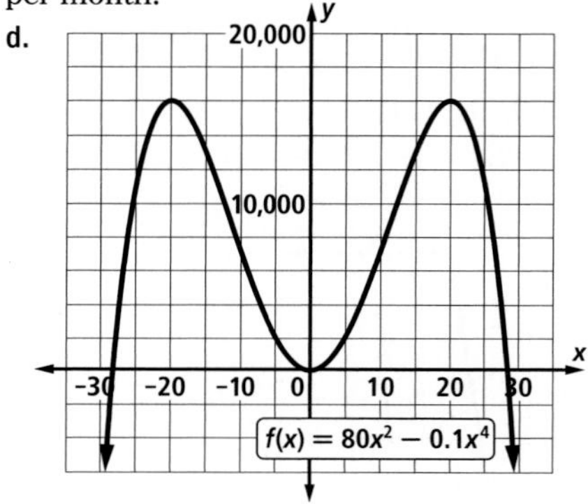

A reasonable domain for this situation is $0 \leq n \leq 28.2843$.
21. No; this expression contains a negative integer power of x. **23.** yes; 2 **25.** 1; 0 **27. a.** True; $\sqrt{12} \cdot \sqrt{3} = \sqrt{36} = \sqrt{2} \cdot \sqrt{18}$ by the Root of a Product Theorem. **b.** False; $\sqrt{-12} \cdot \sqrt{-3} = i\sqrt{12} \cdot i\sqrt{3} = i^2\sqrt{36} = -\sqrt{36} \neq \sqrt{2} \cdot \sqrt{18}$.

Lesson 11-5 (pp. 760-765)

Mental Math a. 12-oz box **b.** \$10-off coupon **c.** before tax **d.** They pay the same amount.
Activity Step 1: $x = \frac{3}{2}$ or $x = -\frac{4}{9}$; $x = \frac{3}{2}$, $x = -\frac{4}{9}$, or $x = -\frac{7}{5}$
Step 2: $Q(x)$: $18x^2$, -12; $P(x)$: $90x^3$, -84 **Step 3:** For both $Q(x)$ and $P(x)$, the denominators of the roots of the equation are factors of the coefficient of the leading term.
Step 4: For both $Q(x)$ and $P(x)$, the numerators of the roots of the equation are factors of the constant term.

Questions

1. 5 is a factor of the leading coefficient, and 7 is a factor of the constant term. **3. a.** $\pm 24, \pm 12, \pm 8, \pm 6, \pm 4, \pm 3, \pm 2, \pm \frac{3}{2}, \pm 1, \pm \frac{3}{4}, \pm \frac{1}{2}, \pm \frac{3}{8}, \pm \frac{1}{4}, \pm \frac{1}{8}$ **b.** $-\frac{1}{2}$ **5. a.** $\pm 14, \pm 7, \pm 2, \pm 1, \pm \frac{2}{7}, \pm \frac{1}{7}$ **b.** There are no rational roots. If we look at the graph, we see that the roots must lie in the ranges $-0.5 < x < 0$ and $3 < x < 3.5$. By testing $-\frac{2}{7}$ and $-\frac{1}{7}$, we find that neither of these values are zeros. **7. a.** $\pm 12, \pm 6, \pm 4, \pm 3, \pm 2, \pm \frac{3}{2}, \pm 1, \pm \frac{1}{2}$

b.

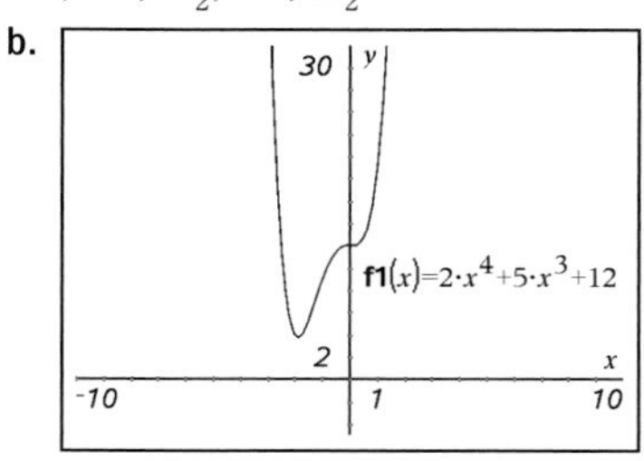

The function does not intersect the x-axis. **9. a.** Answers vary. Sample: $y = x^2 - 2ax + (a^2 - p)$ **b.** Assume that $a + \sqrt{p}$ is rational. Therefore, it should be able to be expressed as $\frac{m}{n}$ and with $n \neq 1$ since $a + \sqrt{p}$ is not an integer. However, according to the Rational-Root Theorem, n is a factor of the leading coefficient, which is 1. Thus, $a + \sqrt{p}$ cannot be rational. **11. a.** $0 \le x \le 9$ **b.** 0, 9, 15 **c.** The beam has no sag when $x = 0$ (the point is on the wall), or $x = 9$ (the point is on the support). $x = 15$ is a zero for the equation, but this value is not in the domain of x in this problem. **13.** about 4.8°

15. a.

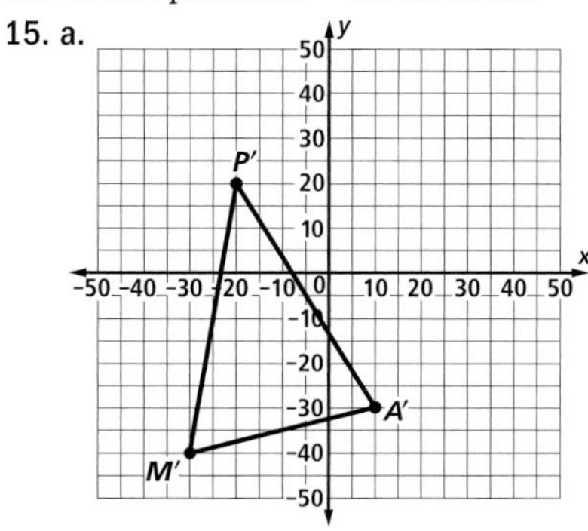

b.

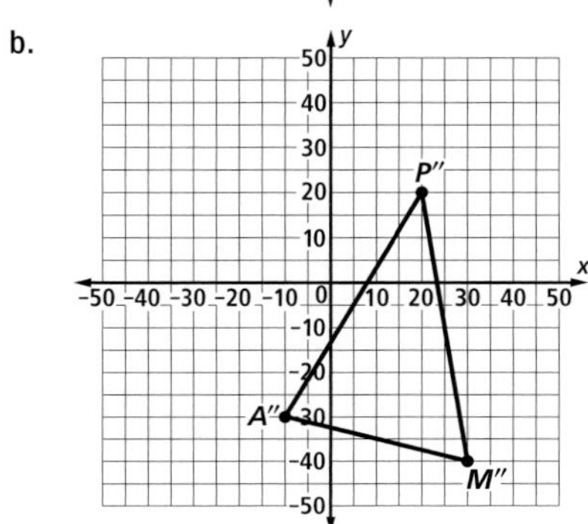

c. a rotation of 180° about the origin

Lesson 11-6 (pp. 766–771)

Mental Math **a.** 2 **b.** 2 **c.** 1 **d.** infinitely many

Activity **Step 1:** $P(3) = 3^3 + 2(3)^2 - 14(3) - 3 = 0$; the Factor Theorem **Step 2:** 2 **Step 3:** 2 roots; The roots of a factor of a polynomial are also the roots of the polynomial itself.

Step 4:

solve$(x^3+2\cdot x^2-14\cdot x-3=0,x)$

$x=\frac{-(\sqrt{21}+5)}{2}$ or $x=\frac{\sqrt{21}-5}{2}$ or $x=3$

Questions

1. Every polynomial equation $P(x) = 0$ of any degree ≥ 1 with complex number coefficients has at least one complex number solution. **3.** C **5.** $x = -\frac{b}{a}$ **7.** $x = -8$, rational; -8 has multiplicity 2 **9.** $z = 3$ and $z = \frac{22}{7}$, rational; $z = 3 + 4i$ and $z = 3 - 4i$, irrational; 3 has multiplicity 4 **11.** 5 **13.** $x = 4 - 2i$ **15. a.** The graph will be translated vertically when k is changed. **b.** $k = 40$ **c.** $k > 40$
17. $p(x) = 3x^3 - 5x^2 - 58x + 40$
19. a. $V(w) = 4w^3 - 30w^2 + 50w$ **b.** no **c.** $w \approx 1.06$
21. 100 **23. a.** $y = 3(x + 3)^2 + 4$

b.

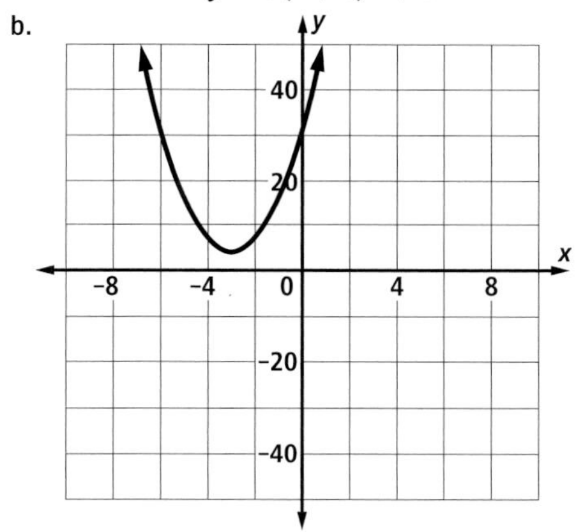

25.

	A	B	C	D	E
◆		=4*a[]^2-13*a[]			
1	3.3	.66			
2	3.4	2.04			
3	3.5	3.5			
4	3.6	5.04			
5	3.7	6.66			
6	3.8	8.36			

B5 =6.66

$y = 6.66$

Lesson 11-7 (pp. 772–777)

Mental Math **a.** $(c^7 + 10)(c^7 - 10)$ **b.** $(r - 5)^2$ **c.** $\pi x^3(x - 13)$ **d.** $(2p + 3q)^2$

Activity 1 Step 1: a–c.

	A x	B	C	D	E
◆		=4*'x^2-5*'x-3			
1	1	-4			
2	2	3	7		
3	3	18	15	8	
4	4	41	23	8	
5	5	72	31	8	
6	6	111	39	8	

D3 =c3–c2

Step 2: a–b.

	A x	B	C	D	E	F
◆		='x^3-				
1	1	-3				
2	2	-1	2			
3	3	7	8	6		
4	4	27	20	12	6	
5	5	65	38	18	6	
6	6	127	62	24	6	

E4 =d4–d3

Step 3: Answers vary. Sample: The fourth set of differences will all be the same.

Activity 2 Steps 1 and 2:

	A x	B	C	D	E	F
◆		=3^x				
1	1	3				
2	2	9	6			
3	3	27	18	12		
4	4	81	54	36	24	
5	5	243	162	108	72	
6	6	729	486	324	216	

C2 =b2–b1

Step 2: Answers vary. Sample: The method of finite differences does not produce a set of constant differences. Instead, the pattern of differences seems to repeat in each column.

Guided Example 2 a. 15; 31; 63; 127 **b.** first row: 15, 31, 63, 127; second row: 16, 32, 64; third row: 16, 32; will not; is not; polynomial

Questions

1. 3 **3.** yes; 12 **5.** Tanner is not using x-values that form an arithmetic sequence. If he rearranged his table and filled in the gaps, he would find a constant set of differences. **7. a.** yes **b.** 4 **9.** yes (degree = 4)
11. a. b; $m + b$; $2m + b$; $3m + b$; $4m + b$ **b.** m, m, m, m; this is a linear function, thus, it has degree 1 and its first differences are equal. **13. a.** 4 by the Number of Roots of a Polynomial Equation Theorem **b.** $\pm1, \pm2, \pm5, \pm10, \pm\frac{1}{3}, \pm\frac{2}{3}, \pm\frac{5}{3}, \pm\frac{10}{3}$ **c.** $x \approx -1.33 + 0.78i$, $x \approx -1.33 - 0.78i$, $x \approx 0.71$, $x \approx 1.96$ **15. a.** $P(x) = -x^3 + 4x^2 - 3$ **b.** 3; $\frac{\sqrt{21}+3}{2}$
17.

$$\text{solve}\left(\begin{bmatrix}4 & -2 & 3\\ 8 & -3 & 5\\ 7 & -2 & 4\end{bmatrix}\cdot\begin{bmatrix}x\\ y\\ z\end{bmatrix}=\begin{bmatrix}1\\ 4\\ 5\end{bmatrix}, x,y,z\right)$$

x=1 and y=3 and z=1

$x = 1, y = 3, z = 1$

Lesson 11-8 (pp. 778-785)

Mental Math a. Answers vary. Sample: 2 **b.** Answers vary. Sample: -8 **c.** 5 or -5 **d.** 4 or -4
Guided Example 2 9, 16, 25, 36; 5, 7, 9, 11; 2, 2, 2; 3; $\frac{1}{3}$; $\frac{1}{2}$; $\frac{1}{6}$; 0; $\frac{1}{3}n^3 + \frac{1}{2}n^2 + \frac{1}{6}n$

Questions

1. They used the method of finite differences. **3.** 190 **5.** 81 **7.** $12 = 4a + 2b + c$, $60 = 25a + 5b + c$, $162 = 64a + 8b + c$ **9.** $a = \frac{1}{2}$, $b = -\frac{1}{2}$, $c = 0$ **11.** $y = \frac{1}{2}x^2 + \frac{1}{2}x + 1$
13. a. $H(x) \approx -0.001x^4 + 0.019x^3 - 0.028x^2 - 0.313x$
b.

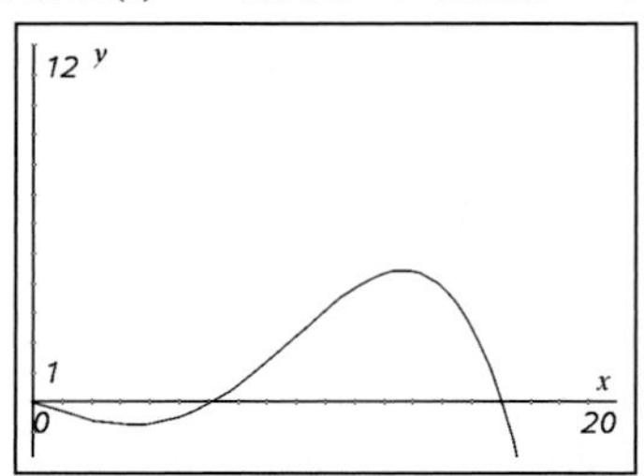

15. a. yes **b.** 3 **17.** \$40,784.87 **19. a.** $\log_7 6$ **b.** log 81 **c.** log 2

Self-Test (pp. 790-791)

1. To calculate the volume, we take the width of the box as $40 - 2x$, the length of the box as $30 - 2x$, and the height of the box as x. Since $V = \ell wh$, $V(x) = (30 - 2x) \cdot (40 - 2x)x = 4x^3 - 140x^2 + 1200x$. **2.** A; Each term of the expansion contains one factor from $(a + b)$, one factor from $(c + d + e)$, and one factor from $(f + g)$. Thus, acf is the only choice that is in the expansion.
3. $z^3 + 2z^2 - 14z + 5$; the standard form of a polynomial has the terms written in descending order by degree. So, we have to expand the factored form and then rearrange the terms. **4.** The degree is the largest sum of the exponents of the variables in any term. Answers vary. Sample: $3xy + z^4$ **5.** $680x^4 + 850x^3 + 1020x^2 + 1105x + 935$; the degree of x in each term is the number of years Francesca has held that summer's savings. **6.** Substitute 0.051 for r, $x = 1.051$; $680(1.051)^4 + 850(1.051)^3 + 1020(1.051)^2 + 1105(1.051) + 935 \approx \$5039.54$
7. a. The degree is the largest sum of the exponents of the variables in any term. The degree of $P(x)$ is 6.
b. A polynomial of degree n has n complex roots. Thus $P(x)$ has 6 complex roots. **8.** According to the Rational-Root Theorem, if $\frac{a}{b}$ is a rational root of a polynomial function, then a is a factor of the polynomial's constant term and b is a factor of the coefficient of the leading term. Here, a is a factor of 11 and b is a factor of 4. Therefore, the possible rational roots are $\pm11, \pm\frac{11}{2}, \pm\frac{11}{4}, \pm1, \pm\frac{1}{2}$, and $\pm\frac{1}{4}$.
9. a. The graph intersects the x-axis 3 times, so there are 3 real zeros. **b.** The function has a total of 5 complex zeros and 3 real zeros, so there are 2 nonreal zeros.

10. a. According to the Rational-Root Theorem, if $\frac{a}{b}$ is a rational root of a polynomial function, then a is a factor of the polynomial's constant term and b is a factor of the coefficient of the leading term. Here, a is a factor of 12, and b is a factor of 1. Therefore, the possible rational roots are ±12, ±6, ±4, ±3, ±2, and ±1. **b.** Looking at the graph, there are two real zeros between consecutive integers that must be irrational because the rational roots are all integer values. The irrational zeros must lie between -1 and 0 and 3 and 4. **11.** Set each factor equal to 0 and solve for x: $(x-2)^3=0, x-2=0, x=2$; $(11x+37)=0, 11x=-37, x=-\frac{37}{11}$; $x^2-7=0, x^2=7, x=\pm\sqrt{7}$. So the zeros of g are $2, -\frac{37}{11}, \sqrt{7}$, and $-\sqrt{7}$. **12.** The multiplicity of a zero r is the highest power of $x-r$ that appears as a factor of the polynomial. The multiplicity of 2 is 3, and the multiplicity of each other zero is 1. **13.** D; D is only true when $x=r$ or $x=s$. The rest are true for all x by the Factor Theorem and the Number of Roots of a Polynomial Equation Theorem. **14.** $\sqrt{21}$ is a solution to $x^2=21$ and a root of $x^2-21=0$. According to the Rational-Root Theorem, if $\frac{a}{b}$ is a rational root of a polynomial, then a is a factor of the polynomial's constant term and b is a factor of the coefficient of the leading term. Here, a is a factor of -21, and b is a factor of 1. Therefore, the possible rational roots are ±21, ±7, ±3, and ±1. If we test these values, none are solutions for the equation $x^2-21=0$. Thus, $\sqrt{21}$ is irrational. **15. a.** Use a CAS: $(y-3)(y^2-5)(y^2+3y+9)$ **b.** Use a CAS or use difference of squares factoring and the quadratic formula on the quadratic factors you found in Part a: $(y-3)(y+\sqrt{5})(y-\sqrt{5})(y+\frac{3}{2}+\frac{3}{2}i\sqrt{3}) \cdot (y+\frac{3}{2}-\frac{3}{2}i\sqrt{3})$ **16.** By the Factor Theorem, a is a zero of r if $y-a$ is a factor of $r(y)$. So by your answer to 15b, the zeros are $3, \sqrt{5}, -\sqrt{5}, -\frac{3}{2}+\frac{3\sqrt{3}}{2}i$, and $-\frac{3}{2}-\frac{3\sqrt{3}}{2}i$ **17.** Factor out the greatest common monomial factor: $2vw(5uv+12)$; these two factors are prime, so the polynomial is factored completely. **18.** Answers vary. Sample: $p(x)=(x+2)(x-6)^2=x^3-10x^2+12x+72$.

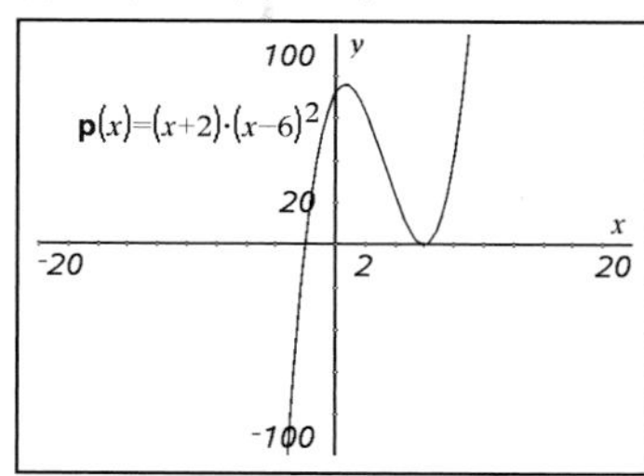

19. a. Yes, the 3rd differences are equal; therefore, f can be modeled by a polynomial. **b.** 3; the 3rd differences are equal, and the 2nd differences are not. **20.** From using the method of finite differences, we find that the 2nd set of differences is constant; therefore, these data can be modeled by a quadratic function. The function has the form $r=at^2+bt+c$. To solve for the coefficients and constant term, we pick three data points and solve. For example, use (-2, 12), (0, 0) and (3, 12).

Solving the system $\begin{cases} 12=4a-2b+c \\ 0=c \\ 12=9a+3b+c \end{cases}$ gives $a=2$, $b=-2$, $c=0$. So, the equation is $r=2t^2-2t$.

Self-Test Correlation Chart

Question	1	2	3	4	5	6	7	8	9	10
Objective(s)	I	A	A	E	H	H	E, F	G	K	G, K
Lesson(s)	11-2	11-2	11-2	11-1, 11-2, 11-3	11-1, 11-8	11-1, 11-8	11-1, 11-2, 11-3, 11-4, 11-6	11-5	11-4, 11-5	11-4, 11-5
Question	**11**	**12**	**13**	**14**	**15**	**16**	**17**	**18**	**19**	**19**
Objective(s)	C	C	F	G	B	C	B	J	D	D
Lesson(s)	11-4, 11-6	11-4, 11-6	11-4, 11-6	11-5	11-3	11-4, 11-6	11-3	11-1, 11-4, 11-5	11-7, 11-8	11-7, 11-8

Chapter Review (pp. 792–795)

1. x^3-x^2+x+3 **3.** $x^3-x^2y-xy^2+y^3$ **5.** $5a^7b^6$; $8a^6$ **7.** $(x-3)^2$ **9.** $(pq+2)(pq-2)(p^2q^2+4)$ **11.** not possible **13.** not possible **15.** $n=0, n=-3, n=\frac{7}{8}$; no multiple roots **17.** $x=0, x=-6$; $x=-6$ is a double root. **19.** 0, 5, -5 **21.** No; there are no constant differences in the 1st through 3rd differences. **23.** No; there are no constant differences in the 1st through 3rd differences. **25. a.** 6 **b.** 18 **27.** B **29.** D **31. a.** yes **b.** no; $(x+\sqrt{42})(x-\sqrt{42})$ **33.** The left side of the equation is not a product. **35.** true **37. a.** 3 **b.** 2 **39. a.** $\pm3, \pm\frac{3}{2}, \pm1, \pm\frac{1}{2}$ **b.** $x=3, x=\frac{1}{2}$ **41. a.** $\pm6, \pm3, \pm2, \pm1, \pm\frac{3}{2}, \pm\frac{6}{5}, \pm\frac{3}{5}, \pm\frac{1}{2}, \pm\frac{2}{5}, \pm\frac{3}{10}, \pm\frac{1}{5}, \pm\frac{1}{10}$

b.

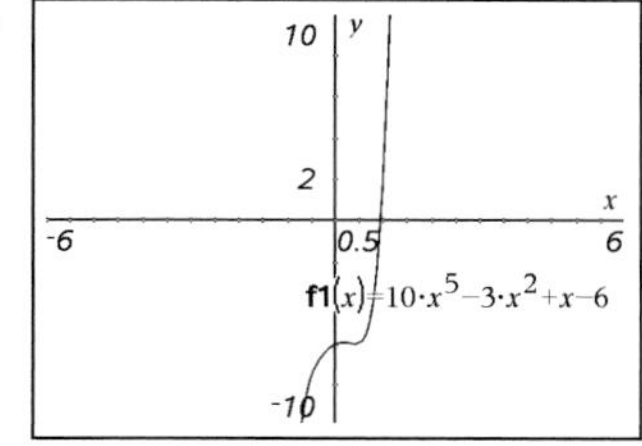

The range of possible rational roots is from $x = -6$ to $x = 6$. By restricting the graph to this range, we see that $f(n)$ only intersects the x-axis once in this interval, and not at any of the possible values that we found in Part a. Therefore, f has exactly one irrational zero.
43. a. $G = n^2 - n$ **b.** 552 **45. a.** $250x^5 + 250x^4 + 250x^3 + 250x^2 + 250x + 250$ **b.** \$1743.83 **c.** about 4.99%
47. $V(s) = 4s^3 - 16s^2 + 15s$ **49.** $4x^3 - 260x^2 + 4000x$
51. a.

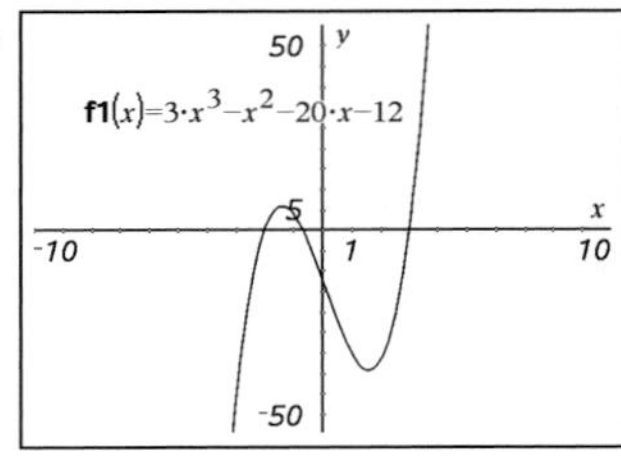

b. $(x - 3)(x + 2)(3x + 2)$ **53. a.** Answers vary. Sample: $h(x) = x(x + 1)(x - 1)(x - 3)$ **b.** $h(x) = 3x^4 - 9x^3 - 3x^2 + 9x$
c.

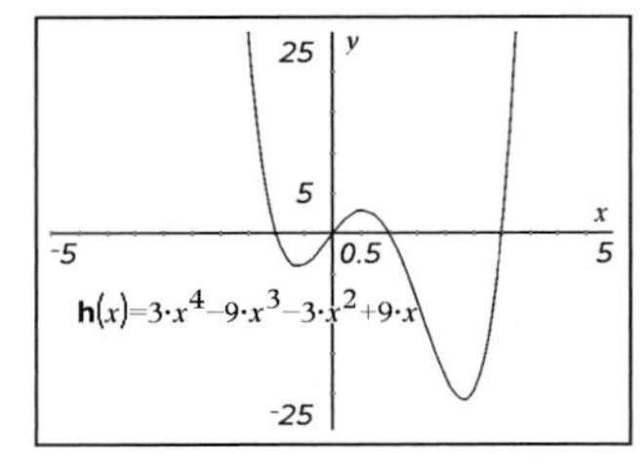

55. -4, -3, -3, -1 **57. a.** $\pm6, \pm3, \pm2, \pm\frac{3}{2}, \pm1, \pm\frac{1}{2}$
b. You should test ±1 and $-\frac{3}{2}$ because the graph indicates that the function does not cross the x-axis around the other values. **c.** There are no rational roots.

Chapter 12

Lesson 12-1 (pp. 798-803)

Mental Math a. $\log_{16} 1742$ **b.** $\log_3 20$ **c.** $r = 3e^t$
d. All are equivalent.
Activity Step 1:

Step 2:

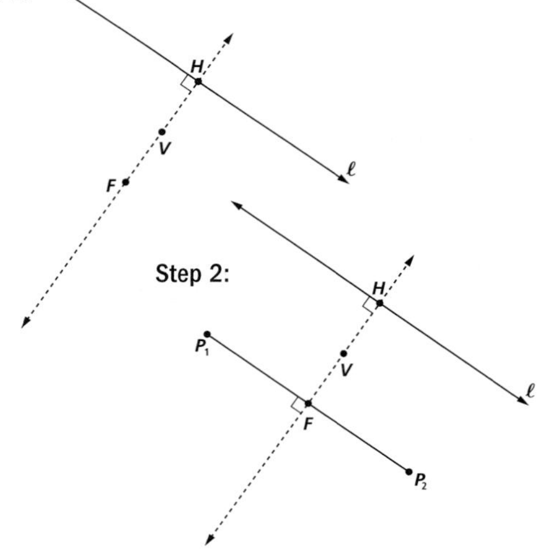

Step 3: a.

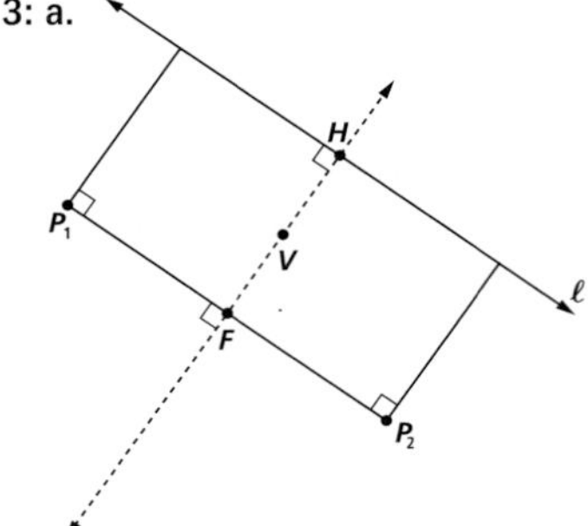

b. FP_1 = perpendicular distance from P_1 to ℓ. P_1 is on the parabola with focus F and directrix ℓ.
c. FP_2 = perpendicular distance from P_2 to ℓ. P_2 is also on the parabola.
Step 4:

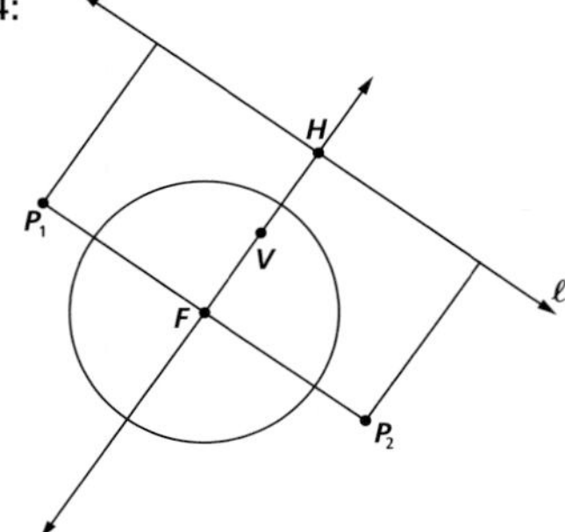

Step 5: a.

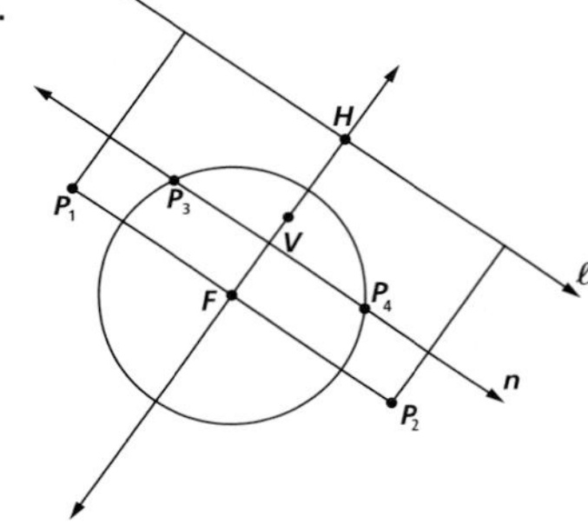

b. Yes; they are equidistant from F and ℓ. (Each distance is r.)
Step 6:

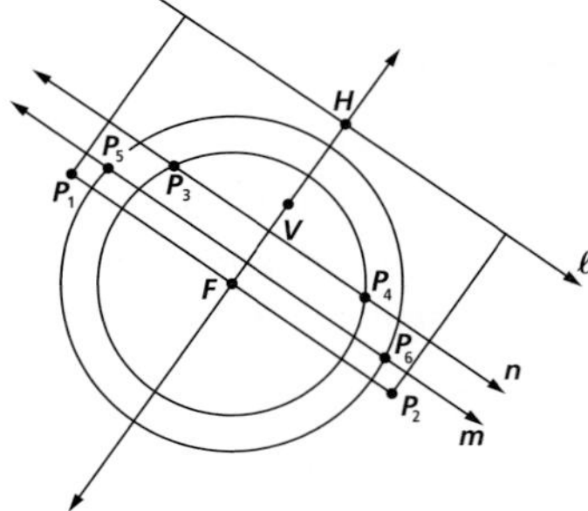

Step 7:

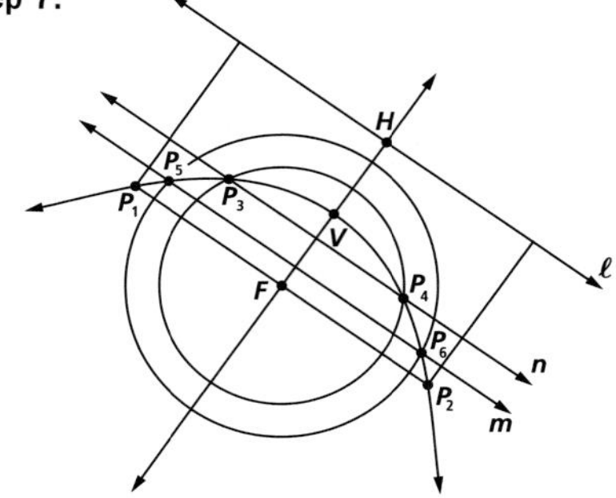

Questions

1. a. No; the focus is defined as a point not on the directrix. **b.** No; the vertex must be equidistant from the focus and directrix, and a point on the directrix has distance zero from the directrix. **3.** false

5. a.

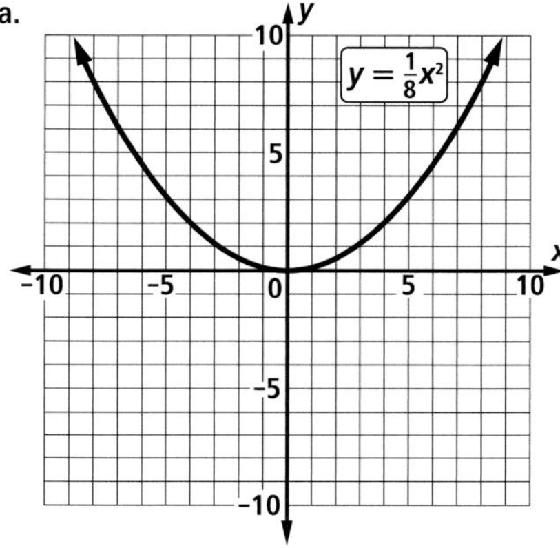

b. focus: (0, 2); vertex: (0, 0); directrix: $y = -2$
c. The distance from (5, 3.125) to (0, 2) is $\sqrt{(5-0)^2 + (3.125-2)^2} = 5.125$, and the distance from (5, 3.125) to $y = -2$ is $3.125 - (-2) = 5.125$.
d. Answers vary. Sample: (8, 8); $\sqrt{(8-0)^2 + (8-2)^2} = 10 = 8 - (-2)$ **7.** $y = -\frac{1}{12}x^2$ **9.** $\left(0, -\frac{1}{8}\right)$; $y = \frac{1}{8}$
11. $\left(-5, \frac{25}{4}\right)$; $y = \frac{23}{4}$ **13. a.** down **b.** $\left(0, -\frac{1}{20}\right)$ **15. a.** $x = \frac{1}{20}y^2$
b. Answers vary. Sample: (0, 0), (20, 20), (20, -20)
17. a. $y = \pm\sqrt{13}$ **b.** $y = -3 \pm \sqrt{13}$ **c.** $y = 169$ **d.** $y = 166$
19. a. $\frac{4}{7}$ **b.** 1000 **21.** C

Lesson 12-2 (pp. 804-809)

Mental Math a. upward **b.** 4.5 $\frac{\text{m}}{\text{sec}}$ **c.** 25 m **d.** yes
Guided Example 2 12; $\frac{17}{2}$; $\frac{27}{2}$; 12; $\frac{17}{2}$; $\frac{729}{4}$
Guided Example 5 1; 1; 24; 25; $y - 5$; 24; 5; $2\sqrt{6}$; 5; $-2\sqrt{6}$; $5 + 2\sqrt{6}$; $5 - 2\sqrt{6}$; 5

Questions

1. $x^2 + y^2 = 230{,}400$ **3.** 34 **5.** Answers vary. Sample: $x^2 + y^2 = 25$, $x^2 + y^2 = 16$

7. center: (0, 0); radius: 11

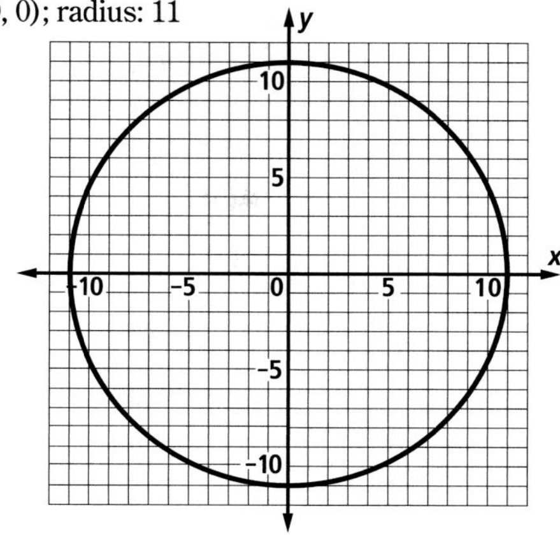

$y = \pm\sqrt{121 - x^2}$ **9. a.** There are no points on the circle where $x = -6$. **b.** There are no points on the circle where $x = 800$. **11. a.** $x^2 + y^2 = 6.25$ **b.** 47,901.4 mph
13. a. $(x-4)^2 + (y+1)^2 = 25$ **b.** Answers vary. Sample: (4, 3); image is (8, 2), $(8-4)^2 + (2+1)^2 = 25$
15. a. (0, 0); maximum **b.** $y = -\frac{1}{4}x^2$ **c.** $x = 0$
17. -4, -1, 1, 4 **19.** $y = -\frac{7}{3}x$

Lesson 12-3 (pp. 810-815)

Mental Math a. 4 **b.** -2, 7, $-\frac{3}{2}$ **c.** 7
Guided Example 3 a. (0, 0); 2.5; $x^2 + y^2 = 6.25$; (0, 0); 9; $x^2 + y^2 = 81$; $x^2 + y^2$; 6.25; $x^2 + y^2$; 81 **b.** 6.25π; 81π; 81π; 6.25π; 74.75π; 234.83

Questions

1. a.

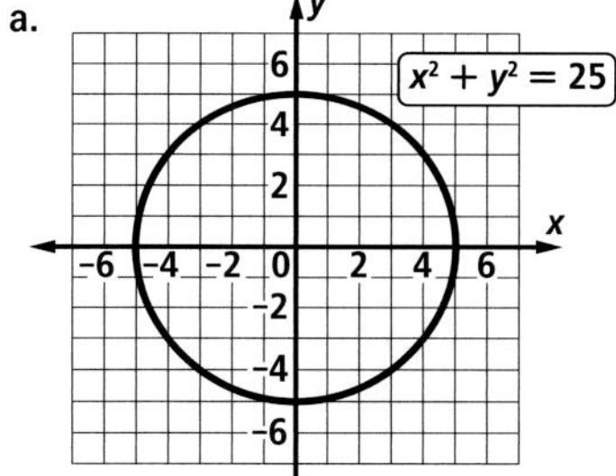

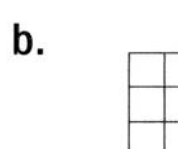
b.

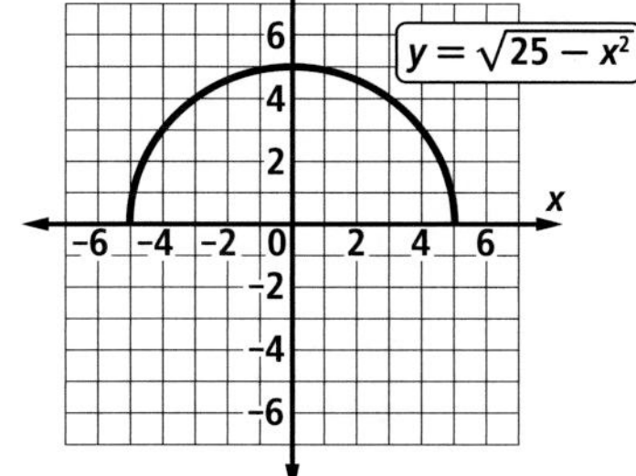

c.

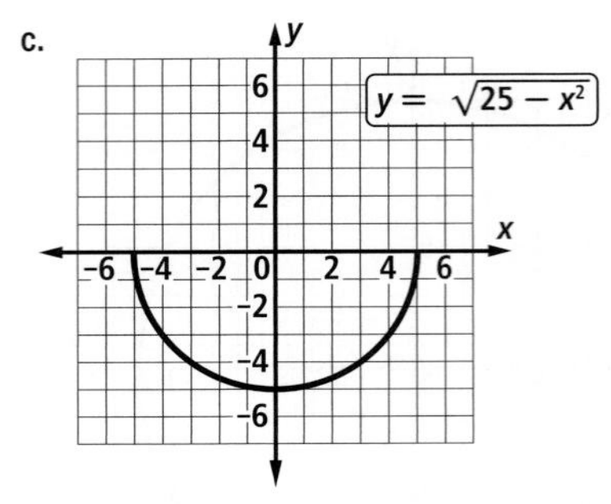

3. 9 ft 8 in. **5.** the interior of the circle C
7. $(x - 2)^2 + (y - 3)^2 > 9$ **9. a.** about 15 ft 5 in.
b. about 14 ft 10 in.

11. $\begin{cases} x < 3.35 \\ x > -3.35 \\ y < 3.35 \\ y > -3.35 \\ x^2 + y^2 > 2.275^2 \end{cases}$

13. For a line ℓ and a point F not on ℓ, a parabola is the set of all points in the plane of ℓ and F equidistant from F and ℓ. **15. a.** 13 **b.** $x^2 + y^2 = 169$ **17. a.** $x^2 + 16x + y^2 + 64$ **b.** $x^2 + 2xy + y^2 + 64$ **c.** $x^2 + 2xy + 16x + y^2 + 16y + 64$ **19. a.** $0 \le x \le 8$ **b.** $0 \le y \le 4$ **21.** No; the pieces do not satisfy the Triangle Inequality. To make a triangle, the sum of the measures of any two sides of the triangle should always be greater than the measure of the third side. Here, $1.5 + 2.3 < 4$.

Lesson 12-4 (pp. 816–823)

Mental Math a. 17 **b.** 11 **c.** 9
Activity Steps 1–3:

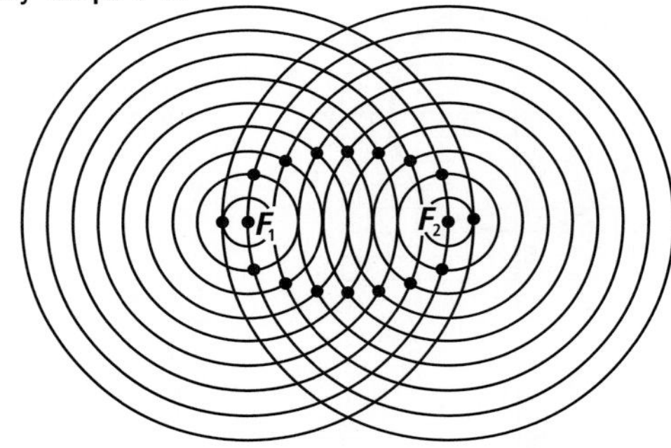

Step 4:

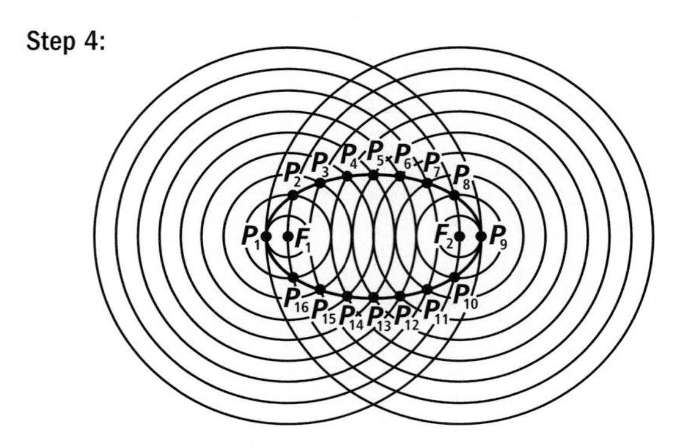

Guided Example 1 a. ± 3; 0; ± 2 **b.** 1; −2; 2 **c.** y-axis; $(x, -y)$; y; $-y$; $\frac{x^2}{9} + \frac{(-y)^2}{4} = 1$; x-axis
Guided Example 2 10; 5; 6; 3; −5; 5; −3; 3; −4; 4; 25; 9
Questions
1. 10 **3. a.** I, J **b.** $\overline{AB}$ **c.** $\overline{CD}$ **5.** major axis: $(0, -b)$, $(0, b)$; minor axis: $(-a, 0)$, $(a, 0)$ **7.** $-a \le x \le a$; $-b \le y \le b$
9.

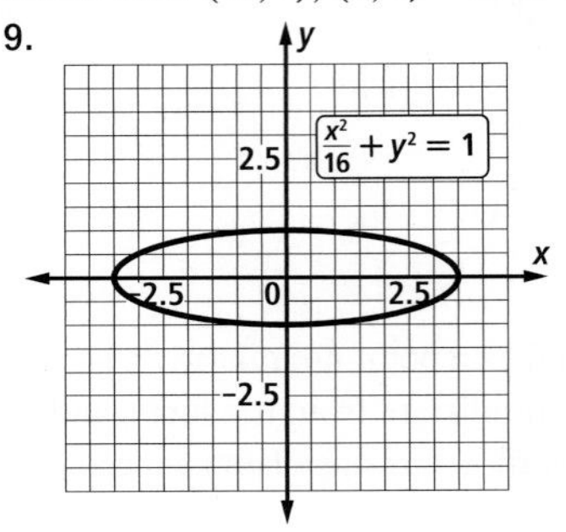

11. a. $\frac{x^2}{64} + \frac{y^2}{16} = 1$ **b.** $\frac{x^2}{64} + \frac{y^2}{16} < 1$ **13. a.** both foci at $(0, 0)$; focal constant 20 **b.** The ellipse is a circle.
15. a. about 43.4 million mi **b.** about 28.6 million mi
c. about 14.8 million mi
17. a.

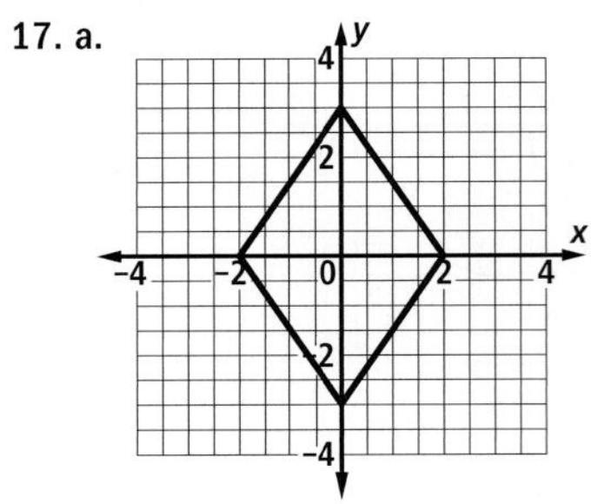

b. major axis: y-axis from −3 to 3; minor axis: x-axis from −2 to 2 **c.** x-intercepts: −2, 2; y-intercepts: −3, 3
d.

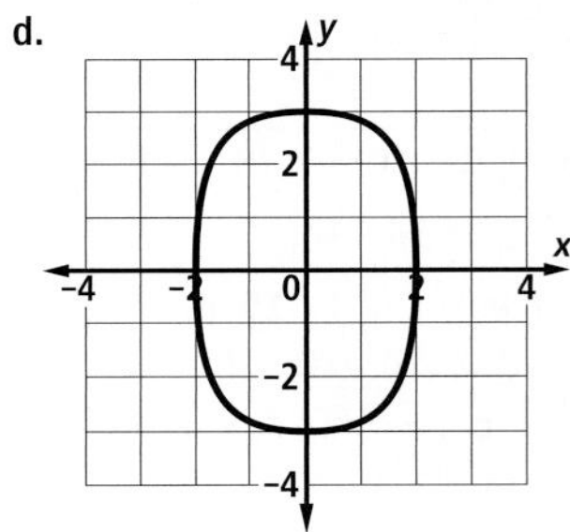

major axis: y-axis from −3 to 3; minor axis: x-axis from −2 to 2 **e.** Answers vary. Sample: They have the same x- and y-intercepts and endpoints of the major and minor axes. The graph from Part a is a polygon made of line segments, whereas the graph from Part d has smooth curves.
19. a. $x^2 + y^2 = 9$ **b.** $\left(x - \frac{3\sqrt{2}}{2}\right)^2 + \left(y - \frac{3\sqrt{2}}{2}\right)^2 = \frac{9}{2}$ **c.** $x^2 + y^2 < 9$ **d.** A: 6π; B: $3\pi\sqrt{2}$ **e.** A: 9π; B: $\frac{9\pi}{2}$
21. $b \approx 35.9$ **23.** $(7x, 8y)$

Lesson 12-5 (pp. 824-830)

Mental Math **a.** $T_{7,-2}$ **b.** $S_{3,2.5}$ **c.** $T_{7,-2} \circ S_{3,2.5}$ **d.** $r_{y=x} \circ T_{7,-2} \circ S_{3,2.5}$

Guided Example $2y$; $\frac{x'}{4}$; $\frac{y'}{2}$; $\frac{x'}{4}$; $\frac{y'}{2}$; $\frac{x}{4}$; $\frac{y}{2}$; 4; 8; 4^2; 2^2; 1; 0; 1; 4^2; 2^2; 0; 1; 1

Questions

1. C **3.** true **5. a.** (5, 0) **b.** $\left(0, \frac{1}{2}\right)$ **c.** $\left(\frac{x}{5}\right)^2 + (2y)^2 = 1$ **7. a.** $S_{4,8}$ **b.** $\left(\frac{x}{4}\right)^2 + \left(\frac{y}{8}\right)^2 = 1$ **c.** 32π **9.** Answers vary. Samples: **a.** $S_{2,2}$ **b.** $S_{1,2}$ **11.** $19{,}973\pi \approx 62{,}746$ million mi^2 **13.** $2b = 8\sqrt{2} \approx 11.31$ **15.** Answers vary. Samples: $\left(\frac{x}{24}\right)^2 + y^2 = 1$; $\left(\frac{x}{12}\right)^2 + \left(\frac{y}{2}\right)^2 = 1$; $\left(\frac{x}{6}\right)^2 + \left(\frac{y}{4}\right)^2 = 1$; $x^2 + \left(\frac{y}{24}\right)^2 = 1$ **17.** iii **19.** ii **21.** i **23.** $n = -0.25$ or $n = -0.75$ **25.** $y = -\frac{3}{7}x + \frac{29}{7}$

Lesson 12-6 (pp. 831-837)

Mental Math **a.** -1 **b.** $\frac{1}{4}$ **c.** no

Activity **Step 1:** 6; 6; 4; 4; 2; 2; yes

Step 2:

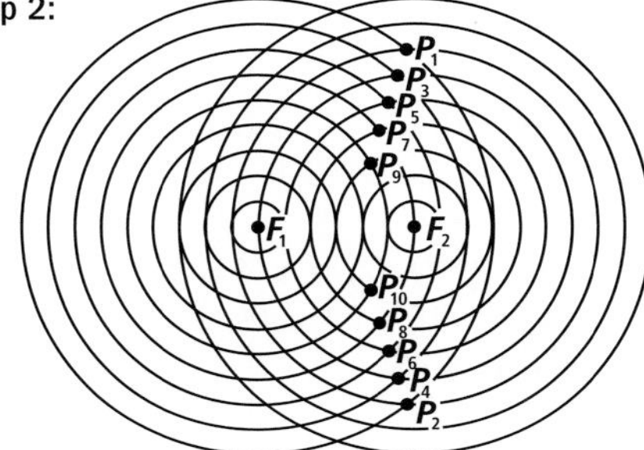

Step 3:

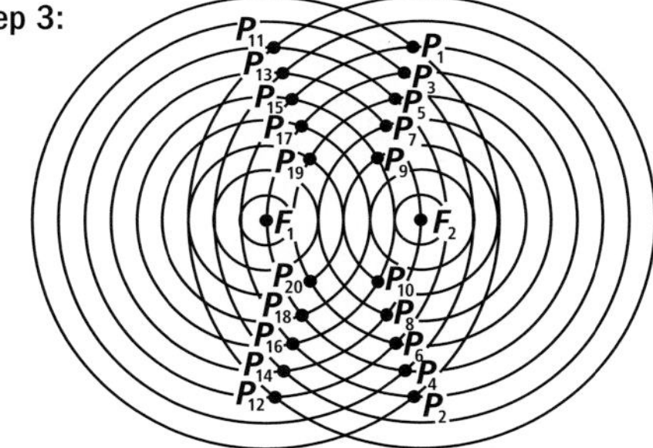

Step 4:

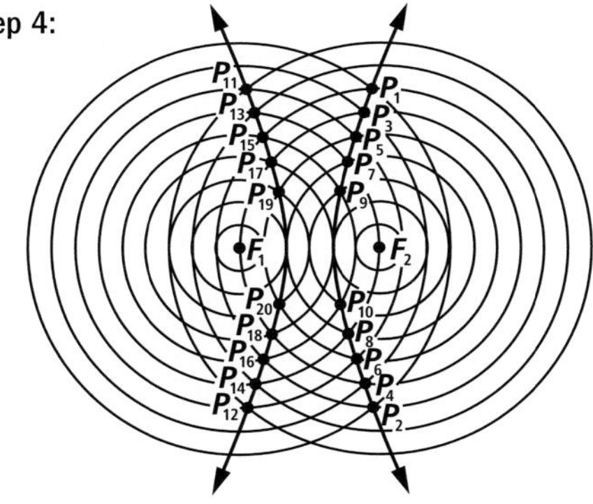

Questions

1. $\frac{x^2}{a^2} - \frac{y^2}{b^2} = 1$ where $b^2 = c^2 - a^2$; $(a, 0)$; $(-a, 0)$
3. (1, 0), (-1, 0); $(-\sqrt{2}, 0)$, $(\sqrt{2}, 0)$; $y = x$, $y = -x$
5. false **7.** Answers vary. Sample: If x is very large, then the difference between $\sqrt{x^2 - 1}$ and $\sqrt{x^2}$ is very small.
9. Answers vary. Sample: It does not include the asymptotes for the parts of the hyperbola in the second and third quadrants. **11. a.** about 6.83 **b.** $\frac{x^2}{11.7} - \frac{y^2}{4.3} = 1$
c.

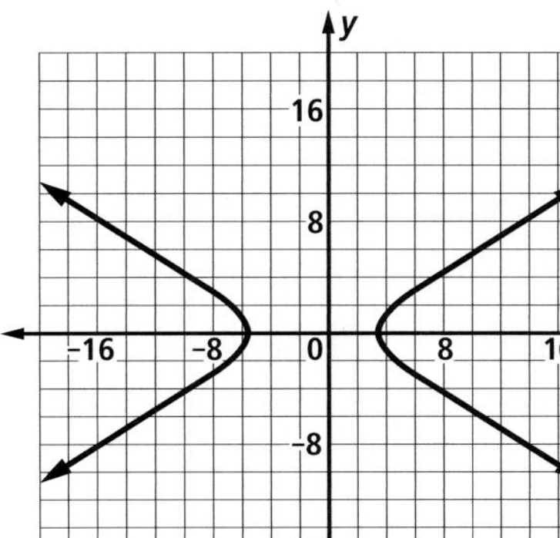

13. $y = \pm\sqrt{x^2 - 1}$

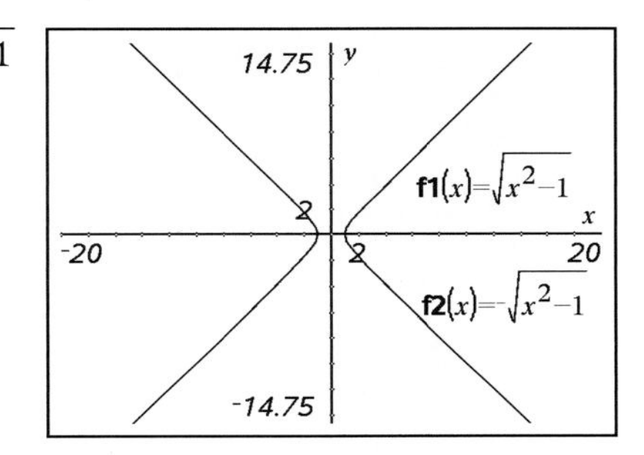

15.

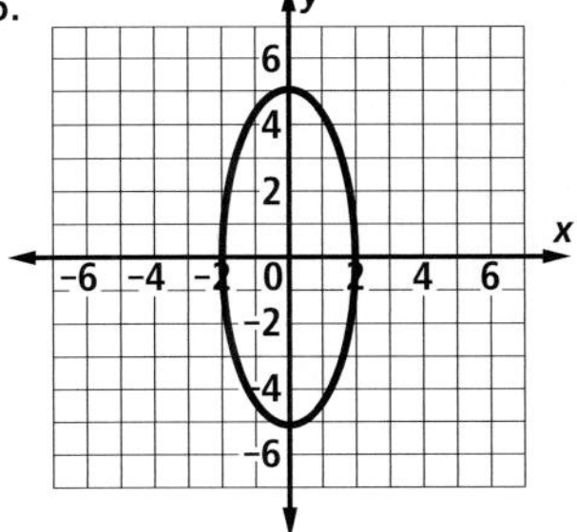

17. a. no closer than 2 ft **b.** $2400\pi \approx 7539.82$ ft^3

Lesson 12-7 (pp. 838-843)

Mental Math **a.** 45° **b.** 60° **c.** 72°

Guided Example 3 $-\sqrt{2k}$; $-\sqrt{2k}$; 8; 8; 8; 64; 32; 32; $\frac{32}{x}$

Questions

1. yes; $x^2 + y^2 - 6x + 14y - 60 = 0$ **3.** yes; $x^2 - 6xy + y^2 + \pi y - \sqrt{11} = 0$ **5. a.** $\left(\sqrt{238}, \sqrt{238}\right)$, $\left(-\sqrt{238}, -\sqrt{238}\right)$ **b.** $2\sqrt{238} \approx 30.85$ **7.** $w = 0$, $d = 0$

9.

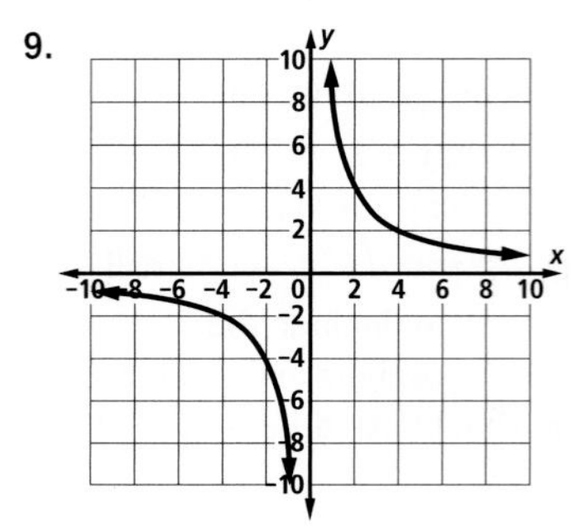

foci: (4, 4), (-4, -4); vertices: $(2\sqrt{2}, 2\sqrt{2})$, $(-2\sqrt{2}, -2\sqrt{2})$; asymptotes: $x = 0$, $y = 0$; focal constant: 8

11. $\frac{1}{4}x^2 - \frac{1}{9}y^2 - 1 = 0$ (or $9x^2 - 4y^2 - 36 = 0$); $A = \frac{1}{4}$, $B = 0$, $C = \frac{1}{9}$, $D = 0$, $E = 0$, $F = -1$ (or $A = 9$, $B = 0$, $C = 4$, $D = 0$, $E = 0$, $F = -36$) **13. a.** Yes; the asymptotes $x = 0$ and $y = 0$ are perpendicular. **b.** Yes; the asymptotes $y = x$ and $y = -x$ are perpendicular. **c.** No; the asymptotes $y = \frac{3}{2}x$ and $y = -\frac{3}{2}x$ are not perpendicular.

15. a.

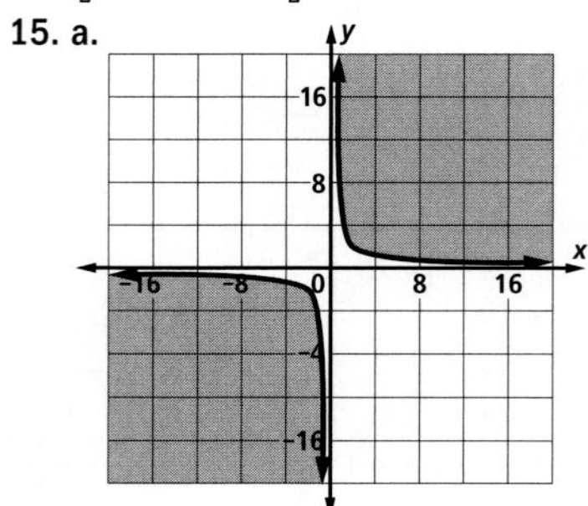

b.

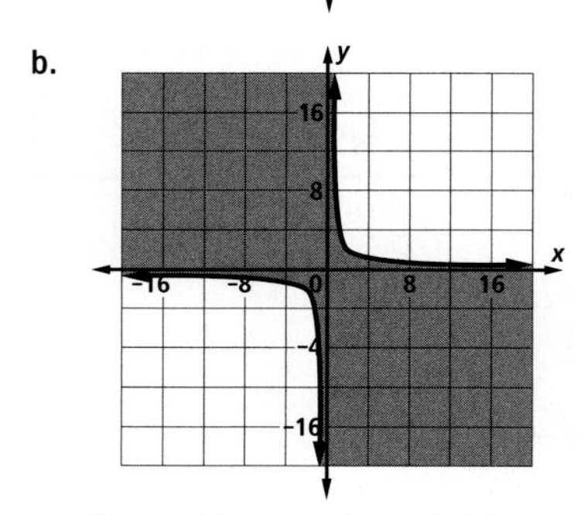

17. C **19.** B **21.** about 401 ft **23.** \$0.90

Lesson 12-8 (pp. 844–849)

Mental Math a. (0, 0) **b.** (-2, 4) and (2, 4) **c.** (0, 0) and (1, 1) **d.** no intersections

Activity Step 1:

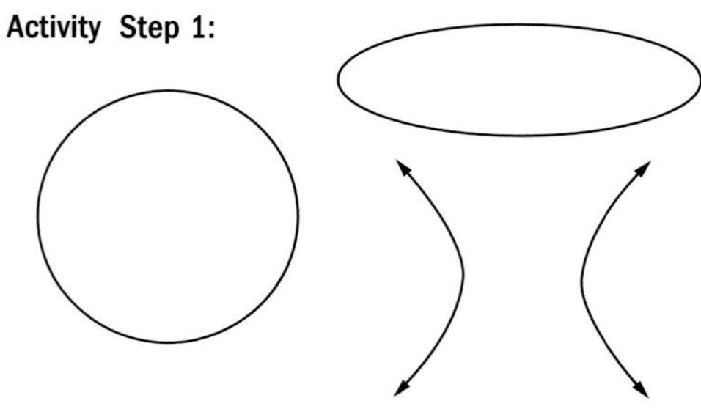

Step 2:

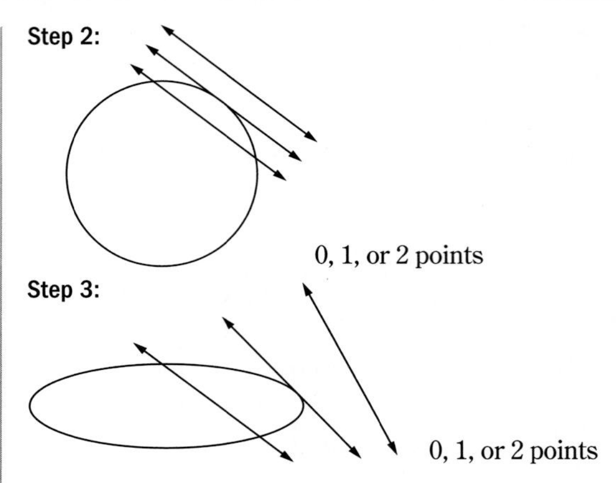

Step 3:

0, 1, or 2 points

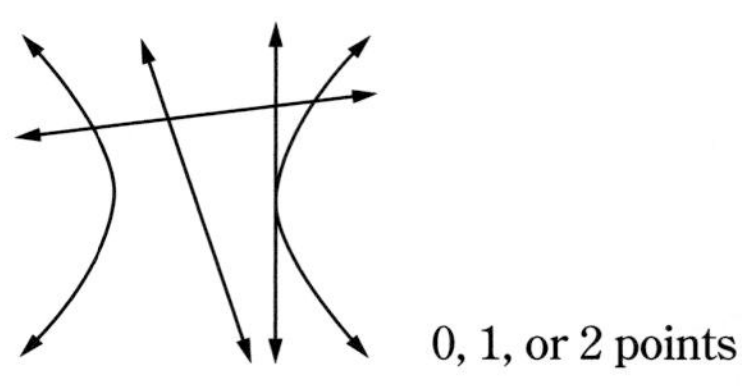

Step 4: 0, 1, or 2; 0, 1, or 2; 0, 1, or 2

Guided Example 3 0; x; x^2; x; 2; 1; -7; 2; 0

Questions

1. 0, 1, or 2 **3. a.** 2 **b.** (-2, -4), (2, 4) **c.** $4 = 2 \cdot 2$; $-4 = 2 \cdot -2$; $4(2)^2 + 2(4)^2 = 16 + 32 = 48$; $4(-2)^2 + 2(-4)^2 = 16 + 32 = 48$

5.

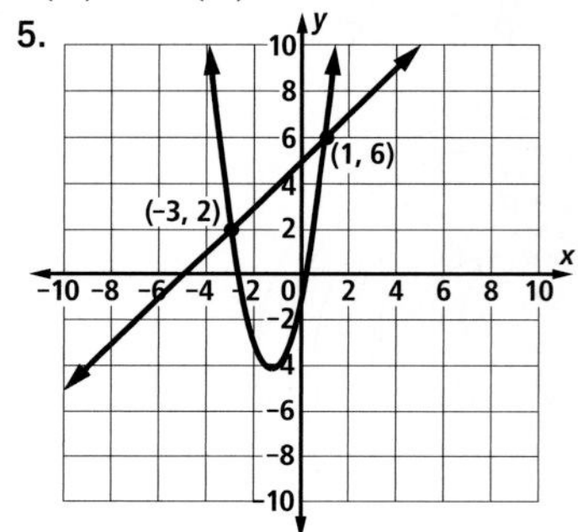

estimated solutions: (-3, 2), (1, 6); exact solutions: (-3, 2), (1, 6) **7.** (1, -2), $\left(-\frac{1}{2}, -\frac{7}{2}\right)$ **9.** $-16 = (-6)^2 + 7 \cdot -6 - 10$; $-16 = -5(-6) - 46$ **11.** A quadratic-linear system can have at most 2 solutions because a straight line and a quadratic curve cannot coincide.

13. Answers vary. Sample: $\begin{cases} x + y = 8 \\ xy = 24 \end{cases}$. Substituting $y = 8 - x$ into the second equation gives $x(8 - x) = 24$, or $x^2 - 8x + 24$. This equation has no real solutions, so the system cannot be solved.

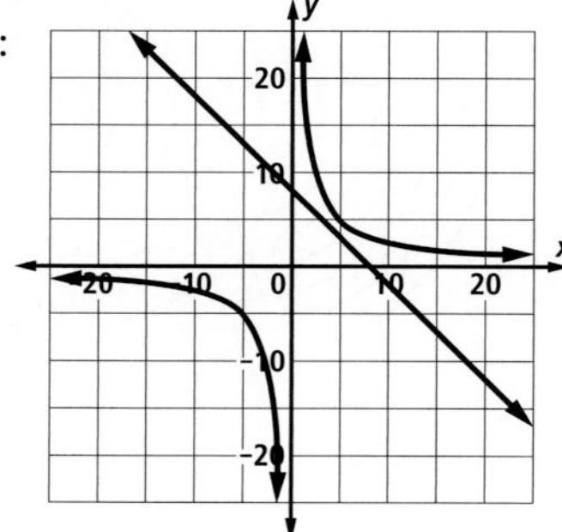

15. (3.79, 1.90), (-3.79, -1.90) 17. $y = \frac{50}{x}$
19. a. difference of squares b. $(r^{10} + t)(r^{10} - t)$
21. a. sum of squares b. not possible 23. $-\frac{7}{2} + 8i$

Lesson 12-9 (pp. 850–855)

Mental Math a. $n > 4t$ b. $\ell \geq 30$ c. $85.9 \leq s \leq 86.9$, or $|86.4 - s| \leq 0.5$ d. $a < 7$

Activity

	Parabola	Circle	Ellipse	Hyperbola
Parabola	0, 1, 2, 3, 4, or infinite	0, 1, 2, 3, or 4	0, 1, 2, 3, or 4	0, 1, 2, 3, or 4
Circle		0, 1, 2, or infinite	0, 1, 2, 3, 4, or infinite	0, 1, 2, 3, or 4
Ellipse			0, 1, 2, 3, 4, or infinite	0, 1, 2, 3, or 4
Hyperbola				0, 1, 2, 3, 4, or infinite

Guided Example 2 ellipse; hyperbola; 9; 3; 15; 13; 52; 4; 2; 2; 2; $\sqrt{7}$; -2; -2; $\sqrt{7}$; 2; $\sqrt{7}$; 2; $-\sqrt{7}$; -2; $\sqrt{7}$; -2; $-\sqrt{7}$

Questions

1. 4 3. (0, 3), (0, -3) 5. a. 2 b. (-1.59, 2.54) and (1.59, 2.54)
7. \$42 in the first month and \$60 in the second month
9. (-4, 3), (4, 3), (-3, -4), (3, -4) 11. (-1, -6)

13. a. $\begin{cases} x^2 + y^2 = 1{,}000{,}000 \\ (x - 200)^2 + (y - 800)^2 = 160{,}000 \\ (x - 1000)^2 + (y - 1100)^2 = 250{,}000 \end{cases}$

b. $x = 600$, $y = 800$; The net is 600 m north and 800 m east of the first boat.

15. $\begin{cases} x + y = 37 \\ xy = 300 \end{cases}$; The solutions are $x = 12$ and $y = 25$ or $x = 25$ and $y = 12$. Mr. Hwan's age is 25 yr, and his baby's is 12 mo. 17. yes; $13y^2 - \frac{1}{2}x + \sqrt{7}y = 0$

19.

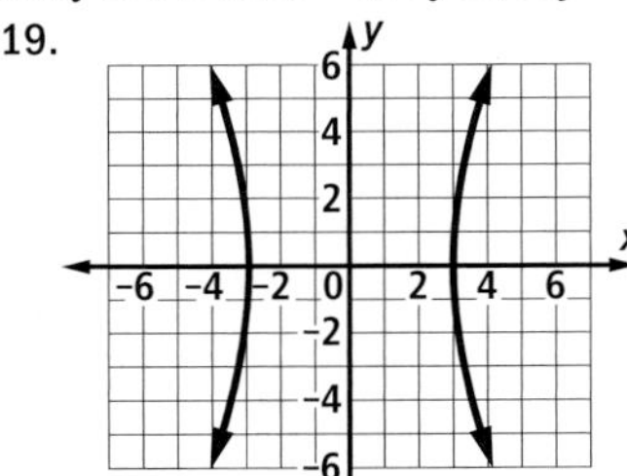

21. Answers vary. Sample: Transformations map each point of a preimage onto a unique point in the image.

23. $\begin{bmatrix} -9 & 14 \\ -8 & 14 \end{bmatrix}$

Self-Test (pp. 860–861)

1. a. $\frac{1}{25}x^2 - \frac{1}{144}y^2 - 1 = 0$ (or $144x^2 - 25y^2 - 3600 = 0$)
b. $A = \frac{1}{25}$, $B = 0$, $C = -\frac{1}{144}$, $D = 0$, $E = 0$, $F = -1$ (or $A = 144$, $B = 0$, $C = -25$, $D = 0$, $E = 0$, $F = -3600$)
c. The equation is of the form $\frac{x^2}{a^2} - \frac{y^2}{b^2} = 1$, so it represents a hyperbola. 2. The interior is the set of points whose distance from (3, -5) is less than 7, so the inequality is $(x - 3)^2 + (y + 5)^2 < 49$. 3. The circle's center shifts to (-2, 5) under the transformation. By the Graph-Translation Theorem, the equation for the image is $(x + 2)^2 + (y - 5)^2 = 1$. 4. a. $\left(0, \frac{1}{4 \cdot \frac{1}{11}}\right) = \left(0, \frac{1}{\frac{4}{11}}\right) = \left(0, \frac{11}{4}\right)$ b. (0, 0)
c. $y = -\frac{1}{4 \cdot \frac{1}{11}} = -\frac{1}{\frac{4}{11}} = -\frac{11}{4}$ 5. The major and minor axes of a circle will be the same length, and the foci will coincide at a single point (the center of the circle).

6. a. $\begin{cases} (n + 70)(p - 2) = 5880 \\ np = 5600 \end{cases}$; $np + 70p - 2n - 140 = 5880$;
$5600 + 70p - 2\frac{5600}{p} - 140 = 5880$; $70p - \frac{11{,}200}{p} = 420$;
$70p^2 - 420p - 11{,}200 = 0$; $p^2 - 6p - 160 = 0$; $p = -10$ or $p = 16$, but since price cannot be negative, the original price was $p = 16$. The new price is \$14. b. 420; $n = \frac{5600}{p} = \frac{5600}{16} = 350$; this year he sold $n + 70 = 420$ pairs. 7. $a = 10$ and $b = 7$, so an equation is $\frac{x^2}{10^2} + \frac{y^2}{7^2} = \frac{x^2}{100} + \frac{y^2}{49} = 1$.
8. $A = \pi ab = \pi(10 \cdot 7) = 70\pi$ 9. $S_{10,7}$; The image of the circle with equation $x^2 + y^2 = 1$ under $S_{10,7}$ is $\frac{x^2}{100} + \frac{y^2}{49} = 1$ by the Circle Scale-Change Theorem.

10.

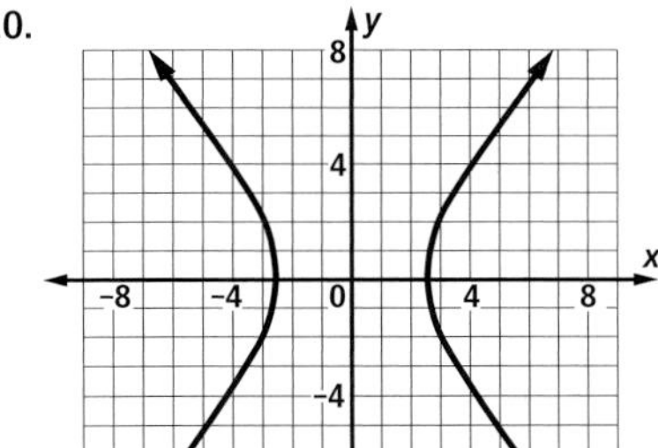

The equation represents a hyperbola with foci at $(\sqrt{41}, 0)$, and $(-\sqrt{41}, 0)$, a focal constant of 10, and vertices (-5, 0) and (5, 0). The asymptotes are $y = \pm\frac{4}{5}x$.

11.

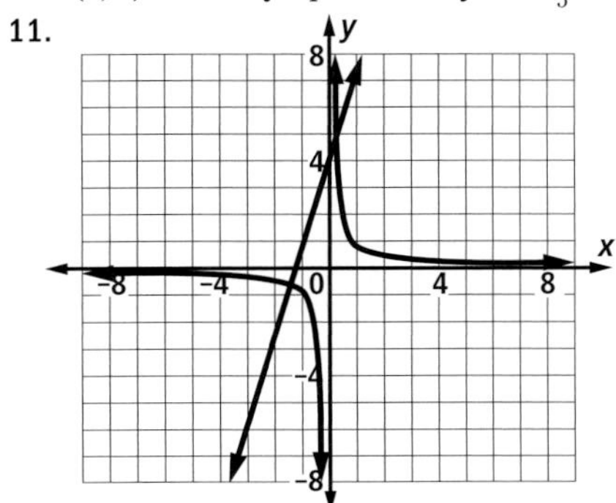

Substitute $2x + 5$ for y in the first equation: $x(2x + 5) = 2$; $2x^2 + 5x - 2 = 0$; Use the quadratic formula to solve for x: $x = \frac{-5 \pm \sqrt{41}}{4}$, or $x \approx 0.35$ or $x \approx -2.85$. Substitute these values into $xy = 2$ to find the y-values: $y \approx 5.70$ or $y = -0.70$. So, the points of intersection are (0.35,5.70) and (-2.85,-0.70). **12.** Substitute $x^2 - 4x + 3$ for y in the second equation: $x^2 + (x^2 - 4x + 3)^2 = 9$; $x^2 + x^4 - 8x^3 + 22x^2 - 24x + 9 = 9$; $x^4 - 8x^3 + 23x^2 - 24x = 0$; $x(x^3 - 8x^2 + 23x - 24) = 0$; $x(x - 3)(x^2 - 5x + 8) = 0$; $x = 0$ or $x = 3$ by the Zero-Product Theorem because $x^2 - 5x + 8 = 0$ has no real solutions. When $x = 0$, $y = 0^2 - 4(0) + 3 = 3$. When $x = 3$, $y = 3^2 - 4(3) + 3 = 9 - 12 + 3 = 0$. So, the solutions to the system are (0, 3) and (3, 0). **13. a.** hyperbola **b.** The foci of the hyperbola with equation $xy = 15$ are $(\sqrt{2 \cdot 15}, \sqrt{2 \cdot 15}) = (\sqrt{30}, \sqrt{30})$ and $(-\sqrt{2 \cdot 15}, -\sqrt{2 \cdot 15}) = (-\sqrt{30}, -\sqrt{30})$, and the focal constant is $2\sqrt{30}$. The graph of $xy = -15$ is the reflection image of the graph of $xy = 15$ over the x-axis, so the foci for $xy = -15$ are $(\sqrt{30}, -\sqrt{30})$ and $(-\sqrt{30}, \sqrt{30})$, and the focal constant is still $2\sqrt{30}$. **c.** Yes; the hyperbola is symmetric over $y = \pm x$. **14.** Area of pool: $A = \pi\left(\frac{15}{2} \cdot 4\right) = 30\pi$; Area of walkway and pool: $A = \pi\left(9 \cdot \frac{11}{2}\right) = 49.5\pi$; Area of walkway: $49.5\pi - 30\pi = 19.5\pi \approx 61.26 \text{ m}^2$

15. Solve the system $\begin{cases} \ell w = 104{,}094 \\ 2\ell + 2w = 1320 \end{cases}$.

$2\ell + 2\left(\frac{104{,}094}{\ell}\right) = 1320$; $2\ell^2 + 208{,}188 = 1320\ell$; $\ell^2 - 660\ell + 104{,}094 = 0$; $\ell \approx 260.7$ or 399.3. Since addition and multiplication are commutative, solving for w would give the same answers. Colorado is longer than it is wide, so $\ell = 399.3$ and $w = 260.7$. The dimensions of Colorado are approximately 399.3 mi wide by 260.7 mi long. **16.** $(5.3 \cdot 10^9) + (9 \cdot 10^7) = 5.39 \cdot 10^9$ km **17.** Answers vary. Sample: A parabola will intersect a circle three times if its vertex is on the highest point of the circle and it opens down. This is the case for the circle and the parabola described by $x^2 + y^2 = 1$ and $y = 1 - x^2$.

18. This set of points is a circle with radius 8 and center (3, 2.5) by the definition of a circle. It has equation $(x - 3)^2 + (y - 2.5)^2 = 64$ because (h, k) is (3,2.5) and $r = 8$.

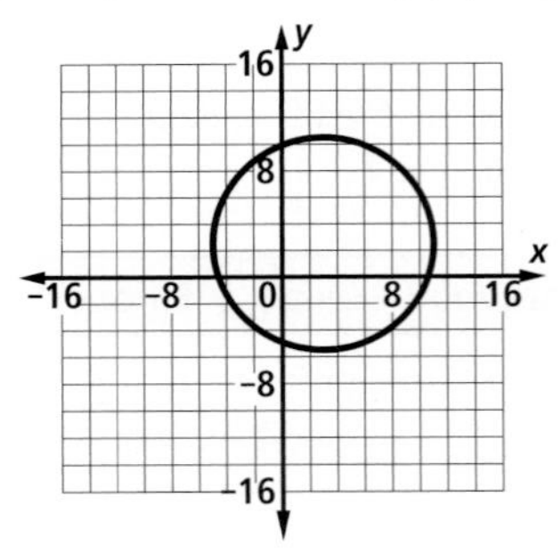

19. If the opening has center (0, 0) and a radius of 7, we can describe the arch with the equation $y = \sqrt{49 - x^2}$. Substitute the spelunker's height for y to find the place farthest from the center that he can stand: $5\frac{8}{12} = 5\frac{2}{3} = \sqrt{49 - x^2}$; $\frac{289}{9} = 49 - x^2$; $x = \sqrt{\frac{152}{9}} \approx \pm 4.1$. The spelunker can stand at most 4.1 ft away from the center.

20.

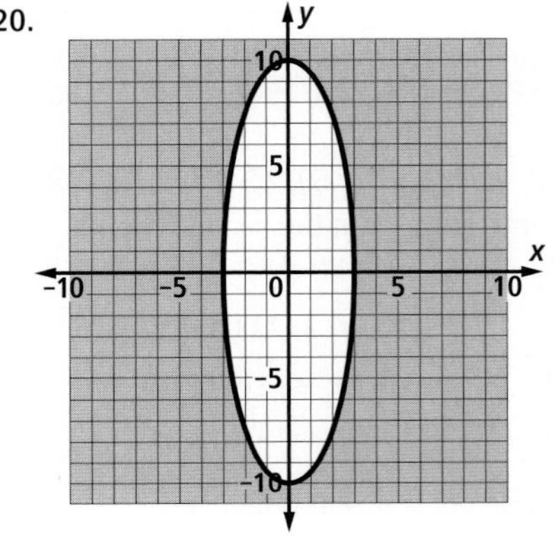

Self-Test Correlation Chart

Question	1	2	3	4	5	6	7
Objective(s)	A, F	B	B	E	F	H	I
Lesson(s)	12-1, 12-2, 12-4, 12-5, 12-6, 12-7	12-1, 12-2, 12-3, 12-4, 12-6, 12-7	12-1, 12-2, 12-3, 12-4, 12-6, 12-7	12-1, 12-2, 12-4, 12-6, 12-7	12-1, 12-2, 12-4, 12-5, 12-6	12-8, 12-9	12-2, 12-4, 12-6, 12-7
Question	**8**	**9**	**10**	**11**	**12**	**13**	**14**
Objective(s)	C	F	E, I	K	D	E, F	G
Lesson(s)	12-5	12-1, 12-2, 12-4, 12-5, 12-6	12-1, 12-2, 12-4, 12-6, 12-7	12-8, 12-9	12-8, 12-9	12-1, 12-2, 12-4, 12-5, 12-6, 12-7	12-2, 12-3, 12-4, 12-5
Question	**15**	**16**	**17**	**18**	**19**	**20**	
Objective(s)	H	G	K	B, L	G	J	
Lesson(s)	12-8, 12-9	12-2, 12-3, 12-4, 12-5	12-8, 12-9	12-1, 12-2, 12-3, 12-4, 12-6, 12-7	12-2, 12-3, 12-4, 12-5	12-3	

Chapter Review (pp. 862–865)

1. $x^2 + y^2 - 14x + 4y - 28 = 0$; $A = 1, B = 0, C = 1, D = -14, E = 4, F = -28$ **3.** $\frac{1}{36}x^2 - \frac{1}{16}y^2 - 1 = 0$ (or $16x^2 - 36y^2 - 576 = 0$); $A = \frac{1}{36}, B = 0, C = -\frac{1}{16}, D = 0, E = 0, F = -1$ (or $A = 16, B = 0, C = -36, D = 0, E = 0, F = -576$) **5.** $x^2 + y^2 - 169 = 0$; $A = 1, B = 0, C = 1, D = 0, E = 0, F = -169$ **7.** $x^2 + y^2 = 144$ **9.** $b = \sqrt{35 - a^2}$ **11.** $x^2 + y^2 > 64$ **13.** $\frac{x^2}{16} + \frac{y^2}{49} = 1$ **15.** $y = \frac{4}{x}$ **17.** $70\pi \approx 219.91$ **19.** the ellipse by 5π or 15.71 units^2 **21.** (0, 8) or $\left(\frac{7}{2}, \frac{81}{4}\right)$ **23.** no solutions **25.** $a = \frac{-4}{3}$ and $b = -3$ or $a = 1$ and $b = 4$

27. a. $\begin{cases} ab = 1073 \\ (a + 3)(b - 7) = 960 \end{cases}$

b. $-\frac{111}{7}$ and $-\frac{203}{3}$ or 29 and 37 **29.** (0, 0); 19 **31. a.** $\left(0, \frac{7}{4}\right)$ **b.** (0, 0) **c.** $y = -\frac{7}{4}$ **33. a.** $\left(0, 2\sqrt{21}\right), \left(0, -2\sqrt{21}\right)$ **b.** 20 **35.** ellipse **37. a.** hyperbola **b.** parabola **c.** ellipse **d.** circle **39.** true **41. a.** $\frac{x^2}{25} + \frac{y^2}{64} = 1$ **b.** ellipse

43. $\begin{cases} x^2 + y^2 \le 250{,}000 \\ x^2 + y^2 \ge 235{,}225 \end{cases}$ **45. a.** If the moving van is in a lane on a two-way road, it will not be able to pass through the tunnel because the tunnel is only 11.5 ft tall 6 ft from the center. The outer corner of the truck would not fit. **b.** Yes, the tunnel is 12.6 ft tall 3 ft from the center, so if the truck drives in the center of the roadway, it will be able to fit through the tunnel with more than 0.5 ft to spare.

47. a. $\begin{cases} x^2 + y^2 \le 5625 \\ (x + 30)^2 + (y - 50)^2 = 5625 \end{cases}$

b. (-74.25, -10.55) or (44.25, 60.55) **49.** The price was \$60 in the first month and \$80 in the second month.

51.

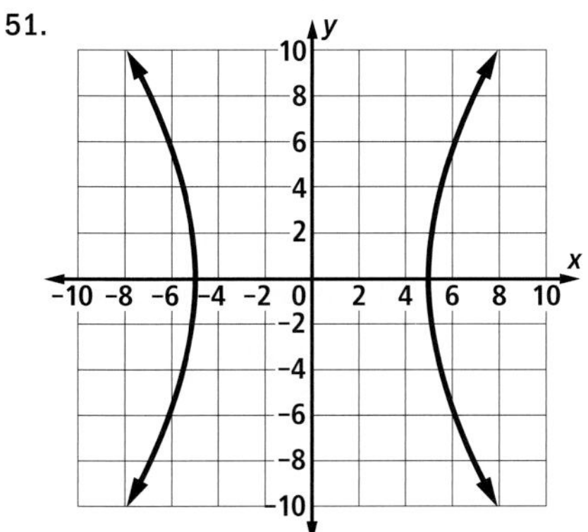

53.

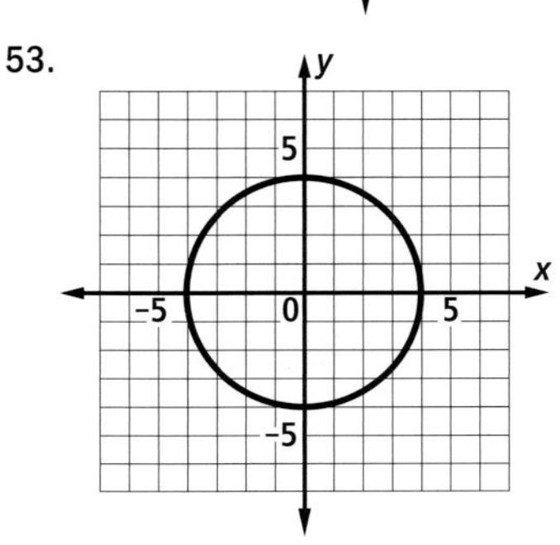

55. $\frac{x^2}{25} + \frac{y^2}{100} = 1$ **57.** B

59.

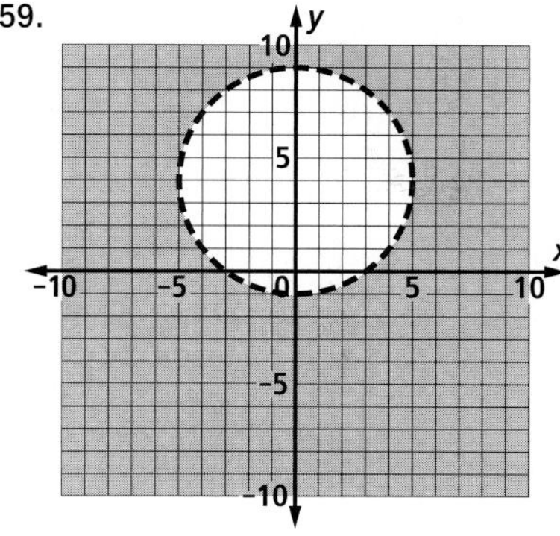

61. Answers vary. Sample: $(x + 1)^2 + y^2 = 9$, $\frac{x^2}{4} - y^2 = 1$

63. The system is: $\begin{cases} x + y = 17 \\ xy = 73 \end{cases}$. It appears on the graph of the system that the functions come very close to each other and might intersect. But, in fact, they do not intersect because there is no real solution to the system. Substituting $y = 17 - x$ into the second equation gives $x(17 - x) = 73$, or $x^2 - 17x + 73 = 0$, which has no real solution. So, the situation is impossible.

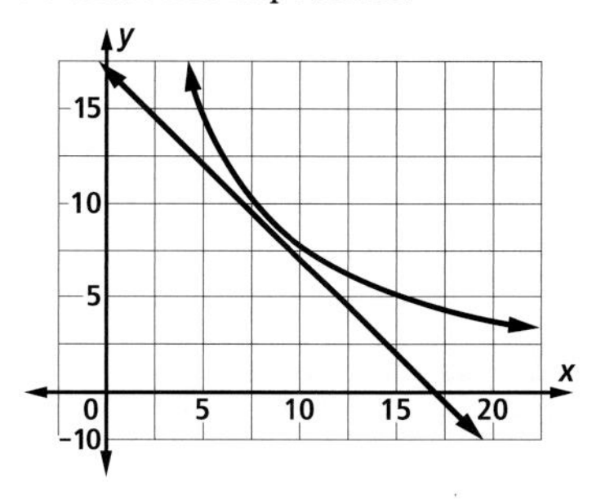

65.

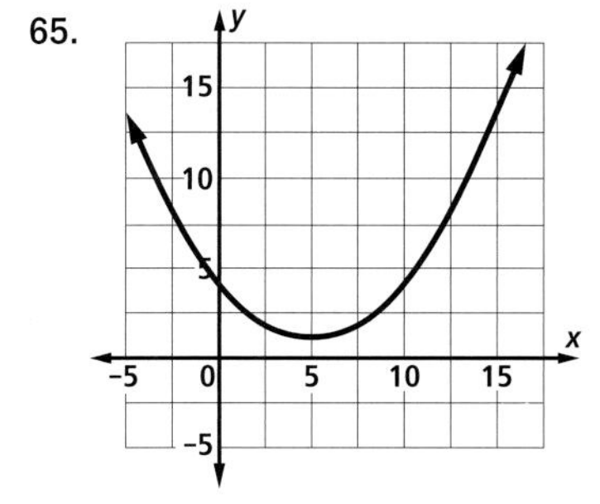

67. **69.**

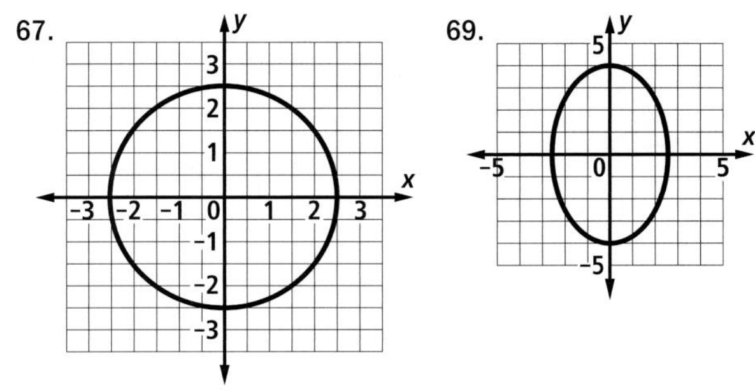

71.

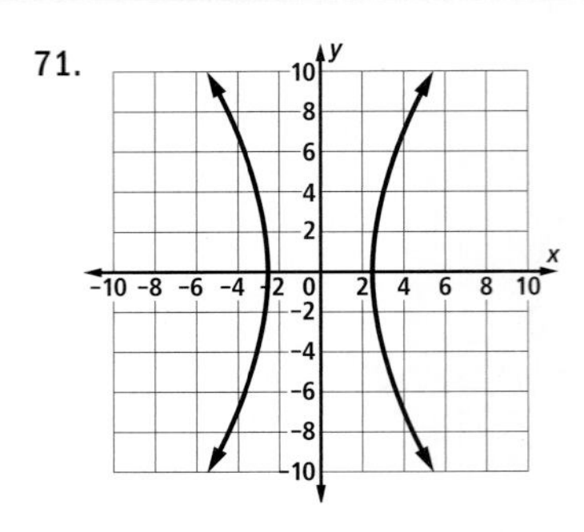

Chapter 13

Lesson 13-1 (pp. 868-875)

Mental Math **a.** -9; -6; -3 **b.** -18 **c.** 291; 294; 297 **d.** 882

Guided Example 1 12; 12; 78; 78

Guided Example 3 **a.** 1; 2; 6; $(4 \cdot 3 + 6)$; $(4 \cdot 500 + 6)$; 10; 14; 18; 2006 **b.** 10; 4; 500; 500; 10; 500; 4; 504,000

Questions

1. arithmetic series **3.** Add the whole numbers from 1 to 100; 5050 **5.** sigma **7. a.** $a_n = a_1 + (n - 1)d$ **b.** $\sum_{i=1}^{n} a_i = \frac{n}{2}(2a + (n-1)d)$ **c.** $\sum_{i=1}^{n} a_i = \frac{n}{2}(a_1 + a_n)$

9. $\frac{500}{2}(10 + 2006) = 504{,}000$ **11.** C **13.** 1850

15. the number of terms **17.** \$2850 **19. a.** $\sum_{i=1}^{100} i^2$ **b.** 338,350 **21.** $\frac{1}{n}\sum_{i=1}^{n} a_i$ **23. a.** -2.5 **b.** 625 **c.** $a_n = 16(-2.5)^{n-1}$ **25.** $y = -\frac{11}{8}x^2 + 7x - \frac{5}{8}$

Lesson 13-2 (pp. 876-882)

Mental Math **a.** yes **b.** no **c.** yes **d.** no

Activity **Steps 1–2:**

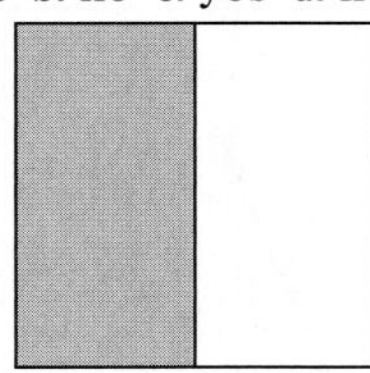

In Step 2, half of the square has been shaded.

Step 3: This region represents $\frac{1}{4}$ of the original square, so $\frac{3}{4}$ of the original square has been shaded.

Step 4:

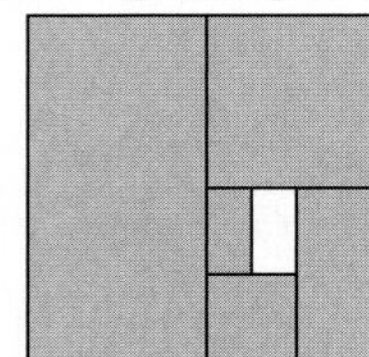

$\frac{1}{2} + \frac{1}{4} + \frac{1}{8} + \frac{1}{16}$; $\frac{1}{2} + \frac{1}{4} + \frac{1}{8} + \frac{1}{16} + \frac{1}{32}$; $\frac{7}{8}, \frac{15}{16}, \frac{31}{32}$

Step 5: $\frac{63}{64}$; the nth term of the series is $\frac{1}{2^n}$, and $S_n = \sum_{i=1}^{n}\left(\frac{1}{2}\right)^n = \frac{2^n - 1}{2^n}$. **Step 6:** The original square will never be entirely shaded because $S_n \neq 1$ for any finite value of n.

Guided Example 1 **a.** $\frac{1}{16}; \frac{1}{32}; \frac{1}{64}; \frac{1}{128}; \frac{1}{256}; \frac{1}{512}; \frac{1}{1024}$ **b.** 10; $k = 1$; $\left(\frac{1}{2}\right)^k$ **c.** $\frac{1023}{1024}$; 0.999

Guided Example 2 **a.** $-\frac{1}{3}; -\frac{1}{3}; -\frac{1}{3}$; 2; $-\frac{1}{3}$; 3; 27; $-\frac{1}{3}$; 4; 27; -9; 3; -1; $\frac{1}{3}$ **b.** 27; $-\frac{1}{3}$; 5; $-\frac{1}{3}, \frac{61}{3}$ **Check:** 27; -9; 3; -1; $\frac{1}{3}, \frac{61}{3}$

Questions

1. $\frac{255}{256}$ **3. a.** 8 **b.** $\sum_{k=1}^{8} 5(2)^{k-1}$ **c.** 1275 **5. a.** 6 **b.** $\sum_{k=1}^{6} 170\left(-\frac{1}{10}\right)^{k-1}$ **c.** ≈ 154.55 **7. a. i.** 18 **ii.** 21 **iii.** 20 **iv.** $\frac{61}{3}$ **b.**

S_2 S_4 S_5 S_3 S_1
12 14 16 18 20 22 24 26 28 30

S_n is between S_{n-1} and S_{n-2}.

9. a. $500(1.04) + 500(1.04)^2 + \ldots + 500(1.04)^7$ **b.** $\sum_{k=1}^{7} 500(1.04)^k$ **c.** \$4107.11

11. a. $r^2 - 1$; $(r - 1)(r^2 + r + 1)$; $(r - 1)(r + 1)(r^2 + 1)$; $(r - 1)(r^4 + r^3 + r^2 + 1)$; $(r - 1)(r + 1)(r^2 + r + 1)(r^2 - r + 1)$ **b.** 1; 0; Suppose $P(r) = r^n - 1$, then $P(1) = 1^n - 1 = 0$ for all n. Thus, by the Factor Theorem, $r - 1$ is a factor of $P(r) = r^n - 1$ for all n. **c.** $n = 2$: $\frac{r^n - 1}{r - 1} = r + 1$; $n = 3$: $\frac{r^n - 1}{r - 1} = r^2 + r + 1$; $n = 4$: $\frac{r^n - 1}{r - 1} = (r + 1)(r^2 + 1)$; $n = 5$: $\frac{r^n - 1}{r - 1} = r^4 + r^3 + r^2 + 1$; $n = 6$: $\frac{r^n - 1}{r - 1} = (r + 1)(r^2 + r + 1)(r^2 - r + 1)$ **13. a.** x^5 **b.** $S_{15} = \frac{x^7(1 - x^{75})}{1 - x^5}$

c.

$\text{expand}\left(\frac{x^7 \cdot (1 - x^{75})}{1 - x^5}\right)$

$x^{77} + x^{72} + x^{67} + x^{62} + x^{57} + x^{52} + x^{47} + x^{42} \ldots$

15. 15,050 **17.** 4230 **19. a.** $f(-3) = 27^{-3} = \frac{1}{19{,}683}$; $f(0) = 27^0 = 1$; $f\left(\frac{2}{3}\right) = 27^{\frac{2}{3}} = 9$ **b.** domain: set of all real numbers; range: set of positive real numbers **c.** $f(x) = \log_{27} x$ **21.** $y - 5 = -\frac{7}{2}(x - 6)$

Lesson 13-3 (pp. 883-888)

Mental Math **a.** 96 **b.** 36 **c.** 111

Activity **Step 1:**

Sentence Number	Number of Words: Paragraph 1	Number of Words: Paragraph 2
1	12	27
2	11	16
3	10	19
4	11	31
5	9	14

Step 2: 10.6; 21.4 **Step 3:** 1.96, 0.16, 0.36, 0.16, 2.56; 31.36, 29.16, 5.76, 92.16, 54.76 **Step 4:** 1.04, 42.64; 1.02, 6.53 **Step 5:** Paragraph one: it has fewer words per sentence on average, and since the standard deviation is much lower, each sentence does not differ much from the average sentence length.

Questions

1. 1.44 **3.** about 5.43 **5.** the sum of all of the scores **7.** the average deviation from the mean **9.** the standard deviation **11.** The results are more spread out in the first option. It has a lower *m.a.d.* and the chances of winning something close to the mean are greater. **13. a.** 11, 5.74 **b.** 12, 5.74 **15.** Answers vary. Sample: {0, 150, 300} and {100, 150, 200} **17. a.** \$10.63 **b.** \$2487.05 **19.** 2.33 m **21.** $2i$ **23.** 0 **25. a.** 95 **b.** at least 90 **c.** 90

Lesson 13-4 (pp. 889-895)

Mental Math a. the set of all real numbers **b.** $\{p \mid p$ is divisible by $6\}$ **c.** the set of all ellipses **d.** $\emptyset$

Activity Step 1: Top row: 6; 24; 720; 5040; 40,320; 3,628,800; Middle row: 6; 24; 120; 5040; 40,320; 362,880; Bottom row: 3; 4; 5; 6; 7; 8; 9; 10

Step 2: The pattern is $n = \frac{n!}{(n-1)!}$. $\begin{cases} f_1 = 1 \\ f_n = n \cdot f_{n-1} \end{cases}$

Guided Example 4 13; 11; 13!; 11!; 2!; 78

Questions

1. a. *PRM, PMR, RPM, RMP, MPR, MRP* **b.** *PRM* **3.** 1, 2, 6, 24, 120, 720, 5040 **5.** Answers vary. Sample: A permutation is a choice of objects where order matters. A combination is a choice of objects where order does not matter. **7.** $\frac{n!}{r!(n-r)!}$ **9.** 10 **11.** 21 **13. a.** 3,921,225 **b.** 1,471,429,260 **c.** about 5.770 quadrillion **15. a.** 177,100; she offers more dye combinations than advertised. **b.** 127,512,000 **17.** The scores in the first set are more spread out. **19. a.** $y = \frac{1}{m}x - \frac{b}{m}$ **b.** They are reciprocals. **c.** when $m = 0$ **21.** Answers vary. Sample: {8, 12, 14, 14}

Lesson 13-5 (pp. 896-902)

Mental Math a. Answers vary. Samples: $(x^2 + 3, 2)$, $(h + hk^3, 4)$, $(\pi, 0)$ **b.** yes **c.** the set of nonnegative integers **d.** no

Activity Step 1: ${}_4C_0 = 1, {}_4C_1 = 4, {}_4C_2 = 6, {}_4C_3 = 4, {}_4C_4 = 1$ **Step 2:** These are the 5 elements in row 4 of Pascal's Triangle. **Step 3:** ${}_7C_0 = 1, {}_7C_1 = 7, {}_7C_2 = 21, {}_7C_3 = 35, {}_7C_4 = 35, {}_7C_5 = 21, {}_7C_6 = 7, {}_7C_7 = 1$ **Step 4:** These are the 8 elements in row 7 of Pascal's Triangle. **Step 5:** ${}_nC_r$ is the $(r + 1)$st element in row n of Pascal's Triangle.

Guided Example 3 Solution 1 8; 5; 8; 5; 56 **Solution 2** 6; 8; 56

Questions

1. The array that later became known as Pascal's Triangle first appeared in the 11th century in the works of Abu Bakr al-Karaji, an Islamic mathematician, and Jia Xian, a Chinese mathematician. **3.** Pascal's triangle is generated as follows: The only element in the top row is 1, and every other row begins and ends with a 1. If x and y are adjacent elements in a row, then $x + y$ is the element immediately beneath and between them. **5.** $\binom{5}{0}$ $\binom{5}{1}$ $\binom{5}{2}$ $\binom{5}{3}$ $\binom{5}{4}$ $\binom{5}{5}$ **7.** 15; 5th element, row 6 **9.** 1; 1st element, row 10 **11.** 21; 6th element, row 7 **13.** 4950 **15.** $\binom{y}{x} = \binom{10}{5}$ **17. a.** 2, 4, 8, 16, 32, 64 **b.** 128 **c.** 2^n **19.** This sequence is formed by the 3rd elements of consecutive rows, beginning with row 2. **21.** 495 **23.** 58 **25.** about 3.99 **27.** $\det\begin{bmatrix} 3 & 1 \\ 6 & 2 \end{bmatrix} = 0$, so its inverse is undefined. **29.** $y = \frac{12}{5}$

Lesson 13-6 (pp. 903-908)

Mental Math a. $r^2 - 2rs + s^2$ **b.** $49p^2 + 126p + 81$ **c.** $4a^2b^2 - 12abc + 9c^2$ **d.** $25m^4k^4 + 10m^2n^3k^4 + n^6k^4$

Activity Steps 1–2:

$a^3 + 3a^2b + 3ab^2 + b^3$	12
$a^4 + 4a^3b + 6a^2b^2 + 4ab^3 + b^4$	20
$a^5 + 5a^4b + 10a^3b^2 + 10a^2b^3 + 5ab^4 + b^5$	30
$a^6 + 6a^5b + 15a^4b^2 + 20a^3b^3 + 15a^2b^4 + 6ab^5 + b^6$	42

Step 2. $n(n + 1)$

Steps 3 and 6.

1, 3, 3, 1	3, 2, 1, 0	0, 1, 2, 3
1, 4, 6, 4, 1	4, 3, 2, 1, 0	0, 1, 2, 3, 4
1, 5, 10, 10, 5, 1	5, 4, 3, 2, 1, 0	0, 1, 2, 3, 4, 5
1, 6, 15, 20, 15, 6, 1	6, 5, 4, 3, 2, 1, 0	0, 1, 2, 3, 4, 5, 6

Step 4: The coefficients form Pascal's triangle. **Step 5:** $\binom{5}{0}$ $\binom{5}{1}$ $\binom{5}{2}$ $\binom{5}{3}$ $\binom{5}{4}$ $\binom{5}{5}$ **Step 7:** The exponents of a start at n and decrease by 1 with each term, and the exponents of b start at 0 and increase by 1 with each term.

Guided Example 3 1; 4; 4; 3; 1; 6; 2; 2; 4; 1; 3; 1; 4; 16; 8; 32; 6; 24; 4; 8; 2; 1

Questions

1. a. $x^2 + 2xy + y^2$ **b.** 1, 3, 3, 1 **3.** $\frac{1}{16} - \frac{1}{2}m^2 + \frac{3}{2}m^4 - 2m^6 + m^8$ **5.** $210x^6y^4$ **7.** $11{,}520n^8$ **9.** $(x + 2)^{14}$ **11.** $(a + b)(a^3 + 3a^2b + 3ab^2 + b^3) = a^4 + 3a^3b + 3a^2b^2 + ab^3 + a^3b + 3a^2b^2 + 3ab^3 + b^4 = a^4 + 4a^3b + 6a^2b^2 + 4ab^3 + b^4 = \sum_{r=0}^{4}\binom{4}{r}a^{4-r}b^r$ **13.** $(1 + 0.003)^3 \approx 1^3 + 3 \cdot 1^2 \cdot (0.003) = 1 + 0.009 = 1.009$

15. a. 1; 11; 121; 1331; 14,641; The digits in each term form a row of Pascal's triangle.
b. $\sum_{r=0}^{4}\binom{4}{r}10^{4-r}1^r = 10{,}000 + 4000 + 600 + 40 + 1 = 14{,}641$
c. $\sum_{r=0}^{5}\binom{5}{r}10^{5-r}1^r = 100{,}000 + 50{,}000 + 10{,}000 + 1000 + 50 + 1 = 161{,}051$ **17.** True; $\frac{n!}{(n-2)!} = \frac{n(n-1)(n-2)!}{(n-2)!} = n^2 - n$; this is the difference of two integers, which will be an integer. **19. a.** $2\sqrt{26}$ **b.** $(0, -\sqrt{26})$, $(0, \sqrt{26})$; $(-\sqrt{15}, 0)$, $(\sqrt{15}, 0)$, **c.** $(0, \sqrt{11})$, $(0, -\sqrt{11})$ **d.** $2\sqrt{26}$ **e.** $\pi\sqrt{390} \approx 62.04$ **21.** $y = 169$ **23.** $z = 100{,}000$

Lesson 13-7 (pp. 909-916)

Mental Math a. 1000 **b.** 1 **c.** 1000 **d.** 499,500

Activity 1 Steps 1–2: Answers vary. Sample:

Trial	Sequence	Number of Heads
1	HHTH	3
2	HHTT	2
3	HTHH	3
4	TTHH	2
5	TTTH	1
6	THHT	2
7	TTTT	0
8	HTHH	3
9	TTTT	0
10	HTHH	3

Number of occurrences of: 0 heads: 2, 1 head: 1, 2 heads: 3, 3 heads: 4, 4 heads: 0 **Step 3:** Answers vary. Sample: The relative frequency for getting 2 heads in 4 flips is 0.39.

Relative Frequency of the Number of Heads in 4 Flips of a Coin

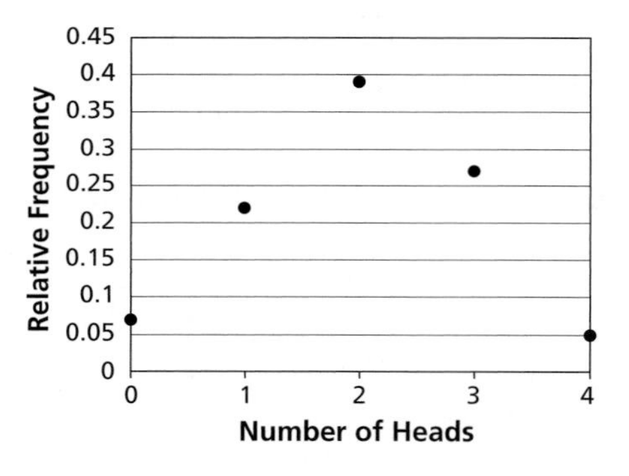

Activity 2 Step 1:

n	0	1	2	3	4
Sequences of 4 Tosses with n Heads	TTTT	HTTT THTT TTHT TTTH	HHTT HTHT HTTH THHT THTH TTHH	HHHT HHTH HTHH THHH	HHHH
y = Number of Sequences with n Heads	1	4	6	4	1

Step 2: **Number of Sequences y with n Heads**

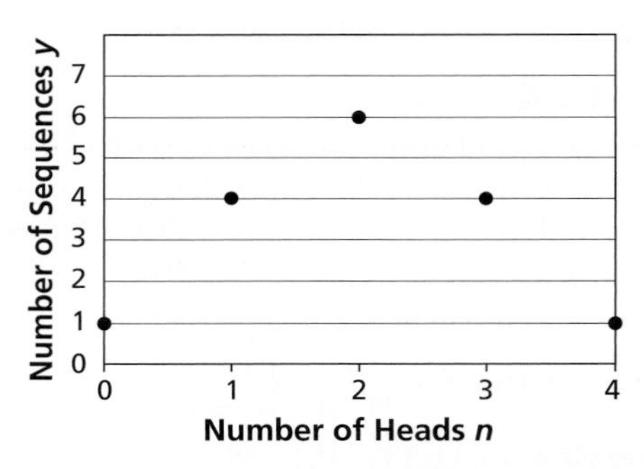

Step 3: The two graphs are nearly identical in shape.

Guided Example 3 $\frac{1}{6}$, $\frac{1}{36}$, $\frac{1}{36}$, $\frac{1}{36}$, $\frac{35}{36}$; $\left(\frac{35}{36}\right)^3$, 0.919; 2, $3 \cdot \frac{1}{36} \cdot \left(\frac{35}{36}\right)^2 \approx 0.0788$; $\binom{3}{2}$, 2, 1; $3 \cdot \left(\frac{1}{36}\right)^2 \cdot \frac{35}{36} \approx 0.00225$; 0; $\binom{3}{3}p^3q^0$; $\left(\frac{1}{36}\right)^3 \approx 0.0000214$

Questions

1. a. 10 **b.** 10 **c.** $\frac{10}{32} = 0.3125$ **3.** $\binom{4}{1}\left(\frac{1}{35}\right)\left(\frac{34}{35}\right)^3 \approx 0.1048$ **5.** $\frac{35}{128} \approx 0.2734$ **7. a.** 0.45 **b.** 0.2475 **c.** 0.495 **9.** about 0.02799 **11.** about 0.0016 **13.** about 0.0231 **15.** RRRR, RRRW, RRWR, RWRR, WRRR, RRWW, RWRW, RWWR, WRRW, WRWR, WWRR, RWWW, WRWW, WWRW, WWWR, WWWW **17.** $a^5 + 5a^4b + 10a^3b^2 + 10a^2b^3 + 5ab^4 + b^5$ **19.** 30, 60 **21.** $t^4 - r^4$ **23.** $\frac{y}{x}$

Lesson 13-8 (pp. 917-921)

Mental Math a. -0.788 **b.** -0.788 **c.** 0.788 **d.** 0.788

Guided Example 1 5; 5!; 51!; 3,819,816; 3,819,816; 175,711,536; 175,711,536; 175,711,536; $5.69 \cdot 10^{-9}$

Questions

1. a game or procedure in which prizes are distributed by pure chance **3.** $\frac{5}{19{,}523{,}504} \approx 0.00000026 \approx \frac{1}{3{,}846{,}154}$ **5.** $\frac{1}{1000}$ **7.** $\frac{1}{76{,}275{,}360}$ **9.** $\frac{5}{324{,}632} \approx 0.0000154 \approx \frac{1}{64{,}935}$ **11.** $\frac{35}{128} \approx 0.2734$ **13.** $\frac{1}{27{,}405}$ **15. a.** 5 **b.** 0 **17.** B; it is equivalent to the equation $f(x) = \left(\frac{1}{5}\right)^x$, which has a growth factor between 0 and 1. **19.** $\frac{8}{1}$

Lesson 13-9 (pp. 922-927)

Mental Math **a.** no **b.** yes **c.** no **d.** yes

Guided Example 1 **a.** 1; $\frac{5}{32}$; $\frac{5}{16}$; $\frac{5}{16}$; $\frac{5}{32}$; $\frac{1}{32}$ **b.** from left to right: $\frac{5}{32}$; $\frac{5}{16}$; $\frac{5}{16}$; $\frac{5}{32}$; $\frac{1}{32}$

Questions

1. a. binomial probability distribution **b.** $P(4) = 0.15625$; this could represent the probability of getting exactly 4 heads or exactly 4 tails in 5 tosses of a fair coin. **3.** $\frac{210}{1024} \approx 0.21$ **5.** $y = \frac{1}{\sqrt{2\pi}}e^{\left(\frac{-x^2}{2}\right)}$ **7. a.** Standardized scores are adjusted so they lie in a normal distribution with a predetermined mean and standard deviation. **b.** Standardized scores make it easy to evaluate an individual score relative to the mean. **9.** 68.2%

11.

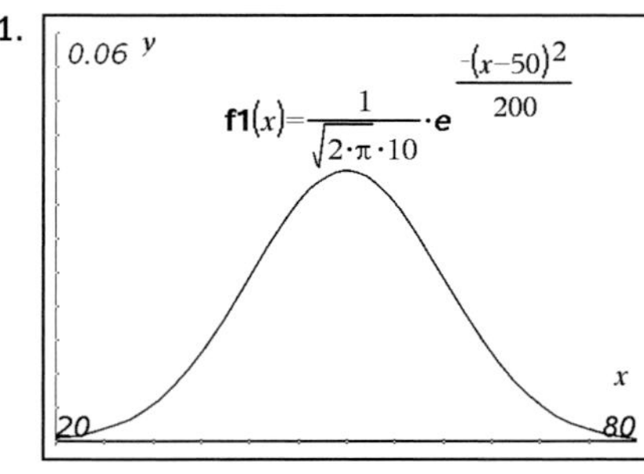

13. a. 15.9% **b.** 68.2% **15.** 770; 21 ft **17.** 0.00129 **19.** false; $\binom{100}{50}\left(\frac{1}{2}\right)^{100} \approx 0.0796 \approx 8\%$ **21.** $7776 - 3240x + 540x^2 - 45x^3 + \frac{15}{8}x^4 - \frac{1}{32}x^5$ **23.** $40i$

Self-Test (pp. 932-933)

1. This is a series with 17 terms where each term is the fourth power of the index variable: $\sum_{i=1}^{17} i^4$.

2. $\sum_{j=0}^{17}(5j+1) = \frac{n}{2}(a_1 + a_n) = 50.5(1 + 501) = 25{,}351$

3. $\mu = \frac{68+69+70+71+71+74+74}{7} = 71$; $m.a.d = \frac{1}{7}\sum_{i=1}^{7}|x_i - \mu| = \frac{1}{7}(|68-71| + |69-71| + |70-71| + |71-71| + |71-71| + |74-71| + |74-71|) = \frac{12}{7}$; $\sigma = \sqrt{\frac{1}{7}\sum_{i=1}^{n}(x_i - 71)^2} = \sqrt{\frac{1}{7}(9+4+1+0+0+9+9)} = \sqrt{\frac{32}{7}} \approx 2.14$

4. The mean team weight is 71 kg. If the standard deviation is 0, then $\sqrt{\frac{1}{7}\sum_{i=1}^{n}(x_i - 71)^2} = 0$, which means that each of the seven team members weighs 71 kg.

5. $(x^2 + 2)^5 = \sum_{r=0}^{n=5}\binom{n}{r}(x^2)^{n-r}2^r = x^{10} + 10x^8 + 40x^6 + 80x^4 + 80x^2 + 32$ **6.** The second term in the expansion is $\binom{4}{1}x^3(3)^1$, so the coefficient is $\binom{4}{1}3 = 12$.

7. $\binom{17}{3} = \frac{17!}{3!14!} = 680$ combinations **8.** By the Number of Permutations Theorem, there are $9! = 362{,}880$ arrangements. **9. a.** $\binom{7}{4} = \frac{7!}{4!(7-4)!} = 35$ **b.** ${}_{164}C_4 = \binom{164}{4} = 29{,}051{,}001$

10. ${}_{37}C_{36} = \binom{37}{36} = \frac{37!}{36!1!} = 37$. This makes sense because each subset of 36 elements is created by removing one element, and there are 37 possibilities. **11.** $\frac{117 \cdot 116 \cdot 115 \cdot 114 \cdot 113}{1} \cdot \frac{112!}{112!} = \frac{117!}{112!}$ **12. a.** $\binom{6}{3} = \frac{6!}{3!(6-3)!} = \frac{6 \cdot 5 \cdot 4}{6} = 20$; This number is the 4th element in row 6 of Pascal's triangle. **b.** This is the 3rd term of the expansion with eight terms, so its coefficient is $\binom{7}{2} = \frac{7!}{2!(7-2)!} = \frac{7 \cdot 6}{2} = 21$. This value is the 3rd element in row 7 of Pascal's Triangle. **13.** This is an arithmetic series with first term 30 and constant difference 2. So, the sum will be $\sum_{i=1}^{30} 30 + 2(i-1) = \frac{30}{2}(30 + 88) = \$1770$ **14. a.** This is an arithmetic series with first term 3 and constant difference 4. Since we know the final term is 87, to find n solve $3 + 4(n - 1) = 87$. $4n - 1 = 87$; $n = 22$. The series can be expressed in sigma notation as $\sum_{i=1}^{22}(4i-1)$. **b.** $\sum_{i=1}^{22}(4i-1) = \frac{22}{2}(3+87) = 990$

15. This is a geometric series with $n = 20$ terms, first term $5^0 = 1$, and constant ratio 5: $\sum_{i=0}^{19}5^i = \frac{a(1-r^n)}{1-r} = \frac{1(1-5^{20})}{1-5} = 23{,}841{,}857{,}910{,}156$ **16.** $\sum_{i=0}^{19}50\left(\frac{4}{5}\right)^i = \frac{50\left(1-\left(\frac{4}{5}\right)^{20}\right)}{1-\frac{4}{5}} = \frac{188{,}535{,}840{,}025{,}698}{762{,}939{,}453{,}125} \approx 247.12$ **17.** There are $2^5 = 32$ possible outcomes. There are $\binom{5}{0} = 1$ possibility for 0 heads, $\binom{5}{1} = 5$ possibilities for 1 head, $\binom{5}{2} = 10$ possibilities for 2 heads, $\binom{5}{3} = 10$ possibilities for 3 heads, $\binom{5}{4} = 5$ possibilities for 4 heads, and $\binom{5}{5} = 1$ possibility for 5 heads. Therefore, the respective probabilities are $\frac{1}{32}, \frac{5}{32}, \frac{5}{16}, \frac{5}{16}, \frac{5}{32}$, and $\frac{1}{32}$. **18.** You have a higher probability of winning in Lottery B. The number of possible combinations for submissions in Lottery A $= \binom{50}{6} = 15{,}890{,}700$. Since the probability of picking each combination is the same, the probability of winning is $\frac{1}{15{,}890{,}700} \approx 6.29 \cdot 10^{-8}$. The number of possible combinations for submissions in Lottery B $= \binom{70}{5} = 12{,}103{,}014$, so similarly, the probability of winning is $\frac{1}{12{,}103{,}014} \approx 8.26 \cdot 10^{-8}$. **19. a.** According to the Normal Distribution Percentages graph, 34.1% + 34.1% = 68.2% of scores are in this range. **b.** $\mu - \sigma = 515 - 114 = 401$ and $\mu + \sigma = 515 + 114 = 629$. So, the scores range from 401 to 629. **c.** $743 = 515 + 228 = \mu + 2\sigma$; therefore, about 2.3% of scores are at or above 743.

20. The probability of r heads in n tosses is $\binom{n}{r}p^r q^{n-r}$. Here, $p = 0.35$, $q = 0.65$, $n = 3$, and $r = 2$; $\binom{3}{2}(0.35)^2(0.65)^1 \approx 0.239$.

21. a.

n	$P(n)$
0	$\frac{1}{64}$
1	$\frac{3}{32}$
2	$\frac{15}{64}$
3	$\frac{5}{16}$
4	$\frac{15}{64}$
5	$\frac{3}{32}$
6	$\frac{1}{64}$

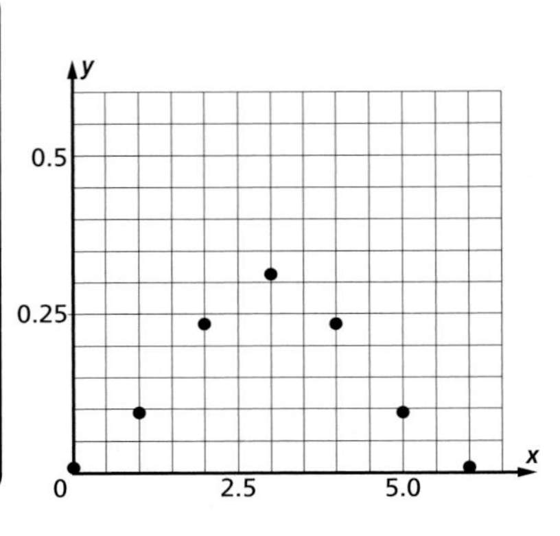

c. $P(n)$ represents the probability of a certain number of outcomes in 6 tosses. For example, $P(5)$ represents the probability that there will be exactly 5 of either heads or tails in 6 fair coin tosses. **22.** $\binom{n}{2} = \binom{n}{n-2}$ because $\binom{n}{2} = \frac{n!}{2!(n-2)!} = \frac{n!}{(n-2)!2!} = \frac{n!}{(n-2)!(n-(n-2))!} = \binom{n}{n-2}$. Therefore, $x = 2$. This value of x can also be deduced from the symmetry of Pascal's Triangle.

Self-Test Correlation Chart

Question	**1**	**2**	**3**	**4**	**5**	**6**	**7**	**8**
Objective(s)	C	C	I	I	E	E	H	H
Lesson(s)	13-1, 13-2, 13-3, 13-4	13-1, 13-2, 13-3, 13-4	13-3, 13-9	13-3, 13-9	13-6	13-6	13-4	13-4
Question	**9**	**10**	**11**	**12**	**13**	**14**	**15**	**16**
Objective(s)	D	D	C	D, F	G	A, C	B	B
Lesson(s)	13-4, 13-5	13-4, 13-5	13-1, 13-2, 13-3, 13-4	13-4, 13-5, 13-6	13-1, 13-2	13-1, 13-2, 13-3, 13-4	13-2	13-2
Question	**17**	**18**	**19**	**20**	**21**	**22**		
Objective(s)	J	J	I	J	K	F		
Lesson(s)	13-7, 13-8	13-7, 13-8	13-3, 13-9	13-7, 13-8	13-9	13-5, 13-6		

Chapter Review (pp. 934-937)

1. 7626 **3.** 8575 **5.** 57 **7.** 157,287 **9.** ≈ 36.75 **11.** -3, 0, 3, 6, 9; 15 **13.** C **15.** $\sum_{i=1}^{41} 3i$ **17.** -40,309 **19.** D **21.** B **23. a.** 56 **b.** 256 **25.** 1 **27.** 532 **29.** $t^5 - 15t^4 + 90t^3 - 270t^2 + 405t - 243$ **31.** $\frac{p^4}{16} + p^3q + 6p^2q^2 + 16pq^3 + 16q^4$ **33.** true **35.** 1 7 21 35 35 21 7 1 **37.** $\binom{x}{y} = \binom{11}{7}$ **39.** The coefficient is the 14th element of row 15 of Pascal's Triangle. **41. a.** \$46 **b.** \$1081 **c.** 141 days **43.** 1230 seats **45.** 3,628,800 **47.** 75,287,520 **49.** 13,280.98 **51.** the 1989 freshman class **53.** Answers vary. Sample: The two classes have different numbers of students, which means that the mean score of incoming 1989 freshmen is weighted less than the mean score of 2006 freshmen. **55.** $\binom{6}{1}\left(\frac{1}{2}\right)^6 = 0.09375$ **57.** 0.027 **59.** 0.42 **61.** No; $\left(\frac{1}{2}\right)^{100}\sum_{k=70}^{100} {}_{100}C_k \neq \left(\frac{1}{2}\right)^{10}\sum_{i=7}^{10} {}_{10}C_i$. **63.** $\frac{1}{1000} = 0.001$ **65. a.** 50% **b.** 68.2% **c.** 4.6%

Glossary

A

absolute deviation The difference $|x_i - \mu|$, where x_i is an element of a data set and μ is the mean of the set. (884)

absolute value The operation or function defined by $|x| = \begin{cases} x \text{ when } x \geq 0 \\ -x \text{ when } x < 0 \end{cases}$; geometrically, the distance of x from 0 on a number line. (380)

absolute-value function The function with equation $f(x) = |x|$. (380)

acceleration The rate of change of the velocity of an object. (12)

algebraic expression See *expression.* (6)

algebraic sentence A sentence in which expressions are related by equality or inequality. (6)

angle of depression The angle between the line of sight and the horizontal when the line of sight points down. (672)

angle of elevation The angle between the horizontal base of an object and the observer's line of sight to the object when the line of sight points up. (665)

annual percentage yield, or APY The rate of interest earned after all the compoundings have taken place in one year. Also called *effective annual yield* or *yield.* (475)

argument of a function The domain variable in a function. (21)

arithmetic mean See *mean of a data set.* (883)

arithmetic sequence A sequence with a constant difference between consecutive terms. Also called *linear sequence.* (196)

arithmetic series An indicated sum of successive terms of an arithmetic sequence. (869)

asymptote A line approached by the graph of a function. (581)

asymptotes of a hyperbola The two lines that are approached by the points on the branches of a hyperbola as the points get farther from the foci. (107)

axis of symmetry of a parabola The line through the focus of a parabola perpendicular to the directrix. (388, 798)

B

base x in the expression x^n. (452)

bel A unit of sound intensity; 10 bels is a decibel. (616)

binomial An expression with two terms. A polynomial with two terms. (375, 738)

binomial coefficients The coefficients of terms in the expansion of $(a + b)^n$, often displayed as the numbers in Pascal's Triangle. (906)

binomial distribution A probability function P resulting from calculations of binomial probabilities. Also called *binomial probabilty distribution.* (923)

binomial expansion The result of writing the power of a binomial as a sum. (903)

binomial experiment A situation in which n independent trials occur, and each trial has exactly two mutually exclusive outcomes. (912)

binomial probability distribution See *binomial distribution.* (923)

boundary of a half plane The line in a plane that separates the half-plane from another mutually exclusive half-plane. (342)

branches of a hyperbola The two separate parts of the graph of a hyperbola. (107)

C

ceiling function The step function $f(x) = \lceil x \rceil$, the least integer greater than or equal to x. Also called *least-integer function* or *rounding-up function.* (204)

ceiling symbol The symbol $\lceil x \rceil$ indicating the least integer greater than or equal to x. (204)

center of a circle The fixed point from which the set of points of the circle are at a given distance. (804)

center of a rotation In a rotation, a point that coincides with its image. (269)

center of a size change The point in a size change of magnitude $k \neq 1$ that coincides with its image. (242)

center of an ellipse The intersection of the axes of an ellipse. (819)

circle The set of all points in a plane at a given distance from a fixed point. **(804)**

closure The property of an operation on elements of a set S when all the results of performing the operation are elements of S. **(262)**

coefficient matrix A matrix that contains the coefficients of the variables in a system of equations. **(336)**

coefficients of a polynomial The numbers $a_n, a_{n-1}, a_{n-2}, \ldots, a_0$ in the polynomial $a_nx^n + a_{n-1}x^{n-1} + a_{n-2}x^{n-2} + \ldots + a_0$. **(730)**

combination Any choice of r objects from n objects when the order of the objects does not matter. **(892)**

combined variation A situation in which direct and inverse variations occur together. **(129)**

common logarithm A logarithm to the base 10. Also called *common log*. **(609)**

common logarithm function The function that maps x onto $\log_{10}x$ for all positive numbers x. Also called the *logarithm function to the base 10*. **(611)**

completing the square A technique used to transform a quadratic from $ax^2 + bx + c$ form to $a(x - h)^2 + k$ form.
(401)

complex conjugate For any complex number $a + bi$, the difference $a - bi$. **(429)**

complex number A number that can be written in the form $a + bi$, where a and b are real numbers and $i = \sqrt{-1}$. **(427)**

composite $g \circ f$ For two functions f and g, the function that maps x onto $g(f(x))$ and whose domain is the set of all values in the domain of f for which $f(x)$ is in the domain of g. **(517)**

composite of two transformations Given transformation T_1 that maps figure G onto figure G' and transformation T_2 that maps figure G' onto figure G'', the transformation that maps G onto G'', the composite of T_1 and T_2, written $T_2 \circ T_1$. **(263)**

composition See *function composition*. **(517)**

compound sentence A sentence in which two clauses are connected by the word *and* or by the word *or*. **(300)**

compounding The process of earning interest on the interest of an investment. **(473)**

concentric circles Circles with the same center but different radii. **(804)**

conic section The intersection of a plane and a double cone. **(838)**

conjugate For any expression of the form $a + \sqrt{b}$, the expression $a - \sqrt{b}$. **(553)**

consistent system A system that has one or more solutions. **(316)**

constant-decrease situation A situation in which a quantity y decreases by a constant amount for every fixed increase in x. **(150)**

constant difference In an arithmetic sequence, the difference of two consecutive terms. **(196)**

constant-increase situation A situation in which a quantity y increases by a constant amount for every fixed increase in x. **(150)**

constant of variation The nonzero real constant k in the equation $y = kx^n$ or $y = \frac{k}{x^n}$ or other equation of a function of variation. **(72)**

constant matrix A matrix that contains the constants on the right sides of the equations in a system. **(336)**

constant multiplier The constant in a geometric sequence. Also called *constant ratio*. **(479)**

constant ratio In a geometric sequence, the ratio of successive terms. Also called *constant multiplier*. **(480)**

constant term, constant In the polynomial $a_nx^n + a_{n-1}x^{n-1} + a_{n-2}x^{n-2} + \ldots + a_0$, the number a_0. **(730)**

constraint A restriction on a variable or variables in a situation. **(299)**

continuous change model The equation $N(t) = N_0e^{rt}$, where N_0 is the initial amount and r is the growth factor over a time t. **(598)**

continuous compounding The limit of the process of earning interest with periods of compounding approaching zero. Also called *instantaneous compounding*. **(596)**

convex region A region of the plane in which any two points of the region can be connected by a line segment which lies entirely in the region. **(354)**

coordinate plane A plane in which there is a one-to-one correspondence between the points in the plane and the set of ordered pairs of real numbers. **(33)**

corollary A theorem that follows immediately from another theorem. (388)

correlation coefficient A number between -1 and 1 that indicates how well a linear equation fits data. (181)

cosine function The correspondence $\theta \rightarrow \cos \theta$ that maps a number θ onto its cosine. (663)

cosine of θ ($\cos \theta$) In a right triangle with acute angle θ, $\cos \theta = \frac{\text{length of leg adjacent to } \theta}{\text{length of hypotenuse}}$, the x-coordinate of the image of (1, 0) under R_θ, the rotation with center (0, 0) and magnitude θ. (663, 684)

counterexample An instance which shows a generalization to be false. (424)

counting numbers See *natural numbers.* (29)

$\cos^{-1} x$ The number between 0 and 180°, or between 0 and π, whose cosine is x. (671)

cube of x The third power of x, x^3. (454)

cube root A cube root t of x, denoted $\sqrt[3]{x}$, is a solution to the equation $t^3 = x$. (487)

cubic polynomial A polynomial of a single variable with degree 3, such as $ax^3 + bx^2 + cx + d$. (731)

cubing function A function f with equation $f(x) = x^3$. (454)

D

data set A collection of elements in which an element may appear more than once. (883)

decade growth factor The ratio of an amount in a specific year to the amount ten years earlier. (542)

decibel (dB) A measure of relative sound intensity; $\frac{1}{10}$ of a bel. (615)

default window The window that is set on an automatic grapher by the manufacturer. (28)

degree of a polynomial in a single variable The largest exponent of the variable in a polynomial. (730)

degree of a polynomial in several variables The largest sum of the exponents of the variables in any term in a polynomial expression. (738)

dependent variable A variable whose value always depends on the value(s) of other variable(s). (15)

depreciation The decrease in value over time of manufactured goods. (587)

determinant of a 2 × 2 matrix For the matrix $M = \begin{bmatrix} a & b \\ c & d \end{bmatrix}$, the number $ad - bc$. (331)

deviation For each value of an independent variable, the difference $p - a$ between the value p of the dependent variable predicted by a model and the actual value a. (178)

difference of two matrices For two matrices A and B with the same dimensions, their difference $A - B$ is the matrix in which each element is the difference of the corresponding elements in A and B. (230)

dimensions of a matrix A matrix with m rows and n columns has dimensions $m \times n$. (222)

direct-variation equation An equation in which one variable is a multiple of another variable or product of variables. (72)

direct-variation function A function that can be described by a formula of the form $y = kx^n$, $k \neq 0$ and $n > 0$. (73)

directly proportional to The situation in which y varies directly as x^n. Also called *varies directly as.* (73)

directrix of a parabola The line such that the distance from it to any point on the parabola is equal to the distance from that point to the focus. (798)

discrete function A function whose domain can be put into one-to-one correspondence with a finite or infinite set of integers, with gaps or intervals between successive values in the domain. (57)

discrete graph A graph that is made up of unconnected points. (57)

discrete set A set in which there is a positive distance greater than some fixed amount between any two elements of the set. (108)

discriminant of a quadratic equation For the equation $ax^2 + bx + c = 0$, the value of the expression $b^2 - 4ac$. (435)

domain of a function The set of values which are allowable substitutions for the independent variable. (27)

double cone The surface generated by a line rotating about an axis that contains a point on the line. (797)

double inequality A sentence that has two inequality symbols. (301)

double root The root of a quadratic equation when the discriminant is 0; the root of a quadratic equation that has only one solution; a root r of a polynomial in x for which $(x - r)^2$ is a factor, but not $(x - r)^3$. Also called a *root with multiplicity 2.* (767)

E

e The constant 2.7182818459... that the sequence of numbers of the form $\left(1 + \frac{1}{n}\right)^n$ approaches as n increases without bound; the base of natural logarithms. (596)

element of a matrix Each object in a matrix. (222)

ellipse Given two points F_1 and F_2 (the *foci*) and a positive number d, the set of points P in a plane for which $PF_1 + PF_2 = d$. (817)

equal complex numbers Two complex numbers with equal real parts and equal imaginary parts. (427)

equal matrices Two matrices that have the same dimensions and in which corresponding elements are equal. (223)

equation A sentence stating that two expressions are equal. (9)

equivalent formulas Two or more formulas for which all values of the variables that satisfy one formula satisfy the other(s). (48)

Euler's $f(x)$ notation Notation in which $f(x)$ represents the value of a function f with argument x. (20)

evaluating an expression Substituting numbers for the variables in an expression and calculating a result. (8)

expanding a polynomial Writing a power of a polynomial or the product of polynomials as a sum. (739)

explicit formula for *n*th term A formula that describes any term in a sequence in terms of its position in the sequence. (54)

exponent n in the expression b^n. (452)

exponential curve The graph of an exponential function. (582)

exponential decay A situation described by an exponential function in which the growth factor is between zero and 1, in which $f(x)$ decreases as x increases. (587)

exponential function A function f with the equation $f(x) = ab^x$ $(a \neq 0, b > 0, b \neq 1)$. (582)

exponential growth A situation described by an exponential function where the growth factor is greater than one. (582)

exponential growth model If a quantity a has growth factor b for each unit period, then after a period of length x, there will be ab^x. (580)

exponential sequence See *geometric sequence.* (479)

exponentiation See *powering.* (452)

expression A combination of numbers, variables, and operations that stands for a number. Also called *algebraic expression.* (6)

exterior of a circle The region outside a circle; the set of points whose distance from the center of the circle is greater than the radius. (811)

extraneous solution A possible solution that is obtained from an equation-solving procedure but that does not check in the original equation. (563)

F

***f*(*x*) notation** The notation used to describe functions, read "f of x." (20)

factor A number or expression which evenly divides a given expression. (745)

factored form of a polynomial A polynomial written as a product of two or more factors. (745)

factorial For any integer $n \geq 2$, the product of the integers from 1 through n, denoted by $n!$. (890)

factorial symbol, ! The symbol used to represent the product of the integers n through 1. (890)

factoring a polynomial The process of rewriting a polynomial as a product of two or more factors. (745)

fair coin, fair die A coin or die that has an equal probability of landing on each of its sides. Also called *unbiased coin* or *unbiased die.* (910)

feasible region The set of solutions to a system of linear inequalities. Also called *feasible set.* (349)

feasible set See *feasible region.* (349)

Fibonacci sequence The sequence 1, 1, 2, 3, 5, 8, 13, ... A recursive definition is

$$\begin{cases} F_1 = 1 \\ F_2 = 1 \\ F_n = F_{n-1} + F_{2n-2} \text{ for } n \geq 3 \end{cases}.$$ (192)

field properties The assumed properties of addition and multiplication of real numbers. (S1)

floor function The step function $f(x) = \lfloor x \rfloor$, indicating the greatest integer less than or equal to x. Also called *greatest-integer function*, *int function*, or *rounding-down function*. (204)

floor symbol The symbol $\lfloor x \rfloor$ indicating the greatest integer less than or equal to x. (204)

focal constant The constant sum of the distances from any point P on an ellipse to the foci. For a hyperbola, the absolute value of the difference of the distances from a point on a hyperbola to the two foci of the hyperbola. (817, 832)

focus, plural *foci* For a parabola, the point along with the directrix from which a point is equidistant. The two points from which the sum (ellipse) or difference (hyperbola) of distances to a point on the conic section is constant. (798, 817, 832)

formula A sentence stating that a single variable is equal to an expression with one or more different variables on the other side. (9)

function A set of ordered pairs (x, y) in which each first component x of the pair is paired with exactly one second component y. A relation in which no two ordered pairs have the same first component x. (15)

function composition The operation that results from first applying one function, then another; denoted by the symbol $\circ$. (517)

G

general form of a quadratic relation An equation of the form $Ax^2 + Bxy + Cy^2 + Dx + Ey + F = 0$, where A, B, C, D, E, and F are real numbers and at least one of A, B, or C is not zero. (796)

geometric mean The nth root of the product of n numbers. (537)

geometric sequence A sequence in which each term after the first is found by multiplying the previous term by a constant. Also called *exponential sequence*. (479)

geometric series An indicated sum of successive terms of a geometric sequence. (877)

gravitational constant The acceleration of a moving object due to gravity, often denoted by g. Near Earth's surface, $g \approx 32 \frac{\text{ft}}{\text{sec}^2} \approx 9.8 \frac{\text{m}}{\text{sec}^2}$. (12)

greatest common monomial factor The monomial with the greatest coefficient and highest degree that is a factor of all the terms of a polynomial. (746)

greatest integer function See *floor function*. (204)

growth factor In the exponential function $y = ab^x$ with $a > 0$, the base b. (582)

H

half-life The amount of time required for a quantity in an exponential decay situation to decay to half its original value. (588)

half-plane Either of the two sets of points, or regions, separated by a line in a plane. (342)

hierarchy A diagram that shows how various ideas are related, with a direction that moves from more specific to more general. (S5)

horizontal asymptote A horizontal line that is approached by a graph as the values of x get very large or very small. (107)

horizontal line A line with an equation of the form $y = b$. (153)

horizontal-line test The inverse of a function is itself a function if and only if no horizontal line intersects the graph of the function in more than one point. (525)

horizontal magnitude The number a in the scale change that maps (x, y) onto (ax, by). (249)

horizontal scale change The stretching or shrinking of a figure in only the horizontal direction; a transformation which maps (x, y) onto (kx, y). (249)

hyperbola The graph of a function with equation of the form $y = \frac{k}{x}$, where $k \neq 0$. For any two points F_1 and F_2 (the *foci* of the hyperbola) and d (the *focal constant* of the hyperbola) with $0 < d < F_1F_2$, the set of points P in a plane that satisfy $|PF_1 - PF_2| = d$. (107, 832)

I

i One of the two square roots of -1, denoted by $\sqrt{-1}$. (421)

identity A relationship that is true for all values of variables in a domain. (688)

identity function The function with equation $f(x) = x$. (454)

2 × 2 identity matrix The matrix $\begin{bmatrix} 1 & 0 \\ 0 & 1 \end{bmatrix}$, which maps each point $\begin{bmatrix} x \\ y \end{bmatrix}$ of a figure onto itself. **(244)**

3 × 3 identity matrix The matrix $\begin{bmatrix} 1 & 0 & 0 \\ 0 & 1 & 0 \\ 0 & 0 & 1 \end{bmatrix}$, which maps each point $\begin{bmatrix} x \\ y \\ z \end{bmatrix}$ of a figure onto itself. **(268)**

identity transformation The size-change transformation of magnitude 1; the transformation in which each point coincides with its image. **(244)**

image The result of applying a transformation to a preimage. **(242)**

imaginary number A number that is the square root of a negative real number. **(421)**

imaginary part Of the complex number $a + bi$, bi. **(427)**

imaginary unit The complex number i. **(421)**

inconsistent system A system that has no solutions. **(316)**

independent events Two or more events in which the occurrence of one event does not affect the probabilities the other events occur. **(453)**

independent variable In a formula, a variable upon whose value other variables depend. **(15)**

index The subscript used for a term in a sequence indicating the position of the term in the sequence. **(54)**

inequality A sentence containing one of the symbols $<, >, \leq, \geq, \neq$, or $\approx$. **(303)**

index variable The variable i under the Σ sign in summation notation. Also called *index.* (871)

input A value of the independent variable in a function. **(15)**

interval The set of numbers x such that $x \leq a$ or $a \leq x \leq b$, where the $\leq$ can be replaced by $<, >$, or $\geq$. **(301)**

int function See *floor function.* **(204)**

integers The set of numbers {... , -3, -2, -1, 0, 1, 2, 3, ...}; the set of natural numbers and their opposites. **(29)**

interior of a circle The region inside a circle; the set of points whose distance from the center of the circle is less than the radius. **(811)**

intersection of two sets The set consisting of those values common to both sets. **(301)**

inverse cosine function, $\cos^{-1}$ For the function that maps x onto $\cos x$, restricted to the domain $0 \leq x \leq \pi$ or $0 \leq x \leq 180°$, the function that maps $\cos x$ onto x. **(671)**

inverse function, f^{-1} The inverse relation formed by switching the coordinates of each ordered pair of f, when this inverse is itself a function. A function that when composed with another function gives the identity function. **(529, 531)**

inverse matrices Two matrices whose product is the identity matrix. **(328)**

inverse of a relation The relation obtained by switching the coordinates of each ordered pair in the relation. **(523)**

inverse sine function, $\sin^{-1}$ For the function that maps x onto $\sin x$, restricted to the domain $-\frac{\pi}{2} \leq x \leq \frac{\pi}{2}$, the function that maps $\sin x$ onto x. **(670)**

inverse-square curve The graph of $y = \frac{k}{x^2}$. **(108)**

inverse tangent function, $\tan^{-1}$ For the function that maps x onto $\tan x$, restricted to the domain $-\frac{\pi}{2} \leq x \leq \frac{\pi}{2}$, the function that maps $\tan x$ onto x. **(671)**

inverse-variation function A function that can be described by a formula of the form $y = \frac{k}{x^n}$, for $k \neq 0$ and $n > 0$. **(79)**

inversely proportional to The situation in which y varies indirectly with x^n. Also called *varies inversely as.* **(80)**

irrational number A real number that is not rational, that is, cannot be expressed as a simple fraction or ratio of the form $\frac{a}{b}$, where a and b are integers and $b \neq 0$. **(29, 383)**

irreducible polynomial See *prime polynomial.* **(748)**

J

joint variation A situation in which one quantity varies directly as the product of two or more independent variables, but not inversely as any variable. **(132)**

L

lattice point A point in a solution set whose coordinates are both integers. **(344)**

leading coefficient In the polynomial $a_n x^n + a_{n-1} x^{n-1} + a_{n-2} x^{n-2} + ... + a_0$, the number a_n. **(730)**

line of reflection The line over which a figure is reflected. (255)

line of sight An imaginary line from one position to another, or in a particular direction. (672)

line of best fit A line that best fits a set of data, found by using regression. Also called *least-squares line* or *regression line.* (177)

line of reflection See *reflecting line.* (255)

line of symmetry For a figure F, a line m such that the reflection image of F over m is F itself. (102)

linear combination The sum of the multiples of two or more variables. (157)

linear-combination method A method of solving systems that involves adding multiples of the given equations. (321)

linear function A function whose graph is a line or part of a line. A function f with the equation $f(x) = ax + b$, where a and b are real numbers. (151)

linear inequality An inequality in which both sides are linear expressions. (342)

linear polynomial A polynomial of the first degree. (731)

linear-programming problem A problem of maximizing or minimizing a quantity based on solutions to a system of linear inequalities. (356)

linear regression A method that uses all the data points to find the line of best fit for those points. (177)

linear scale A scale with units spaced so that the distance between successive units is constant. (617)

linear sequence See *arithmetic sequence.* (196)

log of *x* to the base 10 See *logarithm of x to the base 10.* (608)

logarithm function to the base 10 See *common logarithm function.* (611)

logarithm function with base *b*, $\log_b x$ The inverse of the exponential function with base b, $f(x) = b^x$; the function that maps x onto $\log_b x$ for all positive numbers x. (624)

logarithm of *x* to the base 10 y is the logarithm of x to the base 10, written $y = \log_{10} x$, if and only if $10^y = x$. Also called *log of x to the base 10* or *log base 10 of x.* (608)

logarithm of *a* to the base *b* Let $b > 0$ and $b \neq 1$. Then x is the logarithm of a to the base b, written $x = \log_b a$, if and only if $b^x = a$. (622)

logarithmic curve The graph of a function of the form $y = \log_b x$. (611)

logarithmic equation An equation of the form $y = \log_b x$. (610)

logarithmic scale A scale in which the scale values are the exponents of the powers. (615)

M

matrix subtraction If two matrices A and B have the same dimensions, their difference $A - B$ is the matrix whose element in each position is the difference of the corresponding elements in A and B. (230)

magnitude of a size change In the size change that maps (x, y) onto (kx, ky), the number k. Also called *size-change factor.* (242)

magnitude of a rotation In a rotation, the amount that the preimage is turned about the center of rotation, measured in degrees from –180° (clockwise) to 180° (counterclockwise), $m\angle POP'$, where P' is the image of P under the rotation and O is its center. (269)

major axis of an ellipse The segment that contains the foci of the ellipse and has two vertices of the ellipse as its endpoints. (819)

mapping A synonym for *function.* Also called *map.* (22)

mapping notation The notation $f: x \rightarrow y$ for a function f. (22)

mathematical model A mathematical graph, sentence, or idea that parallels some or all of the structure of a real situation. (16)

matrix A rectangular arrangement of objects or numbers, its *elements.* (222)

matrix addition If two matrices A and B have the same dimensions, their sum $A + B$ is the matrix in whose element in each position is the sum of the corresponding elements in A and B. (228)

matrix form of a system A representation of a system using matrices. The matrix form for $\begin{cases} ax + by = e \\ cx + dy = f \end{cases}$ is $\begin{bmatrix} a & b \\ c & d \end{bmatrix} \cdot \begin{bmatrix} x \\ y \end{bmatrix} = \begin{bmatrix} e \\ f \end{bmatrix}$. (336)

matrix multiplication If A is an $m \times n$ matrix and B is an $n \times p$ matrix, the product $A \cdot B$, or AB, is the $m \times p$ matrix whose element in row i and column j is the product of row i of A and column j of B. **(237)**

matrix product The result of matrix multiplication. **(237)**

maximum The greatest value of a data set or function. **(388)**

mean absolute deviation, *m.a.d.* The mean of the absolute deviations in a data set. **(884)**

mean of a data set The result of dividing the sum of the numbers in a data set by the number of numbers in the set. **(883)**

measure of center A number which in some sense is at the "center" of a data set; the mean or median of a data set. Also called *measure of central tendency.* **(884)**

measure of spread A number, like standard deviation, which describes the extent to which elements of a data set are dispersed or spread out. **(884)**

median When the terms of a data set are placed in increasing order, if the set has an odd number of terms, the middle term; if the set has an even number of terms, the average of the two terms in the middle. **(537)**

method of finite differences The use of successive calculations of differences of values of polynomial functions to determine whether a polynomial function of a particular degree can be an exact model for a set of points. **(774)**

minimum The least value of a set or function. **(388)**

minor axis of an ellipse The segment that has two vertices of the ellipse as its endpoints and does not contain the foci. **(819)**

mode The number or numbers which occur most often in a data set. **(608)**

model for an operation A pattern that describes many uses of that operation. **(7)**

monomial A polynomial with one term. **(738)**

multiplicity of a root For a root r in an equation $P(x) = 0$, the highest power of the factor $x - r$. **(767)**

N

natural logarithm of *m* n is the natural logarithm of m, written $n = \ln m$, if and only if $m = e^n$. **(629)**

natural numbers The set of numbers $\{1, 2, 3, 4, 5, ...\}$, sometimes also including 0. Also called the *counting numbers.* **(29)**

normal curve The graph of a normal distribution. **(924)**

normal distribution A function whose graph is the image of the graph of $y = \frac{1}{\sqrt{2\pi}}e^{\left(\frac{-x^2}{2}\right)}$ under a composite of translations or scale transformations. **(924)**

normalized scores See *standardized scores.* **(925)**

***n*th-power function** The function defined by $f(x) = x^n$, where n is a positive integer. **(454)**

***n*th root** Let n be an integer greater than 1. Then b is an nth root of x if and only if $b^n = x$. **(486)**

***n*th term** The term occupying the nth position in the listing of a sequence. The general term of a sequence. **(197)**

O

oblique line A line that is neither horizontal nor vertical.

one-to-one correspondence A mapping in which each member of one set is mapped to a distinct member of another set, and vice versa. **(242)**

order of operations A set of rules used to evaluate expressions, specifically: 1. Perform operations within grouping symbols from inner to outer; 2. Take powers from left to right; 3. Do multiplications or divisions from left to right; 4. Do additions or subtractions from left to right. **(8)**

output A value of the dependent variable in a function. **(15)**

P

parabola For a line ℓ and a point F not on ℓ, the set of all points in the plane of ℓ and F equidistant from F and ℓ. **(102, 798)**

paraboloid A 3-dimensional figure created by rotating a parabola in space around its axis of symmetry. **(801)**

parallax angle for a star Let P and Q be two positions on Earth and let S be the position of a star. Then the parallax angle θ is half the measure of $\angle PSQ$. **(676)**

Pascal's Triangle The sequence satisfying

1. $\binom{n}{0} = \binom{n}{n} = 1$ for all integers $n \geq 0$ and
2. $\binom{n+1}{r+1} = \binom{n}{r} + \binom{n}{r+1}$ for all integers $0 \leq r \leq n$.

The triangular array

$$\begin{array}{ccccccccccc} & & & & & 1 & & & & & \\ & & & & 1 & 2 & 1 & & & & \\ & & & 1 & 3 & & 3 & 1 & & & \\ & & 1 & 4 & & 6 & & 4 & 1 & & \\ & 1 & 5 & & 10 & & 10 & & 5 & 1 & \\ & & & & & \vdots & & & & & \end{array}$$

where if x and y are located next to each other on a row, the element just below and directly between them is $x + y$. **(898, 867)**

perfect-square trinomial A trinomial of the form $a^2 + 2ab + b^2$ or $a^2 - 2ab + b^2$; the square of a binomial. **(401)**

period The horizontal translation of smallest positive magnitude that maps the graph of a function onto itself. **(694)**

periodic function A function whose graph can be mapped to itself by a horizontal translation. **(694)**

permutation An arrangement of objects in which order matters. **(889)**

pH scale A logarithmic scale used to measure the acidity of a substance. **(618)**

piecewise linear Relating to a function or graph that is described as a union of segments or other subsets of lines. **(171)**

pitch The measure of the steepness of the slant of a roof. **(51)**

point matrix A 2×1 matrix. **(224)**

point-slope form of a linear equation For a line, an equation of the form $y - y_1 = m(x - x_1)$, where (x_1, y_1) is a point on the line with slope m. **(170)**

polynomial equation An equation of the form $y = a_n x^n + a_{n-1}x^{n-1} + ... + a_1 x^1 + a_0$, where n is a positive integer and $a_n \neq 0$. **(729)**

polynomial function A function of the form $P: x \rightarrow P(x)$, where $P(x)$ is a polynomial. **(731)**

polynomial in *x* of degree *n* An expression of the form $a_n x^n + a_{n-1}x^{n-1} + ... + a_1 x^1 + a_0$, where n is a positive integer and $a_n \neq 0$. **(730)**

polynomial model A polynomial equation which fits a data set. **(772)**

power The expression x^n; the result of the operation of powering, or exponentiation. **(452)**

powering An operation by which a variable is raised to a power. Also called *exponentiation.* **(452)**

preimage An object to which a transformation is applied. **(242)**

prime polynomial Over a set of numbers, a polynomial that cannot be factored into polynomials of lower degree whose coefficients are in the set. Also called *irreducible polynomial.* **(748)**

principal The original amount of money invested. **(473)**

probability distribution A function that maps a set of events onto their probabilities. Also called *probability function.* **(923)**

probability of an event If a situation has a total of t equally likely outcomes and e of these outcomes satisfy conditions for a particular event, then the probability of the event is $\frac{e}{t}$. **(453)**

pure imaginary numbers Multiples of the complex number i. **(422)**

Q

quadratic equation An equation that involves quadratic expressions. **(374)**

quadratic equation in two variables An equation of the form $Ax^2 + Bxy + Cy^2 + Dx + Ey + F = 0$, where A, B, C, D, E, and F are real numbers and at least one of A, B, or C is not zero. **(374)**

quadratic expression An expression that contains one or more terms in its variables, such as x^2, y^2, or xy, but no higher powers of x and y. **(374)**

quadratic form An expression of the form $Ax^2 + Bxy + Cy^2 + Dx + Ey + F$. **(374)**

Quadratic Formula If $ax^2 + bx + c = 0$ and $a \neq 0$, then $x = \frac{-b \pm \sqrt{b^2 - 4ac}}{2a}$. **(414)**

quadratic function A function f with an equation of the form $f(x) = ax^2 + bx + c$. **(374)**

quadratic polynomial A polynomial of a single variable with degree 2. **(731)**

quadratic regression A process of finding the model with the least sum of squares of differences from the given data points to the values predicted by the model. (408)

quadratic system A system that involves polynomial sentences of degrees 1 and 2, at least one of which is a quadratic sentence. (844)

quadratic-linear system A quadratic system with at least one linear sentence. (844)

quadratic-quadratic system A system that involves two or more quadratic sentences. (851)

quartic equation A fourth degree polynomial equation. (766)

quartic polynomial A polynomial of a single variable with degree 4. (731)

quintic equation A fifth degree polynomial equation. (766)

R

radian A measure of an angle, arc, or rotation such that π radians = 180 degrees. (712)

radical symbol The symbol $\sqrt{\ }$, as in $\sqrt{2x}$ or $\sqrt[3]{9}$. (537)

radius The distance between any point on a circle and the center of the circle. (804)

random numbers Numbers which have the same probability of being selected. (928)

range of a function The set of values of the dependent variable that can result from all possible substitutions for the independent variable. (27)

rate of change See *slope.* (94)

ratio of similitude In two similar figures, the ratio between a length in one figure and the corresponding length in the other. (245)

rational number A number that can be represented as a simple fraction or ratio of the form $\frac{a}{b}$, where a and b are integers and $b \neq 0$. (29, 383)

rationalizing the denominator The process of rewriting a fraction so that its denominator is a rational number. (551)

real function A function whose independent and dependent variables stand for only real numbers. (26)

real numbers Those numbers that can be represented by finite or infinite decimals. (29)

real part Of the complex number $a + bi$, the real number a. (427)

rectangular hyperbola A hyperbola with perpendicular asymptotes. (842)

recursive formula A set of statements that indicates the first term (or first few terms) of a sequence and tells how the next term is calculated from the previous term or terms. Also called *recursive definition.* (183)

reflecting line The line over which a point is reflected. Also called *line of reflection.* (255)

reflection A transformation under which the image of a point P over a reflecting line m is (1) P itself, if P is on m; (2) the point P' such that m is the perpendicular bisector of the segment connecting P with P' that maps a figure to its reflection image. (255)

reflection image of a point *A* over a line *m* The point A if A is on m and the point A' such that m is the perpendicular bisector of $\overline{AA'}$ if A is not on m. (255)

reflection-symmetric Coinciding with a reflection image of itself. (102)

regression line See *line of best fit.* (177)

relation Any set of ordered pairs. (15)

root of a polynomial For a polynomial function P, a zero of the equation $P(x) = 0$. Also called *zero of a polynomial.* (752)

root with multiplicity 2 See *double root.* (767)

roots of an equation Solutions to an equation. (437)

rotation A transformation with a center O under which the image of O is O itself and the image of any other point P is the point P' such that $m\angle POP'$ is a fixed number (its *magnitude*). (269)

rounding-down function See *floor function.* (204)

rounding-up function See *ceiling function.* (204)

row A horizontal list in a table, rectangular array, or spreadsheet. (222)

row-by-column multiplication The process of obtaining an element in the product of two matrices in which a row matrix is multiplied by a column matrix. (236)

S

scalar multiplication An operation leading to the product kA of a scalar k and a matrix A, in which each element of kA is k times the corresponding element in A. (230)

scalar product The result of scalar multiplication. (230)

scale change The stretching or shrinking of a figure in either a horizontal direction only, in a vertical direction only, or in both directions. A horizontal scale change of magnitude a and a vertical scale change of magnitude b maps (x, y) onto (ax, by), and is denoted by $S_{a,b}$. (249)

scatterplot A plot with discrete points used to display a data set. (178)

semicircle A half-circle. (806)

semimajor axis Half the major axis of an ellipse. (820)

semiminor axis Half the minor axis of an ellipse. (820)

sequence A function whose domain is the set of all positive integers or the set of positive integers from a to b. (53)

set-builder notation The notation $\{x| \ldots\}$ read "the set of all x such that ... ." Also written $\{x: \ldots\}$ (27)

series An indicated sum of terms in a sequence. (869)

shrink A scale change in the horizontal (or vertical) direction in which the absolute value of the magnitude is less than 1. (249)

sigma, Σ The Greek letter that indicates a sum. (871)

sigma notation, Σ-notation A shorthand notation used to restate a series. Also called *summation notation*. (871)

similar figures Two figures such that one is the image of the other under a composite of isometries (reflections, rotations, translations, glide reflections) and size changes. (245)

simple fraction A fraction of the form $\frac{a}{b}$, where a and b are integers and $b \neq 0$. (383)

simple interest The amount of interest I earned when calculated using the formula $I = Prt$, where P is the principal, r is the rate, and t is the time. (477)

sine function The correspondence $\theta \rightarrow \sin\theta$ that maps a number onto its sine. (663)

sine of θ (sin θ) In a right triangle with acute angle θ, $\sin\theta = \frac{\text{length of leg opposite } \theta}{\text{length of hypotenuse}}$; the y-coordinate of the image of (1, 0) under R_θ, the rotation with center (0, 0) and magnitude θ. (663, 684)

sine wave A curve that is the image of the graph of the sine function $s: \theta \rightarrow \sin\theta$ by any composite of translations, scale changes, or reflections. (695)

singular matrix A matrix whose multiplicative inverse does not exist. (330)

sinusoidal Pertaining to sine waves. (695)

size change The transformation that maps the point (x, y) onto (kx, ky); a transformation with center O such that the image of O is O itself and the image of any other point P is the point P' such that $OP' = k \cdot OP$ and P' is on ray OP if k is positive, and on the ray opposite ray OP if k is negative. (242)

$\sin^{-1} x$ The number between -90° and 90°, or between $-\frac{\pi}{2}$ and $\frac{\pi}{2}$, whose sine is x. (670)

size change factor *See magnitude of a size change.* (242)

slope The slope of a line through two points (x_1, y_1) and (x_2, y_2) is the quantity $\frac{y_2 - y_1}{x_2 - x_1}$. Also called *rate of change*. (94)

slope-intercept equation of a line An equation of the form $y = mx + b$, where m is the slope of the line and b is its y-intercept. (151)

solution set of a system The intersection of the solution sets of the individual sentences in a system. (307)

solving a sentence Finding all solutions to a sentence. (40)

solving a triangle Using theorems from geometry and trigonometry to find all the missing measures of sides and angles of a triangle. (700)

square matrix A matrix with the same number of rows and columns. (328)

square root A square root x of t is a solution to $x^2 = t$. The positive square root of a positive number x is denoted $\sqrt{x}$. (381)

square root function The function f with equation $f(x) = \sqrt{x}$, where x is a nonnegative real number. (537)

squaring function The function f with equation $f(x) = x^2$. (454)

standard deviation, *s.d.* Let S be a data set of n numbers $\{x_1, x_2, ..., x_n\}$. Let μ be the mean of S. Then the standard deviation, *s.d.*, of S is given by $s.d. = \sqrt{\frac{\sum_{i=1}^{n}(x_i - \mu)^2}{n}}$. (885)

standard form for an equation of a line An equation for a line in the form $Ax + By = C$, where A and B are not both zero. (159)

standard form of an equation for a parabola An equation for a parabola in the form $y = ax^2 + bx + c$, where $a \neq 0$. (374)

standard form of a polynomial A polynomial written in the form $a_nx^n + a_{n-1}x^{n-1} + ... + a_1x^1 + a_0$, where n is a positive integer and $a_n \neq 0$. (730)

standard form of a quadratic equation An expression of the form $ax^2 + bx + c = 0$, where $a \neq 0$. (374)

standard form of an equation for a hyperbola An equation for a hyperbola in the form $\frac{x^2}{a^2} - \frac{y^2}{b^2} = 1$, where $b^2 = c^2 - a^2$, the foci are $(c, 0)$ and $(-c, 0)$ and the focal constant is $2a$. (833)

standard form of an equation for a quadratic relation An equation of the form $Ax^2 + Bxy + Cy^2 + Dx + Ey + F = 0$, where A, B, C, D, E, and F are real numbers and at least one of A, B, or C is nonzero. (839)

standard form of an equation for an ellipse An equation for an ellipse in the form $\frac{x^2}{a^2} + \frac{y^2}{b^2} = 1$, where $b^2 = a^2 - c^2$, the foci are $(c, 0)$ and $(-c, 0)$ and the focal constant is $2a$. (818)

standard normal curve The graph of a normal distribution. (924)

standard position for an ellipse The position of an ellipse centered at the origin with its foci on an axis. (818)

standard window The default window of a grapher that shows all four quadrants at a reasonably close scale. (28)

standardized scores Scores whose distribution is normal with a predetermined mean and standard deviation. (925)

statistical measure A single number which is used to describe an entire set of numbers.

step function A piecewise function whose graph looks like a series of steps, such as the graph of the function with equation $y = \lfloor x \rfloor$. (204)

stretch A scale change in the horizontal (or vertical) direction in which the absolute value of the magnitude is greater than 1; that is, $|a| > 1$ (or $|b| > 1$). (249)

subscript A number or variable written below and to the right of a variable. (54)

subset A set whose elements are all from a given set. (891)

substitution method A method of solving systems in two or more variables by solving one equation for one variable, substituting the expression for that variable into the other equation(s), and solving the resulting equation(s). (314)

subtraction of matrices Given two matrices A and B having the same dimensions, their difference $A - B$ is the matrix whose element in each position is the difference of the corresponding elements in A and B. (230)

sum of two matrices For two matrices A and B with the same dimensions, the matrix $A + B$ in which each element is the sum of the corresponding elements in A and B. (228)

summation notation A shorthand notation used to denote a series. Also called *sigma notation* or *Σ-notation.* (871)

system A set of conditions joined by the word "and"; a special kind of compound sentence. (307)

T

$\tan^{-1} x$ The number between 0° and 180°, or between 0 and π whose tangent is x. (671)

tangent function The correspondence that maps a number x onto its tangent. (663)

tangent line A line that intersects a circle or ellipse in exactly one point. (846)

tangent of θ ($\tan \theta$) In a right triangle with acute angle θ, $\tan \theta = \frac{\text{length of leg opposite } \theta}{\text{length of leg adjacent to } \theta}$; $\tan \theta = \frac{\sin \theta}{\cos \theta}$, provided $\cos \theta \neq 0$. (663)

term of a polynomial Any one of the separate addends in a polynomial. (730)

term of a sequence An element of a sequence. (53)

theorem In a mathematical system, a statement that has been proved. (88)

transformation A one-to-one correspondence between the points of a preimage and the points of an image. (242)

translation A transformation for all x and y that maps (x, y) onto $(x + h, y + k)$ denoted by $T_{h,k}$. (281)

trial One repetition of an experiment. (912)

triangular number An element of the sequence 1, 3, 6, 10, ..., whose nth term is $\frac{n(n+1)}{2}$. (54)

triangulation The process of determining the location of points using triangles and trigonometry. (703)

trigonometric ratios The ratios of the lengths of the sides in a right triangle. (663)

trinomial A polynomial with three terms. (738)

U

union of two sets The set consisting of those elements in either one or both sets. (302)

unit circle The circle with center at the origin and radius 1 unit. (683)

unit fraction A simple fraction with 1 in its numerator. (918)

V

value of a function For a function f, if $y = f(x)$, the value of y. (21)

variable A symbol that can be replaced by any one of a set of numbers or other objects. (6)

varies directly as See *directly proportional to.* (72)

varies inversely as See *inversely proportional to.* (80)

velocity The rate of change of distance with respect to time. (52)

vertex form of an equation of a parabola An equation of the form $y - k = a(x - h)^2$ where (h, k) is the vertex of the parabola. (388)

vertex of a parabola The intersection of a parabola with its axis of symmetry. (102, 798)

vertical asymptote A vertical line that is approached by the graph of a relation as the values of x approach a particular real number. (107)

vertical line A line in the plane with an equation of the form $x = b$. (153)

vertical magnitude The number b in the scale change that maps (x, y) onto (ax, by). (249)

vertical scale change A transformation that maps (x, y) onto (x, by). (249)

vertices of an ellipse The endpoints of the major and minor axes of the ellipse. (819)

vertices of a hyperbola The points of intersection of a hyperbola and the line containing its foci. (832)

vinculum The bar in a fraction or a radical symbol. (8)

W

whole numbers The set of numbers {0, 1, 2, 3, 4, 5, ... }. (29)

window The part of the coordinate grid shown on the screen of an automatic grapher. (27)

X

***x*-axis** The line in the coordinate plane in which the second coordinates of points are 0. (152)

***x*-intercept** The x-coordinate of the point at which a graph crosses the x-axis. (152)

Y

***y*-axis** The line in the coordinate plane in which the first coordinates of points are 0. (255)

***y*-intercept** The y-coordinate of the point at which a graph crosses the y-axis. (151)

yield See *annual percentage yield.* (475)

Z

zeros of a function For a function f, a value of x for which $f(x) = 0$. (437)

zero of a polynomial See *root of a polynomial.* (752)

zoom A feature on an automatic grapher which enables the window of a graph to be changed without keying in interval endpoints for x and y. (32)

Index

D

E

Q

T

W

X

Y

Z

Photo Credits

Illustration Credits

McGraw Hill Companies, Inc. would like to thank the following illustrator for his contributions: Garry Nichols

Photo Credits

Chapters 1–6

Cover, back: ©Peter J. Robinson/photolibrary; **vi** (l) ©Tomislav Forgo/Shuttterstock, (r) ©Pete Saloutos/zefa Corbis; **vii** (l) ©Tim Tadder/Corbis, (r) ©S.P. Gillette/Corbis; **viii** (l) ©Paul Gilham/Getty Images Sport/Getty Images, (r) ©Sam Kittner/National Geographic/Getty Images; **ix** (l) ©Corbis/SuperStock, (r) ©The Granger Collection, New York; **x** (l) ©Somos Images/Corbis, (r) ©Allen Wallace/Photonica/Getty Images; **xi** (l) ©age fotostock/SuperStock, (r) ©Dennis di Cicco/Corbis; **xii** ©David Madison/The Image Bank/Getty Images; **3** ©Glenn Bartley/All Canada Photos/Getty images; **4-5** ©Tomislav Forgo/Shuttterstock; **7** Courtesy Robert Beerbohm/blbcomics.com; **12** Courtesy Corby Waste/NASA/JPL-Caltech; **16** ©Hannamariah/Shutterstock; **19** ©Nancy R. Cohen/Getty Images; **20** ©The Granger Collection; **21** ©Burke/Triolo/Brand X Pictures; **25** ©Michael-John Wolfe/Shutterstock; **27** ©Stephen Aaron Rees/Shutterstock; **32** ©2008 The Associated Press; **36** ©Tim Platt/Iconica/Getty Images; **39** ©Chuck Pefley/Alamy; **40** ©Image Source Pink/Alamy; **42** ©Chris Hondros/Getty Images Sport/Getty Images; **43** ©Ronald Martinez/Getty Images Sport/Getty Images; **45** ©Image100/Corbis/Punchstock; **51** ©Michael Gunther/www.art-and-archaeology.com; **56** ©Jeff Greenberg/PhotoEdit; **58** Courtesy Mitsumasa Anno/Penguin Group Inc.; **59** ©Hybrid Medical Animation/Photo Researchers, Inc. **60** (l) ©The Bridgeman Art Library, (r) ©Mike Flippo/Shutterstock; **61** ©Mitch Hrdlicka/Getty Images; **70-71** (t) ©Pete Saloutos/zefa Corbis; **71** (b) ©Seb Rogers/Alamy; **77** ©Stock Image/SuperStock; **85** ©Jonathan Daniel/Getty Images Sport/Getty Images; **86** ©Jennifer Westmoreland/Shutterstock; **89** ©Science/Illustration Carin L. Cain; **92** ©Photodisc/Getty Images; **93** ©Don Farrall/Photodisc/Getty Images; **104** ©CreativeAct-Technology Series/Alamy; **112** Courtesy NASA; **117** ©Oliver Furrer/Brand X/Corbis; **119** ©Michael Steele/Getty Images Sport/Getty Images; **130** (t, b) ©Ramiro Posada; **136** (l) ©Tme & Life Pictures/Getty Images, (r) ©Caroline J. Clarke/Shutterstock; **137** ©Lebrecht Music & Arts; **148-149** ©Tim Tadder/Corbis; **150** ©www.RoadsideArchitecture.com; **161** © Image Club; **168** ©Scenics of America/PhotoLink/Getty Images; **181** ©2008 The Associated Press; **185** ©Jim McIsaac/Getty Images Sport/Getty Images; **194** ©Eric Isselee/Shutterstock; **202** ©2008 The Associated Press; **206** ©fotog/Tetra Images/Getty Images; **210** ©Peter Weber/Shutterstock; **211** ©Duomo/Corbis; **220-221** ©S.P. Gillette/Corbis; **225** ©Kalev Leetaru; **226** ©Peter M. Fisher/Corbis/Veer; **228** ©Luigi Petro/Alamy; **233** ©2008 The Associated Press; **235** ©FoodCollection/SuperStock; **240** ©Andrey Kozachenko/Shutterstock; **246** ©Mark Segal/Stone/Getty Images; **249** ©Daryl Benson/Photographer's Choice/Getty Images; **259** ©Glenn Bartley/All Canada Photos/Getty images; **265** ©Big House Productions/Photodisc/Getty Images; **267** ©PhotoAlto/Laurence Mouton/Getty Images; **273** ©Lynn Radeka/SuperStock; **278** (t) ©G. Brad Lewis/Photo Resource Hawaii, (c) ©J Marshall/Tribaleye Images/Alamy, (b) ©Robin Bath/Alamy; **279** ©Royalty-Free/Corbis; **282** ©rfx/Shutterstock; **285** Courtesy University of Chicago; **286** (l) Courtesy Library of Congress, (c) ©akg-images, (r) ©Laurence Monneret/Getty Images; **287** Courtesy NASA; **298** (l) ©Photodisc/Getty Images; **298-299** ©Paul Gilham/Getty Images Sport/Getty Images; **302** ©fine art/Alamy; **305** ©SuperStock, Inc./SuperStock; **312** ©Ariel Skelley/Blend Images/Getty Images; **313** ©David Papas/UpperCut Images/Getty Images; **319** ©Andrew Turner/Camfaud Concrete Pumps Ltd.; **322** ©Sylvain Grandadam/Stone/Getty Images; **326** ©2008 The Associated Press; **331** ©Stephen Kallis, Jr.; **335** ©Travel Ink/Gallo Images/Getty Images; **340** ©2008 The Associated Press; **347** ©U.S. Geological Survey; **352** ©Shalom Ormsby/Stone/Getty Images; **353** ©Mark Weiss/Stone/Getty Images; **356** ©Ted Spiegel/Corbis; **362** (l) ©age fotostock/SuperStock; (r) ©Ian Waldie/Getty Images News/Getty Images; **363** ©Corbis/SuperStock; **372-373** (t) ©Sam Kittner/National Geographic/Getty Images; **373** (b) ©Phillip James Corwin/Corbis; **377** ©age fotostock/SuperStock; **378** ©image100/SuperStock; **390** ©VisionsofAmerica/Joe Sohm/Digital Vision/Getty Images; **391** ©Kim Karpeles/Alamy; **392** ©2008 The Associated Press; **395** ©The Granger Collection, New York; **397** ©flashfilm/Taxi Japan/Getty Images; **399** ©Peter Vanderwarker/The Image Bank/Getty Images; **411** ©2008 The Associated Press; **412** ©AURA/STSci; **418** ©Della Huff; **421** ©North Wind/North Wind Picture Archives; **426** ©Ablestock/Alamy; **431** (t, b) ©Doug Martin/Photo Researchers, Inc.; **438** ©it Stock/PunchStock; **441** ©Thinkstock/PunchStock; **442** ©Ken Welsh/ArtLife Images

Chapters 7–13

450-451 (t) ©Corbis/SuperStock; **451** (b) ©Leslie Richard Jacobs/Corbis; **453** ©Kent Larsson/Stone+/Getty Images; **458** ©2008 The Associated Press; **463** Courtesy NASA/ESA; **464** ©Michael Fay/National Geographic/Getty Images; **470** (t) ©Spectral-Design/Shutterstock; (b) ©FPG Intl./Taxi/Getty Images; **474** ©Keith Brofsky/Getty Images; **475** ©Robert Brenner/PhotoEdit; **476** ©2008 The Associated Press; **478** ©Copestello/Shutterstock; **479** ©Fallon London; **487** Photononstop/Superstock; **491** ©Corbis/SuperStock; **496** ©Car Culture/Getty Images; **498** ©Julie Mowbray/Alamy; **501** ©Blend Images/SuperStock; **502** (t) ©Digital Vision/Getty Images; (b) ©image100/Punchstock; **503** ©G.K. & Vikki Hart/Getty Images; **504** ©The Granger Collection, New York; **505** (l) ©Steve Dunwell/Getty Images; (r) ©Melba Photo Agency/PunchStock; **506** ©RubberBall Productions; **514-515** ©The Granger Collection, New York; **516** ©Thinkstock/JupiterImages; **522** Courtesy NASA, The Hubble Heritage Team, STSci,AURA; **526** Courtesy NASA, ESA, and The Hubble Heritage Team; **536** ©2008 The Associated Press; **538** ©Keith Weller/U.S. Department of Agriculture/Photo Researchers, Inc.; **541** NASA/JPL-Caltech/Cornell University; **544** ©Italian School/The Bridgeman Art Library/Getty Images; **549** ©2008 The Associated Press; **561** image100/SuperStock; **566** Collection of the Australian National Maritime Museum; **568** ©FPG/Taxi/Getty Images; **569** ©2008 The Associated Press; **578-579** ©Somos Images/Corbis; **580** ©Steve Shott/Dorling Kindersley/Getty Images; **583** ©Lawrence Livermore National Laboratory; **585** ©Sean Sprague/Painet; **586** ©Wil Meinderts/Foto Natura/Minden Pictures; **589** ©Burke/Triolo/Brand X Pictures/Jupiterimages; **592** ©Neil Emmerson/Robert Harding World Imagery/Corbis; **594** ©Maximilian Weinzierl/Alamy; **597** ©Dimitri Vervitsiotis/Digital Vision/Getty Images; **602** ©Blend Images/SuperStock; **607** ©arabianEye/Getty Images; **613** ©David Paul Morris/Getty Images News/Getty Images; **616** ©William Radcliffe/Science Faction/Getty Images; **618** ©Adam Teitelbaum/AFP/Getty Images; **619** ©AFP/Getty Images; **620** ©Rob Gendler; **621** ©Peter Cade/Iconica/Getty Images; **628** ©Atlas Photo Bank/Photo Researchers, Inc.; **629** ©The Old Calculator Museum; **631** ©Comstock Images/PictureQuest; **633** ©Pradeep Subramanian; **634** ©Science & Society Picture Library; **638** ©Stephen Dunn/Getty Images Sport/Getty Images; **642** (t, b) Courtesy Scripophily; **644** ©2008 The Associated Press; **648** ©David Young-Wolff/PhotoEdit; **649** (l) ©Nassyrov Rusian/Shutterstock, (r) ©Mark Harwood/Stone/Getty Images; **650** (l) ©2008 The Associated Press, (r) ©Photononstop/SuperStock; **651** ©Dennis Galante/Taxi/Getty Images; **660-661** ©Allen Wallace/Photonica/Getty Images; **665** ©Alan Becker/Photographer's Choice/Getty Images; **668** (t) ©Photodisc/PunchStock, (b) ©Kirk Treakle/Alamy; **673** ©Lee Foster/Lonely Planet Images/Getty Images; **678** ©North Wind/North Wind Picture Archives; **680** ©North Wind/North Wind Picture Archives; **686** ©Jason Hirschfeld/Getty Images News/ Getty Images; **692** ©Corbis/SuperStock; **695** ©The Granger Collection, New York; **696** ©Royalty-Free/Corbis; **698** Courtesy NASA/JPL-Caltech/Cornell; **705** ©Travel Ink/Getty Images; **710** ©2008 The Associated Press; **718** ©Alan Gallery/Alamy; **719** (l) ©kolvenbach/Alamy, (r) ©North Wind/North Wind Picture Archives; **728** (b) ©Dynamic Graphics Value/SuperStock; **728-729** (t) ©age fotostock/SuperStock; **735** ©Ken Chernus/Taxi/Getty Images; **736** ©Photodisc/SuperStock; **737** ©The McGraw-Hill Companies, Inc.; **743** ©C Squared Studios/Getty Images; **758** ©Andy Sacks/Stone/Getty Images; **766** ©The Granger Collection, New York; **781** ©Jorg Greuel/The Image Bank/Getty Images; **784** ©Comstock/Punchstock; **786** ©2008 Masterfile Corporation; **787** ©Jeffrey Coolidge/The Image Bank/Getty Images; **796-797** ©Dennis di Cicco/Corbis; **801** ©Sun Baked; **802** ©Mark Darley/Esto Photographics; **808** ©Allthesky.com Astrophotography; **809** ©2008 The Associated Press; **810** ©Herbert Hartmann/The Image Bank/Getty Images; **812** ©The Bridgeman Art Library/Getty Images; **174** Courtesy NASA; **823** ©David S. Gunderson; **829** © J.B. Spector/Museum of Science & Industry; **831** (l) ©amana images inc./Alamy, (r) ©Kamee14u/Shutterstock; **837** ©Richard Thornton/Shutterstock; **842** ©William H. Edwards/Stone/Getty Images; **848** ©VisionsofAmerica/Joe Sohm/Digital Vision/Getty Images; **849** ©Stephen Schauer/Riser/Getty Images; **852** ©Kraig Scarbinsky/Riser/Getty Images; **854** ©age fotostock/SuperStock; **856** (l) ©2008 The Associated Press, (r) ©Luis Veiga/Photographer's Choice/Getty Images; **857** ©Antonio M. Rosario/The Image Bank/Getty Images; **866-867** ©David MadisonThe Image Bank/Getty Images; **874** ©Purestock/Getty Images; **879** ©Alex Mares-Manton/Asia Images/Getty Images; **881** ©Nick Vedros & Assoc./Stone/Getty Images; **886** ©NBAE/Getty Images; **887** ©The Granger Collection, New York; **889** ©Jeff Greenberg/Alamy; **892** ©Paul Burns/Lifesize/Getty Images; **894** ©Garry Gay/Photographer's Choice/Getty Images; **901** ©Influx Productions/Photodisc/Getty Images; **904** ©Bettmann/Corbis; **909** ©Mario Bruno/Shutterstock; **911** ©2008 The Associated Press; **913** ©Royalty-Free/Corbis; **914** ©WIN-Initiative/Getty Images; **915** ©Cadence Gamache; **916** ©Ingram Publishing/SuperStock; **919** ©Ian Mckinnell/Photographer's Choice/Getty Images; **921** ©Juniors Bildarchiv/Alamy; **927** ©2008 The Associated Press; **928** ©RubberBall/SuperStock; **929** ©Joan Kerrigan/Shutterstock.

Symbols

Symbol	Meaning
$\{x \mid x > n\}$	the set of all x such that x is greater than n
$-x$	opposite of x
$\cap$	intersection
$\cup$	union
$f(x)$	function notation read "f of x"
$f: x \rightarrow y$	function notation read "f maps x onto y"
A'	image of A
S_k	size change of magnitude k
$S_{a,b}$	scale change with horizontal magnitude a and vertical magnitude b
r_x	reflection over the x-axis; transformation with matrix $\begin{bmatrix} 1 & 0 \\ 0 & -1 \end{bmatrix}$
r_y	reflection over the y-axis; transformation with matrix $\begin{bmatrix} -1 & 0 \\ 0 & 1 \end{bmatrix}$
$r_{y=x}$	reflection over the line $y = x$; transformation with matrix $\begin{bmatrix} 0 & 1 \\ 1 & 0 \end{bmatrix}$
r_m	reflection over the line m
R_θ	rotation of magnitude θ *counterclockwise* with center at the origin
R_{180}	rotation of magnitude $180°$; transformation with matrix $\begin{bmatrix} -1 & 0 \\ 0 & -1 \end{bmatrix}$
R_{90}	rotation of magnitude $90°$; transformation with matrix $\begin{bmatrix} 0 & -1 \\ 1 & 0 \end{bmatrix}$
$T_2 \circ T_1$	composite of transformations T_1 and T_2
$T_{h,k}$	translation of h units horizontally and k units vertically
$\parallel$	parallel
$\perp$	perpendicular
$\begin{bmatrix} a & b \\ c & d \end{bmatrix}$	2×2 matrix
M^{-1}	inverse of matrix M
$\det M$	determinant of matrix M

Symbol	Meaning
$\sqrt{}$	radical sign; square root
$\sqrt[n]{x}$	the largest real nth root of x
i	$\sqrt{-1}$
$\sqrt{-k}$	a solution of $x^2 = -k$, $k > 0$
$a + bi$	a complex number, where a and b are real numbers
$g \circ f$	composite of functions f and g
$g(f(x))$	value at x of the composite of functions f and g
$\lvert x \rvert$	absolute value of x
$\lfloor x \rfloor$	greatest integer less than or equal to x
$\lceil x \rceil$	least integer greater than or equal to x
f^{-1}	inverse of a function f read "f inverse"
a^b, a^b	the bth power of a
$\log_b a$	logarithm of a to the base b
e	2.71828…
$\ln x$	natural logarithm of x
$m\angle ABC$	measure of angle ABC
$\sin \theta$	sine of θ
$\cos \theta$	cosine of θ
$\tan \theta$	tangent of θ
rad	radian
a_n	"a sub n"; the nth term of a sequence
$\sum_{i=1}^{n} 1$	the sum of the integers from 1 to n
S_n	the sum of the first n terms of a sequence
$x!$	x factorial
$\binom{n}{r}$, ${}_nC_r$	the number of ways of choosing r objects from n objects
`int`	greatest integer calculator command
`seq`	sequence calculator command
`det`	determinant of a matrix calculator command
`fMax`, `fMin`	maximum or minimum function value calculator command
`stDevPop`	standard deviation calculator command
`nCr`	combination calculator command

Additional Answers

Chapter 8

Lesson 8-7

Activity Page 556

Step 1

x	f1(x):...	f2(x):...	
	(-2)^x	(-7)^x	
2	4.	49.	
4	16.	2.4E3	
6	64.	1.18E5	
8	256.	5.76E6	
10	1.02E3	2.82E8	
12	4.1E3	1.38E10	
2			

x	f1(x):...	f2(x):...	
	(-6)^x	(-5)^x	
2	36.	25.	
4	1.3E3	625.	
6	4.67E4	1.56E4	
8	1.68E6	3.91E5	
10	6.05E7	9.77E6	
12	2.18E9	2.44E8	
2			

Step 3

x	f1(x):...	f2(x):...	
	(-2)^x	(-7)^x	
1	-2.	-7.	
3	-8.	-343.	
5	-32.	-1.68E4	
7	-128.	-8.24E5	
9	-512.	-4.04E7	
11	-2.05E3	-1.98E9	
1			

x	f1(x):...	f2(x):...	
	(-6)^x	(-5)^x	
1	-6.	-5.	
3	-216.	-125.	
5	-7.78E3	-3.13E3	
7	-2.8E5	-7.81E4	
9	-1.01E7	-1.95E6	
11	-3.63E8	-4.88E7	
1			

Every odd power of a negative number is negative; every odd power of an even number is even; and every odd power of an odd number is odd.

Chapter Review Page 574

66a.

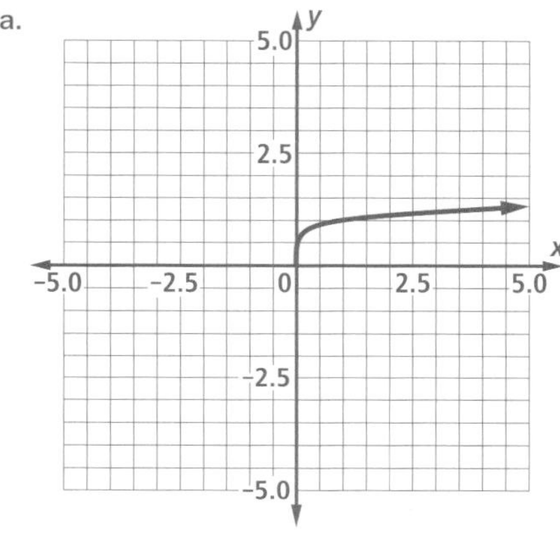

67b. domain: $\{x \mid x \geq 0\}$; range: $\{y \mid y \geq 0\}$

67a.

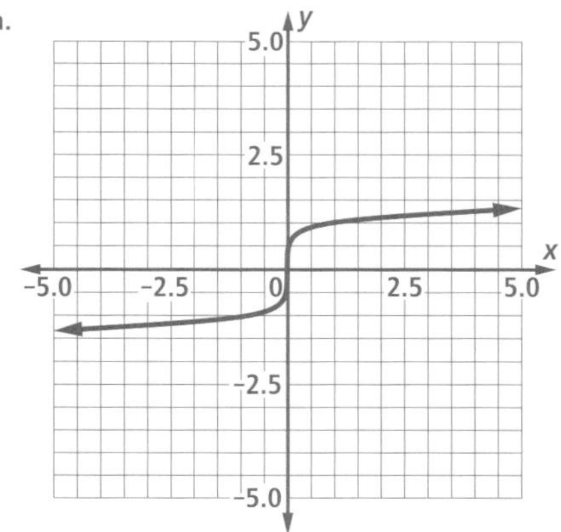

67b. domain: all real numbers; range: all real numbers

Chapter 10

Lesson 10-2
Questions Page 673

1. [2nd][SIN][.][4][7][5][)][ENTER]

9. The line of sight is a transversal for parallel horizontal lines, so the angles of elevation and depression are alternate interior angles and therefore congruent.

22a. range: $0° < y < 90°$

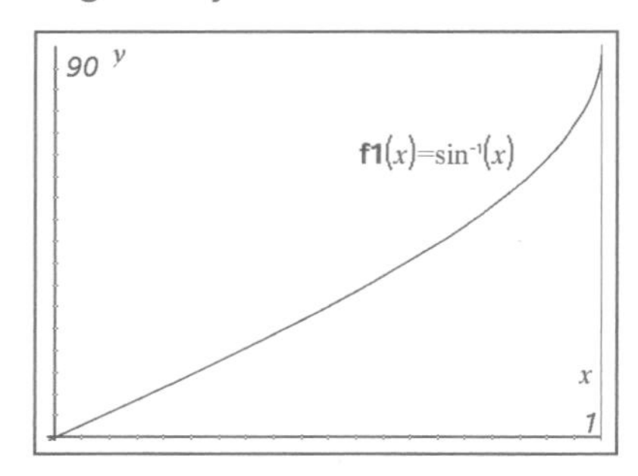

22b. range: $0 < y < 1$

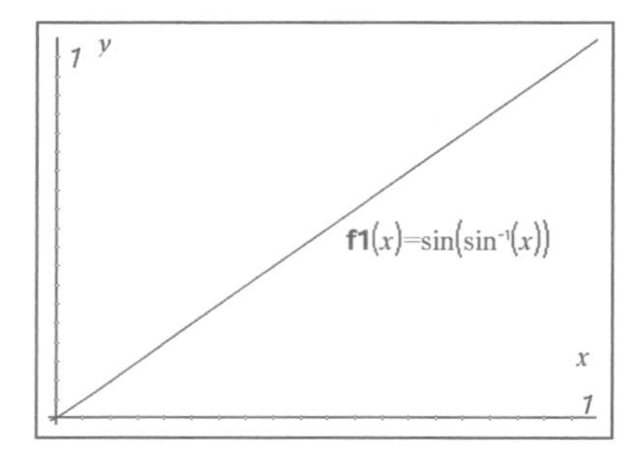

Lesson 10-4
Activity Page 682

Step 2

a. Check students' work. $A_{20} = (\cos 20°, \sin 20°)$

b. Answers vary. Sample: $A_{20} \approx (0.95, 0.35)$

c. $A_{20} = (\cos 20°, \sin 20°) \approx (0.940, 0.342)$

Step 3

a. Check students' work. $A_{40} = (\cos 40°, \sin 40°)$

b. Answers vary. Sample: $A_{40} \approx (0.77, 0.64)$

c. $A_{40} = (\cos 40°, \sin 40°) \approx (0.766, 0.643)$

Step 4

a. Check students' work. $A_{75} = (\cos 75°, \sin 75°)$

b. Answers vary. Sample: $A_{75} \approx (0.97, 0.26)$

c. $A_{75} = (\cos 75°, \sin 75°) = (0.966, 0.259)$

Step 5

a. For any θ, the coordinates of a rotation R_θ centered at (0, 0) of magnitude θ is $(\cos \theta, \sin \theta)$.

b. Answers vary. Sample: $A_{61} \approx (0.49, 0.68)$

c. Answers vary. Sample: $\cos 61° \approx 0.48$; $\frac{0.49 - 0.48}{0.48} \approx 0.02$; $\sin 61° \approx 0.87$; $\frac{0.86 - 0.87}{0.87} \approx -0.01$; both were within 3% of the actual values.

Lesson 10-5
Activity Page 690

Step 1

$C_2 \approx (-0.883, 0.469)$

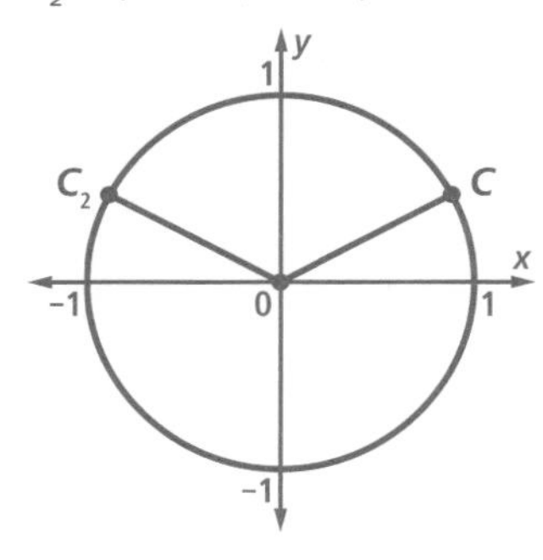

Step 3

$C_4 \approx (0.883, -0.469)$

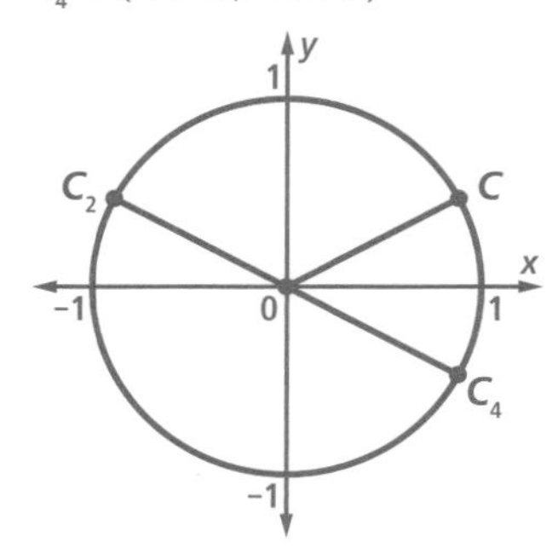

Step 5

$C_3 \approx (\cos 208°, \sin 208°) \approx (-0.883, -0.469)$

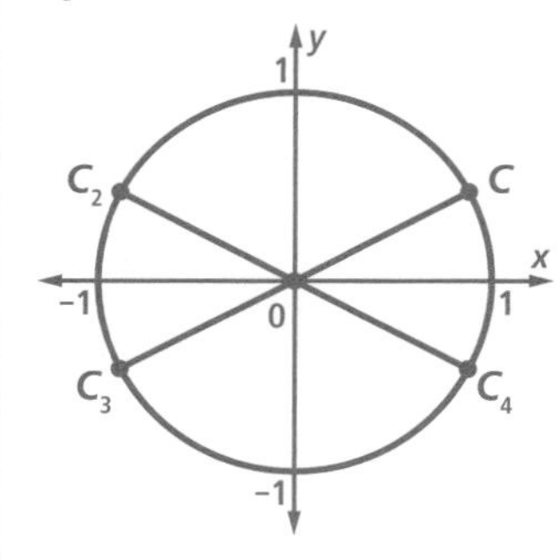

Questions Page 690

18. negative; In Quadrant II, $\cos \theta$ is negative and $\sin \theta$ is positive, therefore $\tan \theta = \frac{\sin\theta}{\cos\theta}$ is negative.

21. The y-coordinates of R_θ and $R_{180°-\theta}$ are the same, and $\sin \theta$ is the y-coordinate of points on the unit circle.

Lesson 10-6
Activity Page 693

Step 1

θ	$\cos \theta$
0°	1.00
15°	0.97
30°	0.87
45°	0.71
60°	0.50
75°	0.26
90°	0.00
105°	-0.26
120°	-0.50
135°	-0.71
150°	-0.87
165°	-0.97
180°	-1.00
195°	-0.97
210°	-0.87
225°	-0.71
240°	-0.50
255°	-0.26
270°	0.00
285°	0.26
300°	0.50
315°	0.71
330°	0.87
345°	0.97
360°	1.00

Step 2

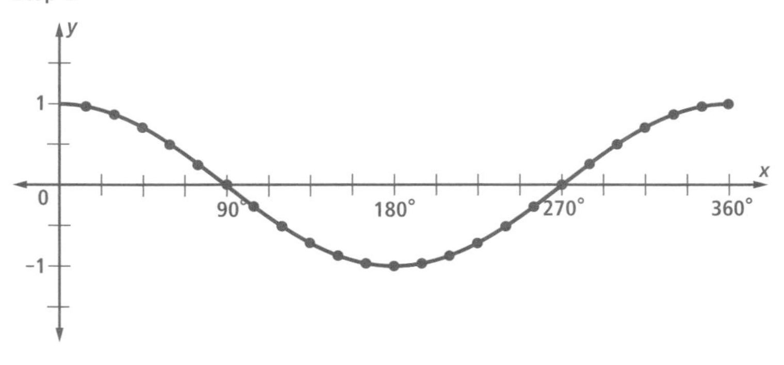

Step 3

The graph is bounded such that $-1 \leq \cos \theta \leq 1$ and has intercepts that are odd multiples of 90°.

Step 4

The largest value is 1 and the smallest value is -1.

Chapter 11

Lesson 11-4
Activity 1 Page 753

Step 1

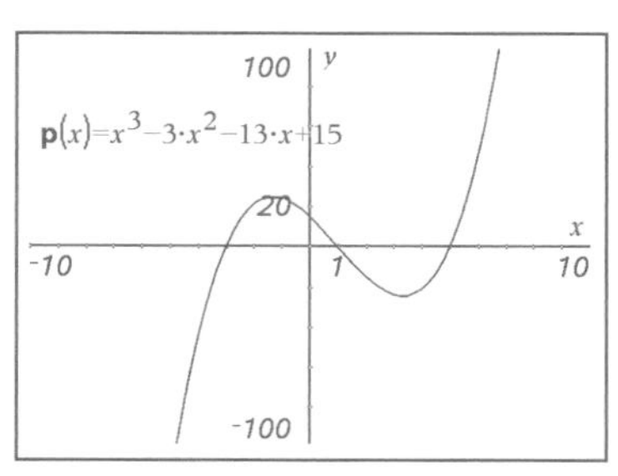

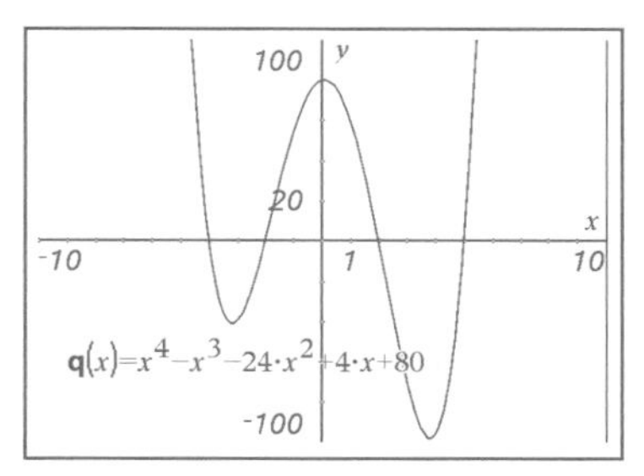

Step 2

$p(x) = x^3 - 3x^2 - 13x + 15$: -3, 1, 5

$q(x) = x^4 - x^3 - 24x^2 + 4x + 80$: -4, -2, 2, 5

Step 3

factor$(x^3-3\cdot x^2-13\cdot x+15)$
$(x-5)\cdot(x-1)\cdot(x+3)$

factor$(x^4-x^3-24\cdot x^2+4\cdot x+80)$
$(x-5)\cdot(x-2)\cdot(x+2)\cdot(x+4)$

Step 4

If r is an x-intercept of the graph of $P(x)$, then $x - r$ is a factor of $P(x)$.

Step 5

Answers vary. Sample: $r(x) = (x + 1)(x - 4)(x - 5) = x^3 - 8x^2 + 11x + 20$

Questions Page 756

29. Answers vary. Sample: $f(x) = (x - 5)(x - 3)(x + 1)$

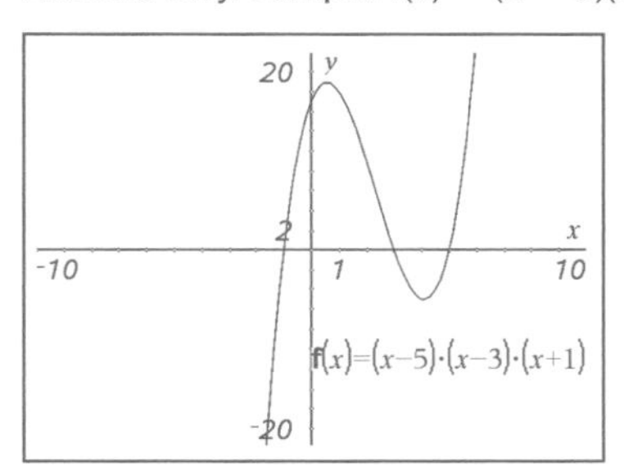

$g(x) = (x - 5)^2(x - 3)^2(x + 1)$

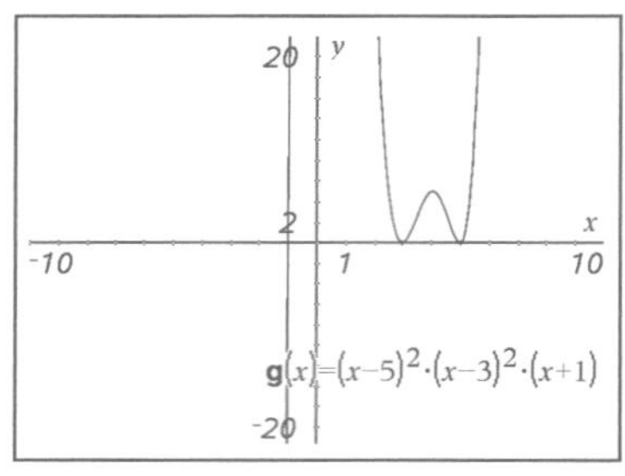

$h(x) = (x - 5)(x - 3)^3(x + 1)$

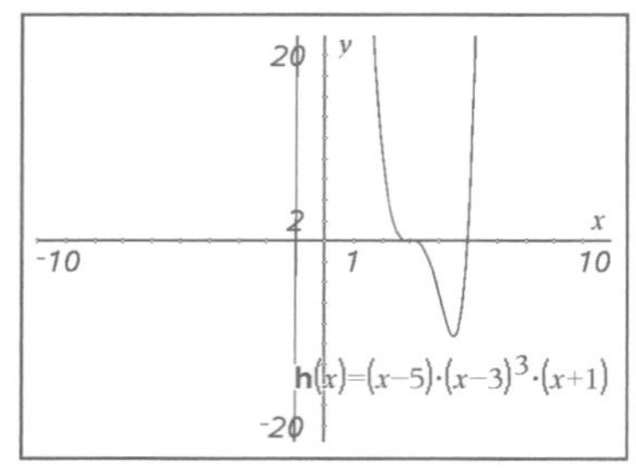

The graph of the function crosses the *x*-axis at a zero of odd multiplicity, and does not cross the *x*-axis at zeros of even multiplicity.

Lesson 11-5
Questions Page 763

3a. $\pm 24, \pm 12, \pm 8, \pm 6, \pm 4, \pm 3, \pm 2, \pm\frac{3}{2}, \pm 1, \pm\frac{3}{4}, \pm\frac{1}{2}, \pm\frac{3}{8}, \pm\frac{1}{4}, \pm\frac{1}{8}$

3b. $-\frac{1}{2}$

4a. $\pm 12, \pm 6, \pm 4, \pm 3, \pm\frac{12}{5}, \pm 2, \pm\frac{6}{5}, \pm 1, \pm\frac{4}{5}, \pm\frac{3}{5}, \pm\frac{2}{5}, \pm\frac{1}{5}$

4b. -1, 1, 2

5a. $\pm 14, \pm 7, \pm 2, \pm 1, \pm\frac{2}{7}, \pm\frac{1}{7}$

5b. There are no rational roots. If we look at the graph, we see that the roots must lie in the ranges $-0.5 < x < 0$ and $3 < x < 3.5$. By testing $-\frac{2}{7}$ and $-\frac{1}{7}$, we find that neither of these values are zeros.

6. $\sqrt[3]{9}$ is a solution to $x^3 = 9$ and a root of $x^3 - 9 = 0$. By the Rational-Root Theorem, if $\frac{a}{b}$ is a rational root, then *a* is a factor of 9, and *b* is a factor of 1. So, the possible roots are ± 9, ± 3, and ± 1. If we substitute these values, we find that none of them is a root of the equation. Therefore, $x^3 - 9 = 0$ has no rational roots, and $\sqrt[3]{9}$ must be irrational.

7a. $\pm 12, \pm 6, \pm 4, \pm 3, \pm 2, \pm\frac{3}{2}, \pm 1, \pm\frac{1}{2}$

7b.

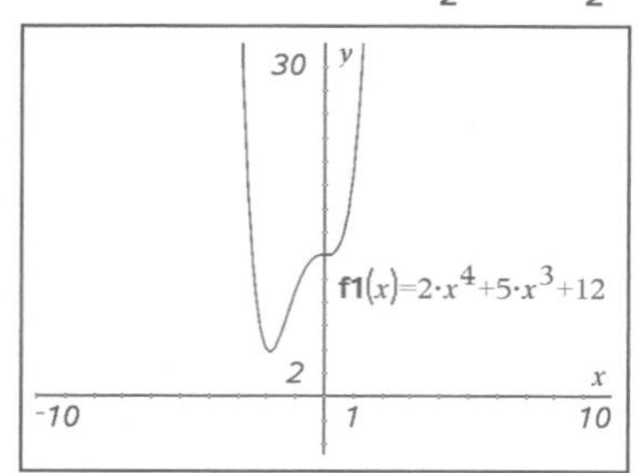

The function does not intersect the *x*-axis.

Chapter 12

Lesson 12-1
Activity Page 799

Step 1

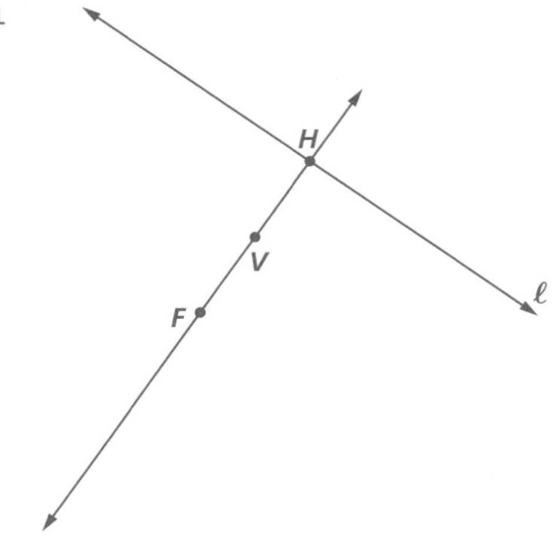

Step 2

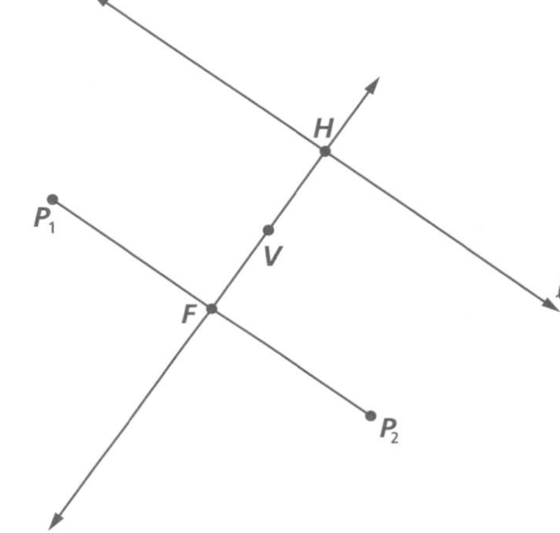

Step 3a

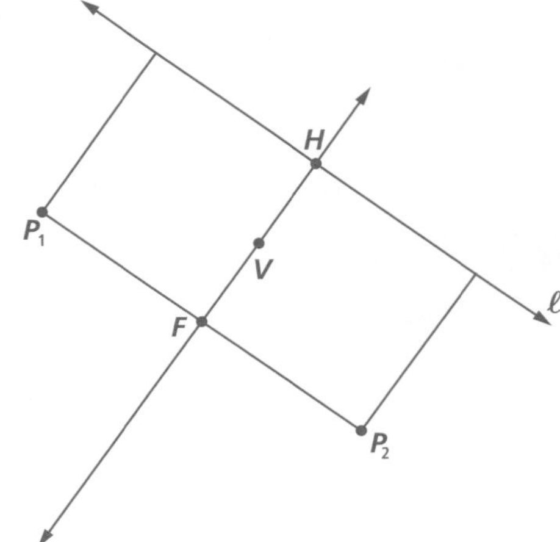

Step 4

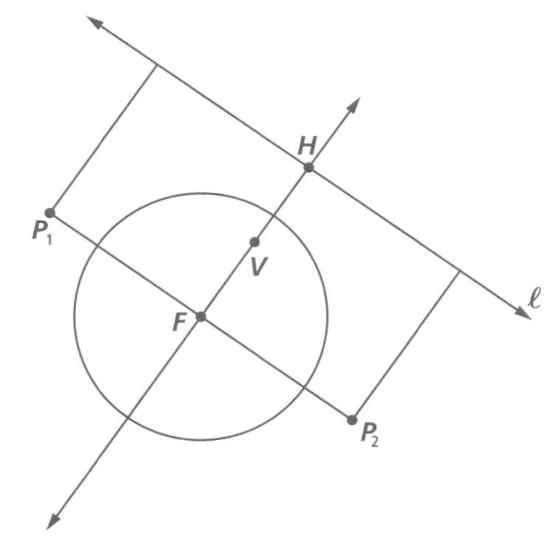

Step 5a

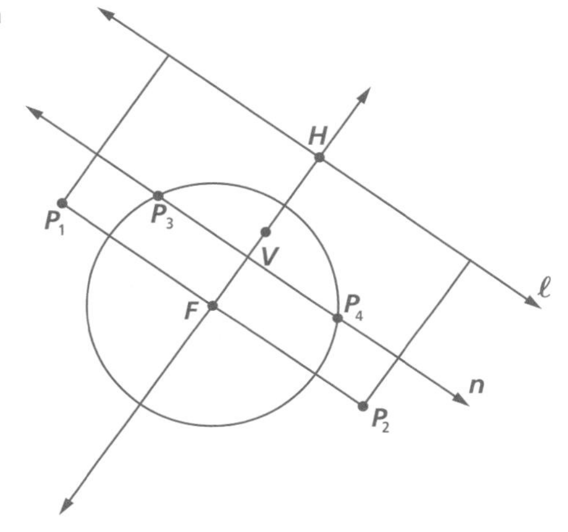

Step 6

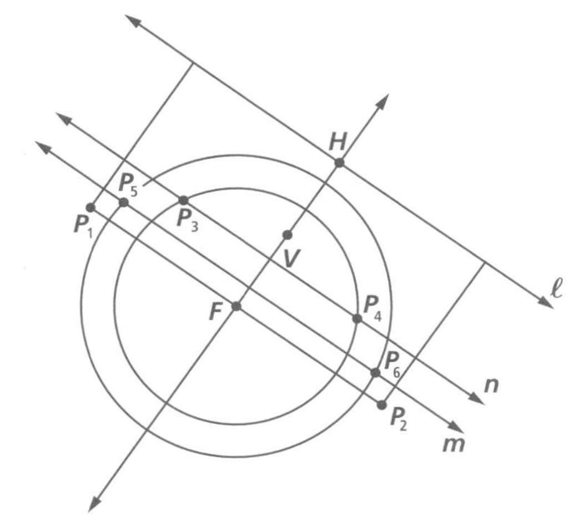

Step 7

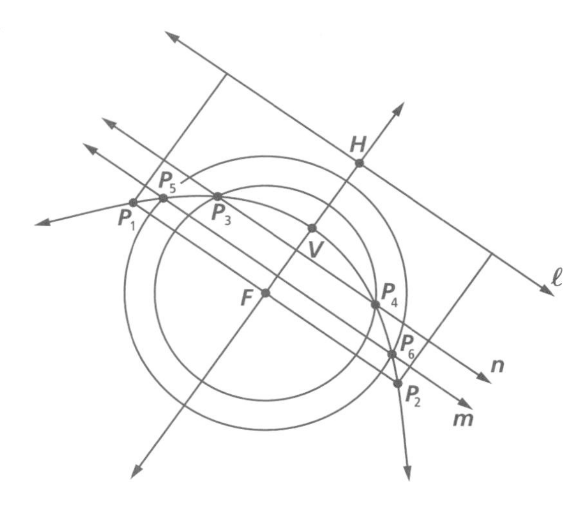

Questions Page 801

12. A parabola is defined as the set of all points in the plane of directrix l and focus F that are equidistant from F and l. Use the distance formula to find an equation for the set of points that are equidistant from $\left(0, \frac{1}{4a}\right)$ and the line $y = -\frac{1}{4a}$. $\sqrt{(x-0)^2 + \left(y - \frac{1}{4a}\right)^2} = \sqrt{(x-x)^2 + \left(y - \left(-\frac{1}{4a}\right)\right)^2}$. So,

$$x^2 + \left(y - \frac{1}{4a}\right)^2 = \left(y + \frac{1}{4a}\right)^2$$

$$x^2 + y^2 - \frac{y}{2a} + \frac{1}{16a^2} = y^2 + \frac{y}{2a} + \frac{1}{16a^2}$$

$$x^2 = \frac{2y}{2a}$$

$$y = ax^2$$

Lesson 12-3
Questions Page 813

1a.

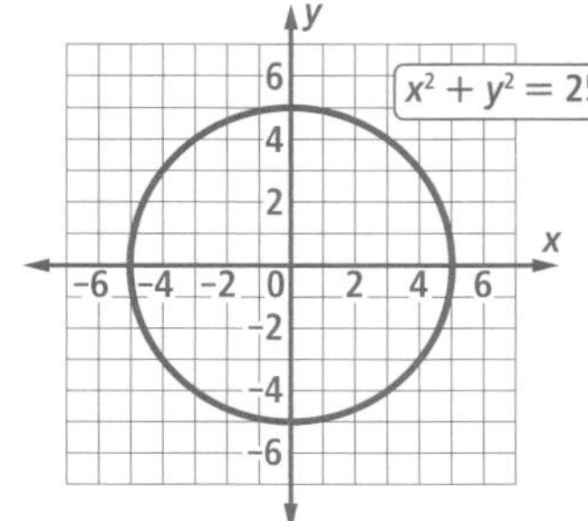

1b.

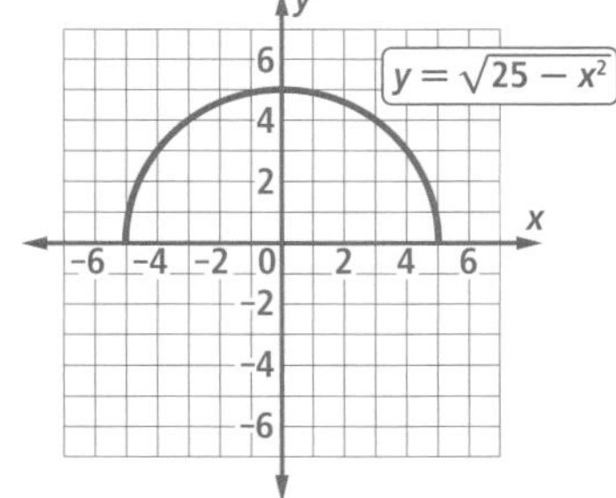

1c.

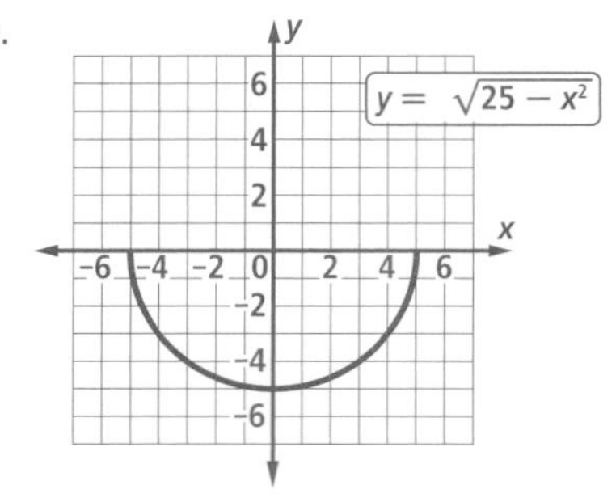

2.

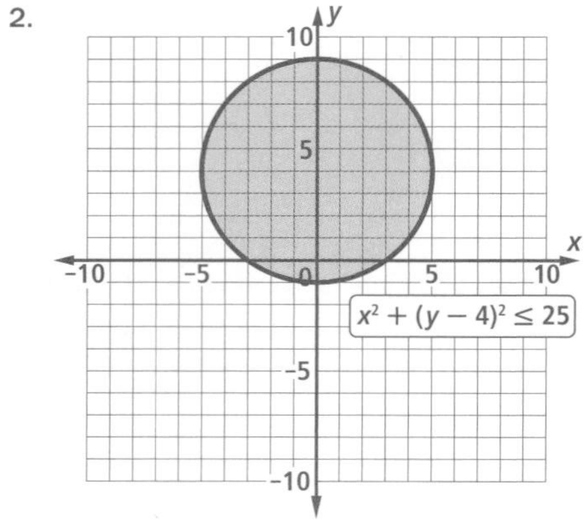

Lesson 12-4

Activity Page 816

Steps 1–3

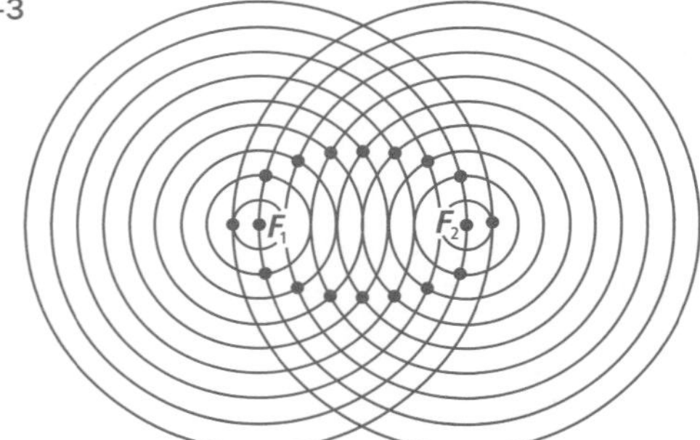

Step 4

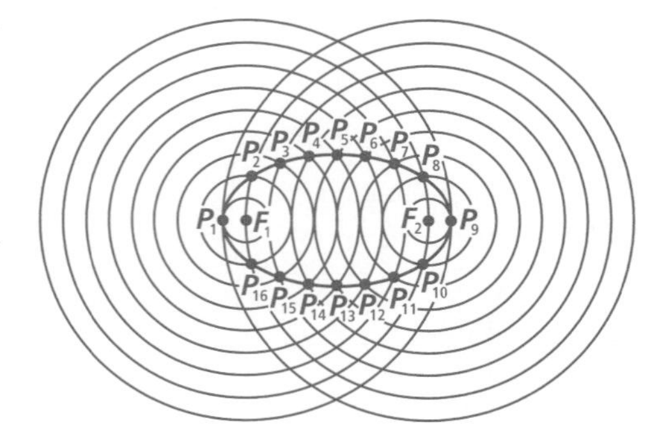

Questions Page 821

17a.

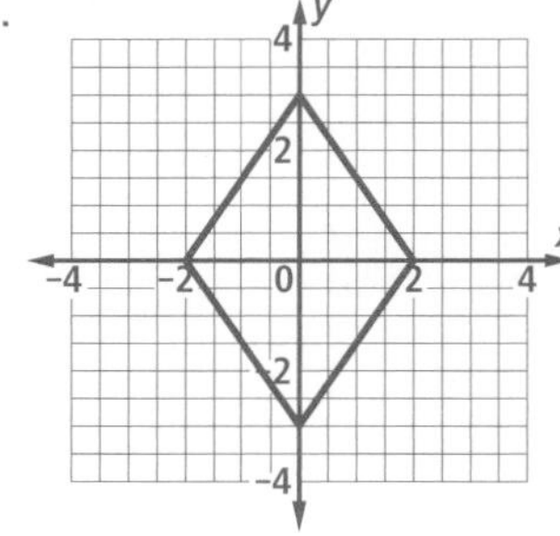

17b. major axis: y-axis from −3 to 3, minor axis: x-axis from −2 to 2

17c. (−2, 0) (2, 0); (0, 3), (0, −3)

17d.

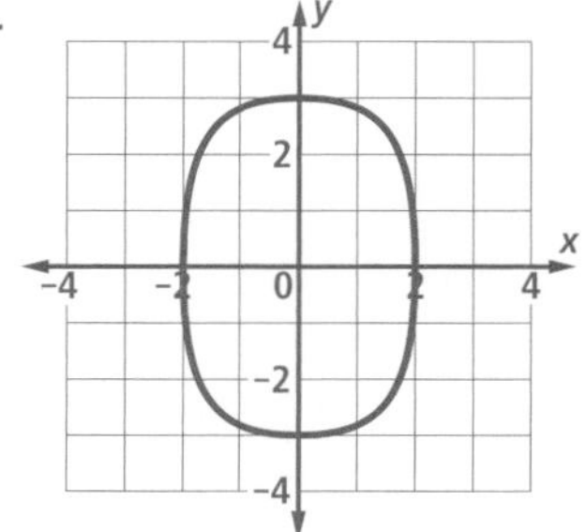

major axis: y-axis from −3 to 3, minor axis: x-axis from −2 to 2

17e. Answers vary. Sample: They have the same x- and y-intercepts and endpoints of the major and minor axes. The graph from Part a is a polygon made of line segments, whereas the graph from Part d has smooth curves.

19a. $x^2 + y^2 = 9$

19b. $\left(x - \frac{3\sqrt{2}}{2}\right)^2 + \left(y - \frac{3\sqrt{2}}{2}\right)^2 = \frac{9}{2}$

19c. $x^2 + y^2 < 9$

19d. A: 6π; B: $3\sqrt{2}$

19e. A: 9π; B: $\frac{9}{2}$

24. Answers vary. Sample: A carpenter's trammel is a tool that acts as a straightedge and stencil when you want to make a circle or ellipse in carpentry. Carpenters might use this to make archways for doors. In order to create an ellipse, you first create x- and y-axes, and then mark the trammel with the lengths of the semimajor and semiminor axes. Then you move the trammel around the axes in order to mark the ellipse.

Lesson 12-6

Questions Page 836

15.

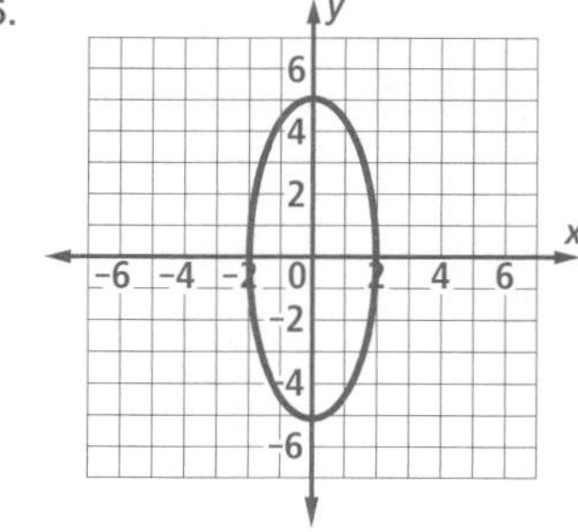

16.

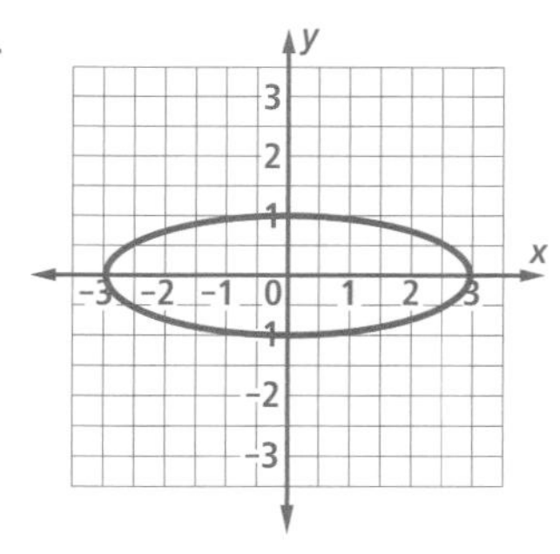

19. Answers vary. Sample: "Ellipsis" means an omission, or the marks that indicate an omission, of one or more words that are implied but must be supplied to make a construction grammatically correct. "Hyperbole" means extreme exaggeration.

20. Answers vary. Sample: To travel between planets, spacecrafts launch so that they enter an irregular orbit around the sun, called a Hohmann Transfer Orbit. They have to time the launch with the orbit of the destination planet so that the elliptical path of their orbit intersects with the orbit of the destination planet. If there is a mistake, the spacecraft may be stuck in the irregular orbit around the sun. Therefore, Verne's characters were partially correct. If misdirected or mistimed, the rocket may be in space for a much longer time than expected. However, they would not travel infinitely through space.

Lesson 12-7

Questions Page 841

24. Answers vary. Sample: If $B = C = 0$, then the graph is concave up when A and E have opposite sign and concave down when A and E have the same sign. If $A = B = C = D = E = 1$, $F < \frac{1}{3}$.

Lesson 12-8

Activity Page 845

Step 1

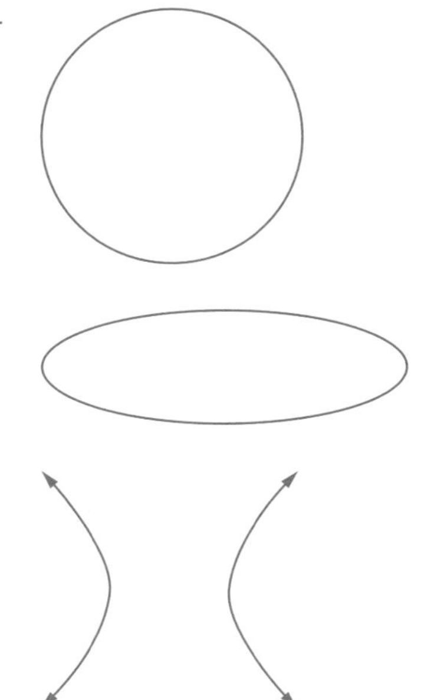

Step 2

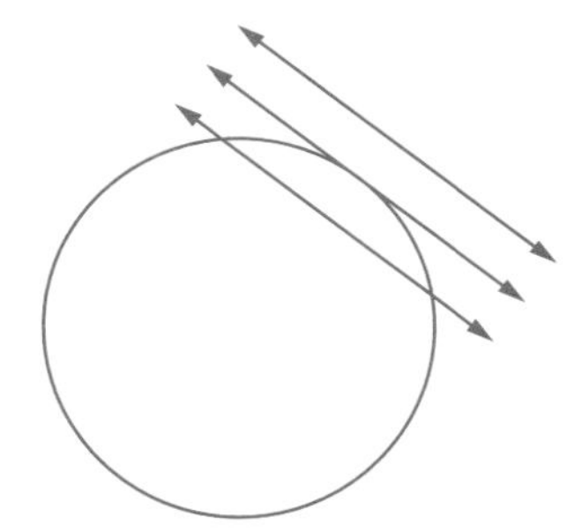

0, 1, or 2 points

Step 3

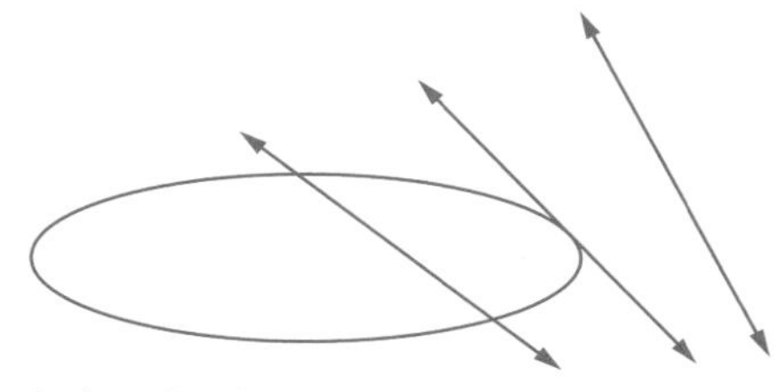

0, 1, or 2 points

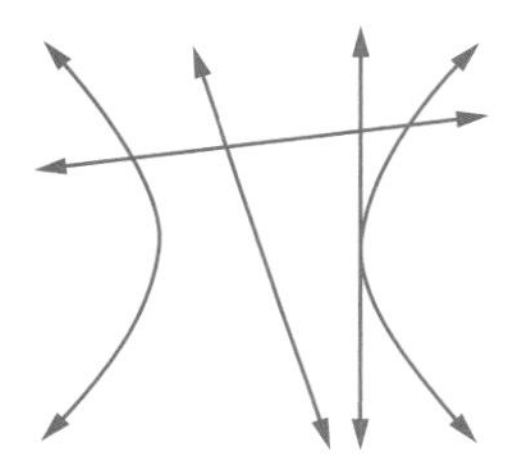

0, 1, or 2 points

Questions Page 847

2.

9
y
(0.5, 8)
f1(x)=10−4·x
(2, 2)
f2(x)=4/x
0.5
x
0.5
6

4.

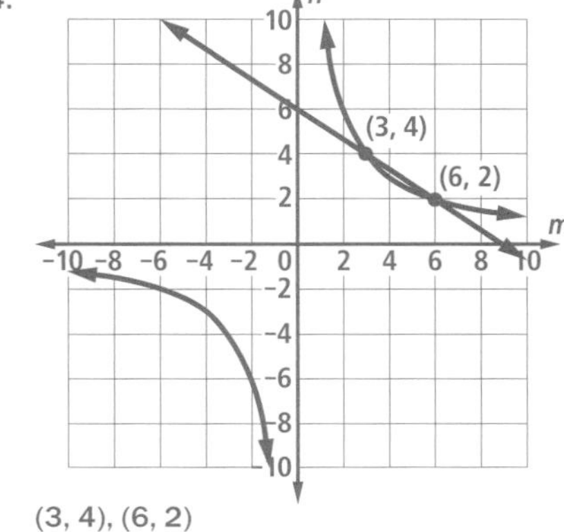

(3, 4), (6, 2)

5.

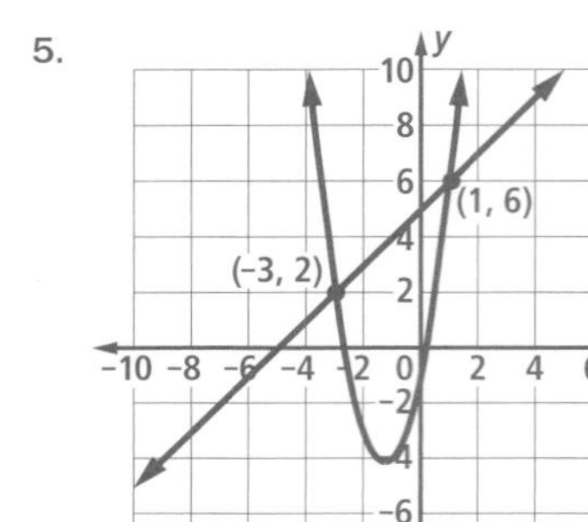

(-3, 2), (1, 6)

11. A quadratic-linear system can have at most 2 solutions because a straight line and a quadratic curve cannot coincide.

13. Answers vary. Sample: $\begin{cases} x + y = 8 \\ xy = 24 \end{cases}$

Substituting $y = 8 - x$ into the second equation gives $x(8 - x) = 24$, or $x^2 - 8x + 24$. This equation has no real solutions, so the system cannot be solved.

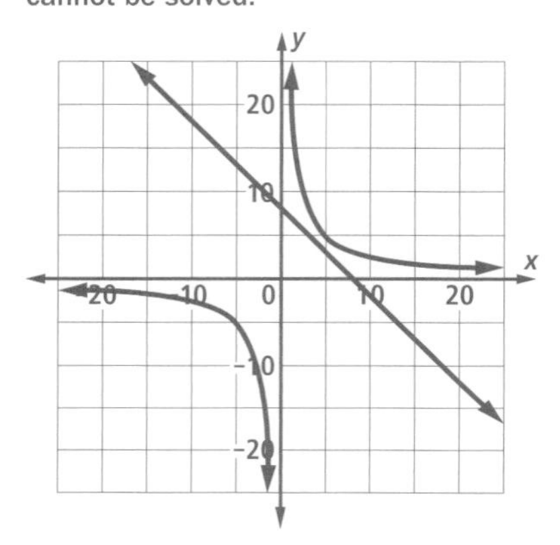

14. (1.05, -2.15), (-0.59, 2.77)

15. (3.79, 1.90), (-3.79, -1.90)

Lesson 12-9

Activity Page 851

	Parabola	Circle	Ellipse	Hyperbola
Parabola	0, 1, 2, 3, 4, or infinite	0, 1, 2, 3, or 4	0, 1, 2, 3, or 4	0, 1, 2, 3, or 4
Circle		0, 1, 2, or infinite	0, 1, 2, 3, 4, or infinite	0, 1, 2, 3, or 4
Ellipse			0, 1, 2, 3, 4, or infinite	0, 1, 2, 3, or 4
Hyperbola				0, 1, 2, 3, 4, or infinite

Questions Page 853

18.

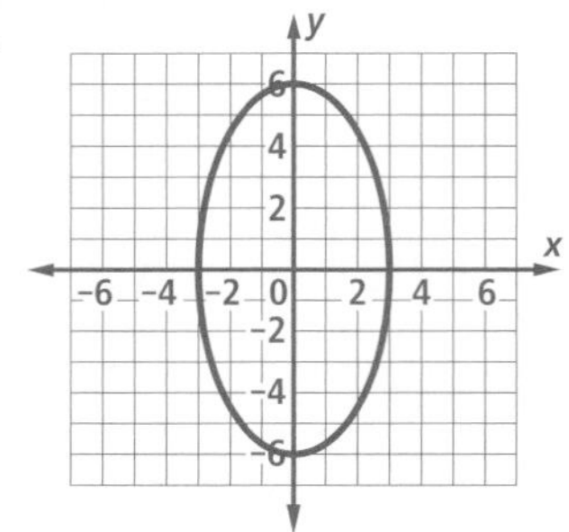

19.

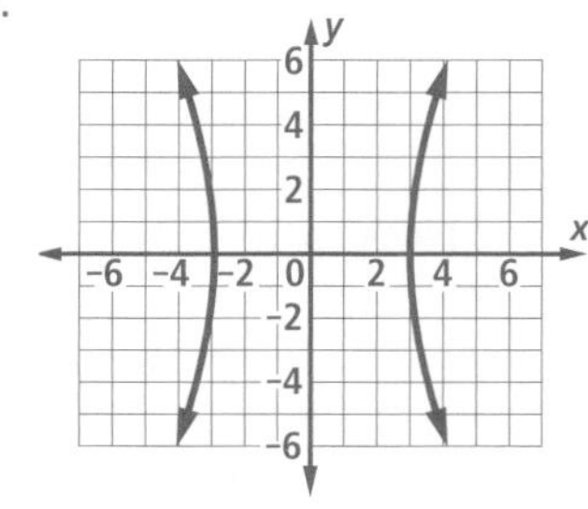

24a. The XSL attack is a technique to test and break the encryption codes used for security in many software applications.

24b. The XSL attack addresses the problem of an overdetermined quadratic system. This is a quadratic system with more equations than unknowns. Many encryption methods can be expressed in terms of these. The XSL attack uses a type of linearization that replaces quadratic terms with independent variables in order to solve the system.

Self-Test Page 860

15. Solve the system $lw = 104{,}094$ and $2l + 2w = 1{,}320$.

$$2l + 2\left(\frac{104{,}094}{l}\right) = 1320$$

$$2l^2 + 208{,}188 = 1320l$$

$$l^2 - 660l + 104{,}094 = 0$$

$l \approx 260.7$ or 399.3. Since addition and multiplication are commutative, solving for w would give the same answers. Colorado is longer than it is wide, so $l = 399.3$ and $w = 260.7$. The dimensions of Colorado are approximately 399.3 mi wide by 260.7 mi long.

18. This set of points is a circle with radius 8 and the center (3, 2.5) by the definition of a circle. It has equation $(x - 3)^2 + (y - 2.5)^2 = 64$ since (h, k) is (3, 2.5) and $r = 8$.

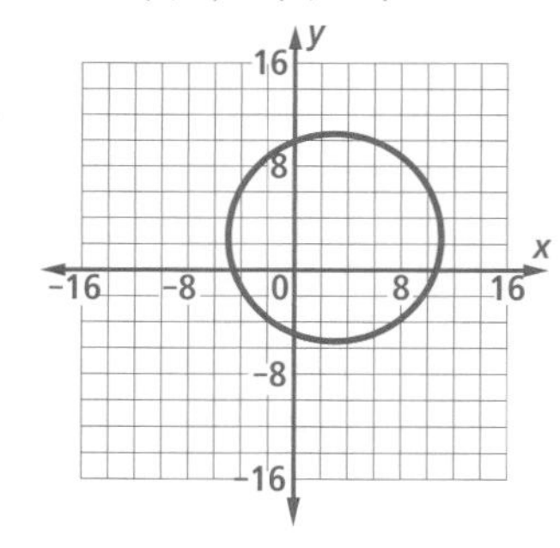

19. If the opening has center (0, 0) and a radius of 7, we can describe the arch with the equation $y = \sqrt{49 - x^2}$. Substitute the spelunker's height for y to find the place farthest from the center that he can stand:

$5\frac{8}{12} = 5\frac{2}{3} = \sqrt{49 - x^2}$

$\frac{289}{9} = 49 - x^2$

$x = \sqrt{\frac{152}{9}} \approx \pm 4.1.$

The spelunker can stand at most 4.1 ft away from the center.

20.

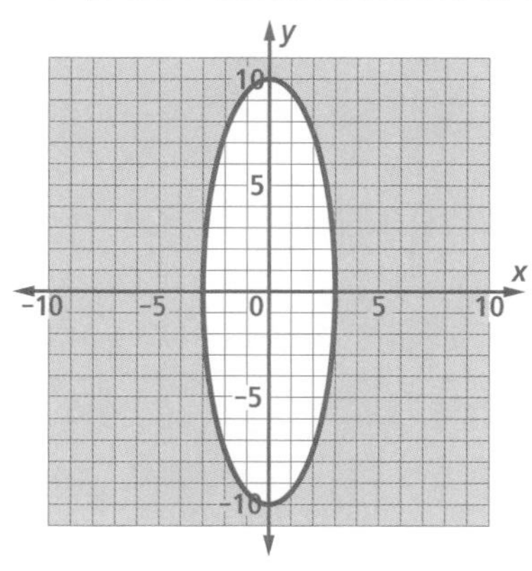

Chapter Review Page 862

59.

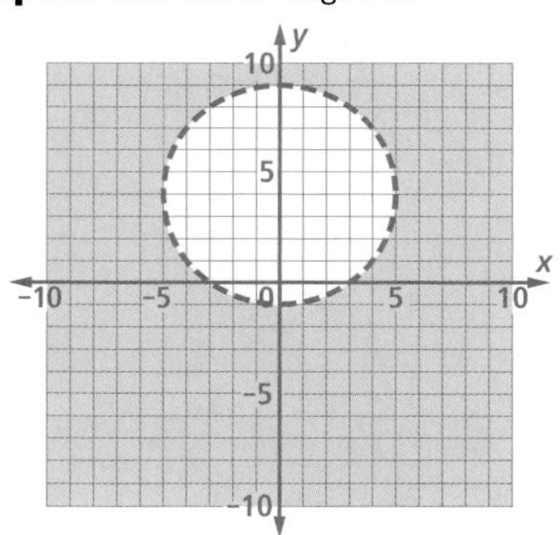

60.

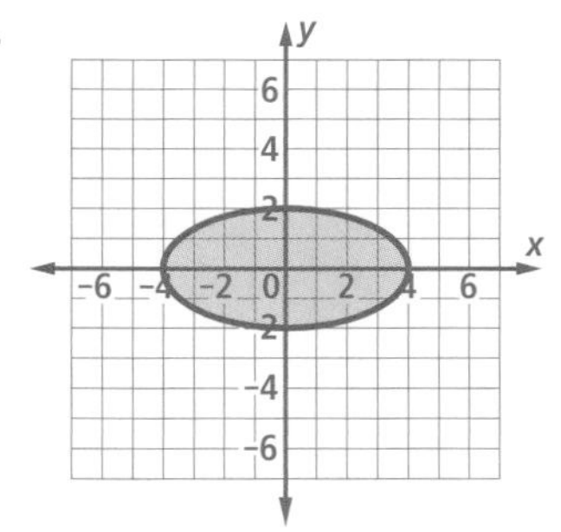

61. Answers vary. Sample: $(x + 1)^2 + y^2 = 9$, $\frac{x^2}{4} - y^2 = 1$

62. Answers vary. Sample: $\frac{x^2}{4} - y^2 = 1$, $xy = 2$

63. The system is: $\begin{cases} x + y = 17 \\ xy = 73 \end{cases}$

It appears on the graph of the system that the functions come very close to each other and might intersect. But, in fact, they do not intersect because there is no real solution to the system. Substituting $y = 17 - x$ into the second equation gives $x(17 - x) = 73$, or $x^2 - 17x + 73 = 0$, which has no real solution. So, the situation is impossible.

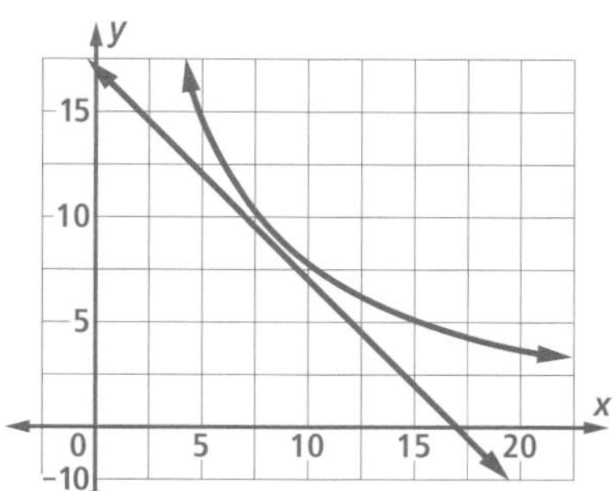

64a.

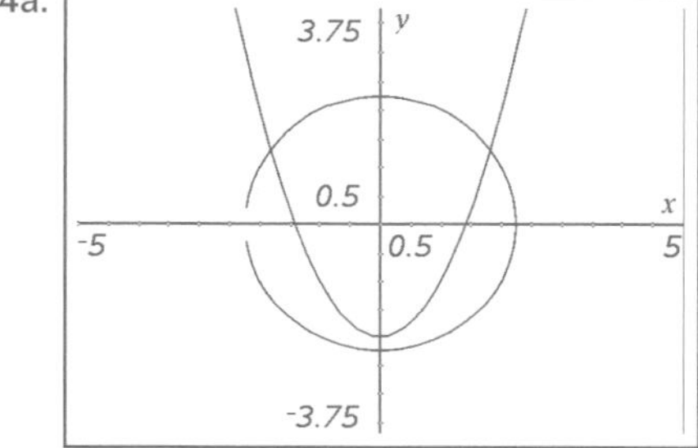

64b. (-1.8, 1.3), (1.8, 1.3)

65.

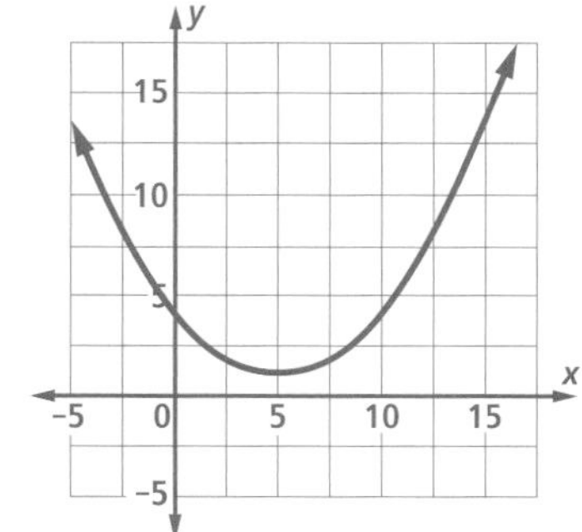

66. Answers vary. Sample:

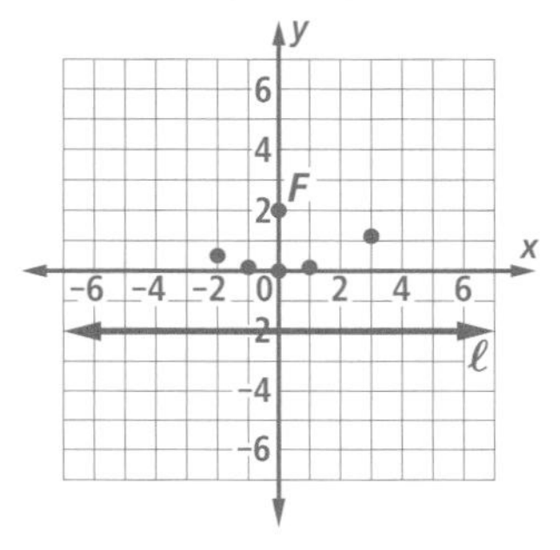

67.

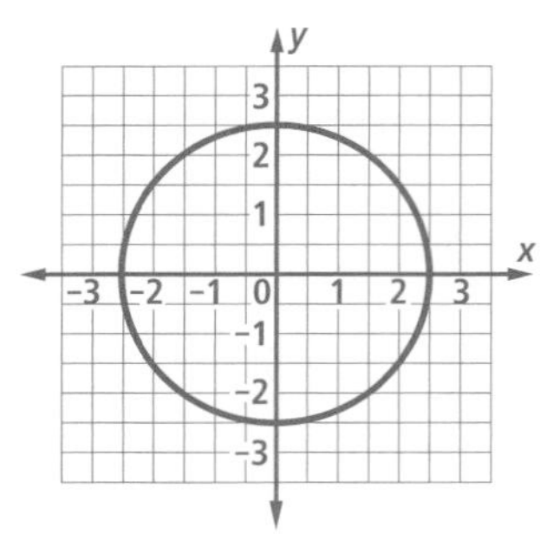

68. Answers vary. Sample:

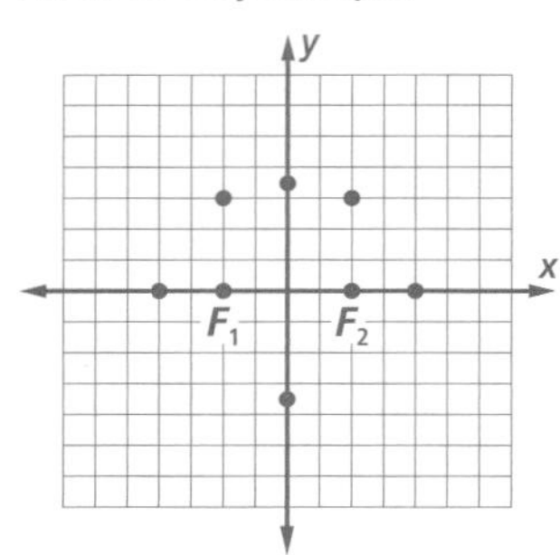

69.

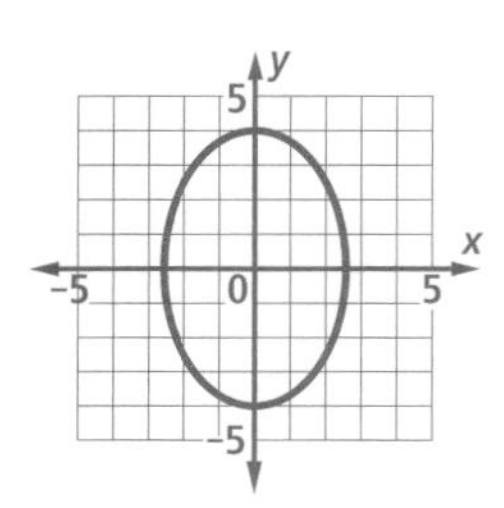

70.

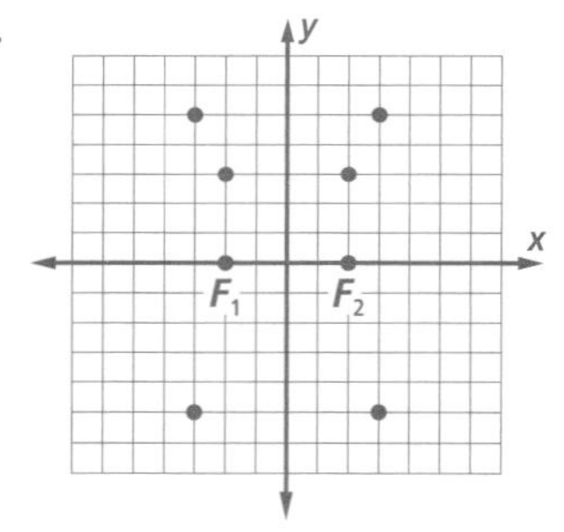

71.

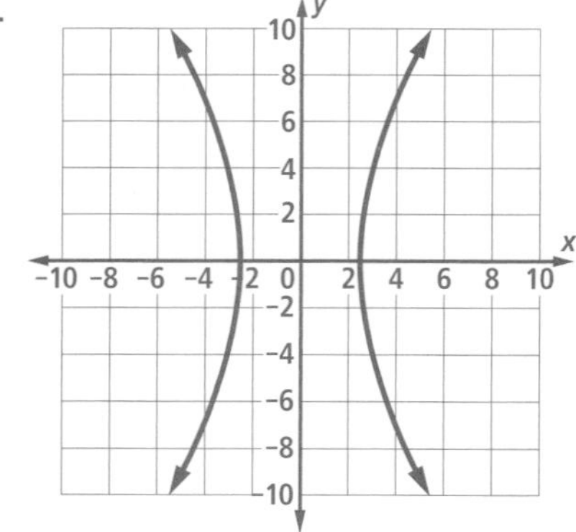

Chapter 13

Lesson 13-2

Activity Page 876

Steps 1–2

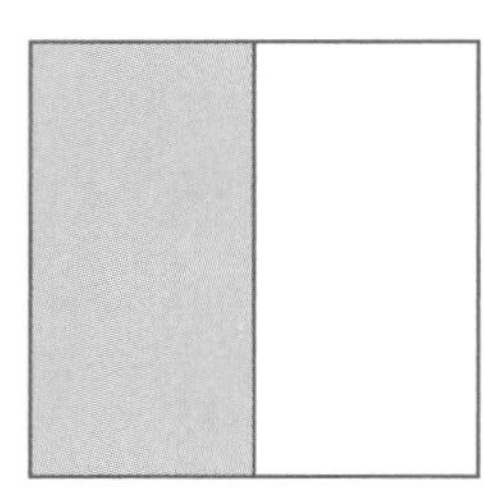

In Step 2, half of the square has been shaded.

Step 3

This region represents $\frac{1}{4}$ of the original square, so $\frac{3}{4}$ of the original square has been shaded.

Step 4

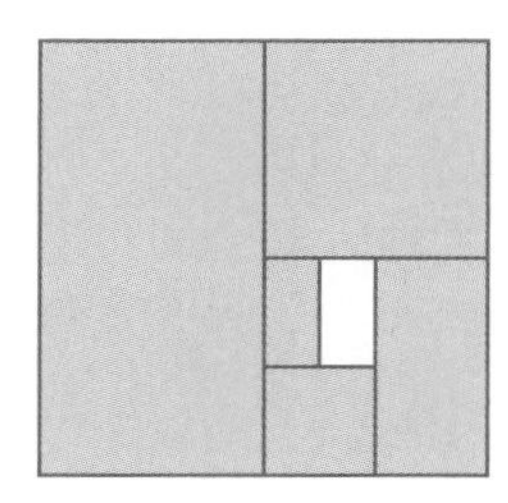

				$\frac{1}{2}+\frac{1}{4}+\frac{1}{8}+\frac{1}{16}$	$\frac{1}{2}+\frac{1}{4}+\frac{1}{8}+\frac{1}{16}+\frac{1}{32}$
			$\frac{7}{8}$	$\frac{15}{16}$	$\frac{31}{32}$

Step 5

$\frac{63}{64}$; the nth term of the series is $\frac{1}{2^n}$, and $S_n = \sum_{i=1}^{n} \left(\frac{1}{2}\right)^n = \frac{2^n - 1}{2^n}$.

Step 6

The original square will never be entirely shaded because $S_n \neq 1$ for any finite value of n.

Lesson 13-7
Activity 1 Page 909

Steps 1–2

Answers vary. Sample:

Trial	Sequence	Number of Heads
1	HHTH	3
2	HHTT	2
3	HTHH	3
4	TTHH	2
5	TTTH	1
6	THHT	2
7	TTTT	0
8	HTHH	3
9	TTTT	0
10	HTHH	3

Number of occurrences of:

0 heads: 2, 1 head: 1, 2 heads: 3,

3 heads: 4, 4 heads: 0

Step 3

Answers vary. Sample: The relative frequency for getting 2 heads in 4 flips is 0.39.

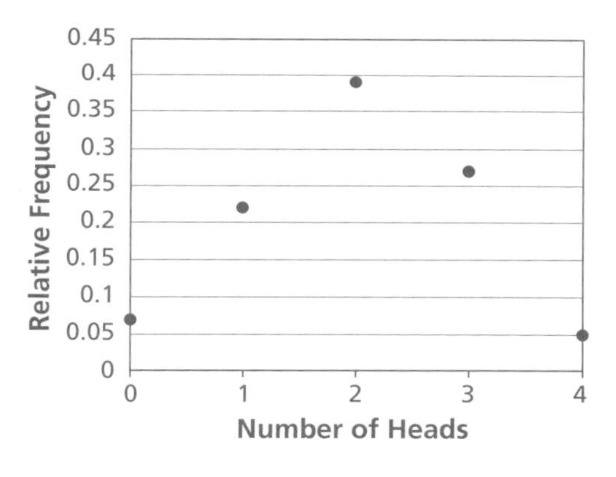

Lesson 13-9
Example 1 Page 922

a. 1; $\frac{5}{32}$; $\frac{5}{16}$; $\frac{5}{16}$; $\frac{5}{32}$; $\frac{1}{32}$

b. from left to right: $\frac{5}{32}$; $\frac{5}{16}$; $\frac{5}{16}$; $\frac{5}{32}$; $\frac{1}{32}$

Self-Test Page 932

13. This is an arithmetic series with first term 30 and constant difference 2. So, the sum will be $\sum_{i=1}^{30} 30 + 2(i - 1) = \frac{30}{2}(30 + 88) = \$1770$

14a. This is an arithmetic series with first term 3 and constant difference 4. Since we know the final term is 87, to find n solve $3 + 4(n - 1) = 87$. $4n - 1 = 87$; $n = 22$. The series can be expressed in sigma notation as $\sum_{i=1}^{22} 4i - 1$.

15. This is a geometric series with $n = 20$ terms, first term $5^0 = 1$, and constant ratio 5: $\sum_{i=0}^{19} 5^i = \frac{a(1 - r^n)}{1 - r} = \frac{1(1 - 5^{20})}{1 - 5} = 23{,}841{,}857{,}910{,}156$

16. $\sum_{i=0}^{19} 50\left(\frac{4}{5}\right)^i = \frac{50\left(1 - \left(\frac{4}{5}\right)^{20}\right)}{1 - \frac{4}{5}} = \frac{188{,}535{,}840{,}025{,}698}{762{,}939{,}453{,}125} \approx 247.12$

17. There are $2^5 = 32$ possible outcomes. There are $\binom{5}{0} = 1$ possibility for 0 heads, $\binom{5}{1} = 5$ possibilities for 1 head, $\binom{5}{2} = 10$ possibilities for 2 heads, $\binom{5}{3} = 10$ possibilities for 3 heads, $\binom{5}{4} = 5$ possibilities for 4 heads, and $\binom{5}{5} = 1$ possibility for 5 heads. Therefore, the respective probabilities are $\frac{1}{32}$, $\frac{5}{32}$, $\frac{5}{16}$, $\frac{5}{16}$, $\frac{5}{32}$, and $\frac{1}{32}$.